ANALYSIS FOR PRODUCTION AND OPERATIONS MANAGEMENT

IRWIN SERIES IN QUANTITATIVE ANALYSIS FOR BUSINESS

CONSULTING EDITOR

ROBERT B. FETTER *Yale University*

BOWMAN & FETTER *Analysis for Production and Operations Management*
Third Edition

BIERMAN, BONINI, FOURAKER, & JAEDICKE *Quantitative Analysis for Business Decisions* Revised Edition

MARTIN *Electronic Data Processing* Revised Edition

MORRIS *Analysis for Materials Handling Management*

FRANK, KUEHN, & MASSY *Quantitative Techniques in Marketing Analysis: Text and Readings*

HOWELL & TEICHROEW *Mathematical Analysis for Business Decisions*

MORRIS *Management Science in Action*

BOWEN *Mathematics: With Applications in Management and Economics*

BERANEK *Analysis for Financial Decisions*

MCMILLAN & GONZALEZ *Systems Analysis: A Computer Approach to Decision Models*

THEODORE *Applied Mathematics: An Introduction: Mathematical Analysis for Management*

ELLIOTT & WASLEY *Business Information Processing Systems*

ROSENTHAL *Numerical Methods in Computer Programming*

Analysis for Production and Operations Management

EDWARD H. BOWMAN
Comptroller and Senior Research Associate

and

ROBERT B. FETTER
Professor of Industrial Administration

YALE UNIVERSITY

A Combined Revision of:

Analysis for Production Management, 1957, 1961

Analyses of Industrial Operations, 1959

Third Edition · 1967
RICHARD D. IRWIN, INC.
Homewood, Illinois

Third Edition

First Printing, January, 1967

Library of Congress Catalog Card No. 66–14548

Printed in the United States of America

Preface

THIS BOOK was first written in the middle fifties when very little formal analytical work was included in the education of the industrial manager, administrator, or engineer. At that time a growing dissatisfaction with production management courses oriented around a description of the many functions, problems, and systems in production, plus an awareness of some of the methods of analysis which had been developed, led us to reorganize the initial production management course offered to juniors and first-year graduate students at M.I.T.'s School of Industrial Management. This book is an outgrowth of the development of this course. Assumed is some previous work by the student in mathematics, computers, economics, and statistics.

The orientation of this book is one of analysis of the economic problems of production and operations management. Economic problems, of course, virtually always have their human and technological aspects. However, where the economical aspects of the problems are prime, certain very pervasive methods of analysis have been developed to cope with them. We attempt in this book to present these methods of analysis, most of which are quantitative and involve mathematics. The organization of the book through its chapters centers on these methods of analysis potentially useful for operations managers in making economic decisions. The text is divided into six sections as follows: I. Orientation; II. Mathematical Programming; III. Statistical Analysis; IV. Economic Analysis; V. Simulation; and VI. Cases.

In virtually all of the chapters of the book we have attempted to teach by example. We are persuaded that the best way to teach these methods of analysis, including their theoretical framework, is in this way. Theory, generalizations, and limitations are presented along with examples. The rationale of each method should become meaningful to the student as he thinks through the illustrations used in the chapter, and as he works through the problems at the end of each chapter. Cases collected from the professional literature that describe the application of management science approaches to real operating problems are presented at the end of the book to supply the student with work closer to industrial reality than the specific problems of each chapter. A next step closer to reality,

v

which we have used with our own students, is to send them into local companies for problem analysis, which includes by necessity what the text lacks—i.e., the difficult tasks of identifying the problem and of securing the proper data for the mathematical analysis. Our objective in this educational effort is to have the student bring an analytical approach to the economic problems of operations management. A willingness and desire to abstract and to relate appropriate theory to the real world is sought. The student is oriented to problem-solving and decision-making. The student is not looking for *any* solution to a problem but for the *best* solution on the basis of the information he has or can make available. He learns to seek these solutions by formal and sometimes powerful methods of analysis. We feel that when the student later comes to a position where he must make decisions or resolve situations for his organization, though he may not take time for the formal analysis presented here, the conceptual frameworks offered will make his decision process a more effective one. Though a good supply of common sense, intuition, and experience will always be valued by the world of affairs, when these are combined with systematic knowledge and analytical methods, they certainly become more useful.

Our experience with the first and revised editions of this book has served to reinforce more than modify the foregoing views. However, we have made a number of revisions and changes in this edition. We have rewritten many of the chapters incorporating new material where it seemed useful. This is especially true in the case of computer applications. A completely new chapter on "Behavior and Heuristics" has been added in order to present some of the techniques, ideas, and philosophy in this area. Finally, we have incorporated a number of articles from our previous book *Analyses of Industrial Operations* as cases for critique and discussion.

As in the past, we are indebted to a number of authors and publishers including Professor Sir Ronald A. Fisher, Cambridge, to Dr. Frank Yates, Rothamsted, and to Messrs. Oliver and Boyd Limited, Edinburgh, for permission to reprint Tables No. III and V from their book *Statistical Tables for Biological, Agricultural, and Medical Research* and Table III from *Statistical Methods for Research Workers* (11th edition); to Prentice-Hall, Inc., and Solomon Asch for permission to quote from *Social Psychology* and F. E. Croxton and D. J. Cowden for permission to reproduce Appendix G1 in *Practical Business Statistics;* to McGraw-Hill Book Co., Inc., and A. M. Mood for permission to reproduce Table II in *Introduction to the Theory of Statistics,* M. E. Munroe, for permission to quote from *The Theory of Probability,* and E. B. Wilson for permission to quote from *An Introduction to Scientific Research;* to the Macmillan Co. and Irwin D. J. Bross for permission to quote from *Design for Decision;* to John Wiley & Sons, Inc., and H. F. Dodge and Harry G. Romig for permission to reproduce Figures 1 and 6 from *Sampling Inspection Tables* and Ralph Barnes for permission to reproduce page 191 from *The Principles of Motion Economy;* to the American Society for Testing Materials for permission to reproduce the table of control chart factors from their *Manual on Quality Control of Materials,* STP 15-C; and to *The Bell System Technical Journal* for permission to quote from W. A. Shewhart's, "Economic Quality Control of Manufactured Product," and F. Thorndike's, "Applications of Poison's Probability Summation," and to the authors of our cases and their publishers, *Management Science, Operations Research, Applied Statistics,* and *Review of Economics and Statistics.*

The authors wish to express gratitude to their many colleagues at M.I.T. who contributed so much in time and effort to this book. Thanks are due to Professors Billy E. Goetz, W. Van Alan Clark, Jr., Albert Rubenstein, Richard Maffei, Gordon Shillinglaw, and John Summerfield. A number of reviewers and users have made many helpful suggestions, all of which have been considered, and many of which have been followed. Several students were especially helpful in a number of ways, including T. M. Mangelsdorf, T. G. Simons, Frederick Langmack, Richard L. Van Horn, Jr., Henry Mintzberg, Richard Egen, George Heidorn, Ted Woronka, and John R. M. Gordon. The imperfections after all this help still fall, of course, to the authors.

New Haven, Connecticut   Edward H. Bowman
January, 1967   Robert B. Fetter

Table of Contents

SECTION V: SIMULATION AND HEURISTICS

SECTION VI: CASE STUDIES IN PRODUCTION AND OPERATIONS MANAGEMENT

APPENDIXES

INDEX

SECTION I

Orientation

CHAPTER 1

Introduction

THIS textbook is an analytical approach to the problems of production and operations management. Production management has many facets, and a systematic presentation of the subject could follow any of a number of directions. The three which appear most relevant would be in terms of the following:

1. Management process.
2. Analytical techniques.
3. Production problems.

Management as a process, especially a feedback control process, is a useful way of viewing the activities of the production manager himself. How does he find problems—a problem in "industrial intelligence," which leads to the allocation of problem solving effort? How does he organize his own activities and that of his group to cope with the problem? Given some solution (this is the process which we focus on here), how is the solution implemented? What kind of controls are then brought to bear to assure stability and continuity in the problem area?

The analytical techniques or methods of analysis which seem to be useful in finding solutions to many production management problems comprise the main part of this book. The philosophy of explicit model building—usually in mathematical form—is reinforced through many kinds of problems and models. It is now possible to say that though the introduction of this kind of thinking to the world's industries may at times be slow, it is sure. More and more companies are finding these analytical techniques useful. While it is true that some industries have made the use of some of these methods—for example, linear programming in the oil industry—routine, we also find them beginning to be

3

used in such other diverse fields as in banking, hospitals, and construction. It is to be expected that, as new methods are developed and new applications made, we shall see them being put to use at an accelerated rate in an increasing variety of enterprises.

A frequent approach to the discussion of management problems is one of codification. An attempt is made to classify the particular group of problems, such as production problems, according to their nature and similarities. With the classification of the problems, generalizations gathered from experience are cited, and a discussion is given of potential solutions to the problems or arrangements of the situations under varying circumstances. Though this will not be the basic approach of this book, a brief presentation will be made here of what seem to be the more important production management problems.

Though the three-way division can be overdrawn, production, distribution, and finance are basic and important functions of a manufacturing business. The organization chart of many firms, particularly those which are too small to require a complex organization structure, usually reveals an executive in charge of each of these functions reporting to the president. The titles of these executives might be vice-president of manufacturing, vice-president of marketing, and secretary-treasurer. One of the disadvantages of overdrawing this functionalization is that many problems will have important facets in all these areas, and in some companies a real difficulty exists in co-ordinating these functional groups for the purpose of resolving such problems.

Production problems in a business, as undoubtedly marketing and financial problems as well, may be classified still further. One way of doing this, which is an abstraction as is any classification, is to indicate that production problems may be essentially of a physical, economic, or human nature. Though most problems will involve all of these, it is felt that one will usually stand out; therefore, a particular set of intellectual disciplines will be most helpful in understanding and resolving that problem. Obviously, this does not mean that knowledge (special or common) of the other areas need be shut off from the problem, but there tends to be a dominant facet to most problems.

The physical or technological problems of production management are the ones that usually stand out to the layman, particularly when he *sees* a production process. Anyone who walks through a steel mill or an automobile factory cannot help but be impressed by the machines and equipment he sees. The physical problems that exist in making a product like steel, for example, are many and varied, such as composition of raw materials, temperature, pressure, rolling rates, cutting and forming, and so forth. In any general discussion of production management, the aspect of the physical problems which stands out most is the great divergence of such problems among industries. For even a superficial understanding of such problems, it would be necessary to discuss those physical problems associated with each of many industries. Considering the manufacturing problems of only shoes, steel, petroleum products, automobiles, and pharmaceuticals, the list of "physical" problems is enormous. The disciplines most helpful for attacking such problems are the natural sciences and engineering. Illustrative of these are physics, chemistry, metallurgy, biology, and civil, mechanical, electrical, and chemical engineering, to mention some of the rather highly (though certainly not completely) developed areas.

The human problems of production management are probably no more a part of production than of marketing, finance, or any other functional area of business. These problems may be divided into those that are individual and those that are social or institutional. The former include problems such as recruiting, hiring, medical care, and so forth. The latter include problems in areas such as organization structure, federal and state law, union relations, employment stabilization, and so forth. Here the list of disciplines which might be helpful would include psychology, social-psychology, sociology, macro-economics, medicine, law, history, and many others.

Finally, there are the essentially economic or operational problems of production management. The relevance of the various problems to be discussed here to the "allocation of scarce resources to alternative ends according to some criteria" may be obvious or obscure. However, even in solving problems which are essentially physical or human, management usually attempts to establish at least an economic relevance. It is the economic aspect of production management that this book will emphasize. However, probably no problem of production management is uniquely physical, economic, or human.

THE FUNCTIONS OF PRODUCTION

In order to gain some insight into the environment within which these economic problems of production management arise, an attempt will be made here to set forth in an orderly fashion a general picture of the major functions of production. These are shown schematically in the figure below and consist of a set of staff activities—product design, process design, supply, production control, quality control, cost control, and maintenance which service the actual production process—and the line operative functions which actually result in the output of the firm.

Two cautions are in order when viewing this schematic representation. First, it is a functional and not an organizational chart. That is, no serious suggestion is being made that any particular firm should organize its personnel to conform to a relationship such as is shown in the chart. This chart is only intended to present in general those functions which constitute production management in the broad sense. Second, it is certainly true that such functions of a firm as finance, distribution, and industrial relations are necessary to the functioning of the enterprise, but they are not given here since they are basic to the *firm* and not just to production.

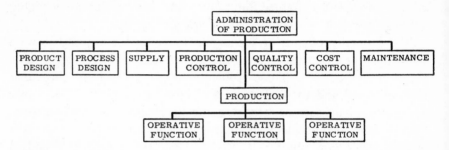

Product design is concerned with the planning involved in determining the attributes of the finished product. The stimulus to new design or redesign usually originates in marketing which reflects consumer preferences and desires. But the actual function is primarily one of engineering and consists of two phases as follows: the mechanics of design—determining primary function or performance of the product; and aesthetics of design—determining appearance, color, etc.

Process design is the planning involved in determining the methods of combining resources to produce the attributes of the finished product as developed by product design. The objective sought is the creation of conditions and methods that will permit the manufacture of a product of the required quality at minimum cost which will meet competitive prices and provide a reasonable profit. The principal phases of this function are plant layout, tool design, and job design.

The function of supply is to provide the materials necessary for production in the proper quantities at the proper time and place, and at the lowest cost consistent with the necessary technical quality. The storage and transportation of these materials and the reclaiming and disposing of scrap and waste are also the work of this function.

The staff control of production in the manufacturing process is the function of determining and regulating those manufacturing activities that relate directly to production, in accordance with manufacturing plans. The type of control used, whether order, flow, or block, depends on the type of manufacturing, i.e., intermittent, continuous, or some combination of the two; but whatever the type, the function may be subdivided into routing, scheduling, dispatching, and follow-up.

Quality control is the function of insuring that the attributes of the product conform to prescribed standards, and that their relationships to one another are maintained. A plan for control of quality must take into consideration the technological aspects of the product, the capabilities of the human and machine inputs to the process, and the cost of producing a given degree of quality. Development of standards serves as the basis for measurement of deviation from desired quality.

Cost control is a phase of the general accounting procedure by means of which details of the costs of materials, labor, and fixed expenses necessary to produce an article are recorded, summarized, analyzed, and interpreted. The cost control activity should seek to predetermine cost figures, on a systematic basis, in order that a standard cost may be set with which the actual cost figures may be compared for purposes of analysis to discover variations from the standard. These variations of actual cost from standards form the basis for study to ascertain the causes of such differences.

The maintenance of plant and equipment, machinery, and tools in a condition that will make possible continuous, economical production is the primary objective of maintenance. Although the performance of the function enters only indirectly into the product, the service performed is necessary for the economical performance of the direct manufacturing functions. The function usually consists of the following tasks: emergency repairs, inspection of machinery and equipment so as to detect wear or impending breakdown, scheduled overhauls or replacements, and the keeping of records of equipment, inspections, and repairs. Development of an economic equipment replacement policy in accordance with technological needs of the company is a function of considerable importance here.

The line production organization is concerned with the direction, supervision, and control of operative performance which leads to the actual physical production of the output of the firm. As such, the final responsibility for quantity, timing, and cost of production rests with the line organization. Thus, while some control functions are performed elsewhere, final authority as to the planning and control of production rests in the line. The functions previously discussed are staff in that they render service to those responsible for operative performance.

Production may be defined as a *process* whereby a set of inputs are converted into a set of outputs. The "process" as here conceived is simultaneously a physical, economic, and human process. The inputs into the process are essentially materials, human skill, and equipment. The outputs of the process are the goods and services desired in the market place. It is the economic problems encountered in this process with which this book is primarily concerned.

THE MAJOR ECONOMIC PROBLEMS OF PRODUCTION MANAGEMENT

The following problems tend to be interrelated. It is not possible to consider a single industry or any part of an industry and enumerate successfully a set of problems which are independent of each other. Further, many of these problems may necessitate the use of disciplines other than those considered here. However, it is their economic aspects which are relevant to the analytical treatment presented in this book.

Inventory

The quantities of goods to be maintained in the plant through the stages of raw materials, work-in-process, and finished goods is one of the major economic problems of production. Inventory must be recorded and accounted for. Purchasing and receiving of the necessary raw materials, parts, and supplies is an associated problem area. Decisions as to the right quantity to make or buy must be made. The timing of this decision must be established. The question (at some higher level) of whether it is more economical to make or buy a material or part must be resolved.

Production Scheduling and Control

The different operations in the manufacturing process must be determined for each product and part. The proper sequence of these operations must be established. The machine to perform each operation must be determined, and a time schedule established. The instructions and information necessary for these decisions and their execution must be available when and where needed. Tooling and fixtures must be provided. Whether or not to make a product at all must be determined. Where demands for the products are uneven, decisions regarding overtime, storage, and employment stabilization must be made. All this complex of interrelated factors which in total determine the structure of the production system at any point in time must be resolved in favor of that set which best accomplishes the objectives of the firm. This kind of problem constitutes one of the more perplexing of the economic problems encountered by production management.

Equipment Selection and Replacement

The proper equipment for a plant to use must be determined initially, and as time passes. As equipment wears out and becomes less efficient and/or new equipment is developed, the problem of economic equipment life must be determined and decisions made among the alternatives available in order to satisfy the objectives of the firm or (at a lower level) the objectives of the specific process. This kind of investment problem is particularly difficult due to the long-term nature of the predictions necessary for its resolution.

Maintenance

Plant and equipment maintenance must be planned for and executed. Maintenance policy must be decided concerning the economics of preventive maintenance versus after-the-breakdown maintenance. Procedures must be established and information gathered which allow for the control of maintenance policy. The size of maintenance crews must also be determined.

Size and Location of Plants

In a sizable firm, a decision must be made as to the proper size of a plant and the related problem of the proper number of plants. The proper location of these plants must also be decided. Because of the long-term nature of decisions such as these, possibilities of future changes must be considered, as well as the decision to tie up substantial capital for long periods.

Plant Layout and Structure

The general layout scheme of the plant must be determined. Decisions must be made, for example, as to whether all equipment necessary to make one product should be located together, influencing, of course, the flow of materials through the plant. The proper amount of each type of equipment must be determined. A decision must be made between a single or multistory plant, as well as other alternatives of construction types.

Quality Control and Inspection

The capability of the various equipment to produce the products specified must be determined. Changes in the process must be detected, understood, and taken into account. The type of inspection, its location, and its frequency must be determined. Some provision must be made for scrap and salvage.

Traffic and Materials Handling

The economics of materials handling into, through, and out of the plant must be understood. The need for, nature, frequency, and quantity of materials handling must be determined.

Methods

Methods and work simplification are a major part of the complex of problems encountered by production management. This includes decisions as regards the method of carrying out the work involved in the entire process, for one man working at his machine(s) or for one sequence of motions by a worker. The economics of work improvement must be understood in making this kind of decision.

Though the above list of problems covers the main areas of economic decision making in production, it is not intended to be exhaustive. Actually, the list of economic problems of production management is virtually endless. Rather than even attempting a complete coverage of these problems, this book presents some of the problems of production management in three different ways. First, some problems are used to illustrate the methods of analysis presented in the chapters. Second, some problems are given after each chapter to enable the reader to become actively involved in the method of analysis by developing his own particularization of the method in "solving" the problem. Finally, various problems are intertwined in the actual production management cases in the latter portion of the book.

Many production problems as described here have their counterparts in railroads, air lines, electric utilities, mines, and so forth. Along with the financial aspects of capital acquisition and the marketing aspects of demand creation, all of these industries have problems analogous to production problems. In many companies in these industries, however, the term *operations* is applied to those groups in the organization that deal with problems of equipment selection and maintenance, facilities and systems structuring, activities and employment scheduling, and so forth. The methods of analysis and the underlying philosophy of abstraction, mathematical model building, and theory application presented here, usually in a manufacturing context, should be equally useful in analyzing operations in this broader classification of industries.

HISTORY OF ANALYTIC METHODS
IN MANAGEMENT

The economic problems just described have been the subject of both theoretical and practical investigation for a long time, in fact, ever since they were recognized as problems. As early as 1832, Charles Babbage, an English mathematician and inventor, voiced concern over uneconomic use of machines and men in the production of goods. In his essay of 1832 on "The Economy of Machinery and Manufacturers," Babbage was concerned with the uses to which machines were put and the organization of people for production. His view was that scientific methods should be applied to the problems of economy in production and general principles determined to guide management. He actually made time studies on pin making and derived some rules for this work. He drew on, and improved, the division of labor idea which had been enunciated by Adam Smith, and he considered the problem of a "fair day's wage for a fair day's work." Even though his thinking did not have a major impact on management of the day, he believed in the necessity of bringing order out of the then chaotic management practices through the use of scientific methods in the management of factories.

The beginning of the "management movement" in the United States is generally marked as 1886, when Henry R. Towne presented his paper, "The Engineer as an Economist," at a meeting of the American Society of Mechanical Engineers. Mr. Towne's views on "successful management" are in part as follows:

To insure the best results, the organization of productive labor must be directed and controlled by persons having not only good executive ability, and possessing the practical familiarity of a mechanic or an engineer with the goods produced and the processes employed, but having also, and equally, a practical knowledge of how to observe, record, analyze, and compare essential facts in relation to wages, supplies, expense account, and all else that enters into or affects the economy of production and the cost of the product. There are many good mechanical engineers;—there are also many good "business men"—but the two are rarely combined in one person. But this combination of qualities, together with at least some skill as an accountant, either in one person or more, is essential to the successful management of industrial work, and has its highest effectiveness if united in one person, who is thus qualified to supervise, either personally or through assistants, the operations of all departments of a business, and to subordinate each to the harmonious development of the whole.

Engineering has long been conceded a place as one of the modern arts, and has become a well-defined science, with a large and growing literature of its own, and of late years has subdivided itself into numerous and distinct divisions, one of which is that of mechanical engineering. It will probably not be disputed that engineering, as affecting the successful conduct of most, if not all, of our great industrial establishments, and that the *management of works* has become a matter of such great and far-reaching importance as perhaps to justify its classification also as one of the modern arts. A vast amount of accumulated experience in the art of workshop management already exists, but there is no record of it available to the world in general, and each old enterprise is managed more or less in its own way, receiving little benefit from the parallel experience of other similar enterprises. Surely this condition of things is wrong and should be remedied. But the remedy must not be looked for from those who are "business men" or clerks and accountants only; it should come from those whose training and experience has given them an understanding of both sides (viz: the mechanical and the clerical) of the important questions involved. It should originate, therefore, from those who are also engineers.

The reaction to these words was not immediately forthcoming, but a small group of engineers headed by Frederick W. Taylor, then at the Midvale Steel Works, began experimenting with a scientific approach to some managerial problems in manufacturing about 1888.

Taylor and his followers were unwilling to rely upon traditional methods and rules governing work which had been handed down from generation to generation through the apprenticeship system. Rather, they emphasized precise measurement of the variables operating in any work situation in their experiments. Taylor spent 20 years measuring relationships between the shape of tools, depth of cut, feed, and speed in the cutting of metals. His *Art of Cutting Metals,* published in 1905, stands today as an authoritative work in this field. His life was devoted to the acquisition of knowledge in management, to replace the rules of thumb in use up until that time. Among areas where Taylor made important contributions are the following:

1. The use of scientific methods of approach in the analysis of management problems.
2. Systematized experimental approach to solving production management problems as illustrated by his pig-iron handling experiment and his shoveling experiment.
3. The discovery of high-speed tool steel.
4. Monumental work on the art of cutting metals.
5. The development of a time study aimed at determining a "fair day's work."
6. His differential piece-rate system designed as a new approach to the problems of designing incentives for work.
7. Development of the concept of staff specialists in industrial organization.

In 1911, Taylor published his *Principles of Scientific Management,* wherein he recommends the following:

1. The development of a science for each element of a man's work.
2. Scientifically, to select, train, and develop workers.
3. The development of a spirit of co-operation between management and workers.

4. The division of the work of an enterprise into equal shares as between management and the workers.

Taylor's ability to sell these ideas to management and workers was considerably less than his ability to develop them. The "Scientific Management Movement" was not well received and, in fact, was fought by many practitioners of management. One of the results of the Congressional Investigation of 1911 into the Taylor and other systems of shop management was a prohibition on the use of stop watches in government service. The "new" managers did little to dispel the notion that "scientific management" and human values were incompatible. It remained for later workers in "scientific management" to dispel the notion, although there are some places where attempts at fact finding in management are still looked upon with suspicion.

The Analysis of Work Methods

Taylor did much pioneering work in the analysis of work methods and recorded his experiments for management use. The examples which he gave in *Principles of Scientific Management* illustrated the tremendous gains possible through discovering the basic elements of any task and attempting to discern through experimentation the principles underlying their performance. In the handling of pig iron, for example, workmen were enabled to load 47 tons a day, as a result of the new methods, against 12 tons previously.[1]

Frank Gilbreth was one of the most widely known men in work simplification. He worked closely with, and was influenced by, Taylor, but he had actually gone a long way in the analysis of work methods before coming into contact with Taylor. His refinements of motion and time study, through utilization of motion pictures, constitute some of today's best practices. His early work was done in the field of construction: notably, with the art of bricklaying. He demonstrated, through his consulting work, the application of the micromotion technique to a tremendous variety of activities in all fields of business and in some fields far removed from business. Together with his wife, Lillian Gilbreth, he made some important contributions to the study of fatigue and that of the psychology of management. Gilbreth and many of those following him made extensive use of schematic models[2] (Chapter 2) in their analysis of work methods.

The present-day practice of industrial engineering comes basically from work in this field. Many refinements of method and measurement

---

[1] F. W. Taylor, *Principles of Scientific Management* (New York: Harper & Bros., 1915), pp. 57–58.

[2] Chapters referred to in parentheses in this section refer to the later chapters of this book.

have been worked out and reported since then, and some of these are given in this book. The essentially nonscientific character of this kind of analysis should become evident to the reader, but the usefulness of such methods should not be underestimated.

Programming Production Activities

The basic economic problem facing any enterprise tends to be one of allocating some scarce resources (men, machines, materials) to some desired outputs. On the level of production activities, this problem tends to be solved in industry by such methods as the graphical technique developed by Henry Gantt. Gantt's progress chart, and its several variations,[3] essentially involves a systematic trial-and-error solution to the allocation problem (Chapter 2). Mathematical methods for solving the general problem of programming economic activities as a whole has been the subject of economic inquiry since Quesnay's *Tableau Economique*. The general equilibrium systems of Walras and Cassel and recent efforts of W. W. Leontief[4] represent more sophisticated treatments. Along with the work on game theory by Weyl[5] and von Neumann[6] came the development of one of the few presently available practical techniques—that of "linear programming" (Chapters 3 and 4). It was not until Dantzig wrote his important paper on the "simplex method" of computation in 1947[7] that practical applications of earlier work in input-output analysis were possible. Recent developments by Dantzig, Charnes, Cooper, and others have made this method of programming practicable in a wide range of actual situations. The problems of developing programming models which take account of uncertainty, of nonlinear programming, and dynamic programming are occupying the attention of scientists, engineers, and economists at the present time.

Statistical Method in Production

The theory of probability and its applications in statistical inference

---

[3] Wallace Clark, *Gantt Chart* (2d ed., London: Sir Isaac Pitman & Sons, Ltd., 1938).

[4] W. W. Leontief, *Structure of the American Economy, 1919–1939* (2d ed.; New York: Oxford University Press, 1951).

[5] H. W. Kuhn and A. W. Tucker, "Contributions to the Theory of Games," *Annals of Mathematical Statistics*, 24 (Princeton: Princeton University Press, 1950).

[6] *Ibid.*; J. von Neumann, "A Model of General Economic Equilibrium," *Review of Economic Studies*, Vol. XIII; and J. von Neumann and O. Morgenstern, *The Theory of Games and Economic Behavior* (Princeton: Princeton University Press, 1947).

[7] G. B. Dantzig, "Maximization of a Set of Linear Functions of Variables Subject to Linear Inequalities," in T. C. Koopmans (ed.), *Activity Analysis of Production and Allocation* (New York: John Wiley & Sons, Inc., 1951).

has been a part of economic analysis for only a short time. Although the economic problems involved in games of chance often provided the spur in the development of the theory, the most significant application of such notions to problems of production management occurred with the work of Walter A. Shewhart at the Bell Telephone Laboratories in the 1920's. This work culminated in the publication of his paper, "The Economic Quality Control of Manufactured Products," in the *Bell Telephone System Technical Journal* in 1930. This paper presented a scientific basis for interpreting significant variations in production output as well as for eliminating causes of variation in such output which do not result from chance (Chapter 5). Shewhart was one of the first to perceive the statistical nature of the problem of control of processes.

Application of this concept in industry was slow to gain acceptance until World War II when it received great impetus. The formation of the American Standards Association Committee on Quality Control and its publications in 1941 and 1942[8] contributed heavily to this growth.

Also, as a result of work done at the Bell Telephone Laboratories by Harold F. Dodge and Harry M. Romig, the concepts and methods of sampling inspection (Chapter 6) as they are known today were developed. The contributions of this work primarily accomplished at the Bell Telephone Laboratories cannot be overemphasized. The application of notions of probability accomplished there have spread into almost all activities of management where planning and control must be accomplished in the face of some uncertainty. The publication in 1941 of the Dodge-Romig Sampling Tables[9] was an extremely important contribution in the application of statistical techniques in industry.

An Englishman, Professor Ronald A. Fisher, is the most influential figure in the development of modern statistical methods. In 1923, he published his first paper on field trials which led to a revolution in agricultural experimentation, and was the starting point for work on the design of experiments (Chapter 7). The Z-test of significance and the arithmetical procedure known as the analysis of variance took their present form at about the same time.

Fisher's *Statistical Methods for Research Workers*[10] was first published in 1925, and has since been through several editions. This book

---

[8] *Control Chart Method of Controlling Quality during Production: American War Standard Z1.3, 1942* (New York: American Standards Association, Inc., 1942).

[9] H. F. Dodge and H. G. Romig, "Single and Double Sampling Inspection Tables," *Bell System Technical Journal*, Vol. XX (January, 1941), pp. 1–61.

[10] R. A. Fisher, *Statistical Methods for Research Workers* (Edinburgh: Oliver & Boyd, Ltd., 1925).

has probably done more than anything else in making research workers in various fields aware of the applications of modern statistical methods to their work. This was followed by work on exact sampling distributions, theory of estimation, the chi-square test of significance, Baye's theorem, and the design of agricultural experiments.

Probability and Management Decisions

An engineer at the Bell Telephone Laboratories, T. C. Fry, presented a series of lectures in 1928 on engineering applications of probability theory. These lectures, which were published in book form,[11] provide the basis for many of the applications of probability theory to economic problems discussed in this book (Chapters 8, 9, and 11).

Much of the wartime work in "operations research," as exemplified by research under the leadership of Professor P. M. S. Blackett of the University of Manchester and in the United States in the Air Force and Navy,[12] contributed heavily to the use of the tools of probability in decision making. Many operational problems were basically those of allocating effort in the face of uncertainty as to enemy strategy. Others were logistics problems concerning the purchase, transport, warehousing, and use of supplies. These and others have their analogies in production, and such military contributions cannot be overlooked.

An application of probability theory which is being increasingly used to solve certain industrial servicing problems is the waiting-line model (Chapter 8). This was developed to solve problems in the design of telephone exchanges but during World War II was used to answer a number of questions concerning the number of servicing channels to provide in the face of random demand for such service. More recently this theory has been applied to the analysis of servicing problems in connection with automatic machinery, maintenance of equipment, design of airports and docking facilities, and similar problems.

A recent work of major potential is *The Theory of Games and Economic Behavior* by John von Neumann and Oskar Morgenstern.[13] This work is making an increasing impact on the growing science of decision making in the face of economic competition.

---

[11] T. C. Fry, *Probability and Its Engineering Uses* (New York: D. Van Nostrand Co., Inc., 1928).

[12] P. M. Morse and G. E. Kimball, *Methods of Operations Research* (Cambridge, Mass.: Technology Press and John Wiley & Sons, Inc., 1951); and J. F. McCloskey and F. N. Trefethen (ed.), *Operations Research for Management* (Baltimore: Johns Hopkins Press, 1954), chap. i.

[13] von Neumann and Morgenstern, *op. cit.*

The Concept of Quantity Planning

The problem of determining optimum inventory levels (Chapters 8 and 9) occupied the attention of a number of investigators in the early 1920's, resulting in the publication during 1925, 1926, and 1927 of several papers, all utilizing essentially the same approach for determining economic purchase quantities.[14] It remained until recently for the basic cost minimization model, which resulted from these investigations, to be modified to account for uncertainty.[15] The general model for determining economic quantities can be considered in a wide range of business applications. In fact, the concept has application wherever such questions as "how many?" or "how much?" must be answered.

Investment Analysis for Production Management

An important method of analysis in the solution of problems in production management is the development and use of a "capital goods model." An explicit formulation of the capital goods problem was given by Eugen von Bohm-Bawerk in 1890.[16] He based his reasoning on the technical superiority of what he calls "roundabout processes of production." In such a process, capital goods are used whose present value, relative to their future, is low. As production occurs over time, these capital goods are transformed into consumer goods. Thus, over time, there is an increase in value above operating costs from which interest flows as a permanent net income. Bohm-Bawerk maintained that a capitalist may exchange capital goods for future goods in the roundabout process. The excess of value provided by such methods is interest. Specific application of such theory to problems of equipment investment were made by Taylor and Hotelling in 1926,[17] and by G. A.

---

[14] Benjamin Cooper, "How to Determine Economic Manufacturing Quantities," *Industrial Management,* Vol. LXXII, No. 4 (1926), pp. 228–33; George F. Mellen, "Practical Lot Quantity Formula," *Management and Administration,* Vol. X, No. 3 (1925), p. 155; H. S. Owen, "How to Maintain Proper Inventory Control," *Industrial Management,* Vol. LXIX, No. 2 (1925), pp. 83–85; H. S. Owen, "The Control of Inventory through the Scientific Determination of Lot Sizes," *Industrial Management,* Vols. LXX and LXXI (1925 and 1926), (nine installments); Gordon Pennington, "Simple Formulas for Inventory Control," *Manufacturing Industries,* Vol. XIII, No. 3 (1927), pp. 199–203; and R. H. Wilson and W. A. Mueller, "A New Method of Stock Control," *Harvard Business Review,* Vol. V (1926–27), pp. 197–205.

[15] Thomson M. Whitin, *The Theory of Inventory Management* (Princeton: Princeton University Press, 1953).

[16] Eugen von Bohm-Bawerk, *Capital and Interest* (London: Macmillan & Co., Ltd., 1890).

[17] J. S. Taylor, "A Statistical Theory of Depreciation," *Journal of the American Statistical Association,* December, 1923; and H. Hotelling, "A General Mathematical Theory of Depreciation," *Journal of the American Statistical Association,* September, 1925.

D. Preinreich in 1940.[18] The basic Preinreich models stand today as definitive, although many models have been used in actual applications (Chapter 10). Among the more important of these are the so-called "engineering economy" models given by Grant, Norton, and others,[19] the MAPI model development by George Terborgh;[20] and the work in capital budgeting by Joel Dean.[21]

Information Handling

The most recent methods of analysis which may provide some insight into important problems in production management are those in the general field of information processing. The birth of information theory may be marked with the publication of *The Mathematical Theory of Communication* by Claude Shannon[22] of the Bell Telephone Laboratories in 1948. Much work in planning and control of production operations takes place in organizations of equipment and people which may loosely be called information processing centers. The analysis of the sources of transmission and reception of information, as well as information generation, may well point the way toward greater efficiency in the design of such organizations.

Norbert Weiner's work on *Cybernetics: or, Control and Communication in the Animal and the Machine*[23] seems to point toward the solution of such problems. The actual application of information theory seems to offer considerable promise toward the solutions of many perplexing problems of production management.

The Future

In view of the increasing interest in the quantitative analysis of management problems and the increasing complexities of business planning and control, the future will be marked by an increased use of such methods as well as much more research aimed at development of newer and better methods. Increased facility with mathematical models

---

[18] G. A. D. Preinreich, "The Economic Life of Industrial Equipment," *Econometrica,* January, 1940, pp. 12–44.

[19] Eugene L. Grant, *Principles of Engineering Economy* (New York: Ronald Press, 1946); and P. T. Norton, *The Selection and Replacement of Manufacturing Equipment,* Bulletin No. 32 (Blacksburg, Va.: Virginia Polytechnic Institute, 1934).

[20] George Terborgh, *Dynamic Equipment Policy* (New York: McGraw-Hill Book Co., Inc., 1949).

[21] Joel Dean, *Capital Budgeting* (New York: Columbia University Press, 1951).

[22] Claude E. Shannon, *The Mathematical Theory of Communication* (Urbana: University of Illinois Press, 1949).

[23] Norbert Wiener, *Cybernetics: or, Control and Communication in the Animal and the Machine* (Cambridge, Mass.: Technology Press, 1948).

will be beneficial to future managers, for this seems the most promising avenue toward better decisions.

Significant research into human behavior must certainly not be overlooked in the development of the management sciences, but effort here will be directed toward the exposition and application of the models whose background has been so briefly traced here. The future use of such methods offers great promise in the satisfaction of human wants. Knowledge concerning the search for new methods and more fruitful applications of present methods is becoming a necessary part of the equipment of successful management.

ANALYSIS

In order to place the analytical techniques in a framework broader than the individual chapters, the following section attempts to make explicit some of the steps found helpful in analyzing problems in the natural sciences, in the social sciences, and in industry. The procedure to be outlined, or something in similar form, has been called the "scientific method," due to its prevalence and usefulness in the physical sciences. Basically it includes the stages of observation, hypothesis, testing, and control. The structure of decision making will also be presented.

OBSERVATION

The first step in the analytical sequence is that of observation. One must "sit with" the problem or situation for a while prior to analysis. It is necessary to watch what actually does happen. The context of the particular problem must be understood. Observation involves also a determination of what the problem actually is. It will be necessary here, in defining any problem to be analyzed, to draw the limits of the problem under investigation. Part of the function of analysis is to segment the total world of reality into understandable parts. These lines of analysis may be somewhat arbitrarily drawn, but it is not possible to attempt to handle all aspects and ramifications of the "problem" simultaneously.

Even the most restricted portions of the real world are too complex to be comprehended in complete and exact detail by human effort. . . . As a consequence it is necessary to ignore most of the actual features of an event under study and abstract from the real situation certain aspects which together make up an idealized version of the real event. This idealization, if successful, provides a useful approximation to the real situation, or rather to certain parts of the real situation.[24]

---

[24] E. Bright Wilson, Jr., *An Introduction to Scientific Research* (New York: McGraw-Hill Book Co., Inc., 1952), pp. 24–25.

An interesting philosophic point is that observation is not possible without at least some tentative hypothesis(es). In order to know what to observe, some ideas as to what might be useful for understanding must exist.

While observing the situation, and specifying the problem, a measurable objective should be established. The analysis centers around a measure of effectiveness, and it is this measure of effectiveness, in a sense, that justifies the analysis. It is the variable of interest. In some cases in which the orientation is not a normative one (accomplishment is not the objective) but understanding alone is sought, the variable of interest may not be an "objective." Sometimes, just these beginnings of analysis —observation, problem specification, picking a measure of effectiveness —and then continued observation with a record of the measure of effectiveness may go a long way towards problem solution.

The selection of this criterion, the measurable objective, must not be a casual decision. Its effect on the whole analysis including the solution will be a major one, and the chance is very real that a good solution to the wrong problem is worse than no solution at all. A twofold discussion of the problem of selecting criteria is presented here. One aspect deals with the concepts of suboptimization. The other deals with the objectives of business. It is necessary to reflect on both of these concepts before attempting to solve production management problems, and in order to evaluate the solutions of others.

ALICE: Would you tell me please which way I ought to go from here?
CHESHIRE CAT: That depends a good deal on where you want to get to.
ALICE: I don't much care where . . .
CHESHIRE CAT: Then it doesn't matter which way you go.[25]

Suboptimization

Suboptimization, as a term, is relatively new.[26] In any sizable organization, problems exist and must be solved within components of the organization. In a manufacturing company, the sales department must solve its problems, the production department must solve its problems, and so forth. Within the production department, particular plants must solve their problems. Within the plants, organizational components have problems which must be solved by their managers. At all of these levels, objectives or measures of effectiveness must be established for the

---

[25] Lewis Carroll, *Alice's Adventures in Wonderland* (London: Macmillan, & Co., Ltd., 1865).

[26] Charles Hitch, "Sub-optimization in Operations Problems," *Journal of Operations Research Society,* Vol. I, No. 3 (May, 1953), pp. 87–99.

particular problems, situations, and departments. A department exists not for its own purposes but for the purposes of the larger organization, of which it is a part.

Ideally, the problems of the smaller department should be solved according to the purposes of the over-all organization. Full optimization requirements include:[27]

1. Consideration of *all* alternatives
2. Consideration of *all* outside events
3. Maximization of the utility function, i.e., the over-all objective of the organization

Realistically, an organizational unit which is several or many layers removed from the top over-all company management may find it difficult or impossible to establish *explicitly* the relevance of each problem it has to the over-all objectives of the organization, to consider all alternatives, and to consider all influences and all side effects. That is, rather than truly optimizing from a company standpoint, the department must suboptimize. It must optimize at its own level. It must solve problems according to objectives which are frequently connected only in an intuitive way to the objectives of the larger organization. If the objectives of the organizational component and the over-all organization cannot be linked explicitly (this does not necessarily mean something which is measurable), they should at least be intuitively consistent. The businessman's intuition is far from obsolete and must be relied upon in many stages of analysis. A criterion which is not explicitly linked to over-all objectives, and yet which seems useful for suboptimization, has been labeled a "proximate criterion." Many, many problems are solved according to proximate criteria.

One of the major problems of the executive is certainly to maintain some consistency throughout his total organization in the selection of objectives. Suboptimization is a natural attribute of an organization. Consistency with the higher level objectives must be given constant attention.

Paraphrased and summarized, Hitch derives the following propositions from economic theory:[28]

1. The criterion for good criteria is consistency with a good criterion at a higher level.

---

[27] Charles Hitch, "Sub-optimization," a chapter in McCloskey and Trefethen, *Operations Research for Management* (Baltimore: Johns Hopkins University Press, 1954).

[28] Charles Hitch, "Sub-optimization in Operations Problems," *Journal of the Operations Research Society*, Vol. I, No. 3 (May, 1953), pp. 87–99.

2. Where there is reasonable question of consistency, the side effects on other operations must be considered.
3. Ratios as criteria may be dangerous, primarily because they ignore magnitudes of both numerator and denominator. (Note that an absolute value used as a criterion—in isolation—may also be dangerous.)
4. A single input, such as labor, should not be emphasized to the exclusion of others.
5. Scarce resources should be equated at the margin in all uses, i.e., have equal marginal rates of substitution in all uses (ratios are involved here). (Chapter 9, Incremental Analysis, discusses this idea further.)

Business Objectives

As indicated in the discussion of suboptimization, in order to solve the economic problems of production management, objectives which are consistent with those of the company should be established. But what are the objectives of the company?

A business accomplishes *many* purposes.

The inclusive context of the processes that occur between men is always a society. . . . *All societies engage in work.* With the aid of tools and skills, men proceed in a special way to provide food, shelter, and clothing. The activities of work occur within a definite framework which regulates the contributions of the members, and which we call its economic organization.[29]

Society accepts a business organization for this production and distribution of goods and services which are purchased in the market place. Also, the distribution of funds for services which are provided to the business makes possible the consumption of the goods produced in the aggregate. Business organizations are a major component in the flow of funds and activity discussed in basic economics.

The specific parties whose purposes a business serves are as follows:

1. The customers who exchange their funds for the product and services;
2. The employees who exchange their services for funds (among other benefits);
3. The owners and creditors who exchange their funds in the forms of equity investments and loans for funds in the forms of dividends, capital gains, and interest payments;
4. Vendors who exchange their supplies for funds; and
5. The government which "exchanges" its services for funds in the form of taxes.

The purposes of all of these parties must be "satisfied" simultaneously for the business to survive. To satisfy any of these parties on a long-term basis, the business must prosper and continue as an economic institution

---

[29] Solomon E. Asch, *Social Psychology* (New York: Prentice-Hall, Inc., 1952), p. 117. Italics added here.

—it must make a profit. It is maintained here that *management's prime responsibility is to look after the firm itself,* which in turn makes all these services possible.

Operationally, the manager makes most decisions on the basis of an objective which serves the effective continuance of the organization. The objective at the firm level will usually be that of profit maximization in the long run within restrictions accepted by the businessman. Decisions made this way consistently should permit the business to continue to serve its many purposes.

Some further statements about the profit maximization statement are called for. Though this decision criterion might be true at the firm level, major problems still exist in selecting operational objectives for lesser organizational components and problems. Because of the many parties served by and serving the organization, some parts of the organization may address themselves especially to the needs and services of these parties, and proximate criteria may be selected according to this orientation. Where conflicts in several objectives seem to arise, they may sometimes be resolved by relating them explicitly to higher level objectives.

The restrictions on the profit maximization process accepted by many businessmen may very well differ. For example, the majority would adhere to the law of the land, some would not. Again, some managements would close a plant in a town abruptly, some managements would close the plant only after substantial efforts to alleviate the problems caused by the closing, and finally some managements would not close the plant at all. "Restrictions" such as these are part of our culture, and as the culture changes so do the restrictions. By no means do all managers make decisions on the basis of the same restrictions or "side conditions."

Of all the parties served by the business, those whose objective is the closest to long-term profit maximization by the managers for the business itself are probably the stockholder-owners. However, even this link is not an exact one. Stockholders come and go—some look for long-term growth with modest current dividends, some look for large current dividends, some look for equity safety, and some look essentially for a capital gain in the stock market.

Finally, some noneconomic decisions will undoubtedly be made by management. Certain employee benefits, or customer services, or stockholder relations, or vendor courtesies, or community benefactions fall outside of the economic sphere. To attribute them to profit maximization seems to be stretching or missing the point.

However, economic problems will normally be resolved according to economic criteria—and this is particularly true of production problems. Where conflicts might arise between economic and noneconomic criteria, the methods of analysis presented here should help resolve the economic problem, and, in addition, should help in the economic evaluation of solutions derived from noneconomic criteria.

HYPOTHESIS

Following the observation of the situation, the specification of the problem, and the selection of a measure of effectiveness or the variable of interest, hypotheses must be formulated. A hypothesis is a possible explanation of the situation observed. It is a tentative theory.

It is at this point that insight, imagination, intuition, and experience all play an important role. On the one hand, experience and familiarity with the subject should help in formulating a hypothesis. On the other hand, a fresh viewpoint may lend the needed spark. These opposites may of course be provided to the analysis by different persons. As we think in terms of what we know, analogy is many times a fruitful source of insight. Previously developed theory may of course also be helpful in hypothesis formulation.

More than one plausible hypothesis may be consistent with the initial observations. Where this is the case, it is usually preferable to use the simplest hypothesis until further investigation causes its rejection.[30] It is difficult to justify the opposite approach.

Following careful observation and reflection, it is necessary to determine or speculate on what aspects of the situation seem to influence the measurable objective. What variables seem to fluctuate with the measure of effectiveness? This list of variables which is tentatively drawn up may be classified two ways for further insight. Which of the variables are important, and which unimportant? Which of the variables are controllable, and which are not controllable?

This selecting of variables from the situation is a form of abstraction. A further form of abstraction is to construct a model which, in some sense, ties all the variables together and establishes the pattern of their relationships.

To describe an organism, we do not try to specify each molecule in it and catalogue it bit by bit, but rather to answer certain questions about it which reveal its pattern . . .[31]

---

[30] Wilson, op. cit., p. 26.

[31] Norbert Wiener, *The Human Use of Human Beings, Cybernetics and Society* (Garden City, N.Y.: Doubleday Anchor Books, 1954), p. 95.

Models

A model is an abstraction. It helps to describe the situation under investigation, and in some sense duplicates it. Models help in picking out those parts of the situation which appear to be most important to the analysis. In a sense, the model is an extension and formalization of the hypothesis.

There are many kinds of models. Physical models are probably most commonly experienced in our society, and most familiarly thought of as models. Model airplanes, ships, cars, houses, trains—the list is a very long one—may serve many purposes. They may be scale models which look like the real object. They may be models which function like the real objects—i.e., fly, move on rails, float, etc. A scale model might be constructed for pleasure. It might be used as part of a group pattern when studying arrangements, as ships in a fleet or chairs in a room. A model's reaction to forces might resemble the reactions of the real object, as, for instance, a model ship in a flow tank. New designs may be tested much more quickly and inexpensively in model than in real form.

Templates, which are small physical models of machinery and equipment, may be used in plant layout. They are arranged and moved around in a scale model of the plant. The physical representation of the equipment and the plant may be two dimensional or three dimensional.

Physical analogues are sometimes very useful for purposes of analysis. An electrical system (an analogue computer) may be constructed which has the same characteristics as another system, such as a complex of gas lines. Manipulation of the computer gives insights into the behavior of the gas system.

Schematic models are another whole classification of models. Diagrams and charts are illustrative of these. In effect, paper and pencil are used to portray some aspect(s) of the real world. Many times the schematic model does not "look like" the part of the physical world it represents. However, someone familiar with the nature of the model can learn a good bit very rapidly about the real world it describes. Schematic models are described in detail in Chapter 2.

Finally, there are the mathematical models. These are the models which are given prominence in this book. Mathematical models or formulas have long been used in the physical sciences, engineering, and some of the social sciences. These are probably the most abstract of any of the models. Mathematics itself has been referred to as a "colossal metaphor."[32] A mathematical model may be simple or complex. It may include but a few or many aspects of the situation. For purposes of analysis, when a satisfactory mathematical model can be built, it is probably the most useful type. It can be related explicitly to the measure of effectiveness. It can be precise. It is easy to manipulate. In many areas of mathematics, the manipulation has already been carried out by the mathematicians and is ready for the analyst to use.

Mathematics and logic are closely related, and in many branches of science forms of mathematics are available which are suitable for the deduction of the consequences of hypotheses. When this is so, much more elaborate and far-reaching deductions become possible because of the great power of mathematical notation and methods, which permit deductions to be made that would be overwhelmingly complex if argued in ordinary language.[33]

No model, physical, schematic, mathematical, or other, *is* the real world, though ". . . some scientists become so devoted to their model (mathematical or verbal) . . . that they will insist that this model is the real world."[34] It is an abstraction from the real world, and at best, it's useful. Usefulness is the proper criterion for judging a model.

A model is neither true or false. The standard for comparing models is therefore dependent on the situation in which it is to be used; it is not *intrinsic* (i.e., dependent only on the model itself).[35]

Obviously, the situation itself, what the problem is, who is analyzing it, and for what purpose, all influence the type of model which will be most appropriate. Because construction of a model helps force selection of the important aspects of the problem, and requires a search for the underlying patterns and structure, it can be a real aid to human comprehension and understanding.

Making the Hypothesis Specific

When a hypothesis has been formed, particularly as a mathematical model, it will be necessary to make it specific. How important are the different variables? To what extent do they influence the measure of effectiveness? What are the powers, the coefficients, the signs? There are at least two approaches to this problem. The usual business method of determining powers and signs is by intuitive and reasoned understanding of the problem, i.e., by answering the question, what makes

---

[32] *Ibid.*

[33] Wilson, *op. cit.*, p. 27.

[34] Irwin D. J. Bross, *Design for Decision* (New York: Macmillan Co., 1953), p. 172.

[35] *Ibid.*

sense? The coefficients—values, costs, speeds, etc.—are determined according to cost accounting and engineering methodologies. They are built up from past records and other sources of information.

A second method is a statistical one. Working from the total picture "backwards," signs, powers, and coefficient values are inferred. This method will be explained in Chapter 8. Of course, these two methods may be combined, and/or used as checks against each other.

The information necessary may be available from past experience, observation, and measurement. It may, in some cases, be necessary or desirable either to do additional observation or actually to generate the information through experiments where possible.

TESTING

When hypotheses have been formulated, it is necessary to test them. The fact that they make sense and are plausible should not be accepted as sufficient evidence of the "goodness" of the model.

They must be tested and substantiated by empirical evidence. It is here that much of business theory is weakest—it has never been explicitly and formally tested. This situation is not likely to be eliminated. Because of the manner in which business data are generated and maintained, it is difficult or impossible to test some models (other than an intuitive check for plausibility). Many inventory models fall into this category.

The testing may be by further observation and measurement or by experiment. A test is considered stronger if it is against new data not known when the hypothesis was formed, i.e., successful prediction rather than successful explanation.[36] Sometimes this is not possible, at least at the time initial decisions must be made. Testing against old data is better than no test at all.

It is interesting to note that Sherlock Holmes usually tested his hypothesis by deduction. From bits and pieces, he induced his general theory. Then, by deduction, he would arrive at a new specific aspect of his general theory. He'd then look for this specific aspect, and if he found it, or substantiated several such deductions by empirical fact, he'd accept the induced general theory. Because of the difficulty of testing the general theory or model itself, deductions therefrom must usually be tested.

In case of conflict, the analysis is sensible when it accepts the real world and rejects the model rather than vice versa.[37] Actually the steps

---

[36] Wilson, *op. cit.*, p. 28.

[37] Bross, *op. cit.*, p. 172.

of observation through model testing will normally be enacted more than once in an analysis. When the first models prove unsatisfactory, new observation, insights, models, and experimentation will be required.

It is well to emphasize here that the models which have been constructed and tested have properly come from thorough observation and reasoned analysis of the situation. Logic, reason, intuition, and all other human mental powers must be exploited at all stages of the analysis. This should protect the analyst against drawing erroneous conclusions from looking only at the numbers themselves.

UNDERSTANDING, PREDICTION, AND CONTROL

When a model has been tested, and is acceptable, then understanding has been added to the problem. A model which usefully describes a given situation is capable of prediction in the sense that changes in the situation can be logically (mathematically) followed through the model to determine changes in the measure of effectiveness. The changes in the measure of effectiveness desired by management may be accomplished by changing the situation in the manner suggested by manipulating the model. Decision rules which aid in managerial manipulation and control of the situation may then be deduced from the model.

DECISIONS

Recently decision making has received a great deal of systematic treatment, with the consequence that an intellectual area known as decision theory now exists. It deals essentially with the steps involved in making decisions, and the conditions under which these steps are taken. The ideas may supply useful ways of thinking about some problems and their resolution. The intention here is to present only briefly the basic structure of these ideas.

A decision is essentially a choice from alternatives. Frequently a production management group is faced with such a choice. A first step then is to identify the alternatives. An extreme position in rational decision theory suggests that *all* the alternatives must be identified. This, of course, is completely infeasible in many real situations. Once the alternatives have been identified, it is then necessary to determine the consequences which stem from each alternative. What will be the consesequences if this particular alternative is chosen for this part of the organization—for the whole organization—today—5 years from now? The major difficulty here is that consequences take place in the future, near and far, many aspects of which are unknown and unknowable. This particular puzzle will be treated later in this chapter.

Following alternative identification and consequence determination, an evaluation of the individual consequence chains must take place. Given several alternatives at this stage, and the consequence chains which stem from each alternative, some mechanism must exist which permits a preference ordering of these consequence chains. In order to choose from among the consequence chains, some evaluation scheme is necessary in order to reveal the preferred consequence chain stemming from an alternative. A nonambiguous answer to this requirement for a *real* analysis is often quite difficult.

The consequences anticipated from an alternative may take place under conditions of certainty, risk, or uncertainty. A classification scheme such as this is a useful way of thinking about problems. Much analysis is carried out with the implicit assumption that a single set of consequences stemming from an alternative can be specified and that these consequences are certain to occur. These unambiguous consequences are evaluated and compared to similarly evaluated consequences stemming from other alternatives. A choice can then be made in favor of that alternative with the most attractive consequences. In a large complex problem, because of the extremely large number of alternatives, this is not a trivial problem, as should become clear while studying Chapters 3 and 4 dealing with mathematical programming.

In many situations the consequences which may stem from an alternative depend on variables which are outside the control of the decision maker. A number of possible consequence chains may be associated with an alternative. There is then some possibility that any one of the consequence chains may follow the choice of the alternative, depending on the uncontrollable variable or variables. Assuming that each consequence chain in the set of possible ones for the alternative can be evaluated or, more particularly, assigned a value, how are the set of values to be resolved in order to associate one value with the alternative (in order to compare it with other alternatives)? Conditions of risk and uncertainty offer two possibilities for resolving this problem.

A rather simplified problem may help to clarify these ideas. For many ceramic products an oven baking process is required. During this process, however, some of the products sometimes break or craze. It is frequently economic to add extra items to allow for this shrinkage. Consider an involved product which is quite difficult to make. A special order for two of these has been received. Should two, or three, or four of these be made for placing in the oven? It depends on how many, if any, will craze; but this is the unknown and uncontrollable element in the problem. Rather than justifying the costs in such a problem they are merely set down in the following table:

Break

		x	y	z
		0	1	2
Produce a	2	10	18	20
b	3	12	12	20
c	4	14	14	14

The numbers within the table correspond to the costs associated with the consequence chains of each alternative (a, b, c) under each of the breakage occurrences (x, y, z). For instance, if 3 units are produced (b), and 2 break (z), the cost will be \$20. The conditions of certainty, risk, and uncertainty may all be illustrated with this simple example. If it is certain that no units will break (x), then alternative a with consequences evaluated at \$10 is the obvious choice. If no one condition of breakage is certain, this simple approach no longer holds true.

If enough information exists about this process that probabilities can be meaningfully assigned to the various breakage possibilities, the *expected value* approach usually associated with conditions of risk can be employed. Assume that you are willing to state that the probability of x occurring is 20 per cent, of y occurring is 70 per cent, and of z occurring is 10 per cent (sum of the probabilities equals 100 per cent). In order to use such probability statements with some confidence, it is advisable to have some assurance concerning the *stability* of the process. Ideas concerning the drawing of inferences from empirical data are presented in Chapters 5, 6, and 7 dealing with statistical analysis.

If alternative a were chosen 100 times, the expected total cost (given the earlier stated probabilities) would be $20 \times 10 + 70 \times 18 + 10 \times 20 = \$1,660$. The average cost would be $1,660/100 = \$16.60$. An expected value is equivalent to an anticipated average. It is the sum of the products of the probability of an occurrence times the value if it does occur. The expression above would be $0.20 \times 10 + 0.70 \times 18 + 0.10 \times 20 = \$16.60$ (i.e., the 100 times is not necessary for the computation). Alternative b presents an expected value of $0.20 \times 12 + 0.70 \times 12 + 0.10 \times 20 = \$12.80$. Alternative c presents an expected value of $14.00 ($1.00 \times 14$). As alternative *b* has the lowest expected value, this alternative would be chosen according to this criterion. Much of the modern analysis of industrial problems taking place today is an attempt to understand and optimize expected values. Much of Chapters 10 and 11 deals with these concepts.

Uncertainty is a condition, as described in the literature,[38] where the alternatives are given, as well as the possible states or consequence chains along with the values of these consequences. What is lacking are the probabilities associated with the states or consequences. Consider the oven crazing problem previously set forth. Now no probability statements can be associated with breakage (x, y, z). Which alternative is to be chosen?

There are a number of ways of developing an answer to this question.[39] The heart of game theory[40] has provided the criterion which has received most attention in the literature—whether this is true in actual decision making is another matter. The idea is to choose the alternative(s) with the best worst outcome (called the minimax, or maximin). In the oven example, alternative *a* has a worst outcome of $20, alternative *b* has a worst outcome of $20, and alternative *c* has a worst outcome of $14. Alternative *c* then is the best choice as it has the best of the worst outcomes. Another way of looking at this is the recognition that it has the best conservative guarantee. Game theory contains much more than this simple notion, presented in a rather limited example, and it is not intended here to extend these ideas. The discussions and problems in this book deal with conditions of certainty or risk as here defined. The common meaning of the term uncertainty (rather than as specially used in this section) is employed later in the book to denote conditions of risk.

REFERENCES ON PRODUCTION PROBLEMS

There are many books which deal with the problems of production. In them can be found descriptions of the problems under varying conditions, and generalizations, considerations, and systems of solution. Books are listed under headings used in the chapter.

---

[38] See R. D. Luce and H. Raiffa, *Games and Decisions* (New York: John Wiley & Sons, Inc., 1957), for an extended discussion of these concepts; and Herbert Simon, *Administrative Behavior* (New York: Macmillan Co., 1957), for a critique of some of the axioms implied.

[39] Luce and Raiffa, *op. cit.*

[40] J. von Neumann and O. Morgenstern, *The Theory of Games and Economic Behavior* (Princeton: Princeton University Press, 1947).

General

ALFORD, L. P., and BANGS, J. R. *Production Handbook.* New York: Ronald Press, 1948.

BUFFA, E. S. *Modern Production Management.* New York: John Wiley & Sons, Inc., 1961.

STARR, M. K. *Production Management: Systems and Synthesis.* Englewood Cliffs, N.J.: Prentice-Hall, Inc., 1964.

Historical

TAYLOR, F. W. *Scientific Management.* New York: Harper & Bros., 1947.

THE TAYLOR SOCIETY, PIERSON, H. S. (ed.). *Scientific Management in American Industry.* New York: Harper & Bros., 1929.

Inventory

FETTER, R. B., and DALLECK, W. C. *Decision Models for Inventory Management.* Homewood, Ill.: Richard D. Irwin, Inc., 1961.

HADLEY, G., and WHITIN, T. *Analysis of Inventory Systems.* Englewood Cliffs, N.J.: Prentice-Hall, Inc., 1963.

LEWIS, HOWARD T., and ENGLAND, WILBUR B. *Procurement, Principles and Cases.* 3d ed. Homewood, Ill.: Richard D. Irwin, Inc., 1957.

MAGEE, JOHN F. *Production Planning and Inventory Control.* New York: McGraw-Hill Book Co., Inc., 1958.

STARR, M. K., and MILLER, D. W. *Inventory Control.* Englewood Cliffs, N.J.: Prentice-Hall, Inc., 1962.

WHITIN, THOMSON M. *The Theory of Inventory Management.* Princeton: Princeton University Press, 1953.

Production Scheduling and Control

EILON, S. *Elements of Production Planning and Control.* New York: Macmillan Co., 1962.

HOLT, C. C.; MODIGLIANI, F.; MUTH, J.; and SIMON, H. A. *Planning Production, Inventories, and Work Force.* Englewood Cliffs, N.J.: Prentice-Hall, Inc., 1960.

KOEPKE, CHARLES E. *Plant Production Control.* New York: John Wiley & Sons, Inc., 1951.

MACNIECE, E. H. *Production Forecasting and Control.* New York: John Wiley & Sons, Inc., 1953.

MAGEE, J. F. *Production Planning and Inventory Control.* New York: McGraw-Hill Book Co., Inc., 1953.

MOORE, FRANKLIN G. *Production Control.* New York: McGraw-Hill Book Co., Inc., 1951.

RITCHIE, W. E. *Production and Inventory Control.* New York: Ronald Press, 1951.

Equipment Selection and Replacement

GRANT, EUGENE L. *Principles of Engineering Economy.* New York: Ronald Press, 1946.

THUESEN, H. G., and FABRYCKY, W. J. *Engineering Economy.* 3d ed. Engle-wood Cliffs, N.J.: Prentice-Hall, Inc., 1961.

Maintenance

Techniques of Plant Maintenance and Engineering. New York: Clapp and Poliak, 1953.

Scale and Location of Plants

HOOVER, EDGAR M. *The Location of Economic Activity.* New York: Mc-Graw-Hill Book Co., Inc., 1948.

Plant Layout and Materials Handling

APPLE, JAMES M. *Plant Layout and Materials Handling.* New York: Ronald Press, 1950.

IRESON, WILLIAM G. *Factory Planning and Plant Layout.* New York: Pren-tice-Hall, Inc., 1952.

MUTHER, RICHARD. *Production Line Techniques.* New York: McGraw-Hill Book Co., Inc., 1944.

Quality Control and Inspection

DUNCAN, ACHESON J. *Quality Control and Industrial Statistics.* 3d ed. Homewood, Ill.: Richard D. Irwin, Inc., 1965.

FEIGENBAUM, A. V. *Quality Control.* New York: McGraw-Hill Book Co., Inc., 1951.

GRANT, EUGENE L. *Statistical Quality Control.* New York: McGraw-Hill Book Co., Inc., 1952.

Methods and Standards

BARNES, RALPH M. *Work Methods Manual.* New York: John Wiley & Sons, Inc., 1946.

NADLER, GERALD. *Motion and Time Study.* New York: McGraw-Hill Book Co., Inc., 1955.

NIEBEL, BENJAMIN W. *Motion and Time Study.* 4th ed. Homewood, Ill.: Richard D. Irwin, Inc., 1967.

Analysis

BAUMOL, W. J. *Economic Theory and Operations Analysis.* Englewood Cliffs, N.J.: Prentice-Hall, Inc., 1961.

BIERMAN, H.; BONINI, C. P.; FOURAKER, L. E.; and JAEDICKE, R. K. *Quantita-tive Analysis for Business Decisions.* Rev. ed. Homewood, Ill.: Richard D. Irwin, Inc., 1965.

BROSS, IRWIN D. J. *Design for Decision.* New York: Macmillan Co., 1953.

BUFFA, E. S. *Models for Production and Operations Management.* New York: John Wiley & Sons, Inc., 1963.

CHURCHMAN, C. W.; ACKOFF, R.; and ARNOFF, E. L. *Introduction to Opera-tions Research.* New York: John Wiley & Sons, Inc., 1957.

HANSMANN, F. *Operations Research in Production and Inventory Control.* New York: John Wiley & Sons, Inc., 1962.

HITCH, CHARLES. "Sub-optimization," a chapter in McCloskey and Trefethen, *Operations Research for Management*. Baltimore: Johns Hopkins University Press, 1954.

KAUFMANN, A. *Methods & Models of Operations Research*. Englewood Cliffs, N.J.: Prentice-Hall, Inc., 1963.

LUCE, R. D., and RAIFFA, H. *Games and Decisions*. New York: John Wiley & Sons, Inc., 1957.

MANNE, A. S. *Economic Analysis for Business Decisions*. New York: McGraw-Hill Book Co., Inc., 1961.

MILLER, D. W., and STARR, M. K. *Executive Decisions and Operations Research*. Englewood Cliffs, N.J.: Prentice-Hall, Inc., 1960.

MORRIS, W. T. *The Analysis of Management Decisions*. Rev. ed. Homewood, Ill.: Richard D. Irwin, Inc., 1964.

SASIENI M.; YASPAN A.; and FRIEDMAN L. *Introduction to Operations Research*. New York: John Wiley & Sons, Inc., 1960.

SIMON, HERBERT. *Administrative Behavior*. New York: Macmillan Co., 1957.

TEICHROEW, D. *An Introduction to Management Science*. New York: John Wiley & Sons, Inc., 1964.

WILSON, E. BRIGHT, JR. *An Introduction to Scientific Research*. New York: McGraw-Hill Book Co., Inc., 1962.

CHAPTER 2

Schematic Models

INTRODUCTION

A VERY large number of the problems of production management have been and are being analyzed through the use of what may be called "schematic models." By this term is meant all those methods for analysis of management problems which involve the graphical representation of the way in which a "system" operates. As such, these techniques as used in management are analogous to the machine designer's blueprint and the electrical engineer's circuit diagram. They represent an abstraction, usually using pencil and paper, of the way in which events are occurring or may occur in the real world. For example, a chart may show the way in which material is being routed from operation to operation. Once drawn, such a chart becomes the starting point for systematic attempts at improvement. Pertinent questions may be asked concerning the way in which the work is being done, as shown on the chart, and avenues toward improvement sought. Basically, then, all schematic methods involve the graphical abstraction of a system with the objective of analysis and improvement through application of known facts and premises. The material which follows this chapter consists of quantitative methods for the analysis of problems in production management. The material of this chapter represents much of what has been called "scientific management." This material thus represents a necessary link between current practice and the more powerful methods of analysis which will be used more and more in management. In fact, the construction of schematic models is often an essential prelude to the framing of a problem for quantitative analysis.

These methods traditionally have constituted (and do so today) the basic tools of the practicing industrial engineer. The electrical engineer may present a design as a circuit diagram of some electrical system to portray all the elements and interconnections necessary for a system whose goal is some useful output. The industrial engineer attempts to do the same thing with respect to production systems. He has to face, however, certain difficulties which are not faced in electrical circuit design. This is primarily because the systems which the industrial engineer portrays almost always involve human beings as basic elements as well as materials and machines.

The electrical engineer may be fairly confident, as a result of his analysis and design, that impressing a given voltage across the input to the system will result in the desired output. The industrial engineer is not nearly so certain that the system he designs will operate as predicted. He impresses "voltage" (wages, working conditions, etc.) at the input, and output occurs in some manner other than predicted because the men in the system did not behave as assumed. The elements which contributed to the behavior of the system as a whole were not explicitly allowed for in the design since their occurrence was not predictable, and even if it had been, the effect would have been largely unknown. This is not intended to introduce despair into this kind of analysis but merely to point out some major difficulties inherent in the use and manipulation of schematic models to portray management systems.

Schematic Methods

The principal schematic methods and those which will be presented here are as follows:

1. Flow process charts and flow diagrams
2. Multiple activity charts
3. Operator charts
4. Routine sequence diagrams
5. Assembly diagrams
6. Gantt charts
7. Block diagrams
8. Organization charts

The above names are given in accordance with general usage and, unhappily, are not mutually exclusive. However, the amount of overlap has been reduced to as low a level as is possible while still maintaining maximum contact with accepted practice.

FLOW PROCESS CHARTS

Flow process charts are schematic representations of the order of occurrence of the events which constitute completion of some desired objective. They usually represent the path of some material or paper past men and machines, although in some cases a man may be followed. They may be drawn on floor plans in order to show distances and directions of flow and the like more clearly. A standard set of symbols in general use is as follows:

○ Operation: Any work done on the material or paper which the chart is following. When blacked in, the symbol represents "do" operations as contrasted to "make-ready" or "put-away."[1]

▢ Inspection: Any comparison with predetermined plans or standards.

⤓ Transporation: Any movement of the material or paper between work stations or to storage.

▽ Storage: Any delay or storage of material, man, or paper (for example, a wait for transportation or filing of a paper).

With the above symbols or a similar set, any procedure for doing work may be portrayed. They may be used to design a proposed procedure or record a procedure to maintain continuity in its use and for use in training. The form on which the process may be entered is quite variable, and an example of a widely used type is shown in Figure 2–1. The job shown is that of trimming the core during the production of a bowling ball. One workman performs the entire sequence of operations, and he is the subject of the chart. Some points to be observed in constructing such a chart are as follows:

1. State clearly the objective of the chart and define the activity to be studied.
2. Orient the chart to a man, material, or paper. Once having determined which is most appropriate, it is helpful to follow the one subject throughout the preparation of the chart without change. If it is better in a given case to follow more than one object, do so separately and show relationship between each of the objects followed.
3. Outline the job from a well-defined starting point to the end in terms of operations, transportations, inspections, and storages. Prepare a brief description of every step in order that none be left out no matter how unimportant it might seem.
4. Connect the appropriate symbols.
5. Record distances involved in transportations and operations on the chart.
6. If appropriate to the analysis, determine and enter time required for the various steps.
7. Summarize the information thus gained in a summary block. The total number of operations, transportations, inspections, and storages should be shown as well as the total distance and time (if appropriate).

---

[1] "Make-ready" operations are all those elements of a job which take place prior to the performance which results in some output, e.g., setups, pre-positioning of tools, and the like. "Put-away" operations are all those elements which follow that performance which results in output such as putting away tools, cleaning up work area, and so forth.

It is usually advantageous to concentrate on the one subject selected for the chart. For example, if a switch is made from man to material and back to the man again, the chart then introduces confusion, whereas

Figure 2–1

FLOW PROCESS CHART

SUMMARY		PRESENT	SAVED
Operations	◯	301	
Transportations	⇨	184	
Storages	▽	0	
Inspections	☐	30	
Total Details		515	
Total Distance		702	
Total Time		24.6 min.	

PROCESS _ Trimming Operation of Bowling Ball Core _ _ _ _ _ _

SUBJECT CHARTED _ _ _ _ Trimming lathe operator _ _ _ _ _ _ _

DATE _ _ _ _ _ _ _ _ _ _ CHARTED BY _ _ _ _ _ _ _ _ _ _ _ _

DETAIL DESCRIPTION (Present / ~~Proposed~~)	OPERATION	TRANSPORT	STORAGE	INSPECTION	DISTANCE	TIME/PROD.	ELIMINATE	COMBINE	SEQUENCE	PLACE	PERSON	IMPROVE	NOTES
1 Place a core on flash trimming table	◯	⇨	▽	☐	4	1							⎫
2 Cut off flash	●	⇨	▽	☐		2							⎬ Repeat 30 times
3 Put the core on storage rack	◯	⇨	▽	☐	4	1							⎭
4 Walk to lathe	◯	⇨	▽	☐	26	4							
5 Carry a core to lathe	◯	⇨	▽	☐	8	2							⎤
6 Chuck core on lathe	◯	⇨	▽	☐		5							
7 Start motor and trim	●	⇨	▽	☐		10							
8 Stop motor	◯	⇨	▽	☐		1							►Repeat ⎤
9 Rechuck the core	◯	⇨	▽	☐		3							10 times
10 Start motor and trim	●	⇨	▽	☐		10							
11 Stop motor	◯	⇨	▽	☐		1							⎦ Repeat 3 times
12 Remove core and place on storage table	◯	⇨	▽	☐		2							⎦
13 Walk to wire wheel	◯	⇨	▽	☐	12	2							
14 Pick up core and buff	●	⇨	▽	☐		3							⎤ Repeat
15 Place core on rail to scale	◯	⇨	▽	☐		1							⎦ 10 times
16 Walk to scale	◯	⇨	▽	☐	7	2							
17 Place core on scale	◯	⇨	▽	☐		1							⎤ Repeat 30
18 Weigh and record	◯	⇨	▽	☐		4							⎬ times
19 Put core on rack	◯	⇨	▽	☐	4	1							⎦
20 Return to lathe	◯	⇨	▽	☐	7	2							
21 Remove scraps and clean lathe	◯	⇨	▽	☐	10	20							
22 Walk to the storage bin	◯	⇨	▽	☐	26	4							

its object is to clear away extraneous matter and focus attention on a particular job. It is also helpful not to attempt to cover too much ground in a single chart. It is more important that the chart be as detailed as necessary for accurate portrayal of the system.

Another type of flow chart is shown in Figure 2–2. Here the manufacture of chocolate candy from cocoa beans is portrayed schematically. No concept is given here of the spatial flow of materials, but a complete picture of the work performed can be obtained from this schematic.

It is often helpful to trace the flow of work on a floor plan as a supplement to the chart. A flow diagram for the job of Figure 2–1 is shown in Figure 2–3. Again this figure is a representation of a portion of the process of producing bowling balls. It shows the work being done in order to cool, trim, and store the core.

Figure 2–2

CHOCOLATE MANUFACTURE—FLOW CHART

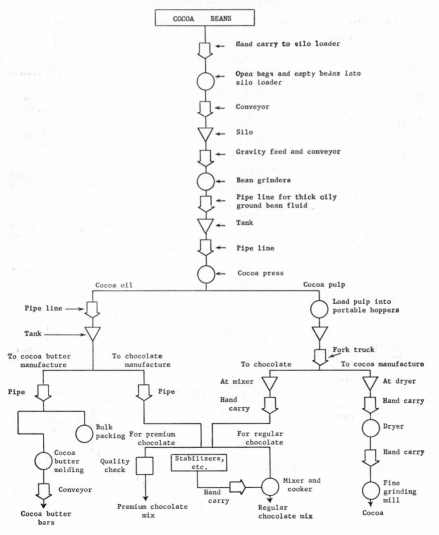

The flow process chart with the accompanying flow diagram now could be used as the basis for a systematic examination of the present method with a view toward its improvement. The first thing to be done is to challenge every detail of the work. This may be done by posing the following kinds of questions:

1. *Why* is the job being done at all? This should always be the first question, and the answer should be definitely established in terms of the objective of the job before going on.
2. *What* is being done? The value of each detail of the work as it contributes to the objective should be established.
3. *Where* is the work being done? Make sure that the work place is the most efficient for the necessary work.

Figure 2–2—Continued

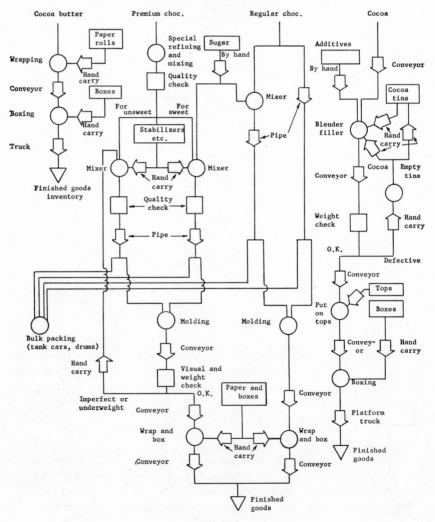

4. *When* is the work being done? The most efficient sequence should be established by questioning the detail of the present sequence.
5. *Who* does the work? Be sure that the right person is doing the work.
6. *How* is the work being performed? Can the work be made simpler and easier for personnel and equipment?

Figure 2–3
BOWLING BALL CORE CONSTRUCTION FLOW DIAGRAM

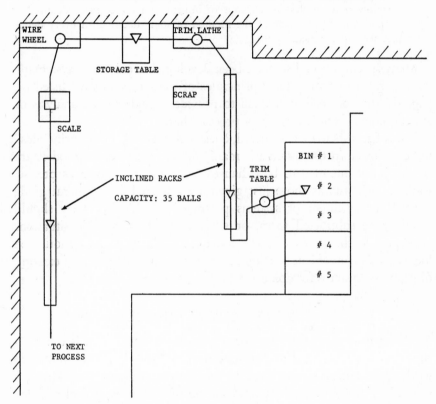

Satisfactory answers should be obtained for these questions before going on with the analysis. It is usually best to concentrate on work which is of the "get-ready" or "put-away" type rather than "do" operations ("do" operations should be blacked in on the flow process chart). Next an attempt may be made to work out a better method.

For this purpose, the following questions may be asked of each detail of the chart:

1. *Can the operation be eliminated?* This question must be answered first since no further work should be done on any detail which can be eliminated. If each operation is justified, transportations and storages should be challenged on the same basis.

2. *Can two or more operations be combined?* This should be done wherever possible to eliminate transportations and delays between operations.
3. *Can the sequence, place, or person be changed?* Here the flow diagram is of importance. Backtracking may be eliminated or cycle time shortened by sequence or place changes. In some cases, work can be done to better advantage by shifting it to another person.
4. *Can the remaining work be improved?* This question should only be asked after the preceding questions have been answered satisfactorily. It is certainly quite useless to attempt to improve an unnecessary detail. No changes should be made in the method of some detail until every detail has been questioned.

Many specific check lists have been developed to aid in the systematic improvement of work. The "principles of motion economy" listed on page 47 may be readily adapted to provide a guide in the analysis of situations represented on a flow process chart.

Lists of factors to be considered, questions to be asked, or "principles" to be followed in the systematic manipulation of schematic models are certainly not intended to be exhaustive nor are they given as precise. Rather, such lists as those just given are intended as a general guide toward improvement of systems portrayed graphically. They should certainly be subtracted from, or supplemented in, specific situations according to the needs of each situation. Such check lists should be looked on as convenient starting points for the improvement of existing or proposed systems for doing work.

MULTIPLE ACTIVITY CHARTS

A second important device for schematic representation is the multiple activity chart. This chart is used to record the times required to do work where both men and machines are involved. Figure 2–4 shows an example of this type of chart representing the assembly of fuel rods for an atomic reactor. The basic symbols used in this kind of chart are as follows:

		Man	*Machine*
■	Independent Activity:	Any work which is independent of the machine or other operator.	Any work which is done by the machine without operator help.
☐	Combined Activity:	Work done with a machine or other operator such as setup or loading.	Operating time when an operator is required.
▨	Idle:	Waiting for machine.	Waiting for operator.

The purpose of the analysis using this chart is to attempt to reduce or eliminate idle operator or machine time. A chart may contain many more than the two columns of Figure 2–4 if more men or machines

Figure 2–4

MAN-MACHINE CHART OF ASSEMBLY OF FUEL RODS FOR ATOMIC REACTOR

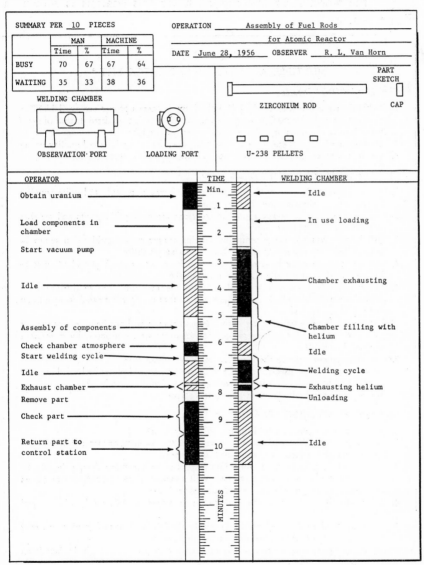

are involved. In the example shown, it might be more profitable for purposes of analysis to break the job down in more detail, especially as regards the one minute allotted to the assembly of components. Even if the time cannot be accurately determined, a simple listing of the activities can often be very helpful. A summary of the chart should be prepared showing the utilization of both men and machines.

Attempts at improvement may be made asking the basic questions; why, where, when, who, and how, followed by detailed analysis of each part of the work. A typical check list for this analysis is shown in Figure 2–5.

Figure 2–5

MULTIPLE ACTIVITY CHART CHECK LIST *

Check List for "DO" Details

1. Is this the right machine for the job, and, if not, is there a proper one available? Can we grind instead of turn? Can we shape instead of mill? Can we ditto instead of type?
2. Are we using the most up-to-date attachments for the job?
3. Are machine feeds and speeds at a maximum, keeping in mind desired quality work?
4. Are the tolerances too tight or too loose for the type of equipment used?

Check List for "MAKE-READY" Details

1. Can we arrange to have tools, blueprints, job instruction card, and office supplies brought out to the machine ahead of time?
2. Can we arrange to have any special instructions accompany blueprints and see that they are faultlessly clear?
3. Will better planning reduce setups by making longer runs possible? Can setups be made during lunch hours or rest periods, or on an off shift?
4. Can maintenance work be done on an off shift or during lunch periods? Can it be done with safety while the machine is running?
5. Can someone else lay out the work place during the setup time? Are we always careful to have the work place laid out the same way so that the operator can develop a habit path?
6. Can the machine be left running with safety so that it will not be necessary to shut it off and turn it on for each operation? Are starting switches properly located? Can a foot pedal be used?
7. Can someone else prepare the materials to better advantage?
8. Can a hopper feed be used to load the machine? Can several pieces be loaded at once? Can loading be combined with unloading? Will pre-positioning help?
9. Are we taking full advantage of guides and stops?

Check List for "PUT-AWAY" Elements

1. Is a limit switch practical for shutting off the machine?
2. Can we use drop delivery to unload the machine? Air, vacuum, or cam action delivery? Can we knock the piece out while loading the next?
3. Can someone else inspect the work? Can inspection be automatic during the DO, or be done by the operator during the DO? Will a sample inspection suffice? Are gauges and measuring devices the easiest and simplest to use?
4. Can a chute be used to take the work to the next operation? Can a floor boy or girl take it away?
5. Can scrap be cleaned up automatically during the DO by means of gravity, air, etc.? Can it be done during lunch periods or during an off shift?
6. Can the complete setup be removed as an assembly and, if necessary, be broken down in the tool crib?
7. Can someone else return tools, excess materials, and supplies?

---

* Compiled by Professor Herbert F. Goodwin of the School of Industrial Management, Massachusetts Institute of Technology.

OPERATOR CHARTS

The operator chart is a detailed presentation of the motions of a man in performing a job. The same symbols may be used as in the flow process chart, but they refer here to the work of the human body. An operator chart for the assembly of a fountain pen is shown in Figure 2–6.

Figure 2–6

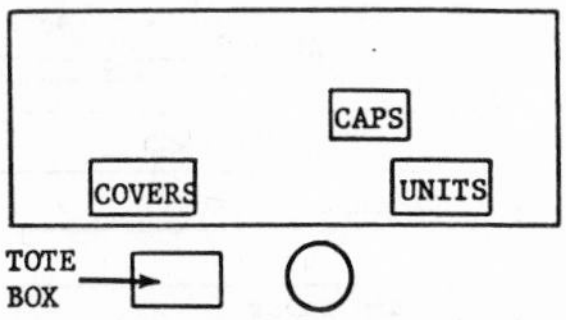

OPERATOR CHART OF FOUNTAIN PEN ASSEMBLY—PRESENT METHOD

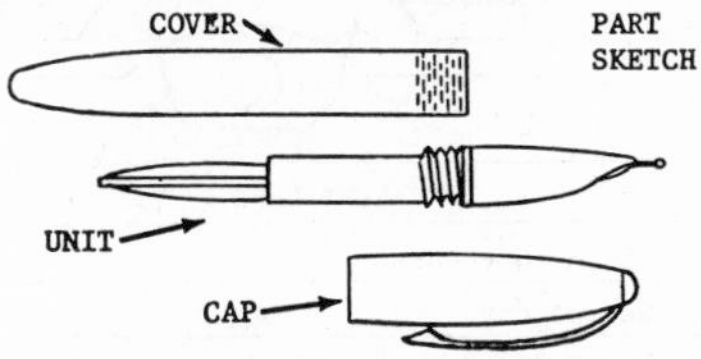

The same questions and check list as for the flow process chart may be applied to the operator chart in order to improve the method. A chart for a possible improved method resulting from such an analysis is shown in Figure 2–7. It should be noticed that the proposed method requires

21 steps for each hand, as against 12 for the present, but results in twice the production per cycle. Further, all delays have been eliminated and both hands work symmetrically. This last is certainly a much more

Figure 2–7

OPERATOR CHART OF FOUNTAIN PEN ASSEMBLY—PROPOSED METHOD

~~PRESENT~~ PROPOSED	METHOD					OPERATOR CHART	PAGE _1_ OF _1_
SUMMARY	OPER O	TRAN ⇨	STOR ▽	INSP ☐	TOTAL STEPS	OPERATION _PEN ASSEMBLY_	
LEFT HAND	14	7	0	0	21		
RIGHT HAND	14	7	0	0	21	DATE JUNE 23 OBSERVER *R. L. Van Horn*	

WORK SPACE LAYOUT

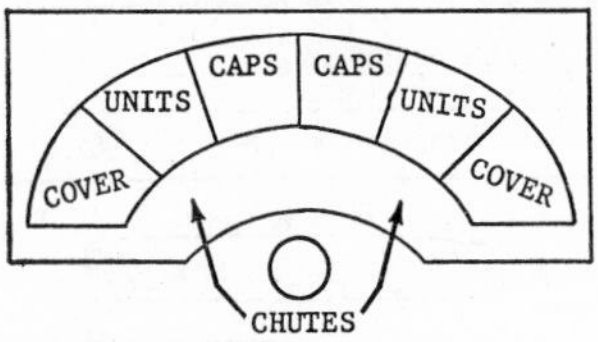

PART SKETCH

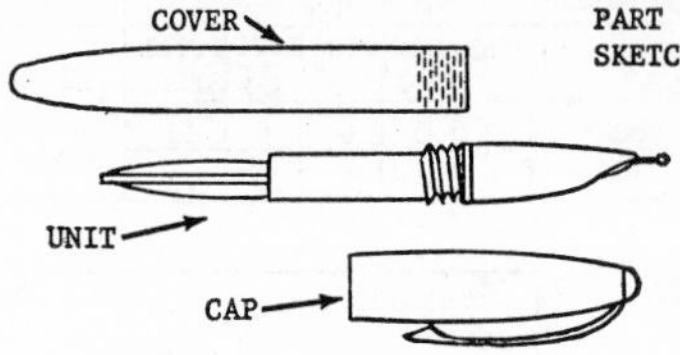

LEFT HAND			RIGHT HAND
1. Reach to covers	⇨	⇨	1. Reach to covers
2. Select cover	O	O	2. Select cover
3. Grasp cover	O	O	3. Grasp cover
4. Carry to fixture	⇨	⇨	4. Carry to fixture
5. Position in fixture	O	O	5. Position in fixture
6. Release cover	O	O	6. Release cover
7. Reach to unit	⇨	⇨	7. Reach to unit
8. Select unit	O	O	8. Select unit
9. Grasp unit	O	O	9. Grasp unit
10. Carry to cover	⇨	⇨	10. Carry to cover
11. Assemble to cover	O	O	11. Assemble to cover
12. Reach to caps	⇨	⇨	12. Reach to caps
13. Select cap	O	O	13. Select cap
14. Grasp cap	O	O	14. Grasp cap
15. Carry to unit	⇨	⇨	15. Carry to unit
16. Position cap	O	O	16. Position cap
17. Assemble on unit	O	O	17. Assemble on unit
18. Lift assembly	O	O	18. Lift assembly
19. Carry to drop chute	⇨	⇨	19. Carry to drop chute
20. Position assembly	O	O	20. Position assembly
21. Release assembly	O	O	21. Release assembly

restful scheme of work than asymmetrical motions. A useful check list in examining such situations as this is shown in Figure 2–8.

ROUTINE SEQUENCE DIAGRAMS

Diagrams representing the flow of information (e.g., in a production control system) may be called routine sequence diagrams or information flow charts. They show the way in which information, both oral and written, flows from points of origin to destinations, as well as showing the work done in preparing, processing, and using this information. In

---

Figure 2–8

PRINCIPLES OF MOTION ECONOMY*

A. Use of the Human Body

1. The two hands should begin, as well as complete, their motions at the same instant.
2. The two hands should not be idle at the same instant except during rest periods.
3. Motions of the arms should be in opposite and symmetrical directions, instead of in the same direction, and should be made simultaneously.
4. Hand motions should be confined to the lowest classification with which it is possible to perform the work satisfactorily; classification of motions from lowest to highest are as follows: (1) finger, (2) hand, (3) wrist, (4) arm, (5) trunk.
5. Momentum should be employed to assist the worker wherever possible, and it should be reduced to a minimum if it must be overcome by muscular effort.
6. Continuous curved motions are preferable to straight-line motions involving sudden and sharp changes in direction.
7. Ballistic movements are faster, easier, and more accurate than restricted fixation or "controlled" movements.
8. Rhythm is essential to the smooth and automatic performance of an operation, and the work should be arranged to permit easy and natural rhythm wherever possible.

B. Arrangements of the Work Place

1. Definite and fixed stations should be provided for all tools and materials.
2. Tools, materials, and controls should be located around the work place and as close in front of the worker as possible.
3. Gravity feed bins and containers should be used to deliver the material as close to the point of assembly or use as possible.
4. "Drop deliveries" should be used wherever possible.
5. Materials and tools should be located to permit the best sequence of motions.
6. Provisions should be made for adequate conditions for seeing. Good illumination is the first requirement for satisfactory visual perception.
7. The height of the work place and the chair should preferably be so arranged that alternate sitting and standing at work are easily possible.
8. A chair of the type and height to permit good posture should be provided for every worker.

C. Design of Tools and Equipment

1. The hands should be relieved of all work that can be performed more advantageously by the feet or other parts of the body.
2. Two or more tools should be combined whenever possible.
3. Tools and materials should be pre-positioned wherever possible.
4. Where each finger performs some specific movement, such as typewriting, the load should be distributed in accordance with the inherent capacities of the fingers.
5. Handles, such as those used on cranks and large screwdrivers, should be designed to permit as much of the surface of the hand to come in contact with the handle as possible. This is particularly true when considerable force is exerted in using the handle. For light assembly work the screwdriver handle should be so shaped that it is smaller at the bottom than at the top.
6. Levers, crossbars, and handwheels should be located in such positions that the operator can manipulate them with the least change in body position and with the greatest mechanical advantage.

---

* Ralph Barnes, *Time and Motion Study* (3d ed.; New York: John Wiley & Sons, Inc., 1949), p. 191.

analyzing such procedures, the routine sequence diagram gives an overall picture of the system, as well as relationships within the system. Figure 2–9 is a typical routine sequence diagram showing a part of a production control system for the production of rubber covered rollers to customer order. Across the top of the chart are listed the departments or organizational units involved in the procedure, while the steps in the procedure are either given in a separate list or along the left edge of the chart. The standard process chart symbols are used to indicate the kind of activity involved at each step.

The description of each step is as follows:

1. Customer's order received.
2. Customer's order filed; one copy typed for salesman's reference. Factory order made up in triplicate:
   a) Office file
   b) Factory action
   c) Shipping and receiving
3. Copy given to salesman for customer.
4. Upon arrival of roller:
   a) Serial number stamped on roller shaft and noted on shipping's copy of factory order (serial numbers are assigned by sequence of arrival).
   b) Roller department clerk notes serial number in a pocket record book.
5. Roller department clerk takes shop copy of factory order from pending file and makes a serial number entry (factory order is now activated and proceeds to scheduling).
6. Schedule card is made out and placed in ring binder which is used as a schedule priority file.
   Delivery date entered on factory order.
   Daily summary sheet is sent to the roller department office (9).
7. Factory order sent to shop foreman's desk (first pigeon hole).
8. Daily compound order sheet sent to mill room foreman (10).
   Daily "rolls to be transferred" sheet sent to shop foreman.
11. Factory order shifted to "prepared and stripped" pigeon hole when report of roller progress is received from shop.
12. Factory order shifted to "stock ready" pigeonhole when report from mill room indicates rubber stock is ready for calendering.
   Daily "covering ticket" (or calendar sheet) in triplicate is sent by foreman to:
   a) Shop file
   b) Calendering crew (in mill room) (17)
   c) Roller coverers (in roller shop) (18)
13. Factory order shifted to "ready in all respects" slot when calendered stock is ready.
14. Factory order shifted to "covered and cured" when roller is ready for skimming.
15. Factory order shifted to "ready for grinding" after skimming operation.
16. Finished roller is inspected. Inspector completes quality control sheet

Figure 2-9

INFORMATION FLOW CHART I—ROLL PROCESSING

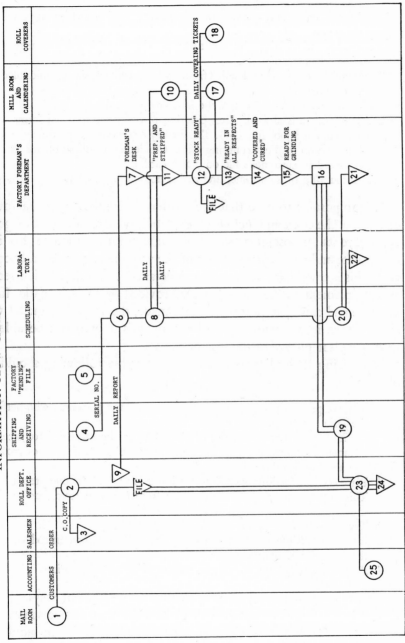

(for large rollers only) and attaches it to the factory order; one copy goes to scheduling (20).

Factory order and quality control sheet go with roller to shipping department.

19. Factory order and quality control sheet return to roller department office, after shipment of roller.
21. Schedule ticket completed (from quality control sheet) and filed by shop foreman.
22. Quality control copy enters the laboratory records.
23. The job file is cleared. After entering prices, the completed forms enter a "completed job" file (24). The factory order office copy carries pricing information to the accounting office. Condensed information for this job is placed in customer's file on 5 × 7 card.
25. Accounting bills customer and makes accounting entries.

It is important to note that the written descriptions carry far more detail than the chart and include all explanatory material. If the diagram is to serve its purpose, it must include enough information so that it is a complete and true representation of the way the system actually operates. This is true of any such model. A detailed verbal description serves as a supplement to the over-all view provided by the schematic. If an accurate and complete portrayal is not made, the schematic model will either prove inadequate as a tool for analysis or will not be able to convey a clear picture of the system.

In drawing these diagrams, such points as the following should be observed:

1. Observe procedures at each level and talk with the personnel who perform the tasks involved.
2. Do not cramp the schematic. Clarity must not be sacrificed for size.
3. Arrange functional headings so that the necessity for flow lines crossing one another is minimized.
4. Place each succeeding operation at a lower level than the one preceding it. This will permit reading the diagram from top to bottom, and make it easier to locate successive steps.
5. Try to avoid long vertical flow lines if possible.
6. Identify multiple copies by color or letter rather than introduce more than one set of numbers.
7. Alternate procedures should be shown wherever appropriate.

This type of diagram can be drawn in many different ways. Figure 2–10 illustrates one of these. It represents the same system shown in Figure 2–9. This type of chart is sometimes very useful in gathering information on a system. It helps get details down accurately and in orderly fashion, and is simpler to prepare than some of the other charts. It might be the work sheet from which Figure 2–9 is constructed.

Routine sequence diagrams are often more than just useful supplements to written descriptions of information systems. Their most important contributions can be made when established systems are reviewed for possible improvement or new systems are designed. They combine the mechanics of the procedure, and the flow of information in a single document making possible easy manipulation by the system

Figure 2–10

INFORMATION FLOW CHART II—ROLL PROCESSING

PAPER OR INFORMATION (0 = BY OR FROM, 1 = TO)	MAIL ROOM	ROLL DEPT. OFFICE	SALESMAN (CUSTOMER FILE)	ROLL DEPT. OFFICE FILE	SHIPPING AND RECEIVING	FACTORY "PENDING" FILE	SCHEDULING	SHOP FOREMAN'S DESK	"PREP. & STRIP" PIGEON HOLE	"STOCK READY" PIGEON HOLE	"READY IN ALL RESPECTS" PIGEON HOLE	"COVERED & CURED" PIGEON HOLE	"READY FOR GRINDING" PIGEON HOLE	SHOP FILE	MILL ROOM FOREMAN	CALENDERING CREW	ROLLER COVERERS	QUALITY CONTROL INSPECTION	COMPLETED JOB FILE	ACCOUNTING OFFICE	LABORATORY RECORD	CUSTOMER
1. Customer Order	0	1																				
2. Factory Order--Copy A		0	1																			
Copy B		0			1																	
Copy C		0		1																		
3. Customer Order Copy		0	1																			
4. Factory Order--Copy C				0		1																
5. Factory Order--Copy B					0	1																
6. Schedule Card							0															
Daily Summary Sheet	1						0															
7. Factory Order (B and C)							0	1														
8. Daily Compound Order Sheet							0								1							
"Rolls to Be Transferred" Sheet							0	1														
11. Factory Order (B and C)								0	1													
10. Mill Room Report								1								0						
12. Factory Order (B and C)									0	1												
Daily "Covering Ticket"--Copy A								0								1						
Copy B								0									1					
Copy C								0										1				
17. Calendered Stock Ready								1								0						
13. Factory Order (B and C)										0	1											
14. Factory Order (B and C)											0	1										
15. Factory Order (B and C)												0	1									
16. Quality Control Sheet--Copy A						1												0				
Copy B					1													0				
Factory Order (B and C)													0					1				
Factory Order (B and C)					1													0				
Quality Control Sheet (B)																						
19. Factory Order (B and C)	1			0																		
Quality Control Sheet (B)																						
23. Factory Order (B)	0																		1			
Quality Control Sheet (B)																					1	
Factory Order (C)	0																				1	
Condensed Job Info. (5x7 Card)	0	1																				
21. Schedule Ticket							0									1						
22. Quality Control Sheet (A)							0														1	
25. Bills																				0		1
Accounting Entries																				0		

analyst. Some important facts which are often brought out by these schematics are as follows:

1. The complexity of the system.
2. The presence of excess paper work.
3. The accumulation of files which have no use.
4. The level in the organization at which important control decisions are made.
5. The amount and kind of information available at each step in the system.
6. Opportunities for decentralization of control, both within the system and in its relation to higher level control within the firm.

This list is far from exhaustive and is only intended to show the kind of questions which studies of this type of chart may suggest. Moreover, the mere act of collecting data and drawing the chart is often beneficial in focusing attention on the system, in clearing up misunderstandings, and in indicating minor gaps in control procedures.

ASSEMBLY DIAGRAMS

An assembly diagram is used to set forth the time requirements and necessary sequencing in the manufacture of a product. The horizontal scale of this diagram represents time, while the required parts are listed

Figure 2–11
ASSEMBLY DIAGRAM

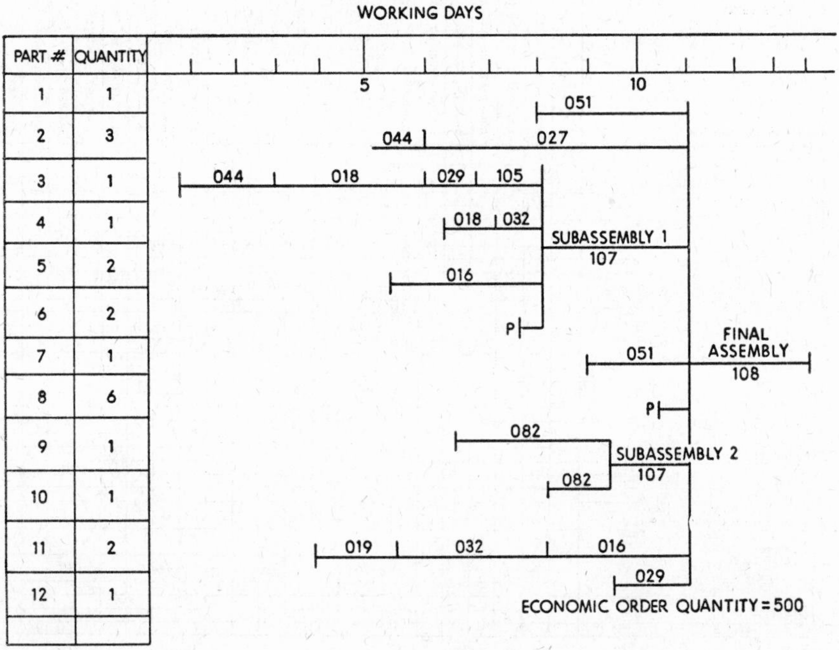

vertically. Figure 2–11 shows such a diagram for the production of a product in a job shop. The economical order quantity is 500, and the diagram is set up for this quantity. The diagram is drawn, beginning at the relative or desired finish date and working from right to left. Setup time, process time, and move time should all be included for each part; subassembly and final assembly and maximum possible overlap of operations should be achieved. In this way, the resulting production time will be as short as possible.

The diagram shows clearly when each part or subassembly will have to be put into operation in order to complete production in the minimum time. Purchased parts are labeled "P," and the diagram can be expanded to show necessary purchase time or can only show time at which such parts must be available in inventory, as is done in Figure 2–11. Here parts No. 6 and No. 8 are shown as being purchased and are required in inventory one day ahead of use. The departments where each part is to be manufactured are shown on the time line. For example, part No. 3 is manufactured in the required quantity by routing through Departments 44, 18, 29, and 105 requiring 2, 3, 1, and 1 days, respectively, to reach subassembly 1 in Department 107. With this diagram when an order is received from a customer or from an inventory section, the manufacturing requirements are immediately known, and a calendar scale entered along the top of the diagram to give the start dates and purchasing requirements necessary to complete the order. The finish date may also be estimated accurately. As will be shown next, this kind of device may be of considerable aid in programming production.

GANTT CHARTS

In planning production, the manager must allocate the various available capacities to the output which is desired. He must plan for the best use of the firm's facilities and then control the operations in accordance with these plans. Perhaps the most widely used device for such work is the Gantt chart.

The concept of the Gantt chart is simple. Vertically are listed the kinds of capacities to which the various requirements must be allocated or orders to which capacities are to be apportioned. The horizontal axis represents the available time for this work. Allocation is accomplished by assigning the times necessary for performance of the given tasks to the available capacities or requirements by trial and error until some feasible fit is discovered. This, then becomes the program for the time covered by the chart, and the chart may be used as a control device on performance. As the passage of time reveals under- or overperformance, the various allocations can be shifted to conform with new information.

Although the notation and symbols used in constructing Gantt charts vary with the individual or firm, the following are in common use:

This indicates date or hour when work is to be begun.

This indicates date or hour on which work is to be completed.

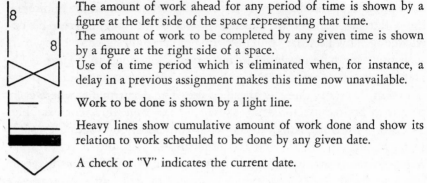

The amount of work ahead for any period of time is shown by a figure at the left side of the space representing that time.

The amount of work to be completed by any given time is shown by a figure at the right side of a space.

Use of a time period which is eliminated when, for instance, a delay in a previous assignment makes this time now unavailable.

Work to be done is shown by a light line.

Heavy lines show cumulative amount of work done and show its relation to work scheduled to be done by any given date.

A check or "V" indicates the current date.

In addition to the above, various sets of symbols may be devised in connection with each application to convey any information necessary in the specific situation.

A large number of variations of the basic concept of Gantt charts are in use in industry today. Peg boards with different colored pegs used to represent the symbols given above and a vertical string showing the current date are quite common. Racks in which can be placed order cards opposite each capacity are a simple variation. One in common use is a board with capacities in the left-hand column and clips strung out horizontally opposite each capacity. Paper tapes of length corresponding to the time requirements for an order are prepared and clipped opposite the capacities. A fit is obtained by moving the paper tapes around. Rescheduling is simplified by this device.

Examples of Gantt Charts

A Gantt layout chart for a milling department is shown in Figure 2–12. This chart shows work scheduled and completed as of the end of work on Wednesday. The letters represent explanations for the conditions shown on the chart according to the following key:

R = down for repairs
A = operator absent
I = idle capacity
M = lack of materials
P = power failure
T = lack of tools

The amount of work scheduled for each machine is shown by a light line, and the amount completed by the heavy lines. The numbers above the light lines refer to the factory order being processed. As of Wednesday evening, miller No. 4 has no work scheduled, and work which has been delayed has been rescheduled on machines Nos. 5, 7, and 10. Machine No. 1 is down for repairs, and no attempt has yet been made to reschedule the work allotted to it. Machine No. 6 has been scheduled for a new order based on work done ahead of schedule.

An example of a load chart, which shows the work load of a foundry, is shown in Figure 2–13. The light lines represent work scheduled by

Figure 2–12
GANTT LAYOUT CHART

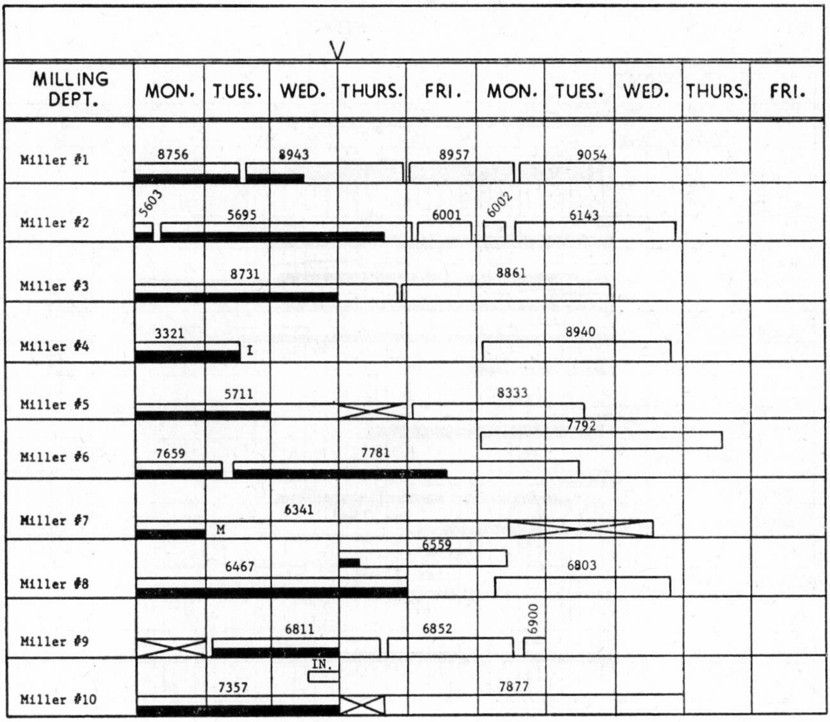

MILLING DEPT.	MON.	TUES.	WED.	THURS.	FRI.	MON.	TUES.	WED.	THURS.	FRI.
Miller #1	8756		8943		8957		9054			
Miller #2	5603	5695			6001	6002	6143			
Miller #3		8731			8861					
Miller #4	3321	I				8940				
Miller #5		5711			8333					
Miller #6	7659			7781		7792				
Miller #7		6341	M							
Miller #8		6467		6559		6803				
Miller #9			6811		6852	6900				
Miller #10		7357	IN.			7877				

periods; heavy lines, cumulative work ahead; and broken lines, work not completed and therefore carried over from previous periods. The planned utilization of the facilities of the foundry can be seen at a glance from this chart, and plans revised to obtain better use of facilities whenever appropriate. The method of solution is, of course, trial and error.

Figure 2–14 illustrates a Gantt progress chart used to program and control a set of manufacturing orders. The heavy lines represent completion of work and provide a basis for action by the control center.

The procedure followed in preparing all of these charts is essentially the same and involves the following steps:

1. List all available capacities or requirements vertically.
2. Show available time chronologically on the horizontal axis.
3. Compute time necessary to produce all outstanding orders on each capacity.
4. Fit time blocks from (3) on the chart, attempting to produce all requirements in a minimum elapsed time.
5. As time goes on keep extending the available time and scheduling new orders or rescheduling delayed orders, always searching for a "better" fit.

These basic graphical programming methods are used in industry in almost infinite variety tailored to fit specific situations. A common

Figure 2–13
GANTT LOAD CHART

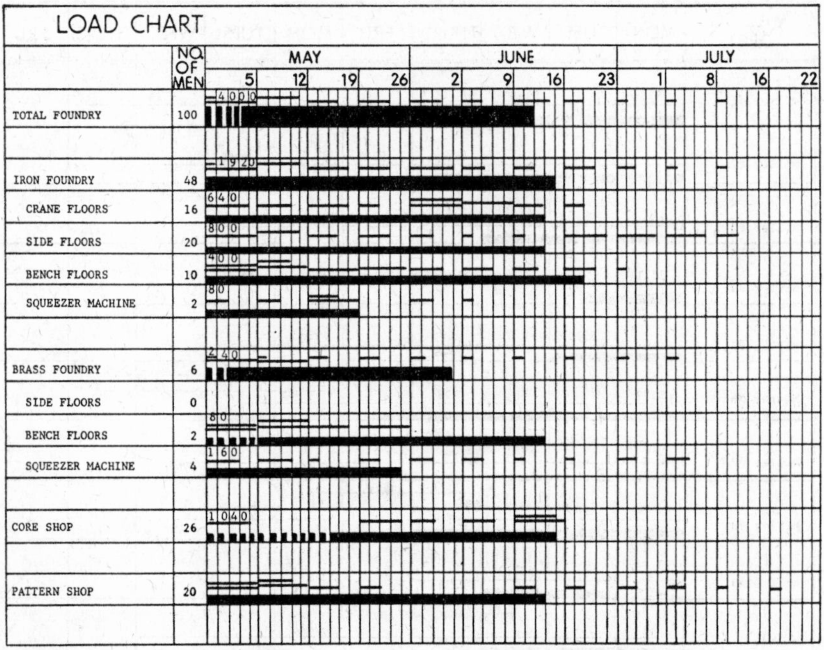

LOAD CHART	NO OF MEN	MAY				JUNE				JULY			
		5	12	19	26	2	9	16	23	1	8	16	22
TOTAL FOUNDRY	100	4000											
IRON FOUNDRY	48	1920											
CRANE FLOORS	16	640											
SIDE FLOORS	20	800											
BENCH FLOORS	10	400											
SQUEEZER MACHINE	2	80											
BRASS FOUNDRY	6	240											
SIDE FLOORS	0												
BENCH FLOORS	2	80											
SQUEEZER MACHINE	4	160											
CORE SHOP	26	1040											
PATTERN SHOP	20												

variation is to place all job orders to be done on cards and shuffle these cards according to some priority system such as "first come, first served" until a "good" program in terms of start dates is achieved. All such methods are essentially time based, trial-and-error allocations of capacities.

Probably the most fruitful current development is the simulation of these methods using high-speed computers. Since the graphical techniques just outlined essentially involve the fitting of some predetermined requirements to some available capacities by trial and error, it is certainly feasible to set up a machine to make the trials rather than doing them by hand. Certainly a high-speed computer can make many more trials in a given period than a man or even a large group of men. In fact, some manufacturing situations are so complex that even a feasible solution, one that will work, is difficult to obtain by hand.

The concept of computer simulation is simple. Given the requirements and restrictions of some manufacturing program, the machine is directed to "search" for a "fit" of all the requirements with the available capacities by successive trials. Recognizing that the number of such trials may be very large in a complex situation, some restrictions usually must be placed on the selection of these trials.[2] A more complete description of the nature of such simulators is given in Chapter 11.

Figure 2–14

GANTT PROGRESS CHART

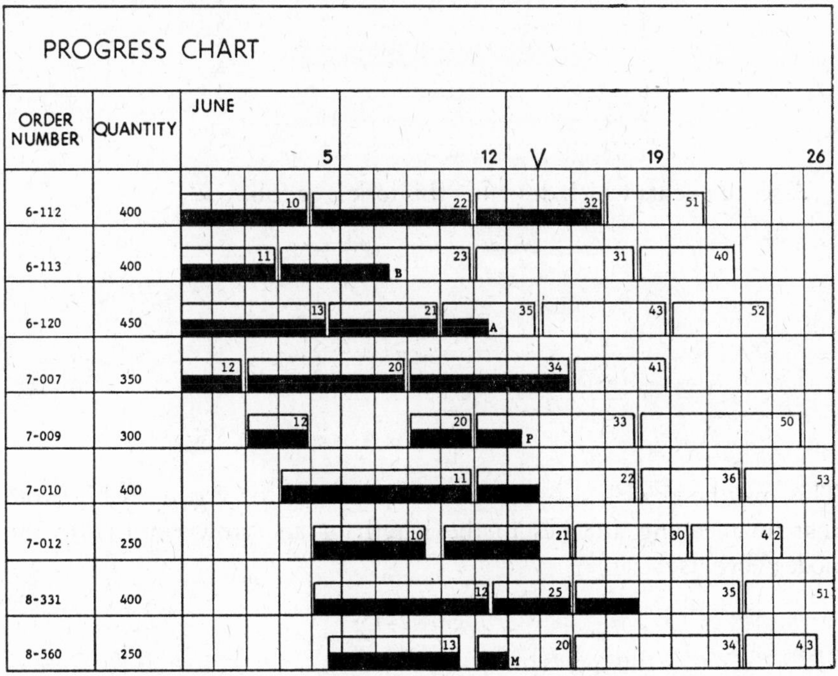

Critical Path Analysis

The Gantt chart has many limitations, not the least of which is one's inability with such a device to pinpoint clearly interferences in project scheduling due to sequencing restrictions. Such restrictions are often important on complex tasks and make it difficult for management to control project completion time. On the other hand, the existence of

[2] W. E. Andrus, Jr., and A. L. Becker, "A Production Schedule Computed on the IBM 701," *IBM Technical Report*, 1953.

usable slack in a system if highlighted by the method would make it easy for a manager to shift resources to tasks more critical to progress.

A better approach to progress control in complex projects is given by what have become known as critical path methods. The essence of this approach lies in the preparation of a network of events each representing the completion of a task included in the project. Consider, for example, a project made up of ten tasks defined as follows:

Task	Time Required	Predecessors
1	7	None
2	12	None
3	3	None
4	3	1
5	6	4
6	10	5
7	2	2
8	7	3
9	14	3
10	1	7,8

A set of events which describes this task is as follows:

Event	Tasks Completed
1	None
2	1
3	4
4	5
5	3
6	2
7	7,8
8	6,9,10

This may be described by the directed network of Figure 2–15. Note that no meaning attaches to the length of an arrow connecting the nodes (events).

Figure 2–15

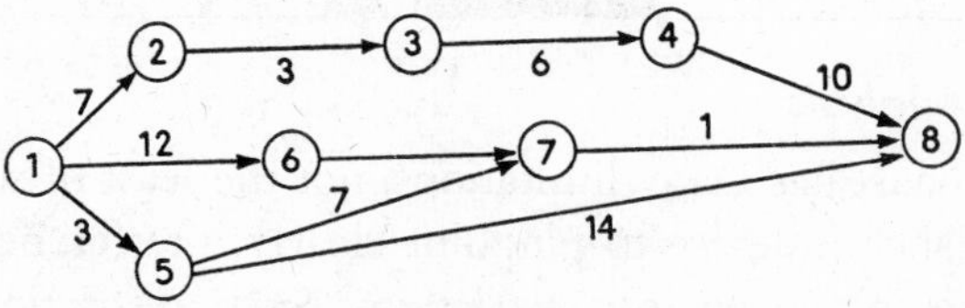

The time requirements for completion of the project may be described using the following notation:

(i,j) = a task beginning at event i and ending at event j $(i < j)$,
P = a project made up of a set of tasks (i,j),

y_{ij} = duration of task (i,j),
t_i^0 = earliest time for event i,
t_i^1 = latest time for event i,
λ = project completion time,
n = number of events in the project.

Then, if starting time is set at zero,

$$t_1^0 = 0 ,$$
$$t_j^0 = \text{MAX}[y_{ij} + t_i^0 | i < j, (i,j)\epsilon P], 1 \le j \le n , \qquad (1)$$
$$t_i^1 = \text{MIN}[t_j^1 - y_{ij} | i < j, (i,j)\epsilon P], 0 \le i \le n - 1 . \qquad (2)$$

Equation (1) specifies that for all tasks terminating in a given event j and which are elements of the project set, the earliest time for event j is the largest of the sum of the earliest time for the immediately preceding event (i) and the time necessary to get from i to j. For example, the earliest time for event 7 in the given network can be determined by observing that

$$\begin{aligned} t_7^0 &= \text{MAX}[y_{67} + t_6^0, y_{57} + t_5^0] \\ &= \text{MAX}[2 + 12, 7 + 3] \\ &= 14 . \end{aligned}$$

Starting with t_1^0, all earliest times can be determined with the earliest time for event n being the project completion time.

Then equation (2) can be used to determine the latest times for all events by fixing t_n^1 at some value λ. If we let λ be t_n^0, then, for example

$$\begin{aligned} t_5^1 &= \text{MIN}[t_8^1 - y_{58}, t_7^1 + y_{57}] \\ &= \text{MIN}[\lambda - 14, (\lambda - 1) - 7] \\ &= \lambda - 14 . \end{aligned}$$

since $t_7^1 = \lambda - y_{87}$. With $\lambda = 26$, $t_5^1 = 12$. Thus, the earliest completion time for a job would be $(t_i^0 + y_{ij})$ and the latest start time $(t_j^1 - y_{ij})$.

Given these definitions, Table 2–1 showing all event times may be constructed. It is easy to see that if the maximum time available for a task is equal to the task time the task is "critical" in that any change in start date or increase in task time will delay the project by the amount of the change. Of course, for there to be a "critical path" at all, λ must equal t_n^0.

One difficulty which often arises in the construction of project networks is illustrated in Figure 2–16a. Here events 5 and 8 are connected by two tasks (A and B) requiring different times for their completion. Thus, task (5, 8) is defined ambiguously and our computational proce-

Table 2-1

EVENT TIMES FOR PROJECT NETWORK

Task (i,j)	Task Time (y_{ij})	Earliest Start (t_i^0)	Latest Start $(t_j^1 - y_{ij})$	Earliest Finish $(t_i^0 + y_{ij})$	Latest Finish (t_j^1)	Maximum Time Available $(t_j^1 - t_i^0)$	"Critical"
1,2	7	0	0	7	7	7	Yes
2,3	3	7	7	10	10	3	Yes
3,4	6	10	10	16	16	6	Yes
1,6	12	0	11	12	23	23	No
5,7	7	3	18	10	25	22	No
6,7	2	12	23	14	25	13	No
4,8	10	16	16	26	26	10	Yes
5,8	14	3	12	17	26	23	No
7,8	1	14	25	15	26	12	No

dure will not work. In order to resolve this difficulty, an event 6 is defined signaling the completion of task *B* and 8 is reserved for task *A*. The network is closed by a "dummy" task *C* requiring zero time as shown in Figure 2–16*b*.

Figure 2–16

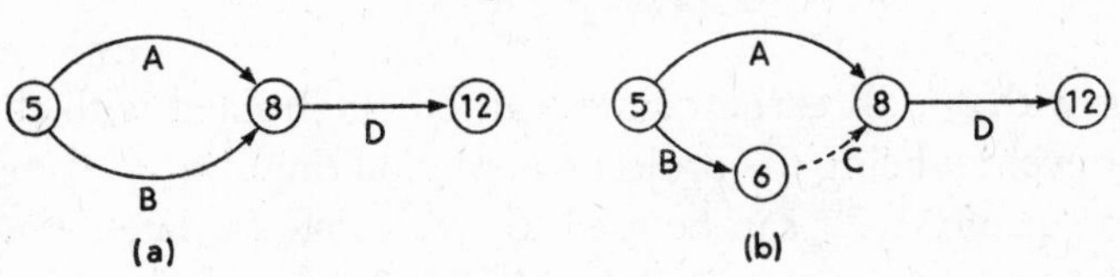

(a)   (b)

Even though this kind of project description is superior in many ways to the Gantt chart, it is more difficult to construct and still leaves the decision problems posed in project planning unresolved. One gets information concerning the effect on project time of alternative start-finish times but in no sense obtains a "solution" to the planning problem. The interested reader is referred to sources given at the end of this chapter for extensions and variations on this technique.

BLOCK DIAGRAMS

Block diagrams, while simple in conception, are often useful in the portrayal of routine systems in management, particularly information systems.[3] For example, a simple information system may be portrayed as

[3] Recently the terms *block diagram* and/or *flow chart* have been applied to the graphical device used to portray the steps to be taken by an electronic computer in performing some given operation. This is an important technique but should not be confused with the techniques described here. For descriptions of these, see E. W. Martin, Jr., *Electronic Data Processing: An Introduction* (rev. ed.; Homewood, Ill.: Richard D. Irwin, Inc., 1965).

shown in Figure 2–17, and this may serve as the basis for the analysis of such a system. A more realistic block diagram of an information system which might be encountered in management is shown in Figure 2–18. Here one might be portraying a system which involves the source telling his assistant to prepare a tabulation of orders received during the last month and to transmit a summary by telephone to the manager of the Boston office. Semantic noise is introduced through the assistant's interpretation of the source's instructions. The encoding process involves tabulating and summarizing the required information according

Figure 2–17

BLOCK DIAGRAM OF INFORMATIONAL SYSTEM

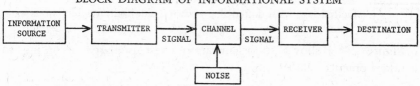

to the interpretation of instructions. The telephone is the transmitter, and the noise introduced is mechanical. The decoder is the secretary in the Boston office who may introduce semantic noise through her interpretation of the kind of information her boss is interested in seeing, and this final interpretation is what eventually gets to the destination in response to the instructions at the source. The block diagram provides a clearer and more accurate portrayal of the system by which information

Figure 2–18

BLOCK DIAGRAM OF COMMUNICATION PROCEDURE

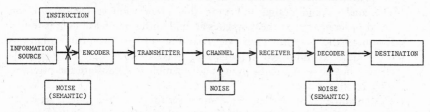

on orders is sent to the Boston office than a verbal description. Also, it may provide the basis for examination and understanding of the process with a view toward improvement.

ORGANIZATION CHARTS

While organization charts might be placed in the category of block diagrams, usage indicates their separation in a different category. An organization chart is designed to show the relationhips between people or functions or both which exist currently in the carrying out of the activities of a business firm. Such a chart is a useful device in that it portrays the relationship between people and function, and in its preparation forces the management of a firm to define these relationships.

There are many ways of drawing organization charts, but one will be presented here which experience indicates is useful and clear in portraying "line-and-staff" type of organization structure, by far the most prevalent in modern business. The basic instructions for the preparation of this chart are as follows:

——————— Solid lines indicate *authority-responsibility-accountability* relationships.

--------- Dotted lines indicate specialized advisory relationship.

□ Solid box indicates permanent organization.

⌐⌐⌐¬ Dotted box with dotted line entering side indicates temporary outside advisor.

Figure 2–19 shows an organization chart prepared according to standard practice.

THE USES OF SCHEMATIC METHODS

It should be apparent from the preceding discussion that schematic models have seen and will continue to see very wide use in management. A summary of the major uses for these tools is as follows:

1. The analysis of work methods—whether known as motion study, work simplification, or methods improvement. This kind of activity makes wide use of schematic methods. In fact, these constitute the principal tool in the pursuit of better ways of performing work.
2. Plant layout—the preparation of schematics representing floor plans and templates for the equipment to be used is the principal method of layout. The analysis and design following this preparation is trial and error, i.e., the planner moves the templates around until some feasible fit is found.
3. Routing—the determination and recording of manufacturing routes is often best accomplished through the use of schematics. Flow process charts, routine sequence diagrams, and assembly diagrams are the principal tools for this purpose.
4. Design and analysis of control systems—for this work the routine sequence diagram is the principal tool. The portrayal of information flow and processing is best accomplished by this device, although the block diagram may be used for simple systems or where great detail is not desired.
5. Production programming—the Gantt chart is widely utilized to get some feasible allocation of requirements to available capacities. Essentially this is also a trial-and-error method, but the visual technique often allows one to find not just a feasible but a "better" program.
6. Organizational planning—this may be accomplished through the joint use of many schematic methods but principally flow process charts, routine sequence diagrams, and organization charts are most useful. Communication paths within organizations should form a major part of organizational analysis and design, and schematic methods are the principal technique here.

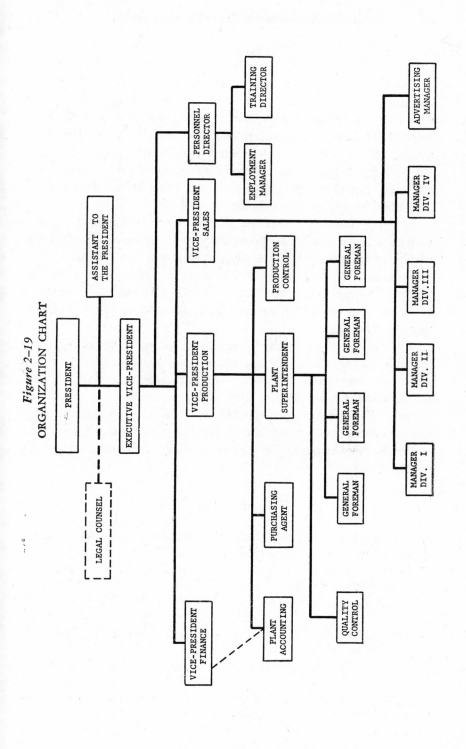

Figure 2-19
ORGANIZATION CHART

SUMMARY

The above listing of uses of schematic methods is certainly open-ended and is only presented to show the very wide range of application which these techniques enjoy. They form a major portion of the kit of tools of the industrial engineer. In many cases in the application of mathematical models to the solution of production management problems, a schematic is useful in setting up the more formal model. The schematic can show qualitatively the relationships which are to be formalized for quantitative solution.

In a large number of problem situations, manipulation of a system with the objective of improvement may not be economic by other than graphic techniques. While it is certainly true that many multiple-activity situations may be presented for solution in mathematical form (see Chapter 3), yet it is also true that many do not warrant such treatment, as the number of alternatives may be so few that it is economical to examine all of them.

It is also true that in many situations the schematic model represents the only tool available for use in problem solving. This is almost universally true today when the problem involves the analysis of methods by which people perform work where such work is not machine-oriented. The importance of these kinds of models to production management cannot be overemphasized, but at the same time, the informal manipulation, which is the only means of solution they afford, must also be recognized.

REFERENCES

1. ALFORD, L. P., and BANGS, J. R. *Production Handbook,* Secs. 2 and 3. New York: Ronald Press, 1948.
2. BARNES, RALPH M. *Motion and Time Study.* 3d ed. New York: John Wiley & Sons, Inc., 1949.
3. BERGE, C. *The Theory of Graphs.* New York: John Wiley & Sons, Inc., 1962.
4. BUFFA, E. S. *Modern Production Management.* New York: John Wiley & Sons, Inc., 1961.
5. CLARK, WALLACE. *The Gantt Chart.* London: Sir Isaac Pitman & Sons, 1938.
6. KELLEY, J. E., JR. "Critical-Path Planning and Scheduling: Mathematical Basis," *Operations Research,* Vol. IX, No. 3 (May–June, 1961), pp. 296–320.

7. MUNDEL, MARVIN E. *Motion and Time Study.* 2d ed. New York: Prentice-Hall, Inc., 1955.

8. NADLER, GERALD. *Motion and Time Study.* New York: McGraw-Hill Book Co., Inc., 1955.

9. NIEBEL, BENJAMIN W. *Motion and Time Study.* 4th ed. Homewood, Ill.: Richard D. Irwin, Inc., 1967.

10. RITCHIE, W. E. *Production and Inventory Control.* New York: Ronald Press, 1951.

PROBLEMS

1. The Hydrolite Company makes waterfall spray paint booths to order. On Monday, June 6, they received an order for one $18' \times 7' \times 5'$ spray booth. The basic booth is built in the metal forming department, and three days will be required to build it. Steel used in the booth is delivered one week after ordering. The special brass fittings used require four weeks for delivery after ordering.

   Once the unit is built, it is finished in the painting department, a job which requires four days.

   The lighting unit requires one day in the electrical department to assemble, wire, and test. Lights are delivered three days after ordering; fixtures, five days; and the safety shields, two weeks.

   The water recirculator and filter is constructed in the pump department and requires seven days to assemble and adjust. The pump and pump motor must be ordered four weeks before delivery.

   Final assembly takes one week and is not started until all components are on hand. When complete, the unit is taken to its location and installed in two days. Pipe, etc., to connect up the booth during installation must be ordered three days before it is needed. The purchaser is given two weeks' advance notice of installation so that he may install the necessary water pipes, power lines, and foundation.

   Neither the company nor its suppliers work weeks ends, hence all times are weekdays only.

   Assuming the company starts ordering parts tomorrow and does not keep any more inventory on hand than necessary:
   a) When will the booth be ready for use?
   b) At what time should each order and process be started provided that the company wishes to keep inventory as small as possible?

2. The Fit-Rite Garment Company, located in Lowell, Massachusetts, is the manufacturer of knitted rayon garments. The company buys rayon thread, knits and bleaches the cloth, and then cuts and sews the cloth into garments. Faced by falling profits, the company's owners are interested in improving the efficiency of the manufacturing processes. The president believes that a work simplification program will help and has asked that the plant be studied.

A preliminary survey disclosed that knitting and bleaching operations were done entirely by expensive machinery and, at present, offered little possibility for change. On sewing operations the company uses a standard method, developed as a result of extensive studies in the industry. All cutting room operations are done by hand and involve considerable time. The present method was developed 37 years ago when the company was founded.

In the cutting room, the general procedure is to cover the lay-up tables with dozens of layers of cloth. Patterns are placed on top of the cloth, and all the layers cut simultaneously in the shape of the pattern. All jobs are done to order only; therefore, the patterns used on each lay are different. The cutting room personnel do not look for defects in the cloth. After the parts have been sent to the sewing room, girls inspect them and reject parts with defects.

The cutting room employs seven men. All the men are skilled workers and can perform any of the several jobs in the room.

Before starting a job, one of the men will walk to the bleaching room (see Fig. 2–20) and carry back a roll of cloth to the storage racks. When he has

Figure 2–20

CUTTING ROOM FLOOR PLAN

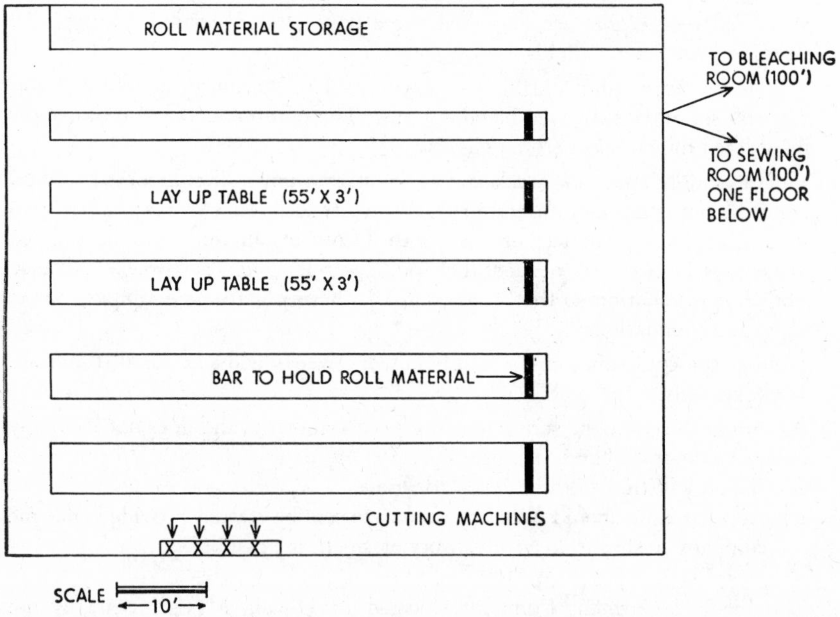

enough cloth to complete a lay, he picks up a roll and places it on the lay-up table. After removing the paper wrapping from the roll, the operator inserts it in the table-holding fixture. He then picks up the edge of the cloth and carries it to the far end of the table. He returns, smoothing the cloth and keeping the edges of the stack even. When he reaches the holder, he cuts off the cloth from the roll and starts over again. On an average job he repeats this process 218 to 288 times. At the end, the layers are counted to see that the stock is of the desired ply.

Once the lay is complete, two of the men and the factory superintendent decide on the best way to arrange the pattern so that waste material is kept at a minimum. The patterns used are cardboard pieces which have been cut in the shape of the desired garment. When the men have found the desired arrangement, the pattern outline is traced in pencil on the top layer of material. One man cuts the parts out with a vibrating blade cutter (see Fig. 2–21). The second man follows the first along the table and ties the parts

Figure 2–21

VIBRATING BLADE CUTTER

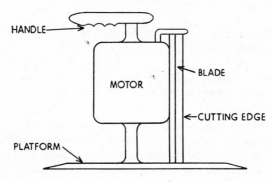

SAMPLE PATTERN LAYOUTS

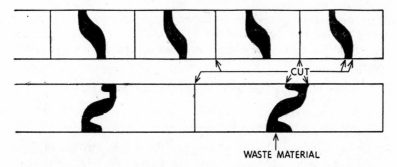

into bundles of three dozen. The bundles are stacked into a car and taken to the sewing room on the floor below. The cutting room operator removes the bundles and takes the car back to the cutting room.

Material Specification
Rolls of tubular rayon
Length—200 yards
Width—24 inches
Weight/roll—60 lbs.

Cutting Room Operators
No. employed—7
Wage rate—$2.00/hr.

Approximate Times for a 288-Ply Lay   *Hours*

Load material on bar, lay 288-ply, count...8.50
Transfer material from bleaching to storage racks..................................0.75
Pick up, tie, and stack bundles..0.75
Cut out garments...0.75
Transfer material from rack to table and unwrap....................................0.50
Find superintendent, decide on pattern arrangement..............................0.25
Transfer to sewing, unload, return..0.25
Place and mark and remove pattern..0.25

a) Make up a flow process chart for the processing of rayon cloth from bleaching to sewing following the material.

b) Make a flow process chart following the man.

c) Make up a flow process chart for your proposed method. Explain briefly why you made your changes.

3. Prepare flow diagrams for the process described in Problem No. 2 and for a new flow which may improve that process.

4. The Arrow Manufacturing Company is a small independent company engaged in the design and manufacture of heat exchangers, chemical distilling equipment, and expansion joints.

The manufacturing section is in a single-story building 200′ × 150′ with a 100′ × 180′ storage yard outside. The offices are located on a balcony over one section of the manufacturing area, and the storeroom is in the basement of the same building. The engineering section has one floor of a building a block away. The president and the vice-president in charge of sales are located with the engineering section. Figure 2–22 shows the general layout.

A large portion of the business is in the design and process engineering field. There are 100 engineers and draftsmen engaged in this design and process engineering. The organization chart, Figure 2–23, gives a rough breakdown of employees.

In the manufacturing end of the company, the sales volume has gone from over $1,000,000 in 1948 to about $5,000,000 in 1952, with an estimated $8,000,000 for 1953. The present sales are broken down approximately as follows:

Special Distillation Equipment (requires special design and engineering)...35%
Government Contracts..50%
Regular Line of Expansion Joints...15%

Studies have indicated to the management that the regular line of expansion joints give a higher return on investment than do the other products. There has been a trend, however, toward the regular line of expansion joints becoming a smaller percentage of total sales. In 1951 they were over 20 per cent of sales, and in 1952 sales had dropped to about 15 per cent. This decrease in percentage of total sales is due to the expansion joint sales not growing as rapidly as the others.

The regular line of expansion joints are sold out of a catalogue, although no finished units are presently carried in stock. The materials are carried in stores and are made up to order. Orders may be from one to one hundred and are in sizes from 4″ diameter to over 30″ diameter. Superficial studies have been made for a finished inventory stock, but no action has yet been taken in this direction. The other lines of distilling columns, heat exchangers, evaporators, etc., are designed and made to order. Some of these orders are similar to previous orders, and old drawings need only be revised; in other cases a complete process engineering and design job is involved.

Sales forecasts are made on the regular line of expansion joints based on past seasonal experience combined with forecasts of the industrial construction

Figure 2–22
PLANT LAYOUT

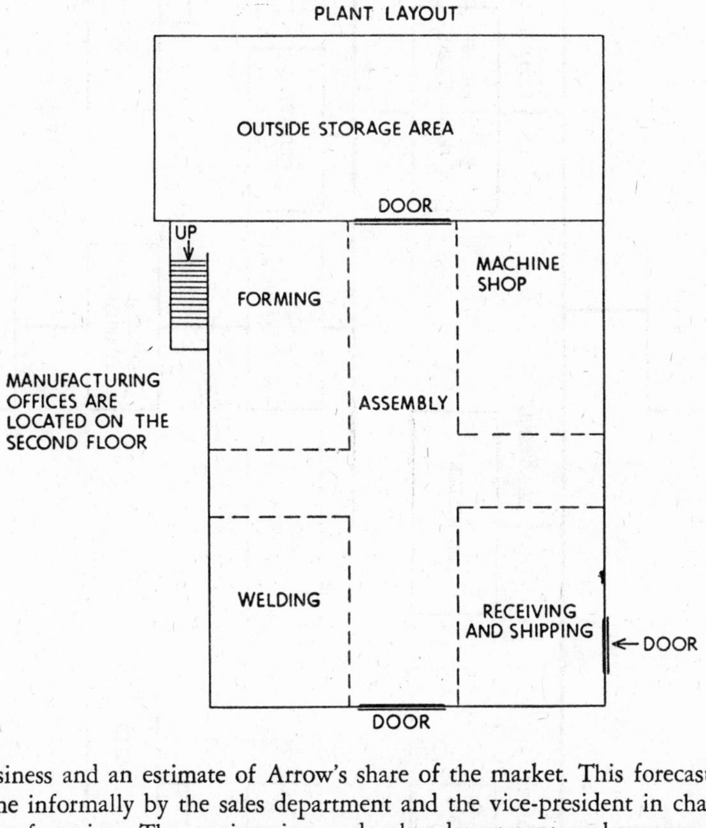

PLANT LAYOUT

business and an estimate of Arrow's share of the market. This forecasting is done informally by the sales department and the vice-president in charge of manufacturing. The engineering and sales department make general estimates of the volume of sales in specialized chemical equipment, but no effort is made to estimate specific types of units because each job is an individual problem. The nature of much of the specialized equipment is such that the orders are discussed and placed well in advance of the required delivery date.

The manufacturing operation consists of cutting and forming sheet metal tubing, machining castings, welding, machining fittings from bar stock, heat treating, stamping and drawing various components, and assembly of these

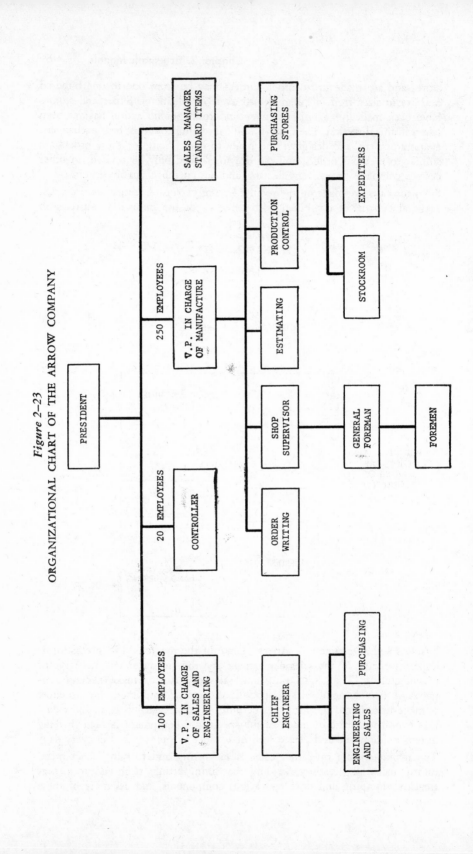

Figure 2–23

ORGANIZATIONAL CHART OF THE ARROW COMPANY

items to form a finished unit. The sequence of operations does not follow any set pattern, and in some cases one operation is not dependent upon another. The general sequence of operations is established by the engineering section on the drawings and specifications, but considerable freedom is permitted to the various foremen.

The flow of paper and information relative to the manufacture of an item is described below.

In following this flow of information, it should be noted that the vice-president in charge of manufacturing keeps a close, informal check on production control.

1. The customer's order is received and is sent to the order writing department where it is put on a standard sales order form and is run off on ditto.

2. The ditto copies of the sales order are distributed as follows:
   a) Order writing file.
   b) Acknowledgment copy to customer giving order number, file number, shipment date, etc.
   c) Sales control copy to sales office for record, and copy for price information.
   d) Copy to engineering department for notation of drawings required, for new drawings, specifications, and bills of material.
   e) Production control for information and notice of new order.
   f) Accounting: 3 copies of invoice
                    1 copy for cost control
                    1 copy for files
   g) 3 copies to shipping to hold until order comes through.

3. On receipt of sales order, the engineering department prepares drawings, specifications, and bills of material. These are distributed as follows:
   a) Order writing department for incorporation in a factory order (step 5).
   b) Production control for record and information.
   c) Shop supervisor and foremen for information.
   In the case of the regular line of expansion joints, engineering does not prepare drawings or B/M's, and steps 3 and 4 are effectively eliminated.

4. The production control department advises the order writing department on the required delivery dates for material. These dates are figured by working back from the delivery date for the finished item and the estimated times needed in the manufacturing sections. A Kardex Visual file is kept for each order on which the estimated man-hours required in each section are posted. This file provides the basis for determining shop load and for setting the dates when material must be on hand for each job.

5. On receipt of the drawings and B/M's from engineering, and material delivery time information from production control, the order writing department makes up a factory order on ditto. This factory order comprises the authority which will start an order into production. It incorporates all the information on materials required and dates when it

must be on hand, references to drawings, and sequence of operations as established by engineering.

This factory order is sent to production control for file, and nine (9) copies are sent to the stores record section for action on materials supply.

6. The stores record section takes the nine (9) copies of the factory order which has a detailed listing of materials required and checks them against their stock records. This section punches items which can be supplied from stores so that all nine (9) copies are coded as to which items can be supplied.

The function of this coded factory order is to notify the storeroom of allocated material, notify purchasing of what they must procure, and to notify the shops of the general materials status.

Distribution of these punched copies is as follows:

a) Stockroom—to cut out parts to the job. This is done physically by use of bins with job order numbers on them.

b) Three (3) copies to purchasing for action in procuring materials not on hand.

c) One (1) copy to expediting to follow up the purchasing section.

d) Two (2) copies to shipping and receiving for information.

e) One (1) copy to the shop superintendent as advance notice of the source of materials and dates when they should be available.

7. The purchasing department places the order as required and sends one copy of the factory order with the purchase order number to expediting for future follow-up.

8. Receipt of the factory order by the production control department is their authority to schedule the order into production. A monthly orders on hand sheet is made up, listing the orders in the general sequence in which they will go into the shops. The sequence of orders is based upon the order in which they were received and the availability of facilities for the operations required. An important column on this sheet is the one indicating material shortages on each job and the date when delivery is expected. Copies are run off on ditto and are distributed to the various sections.

9. The shop superintendent sits down with his foremen and, using the orders on hand sheet and the factory orders, does the final scheduling of jobs into his shops. The foremen prepare a materials requisition for materials required and draw these from the storeroom where they have previously been cut out to the job.

10. The orders on hand sheet is followed closely by the expediters in the production control section to follow-up materials shortages holding up jobs.

11. The accounting department collects man-hour figures weekly and reports these to production control. These man-hour figures (hours actually expended on a job) are posted in the Kardex file for each job next to the estimated hours which were entered when the job was originally figured. This comparison of actual man-hours to estimated hours is the only automatic check which production control has on the progress of each job. This control depends upon the accuracy of the original estimate to give

a reasonable progress picture. It has been found that the average variation is about 10–15 per cent with some running to 100 per cent. Production control is verbally notified when a section finishes an order, and a notation is made on the Kardex file.

12. When a job reaches the shipping section, notice of completion and shipment is sent out by the shipping section.

   a) Make up a routine sequence diagram for the operations described.

   b) What recommendations would you make? Why?

5. A manufacturer of industrial rollers has the following orders outstanding on Tuesday, April 5.

Order No.	Size (Inches)	Date Received	Date Promised
B-7512......................	26 × 117	3/31	4/19
B-7538......................	34 × 264	3/10	4/20
B-7579......................	13 × 104	3/22	4/20
B-7547......................	15 × 166	3/21	4/20
B-7803......................	32 × 242	3/28	4/21
B-7500......................	32 × 242	3/25	4/21
B-7514......................	23 × 168	4/5	4/21
B-7510......................	22 × 155	3/30	4/22
B-7511......................	18 × 114	3/31	4/25
B-7670......................	25 × 168	2/17	4/25
B-7404......................	26 × 238	3/28	4/25

Processing times are given below for a standard roller which is 24″ in diameter and 150″ long. All rollers are covered to a thickness of $3\frac{1}{4}$″. Operations which are starred (*) have variable process times directly proportional to the surface area.

   a) Construct a Gantt chart showing the minimum time schedule necessary for the given orders, assuming there are no orders currently in the shop.

   b) If an order for covering a 20″ × 150″ roller comes in on April 7, what is the quickest delivery that can be given?

   c) If the order of April 7 is given priority over all other orders in the shop, how soon can it be delivered? What effect does this have on the delivery dates of the other orders?

Process	Time (Hrs.)	Setup Time	Machine	No. of Shifts
1. Cementing...........	0.80*	0	Roller stands	1
Holding...........	10 (min.)	0	Roller stands	
2. Covering...........	12.5*	0.5	Covering table (3 available)	1
3. Wrapping...........	1.1	0.2	Lathe No. 1	1
4. Vulcanizing.........	24	0.4	Vulcanizer (2 available)	3
5. Unwrapping⎫ .... Shimming ⎬	2.5*	0.2	Lathe No. 2	2
Holding...........	10 (min.)			
6. Grinding...........	8*	0.3	Grinder	2
7. Inspection...........	12	0	Roller stands	1
8. Packing............	1	0		1

6. The following is a set of activities required in the replacement of a pipeline:[4]

ACTIVITY	DESCRIPTION	IMMEDIATE PREDECESSOR	NORMAL		CRASH	
			Duration (Hours)	Cost ($)	Duration (Hours)	Cost ($)
AA......	Lead time	None	10	—	10	—
AB.......	Delivery of line to maintenance	None	16	—	16	—
A........	Develop material list	AA	8	100	8	100
B........	Deactivate old line	A,AB	8	150	8	150
C........	Erect scaffold	A	12	300	8	450
D........	Remove scaffold	I,M	4	100	2	170
E........	Procure pipe	A	200	850	130	1,100
F........	Prefab pipe sections	E	40	1,200	25	2,000
G........	Place new pipe	F,J,L	32	800	12	1,900
H........	Weld pipe	G,K	8	100	4	300
I........	Fit-up pipe and valves	H	8	100	4	250
J........	Procure valves	A	225	300	140	600
K........	Place valves	J,L	8	100	4	250
L........	Remove old pipe and valves	B,C	35	400	18	1,000
M.......	Insulate pipe	H	24	300	12	700
N........	Pressure test	I	6	50	3	100
O........	Clean-up and start-up	D,N	4	100	2	200

a) Set up a project network and determine the earliest and latest start and finish times for all activities on a normal basis.

b) What is the project cost?

c) Suggest some activities to be substituted on a crash basis and compute the new project cost.

[4] Adapted with permission from a paper by J. E. Kelley, Jr., of Mauchly Associates, Inc., "Critical-Path Planning and Scheduling: Mathematical Basis," *Operations Research*, Vol. IX, No. 3 (May–June, 1961).

SECTION II

Mathematical Programming

The economic problem facing the production planner is one of allocating various scarce resources (men, machines, materials) to the attainment of some objective. This problem most often calls for the programming of several interdependent activities in order to obtain some given or alternative outputs. Most production processes consist of some series of concurrent and sequential operations with either fixed or alternative inputs and limiting capacities.

The production of a product might involve, for example, a punch-press operation followed by the assembly of the punchings, the concurrent manufacture of another component, and final assembly and packing. If only one variety of this product is made to a constant demand, the important problems concern the basic decisions about lot size, materials inventories, equipment, layout, and method. However, the production planner is often faced with economic alternatives as regards the use of the firm's facilities.

For example, in the given case, a variety of products might be made, utilizing the same basic capacities. Production management must decide on the most profitable allocation of available capacities over time among the various products to meet anticipated demand for each. The problem is magnified when the demand is subject to fluctuation from one period to the next and the amount of this fluctuation is uncertain. Consider, for example, the problems faced by the foreman of a milling department in the manufacture of a number of sizes of some component part. A schedule of requirements stipulates when each size will be needed and in what quantity. The foreman has available a number of machines of differing capacities and efficiencies. He must allocate the output requirements to these machines so that he attains his objective, e.g., minimum cost. This is a problem in programming and may be attacked by graphical or mathematical techniques.

The preceding chapter has dealt with a schematic technique (Gantt charts). The following section will present mathematical methods of analysis for programming.

CHAPTER 3

Linear Programming

MANY manufacturing problems can be thought of in terms of the economist's "most efficient allocation of scarce resources to multiple ends." The conventional routing problem in which jobs must be assigned to men and machines within a certain time period is an example. Most jobs can be handled by several of the machines, but some machines are better than others for certain jobs. The time available on each machine is limited, and other restrictions on routing probably also exist. Given these limiting conditions, many allocations of machines to jobs might be possible. The problem is to choose the best one.

The choice of the best solution in a case such as this is a problem in suboptimization. According to what criterion is the solution to be judged? One solution might yield a minimum of machining cost. Another solution might minimize total machining time. Obviously, it is necessary to choose the objective to be considered in making this allocation, and the choice should be consistent with the objectives of the larger organization of which the shop in question is a part.

In some cases, the number of choices is so few that each one can be examined and the proper solution chosen by inspection. However, in other cases the number of distinct solutions might run into many thousands. In a case of the latter type, linear programming has been helpful. Linear programming is a method of planning whereby some objective function is minimized or maximized while at the same time satisfying the various restrictions placed on the potential solutions. The meaning of the adjective "linear" should become clear through the following examples. While the linear nature of the problem structure might appear at first excessively restrictive, it has not proved so in practice. This is particularly so when the pragmatic position is taken and the question asked is not "Is the model 'true'?" but "Is the model useful?"

A GRAPHICAL EXAMPLE OF PRODUCTION ALTERNATIVES

A simplified case will be used as an example to illustrate the general nature of the methods of linear programming. The more general algebraic methods become rather involved, and an understanding of a relatively simple graphical solutions should facilitate understanding of the algebraic method.

Consider a shop in which large metal parts are stamped from sheet metal, formed into shape, welded at the corners, and then painted. At present two parts, A and B, are in demand; and as this shop is but a small supplier among many, it can sell either part to the extent of the shop capacity at the market price. Each of the four processes, stamping, forming, welding, and painting, has a capacity limitation. That is, 30,000 seconds per day on the stamping and forming machines, 20,000 seconds in welding, and 40,000 seconds in the paint booth.

Each unit of part A takes 10 seconds on the stamping machine, 15 seconds on the forming machine, 6 seconds in welding, and 10 seconds in the paint booth. Similarly, each unit of part B takes 20 seconds on the stamping machine, 5 seconds on the forming machine, 3 seconds in welding, and 8 seconds in the paint booth. The equipment does not have to be set up or adjusted for the different parts.

Each unit of part A sold yields a contribution to profit and overhead of 2 cents. Each unit of part B sold yields a contribution to profit and overhead of 3 cents. Contribution to profit and overhead is essentially selling price minus variable cost. For instance, part A might sell for 8 cents and have a variable cost of 6 cents, including such elements as direct labor, sheet steel, paint, and power. For each additional unit of A manufactured and sold, an additional expense of 6 cents is incurred (all costs and prices are constant in the range of quantities used by the shop). Therefore each unit of A yields 2 cents (8 minus 6) to be used in covering fixed expenses, such as the salary of the foreman and rent of the building. The total of these yields should exceed the fixed costs. Otherwise, a loss is incurred during the period.

The objective chosen for this problem will be to maximize the contribution to overhead and profit of this operation. Other things being equal, this will yield a maximum profit (or a minimum loss) for the period.

This problem may be illustrated and solved graphically as in Figure 3–1. Number of units of part A is plotted on the vertical axis. Number of units of part B is plotted on the horizontal axis. The line representing the capacity of the stamping machine is drawn from 3,000 on the A-axis to 1,500 on the B-axis. That is, if all of the capacity of the stamping machine is used on part A, 30,000 seconds ÷ 10 seconds per unit = 3,000 units of A can be stamped; or if all of the capacity of the stamping

Figure 3–1
GRAPHICAL SOLUTION OF TWO-DIMENSIONAL PROGRAM

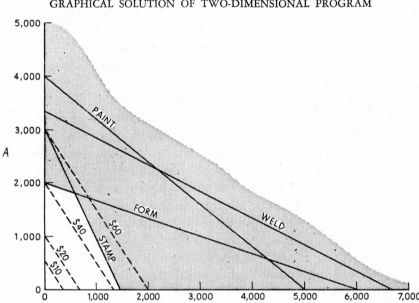

machine is used on part B, 30,000 seconds ÷ 20 seconds per unit = 1,500 units of B can be stamped.

Note that it is possible to divide the stamping machine time between parts A and B. For instance, half of the 30,000 available seconds could be devoted to A, and half to B. In this case, 15,000 seconds ÷ 10 seconds per unit = 1,500 units of A and 15,000 seconds ÷ 20 seconds = 750 units of B could be stamped. This production possibility also lies on the stamping capacity line as drawn. All possible divisions of stamping time between A and B, if the capacity is completely used, lie on this straight line. This is one reason for the name "linear" programming. If the actual production possibility line may not be approximated sufficiently well by a straight line, the straightforward algebraic method of solution to be illustrated may not be used but must be modified.

This line represents the total capacity of the stamping machine. While it is possible to operate the machine at less than full capacity and, therefore, be at a point nearer the origin than this line, it is not possible to exceed the capacity. Graphically, this means that the point of production (units of A and B) may not be farther from the origin than the capacity line as drawn.

Similarly, capacity lines can be drawn representing the forming machine, the welding equipment, and the paint booth. For the forming machine the A-axis intercept would be $30,000/15 = 2,000$ and the B-axis intercept would be $30,000/5 = 6,000$. For the welding equipment the A-axis intercept would be $20,000/6 = 3,333$ and the B-axis intercept would be $20,000/3 = 6,667$. For the paint booth the A-axis intercept would be $40,000/10 = 4,000$ and the B-axis intercept would be $40,000/8 = 5,000$.

The actual production possibility chosen must be within the range of possibility for all capacities. This means, graphically, that the point must be on the origin side of all capacity lines. The clear or nonshaded area represents these production choices which are technically feasible. Though a great number of choices are possible, they are all within this nonshaded area bounded by the A- and B-axes (no negative production is possible) and segments of the stamping and forming capacity lines. Note that under present circumstances, the welding and painting capacities in no sense limit the production of parts A and B. Under such circumstances if funds were available for expansion, they should certainly not be devoted to the paint booth or welding equipment.

The Objective Function

The graphical portrayal so far has dealt with technical restrictions. Economics as such has not been introduced. Now, however, it is necessary to bring in the economic criterion or objective in order to choose the desirable solution. As a starting point, consider the possibility of making a total contribution to overhead and profit, for this shop, of $10. There are actually many ways of doing this. If it is all to come from part A, then $10/\$0.02 = 500$ units would do this. Similarly, if it is all to come from part B, then $10/\$0.03 = 333$ units would do this. A combination of $7/\$0.02 = 350$ units of A and $3/\$0.03 = 100$ units of B would also yield the $10. All of the $10 income possibilities can be represented graphically by the straight dashed line labeled $10 in Figure 3–1. Since the contribution per unit of product is constant over the range which is possible, a parallel line representing a contribution of $20 can be drawn twice as far out. This proportionality is another reason for the term "linear" programming. Since the objective is to maximize the contribution to overhead and profit, it is desirable to select an "iso-revenue" or equal-contribution line which is as far out as possible. Note that the $60 iso-revenue line does not intersect the technically feasible area at any point. Therefore, this contribution is not possible. The equal-contribution line which is farthest out and still touching the technically feasible area is the $54 line. The $54 line just touches this area where the forming and stamping lines cross at the point representing 1,800 units of A and 600 units of B. At this combination the contribution to overhead and profit will be $54, and this is the maximum contribution (within the capacity restrictions).

A Three-Dimensional Problem

Suppose that a new metal part, C, is added to the shop. Each unit of part C takes 8 seconds on the stamping machine, 6 seconds on the forming machine, 10 seconds on the welding equipment, and 25 seconds in the paint booth. Each unit of part C yields a contribution to profit and overhead of $2\frac{1}{2}$ cents. What, now, is the best combination of parts A, B, and C to make in the shop?

This problem may at least be conceptualized geometrically. On Figure 3–1 a third axis may now be added to the first two. The C-axis may be conceived as coming vertically out from the page. The problem is now to pick the best production possibility; that is, the number of parts A, B, and C which can be represented by a point in space defined by its relation to the three different axes. Now, however, rather than lines representing the capacity restrictions, planes or surfaces make the representation. As in the first problem, the capacity restriction of the stamping machine intersects the A-axis at 30,000/10 = 3,000 units, and intersects the B-axis at 30,000/20 = 1,500. In addition, the capacity restriction of the stamping machine intersects the C-axis at 30,000/8 = 3,750 units.

This point is on the C-axis which comes up vertically from the page, as represented in Figure 3–2. The plane which passes through these three points represents the stamping machine capacity restriction. The production possibility chosen may not fall above this plane. Similar planes may be constructed for the other three capacity restrictions. The technically feasible production possibilities are within the enclosed space formed by the four planes representing the four different processes and the three planes formed jointly by the A- and B-axes, the B- and C-axes, and the A- and C-axes (again negative production is not possible).

An iso-revenue plane may be constructed similar to the line representing $10. Three points on this plane would be $10/$0.02 = 500 units of A (no B or C), $10/$0.03 = 333 units of B (no A or C), and $10/$0.025 = 400 units of C (no A or B). Any point on the plane passing through these three points represents an income of $10. Similarly, planes of $20, etc., may be constructed. In this case, the plane farthest from the origin which still touches the enclosed space represents the best production scheme. This would be the production possibility (*A, B,* and *C*) which, while technically feasible, maximizes the contribution to overhead and profit. In certain cases the scheme which does

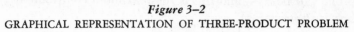

Figure 3–2

GRAPHICAL REPRESENTATION OF THREE-PRODUCT PROBLEM

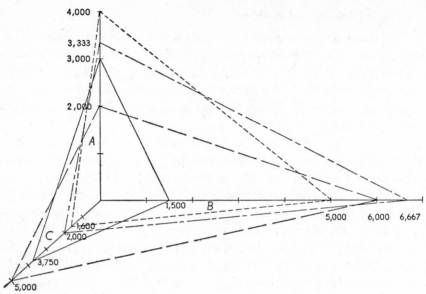

this could specify that only one or two of the metal parts be made.

It can be seen that the three-dimensional case, while possible to visualize, becomes rather awkward. When more than three dimensions are necessary—20 products and 10 processes, for instance—geometric solution becomes impossible. This would certainly be the case in most industrial problems. For this type of problem an algebraic method of solution called the simplex method has been developed.[1]

THE SIMPLEX METHOD

The simplex method is an algebraic procedure which, through a series of repetitive operations, progressively approaches, and ultimately reaches, an optimum solution. The procedure may be summarized briefly as follows:

---

[1] G. B. Dantzig, "Maximization of a Linear Function of Variables Subject to Linear Inequalities," T. C. Koopmans (ed.), *Activity Analysis of Production and Allocation,* Cowles Commission Monograph 13 (New York: John Wiley & Sons, Inc., 1951), chap. xxi.

1. The problem is framed, and all relevant initial relationships are determined.
2. An initial solution is determined.
3. Alternative changes to this solution are evaluated.
4. The alternative with the largest favorable cost or revenue difference per unit is selected.
5. A new solution is determined introducing the favorable alternative.
6. Steps 3 through 5 are repeated to derive successively better solutions, i.e., the process is iterative.
7. When, at any stage, step 3 evaluates no alternative choices favorably, the procedure is complete; there is no better solution.

This method takes on tangible meaning best through an example. Using the example previously discussed of the shop with three parts (A, B, and C), the following notation is given:[2]

Number of units of part A manufactured $= X_A$.
Number of units of part B manufactured $= X_B$.
Number of units of part C manufactured $= X_C$.

Seconds required per unit of A on stamping machine $= t_{As}$.
Seconds required per unit of B on stamping machine $= t_{Bs}$.
Seconds required per unit of C on stamping machine $= t_{Cs}$.

Seconds required per unit of A on forming machine $= t_{Af}$.
Seconds required per unit of B on forming machine $= t_{Bf}$.
Seconds required per unit of C on forming machine $= t_{Cf}$.

Seconds required per unit of A on welding equipment $= t_{Aw}$.
Seconds required per unit of B on welding equipment $= t_{Bw}$.
Seconds required per unit of C on welding equipment $= t_{Cw}$.

Seconds required per unit of A in paint booth $= t_{Ap}$.
Seconds required per unit of B in paint booth $= t_{Bp}$.
Seconds required per unit of C in paint booth $= t_{Cp}$.

Profit per unit of $A = P_A$.
Profit per unit of $B = P_B$.
Profit per unit of $C = P_C$.

The objective function to be maximized is

$$Z = X_A P_A + X_B P_B + X_C P_C.$$

Then the amount of stamping time utilized is equal to the number of units of part A multiplied by time per unit A, plus the number of units of part B multipled by time per unit B, plus the number of units of part C multiplied by the time per unit C. Similar expressions hold for forming, welding, and painting time utilized as follows:

---

[2] The notation used is mnemonic (memory aiding) to aid the reader in understanding what takes place in the various steps in the following procedure.

$$X_{A}t_{As} + X_{B}t_{Bs} + X_{C}t_{Cs}$$
$$X_{A}t_{Af} + X_{B}t_{Bf} + X_{C}t_{Cf}$$
$$X_{A}t_{Aw} + X_{B}t_{Bw} + X_{C}t_{Cw}$$
$$X_{A}t_{Ap} + X_{B}t_{Bp} + X_{C}t_{Cp}$$

The conditions inherent in the shop indicate that these total times cannot exceed the process capacities of 30,000, 30,000, 20,000, and 40,000 seconds.

$$X_{A}t_{As} + X_{B}t_{Bs} + X_{C}t_{Cs} \leq 30{,}000$$
$$X_{A}t_{Af} + X_{B}t_{Bf} + X_{C}t_{Cf} \leq 30{,}000$$
$$X_{A}t_{Aw} + X_{B}t_{Bw} + X_{C}t_{Cw} \leq 20{,}000$$
$$X_{A}t_{Ap} + X_{B}t_{Bp} + X_{C}t_{Cp} \leq 40{,}000$$

The time requirement for $X_A = X_{A}t_{As} + X_{A}t_{Af} + X_{A}t_{Aw} + X_{A}t_{Ap}$.
The time requirement for $X_B = X_{B}t_{Bs} + X_{B}t_{Bf} + X_{B}t_{Bw} + X_{B}t_{Bp}$.
The time requirement for $X_C = X_{C}t_{Cs} + X_{C}t_{Cf} + X_{C}t_{Cw} + X_{C}t_{Cp}$.

As no negative production is possible, the following holds:

$$X_A, X_B, X_C \geq 0 .$$

Notice that all of the expressions given, including the constraints and the function to be maximized, are in only the first power, i.e., they are in linear form. This general algebraic statement of the problem is generic to linear programming and does not apply only to the simplex method.

Since the simplex method requires equalities ($=$) rather than inequalities ($\leq$, $\geq$) for solution, "slack variables" are introduced into the expressions for capacity restrictions. Technically, the slack variables in this case correspond to idle time in the processing capacity. Computationally, they represent fictitious products made using the particular process, and in effect, the equation expresses the fact that the time used in production plus the time not used (or slack time) is equal to the total time. Let s represent the fictitious product or slack variable for stamping time, f for forming time, w for welding time, and p for painting time. X_s, X_f, X_w, and X_p will then represent the amounts of the slack variables. The coefficient (t_{ss}, t_{ff}, t_{ww}, and t_{pp}) in each case is defined as one, that is, by definition it takes one second to "make" a fictitious product in each capacity. Again these slack variables really represent idle time, and the convention adopted here is used for computational convenience. This gives:

$$X_{A}t_{As} + X_{B}t_{Bs} + X_{C}t_{Cs} + X_s 1 = 30{,}000$$
$$X_{A}t_{Af} + X_{B}t_{Bf} + X_{C}t_{Cf} + X_f 1 = 30{,}000$$
$$X_{A}t_{Aw} + X_{B}t_{Bw} + X_{C}t_{Cw} + X_w 1 = 20{,}000$$
$$X_{A}t_{Ap} + X_{B}t_{Bp} + X_{C}t_{Cp} + X_p 1 = 40{,}000$$

The first equation of the above set states that the time devoted to product A on the stamping equipment (number of units multiplied by time per unit), plus the amount of time devoted to B on stamping, plus the time devoted to C on stamping, plus the time devoted to slack variable or idle time on stamping is equal to the total time available on the stamping equipment.

It is possible to put this same set of equations into the form of a table or tableau in which the column headings represent identical coefficients in each row of the particular column, as shown in Table 3–1a.

Table 3–1a
TABLES OF COEFFICIENTS FOR SIMPLEX SOLUTION

X_A	X_B	X_C	X_s	X_f	X_w	X_p	
t_{As}	t_{Bs}	t_{Cs}	1	0	0	0	30,000
t_{Af}	t_{Bf}	t_{Cf}	0	1	0	0	30,000
t_{Aw}	t_{Bw}	t_{Cw}	0	0	1	0	20,000
t_{Ap}	t_{Bp}	t_{Cp}	0	0	0	1	40,000

The first row representing stamping time (at present) can be read $X_A t_{As} + \ldots + X_p 0 = 30,000$. The other rows are similar. For purposes of problem solution the columns representing the slack variables would be placed to the left side of the table, as in Table 3–1b.

Table 3–1b
FIRST TABLE IN SIMPLEX COMPUTATION

	X_s	X_f	X_w	X_p	X_A	X_B	X_C	
X_s	1	0	0	0	10	20	8	30,000
X_f	0	1	0	0	15	5	6	30,000
X_w	0	0	1	0	6	3	10	20,000
X_p	0	0	0	1	10	8	25	40,000

The problem now presents seven variables and four equations (the additional variables are needed to make the inequalities into equalities). This means that the number of solutions to this problem is extremely large. However, some of these solution will be preferable to others according to the objective function. It is normally possible to get an *optimum* solution to n simultaneous equations with positive values assigned to only n unknowns (or less in the unusual case labeled degeneracy in linear programming). Normally only one set of n unknowns (from a larger set m), which satisfies the n equation, will optimize (maximize or minimize) the objective function. The computational procedure developed here picks the particular set of n unknowns, from the larger set of m unknowns, which optimizes the objective function. The procedure, while always satisfying the n equations with n unknowns, progressively selects new unknowns to bring into the solution one at a time (and therefore old unknowns to take out as the number being used always equals n). Ultimately the optimum set is chosen, and the unique set of values they require is revealed.

The solution systems in linear programming actually consist of the manipulation of a set of simultaneous (linear) equations. The problem here exists because there are more unknowns (including explicit statements of the slacks) than equations. That is, many possible values for the unknowns could satisfy the equations. This is the opposite problem from the statistical one where there are more equations than unknowns, and because no values of the unknowns will simultaneously satisfy all of the equations, some criterion, such as least squares (multiple regression), must be used to choose the "best" values for the unknowns. The simplex method of linear programming consists of a series of steps whereby one of the equations—the objective function—is optimized while the other equations—the constraints—are being manipulated.

Computational Procedure

A first stage solution can be represented, as in Table 3–1*b,* by arranging the appropriate slack variables as row headings corresponding to the total number of seconds in the last column. The actual values of the seconds required per unit, which have been given, are inserted in place of the t's.

The solution at this stage indicates that X_s equals 30,000 units, X_f equals 30,000 units, X_w equals 20,000 units, and X_p equals 40,000 units. In effect, this means that these amounts of idle time are to be assigned to the four processes. Of course, this means that no real production is to be carried out. The advantage of this starting point is that it is technically feasible and also easy to formulate. This is equivalent in the graphical solution to starting at the origin, before pushing the iso-revenue line or plane out as far as possible into the restriction area or space.

At the origin all slack variables, which are the ones used in the initial solution, are independent of each other. They are unique to their equations. The columns underneath each slack variable have zeros in every cell other than the one corresponding to itself in the row headings. This is so because the table also represents physical rates of substitution between products in the solution (s, f, w, and p) and products not in the solution which might be brought in (A, B, and C). The numbers in each column represent these rates. For instance, for every unit of A brought into the solution, 10 units of s, 15 units of f, 6 units of w, and 10 units of p must all come out of the solution. Expressed another way, for each unit of metal part A produced, there would be 10 seconds less of idle time on the stamping machine, 15 seconds less of idle time on the forming machine, 6 seconds less of idle time on the welding machine, and 10 seconds less of idle time in the paint booth. The other columns have similar interpretations.

Similar to a certain point in the graphical solutions, the discussion and table have centered around technical not economic aspects of the problem. All values in the table have technical meanings. It is now necessary to introduce economic considerations in order to determine in what way to modify the initial solution. The unit contributions can be placed above (and next to) the products—idle time or slack variables having a direct contribution to overhead and profit of zero, that is, no real production means no contribution.

At this point the objective function, Z, which is to be maximized is:

$$Z = X_A P_A + X_B P_B + X_C P_C + (X_s + X_f + X_w + X_p)(0)$$
$$= (0)(2) + (0)(3) + (0)(2.5) + (30,000 + 30,000 + 20,000 + 40,000)(0)$$
$$= 0 .$$

It is now possible to determine which potential product it would be most advantageous to bring into the solution. As the numbers within the table represent rates of substitution, it is possible to determine the net value per unit in bringing a product into the solution. For instance, for each unit of A the gross return is 2 cents. From this is subtracted the amount of contribution which must be taken out of the solution in order to bring in the unit of A. Ten units of s must be removed at a profit of zero each, 15 units of f at a zero profit, 6 units of w at a zero profit, and 10 units of p at zero profit. This calculation is shown beneath the X_A column (Table 3–1c). Obviously the net and gross contribution per unit are the same in this instance. This, of course, is not always the case. Similar calculations may be made for X_B and X_C. A row including these net evaluations will be included, and labeled N (net).

With these calculations the first choice is now available. The product which yields the greatest net contribution is brought into the solution.[3]

---

[3] The procedure outlined here is an "efficient" procedure, as it leads to a final solution in the fewest *expected* number of changes on the basis of the information available. If

Table 3–1c
FIRST STEP IN SIMPLEX SOLUTION

	0 X_s	0 X_f	0 X_w	0 X_p	2 X_A	3 X_B	2.5 X_C		
0 X_s	1	0	0	0	10	20	8	30,000	/20 = 1,500
0 X_f	0	1	0	0	15	5	6	30,000	/ 5 = 6,000
0 X_w	0	0	1	0	6	3	10	20,000	/ 3 = 6,667
0 X_p	0	0	0	1	10	8	25	40,000	/ 8 = 5,000
N					2 -10×0 -15×0 -6×0 -10×0	3 -20×0 -5×0 -3×0 -8×0	2.5 -8×0 -6×0 -10×0 -25×0		
					2	3	2.5		

This is B, with a contribution of 3. Because each unit of B yields 3 cents, as many units as technically possible are to be brought into the solution because there is no falling off or decrease in returns to scale from B. This is a problem in "linear" programming.

Additional calculations must be made in order to make a second choice with Table 3–1c. The number of units of the new product to bring in and the product which is to come out of the solution (in this first case the idle time to be completely used up) must be determined. For each unit of B brought into the solution, 20 units of s, 5 units of f, 3 units of w, and 8 units of p must be taken from the solution. This is due to the fact that all capacities are completely utilized or accounted for (including idle time), and as the numbers in the table represent physical rates of substitution, they represent the rates at which certain products must be subtracted if other products are to be added, in order

---

another whole set of computations is made for each table to determine the total contribution a product will make (rather than contribution per unit), then the expected number of changes required for the final solution would be even less. This total contribution is the product of contribution per unit and number of units which can be brought in. This would mean more computations per table with an expectation of making fewer tables. The reverse of this is also true. If the first (or any) product with a favorable contribution is brought into the solution, this would reduce the number of computations per table but increase the expected number of tables for the final solution. Picking the product with the largest net contribution per unit, which is the procedure described here, is analogous in the graphical solution to going along the axis most nearly parallel (smallest difference angle) to the normal (perpendicular) to the objective function's line or plane. As long as the contribution of the product brought into the solution is favorable, the solution is being improved and an optimum solution will ultimately be obtained. This is due to the fact that the restriction space is everywhere convex, meaning that there are no "local" optima (or blind alleys).

that the solution remains within all the physical capacities. This corresponds graphically to moving along boundary lines of the feasible space.

In this case no more that 30,000 units of s, nor 30,000 units of f, nor 20,000 units of w, nor 40,000 units of p may be subtracted from the solution. This is generally equivalent to stating that no negative production is possible. Dividing these limits by the appropriate rates of substitution will yield four simultaneous limits to the number of units of B which can be brought into the solution. This calculation is shown beyond the right end of the appropriate rows in Table 3–1c. It can be seen that 1,500 is the smallest capacity restriction and, therefore, the largest number of units of B which can be brought into the solution. This takes all units of s out of the solution. There are no more to subtract. This is equivalent in the graph to going out along the B-axis from the origin until the first capacity line is reached or in the three-dimensional presentation to going out along the B-axis from the origin until the first capacity plane is reached. It is not technically possible to go beyond these limits because all of at least one kind of capacity is fully utilized by making 1,500 units of part B. As it is X_s which is subtracted to zero, and therefore removed from the solution, the capacity fully utilized is the stamping machine.[4]

At each stage of solution (or table) two choices are required, as follows:

1. The product, not presently in the solution, to bring into the solution. When no new product will yield a positive net contribution, the problem is solved, i.e., there is no product not in the *solution* which will yield a net profit if brought in. If two or more products yield equally large contributions, any one of them may be chosen.
2. The number of units of this product which may be brought into the solution. This number of units is restricted by the number of units of a prod-

---

[4] In the simplex calculation, more than one product in the solution may have the same lower figure limiting the number of units of the new product to be brought into the solution. This same lower limiting number might be zero. This is a case of "degeneracy." There is no problem as to how many units of the new product to bring in, as this is given by the several lower limits (which may be zero). However, since the products which are "limiting" will now all go to zero, if not already there, there is some question as to which product to remove from the solution set represented by the row headings in the table. This problem is resolved by starting at the left-hand side of the table for each of the variables in question and progressively dividing each column's coefficients, or rates of substitution, by the rate of substitution of the new product coming into the solution in the same row—the coefficient used for the original division. In the first column where the resulting ratios are not equal, the product corresponding to the row with the smallest algebraic ratio is the one removed from the solution set. Therefore, *only one product is removed from each solution set per table. The number of rows in each table remains constant.*

See A. Charnes, W. W. Cooper, and A. Henderson, *An Introduction to Linear Programming* (New York· John Wiley & Sons, Inc., 1953).

uct presently in the solution, which due to the substitution or exchange go to zero. Therefore this choice also yields the product which must be taken out of the solution.

A new table is then constructed. The column headings remain the same, as they represent the full range of choices available, the total number of variables in the problem. The row headings in Table 3–2a have changed due to the fact that X_S has been removed and X_B inserted.

Table 3–2a
BASIS AT SECOND STEP IN SIMPLEX SOLUTION

	0 X_s	0 X_f	0 X_w	0 X_p	2 X_A	3 X_B	2.5 X_C	
X_B								1,500
X_f								22,500
X_w								15,500
X_p								28,000
N								

The new stage in the solution is now determined. X_B equals 1,500 units in the solution. X_f, X_w, and X_p no longer have their original number of units in the solution because 1,500 units of B have been brought in. From the rates of substitution the number of units of f, w, and p subtracted may be determined, i.e., $1,500 \times 5 = 7,500$, $1,500 \times 3 = 4,500$, and $1,500 \times 8 = 12,000$. The f units remaining (the new X_f) are $30,000 - 7,500 = 22,500$. The w units remaining (the new X_w) are $20,000 - 4,500 = 15,500$. The p units remaining (the new X_p) are $40,000 - 12,000 = 28,000$. The same figures for Table 3–2a could have been determined by multiplying the number in the previous solution by the proportion of the capacity remaining, giving:

$$X_f = 30,000 \times \frac{6,000 - 1,500}{6,000} = 22,500$$

$$X_w = 20,000 \times \frac{6,667 - 1,500}{6,667} = 15,500$$

$$X_p = 40,000 \times \frac{5,000 - 1,500}{5,000} = 28,000$$

Probably the most tedious and time-consuming part of the simplex method yet remains. At this new stage of solution with this new table, new rates of physical substitution are necessary. That is, new coefficients must be determined to insert within the table. This is due to the fact that the coefficients in a particular column represent the rates of substitution of the column heading with each respective row heading. In each new table the column headings remain the same, but the row headings change (a new set of variables represent the solution). The products which may be brought into the solution are expressed in terms of this new set of variables. The coefficients for the new table (3–2) are

Table 3–2b

SECOND TABLE IN SIMPLEX COMPUTATION

	0 X_s	0 X_f	0 X_w	0 X_p	2 X_A	3 X_B	2.5 X_C		
3 X_B	$\frac{1}{20}$	0	0	0	$\frac{1}{2}$	1	$\frac{2}{5}$	1,500	$/\frac{2}{5} = 3{,}750$
0 X_f	$-\frac{1}{4}$	1	0	0	$12\frac{1}{2}$	0	4	22,500	$/4 = 5{,}625$
0 X_w	$-\frac{3}{20}$	0	1	0	$4\frac{1}{2}$	0	$8\frac{4}{5}$	15,500	$/8\frac{4}{5} = 1{,}762$
0 X_p	$-\frac{2}{5}$	0	0	1	6	0	$21\frac{4}{5}$	28,000	$/21\frac{4}{5} = 1{,}283$
N	$\begin{array}{l}0\\-\frac{1}{20}\times 3\\-(-\frac{1}{4})\times 0\\-(-\frac{3}{20})\times 0\\-(-\frac{2}{5})\times 0\end{array}$				$\begin{array}{l}2\\-\frac{1}{2}\times 3\\-12\frac{1}{2}\times 0\\-4\frac{1}{2}\times 0\\-6\times 0\end{array}$		$\begin{array}{l}2.5\\-\frac{2}{5}\times 3\\-4\times 0\\-8\frac{4}{5}\times 0\\-21\frac{4}{5}\times 0\end{array}$		
	$-\frac{3}{20}$				$\frac{1}{2}$		1.3		

derived from the old table (3–1). First use the expression for the rates of substitution from the previous table (3–1c) for the product brought into the new solution (X_B, that is,

$$B = 20s + 5f + 3w + 8p .$$

The product removed from the old solution (s) may, by algebraic manipulation, be expressed in terms of the new solution set showing rates of substitution with the new set. Dividing by 20,

$$\frac{1}{20}B = s + \frac{1}{4}f + \frac{3}{20}w + \frac{2}{5}p$$

and

$$s = \frac{1}{20}B - \frac{1}{4}f - \frac{3}{20}w - \frac{2}{5}p .$$

Note that the negative signs in Table 3–2b are consistent with the equation. These numbers, i.e., $-\frac{2}{5}$, represent rates of substitution also, but in this case (with a negative sign) this means that every unit of s brought into the solution would require an additional $\frac{2}{5}$ of a unit of p also to be brought into the solution. At this stage in the solution the only way to increase s (generate idle time in stamping) is to eliminate units of B which will also generate more idle time in painting or units of p in the ratio of 2 to 5. When a product to be brought into the solution has negative rates of substitution (meaning some products presently in the solution are to be increased), then these products presently in the solution do not restrict the number of units of the new product which may be brought in. They are not decreasing toward zero but are increasing. It is only products divided by positive rates of substitution which limit the number of units to be brought into the solution. With the expression for s in terms of the new solution set, it is possible to express all other possible products in terms of the solution set, i.e., the products in the row headings corresponding to the number of units to be made (in the last column). For the columns headed by products in the present solution, the coefficient in the row opposite each product is one; all others in the column are zero. This is equivalent to saying that for each unit of f brought into the present solution, one unit of f must be taken out, with nothing else changed.

From the previous table $(3-1c)$:

$$A = 10s + 15f + 6w + 10p .$$

Substituting the new expression for s gives:

$$
\begin{aligned}
A &= 10(\tfrac{1}{20}B - \tfrac{1}{4}f - \tfrac{3}{20}w - \tfrac{2}{5}p) + 15f + 6w + 10p \\
&= \tfrac{1}{2}B - 2\tfrac{1}{2}f - 1\tfrac{1}{2}w - 4p + 15f + 6w + 10p \\
&= \tfrac{1}{2}B + 12\tfrac{1}{2}f + 4\tfrac{1}{2}w + 6p \text{ (which is inserted in Table 3-2}b \\
&\qquad\qquad \text{in column } X_A)
\end{aligned}
$$

Similarly,

$$
\begin{aligned}
C &= 8s + 6f + 10w + 25p \\
&= 8(\tfrac{1}{20}B - \tfrac{1}{4}f - \tfrac{3}{20}w - \tfrac{2}{5}p) + 6f + 10w + 25p \\
&= \tfrac{2}{5}B + 4f + 8\tfrac{4}{5}w + 21\tfrac{4}{5}p \text{ (Table 3-2}b, \text{ column } X_C) .
\end{aligned}
$$

To demonstrate a point,

$$
\begin{aligned}
B &= 20s + 5f + 3w + 8p \\
&= 20(\tfrac{1}{20}B - \tfrac{1}{4}f - \tfrac{3}{20}w - \tfrac{2}{5}p) + 5f + 3w + 8p \\
&= 1B - 5f - 3w - 8p + 5f + 3w + 8p \\
&= 1B + 0f + 0w + 0p \text{ (Table 3-2}b, \text{ column } X_B) .
\end{aligned}
$$

Two choices are again required, as follows:

1. The most profitable product to bring in.
2. The limiting product and therefore the one which is completely subtracted and comes out of the solution set.

Notice that it is necessary to treat slack variables like all other variables and therefore to evaluate their contribution if brought into the solution at any stage.

Thus X_C comes in and X_p goes out. Similar computations and tables are made until the net valuations of all products (variables) not in the solution are zero and negative.

Table 3–3

THIRD TABLE IN SIMPLEX COMPUTATION

	0 X_s	0 X_f	0 X_w	0 X_p	2 X_A	3 X_B	2.5 X_C		
$3X_B$	0.057	0	0	−0.018	0.392	1	0	987	/ 0.392 = 2,520
$0X_f$	−0.178	1	0	−0.184	11.396	0	0	17,368	/11.396 = 1,525
$0X_w$	0.012	0	1	−0.404	2.076	0	0	4,210	/2.076 = 2,032
$2.5X_C$	−0.018	0	0	0.046	0.276	0	1	1,283	/0.276 = 4,650
	0 −0.057 × 3 −(−0.178) × 0 −0.012 × 0 −(−0.018) × 2.5			0 −(−0.018) × 3 −(0.184) × 0 −(0.404) × 0 −0.046 × 2.5	2 −0.392 × 3 −11.396 × 0 −2.076 × 0 −0.276 × 2.5				
N	−0.126			−0.061	0.134	(product to bring in)			

Solving for quantities of products in the solution set for Table 3–3 gives:

$$X_B = 1,500 - \tfrac{2}{5} \times 1,283 = 987 ,$$
$$X_f = 22,500 - 4 \times 1,283 = 17,368 ,$$

and

$$X_w = 15,500 - 8\tfrac{4}{5} \times 1,283 = 4,210 .$$

Solving for rates of substitution for Table 3–3 gives:

$$C = \tfrac{2}{5}B + 4f + 8\tfrac{4}{5}w + 21\tfrac{4}{5}p \text{ (from Table 3–2b)}$$
$$0.046C = 0.018B + 0.184f + 0.404w + p$$
$$p = 0.046C - 0.018B - 0.184f - 0.404w \text{ (Table 3–3)}$$

Also

$$s = \tfrac{1}{20}B - \tfrac{1}{4}f - \tfrac{3}{20}w - \tfrac{2}{5}p \text{ (Table 3–2b)}$$
$$= \tfrac{1}{20}B - \tfrac{1}{4}f - \tfrac{3}{20}w - \tfrac{2}{5}(0.046C - 0.018B - 0.184f - 0.404w)$$
$$= \tfrac{1}{20}B - \tfrac{1}{4}f - \tfrac{3}{20}w - 0.018C + 0.007B + 0.072f + 0.162w$$
$$= 0.057B - 0.178f + 0.012w - 0.018C \text{ (Table 3–3)}$$

and

$$A = \tfrac{1}{2}B + 12\tfrac{1}{2}f + 4\tfrac{1}{2}w + 6p \text{ (Table 3–2b)}$$
$$= \tfrac{1}{2}B + \cdot 12\tfrac{1}{2}f + 4\tfrac{1}{2}w + 6(0.046C - 0.018B - 0.184f - 0.404w)$$
$$= 0.5B + 12.5f + 4.5w + 0.276C - 0.108B - 1.104f - 2.424w$$
$$= 0.392B + 11.396f + 2.076w + 0.276C .$$

The remaining table(s) are derived in stages similar to those followed with the earlier tables:

1. The variables with positive values are listed to the left of the table, and used as row headings.
2. The values which these variables take are listed at the end of their respective rows. (In this problem, this is one solution to the four equations, using four of the seven unknowns.)
3. The rates of substitution within the table between variables in the solution basis and variables not in the solution (all of which take a zero value) are developed from the rate of substitution in the previous table.
4. Variables not in the solution are evaluated (net) one at a time, in order to choose one to bring into the next table.
5. The number of units permissible for the new variable in the next table is determined.

Table 3-4

	0 X_s	0 X_f	0 X_w	0 X_p	2 X_A	3 X_B	2.5 X_C	
3 X_B	0.063	−0.034	0	−0.012	0	1	0	390
2 X_A	−0.016	0.088	0	−0.016	1	0	0	1,525
0 X_w	0.044	−0.182	1	−0.371	0	0	0	1,044
2.5 X_C	−0.014	−0.024	0	0.050	0	0	1	862
N	−0.122	−0.014		−0.057				

As all net contributions in Table 3-4 are computed to be negative, i.e., −0.122, −0.014, and −0.057, the problem is solved. Contribution to profit and overhead will be maximized when 1,525 units of product A, 390 units of product B, and 862 units of product C are manufactured (and there are 1,044 slack seconds in welding). The total contribution at each table or stage in the solution may be readily computed from the objective function:

$$Z = X_A P_A + X_B P_B + X_C P_C + (X_s + X_f + X_w + X_p)(0).$$

This gives for Table 3-1:

$$Z_1 = (0)(2) + (0)(3) + (0)(2.5) + (30,000 + 30,000 + 20,000 + 40,000)(0)$$
$$= 0.$$

For Table 3-2:

$$Z_2 = (0)(2) + (1,500)(3) + (0)(2.5) + (0 + 22,500 + 15,500 + 28,000)(0)$$
$$= 4,500 \text{ cents}.$$

For Table 3-3:

$$Z_3 = (0)(2) + (987)(3) + (1,283)(2.5) + (0 + 17,368 + 4,210 + 0)(0)$$
$$= 6,169 \text{ cents}.$$

For Table 3–4:

$$Z_4 = (1,525)(2) + (390)(3) + (862)(2.5) + (0 + 0 + 1,044 + 0)(0)$$
$$= 6,375 \text{ cents}.$$

Note that the introduction of the new product C has raised the maximum contribution from $54.00 (page 81) to $63.75.

Implicit Values and the Dual

Given the optimum solution which has just been derived by the simplex method of linear programming, note that the three variables (slack time) not in the solution basis ($s, f,$ and p) have net evalutations at the bottom of their columns. The fact that these are all negative assures that the solution reached at this stage is the optimum one. Consider further, however, the meaning of these net evaluations.

The variable p takes a net evaluation of -0.057 cents. This means that a unit of this variable (slack seconds in painting) introduced into the solution at this final stage would reduce the objective function (contribution to overhead and profit) by 0.057 cents. If in fact the original capacity of painting had been one second less than the 40,000, the optimum solution would have a value of 0.057 cents less. Similarly, if the original capacity of painting had been one second larger than the 40,000, the optimum solution would have a value of 0.057 cents more. In other words, the net evaluation at this stage represents the *worth* of a marginal unit of painting capacity implied by the solution (implicit value—shadow price is a term also used here). In an economic sense, the total value of the painting capacity could be set at $(0.057)(40,-000) = 22.80$. The other two capacities with no slack in the solution are s and f and take similar total implicit values of $(0.122)(30,000) = 36.60$ and $(0.014)(30,000) = 4.20$. In total these values equal $22.80 + 36.60 + 4.20 = 63.60$, which differs from $63.75, the optimal value of the objective function, only due to rounding errors in computation. In other words, with an optimum solution, the values imputed to the variables not in the solution basis in total equal the value of the objective function. This introduces the concept of the dual in linear programming.[5]

Every linear programming problem has a dual problem associated with it. For instance, in the problem illustrated, the method of solution

---

[5] See Robert Dorfman, Paul A. Samuelson, and Robert M. Solow, *Linear Programming and Economic Analysis* (New York: McGraw-Hill Book Co., Inc., 1958), for an extended discussion of these concepts.

chosen seeks to choose the quantity of each metal part to make, which maximizes the returns from the parts and at the same time does not violate the capacity restrictions. The dual to this problem would have been to choose the value or "price" to assign to each unit of process which would minimize the value of the total input or processes used, while at the same time not violate the contribution per unit or price for each part as a lower limit. *Solving one problem also solves the other.*

The problem used to illustrate this chapter may be represented by the following expressions reading horizontally:

$$
\begin{array}{cccccc}
 & & & & & \text{Min.} \\
10X_A &+& 20X_B &+& 8X_C &\leq& 30,000 \\
K & & K & & K & & K \\
+ & & + & & + & & + \\
15X_A &+& 5X_B &+& 6X_C &\leq& 30,000 \\
L & & L & & L & & L \\
+ & & + & & + & & + \\
6X_A &+& 3X_B &+& 10X_C &\leq& 20,000 \\
M & & M & & M & & M \\
+ & & + & & + & & + \\
10X_A &+& 8X_B &+& 25X_C &\leq& 40,000 \\
N & & N & & N & & N \\
\geq & & \geq & & \geq & & \\
\end{array}
$$

$$\text{Max.}\quad 2X_A + 3X_B + 2\tfrac{1}{2}X_C$$

The dual to this same problem may be represented by the above expressions reading vertically. These expressions are written below in regular form:

$$
\begin{array}{l}
10K + 15L + 6M + 10N \geq 2 \\
20K + 5L + 3M + 8N \geq 3 \\
8K + 6L + 10M + 25N \geq 2\tfrac{1}{2} \\
\text{Min. } 30,000K + 30,000L + 20,000M + 40,000N
\end{array}
$$

Had the dual problem been solved using the simplex method, the values of A, B, and C could have been determined from the net evaluation row (for their slacks) in the final simplex table. The value of the dual objective function is $30,000(\$0.122) + 30,000(\$0.014) + 20,000(0) + 40,000(\$0.057) = \$63.60$ (given earlier). (In this solution, additional welding capacity would have zero value, and welding is equivalent to a "free good" in economic theory.) Because of the possibility of fewer constraint equations in the dual statement (as in this problem), conversion to the dual may be made for computational efficiency.

Checking

It is possible to check the technical feasibility of the final answer to insure that no capacities are violated:

	Capac-ity	Part A	Part B	Part C	Total
Stamping	30,000	$1,525 \times 10 = 15,250$	$390 \times 20 = 7,800$	$862 \times 8 = 6,896$	29,946
Forming	30,000	$1,525 \times 15 = 22,875$	$390 \times 5 = 1,950$	$862 \times 6 = 5,172$	29,997
Welding	20,000	$1,525 \times 6 = 9,150$	$390 \times 3 = 1,170$	$862 \times 10 = 8,620$	18,940
Painting	40,000	$1,525 \times 10 = 15,250$	$390 \times 8 = 3,120$	$862 \times 25 = 21,550$	39,920

In this case theoretically all capacities but welding ($X_w = 1,044$) should be fully utilized. Because of the rounding off of numbers during the solution, this is not quite the case. However, there is less than a quarter of a per cent slack in any of the other capacities.

For purposes of supplying a running check on the simplex calculations, the net evaluation row (N) for each table can be calculated in the same manner as the coefficients in the other rows. As an example in computing the values for Table 3–3 from Table 3–2, the calculations could have been as follows:

$$C = \tfrac{2}{5}B + 4f + 8\tfrac{4}{5}w + 21\tfrac{4}{5}p + 1.3N \text{ (from Table 3–2b)}$$
$$0.046C = 0.018B + 0.184f + 0.404w + p + 0.060N$$
$$p = 0.046C - 0.018B - 0.184f - 0.404w - 0.060N \text{ (Table 3–3)}$$

This net evaluation figure of -0.060 could then be used as a check against the -0.061 determined independently (a rounding error of 0.001 is present). The evaluation figure can be included in similar fashion for all the variables. Thus the same evaluation figures will be determined two separate ways providing a check on the computations for the whole table.

Relation of Products to Processes

Where there are fewer products than processes, only a number of processes equal to, or less than, the number of products will be fully used, as in the example. Where the number of products is equal to the number of processes, all processes may be fully utilized, and all products may be made. Where the number of products exceeds the number of processes, only a number of products equal to, or less than, the number of processes will be made. In all cases, the smaller number is the limiting one. This may be represented geometrically by considering two very simple cases: 1 product and 2 processes, and 2 products and 1 process.

Process x Process y

0   Product A

Only process x is fully used; while process y is partly used.

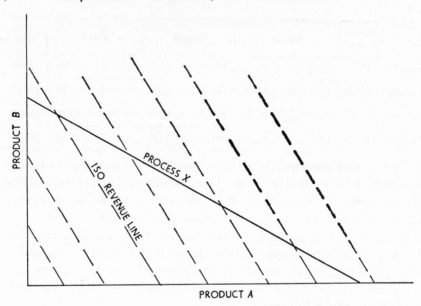

Only product A should be made; while no product B should be made.

This information about the number of products and the use of processes in the solution may be deduced from the simplex table. The number of products in the final solution (real and slack) is equal to the number of rows in the table which is equal to and determined by the number of constraints (number of processes in this case) on the solution. Therefore, no more products than there are processes or constraints will be made. Also, if the number of processes exceeds the number of products, then the difference will be represented by slack variables (idle capacities) with positive values. If, in the case with fewer processes than products, other constraints are added to the problem, such as certain sales requirements that must be met, then each additional constraint will provide either a real or slack variable in the final solution.

It is well to point out that it is always fairly simple to test the technical feasibility of a proposed solution, and also to evaluate it economically. The variables with positive values would be inserted into the constraint equations to assure that they had not been violated. The variables could then be inserted into the objective function in order to evaluate the solution. Therefore, if the number of possible solutions is small enough, and their nature easy to determine, it might be simpler and faster to make these tests and evaluations rather than using the simplex method. However, as variables are added, the potential number of solutions increases rapidly to a point where this is not possible. In some cases, however, where the nature of the problem neither justifies testing all possible solutions nor the use of the simplex method, the problem may be made explicit as is done at the first stage of the simplex method, and then a few of the more likely solutions tested and evaluated. This method might work quite satisfactorily, especially where the user had a good bit of experience with the particular problem. Other methods of solving linear programming problems are discussed in the next chapter.

Where many extensive linear programming problems remain to be solved, it may be well to put them on a computer. Several computers have been programmed to handle the simplex method, and the Armed Forces and some companies are currently solving linear programming problems with the use of these machines.

Slack Variables

Where equalities rather than inequalities exist in the problem restrictions, slack variables are used as a starting point in each equation of constraint or restriction for computational convenience. Because the initial solution which automatically supplies all the necessary rates of substitution is a solution at the origin, all variables with positive values at the origin are slack variables. As in the illustration, a slack variable takes the numerical value of each equation. (All time is idle time.) However, in many problems, no slack is allowed, such as a requirement that a capacity be fully utilized, or that a specific amount of raw material be used, or that a specific number of pounds be included in a package.

In cases such as these a slack variable, called an artifical slack variable, is included in the equation and is used as a starting point. However, because no slack is permitted in the final answer, a large positive cost or negative profit (M) is associated with the slack variable rather than a zero cost or profit. The method of computation and evaluation is the same as in the example given, except that when an "M" or any fraction of an "M" is included in the valuation of a potential choice it is considered sufficiently large to drive the associated artificial slack variable out of the solution. In other words, the economic penalty is so heavy that it removes what would have been technically not feasible.

As an example, if components A, B, and C going into a single package must equal 5 pounds (along with other restrictions), an initial constraint equation for a package would be:

$$X_A + X_B + X_C = 5 .$$

The artificial slack variable, S_a, would make the equation:

$$X_A + X_B + X_C + S_a = 5 .$$

It is obvious that S_a must equal zero, but it is included in the equation so that the simplex method may be used. The high cost of S_a, M, will drive it out of the solution.

It is possible to use the simplex method either to maximize or minimize a linear function. In analyzing problems of production management, the desire might well be to minimize a set of costs or a set of times. In this case, assuming cost is a positive figure, the largest negative number is chosen from the column footings of each table to bring a variable into the solution until all values at the column footings are zero or positive. Otherwise, the procedure is identical.

However, frequently in minimizing a linear function, one or some of the equations of constraint have a negative slack variable. For instance, if the sum of all components going into a package must be greater than, or equal to, a pound, then the slack variable (S) will be negative, i.e.:

$$X_1 + X_2 \cdots + X_n \geqq 1 \text{ pound, or}$$
$$X_1 + X_2 \cdots + X_n - S = 1 \text{ pound.}$$

That is, the sum of the actual components may equal one pound if there is no slack, or they may exceed one pound requiring some value for S to reduce the equation to one pound. However, for the initial solution or starting point for the simplex method, the slack variable used for each equation should be nonnegative. The method for handling this is the same as where the actual constraint is an equality rather than an inequality. An artificial slack variable is inserted into the equation with an extremely large positive cost (M), and so the economic choices involved in the solution drive this variable, which is technically not feasible, out of the solution. The other slack variable in the equation which may have a value in the solution (more than a pound in the package) has a cost of zero, similar to the slack variables in the metal parts problem illustrated. The equation of constraint would be:

$$X_1 + X_2 \cdots + X_n - S + S_a = 1 .$$

Each of these variables including S (with cost zero) and S_a (with cost M) would be a column heading in the simplex table. However, only S_a (the slack variable with a $+1$ coefficient) would be in the initial solution representing the origin.

Uses of Linear Programming

Many kinds of problems may be placed into a linear programming framework. Undoubtedly more uses will be made of the methods of solution as time progresses. A number of developments are currently being worked on including possible integer requirements,[6] inclusion of probability distributions explicitly into the linear program,[7] parametric programming,[8] and nonlinear programming.[9]

Some examples of the kinds of problems which can be and have been solved by these methods include the following:

1. Mixing Problem:

    A product or good is composed of several ingredients yielding the desired characteristics of the product and with varying cost. The least costly mix of ingredients which meets the characteristic requirements of the product is obtained. This has been applied to a wide variety of situations from gasoline blending at refineries to cattle feed mixing on farms.

2. Job Assignment Problems:

    A number of jobs or products must be handled by various men and/or machines. The least costly assignment is made. The Army has used linear programming to assign men to jobs, while industry has used it to assign orders to machines.

3. Capacity Allocation Problem:

    Limited capacity is allocated to products in order to yield maximum profits.

4. Production Scheduling:

    An uneven sales demand is met by a production schedule over a period of time with given penalties for storage and overtime, or "undertime" production.

5. Transportation Problems:

    The simplex method may be used to select a least costly shipment schedule from various plants with given capacities and costs to various distribution centers with given demands and given costs of transportation. The "transportation" method of solving linear programming problems is particularly suited to solve such problems and is presented in the following chapter.

6. Purchasing:

    Where multiple complex bids must be evaluated, such as by the Armed Services, linear programming can help make the choice of suppliers and demonstrate that the lowest cost arrangement has in fact been selected. Where a number of jobs must be done and it is possible to buy or subcontract some of the parts or jobs, linear programming can help choose between the firm's own departments and outside suppliers in order to ac-

---

[6] R. Gomory, "Outline of an Algorithm for Integer Solutions to Linear Programs," *Bull. Am. Math. Soc.,* September, 1958.

[7] Allen R. Ferguson and George B. Dantzig, "The Allocation of Aircraft to Routes—an Example of Linear Programming under Uncertain Demand," *Management Science,* October, 1956.

[8] W. W. Garvin, H. W. Crandall, J. B. John, and R. A. Spellman, "Applications of Linear Programming in the Oil Industry," *Management Science,* July, 1957.

[9] Robert Dorfman, Paul A. Samuelson, and Robert M. Solow, *Linear Programming and Economic Analysis* (New York: McGraw-Hill Book Co., Inc., 1958), chap. viii.

complish the whole job at minimum cost, or minimum time if this is the important variable.

7. Uses within the Method:

The simplex method automatically assigns values to unused slack variables (capacity completely used, or restriction exactly satisfied). It, therefore, indicates the value to the firm of increasing by a unit each limiting capacity. This might be useful in investment decisions. It would also indicate the least cost per unit of additional weight placed in a package.

It is also possible to determine the difference in costs or profits between the "best" solution and some other solution. This other solution might be the one used historically, or might be one determined by the simplex method with different constraints (e.g., the sales department requires at least 100 units of each product). Some quantitative guide is then available to management in evaluating its choice.

Solution by Computer

As an aid to the student, a computer program written in FORTRAN II-D has been prepared which solves small linear programming problems of the type used as illustrations in this book. The computations are carried out in the same step-by-step manner and the output is in the same form as the tableaus shown in this chapter. The program together with the input data and the output for the problem used as the main illustration in this chapter is given in the Appendix to this chapter. This run was made on an IBM 1620 computer, and the program is dimensioned to take a problem consisting of up to 10 rows and 20 columns. It would be easy to redimension for larger problems, but due to the step-by-step nature of the computations, it is not recommended that this program be used other than for teaching purposes.

SUMMARY

Linear programming is a methodology whereby a linear function is optimized (minimized or maximized), subject to a set of linear constraints in the form of equalities or inequalities (more than or less than). Symbolically this may be expressed as follows for the illustrative problem in this chapter:

$$Z = \text{MIN} \sum_i P_i X_i$$

subject to nonnegativity constraints on the variables

$$X_i \geq 0$$

and capacity constraints of the form

$$\sum_j t_{ij} X_i \leq b_i .$$

This formulation may be called the product-mix problem. Examples of other problems which may be formulated as linear programming problems are the following:

Blending

$$Z = \text{MIN} \sum_i C_i X_i$$

subject to

$$X_i \geq 0$$
$$\sum a_{ij} X_i \geq S_j \text{ (or } \leq S_j)$$

in which

X_i = amount of ith ingredient ,
a_{ij} = contribution of a unit of ith ingredient to satisfaction of specification j ,
S_j = specification j ,
C_i = cost of ith ingredient .

Make or Buy

$$Z = \text{MIN} \sum_{ij} c_{ij} X_{ij}$$

subject to

$$X_{ij} \leq 0$$
$$\sum_i a_{ij} X_{ij} \leq C_j$$
$$\sum_j X_{ij} = D_i$$

in which

X_{ij} = amount of ith product made with j^{th} capacity (capacity may be of same type but $j = 1$ might be owned and $j = 2, 3, \ldots$ that of potential suppliers),
a_{ij} = amount of jth capacity required per unit of product i,
c_{ij} = cost of jth capacity required per unit of product i,
C_j = amount of jth capacity available,
D_i = demand for i^{th} product.

Production Scheduling

$$Z = \text{MIN} \sum_{ijkl} c_{ijkl} X_{ijkl}$$

subject to

$$X_{ijkl} \geq 0$$

$$\sum_{ik} X_{ijkl} \leq C_{jl}$$

$$\sum_{jl} X_{ijkl} = D_{ik}$$

in which

X_{ijkl} = amount of ith product made in j^{th} period using l^{th} capacity for sale in k^{th} period,

D_{ik} = demand for i^{th} product in k^{th} period,

C_{jl} = capacity of type l available in period j,

c_{ijkl} = cost of making i^{th} product using l^{th}, capacity in j^{th} period for sale in k^{th} period.

Of course, this is only a small subset of the kinds of problems which lend themselves to this approach. The problems at the end of this chapter offer the opportunity to formulate and solve a variety of these and observe the potential results of applications.

A method for solving a mathematical problem has been demonstrated in this chapter. If the mathematical problem corresponds closely to a problem in the real world, then the solution to the mathematical problem should yield useful insights into the solution to the problem in the real world. The more distant the relationship is between the mathematical problem and the real problem, the less useful will be the solution of the former to the solution of the latter. It is this relationship which is of real importance to managerial decision making. Though many instances will not justify a complete and formal solution to a problem, the linear programming framework presented here may well provide a useful way of thinking about the problem.

REFERENCES

1. CHARNES, A.; COOPER, W. W.; and HENDERSON, A. *An Introducton to Linear Programming*. New York: John Wiley & Sons, Inc., 1953.

2. CHARNES, A., and COOPER, W. W. *Management Models and Industrial Applications of Linear Programming* (2 volumes). New York: John Wiley & Sons, Inc., 1961.

3. DANTZIG, G. B. *Linear Programming and Extensions*. Princeton: Princeton University Press, 1963.

4. DORFMAN, ROBERT. "Mathematical, or 'Linear' Programming: A Nonmathematical Exposition," *The American Economic Review*, December, 1953.

5. DORFMAN, ROBERT; SAMUELSON, PAUL A.; and SOLOW, ROBERT M. *Lin-*

ear Programming and Economic Analysis. New York: McGraw-Hill Book Co., Inc., 1958.

6. GARVIN, W. W. *Introduction to Linear Programming.* New York: McGraw-Hill Book Co., Inc., 1960.

7. GASS, S. I. *Linear Programming.* New York: McGraw-Hill Book Co., Inc., 1964.

8. HADLEY, G. *Linear Programming.* Reading, Mass.: Addison-Wesley Publishing Co., 1962.

9. KOOPMANS, T. C. (ed.). *Activity Analysis of Production and Allocation.* Cowles Commission for Research in Economics 13. New York: John Wiley & Sons, Inc., 1951.

APPENDIX TO CHAPTER 3

The following program computes the solution to a linear programming problem in the manner used in this chapter for the illustrative problem. The tableau may be printed at each iteration giving one detailed information on the course of the computations. The example for which input and output are shown is the four-process, three-product problem used throughout Chapter 3.

Input Variable Dictionary

PROB —alphameric problem label (up to 6 characters)

NXI(I) —numbers (subscripts) of variables in initial solution in row order

B(I) —right-hand side values for initial solution in row order

CJ(J) —costs of variables (program minimizes objective function so that maximization requires that objective function be multiplied by -1.)

NXJ(J) —numbers (subscripts) of all variables in column order

A(I, J) —tableau entries (by row and column)

Program Listing

```
  C      SIMPLEX ALGORITHM  -  2/22/65  -  GEH
  C
         DIMENSION CI(10),NXI(10),B(10),CJ(20),NXJ(20),
        1           A(10,20),Z(20),ZC(20)
  C
  C      READ DATA.
  C
       1 READ 901, PROB,M,N,KODE
         READ 902, (NXI(I),I=1,M)
         READ 903, (B(I),I=1,M)
         READ 903, (CJ(J),J=1,N)
         READ 902, (NXJ(J),J=1,N)
         DO 7 I=1,M
       7 READ 903, (A(I,J),J=1,N)
  C
  C      SETUP CI.
  C
         DO 15 I=1,M
         DO 15 J=1,N
         IF (NXI(I)-NXJ(J)) 15,14,15
      14 CI(I) = CJ(J)
      15 CONTINUE
         ITER = 0
  C
  C      COMPUTE Z AND ZC.
  C
      21 DO 25 J=1,N
         Z(J) = 0.0
         DO 24 I=1,M
```

```
      24 Z(J) = Z(J)+CI(I)*A(I,J)
      25 ZC(J) = Z(J)-CJ(J)
         OBJ = 0.0
         DO 28 I=1,M
      28 OBJ = OBJ+CI(I)*B(I)
C
C        PUNCH TABLEAU.
C
         PUNCH 910, PROB,ITER
         N1 = 1
         N2 = 5
      43 IF (N2-N) 45,45,44
      44 N2 = N
      45 PUNCH 911, (CJ(J),J=N1,N2)
         PUNCH 912, (NXJ(J),J=N1,N2)
         DO 48 I=1,M
      48 PUNCH 913, CI(I),NXI(I),B(I),(A(I,J),J=N1,N2)
         PUNCH 914, OBJ,(Z(J),J=N1,N2)
         PUNCH 915, (ZC(J),J=N1,N2)
         IF (N2-N) 52,55,55
      52 N1 = N1+5
         N2 = N2+5
         GO TO 43
      55 PUNCH 916
         ITER = ITER+1
C
C        DETERMINE PIVOT COLUMN.
C
         ZCM = ZC(1)
         JM = 1
         DO 109 J=2,N
         IF (KODE) 106,105,106
     105 IF (ZC(J)-ZCM) 107,109,109
     106 IF (ZC(J)-ZCM) 109,109,107
     107 ZCM = ZC(J)
         JM = J
     109 CONTINUE
C
C        CHECK FOR OPTIMAL.
C
         IF (KODE) 122,121,122
     121 IF (ZCM) 131,123,123
     122 IF (ZCM) 123,123,131
     123 PUNCH 917
         GO TO 1
C
C        DETERMINE PIVOT ROW.
C
     131 XM = 1.0E40
         IM = 0
         DO 139 I=1,M
         IF (A(I,JM)) 139,139,135



     135 XX = B(I)/A(I,JM)
         IF (XX-XM) 137,139,139
     137 XM = XX
         IM = I
     139 CONTINUE
         IF (IM) 141,141,151
     141 PUNCH 918
         GO TO 1
C
C        PERFORM PIVOT OPERATION.
C
     151 XX = A(IM,JM)
         B(IM) = B(IM)/XX
         DO 154 J=1,N
     154 A(IM,J) = A(IM,J)/XX
         DO 161 I=1,M
         IF (I-IM) 157,161,157
     157 XX = A(I,JM)
         B(I) = B(I)-XX*B(IM)
         DO 160 J=1,N
     160 A(I,J) = A(I,J)-XX*A(IM,J)
     161 CONTINUE
         CI(IM) = CJ(JM)
         NXI(IM) = NXJ(JM)
         GO TO 21
C
     901 FORMAT (A4,6X,3I3)
     902 FORMAT (24I3)
     903 FORMAT (7F10.0)
     910 FORMAT (8HPROBLEM A4,10X,9HITERATION I3//)
     911 FORMAT (28X,5F10.0)
     912 FORMAT (28X,5(6H   X(I2,2H) ))
     913 FORMAT (F8.0,5H   X(I2,1H),F10.3,1X,5F10.3)
     914 FORMAT (/15X,F10.2,3X,5F10.2)
     915 FORMAT (28X,5F10.2////)
     916 FORMAT (79X,1H-)
     917 FORMAT (22HOPTIMAL SOLUTION FOUND/79X,1H-)
     918 FORMAT (18HUNBOUNDED SOLUTION/79X,1H-)
         END
```

Input Data

```
*DATA
BOOK          4   7   1
  1   2   3   4
    30000.        30000.     20000.     40000.
       0.            0.         0.         0.        -20.       -30.       -25.
  1   2   3   4   5   6   7
    1.                                             10.        20.        8.
              1.                                   15.         5.        6.
                        1.                          6.         3.       10.
                                  1.               10.         8.       25.
```

Sample Output

			0.	0.	0.	0.	-20.
			X(1)	X(2)	X(3)	X(4)	X(5)
0.	X(1)	30000.000	1.000	0.000	0.000	0.000	10.000
0.	X(2)	30000.000	0.000	1.000	0.000	0.000	15.000
0.	X(3)	20000.000	0.000	0.000	1.000	0.000	6.000
0.	X(4)	40000.000	0.000	0.000	0.000	1.000	10.000
		0.00	0.00	0.00	0.00	0.00	0.00
			0.00	0.00	0.00	0.00	20.00

			-30.	-25.	
			X(6)	X(7)	X(
0.	X(1)	30000.000	20.000	8.000	
0.	X(2)	30000.000	5.000	6.000	
0.	X(3)	20000.000	3.000	10.000	
0.	X(4)	40000.000	8.000	25.000	
		0.00	0.00	0.00	
			30.00	25.00	

PROBLEM BOOK   ITERATION 1

			0.	0.	0.	0.	-20.
			X(1)	X(2)	X(3)	X(4)	X(5)
-30.	X(6)	1500.000	.050	0.000	0.000	0.000	.500
0.	X(2)	22500.000	-.250	1.000	0.000	0.000	12.500
0.	X(3)	15500.000	-.150	0.000	1.000	0.000	4.500
0.	X(4)	28000.000	-.400	0.000	0.000	1.000	6.000
		-45000.00	-1.50	0.00	0.00	0.00	-15.00
			-1.50	0.00	0.00	0.00	5.00

			-30.	-25.	
			X(6)	X(7)	X(
-30.	X(6)	1500.000	1.000	.400	
0.	X(2)	22500.000	0.000	4.000	
0.	X(3)	15500.000	0.000	8.800	
0.	X(4)	28000.000	0.000	21.800	
		-45000.00	-30.00	-12.00	
			0.00	13.00	

PROBLEM BOOK   ITERATION 3

			0. X(1)	0. X(2)	0. X(3)	0. X(4)	-20. X(5)
-30.	X(6)	392.354	.063	-.034	0.000	-.012	0.000
-20.	X(5)	1523.138	-.015	.087	0.000	-.016	1.000
0.	X(3)	1032.194	.043	-.182	1.000	-.370	0.000
-25.	X(7)	865.191	-.014 .	-.024	0.000	.050	0.000.

		-63863.17	-1.23	-.12	0.00	-.57	-20.00
			-1.23	-.12	0.00	-.57	0.00

			-30. X(6)	-25. X(7)	X(
-30.	X(6)	392.354	1.000	0.000	
-20.	X(5)	1523.138	0.000	0.000	
0.	X(3)	1032.194	0.000	0.000	
-25.	X(7)	865.191	0.000	1.000	

		-63863.17	-30.00	-25.00
			0.00	0.00

OPTIMAL SOLUTION FOUND

PROBLEMS

1. An automobile plant manufactures automobiles and trucks.[10] The plant is organized into four departments: (1) sheet metal stamping, (2) engine assembly, (3) automobile final assembly, and (4) truck final assembly— raw materials, labor and other inputs being available at constant prices within the demand range of the plant.

Department capacities limited as follows:

Metal stamping	25,000 autos	or	35,000 trucks per month
Engine assembly	33,333 autos	or	16,667 trucks per month
Auto assembly	22,500 autos per month		
Truck assembly			15,000 trucks per month

"The sales value of an automobile is $300 greater than the total costs of purchased materials, labor, and other direct cost attributable to its manufacture"; the truck yields $250 by the same measure. These are contributions to profit and overhead per unit.

a) Solve for this plant's optimum program by graphical methods.

b) What is the best schedule if one auto's "contribution" per unit is $500?

c) As the ratio of contributions of autos to trucks changes, what are the crucial ratios where the economic program changes?

2. Following World War II, the Bonhorn Rug Company could sell all the carpeting it could manufacture. It appeared that this would be the situation for the next several years. Their problem was how to best utilize their capacity

---

[10] Robert Dorfman, "Mathematical or 'Linear' Programming: A Nonmathematical Exposition," *The American Economic Review*, December, 1953.

during this seller's market. All of the large competitors in the industry charged about the same prices for given types and grades of carpeting, and Bonhorn accepted these prices as given restrictions. The two basic types of carpet manufactured by Bonhorn were velvet and axminster. Both of these types had to go first to the dye house and then to the weaving rooms. The capacity restriction in the dye house was 320 hours/time period. In velvet weaving, it was 400 hours/time period, while in axminster weaving, it was 160 hours/time period.

There were six product possibilities which shall be labeled for convenience 1 through 6. They required, respectively, 0.1, 0.2, 0.3, 0.4, 0.5, and 0.6 hours of dye house capacity per yard; 0.7, 0.6, 0.5, 0.4, 0, and 0 hours of velvet weaving capacity per yard; and 0, 0, 0, 0, 0.8, and 0.9 hours of axminster weaving capacity per yard. The contribution to overhead and profit per yard for the various products were, respectively, $5, $7, $7, $10, $20, and $30. This "contribution" is essentially price minus variable costs.

a) For maximum contribution to overhead and profits, what would have been the best production schedule for a time period?

b) The sales department felt it was advisable, considering the long run, to produce and sell at least 50 yards of each product (1 through 6) per time period. With this added restriction, what would be the difference in contribution to profit and overhead relative to the schedule determined in (a)?

3. A plant has 3 lathes, L_1, L_2, L_3, and 2 grinders, G_1, G_2, available for the machining of 4 products, P_1, P_2, P_3, P_4. Given the data below, find the most profitable allocation of machines among the 4 products. Setup times are negligible.

Unit Profits		A	P_1—$2.00 t	P_2—$1.50 t	P_3—$3.00 t	P_4—$4.00 t
Lathe Alternatives	L_1	32	0.7	—	—	0.6
	L_2	40	0.4	0.2	0.9	0.4
	L_3	28	0.3	0.1	—	—
Grinder Alternatives	G_1	36	—	0.6	0.4	0.6
	G_2	40	—	0.4	—	0.5

Column A shows the available capacity in hours per week of each machine. The t's are the unit machining times in hours for the various P's on the machines which can handle them. Note that P_2, P_3, and P_4 require both lathe and grinding operations, while P_1 requires no grinding. Each of the products can be made on any machine opposite which a time value appears. For example, P_1 can be made on L_1, L_2, or L_3.

a) Set up the problem for solution by the simplex method.

b) Solve the problem.

4. Given the following data on demand and production:

> 22 units to be sold in period 1
> 40 units to be sold in period 2
> Regular production capacity—25 units/time period
> Overtime production capacity—10 units/time period
> Overtime penalty—$2.00/unit
> Storage penalty—$1.00/unit/time period

a) Place this problem within the framework of the simplex method of linear programming.

b) Solve the problem by the simplex method.

5. A small machine shop has two tools and two products. The relevant parameters of the situation are shown below:

	0 X_3	0 X_4	3¢ X_1	4¢ X_2	Capacity
Machine Tool 1	1	0	3	5	4,200
Machine Tool 2	0	1	6	3	4,200

a) What function is to be maximized?

b) What is the significance of the column $(3, 6)$?

c) What is the significance of the row $(1; 0; 3; 5; 4,200)$?

d) What is the optimal production plan?

e) What is the optimum value of the profit function?

6. A manufacturer of paint solvents has the following problem. His product includes the following four characteristics and specifications (among others).

> Combustion point $\geq$ 250°
> Specific weight $\leq$ 1.00
> Alpha content $\leq$ 10% (by volume)
> Beta content $\leq$ 1% (by volume)

He may purchase the following raw materials to mix for his product. All mixing as far as the above characteristics are concerned results in linear combinations.

> *r*..........................$0.20/gallon
> *s*.......................... 0.18/gallon
> *t*.......................... 0.23/gallon

The raw materials possess the following characteristics:

	r	*s*	*t*
Combustion point	250°	240°	260°
Specific weight	0.92	1.06	0.98
Alpha content (by volume)	10.2%	9.5%	9.5%
Beta content (by volume)	0.9%	0.8%	1.0%

What is the economic mix of inputs *r*, *s*, and *t* which satisfies the product requirements?

a) Set up this problem in simplex form.

b) Solve the problem.

7. A company manufactures three products—A, B, and C—and in doing so utilizes four capacities—grinding, turning, assembly, and testing. The capacity requirements per unit of product in hours are as follows:

	Grinding	Turning	Assembly	Test
A.....................	0.03	0.10	0.30	0.08
B.....................	0.01	0.04	0.20	0.08
C.....................	0.03	0.20	0.25	0.08

The available capacities per month are:

Grinding...1,000 hours
Turning..4,000 hours
Assembly...9,000 hours
Test...3,000 hours

And the minimum monthly sales requirements are:

A..9,000 units
B..9,000 units
C..6,000 units

The profit per unit sold of each product is 5 cents for A, 4 cents for B, and 3 cents for C. All produced above the minimum can be sold for this amount. What quantities of each product should be produced next month for maximum profit?

a) Set up this problem for solution by the simplex method of linear programming, with the first table complete.

b) What product will be brought in and what capacity taken out at the first step?

c) How many units of this product will be brought in at the first step?

d) Solve for the best program.

8. The Magnavolt Company makes four types of television sets. Each set can be made by two different methods, one of which has two processes and the other three. Data on the operation is given below.

Set Type	1	2	3	4
Price to distributor................	$500	$400	$300	$200
Cost—Method X.................	$350	$300	$300	$300
Cost—Method Y.................	$485	$350	$220	$140
Quantity that can be sold..........	1,000	3,000	6,000	10,000

MANUFACTURING TIMES (HOURS)

Type	1	2	3	4
Method X, Process A..........	3.00	2.00	2.00	1.50
B..........	10.00	9.00	8.30	7.20
C..........	1.30	0.80	0.60	0.00
Method Y, Process D..........	0.00	0.00	1.25	2.00
E..........	15.00	14.00	2.00	1.00

PROCESS

	A	B	C	D	E
Hours available	10,000	40,000	5,000	10,000	10,000

a) Set up the data given in simplex form.

b) The above problem can be solved by a simple two-dimensional graphical approach if it is carefully examined. In this manner, solve for the best production program.

9. A manufacturer has jobs *A*, *B*, *C*, and *D* which must be produced next month. The following table shows the number of hours required to *complete* each job in each of the manufacturer's shops, *x*, *y*, and *z*, and the cost per hour and hours available. It is possible to split the jobs between shops.

Shop	Hours Required per Job				Cost per Hour	Hours Available
	A	B	C	D		
x	32	151	72	118	$89	160
y	39	147	61	126	81	160
z	46	155	57	121	84	160

a) Set up this problem as a linear programming problem.

b) Schedule this production for minimum cost by the simplex method.

c) What is the cost for each job?

10. From the table which follows:

a) State algebraically the objective function—profit maximization.

b) State algebraically the problem constraints.

c) Set up the first simplex table.

d) Solve the problem, i.e., amounts of the processes to be used and total net value received.

POSSIBLE PRODUCTION PROCESSES

	1	2	3	4	Amounts Available
Material, tons	100	100	100	100	1,500
Primary, %	7	5	3	2	100
Secondary, %	3	5	10	15	100
Output value	$1,110	$1,120	$1,130	$1,150	
Material cost	1,000	1,000	1,000	1,000	
Other direct costs	50	60	40	60	
Net value	60	60	90	90	

For example, one unit of process 1 will treat 100 tons of material, use 7 per cent of the primary capacity, 3 per cent of the secondary capacity, and yield a net value of $60.

11. Given the answers to the main problem used for illustration in this chapter, pages 82–97, if the problem conditions were assumed to be stable:

a) How much money should the shop be willing to spend for an additional unit of stamping capacity?

b) With larger investments in increased stamping capacity, what kind of a schedule of investment value as a function of increasing additional capacity can be set up?

c) If additional stamping capacity were "almost" free, how much capacity would be justified?

12. In the main problem used to illustrate this chapter, pages 82–97, consider that varying quantities of product *B* are to be *required* (from zero to infinity).

   a) As the quantity of *B* *required* goes from zero to infinity, what happens to the value of the objective function?

   b) Can a meaningful value for a unit of product *B* (equal to or different from its nominal 3 cents) be determined as the quantity of *B* required goes from zero to infinity?

13. In the main problem used to illustrate this chapter, pages 82–97, if the amount of product *A* which can be sold is unknown but can be estimated as a normal distribution with a mean of 1,000, and a standard deviaton of 200, what kind of a solution would you propose?

14. In the main problem used to illustrate this chapter, pages 82–97, if all products, *A, B,* and *C,* must have quantity answers in integer hundreds (e.g., 800, 900, 1,000, 1,100, etc.), what approach and what answer do you propose?

15. In the main problem used to illustrate this chapter, pages 82–97, if the forming operation is no longer required on products, *A, B,* and *C,* what is the optimum schedule?

16. With the following information:

   a) Completely set up first simplex table.

   b) Solve for least cost mix.

FOUNDRY	SCRAP PILES AVAILABLE				
	1	2	3	4	5
% *A*	0.43	0.36	0.52	0.31	0.45
% *B*	0.41	0.45	0.32	0.50	0.37
% *C*	0.03	0.02	0.05	0.04	0.06
Other	0.13	0.17	0.11	0.15	0.12
Total Pounds Weight	700	620	930	210	60

Scrap is not salable *as such.*
Price/pound to purchase:

A	*B*	*Other*
17 cents	23 cents	6 cents

Product specification to be made:

$A = 50\%, B \geq 30\%, B \leq 35\%, C \leq 3\%$
Weight $= 2{,}000$ pounds

Components A, B, and/or other may be purchased as such; scrap is "free."

17. A company with two plants has received the following orders for shipment next week:

		SHIPPING COST/UNIT	
DESTINATION	UNITS ORDERED	From Plant No. 1	From Plant No. 2
A........................	500	$1.00	$5.00
B........................	300	2.00	3.00
C........................	1,000	3.00	2.00
D........................	200	4.00	1.00

Each unit of product must be machined and assembled. The costs, requirements, and availabilities are as follows:

	Hours/Unit	Cost/Hour	Hours Available
Plant No. 1:			
Machining..............	0.10	$4.00	120
Assembling.............	0.20	3.00	240
Plant No. 2:			
Machining..............	0.12	3.80	120
Assembling.............	0.22	3.00	240

In which plants should these orders be manufactured?

a) Set up this problem in order to obtain a least cost solution by the simplex method of linear programming.

b) Make one iteration showing the variable brought in, the variable removed, new exchange rates, and the change in the value of the objective function.

18. Formulate Problem No. 7, Chapter 2, as a linear programming problem with the objective function that of minimizing costs. What basic assumption concerning the costs is necessary for this formulation? Show completely the simplex tableau for your formulation. What special requirements, if any, must be satisfied in order to obtain a solution to this problem?

CHAPTER 4

Special Programming Methods

SOME types of linear programming problems may be handled by less tedious methods than the simplex method. The transportation method is an example of such a method and is presented in this chapter. Dynamic programming, a method applicable to a more general class of problems, is also presented.

TRANSPORTATION METHOD OF LINEAR PROGRAMMING

The transportation method, as its name suggests, was developed for problems involving a number of shipping sources and a number of destinations. For a given time period, each source has a certain maximum capacity and each destination has a certain requirement. There is a given cost per unit (pound, ton, barrel, etc.) for shipment from each source to each destination. The objective is to satisfy the destination requirements within the capacity restrictions of the sources with the minimum total cost (the objective function).

A number of different types of problems, such as transportation shipments, machine assignment, and storage and overtime scheduling, can be placed within the transportation framework of analysis. These will be discussed following the method itself.

Steps in the Transportation Method

Any problem which can be solved by the transportation method can be solved by the more general simplex method. The transportation method of solving linear programming problems is basically very similar to the general simplex method, and in a sense is a special case of it. The nature of the steps in both of these procedures is as follows:

1. The problem is framed.
    a) All requirements are explicitly stated.

115

    b) Any permissible slack in the system is explicitly stated.
    c) All appropriate costs and/or revenues are determined.
    d) An objective function is determined.
    e) The computational framework is established.
2. An initial solution is determined.
    a) The initial solution must be technically feasible, i.e., it must meet all restrictions.
    b) It may be nonsense economically.
3. Alternative choices are evaluated.
    a) Changes in the solution are made one at a time.
    b) The evaluation is of the *complete* effect of each change for the incremental unit added. (The value of both the transportation and the general simplex computational techniques is that this evaluation of the complete effect of each change is straightforward and therefore can be delegated to a clerk or computing equipment.)
4. The alternative with the largest favorable cost or revenue difference per unit is selected. On the basis of limited information, this is an "efficient" procedure. Alternatives to this choice will be discussed.
5. The number of units to be included in this change is determined.
    a) Because of the linear nature of the model, each unit contributes the same cost or revenue difference.
    b) The limit on the number of units involved in the particular change is technical feasibility (nonnegative requirements).
6. A new solution is determined.
    a) The elements to change and the number of units to include have been previously determined.
7. Steps three through six are repeated. The process is iterative.
8. When step 3 evaluates no alternative choices favorably, the procedure is complete; there is no better solution.

A transportation method example should make this procedure more meaningful.

A Transportation Problem

Consider the problem of three factories supplying a product to five warehouses. Some difference exists in the manufacturing costs, and the cost of shipment varies for the fifteen different plant to warehouse routes. Each plant has a certain maximum capacity restriction per month. Each warehouse has a certain sales requirement. All of this may be shown in tabular form (the computational framework). See Table 4–1.

The foot of each column expresses the sales requirement for the warehouse heading the column. The end of each row expresses the capacity restriction for the factory heading the row. The sales requirements must be satisfied (in this problem) exactly, that is, they may be neither overfulfilled nor underfulfilled. The capacity restrictions of the factories may not be exceeded, but smaller figures may be chosen.

Table 4-1

TRANSPORTATION COSTS AND REQUIREMENTS

		Destination (Outputs)						Capacity Restriction
	Warehouses / Factories	A	B	C	D	E	Slack	
Sources (Inputs)	x	0.37	0.27	0.28	0.34	0.31	0	100
	y	0.29	0.31	0.32	0.27	0.29	0	125
	z	0.33	0.26	0.35	0.30	0.30	0	150
Sales Requirement		50	60	70	80	90	25	375

The figures within the table (i.e., $yD = 0.27$) represent the cost to manufacture one unit of product at a given plant (y), and ship it to a given warehouse (D). Thus, each cost in the table is a combination of manufacturing and shipping costs. The cost involved is the variable cost per unit, i.e., the cost affected by the decision made in the problem. If ten additional units are made at plant y and shipped to warehouse D, an additional \$2.70 (10×0.27) will be spent by the firm.

As the total capacity of the factories exceeds the total requirements of the warehouses, there is some idle capacity or slack in the system. The amount of slack here is 25 units $[100 + 125 + 150 - (50 + 60 + 70 + 80 + 90)]$, and a column is provided for it. The direct cost associated with idle capacity (goods neither produced nor shipped) is zero, as in the simplex method. Part of the problem, of course, is to determine which factory(ies) should have idle capacity and how much.

Several points should be made here. The total sales requirements or outputs must equal the total capacity restrictions or inputs in order to use the transportation procedure. Where this is not initially the case, a slack row or column is included to provide for the difference. Like the general simplex method, the transportation method requires equalities rather than inequalities. The cost per unit in each cell route represents a linear function, i.e., each unit adds the same amount to costs. Finally, units may be transferred within the schedule on a one-for-one basis. That is, within a source capacity restriction, if one unit is subtracted from a destination, one unit, no more and no less, may be added from the same source to another destination. Likewise, it is meaningful to transfer one unit assigned to a destination from one source to another. With respect to the last two points—the linearity of costs and the homogeneity of units—a slight discrepancy might exist between the symbolic world and the real world. Just as in the general simplex method, if the pragmatic position is taken, the question will not be "Is the model true?" but, "Is the model useful?"

The objective in such a situation is to satisfy all sales requirements of the warehouses within the capacity restrictions of the factories at minimum total cost.

In line with the procedure outlined initially, step one is completed, and the problem has been framed as follows:

1. All requirements have been explicitly stated:
   a) The warehouse sales
   b) The factory capacities
2. The total slack is explicitly stated (25 units).
3. The manufacturing plus transportation costs per unit are stated in the table.
4. The objective is stated.
5. The table for implementing the transportation method has been constructed. Actually two tables could have been used; one for the costs and one for the capacities and requirements (together considered the "rim requirements").

Initial Solution

The next step is to determine an initial solution. This means that the requirements must be satisfied within the capacity restrictions. A number of methods exist for securing an initial solution. The particular initial solution chosen may have some effect on the number of steps required to obtain the final solution.

One way of getting an initial solution is to use the existing solution to the problem if there is one. The requirement of an initial solution (and every other solution) is that the destination requirements be satisfied within the source capacities (the rim requirements must be met). The main advantage of starting with an existing solution rather than a random solution is that judgment and experience have previously gone into this solution.

A second method of reaching an initial solution is by inspection. Some routes (source-destination) are less costly than others. This can be read right from the table. However the nature of a linear programming problem includes the characteristic that the second, third, and n order effects (if it's used here it won't be available there) must be considered in determining the best solution. However, even a cursory analysis of the two tables—one for the incremental costs and one for the rim requirements—will indicate that some routes are probably better than others, considering the effects their choice has on the rest of the solution. The smaller the table (sources × destinations), the more effective this method will be. Experience in seeing what the second and third order effects will be should make this method yield a solution closer to the final best solution. See Table 4–2 for one possible initial solution by inspection. The shipment schedule is shown in the lower right-hand corner of each cell or route which is used.

Table 4–2

INSPECTION SOLUTION OF TRANSPORTATION PROBLEM

	Warehouses / Factories	DESTINATIONS						Capacity Restriction
		A	B	C	D	E	Slack	
SOURCES	x	0.37 / 5	0.27	0.28 / 70	0.34	0.31	0 / 25	100
	y	0.29 / 45	0.31	0.32	0.27 / 80	0.29	0	125
	z	0.33	0.26 / 60	0.35	0.30	0.30 / 90	0	150
Sales Requirement		50	60	70	80	90	25	375

An analogous but more formal method than inspection for determining the initial solution is the mutually preferred method.[1] In this method all routes (source i to destination j) that have the lowest cost (or the highest profit, given a problem of maximization rather than minimization) in both their row and their column are used. The limit to their use—to satisfy the rim requirements—is the lower figure of the source capacity and the destination requirement. It is not possible to exceed the capacity, nor, in this case, to overship to a destination. These routes are termed "mutually preferred" as they are "best" in both their row and column.

Ignoring the slack column for the moment, from Table 4–1, it can be seen that yD and zB are mutually preferred routes. The next step in the mutually preferred procedure is to set up a new table with these routes removed. This is done by removing the respective rows or columns with the limiting quantities. For instance, in the case with yD, column D had 80 units and row y had 125 units, so 80 units are

---
[1] H. S. Houthakker, "On the Numerical Solution of the Transportation Problem," *Journal of the Operations Research Society of America*, Vol. III (1955), p. 210.

assigned to yD, column D is eliminated, and row y is reduced to $125 - 80 = 45$ units. Table 4–3a would be the next step, from which yA and xC would then be the mutually preferred routes which would be subtracted yielding Table 4–3b. From this table, zE would be subtracted

Table 4–3a

NEW TABLE—"MUTUALLY PREFERRED" SOLUTION

	A	C	E	Slack	
x	0.37	0.28	0.31	0	100
y	0.29	0.32	0.29	0	45
z	0.33	0.35	0.30	0	90
	50	70	90	25	235

Table 4–3b

	A	E	Slack	
x	0.37	0.31	0	30
z	0.33	0.30	0	90
	5	90	25	120

as the mutually preferred route, forcing assignments into xA and xSlack to satisfy the rim requirements. Higher order effects may be considered in the mutually preferred method, thus permitting a bit of juggling after the first solution and before formal evaluation takes place.

A fourth method of determining an initial solution is the northwest corner rule.[2] Following this procedure, a start is made in the upper left-hand corner—the northwest corner. This route is fully used, meaning that either the destination requirement is fully satisfied or the source capacity is completely used, depending on which number is lower. The remainder of either the destination requirement or the source capacity is then assigned to the next row(s) or column(s) until it is fully used. Following this procedure, the table is filled in from the upper left cell to the lower right, using up fully a destination requirement, and then a source capacity, then a destination requirement, etc. Table 4–4 shows the results of this procedure.

This procedure is essentially a random one in that the orders of the rows and columns determine the initial solution, and these orders are random. The northwest corner system has the advantage of supplying

---

[2] A. Charnes and W. W. Cooper, "The Stepping Stone Method of Explaining Linear Programming Calculations in Transportation Problems," *Management Science,* Vol. I, No. 1 (October, 1954), p. 49.

Table 4–4

NORTHWEST CORNER SOLUTION

		DESTINATIONS						Capacity Restriction
	Warehouses / Factories	A	B	C	D	E	Slack	
SOURCES (INPUTS)	x	0.37	0.27	0.28	0.34	0.31	0	100
		/50	/50					
	y	0.29	0.31	0.32	0.27	0.29	0	125
			/10	/70	/45			
	z	0.33	0.26	0.35	0.30	0.30	0	150
					/35	/90	/25	
Sales Requirement		50	60	70	80	90	25	375

a straightforward initial solution, which would be useful, for instance, in machine computing.

Step two is now complete—an initial solution has been determined by one of the methods demonstrated. This is analogous in the general simplex method to the initial solution in which all capacity scheduled is idle capacity to provide a starting point which leads into the procedure of solution.

Evaluation

Step three must now be undertaken wherein alternative choices are evaluated. As in the general simplex method, the incremental (per unit) gain or loss associated with bringing each alternative into the solution is computed. In the transportation method, the alternatives are the unused routes. The main body of the procedure, in both the transportation method and the general simplex method, is for the purpose of facilitating the evaluation of the complete effect of one unit being added to an alternative choice. Since it is the complete effect which is determined, the alternative with the most favorable result is chosen.

Table 4–4 will be used as a starting point. The figure at the top of each cell is the direct variable cost per unit. The figures in the lower right-hand corner of some of the cells give the number of units to be shipped via this route in the initial solution. These scheduled shipments (including the slack) in each row add up to that row's capacity; these scheduled shipments in each column add up to that column's requirements, i.e., the rim requirements have been satisfied. Those cells which do not have scheduled shipments are the alternative choices. Each cell which is not used must be evaluated. This evaluation shows the net total effect of adding one unit to the cell route.

Route yA will be used to illustrate this evaluation. If one unit is added to cell yA, its shipment cost is 29 cents. However, *as rim requirements must be satisfied,* if the unit is added to yA, a unit must be subtracted from xA in order that the A column cells still total a shipment of 50 units. This unit which is subtracted from xA saves a shipping cost of 37 cents. However, as a unit is subtracted from xA, a unit must be added to xB in order that the row x shipments still equal 100 units. Notice, only those cell routes which are now used are considered in this adjustment as *only one new cell at a time is evaluated.* If a unit is added to xB, an additional shipping cost of 27 cents is incurred. Again, considering the rim requirements, if a unit is added to xB, a unit must be subtracted from yB in order that column B will still total 60. The unit subtracted from yB saves 31 cents in shipping costs. The unit subtracted from yB enables row y to still total 125 as a unit had been tentatively added to yA at the start of the procedure. This procedure is now back where it started. Tentatively, a unit has been added to yA, subtracted from xA, added to xB, and subtracted from yB. The rim requirements are still satisfied. However, and this is the purpose of the procedure, a cost change has taken place; 29 cents has been added, 37 cents subtracted, 27 cents added, and 31 cents subtracted, or a net cost of 12 cents has been subtracted $(+ 29 - 37 + 27 - 31 = -12)$. This means that every unit added to route yA saves 12 cents according to the adjustments given above. The cost of not using this route is 12 cents per unit. It would certainly be worthwhile to use this route if this were the only choice available. However, other alternative routes might be even more profitable.

The evaluation could just as well have taken the reverse of this route. If a unit is added to yA, one must be subtracted from yB, one must be added to xB, and one must be subtracted from xA $(+ 29 - 31 + 27 - 37 = - 12)$.

One more alternative cell route will be evaluated to demonstrate the procedure further. This time x slack will be evaluated. If a unit is added to x slack, the additional direct cost is zero—the cost in the table. This is because the direct cost of, in effect, not manufacturing a unit at plant x is zero. The indirect cost is being evaluated. If a unit is added to x slack, a unit must be subtracted from xB, and 27 cents is saved. The unit cannot be subtracted from xC, xD, or xE because there is nothing to subtract. It cannot be subtracted from xA because column A must total 50, and no other cell in column A can be increased because they are not presently used and the procedure evaluates only one alternative at a time. If a unit is subtracted from xB, one must be added to yB at a cost of 31 cents; yC cannot be used to balance off yB because no opportunity for adjustment exists in column C so that it can still total 70. Therefore, if a unit is added to yB, a unit must be subtracted from yD at a saving of 27 cents. If a unit is subtracted from yD, a unit must be added to zD at a cost of 30 cents. If a unit is added to zD, a unit must be subtracted from z slack at a zero saving. The slack column now totals 25, as a unit was tentatively added to x slack at the start of the procedure. The total net difference in cost is $(+0 - 27 + 31 - 27 + 30 - 0 = +7)$ a 7-cent *increase* in cost per unit added to x slack. This means that any slack permitted in factory x at this stage of the solution would have a total effect of increasing costs by 7 cents per unit. Table 4–5 shows all of the alternative routes evaluated. The evalua-

Table 4–5

EVALUATION OF ALTERNATIVES—INITIAL SOLUTION

	Warehouses / Factories	DESTINATIONS						Capacity Restriction
		A	B	C	D	E	Slack	
SOURCES	x	0.37	0.27	0.28	0.34	0.31	0	100
		50	50	0.00	+0.11	+0.08	+0.07	
	y	0.29	0.31	0.32	0.27	0.29	0	125
		−0.12	10	70	45	+0.02	+0.03	
	z	0.33	0.26	0.35	0.30	0.30	0	150
		−0.11	−0.08	0.00	35	90	25	
Sales Requirement		50	60	70	80	90	25	375

tion (opportunity cost) is shown in the lower left-hand corner of the unused cells.

According to the system of computation and signs used here, a negative evaluation means the cells offer an opportunity for cost savings, and a positive evaluation means the cell, if used, would incur a cost penalty. A different system of signs could have been used in the computation, i.e., a plus for a cost saving or profit increase and a minus for a cost increase or profit decrease. The important point is that the system be meaningful to the user. Basically, the same procedure would be used if the problem were one of maximization rather than minimization as this one is. In the case of maximization (with profit figures for instance) using the system of signs presented here, if the "cost" matrix here represented contribution to profit per unit, the positive evaluations would be desirable and the negative ones undesirable.

Step three has now been completed—all alternative choices have been evaluated. Step four is completed by inspection. The change with the largest favorable cost difference per unit is yA, with a saving of 12 cents per unit. This is the first change to be made. The next question is how many units to place in cell route yA. As in the general simplex method, because of the linear nature of the model, each unit contributes the same cost difference and therefore as many units as possible are placed on the new route. How many are possible?

Altering the Solution

Cell yA, which is the new route "being brought into the solution," was the first one evaluated for demonstration purposes. Consider the nature of the evaluation. If a unit is added to yA, it must be subtracted from xA, added to xB, and subtracted from yB in order that the rim requirements be satisfied. If 5 units are added to yA, 5 units must be subtracted from xA, added to xB, and subtracted from yB. Therefore, the limitation to the number of units that can be added to yA is the number of units that can be subtracted from xA or from yB. For every unit that is added to yA (and xB), a unit must be subtracted from xA and yB. The smaller number of units currently scheduled in xA or yB is therefore the limit to which units can be added to yA. No more units can be subtracted than are there. This is due to the nonnegative requirement. No negative shipments are permitted—the process is not reversible. If sending fewer units from factory x to warehouse A saves 37 cents per unit, this does not mean that sending units from warehouse A to factory x also saves 37 cents per unit.

In this case yB has the lower number, 10, and therefore only 10 units can be added to yA. The procedure described here is "efficient" in the sense that with limited information, and knowing only contribution per unit, if the route with the largest contribution per unit is brought into the solution, the expected or average number of "tables" to the final solution will be minimized. However, if for each route favorably evaluated, the number of units which might be brought in is determined, and if this number is then multiplied by the contribution per unit, then the route with the largest product (total contribution) should be brought in. Though this will further reduce the expected number of tables, it would require a whole additional *set* of calculations for each table.

Step five is completed as the number of units to be included has been determined. Ten units, therefore, are subtracted from xA and yB, and added to xB and yA. This, of course, means that yB is no longer a used route—it "comes out of the solution." Step six is completed as a new solution has been determined. This new solution is shown in Table 4–6. As step seven indicates, steps three through six are now repeated—the process is iterative. The evaluations for the new solution, step three, are also included in Table 4–6.

Table 4–6

SECOND TABLE IN TRANSPORTATION PROBLEM

		DESTINATIONS (OUTPUTS)						Ca-pacity Restrictions
Warehouses / Factories		A	B	C	D	E	Slack	
SOURCES (INPUTS)	x	0.37 / 40	0.27 / 60	0.28 / −0.12	0.34 / −0.01	0.31 / −0.04	0 / −0.05	100
	y	0.29 / 10	0.31 / +0.12	0.32 / 70	0.27 / 45	0.29 / +0.02	0 / +0.03	125
	z	0.33 / +0.01	0.26 / +0.04	0.35 / 0.00	0.30 / 35	0.30 / 90	0 / 25	150
Sales Requirement		50	60	70	80	90	25	375

Note in evaluating zB, the path of adjustments is $+zB - xB + xA - yA + yD - zD$, or $+26 - 27 + 37 - 29 + 27 - 30 = +4$ cents. In Table 4–6, xC is the most favorable change. The evaluation route was $+xC - xA + yA - yC$. Of the two cells being reduced, xA has the smaller number of units, 40. Therefore, 40 units are added to xC, and the appropriate adjustments are made in xA, yA, and yC to agree with the rim requirements. Table 4–7 shows the new solution and the evaluation of its alternative routes.

In Table 4–7, zB is the most (and only) favorable change. The evaluation route was $+zB - xB + xC - yC + yD - zD$. In this case,

Table 4–7

THIRD TABLE IN TRANSPORTATION PROBLEM

		DESTINATIONS (OUTPUTS)						Capacity Restriction
	Warehouses / Factories	A	B	C	D	E	Slack	
SOURCES (INPUTS)	x	0.37 +0.12	0.27 /60	0.28 /40	0.34 +0.11	0.31 +0.08	0 +0.07	100
	y	0.29 /50	0.31 0.00	0.32 /30	0.27 /45	0.29 +0.02	0 +0.03	125
	z	0.33 +0.01	0.26 −0.08	0.35 0.00	0.30 /35	0.30 /90	0 /25	150
Sales Requirement		50	60	70	80	90	25	375

three cells are being decreased (and three increased). Of the cells being reduced, yC has the smallest number of units, 30. Therefore, 30 units are added to zB, and the appropriate adjustments made in xB, xC, yC, yD, and zD to agree with the rim requirements.

Table 4–8 shows the new solution and the evaluation of its alternative routes.

Table 4–8

FOURTH TABLE IN TRANSPORTATION PROBLEM

		DESTINATIONS (OUTPUTS)						Capacity Restriction
	Warehouses / Factories	A	B	C	D	E	Slack	
SOURCES (INPUTS)	x	0.37 +0.04	0.27 /30	0.28 /70	0.34 +0.03	0.31 +0.00	0 −0.01	100
	y	0.29 /50	0.31 +0.08	0.32 +0.08	0.27 /75	0.29 +0.02	0 +0.03	125
	z	0.33 +0.01	0.26 /30	0.35 +0.08	0.30 /5	0.30 /90	0 /25	150
Sales Requirement		50	60	70	80	90	25	375

Note in evaluating xA, the path of adjustment is $+ xA - yA + yD - zD + zB - xB$, or $+ 37 - 29 + 27 - 30 + 26 - 27 = + 4$ cents. In this table x slack is the most (and only) favorable change. Note that in the previous table there was only one favorable change indicated, and the change was made. This brought about a new favorable change. As solutions replace each other, it should be apparent that the desirability of alternative routes changes. It is recalled that the evaluation of alternatives for the first solution indicated that x slack had a value $+ 0.07$ at that stage of the solution.

The evaluation route of x slack (this time) was $+ x$ slack $- z$ slack $+ zB - xB$. Of the cells being reduced, z slack has the limiting number of units, 25. Therefore, 25 units are added to x slack, and the appropriate adjustments made in z slack, zB, and xB, to agree with the rim requirements. Table 4–9 shows the new solution and the evaluation of its alternatives.

Table 4–9
FINAL SOLUTION OF TRANSPORTATION PROBLEM

		DESTINATIONS (OUTPUTS)						Capacity Restrictions
	Warehouses / Factories	A	B	C	D	E	Slack	
SOURCES (INPUTS)	x	0.37 / +0.04	0.27 / /5	0.28 / /70	0.34 / +0.03	0.31 / 0.00	0 / /25	100
	y	0.29 / /50	0.31 / +0.08	0.32 / +0.08	.27 / /75	0.29 / +0.02	0 / +0.04	125
	z	0.33 / +0.01	0.26 / /55	0.35 / +0.08	0.30 / /5	0.30 / /90	0 / +0.01	150
Sales Requirement		50	60	70	80	90	25	375

Step seven is now complete, as steps three through six have been repeated until no alternative choices give a favorable valuation. There is no better solution. Cell route xE has an evaluation of 0.00, meaning that the cost of the solution would not change if xE were used. There are alternative best solutions having the same cost.

An evaluation of the solutions at the initial and final stages should be of interest. For Table 4–5, the result of following the northwest corner rule gives:

$50 \times 0.37 + 50 \times 0.27 + 10 \times 0.31 + 70 \times 0.32 + 45 \times 0.27 + 35 \times 0.30$
$+ 90 \times 0.30 + 25 \times 0 = 18.50 + 13.50 + 3.10 + 22.40 + 12.15 + 10.50$
$+ 27.00 + 0 = \$107.15$.

A similar evaluation of the final solution, Table 4–9, yields $98.50. In this example, notice that Table 4–2, a solution by inspection, looks fairly similar to the computed solution, and gives a cost of $98.70, only 20 cents more than the computed solution. In cases of a very small table, as the example given here, informal methods should yield a solution close to that given by the formal method. It is in the case of large tables (complex problems) that informal methods are much less satisfactory.

One method for saving computation time is to go on to another solution when an alternative route is favorably evaluated (possibly considering its magnitude), rather than evaluating each alternative for each solution. Adhering strictly to the formal method of evaluating every alternative and selecting the most favorable will yield a final solution in the *fewest expected number of tables.* However, the time saved in evaluating only some of the alternatives in each table may more than offset potential extra tables. This, of course, would be particularly true where a new table is determined by a few erasures on paper or a blackboard.

Alternative Evaluation Procedure

A method of evaluation of unused routes using the concept of implicit costs is also available for solving transportation problems of linear programming. It has the advantage of speed, but the disadvantage of its rationale being somewhat obscure.

An outside row and column are added to Table 4–4 (northwest corner solution), page 129, making Table 4–4a. These outside cells contain the "key values" of the rows and columns. Since the key values are relative, it is convenient to start with a zero value for either the first row or first column (here row x or column A). Then using those cells with shipments scheduled (variables in the solution), xA, xB, yB, yC, yD, zD, zE, and zSlack. The other key values are chosen so that the sum of the key row value and key column value equals the cost in the used cells. For instance, key value of $x(0)$ + key value of $A(0.37)$ = the cost of $xA(0.37)$; $x(0) + B(0.27) = xB(0.27)$; $y(0.04) + B(0.27) = yB(0.31)$; and so forth. Starting with the value zero for row x, it is the key values which are determined from the costs of the used cells (not vice versa). Notice it is the specific solution to the problem which determines these key values, and with a given

Table 4-4a

NORTHWEST CORNER SOLUTION

Key Value	⟶	0.37	0.27	0.28	0.23	0.23	-0.07	
↓		A	B	C	D	E	Slack	Capacity
0	x	0.37	0.27	0.28	0.34	0.31	0	100
				0.28	0.23	0.23	-0.07	
		/50	/50	0	+0.11	+0.08	+0.07	
0.04	y	0.29	0.31	0.32	0.27	0.29	0	125
		0.41				0.27	-0.03	
		-0.12	/10	/70	/45	+0.02	+0.03	
0.07	z	0.33	0.26	0.35	0.30	0.30	0	150
		0.44	0.34	0.35				
		-0.11	-0.08	0	/35	/90	/25	
	Requirements	50	60	70	80	90	25	375

solution the values are unique (with the exception that a constant could be added to all row key values and subtracted from all column key values—these values are relative, but their respective sums are not).

The meaning of these values is to be found in their sums. As the sum of a row and column key value corresponding to a variable in the solution (i.e., positive shipment cell) equals the cost of that cell, the sum of a row and column key value corresponding to a variable *not* in the solution (i.e., zero shipment cell) equals the *implicit* cost of that cell. For instance, the present solution implies that xD has a cost of 0.23 or higher (the number to the right and underlined in the cell). In fact the cost in xD is 0.11 higher than 0.23 (0.34), so there is nothing inconsistent between the real cost in this cell and the value implied by this solution if it is to be a least cost solution. However, the implicit cost of yA is 0.41. That is, this solution if it is to be a least cost solution implies that yA has a cost of 0.41 or higher. In fact yA has a cost of 0.29, which is -0.12 lower than the implicit value. This is the same evaluation (-0.12) which had been obtained by the former procedure (Table 4-5). The evaluation figures obtained throughout Table 4-4 with the key value procedure are identical to those obtained in Table 4-5.

Choosing an attractive alternative and bringing in as many units as possible, a new table in the solution is determined as before. For each new table or iteration in the solution, new key values, implicit values, and evaluation of unused cells are determined.

Degeneracy

Another method for saving computation time is to start with a solution close(r) to the final one. Solution by inspection or the more formal mutually preferred method should give such an initial solution. However, there is more chance of a "degenerate" solution when done by inspection, making necessary certain adjustments. Table 4-2, the solution by inspection given here, is such a case. Table 4-2 is reproduced here.

When an attempt is made to evaluate the alternative cell routes, the need for adjustment becomes clear. To evaluate zA, it is necessary that a used cell route in the same row as zA have another used cell route in its column. This is not the case. For instance zB is used, but neither yB nor xB is. The nature of the evaluation procedure is that one unit is traded back and forth between used cell routes (used, except for the one being evaluated) within the rim requirements.

Table 4-2

INSPECTION SOLUTION OF TRANSPORTATION PROBLEM

		DESTINATIONS (OUTPUTS)						Capacity Restrictions
SOURCES (INPUTS)	Warehouses / Factories	A	B	C	D	E	Slack	
	x	0.37 /5	0.27	0.28 /70	0.34	0.31	0 /25	100
	y	0.29 /45	0.31	0.32	0.27 /80	0.29	0	125
	z	0.33	0.26 /60	0.35	0.30	0.30 /90	0	150
Sales Requirements		50	60	70	80	90	25	375

Where it is not possible to evaluate all unused cells due to a smaller number of cells used than rim minus one (the number of constraints), the problem is degenerate and a special procedure is necessary.

For computation purposes in degeneracy, a cell is considered artificially used where necessary and an ϵ (epsilon) is placed in the lower-right-hand corner and treated just as though it represented a very small quantity to be shipped via that cell route.[3] An ϵ is placed in cell yB and is therefore considered in use and the remaining cells evaluated. The result of this process is shown in Table 4–10.

Table 4–10

ILLUSTRATION OF THE USE OF ϵ IN TRANSPORTATION PROBLEMS

		DESTINATIONS (OUTPUTS)						Capacity Restriction
	Warehouses / Factories	A	B	C	D	E	Slack	
SOURCES (INPUTS)	x	0.37	0.27 / 5 / −0.12	0.28 / 70	0.34 / −0.01	0.31 / −0.12	0 / 25	100
	y	0.29 / 45	0.31 / ϵ	0.32 / +0.12	0.27 / 80	0.29 / −0.06	0 / +0.08	125
	z	0.33 / +0.09	0.26 / 60	0.35 / +0.20	0.30 / +0.08	0.30 / 90	0 / +0.13	150
Sales Requirements		50	60	70	80	90	25	375

The method of solution is carried forward as before. The most favorable evaluation is followed through; ϵ is treated as a very small number. For instance, if this cell were involved in the evaluation procedure of the most favorable cell, and it were the limiting number, as it would be if a tentative unit were being subtracted from it, the amount transferred would be ϵ. Once inserted, an ϵ stays in the table until the solution is completed, or until the ϵ is formally removed by the procedure through subtractions. If one or more ϵ's exist in the final solution, they are ignored. That is, if a cell route has only an ϵ, it is not used; if ϵ's are added to, or subtracted from, other numbers (i.e., $50 - \epsilon$), these other numbers (i.e., 50) are used in the final schedule. If a solution at any stage has fewer cells occupied than the number of rim requirements (i.e., capacity restrictions plus sales requirements) minus one, then it is degenerate. This merely means that these ϵ adjustments must be made. This is analogous to the general simplex method in which the number of variables kept in the solution must be equal to the number of constraint equations, or rows, in the simplex table.

---

[3] Charnes and Cooper, *op. cit.*

A further explanation should be included with the inspection method of determining an initial solution. Rather than using less cell routes than rim requirements minus one, and therefore requiring epsilons (ϵ), the initial solution may use more cell routes than rim requirements minus one. A reduction in the number of used cell routes is necessary if this is the case. It will always be possible to reduce the number of used cell routes to the number of rim requirements minus one (and sometimes less than this number incurring degeneracy). This can be done by finding four (or six or eight, etc.) used cell routes which form a closed system as far as shifting units are concerned as below:

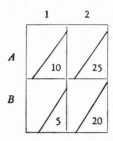

A shift may be made here from $A1$ and $B2$ to $B1$ and $A2$, or vice versa. That is, 10 units may be subtracted from $A1$ and $B2$ and added to $B1$ and $A2$. This would eliminate $A1$ as a used cell route. On the other hand, 5 units may be subtracted from $B1$ and $A2$ and added to $A1$ and $B2$. This would eliminate $B1$. The choice as to which switch to make may be made on the basis of economics (relative costs or profits) or on a random basis to obtain an acceptable initial solution. Where more cell routes are used than rim requirements minus one, switches of this type will always be available.

As opposed to degeneracy, in which all routes may not be evaluated without the ϵ adjustment, the case of superfluous routes should reveal itself with the possibility of more than one evaluation for an unused cell. This will indicate a need for adjustment as proper solutions provide unique evaluations for each new possible route. There must be only one value.

Another way of explaining this same point is to indicate that all routes in the solution are to be used to their fullest extent (without calling for new routes). In the figure above, none of the cells $A1$, $A2$, $B1$, or $B2$ are used as fully as they might be, i.e., $A1$ and $B2$ could contain 5 more units, or $B1$ and $A2$ could contain 10 more units. Analogous to the simplex graphical description, a solution must be at one of the extreme points in the possibility space in order to evaluate completely all of the next possible changes. The point will be repeated for emphasis—the number of used cell routes in each table should be equal to the rim requirements minus one.[4]

If, for some reason, a cell route is not technically feasible (i.e., this machine just can't make that product) or management wishes to eliminate the possibility of its use, the same procedure may be used as in the general simplex method. A cost of $M can be used for this cell: $M is considered to be extremely large, and will therefore always be driven out of the solution. That is, economic considerations will eliminate solutions which are not technically feasible. The procedure used is precisely the same as the regular transportation method. A simpler way of handling the same problem is merely to cross out the cells in question and never use nor evaluate them.

Simplex Comparison

For purposes of comparison, the initial *simplex*[5] table for the problem used to illustrate the transportation method (Tables 4–1 through 4–10) is given in Figure 4–1.

Figure 4–1

SIMPLEX TABLE FOR TRANSPORTATION PROBLEM

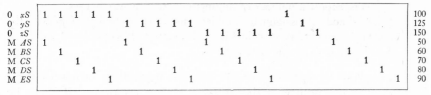

		0.37	0.27	0.28	0.34	0.31	0.29	0.31	0.32	0.27	0.29	0.33	0.26	0.35	0.30	0.30	0	0	0	M	M	M	M	M	
		xA	xB	xC	xD	xE	yA	yB	yC	yD	yE	zA	zB	zC	zD	zE	xS	yS	zS	AS	BS	CS	DS	ES	
0	xS	1	1	1	1	1											1								100
0	yS						1	1	1	1	1							1							125
0	zS											1	1	1	1	1			1						150
M	AS	1					1					1								1					50
M	BS		1					1					1								1				60
M	CS			1					1					1								1			70
M	DS				1					1					1								1		80
M	ES					1					1					1								1	90

The costs per unit are written adjacent to each route. The slack variables are designated xS, yS, zS, AS, BS, CS, DS, and ES. Note that the capacity slacks have a cost per unit of zero as in the transportation table. The sales requirement slacks have a cost per unit of M, an extremely large positive cost. This is due to the fact that requirement slacks represent nonfulfillment of committments which in this case is not permissible. The high cost associated with these variables will drive

---

[4] An initial solution in a very unusual case may have positive values assigned to the proper number of cell routes, that is, rim requirements minus one, and really be a combination of (1) a set of routes which may be reduced and (2) degeneracy. In this case, the routes should be reduced, fully utilizing those routes which remain, and ϵ's should then be inserted where needed.

[5] See previous chapter for a fuller discussion of the general simplex method necessary to appreciate this comparison.

them out of the solution. These must be provided in the simplex method so that the initial solution is at the origin, i.e., all positive values are slacks.

The evaluations of the possibilities below the table would show a large savings or decrease in cost per unit (such as $0.37 - M$), which will ultimately drive all these nonfulfillment slacks out of the solution. The method of solution of this problem in the general simplex framework is straightforward, and it is described in the previous chapter.

The two main purposes for making this comparison are as follows:

1. All coefficients within the table are either zero or one—this will help identify problems which may be placed within the transportation framework.

2. The number of rows in the table, or constraints on the problem, is eight, the number of rim requirements minus one in the transportation matrix. These provide for the same number of variables in the solution—one for each equation.

Uses of Transportation Procedure

A number of types of problems can be placed within the framework of the transportation method of linear programming. Some of these are as follows:

1. Conventional transportation problems in which a number of sources, such as plants, supply a number of destinations, such as warehouses.
2. Machine and job assignment problems in which a number of jobs can be done on a number of machines or by a number of people.
3. Scheduling over several time periods.

These types of applications are mainly suggestive, rather than inclusive. It is the nature of the problem that is important; if it can be considered a source-destination or input-output problem conforming to the attributes discussed here, it might be possible to place it within the framework of the transportation method of linear programming. These attributes, particularly linearity, homogeneity, and certainty, while not strictly met, may be sufficiently well approximated to permit use of the method.

The time period problem might be explained further. The sales experience of many manufacturers follows a seasonal pattern. Either production can be constant with fluctuating inventories or inventories can remain constant with fluctuating production. Some combination of the two is also possible. This problem may sometimes be conceived as a problem of balancing overtime costs (fluctuating production) with storage costs (fluctuating inventories). In this case, each production possibility (regular time and overtime) in each time period may be considered a source of input. Each sales requirement (i.e., product group) in each time period may be considered a separate destination or output. The nature of the costs in the "cell routes" in the table is a combined production cost (regular or overtime) plus a storage cost for the appropriate number of time periods. A general table for this problem is shown in Table 4–11.[6]

Table 4–11

PRODUCTION SCHEDULING BY THE TRANSPORTATION METHOD

Sales Periods (Destination)

		$Sales_1$	$Sales_2$	$Sales_3$	$Sales_n$	$Inventory_n$	Slack	Total Capacities
	$Inventory_0$	0	C_I	$2C_I$	$(n-1)C_I$	nC_I	0	I_0
Production	$Regular_1$	C_R	C_R+C_I	C_R+2C_I	$C_R+(n-1)C_I$	C_R+nC_I	0	R_1
Periods	$Overtime_1$	C_O	C_O+C_I	C_O+2C_I	$C_O+(n-1)C_I$	C_O+nC_I	0	O_1
(Source)	$Regular_2$	✕	C_R	C_R+C_I	$C_R+(n-2)C_I$	$C_R+(n-1)C_I$	0	R_2
	$Overtime_2$	✕	C_O	C_O+C_I	$C_O+(n-2)C_I$	$C_O+(n-1)C_I$	0	O_2
	$Regular_3$	✕	✕	C_R	$C_R+(n-3)C_I$	$C_R+(n-2)C_I$	0	R_3
	$Overtime_3$	✕	✕	C_O	$C_O+(n-3)C_I$	$C_O+(n-2)C_I$	0	O_3
	$Regular_n$	✕	✕	✕	C_R	C_R+C_I	0	R_n
	$Overtime_n$	✕	✕	✕	C_O	C_O+C_I	0	O_n
	Total Requirements	S_1	S_2	S_3	S_n	I_n	*	

* Slack total $= I_0 + R + O - S - I_n$.

Notation:
I_i = Inventory at the end of the ith time period.
R_i = Maximum number of units which can be produced during ith time period on regular time.
O_i = Maximum number of units which can be produced during ith time period on overtime.
S_i = Number of units of finished product to be sold (delivered) during ith time period.
C_R = Cost of production per unit on regular time.
C_O = Cost of production per unit on overtime.
C_I = Cost of storage per unit per time period.

Virtually half such a transportation matrix is crossed out, as it is not possible to deliver in a period previous to that made or shipped. This facilitates a more rapid solution.[7]

Many transportation problems, such as plants and warehouses, can

[6] E. H. Bowman, "Production Scheduling by the Transportation Method of Linear Programming," *Journal of the Operations Research Society,* February, 1956.

[7] In effect, this formulation of the problem places an infinite cost on supplying sales in one period from subsequent periods. In many cases, "back ordering" may be possible. Some finite cost must then be placed on this time lag. One way of looking at this problem is to consider it as a combination of storing inventory and/or storing customer orders, both processes having their own costs.

be extended to include the time period problem where this is meaningful. If requirements of the warehouses fluctuate during the year, as in the case, for example, of a seasonal pattern, the problem becomes one of determining whether to use the more favorable routes (revealed by the regular transportation method) during slack periods and incur storage costs or use the less favorable—more expensive—routes during peak periods and not incur the storage costs. This problem may be placed within the above time period framework by considering each plant in each time period a separate source and each warehouse in each time period a separate destination. Each cost figure in the matrix will be a combination of manufacturing, transportation, and storage costs. It is also possible to extend this same method to the multiproduct case.

DYNAMIC PROGRAMMING

Dynamic programming is a mathematical method of analysis which has been developed over the last 10 years. It has been applied to a number of classes of problems involving the following characteristic features:[8]

   a) The situation involves multistage processes containing a large number of variables.
   b) The relationship between the stages is not a complex one.
   c) At each stage, the state of the process is described by a small number of parameters.
   d) The effect of a decision at any stage is to transform this set of parameters into a similar set.

The basic feature of dynamic programming is that the optimum decision is reached stepwise, proceeding from one stage to the next. Stages in the problem need not be in terms of time. An optimum solution set is determined, given any conditions in the first stage. Then this optimum solution set (from the first stage) is integrated with the second stage to obtain a new optimum solution set, given any conditions. Then, in a sense ignoring the first and second stages as such, this new optimum solution set is integrated with the third stage to obtain still a further optimum solution set (or decision) under any conditions. This new solution is integrated with the fourth stage, and so forth. At each stage an optimum solution from all previous stages, under any conditions, is carried into the next stage. It is this optimum solution which is carried forward rather than all the previous stages. Bellman summarizes this

[8] Richard Bellman, "Some Applications of the Theory of Dynamic Programming—A Review," *Journal of the Operations Research Society of America*, August, 1954, pp. 275–88.

concept in a "Principle of Optimality: An optimal policy has the property that whatever the initial state and initial decision are, the remaining decisions must constitute an optimal policy with regard to the state resulting from the first decision."[9]

In effect this solution procedure, which is the heart of dynamic programming, transforms one n dimensional problem into n one (or possibly two) dimensional problems which are individually much easier to solve. In a problem involving a large number of stages, the computational mechanics may be rather lengthy, especially if there are a large number of conditions to keep track of, but in these cases computing equipment may make the procedure feasible. The problems can involve nonlinearity and uncertainty (represented by probability distributions) and still be handled by the methodology of dynamic programming.[10]

It is quite probable that more work will be done on dynamic programming in the near future, and more become known about its more pertinent applications.

A Package Problem

To illustrate the methods here, a very simple problem will be solved centering around the indivisibility of the components of a "package." The objective is to maximize the value of the package, given in the data of Table 4–12.

Table 4–12

Component		Weight	Value
A.....................		7 lbs.	$9
B.....................		5	4
C.....................		4	3
D.....................		3	2
E.....................		1	½

Total weight ≤ 13 pounds

As all weights can be expressed in terms of integral pounds, all possible conditions vary from 0 to 13 pounds by integers. These conditions may be listed down the first column of solution Table 4–13. The first stage in the multistage problem may be developed as component A (or any other of the components in this problem).[11] Component

---

[9] *Ibid.,* p. 285.

[10] See for example, "The Inventory Problem" by Laderman, Littauer, and Weiss, *Journal of the American Statistical Association,* Vol. XLVIII (December, 1953), pp. 717–32.

[11] In a multi-time stage process, the last time period is the one solved first, and the problem worked backwards timewise.

Table 4–13

w	$f_1(w)$ A Value	$f_1(w)$ A Units	$f_2(w)$ B(+A) Value	$f_2(w)$ B(+A) Units	$f_3(w)$ C(+A,B) Value	$f_3(w)$ C(+A,B) Units	$f_4(w)$ D(+A,B,C) Value	$f_4(w)$ D(+A,B,C) Units	$f_5(w)$ E(+A,B,C,D) Value	$f_5(w)$ E(+A,B,C,D) Units
1	0	0	0	0	0	0	0	0	$ ½	0 1
2	0	0	0	0	0	0	0	0	1	0 1 2
3	0	0	0	0	$ 3	0 1	$ 2	0 1	2	0 1 2 3
4	0	0	$ 4	0 1	4	0 1	3	0 1	3	0 1 2 3 4
5	0	0	4	0 1	4	0 1	4	0 1 2	4	0 1 2 3 4 5
6	0	0	9	0 1	9	0 1 2	4	0 1 2	4½	0 1 2 3 4 5 6
7	$ 9	1	9	0 1	9	0 1 2	9	0 1 2	9	0 1 2 3 . . 7
8	9	1	9	0 1	9	0 1 2	9	0 1 2 3	9½	0 1 2 3 . . 8
9	9	1	9	0 1	12	0 1 2	9	0 1 2 3	10	0 1 2 3 . . 9
10	9	1	13	0 1 2	13	0 1 2 3	11	0 1 2 3	11	0 1 2 3 . . 10
11	9	1	13	0 1 2	13	0 1 2 3	12	0 1 2 3 4	12	0 1 2 3 . . 11
12	9	1	13	0 1 2	13	0 1 2 3	13	0 1 2 3 4	13	0 1 2 3 . . 12
13	9	1	13	0 1 2	13	0 1 2 3	13	0 1 2 3 4	13½	0 1 2 3 . . 13

A takes the second column in the table, and the values in the column are the optimum values of the function corresponding to the conditions in the first column for the first stage (component A). For instance, under the conditions of 1 pound through 6 pounds, the function, which is to be an optimum under all conditions f_1, takes on the value of zero, as no units which weigh 7 pounds can be included. From 7 pounds through 13 pounds, either one or zero units may be used, and the function takes on the value of \$9.00, as one unit of A gives a higher value to the function than zero units of A. These alternatives, 0 and 1, are shown in the column adjacent to the column for A, and the number in boldface print represents the choice at that point.

The third headed column represents the solution set at the second stage of the multistage chain. It represents an optimum solution under all conditions (weights of 1 through 13) of a combination of component B and an optimum at the previous stage (stage 1—no longer thought of as component A). Weights of 1 through 4 still take no units. Weight 5 will take one unit of component B at a \$4.00 value (or zero units); so will weights 6, 7, 8, and 9. However, though weight 7 will take one unit of component B at a \$4.00 value, it will also take zero units of B, allowing the 7 pounds for the previous stage optimum, which at 7 pounds is one unit of component A at a \$9.00 value. The solution at each stage is to be an optimum solution, so the larger value (\$9.00) with its associated components is taken. That is, each row in the column representing the second stage represents the optimum combination at that weight (condition) of the optimum from the new stage, plus the optimum from the previous stage for the allowable condition.

Better illustrations of the procedure may be obtained from later stages. At stage four $[f_4(w);\ A,\ B,\ C,\ \text{and}\ D]$, the component being added at the stage is D. D weighs 3 pounds per unit and has a \$2.00 value. At the conditions where weight equals 10, the number of units of D can be 0, 1, 2, or 3. At zero, the function takes its value from the previous stage at $w = 10$, or \$9.00. At one, the function is the sum of \$2.00 (for 1 unit of D) plus $f_3(w) = \$9.00$ at $w = 7$ which sum gives \$11. The function $f_3(w) = \$9.00$ at $w = 7$ is used here as 1 unit of D weighs 3 pounds, which at $w = 10$ leaves 7 pounds to be used. The \$9.00 with its specified components is the best possible (optimum) use of the 7 pounds up to stage three. At 2 units of D, the function is the sum of \$4.00 (for 2 units of D) plus $f_3(w) = \$3.00$ at $w = 4$, which is \$7.00. At 3 units of D, the function is the sum of \$6.00 (for 3 units of D) plus $f_3(w) = 0$ at $w = 1$, which is \$6.00. The optimum value at stage four, $w = 10$ pounds is taken from \$9.00, \$11.00, \$7.00, and

$6.00, or $11.00 where D equals one (the number of units in boldface print in the adjacent column). Some record keeping to identify the components associated with the optimum value is necessary, e.g., at this stage 1 unit of component D and 1 unit of component A, so that the problem solution will yield not only the maximum value but also the components that make this up.

The Functional Equations

Summarized, the procedure at each stage for each condition is to maximize the sum of the value added at that stage and the optimum from the previous stage under the appropriate condition (remaining weight). Symbolically, this may all be expressed as follows:

$$\text{Max.} \Sigma\ v_i x_i = f_5(w)$$
$$\text{subject to } \Sigma w_i x_i \leq 13$$

. . . .

$$f_1(w) = \text{max. } 9\ x_1$$
subject to $0 \leq x_1 \leq \left[\dfrac{w}{7}\right]$ where $\left[\ \ \right]$ denotes an integer

. . . .

$$f_2(w) = \text{max. } [4x_2 + f_1\ (w - 5x_2)]$$
$$0 \leq x_2 \leq \left[\dfrac{w}{5}\right]$$

. . . .

$$f_3(w) = \text{max. } [3x_3 + f_2\ (w - 4x_3)]$$
$$0 \leq x_3 \leq \left[\dfrac{w}{4}\right]$$

. . . .

$$f_4(w) = \text{max. } [2x_4 + f_3\ (w - 3x_4)]$$
$$0 \leq x_4 \leq \left[\dfrac{w}{3}\right]$$

. . . .

$$f_5(w) = \text{max. } [\tfrac{1}{2}x_5 + f_4\ (w - 1x_5)]$$
$$0 \leq x_5 \leq \left[\dfrac{w}{1}\right]$$

. . . .

Generally, the form of these equations is:

$$f_n(w) = \text{max. } [v_n x_n + f_{n-1}\ (w - w_n x_n)]$$
where f_{n-1}, f_{n-2}, etc., are themselves maximized functions.

As a further explanation of the procedure, and the functional equations, consider the second stage:

$$f_2(w) = \text{max. } [4x_2 + f_1\ (w - 5x_2)]$$
$$0 \leq x_2 \leq \left[\dfrac{w}{5}\right]$$

For each possible value of w, e.g., 0,1,2,3, . . . 11,12,13, x_2 is restricted to an integer value between 0 and $\dfrac{w}{5}$ (as each unit of x_2 weighs 5 pounds). *All* values of $f(w)$ must be calculated for all the values of x_2 possible at each weight. Table 4–14 contains all this information.

Table 4–14

w_i	$0 \leq x_2 \leq \left[\dfrac{w}{5}\right]$	$4x_2 + f_1(w - 5x_2)$	Maximum of $f_2(w_i)$
0	0	$4(0) + f_1(0) = \$0$	0
1	0	$4(0) + f_1(1) = \$0$	0
2	0	$4(0) + f_1(2) = \$0$	0
3	0	$4(0) + f_1(3) = \$0$	0
4	0	$4(0) + f_1(4) = \$0$	0
5	0	$4(0) + f_1(5) = \$0$	
	1	$4(1) + f_1(0) = \$4$	$\$4$
6	0	$4(0) + f_1(6) = \$0$	
	1	$4(1) + f_1(1) = \$4$	$\$4$
7	0	$4(0) + f_1(7) = \$9$	$\$9$
	1	$4(1) + f_1(2) = \$4$	
8	0	$4(0) + f_1(8) = \$9$	$\$9$
	1	$4(1) + f_1(3) = \$4$	
9	0	$4(0) + f_1(9) = \$9$	$\$9$
	1	$4(1) + f_1(4) = \$4$	
10	0	$4(0) + f_1(10) = \$9$	$\$9$
	1	$4(1) + f_1(5) = \$4$	
	2	$4(2) + f_1(0) = \$8$	
11	0	$4(0) + f_1(11) = \$9$	$\$9$
	1	$4(1) + f_1(6) = \$4$	
	2	$4(2) + f_1(1) = \$8$	
12	0	$4(0) + f_1(12) = \$9$	
	1	$4(1) + f_1(7) = \$13$	$\$13$
	2	$4(2) + f_1(2) = \$8$	
13	0	$4(0) + f_1(13) = \$9$	
	1	$4(1) + f_1(8) = \$13$	$\$13$
	2	$4(2) + f_1(3) = \$8$	

Following this procedure of dynamic programming stage by stage will yield, as shown, $f_5 = 13\frac{1}{2}$, with one unit of E, no D's or C's, one B, and one A.

A further brief illustration of these methods may be made by adding a volume parameter to basically the same type of problem as the previous one, as shown in Table 4–15.

Before setting down the functional equations of dynamic programming for this problem, it should be pointed out that component E is everywhere inferior (or equal) to component D, and may, therefore, be eliminated immediately from the problem. That is, E has the same value

Table 4-15

Component	Weight(w)	Volume(l)	Value(v)	Functional Equation $f(w,l)$
A................	5	6	4	$f_1(w,l)$
B................	4	5	3	$f_2(w,l)$
C................	3	3	2	$f_3(w,l)$
D................	7	10	7	$f_4(w,l)$
E................	8	11	7	$f_5(w,l)$

Maximize $\Sigma v_i\, x_i$
Subject to $\Sigma x_i\, w_i \leq 13; \Sigma x_i\, l_i \leq 14$

as *D*, and is larger in both weight and volume. For any conceivable use for component *E*, *D* may be used with the same value and release both weight and volume for other use. The functional equations for this problem are as follows:

$$f_1(w, l) = \max. \; 4x_1$$
$$0 \leq x_1 \leq \left\lfloor \frac{w}{5} \right\rfloor , \left\lfloor \frac{l}{6} \right\rfloor$$

. . . .

$$f_2(w, l) = \max. \; [3x_2 + f_1(w - 4x_2, l - 5x_2)]$$
$$0 \leq x_2 \leq \left\lfloor \frac{w}{4} \right\rfloor , \left\lfloor \frac{l}{5} \right\rfloor$$

. . . .

$$f_3(w, l) = \max. \; [2x_3 + f_2(w - 3x_3, l - 3x_3)]$$
$$0 \leq x_3 \leq \left\lfloor \frac{w}{3} \right\rfloor , \left\lfloor \frac{l}{3} \right\rfloor$$

. . . .

$$f_4(w, l) = \max. \; [7x_4 + f_3(w - 7x_4, l - 10x_4)]$$
$$0 \leq x_4 \leq \left\lfloor \frac{w}{7} \right\rfloor , \left\lfloor \frac{l}{10} \right\rfloor$$

. . . .

As in the previous problem, a tabular method could be used for the mechanics of the iterative solution to this problem, but in this case the allowable conditions involve not only weight from 1 to 13 but also volume from 1 to 14. A table for each of the four functional equations, one for each stage or component, would be needed. Table 4–16 is an illustration for component *A*.

In each of the four tables there would be, progressively inserted, a value in each of the $13 \times 14 = 182$ cells in the table. For instance, in the functional equation in stage four, the expression $f_3\,(w - 7x_4, l - 10x_4)$, given a value for x_4, corresponds to a specific cell in the

Table 4–16

w/l	1	2	3	4	5	6	7	8	9	10	11	12	13	14
1.......	0	0	0	0	0	0	0	0	0	0	0	0	0	0
2.......	0	0	0	0	0	0	0	0	0	0	0	0	0	0
3.......	0	0	0	0	0	0	0	0	0	0	0	0	0	0
4.......	0	0	0	0	0	0	0	0	0	0	0	0	0	0
5.......	0	0	0	0	0	4	4	4	4	4	4	4	4	4
6.......	0	0	0	0	0	4	4	4	4	4	4	4	4	4
7.......	0	0	0	0	0	4	4	4	4	4	4	4	4	4
8.......	0	0	0	0	0	4	4	4	4	4	4	4	4	4
9.......	0	0	0	0	0	4	4	4	4	4	4	4	4	4
10.......	0	0	0	0	0	4	4	4	4	4	4	8	8	8
11.......	0	0	0	0	0	4	4	4	4	4	4	8	8	8
12.......	0	0	0	0	0	4	4	4	4	4	4	8	8	8
13.......	0	0	0	0	0	4	4	4	4	4	4	8	8	8

table for stage three. It can be seen that though dynamic programming may cut through the mathematical complexity of a problem, its computational phase may be rather lengthy, as is also, of course, the case with the general simplex method of linear programming.

Procurement Problem

A further example of dynamic programming may help in understanding the essence of the ideas presented here. In fact each problem which takes a dynamic programming framework will probably require its own individual structure. Some of these structures permit solution by mathematical deduction, while others permit modifications or simplifications in the general method presented here. Though the procurement problem to be described permits such a modification,[12] it will be presented in its more general form here.

Table 4–17

Quantity	Procurement Cost*	Carrying Cost between Months
10..................	$ 500 + A	$ 10
20..................	900 + A	20
30..................	1,250 + A	35
40..................	1,600 + A	50
50..................	1,900 + A	70
60..................	2,175 + A	90
70..................	2,375 + A	120 Max. storage
80..................	2,525 + A	...
90..................	2,625 + A	...
100..................	2,700 + A	...
110..................	2,775 + A	...
120..................	2,825 + A	...

* See Table 4–18.

[12] See Harvey M. Wagner and Thomson M. Whitin, "Dynamic Version of the Economic Lot Size Model," *Management Science,* October, 1958.

Table 4–17 presents the cost to procure different quantities and the cost to carry or inventory different amounts between time periods. As can be seen, an additional procurement cost exists which depends on the period of procurement. This is shown in Table 4–18 along with the

Table 4–18

Month	A*	Requirement
January..................	$ 0	40
February.................	0	30
March...................	200	20
April....................	300	60
May.....................	100	40
June....................	0	30
July....................	0	40
August..................	300	40
September...............	200	30
October.................	500	40
November...............	100	20
December...............	0	10

* See Table 4–17.

requirement for each time period. The requirements of each time period must be met (units consumed). They must either be procured within the time period, or earlier, in which case they would be inventoried between periods. In total, 400 units are required. If 40 units were procured in each of the first ten periods, the associated costs would be as follows:

Month	Requirement	Procurement	Cumulative Carried Over	Procurement Cost	Carrying Cost
January........	40	40	0	$1,600 + 0	$ 0
February......	30	40	10	1,600 + 0	10
March........	20	40	30	1,600 + 200	35
April.........	60	40	10	1,600 + 300	10
May..........	40	40	10	1,600 + 100	10
June..........	30	40	20	1,600 + 0	20
July..........	40	40	20	1,600 + 0	20
August........	40	40	20	1,600 + 300	20
September.....	30	40	30	1,600 + 200	35
October.......	40	40	30	1,600 + 500	35
November.....	20	0	10	0	10
December.....	10	0	0	0	0
				$16,000 + $1,600 + $205 = $17,805	

In formulating this problem, the variable condition at each stage (deriving from earlier stages) is the inventory carried into the stage. The decision variable is the amount to procure in each stage, given the inventory position at the beginning of the stage. A maximum of 70 is placed on inventory, and this may range from 0 to 70. In Table 4–19

Table 4-19

Inventory	December (10)	November (20)	October (40)	September (30)
0	$\overline{10}$/\$500 (\$500)	$\overline{30}$/\$1,360, 20/\$1,500 (\$1,360)	$\overline{70}$/\$2,920, 60/\$3,195, 50/\$3,420, 40/\$3,460 (\$2,920)	$\overline{100}$/\$3,065, 90/\$3,435, 80/\$3,815, 70/\$3,985, 60/\$4,555, 50/\$4,565, 40/\$4,530, 30/\$4,370 (\$3,065)
10	$\overline{0}$/\$10 (\$10)	$\overline{20}$/\$1,020, 10/\$1,030 (\$1,020)	$\overline{60}$/\$2,730, 50/\$2,930, 40/\$3,130, 30/\$3,120 (\$2,730)	$\overline{90}$/\$3,000, 80/\$3,345, 70/\$3,675, 60/\$3,795, 50/\$4,290, 40/\$4,275, 30/\$4,190, 20/\$4,030 (\$3,000)
20	$\overline{0}$/\$20 (\$20)	10/\$630, $\overline{0}$/\$520 (\$520)	$\overline{50}$/\$2,465, 40/\$2,690, 30/\$2,790, 20/\$2,780 (\$2,465)	$\overline{80}$/\$2,910, 70/\$3,205, 60/\$3,485, 50/\$3,530, 40/\$4,000, 30/\$3,935, 20/\$3,850, 10/\$3,640 (\$2,910)
30	$\overline{0}$/\$35 (\$35)	$\overline{0}$/\$45 (\$45)	$\overline{40}$/\$2,180, 30/\$2,305, 20/\$2,455, 10/\$2,395 (\$2,180)	$\overline{70}$/\$2,775, 60/\$3,020, 50/\$3,225, 40/\$3,245, 30/\$3,665, 20/\$3,600, 10/\$3,465, 0/\$2,920 (\$2,775)
40	$\overline{0}$/\$50 (\$50)		30/\$1,845, 20/\$1,970, 10/\$2,070, $\overline{0}$/\$1,410 (\$1,410)	$\overline{60}$/\$2,590, 50/\$2,760, 40/\$2,940, 30/\$2,910, 20/\$3,330, 10/\$3,215, 0/\$2,780 (\$2,590)
50	$\overline{0}$/\$70 (\$70)		20/\$1,515, 10/\$1,590, $\overline{0}$/\$1,090 (\$1,090)	$\overline{50}$/\$2,335, 40/\$2,480, 30/\$2,610, 20/\$2,580, 10/\$2,950, 0/\$2,535 (\$2,335)
60	$\overline{0}$/\$90 (\$90)		10/\$1,135, $\overline{0}$/\$610 (\$610)	$\overline{40}$/\$2,055, 30/\$2,150, 20/\$2,280, 10/\$2,200, 0/\$2,270 (\$2,055)
70	$\overline{0}$/\$120 (\$120)		$\overline{0}$/\$165 (\$165)	30/\$1,735, 20/\$1,830, 10/\$1,910, $\overline{0}$/\$1,530 (\$1,530)

starting with the last period in time, the possible procurements are itemized, costed out (including the appropriate cost from the following stage in time), and the conditional optimum is chosen (the choice is underlined and the cost is placed in parentheses at the end of the row). Only four stages are presented in the illustration.

In each case as costs are built up in a particular stage, the effect that a procurement decision will have on inventory and therefore costs at a succeeding stage may be read right from that stage, as optimum decisions have already been made and their costs noted.

For instance, if 30 units of inventory have been brought into September from earlier months, a number of procurement decisions between 70 and 0 may be made. One of these is for 50 units. How is such a choice to be costed? The procurement cost for 50 in September is $1,900 + $200. The inventory cost of the 30 carried into September is $35. So far these costs total $2,135. What will be the costs included for the future periods, October, November, and December? In fact many sets of decisions could be made in these future 3 months. However, the essence of dynamic programming and its periodic conditional optimizing is that the optimum decisions have already been worked out for these future months. With 30 beginning inventory plus 50 procured, minus the 30 required, the inventory carried into October would be 50. The best decisions with 50 carried into October (and decisions on through November and December) have already been worked out and their total costs accumulated and noted in the Table 4-19, $1,090. This makes a total cost of $3,225 ($2,135 + $1,090). All other costs in the Table 4-19 have been built up in the same manner.

Bellman cites the following as typical multistage problems:[13]

1. A production scheduling problem.
2. An equipment purchase problem.
3. An employment stabilization problem.
4. An optimal inventory problem.
5. An engineering control problem.
6. A reinvestment of earnings problem.
7. Production bottleneck problems.
8. Learning and testing theory.

The simple illustrative problems worked through in this section have served merely the purpose of demonstrating the nature of dynamic programming. For applications to more involved problems, reference should be made to *Dynamic Programming,* by Richard Bellman, Princeton University Press, 1957.

---

[13] Bellman, *op. cit.*

SUMMARY

In this chapter and the previous one the basic ideas of mathematical programming have been presented. The nature of the linear programming procedure was explained, using a graphical example. However, as most real problems are substantially more involved than those which can be solved graphically, more powerful methods must be used. The general simplex method, an iterative algebraic algorithm, has been explained and illustrated. Dynamic programming has also been described briefly. However, in large problems the amount of computation involved in mathematical programming may be prodigious. For some problems, the only feasible way of solution has been by computing equipment. For other problems having certain characteristics, shorter methods of computation are possible. One of these methods, the transportation method, has been presented in this chapter. As mathematical programming is a relatively recent method of analysis, the chances are good that as time passes both more problems will be placed within these frameworks and additional modified solution systems will be developed.

REFERENCES

1. BELLMAN, RICHARD. *Dynamic Programming.* Princeton: Princeton University Press, 1957.
2. BELLMAN, RICHARD, and DREYFUS, STUART. *Applied Dynamic Programming.* Princeton: Princeton University Press, 1962.
3. CHARNES, A., and COOPER, W. W. "The Stepping Stone Method of Explaining Linear Programming Calculations in Transportation Problems," *Management Science,* Vol. I, No. 1 (October, 1954).

PROBLEMS

1. The Fairbanks Fastener Corporation manufactures a variety of fasteners for both industrial and consumer markets. The various items are produced and sold in widely varying quantities. The various items are produced and sold in widely varying quantities. The demand for some items is relatively stable throughout the year; for others the demand fluctuates seasonally or otherwise.

   Depending upon which jobs the foreman assigns to each machine, he influences the costs incurred in producing the items. This is caused by factors such as the following: some machines are faster than others; particular items produced on particular machines require closer attention from the operator, the machines have varying operating costs depending upon capacity, age, state of wear, etc. While he can influence the total operating costs of his department, the foreman faces a formidable task of actually achieving the minimum possible costs.

   Typical of the problem facing each foreman every week is that which was faced by Mr. Fordham, foreman of Department 463. There are seven presses in this department with varying operating speeds. The hours available on each press for this week were as follows:

Machine	Productive Capacity	Hours Available
M-1	40,000 parts/hour	10
M-2	40,000 parts/hour	40
M-3	40,000 parts/hour	40
M-4	30,000 parts/hour	20
M-5	30,000 parts/hour	40
M-6	10,000 parts/hour	35
M-7	10,000 parts/hour	40

The schedule for this week furnished by the production control section called for manufacturing eight items from the firm's "Hold-Tite" line. The quantities of each were as follows:

Item	Quantity
P-1	625,000
P-2	950,000
P-3	275,000
P-4	330,000
P-5	450,000
P-6	500,000
P-7	460,000
P-8	710,000

In conjunction with the cost accounting department, Mr. Fordham had been able to arrive at the cost which should be associated with producing each of the items on each of the seven presses. The following matrix summarizes this data. The blank spaces mean that the item cannot be produced on that particular machine for one reason or another.

Using these costs, Mr. Fordham juggled his machine assignment around as best he could. However, both he and the manufacturing superintendent

Cost ($) per Thousand Pieces

	M-1	M-2	M-3	M-4	M-5	M-6	M-7
P-1	0.11	0.10	0.09	0.15	0.12	0.31	0.46
P-2	0.10	0.10	0.09	0.15	0.12	0.31	0.46
P-3	0.20	0.15	0.20	0.25	0.25	0.60	0.90
P-4	—	—	—	0.15	0.10	0.31	0.42
P-5	—	—	—	0.15	0.12	0.31	0.31
P-6	—	—	—	—	0.15	0.31	0.33
P-7	—	—	—	—	—	0.31	0.35
P-8	—	—	—	—	0.14	0.31	0.37

were cognizant of the virtual impossibility of knowing whether the lowest cost schedule actually was used.

In order to attempt to make the foreman's jobs easier in this respect, the manufacturing superintendent requested the engineering department to determine whether linear programming could be used. After studying the problem, the engineering department concluded that the problem was readily solvable using linear programming. However, the general linear programming procedure called the "simplex method" is somewhat laborious. If the problem had certain characteristics, or could be manipulated to have them, it would be possible for the "transportation procedure" to be used. This procedure is much shorter than the "simplex method."

The engineering department immediately recognized that setup costs would not fit into the transportation method. However, further investigation revealed that whenever any press was set up to run one item of the "Hold-Tite" line, only a few minutes were required to change the set up to another item from the line. It appeared, therefore, that setup costs could be ignored.

a) Discuss the machine assignment problem in Department 463 with a view toward determining whether the problem is in a form, or can be put in a form, so that it can be solved by the "transportation-problem procedure."

b) Determine the lowest total cost machine assignment for department 463 for the week given, using any appropriate procedure.

c) What is the cost of the "best" machine assignment?

2. The Atlas Steel Company has three iron mines and five steel mills. Ore transportation costs are shown below:

		MILLS					CAPACITIES
		D_1	D_2	D_3	D_4	D_5	
Mines	O_1.............	4	2	3	2	6	8
	O_2.............	5	4	5	2	1	10
	O_3.............	6	5	4	7	3	14
Requirements..........		4	5	7	8	8	

From above cost, requirements, and capacities matrix, what is the best shipments schedule?

3. Given the following:

Two plants: A and B

Three distribution warehouses: $x, y,$ and $z.$

Three time periods (months): 1, 2, and 3.

Plant A can produce 100 units of product each month.

Plant B can produce 75 units of product in each of months 1 and 2, and 50 units of product in month 3.

The demand for the product, by month, at each distribution warehouse is as follows:

Month/Warehouse	x	y	z
1..........................	40	50	60
2..........................	60	50	40
3..........................	60	60	60

Product manufactured at Plant A costs $1.00 to store one unit from one month to the next.

Product manufactured at Plant B costs $2.00 to store one unit from one month to the next.

There is no storage cost within one month.

Manufacturing cost at Plant A is $7.00 per unit.

Manufacturing cost at Plant B is $5.00 per unit.

Cost to transport one unit of product from a plant to a warehouse is given below:

Plant/Warehouse	x	y	z
A..........................	$1	$2	$1
B..........................	0	1	2

Within the framework of the transportation method, determine the minimum cost over-all schedule of production, storage, and transportation for the two plants, three warehouses, and three time periods.

4. A company makes red, yellow, and blue products. The demand (expressed in plant hours) for the third quarter follows:

	Red	Yellow	Blue
July.........................	60	40	50
August.....................	70	90	60
September..................	90	130	120

The products may be made in regular time or overtime. The available plant time in the third quarter follows:

	Regular Time	Overtime
July.........................	150	150
August.....................	80	120
September..................	150	150

To store one hour's production from one month to the next incurs the following expense:

Red.......................... 20 cents
Yellow...................... 30 cents
Blue........................ 35 cents

To produce in overtime has the following penalty per hour's production.

Red.......................... .35 cents
Yellow........................ .40 cents
Blue.......................... .50 cents

a) Compute the best schedule available.
b) What does your best schedule cost?

5. Do Problem No. 4 of Chapter 3 by the transportation method.

6. Department *A* has five operators, and each operator can run any of the given machines. However, the operators' ability to run the different machines varies. The daily contribution to profit and overhead resulting from each operator running each machine is shown in the matrix below. Each operator must work for the full day on the same machine.

OPERATOR	MACHINE				
	1	2	3	4	5
A........................	$5	$5	$3	$2	$6
B........................	3	1	2	1	4
C........................	3	7	8	1	5
D........................	6	2	9	2	3
E........................	1	4	4	1	2

What is the best assignment of operators?

7. The Airlane Products Corporation has a plant made up of five separate buildings scattered around the outskirts of a city and the only railroad freight dock is in the center of the city. Normally the company's own trucks carry all the materials needed; however, due to a recent strike next month's shipments will be very heavy. The trucking companies have bid on the amount they can carry and the price per hundred pounds to various buildings. The results are as follows:

BUILDINGS	TRANSPORTATION METHODS				BUILDING REQUIREMENTS
	Own Trucks	1	2	3	
A........................	10	8	2	7	500
B........................	6	9	5	1	700
C........................	4	3	7	5	200
D........................	7	2	4	6	900
E........................	5	9	8	4	700
Hauling Capacity........	800	1,000	700	500	3,000

Find the best program for carrying the material.

8. Three plants, *A, B,* and *C,* can make two products *x* and *y.* The plants can work regular time and overtime, and 2 time periods are to be scheduled. Product *x* requires 2 hours per unit to be made in all plants. Product *y* requires 3 hours per unit to be made in all plants.

Product requirements (in units) follow:

PRODUCT	PERIOD	
	1	2
x	100	135
y	210	210

Plant capacities (in hours) follow:

PLANT	PERIOD	
	1	2
A regular time	100	100
A overtime	50	50
B regular time	200	200
B overtime	50	—
C regular time	500	500
C overtime	100	100

Cost per unit follows:

PLANT	PRODUCT	
	x	*y*
A regular time	$1.50	$2.20
A overtime	1.75	2.60
B regular time	1.60	2.25
B overtime	1.90	2.50
C regular time	1.70	2.30
C overtime	1.80	2.65

Cost of storage per unit per time period:

Plant *A*..................$0.20
Plant *B*.................. 0.15
Plant *C*.................. 0.10

Solve this problem by the transportation method of linear programming (making any adjustments necessary). Give total cost of your schedule.

9. Products *A, B, C,* and *D* can be made on machines *x, y,* and *z.*
The cost per unit is as follows:

	A	B	C	D
x....................	$0.42	$0.36	$0.29	$0.31
y....................	0.27	0.28	0.15	0.19
z....................	0.21	0.31	0.17	0.22

The time in minutes required per unit of product is as follows:

	A	B	C	D
x...............	9	9	9	9
y...............	7	7	7	7
z...............	6	6	6	6

The units of product required are as follows:

A	B	C	D
200	200	150	300

The amount of time in minutes available is as follows:

x	y	z
4,000	2,000	1,500

The cost for the above schedule is to be minimized.

a) Express the constraints and objective of this problem in algebraic form.

b) Lay out the first table for the general simplex method.

c) Convert the above problem into the transportation form.

d) What is the cost of the optimum assignment?

10. A manufacturer of heavy equipment has the problem of determining the number of units of each of three items to pack in a repair kit whose total cost (c) cannot exceed $320. Part 1 costs $30; part 2, $40; and part 3, $60. The field utility in dollars of a unit of each part decreases as more are added according to the following schedules (estimated by multiplying the value in use by the probability of use):

x No. of Parts in Kit	$g(x_1)$ Utility of Parts No. 1	$g(x_2)$ Utility of Parts No. 2	$g(x_3)$ Utility of Parts No. 3
1.....................	70	140	200
2.....................	130	220	300
3.....................	190	300	380
4.....................	240	350	440
5.....................	280	400	490
6.....................	320	430	530
7.....................	350	450	550
8.....................	380	480	570
9.....................	390	490	590
10....................	400	500	600

The problem is to determine the number of parts of each type to pack in the kit to maximize its field utility and not exceed a cost of $320.

a) Express the general form of the dynamic programming functional equations for this problem.

b) Determine the contents and the field utility of the repair kit.

11. Transportation costs are included within the following table:

WAREHOUSES	PLANTS			REQUIREMENTS
	x	*y*	*z*	
A....................	$10	$ 20	$ 30	25
B....................	15	40	35	115
C....................	20	15	40	60
D....................	20	30	55	30
E....................	40	30	25	70
Capacities............	50	100	150	

a) State the objective function.

b) Solve for the optimum scheme and determine its cost.

12. A manufacturing firm has two plants and makes three products for national distribution. Each of the products requires both foundry and machining capacity in the plant used to produce that product (per unit) as follows:

	Product 1	Product 2	Product 3
Foundry hours.............	1	2	2
Machining hours..........	3	1	4
Selling price..............	$20	$15	$40
Material cost.............	$ 2	$ 3	$10

The direct labor costs of an hour of each capacity at the two plants are as follows:

	Plant 1	Plant 2
Foundry.....................	$3.00 (1,600)	$3.50 (3,200)
Machining..................	$2.50 (3,200)	$2.50 (3,200)

The figures in parentheses represent the maximum number of hours of each type of capacity available per month.

a) The company wishes to determine the most profitable product mix assuming all production can be sold and no change is contemplated in plant capacity. Set up a linear model for the solution of the problem.

b) The company has determined the least cost shipping area from each of the plants and the demand for each product in each plant's area is as follows:

	Plant 1	Plant 2
Product 1.................	200	200
Product 2.................	500	300
Product 3.................	700	300

It costs the company a premium of $1.00 per unit of product which must be shipped out of one plant's least cost shipping area. Set up a linear model to determine the least cost production program to meet these demands.

13. A trucking firm must transport trailers as demanded by its customers. The following is a typical problem faced by the dispatcher:

TRACTORS	TRAILERS					
	1	2	3	4	5	
A..............	20	51	25	95	60	3
B..............	32	27	16	52	72	8
C..............	58	82	12	81	41	6
D..............	41	42	10	81	33	5
	9	5	1	3	2	

He must assign the tractors located at points A, B, C, and D to the trailers located at points 1, 2, 3, 4, and 5 so as to minimize the mileage traveled by the tractors. The mileages are shown in the body of the table. Determine the optimal assignment by the use of linear programming.

14. Complete the dynamic programming approach to the procurement scheduling problem which has been started on pages 143–46.

15. What other approaches (in addition to straightforward dynamic programming) can be worked out for the procurement scheduling problem which has been started on pages 143–46.

16. Using Table 4–16, page 143, for component A as the first stage in the package problem with weight and volume constraints, set up the appropriate table for component B as the second stage in the problem solution.

17. Determine the minimum cost transportation schedule:

Territories

Plants		A	B	C	D	E	F	G	H	Cap.
	x	$45	$63	$55	$51	$59	$43	$48	$60	450
	y	$39	$47	$42	$40	$50	$37	$46	$53	325
	z	$51	$57	$60	$53	$56	$50	$57	$54	375
Requirements		75	120	90	310	60	135	185	105	

18. Seven field repair crews are now available to assign to the next seven field repair jobs. It is desirable to minimize the total miles traveled by these crews. The table below contains these mileage figures:

Jobs

		1	2	3	4	5	6	7
	1	150	206	127	305	172	209	300
	2	143	172	186	205	215	300	286
	3	305	172	180	145	237	261	280
Crews	4	270	245	231	206	195	300	206
	5	235	297	210	211	226	200	274
	6	291	190	273	195	236	197	215
	7	204	221	297	173	207	195	236

19. Set up the functional equations for the 12-month procurement scheduling problem used to illustrate dynamic programming, pages 143–46.

20. The objective of this problem is to determine minimum costs. The products are A, B, and C; the machines are x, y, and z; the subcontractor is R; and there is one time period.

Demand:

A	B	C
40 units	60 units	80 units

Capacities:

x	y	z	R
20 hours	30 hours	30 hours	∞ hours and units

Time requirements, hours per unit:

	A	B	C
x	0.2	0.3	0.4
y	0.4	0.6	8.3
z	0.2	0.3	0.4

Variable costs per unit:

	A	B	C
x	$2.00	$3.00	$ 4.00
y	$4.00	$6.00	$83.00
z	$3.00	$4.50	$ 6.00
R	$5.00	$5.00	$ 5.00

a) Completely set up first simplex table.
Determine which new variable to bring into the solution for the next table.
Tell how many units to bring in.
b) Put problem into transportation form.
Explain any modifications or adjustments necessary.
Solve for an optimum solution.

SECTION III

Statistical Analysis

Modern statistical methods find wide application in production management. Variation in the output of a process, whether it be quality, quantity, or cost which is the measured characteristic of output, is the rule rather than the exception. Knowledge concerning the expected variation is essential if control is to be instituted over a process. Decisions as to whether a process is giving the desired output can only be made if the manager knows what to expect of a process and can decide precisely when a process is not meeting these expectations. The statistical control concept provides for this kind of decision.

In many cases, inferences must be drawn about the output of some process based on less than complete information. When this is necessary, formal sampling plans provide the manager with good decision rules. The economic criteria which establish the necessity for the use of sampling plans should be known and understood by management.

Industrial experimentation is seeing wider and wider use in industry today as the means whereby useful information may be gathered economically and with greatest efficiency. Decisions should always be based on the best and most complete information which it is feasible to get. Modern statistical techniques aim at the efficient gathering and utilization of information.

CHAPTER 5

Statistical Control

IN ANY process in which output is expected to conform to some measurable characteristic, variation in this output will occur. Thus, if a machining process is producing a product which is judged by a dimension, a blending process, a product judged by a volumetric content, or a manufacturing process, a level of performance judged by a cost, in each case the decision problem faced by management with respect to this output is the same. A decision must be made as to whether the observed variation between an actual output measurement and the established standard is "acceptable" or constitutes an exception to acceptable performance and therefore should be the basis for some corrective action.

The reasons for the output variation are not very hard to find, although their quantitative evaluation may be quite difficult.[1] Any production process is concerned basically with the conversion of a set of inputs into a set of outputs. We can expect variation in the inputs to occur over time as well as variation in the conversion process. The important question of concern to management is whether or not the variation in the process is stable over time or unstable. That is, are there cause factors operating with respect to inputs, the conversion process, and the measurement of outputs which are unchanging (stable cause system) or changing (unstable cause system). If, for example, we operate for a period with a given set of machines, setup men, and operators and these are the major sources of output variation, one would expect stability in the observed variation in output. However, if there were a high rate of turnover among setup men, and the level of training and skill exhibited by the group was therefore changing from time to time, one would expect this instability to be reflected in output variation insofar as setup men influenced this variation to any extent.

---

[1] See Chapter 7.

Thus, the problem of control is to detect changes in any given process as reflected by observation of output variation. What is required is a tool which will aid in the process of judging whether or not an observed variation in output represents an exception or an expected occurrence. The statistical control concept forms the basis for a quantitative tool to serve this need.

THE CONCEPT OF STATISTICAL CONTROL

Broadly speaking, the objective of control in production is to get assurance that operations occur according to plans. This implies that in order to control a process, one must predict the behavior of the process. Through past experience, one is able at least to determine the limits within which any given characteristic has varied. By assuming that the same set of causal factors will continue to operate in the future, it is usually possible to make a prediction of the expected behavior of the process. Then, of course, if a change occurs in the cause system which produced the past variation, this fact should be quickly apparent through a change in the variation of current output.

Consider, for example, a turning process whose output is a shaft where the diameter is critical and is specified as $4.000'' \pm 0.002''$. The probability[2] that the process will turn out a shaft whose diameter is *exactly* $4.000''$ is very low. One does expect, however, that the process will turn out a high proportion of product within the specification limits. The inputs to this process are the machine, the operator, the materials, the work method, temperature, humidity, measuring instruments, to mention some of the more important. Over the course of a production run, variation in these input factors will occur. This variation will in turn result in some variation in the measured characteristic of output, the shaft diameter. One expects this variation to be relatively stable over time. That is, as long as the variation is due to the chance coming together of a particular set of input levels each time a unit of output is produced, the variation which is observed in the measured characteristic may be attributed to some stable system of chance causes. The observed variation is inherent in the process, and in order to change it, the process itself must be changed.

If observations tell us that 20 per cent of the output of the process is outside the specification limits, it might be profitable to spend money in order to reduce the extent of variation in those input factors which are most significant in producing output variation. For example, one

---

[2] "Probability" is defined here as the relative frequency of an event. If an event has occurred in m ways, n of which are considered "successful," then the probability of a successful event is n/m.

might buy a better machine, hire a more skilled operator, get better measuring instruments, or use better materials. Any change of this kind should result in a new system of chance causes which exhibits stability in terms of its variability.

Variation which is unstable may also be introduced into a process. For example, if the tools which are used wear as they are used, one expects a *change* in the process variation which is unidirectional, i.e., in the direction of poorer dimensional stability. If the operator becomes, in some way, emotionally upset, or changes his work method; if a supplier begins sending material of different quality; or if the atmosphere becomes filled with dust from some source, any or all of these may cause instability to be introduced into the process. The result will tend to be some systematic bias in the measured characteristic of the output. This bias is due to the presence in the process of some *assignable cause of variation*. As long as no such causes are present, one expects behavior according to the inherent capabilities of the process. When some nonrandom cause *is* present in such a system, then its presence may be detected as an *unexpected* variation in the system measurements.

The concept of statistical control is one of the most useful tools of production management yet developed and rests on three postulates as follows:[3]

1. All chance systems are not alike in the sense that they enable us to predict the future in terms of the past. That is, you might be willing to gamble on the outcome of a coin-tossing game to be played next month, but not on the outcome of a particular horse race.
2. Constant systems of chance causes do exist in nature. Our ability to produce mortality tables is prime evidence of the existence of such systems.
3. Assignable causes of variation may be found and eliminated. As indicated previously, a measurable characteristic from a process may be thrown outside its predicted limits, i.e., out of control, by the introduction of known causes. Unknown causes may have the same effect. Abundant evidence exists today, as will be shown, that such causes can be discovered and eliminated.

Having established the basic concept of statistical control, the specific nature of such control systems in their application to production processes can be set forth.

The Statistical Nature of Production Processes

A production process consists of a series of inputs designed to produce some given output. Typical classes of inputs are men, equipment, materials, etc. Variations in these input factors occur, over time, as do

[3] W. A. Shewhart, "Economic Quality Control of Manufactured Product," *Bell System Technical Journal,* April, 1930, pp. 367–72.

variations in the relationships of the inputs to each other. These variations in the input factors constitute a cause system which produces some variation in the uniformity of output. Assuming that the variation within, and between, input factors is stable, then the variation in output will be stable, and therefore predictable. The introduction of some change in the input variation or of some previously absent cause of variation should quickly be made known by some change in the output variation. The objective of *statistical control* is to set up a formal control system whereby such changes in the chance cause system operating in a given situation may be made known and action taken accordingly.

For example, the variation in the cost of producing some item may be discovered by an analysis of past performance. Through application of the technique of statistical control, the expected value and limits of variation of this cost with a stable chance cause system may be discovered, and thus a mechanism established for identifying assignable causes of variation in cost. Furthermore, the technique aims at improving the cost performance by the following:

1. Directing attention at both mean cost and variation in cost.
2. Discovering causes for good, as well as poor, cost performance.

The statistical control technique may be used in the control of machine breakdowns in order to discover the presence of assignable causes, as well as to gauge the effectiveness and economic worth of a preventive maintenance program. It may be used in the analysis and control of production rates, accidents, personnel turnover, and, in fact, in most situations where control is desired over some process which may be typified by some measurable characteristic.

The Statistics of Process Output

The control chart is a device which takes advantage of the statistical nature of output in order to control a process. Consider a production process producing output the first n units of which are characterized by a set of measurements $x_1, x_2, x_3, x_4, \ldots x_i, \ldots x_n$. The only stipulation placed on this set is that it be ordered in time with respect to the process. That is, x_1, was produced before x_2 and so on. From this experience with the process, it is desired to set up a prediction of the expected behavior of future output so that decisions can be made as to whether or not corrective action is warranted with respect to any specific observed variation in output.

Output from a process may be characterized in a number of ways, but it is necessary to select some method of describing current output that is useful as a predictor of future output. Two statistics of considerable utility for such purposes are the mean and standard deviation of the underlying distribution which characterizes the process. Assuming that the data generated arose from a stable set of causes, these can be estimated as

$$\bar{x} = \frac{\sum\limits_{i=1}^{n} x_i}{n} \tag{1}$$

and

$$s_x = \sqrt{\frac{\sum\limits_{i=1}^{n} (x_i - \bar{x})^2}{n-1}} \tag{2}$$

where $\bar{x}$ and s_x are estimates of the population mean, μ_x, and standard deviation σ_x, respectively.

However, these estimates do not necessarily provide a prediction of the expected behavior of the process except insofar as the assumption that during the period represented by the x_i, there was a constant, underlying generating process in effect. If, for example, the mean of the process changed during this period, the calculation of $\bar{x}$ and s_x as shown in (1) and (2) would not be meaningful since in reality data from two or more populations are represented in the x_i. In order to get a useful prediction, one would first have to test the hypothesis that the data were generated by a constant cause system and come to some conclusion about the character of the distribution.

Assume that the output of some process may be characterized by the measurement of, say, a diameter, and that this diameter has been specified as 2.0030″ ± 0.0025″. Measurements are taken of this characteristic as output occurs, and a set of these measurements obtained as shown in Table 5–1 (reported in ten-thousandths of an inch above 2.0000″).

These data in Table 5–1 are arranged in a frequency distribution in Table 5–2. The class interval is selected so that the average of the data (2.0030) is at or near the midpoint of an interval, and so that the frequency in each interval gives the clearest possible clue as to the shape of the distribution.

The symmetry of this distribution is quite apparent, and a test for goodness of fit (the chi-square test) shows that the distribution of meas-

Table 5-1

1	2	3	4	5	6	7	8	9	10
47	31	19	29	40	31	19	24	28	41
32	34	37	43	18	29	1	30	39	42
44	12	31	25	30	52	30	21	23	32
35	21	27	22	11	29	30	37	21	28
33	24	23	37	21	21	28	32	41	46
33	47	45	33	18	18	34	25	32	27
34	35	26	29	36	26	39	24	46	42
34	23	37	32	34	20	17	22	12	34
34	38	33	30	26	30	29	16	14	22
34	40	12	13	35	20	25	35	23	34

urements may be assumed normal. The mean of the set of 100 measurements is (refer to Glossary, Appendix I, for definitions):

$$\bar{x} = \frac{\Sigma x_i}{n} = 29.38 \, ,$$

and an estimate of the standard deviation of the population, σ_x, is:

$$s_x = \sqrt{\frac{\Sigma(x_i - \bar{x})^2}{n - 1}} = 9.4 \, .$$

Table 5-2

FREQUENCY DISTRIBUTION—SHAFT DIAMETERS

Class Interval	Frequency
1.9995–2.0004	1
2.0005–2.0014	6
2.0015–2.0024	24
2.0025–2.0034	43
2.0035–2.0044	20
2.0045–2.0054	6
2.0055–2.0064	0

The normal distribution is given by the following:[4]

$$f(x) = \frac{1}{\sigma_x \sqrt{2\pi}} e - \frac{1}{2} \left(\frac{x_i - \mu}{\sigma_x} \right)^2$$

where

x_i = population members (i = 1, 2, 3, . . .),
μ = mean of the population,
σ_x = standard deviation of the population.

This distribution is symmetrical about the mean, and definite areas are
included within known deviations on either side of the mean as follows:

---

[4] $f(x)$ denotes a continuous density function, the relative area under which gives
the probability of x occurring in any given interval. This distribution is the familiar bell-
shaped curve.

.1. $\mu \pm \sigma_x$ includes 68.26 per cent of the area under the curve.
2. $\mu \pm 2\sigma_x$ includes 95.45 per cent of the area under the curve.
3. $\mu \pm 3\sigma_x$ includes 99.73 per cent of the area under the curve.
4. $\mu \pm 4\sigma_x$ includes 99.99 per cent of the area under the curve.

The following figure illustrates the area within $\mu \pm \sigma_x$:

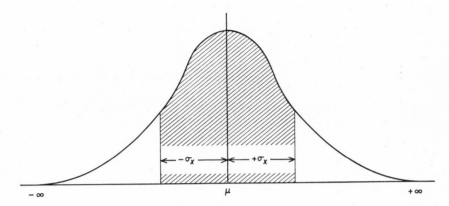

The shaded portion of the area under the curve represents 68.26 per cent of the items in the population. Portions of the area under a normal curve may be found using the Table A in Appendix II which shows areas from $-\infty$ to any desired positive deviation measured in standard deviation units, as shown in the following figure:

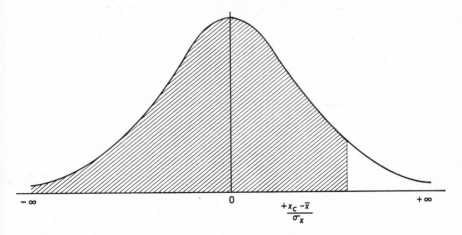

If it is desired to find the area up to $x = 2.00\sigma_x$, the shaded portion will include 0.9772 of the total area under the curve, as may be read directly from the table. In order to determine the area from $-2\sigma_x$ to $+2\sigma_x$, it is necessary to subtract 0.5000 from the above to get the area between

0 and $+2\sigma_x$ and multiply the result by 2, thus obtaining 0.9544 as the fraction of the total area between these limits.

Using the normal table, Table A, in Appendix II, the percentage of output which may be expected to fall within the specification limits in our example, so long as the cause system does not change, may be determined as follows:

1. The specification limits vary from 2.0005″ to 2.0055″. In standard deviation units this range is from

$$\frac{2.0005 - 2.0030}{9.4 \times 10^{-4}} \text{ to } \frac{2.0055 - 2.0030}{9.4 \times 10^{-4}}, \text{ or from } -2.66\ s_x \text{ to } +2.66\ s_x.$$

2. The area under the normal curve between these limits, from the table, is 99.22 per cent $[(0.9961 - 0.5000)2 \times 100]$.

In the first 100 items from the process, one is out of specification limits, which is not far from expectations. However, the above analysis does not satisfy the objective of control, since a basis for action must be available on a continuous basis.

As long as one has assurance that a normal population of measurements flows from the process over which it is desired to institute control, expectations may be set up as shown in Figure 5–1. Here k enables one

Figure 5–1

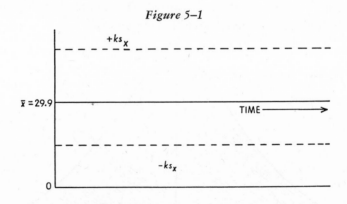

to predict the proportion of observations which can be expected within the given limits. Observations are plotted in their order of occurrence, and inferences drawn as to whether the process is as it was when $\bar{x}$ and s_x were first computed or has changed due to the presence of assignable causes. As long as the proportion outside of limits does not exceed expectations (based on the selection of k), and as long as the distribution of measurements remains symmetrical, one may infer that the process is in control at the given limits. Specification limits may be plotted on the chart to give a visual indication of the ability of the process to produce technically acceptable product.

This, however, does not get at the basic problem of control which is first of all to test the hypothesis that the process is in control and, having once accepted it, continue monitoring the process by repeating the test at appropriate intervals.

The Concept of Rational Subgroups

Consider again the process from which we have obtained an initial set of values $x_1, x_2, \ldots, x_n$ but we have no knowledge as to the stability or lack of stability exhibited by the process. If the process changed in its centering during this initial period, as for example in Figure 5–2, then

Figure 5–2

EFFECT OF CHANGE IN PROCESS CENTERING

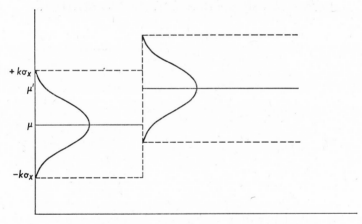

the computations of $\bar{x}$ and s_x shown earlier are not valid. We would be pooling observations from two different underlying populations, one with mean μ and the other with mean μ', and our estimates would only be weighted averages of the statistics of both processes. It is easy to see that the problem of estimation of process characteristics could be solved by dividing the output according to the time at which the process changed.

Since this is unknown, we might consider subdividing the observations into smaller sets each one of which provides estimates of the process characteristics. Then if a change of the kind shown occurred, only one of the subgroups at most would provide an invalid estimate.

If the process change occurred as shown in Figure 5–3, the estimates provided by these subgroups might still be reasonable if the subgroup size were small. Then the envelope of the estimates would approximate the actual behavior of the process.

If we divide our n observations into $[n/r]$ subgroups of r observations each preserving the order of observation between subgroups, we can compute $[n/r]$ estimates of $\bar{x}$ and s_x and we have two ordered sets of statistics as estimates of the process behavior. The value of r is arbitrary and depends largely on one's expectations as to the likelihood of a process change occurring at all.

If the process is such that if changes occur they are abrupt and of short duration, the sample should be taken over as short a period as possible since it is desirable to insure that if a change occurs it does so between samples rather than within a sample. If the process is subject to slow continuous change, then again sample size should be small so that

Figure 5–3

CONTINUOUS SLOW CHANGE IN PROCESS CENTERING

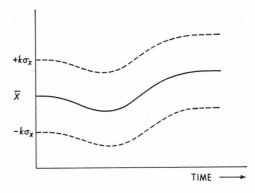

the process variation within the sample be small relative to that between the sample. In any case, the arguments in favor of small subgroups are persuasive but the choice of interval between subgroups is more difficult. The economics of this choice will be discussed later.

The Central Limit Theorem and Control Charts

In order to institute and maintain process control, it is necessary to be able to state one's prior expectations concerning process output and then to test the hypothesis that these expectations are being satisfied. If we know nothing about the process except that we have a set of observations of output generated over some initial production period, what can be stated as our expectations concerning this process? The addition to our data gathering process of the subgrouping procedure makes it possible to set up an hypothesis otherwise unavailable to us.

Consider the set of 100 measurements given in Table 5–3 as divided into subgroups of five in which the order of production is preserved as between subgroups. Each sample provides us with an estimate of μ_x and σ_x as shown in Table 5–3. Thus the behavior of the process mean is estimated by each of the 20 values of $\bar{x}$ and we can immediately hypothesize that if the process centering was unchanged during this period they are all estimates of the same population value, μ_x.

According to the central limit theorem[5] the statistics of observations drawn from nonnormal populations will exhibit nearly normal behavior. Of course, such behavior will be more closely normal the closer the

Table 5–3

MEASUREMENT OF SHAFT DIAMETERS IN ORDER PRODUCED

SAMPLE No.	OBSERVATIONS					$\bar{x}$	s_x	R
	A	B	C	D	E			
1.....	47	32	44	35	33	38.2	6.5	15
2.....	33	34	34	34	34	33.8	0.4	1
3.....	31	34	12	21	24	24.4	8.7	22
4.....	47	35	23	38	40	36.6	10.4	24
5.....	19	37	31	27	23	27.4	7.0	18
6.....	45	26	37	33	12	30.6	12.4	33
7.....	29	43	25	22	37	31.2	8.7	21
8.....	33	29	32	30	13	27.4	8.2	20
9.....	40	18	30	11	21	24.0	11.2	29
10.....	18	36	34	26	35	29.8	7.7	18
11.....	31	29	52	29	21	32.4	11.6	31
12.....	18	26	20	30	20	22.8	4.7	12
13.....	19	1	30	30	28	21.6	12.4	29
14.....	34	39	17	29	25	28.8	8.4	22
15.....	24	30	21	37	32	28.8	6.4	16
16.....	25	24	22	16	35	24.4	6.8	19
17.....	28	39	23	21	41	30.4	9.1	20
18.....	32	46	12	14	23	25.4	14.0	34
19.....	41	42	32	28	46	37.8	7.5	18
20.....	27	42	34	22	34	31.8	7.6	20

underlying population is to a normal distribution, but the principle applies in any case.

If the basic distribution were rectangular, that is, the probability of each observation the same and samples of 5 drawn from this population, the distribution of sample means would be normal. The most likely value (the *central* value) would be the mean of the population since if the sampling is random there would be no bias toward extreme (tail) values within any one sample. If the sample size were larger, the

[5] M. E. Munroe, *Theory of Probability* (New York: McGraw-Hill Book Co., Inc. 1951).

only effect would be to reduce the variance of the distribution of sample means while preserving its normal shape.

Each subgroup mean is a random event and the standard deviation of the distribution of these means is

$$s_{\bar{x}} = \frac{s_x}{\sqrt{n}}. \tag{3}$$

It should be easy to see that the expected mean of this new distribution is the same as that of the original population, that is, the expected value of the mean of a subgroup is

$$E(\bar{x}) = E\left[\frac{1}{n}(x_1 + x_2 + \ldots + x_n)\right]$$

$$= \frac{1}{n}[E(x_1) + E(x_2) + \ldots + E(x_n)]$$

$$= \mu$$

where

$$E(\ ) = \text{expected value of variable in } (\ ),$$
$$n = \text{number of observations in subgroup},$$
$$\mu = \text{population mean}.$$

The variance of the subgroup means can be determined by noting that

$$\bar{x} = \frac{1}{n}(x_1 + x_2 + \ldots + x_n).$$

Then

$$\text{var}(\bar{x}) = \text{var}\left[\frac{1}{n}(x_1 + x_2 + \cdots + x_n)\right]$$

$$= \frac{1}{n^2}[\text{var}(x_1) + \text{var}(x_2) + \cdots + \text{var}(x_n)].$$

Where var( ) = variance of variable in parentheses. Since var(x_i) is everywhere the same,

$$\text{var}(\bar{x}) = \frac{n \, \text{var}(x_i)}{n^2}$$

$$= \frac{\sigma_x^2}{n}.$$

An estimate of the standard deviation of a distribution can then be obtained as

$$s_{\bar{x}} = \frac{s_x}{\sqrt{n}}.$$

Further, the standard deviation of each subgroup may be determined, and these values arrayed in a frequency distribution will have a standard deviation (s_s) approximately equal to $s_x/\sqrt{2n}$, where n is the subgroup size. The tendency toward normality is more pronounced the larger n is, but for control chart purposes subgroup sizes of 4, 5, or 6 are most common for several reasons.

The reader is urged to verify for himself the facts given above by actual experience. An ordinary deck of playing cards can provide, for example, a rectangular distribution from which samples may be drawn for this purpose.

With respect to the sample means of Table 5–3, we may now hypothesize that, for example, 95.4 per cent of them will fall in the interval $-2s_{\bar{x}} < \bar{x} < 2s_{\bar{x}}$ if the process was unchanged during the initial observation period ($\bar{x}$ signifies the mean of the subgroup means). The problem facing us in testing this hypothesis is to calculate $s_{\bar{x}}$.

If we calculate s_x in the usual way by pooling all observations and the hypothesis is not true, then we have lost the ability to test for this. However, we have 20 independent estimates of this statistic and even if the process has changed centering, the subgroup standard deviations provide us with estimates of the process variation over a short enough period that their reliability should be high. Thus the estimate we will choose will be that given by the *average* of these 20 estimates, that is,

$$s_x = \frac{\sum_i s_{xi}}{N} \tag{5}$$

in which

$$s_{xi} = \text{subgroup standard deviation} ,$$
$$N = \text{number of subgroups} .$$

In this case, the average of these estimates is 8.5 and $s_{\bar{x}}$ may be estimated as $8.5/\sqrt{5}$, or 3.8. Our expectations can be set up as shown in Figure 5–4 with the central line corresponding to the expected mean $\bar{x}$ (where $\bar{x}$ signifies the mean of the means of the subgroups), and limit lines corresponding to standard deviations from the mean. Then the results of measurements of successive groups of five may be plotted and statements made on a continuing basis as to the probability that the cause system has changed, i.e., that an assignable cause of variation is present. For the twenty subgroups plotted, all fall within $\pm 3s_{\bar{x}}$. From the normal table, the expectation for each subgroup value within $\pm 3s_{\bar{x}}$

Figure 5-4

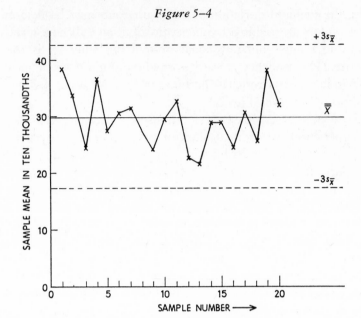

is 99.73 per cent, i.e., there are only about 3 chances in 1,000 that a point will fall outside the $\pm 3s_{\bar{x}}$ limits as long as no assignable causes of variation are present. This, therefore, is the probability of mistakenly inferring that the process is out of control when it is really still in control. If one were to use $\pm 2s_{\bar{x}}$ limits, based on the normal distribution, about 4.5 times out of 100 it would be inferred that the process was out of control when nothing was really wrong. Clearly, wider limits decrease the probability of making this kind of error.

However, wider limits decrease the probability that a change in the process average will be detected quickly. The chance of inferring that

Figure 5-5

SHIFT IN PROCESS AVERAGE—VARIATION CONSTANT

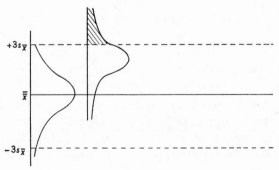

the process is still in control when it really isn't is increased quite sharply when one uses, say, $\pm 4s_{\bar{x}}$ limits. The exact probability of making this kind of an error depends on the magnitude of the shift which occurs in the average. If the average changes from 29.4 to 37.0, the situation is as shown in Figure 5–5, where the first distribution is the expected one and the second the actual. The shaded area represents the probability that the shift will be detected by any single subgroup taken following the change. From the normal table this may be computed as approximately 16 per cent of the total area. The probability that the change will be detected at all is equal to $1 - (0.84)^N$, where N is the number of successive subgroups.[6] Thus, for example, there is an even chance of catching a shift of this magnitude in four successive subgroups taken after the shift has occurred.

It is plain that the control chart for means primarily allows detection of shifts in the process average and assumes that process variation remains essentially constant. It is quite possible that the same value for the mean of a subgroup could conceal a shift in the variability of the process as shown in Figure 5–6.

Figure 5–6

SHIFTS IN PROCESS VARIATION—MEAN CONSTANT

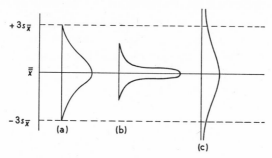

All the distributions of $\bar{x}$ values in Figure 5–6 have the same means but different variations. The $\bar{x}$ chart alone would tend to conceal these differences. That is, the means of the distributions would all plot as the same point. There is some chance that a sample drawn from distribution (c) would give a value of $\bar{x}$ outside the control limits, but this is not an efficient means for detecting such shifts in the variability of a process.

---

[6] The probability of *not* detecting the shift on any one subgroup is $(1 - 0.16) = 0.84$. The probability of not detecting the shift on two successive subgroups is the probability that it was not detected on the first (0.84) times the probability that it will not be detected on the second (0.84). The probability of detecting the shift on N subgroups, then, is one minus the probability of not detecting it $(0.84)^N$.

In order to exercise greater control over the process, it is necessary to have a chart which will reveal changes in variation. The standard deviation of each subgroup could be computed, and the expected values for the resulting distribution of standard deviations used for control. In our example, the standard deviation estimated for all 20 samples, 8.5, would constitute the central line, and an estimate of the standard deviation of the distribution of standard deviations σ_σ computed from

$$s_s = \frac{s_x}{\sqrt{2n}} = \frac{9.4}{\sqrt{10}} = 3.0$$

would be used in setting limits.

The resulting control chart using $\pm 3s_s$ limits is plotted in Figure 5–7.

Figure 5–7

CONTROL CHART FOR STANDARD DEVIATION

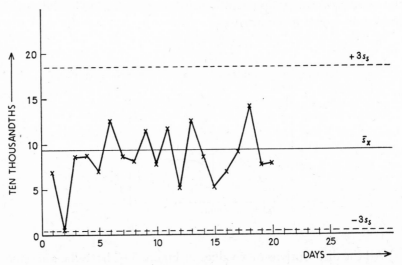

$\bar{X}$ and R Control Charts

In most industrial work, the difficulty of computation makes the use of a standard deviation chart impractical. Fortunately, for small samples another measure of variation, the range, is sufficiently stable to be useful. As long as the subgroup size is small, the difference between the highest and lowest value in the subgroup can be used as a satisfactory measure of variation. In order to use the range[7] for control chart

---

[7] Range equals difference between highest and lowest measurement within the subgroup.

purposes, the relationship between the range and σ_x must be established. Consider the following generating process. Draw from a normal population of known characteristics random samples of size n and for each compute the range, R. Then the ratio R/σ_x may be determined and estimates formed of the characteristics of the distribution of R/σ_x for any sample size n. This has been done, and the results are tabulated as the distribution of the relative range, $w = R/\sigma_x$ in Table D, Appendix II. The mean, $\bar{w}$ for each sample size is called d_2 and can be used to obtain an estimate of σ_x if one has an estimate of the expected range. Since $w = R/\sigma_x$, an estimate of σ_x, s_x, can be obtained from

$$s_x = \frac{R}{d_2}.$$

Usually the best estimate available of the expected range is $\bar{R}$, the average of values of the range for N subgroups. The more subgroups available, the better the estimate of σ_x that is obtained.

In the example used previously, $\bar{R}$ may be computed from Table 5–3 as

$$\bar{R} = \frac{422}{20} = 21.1$$

and an estimate of σ_x obtained as

$$s_x = \frac{21.2}{2.326} = 9.1 ,$$

where $d_2 = 2.326$ for samples of 5. This can be compared with the value of 8.5 obtained by the use of equation (2).

In order to set up a control chart to detect changes in variation, it is necessary to estimate σ_R, the standard deviation of the population of ranges drawn from a stable process. Assuming the process is in control (within subgroups), the distribution of the relative range can be used again. For any sample size n, σ_w, the standard deviation of the sample values of R/σ_x, may be determined and has been tabulated in Tables D and (as d_3) F, Appendix II. Then an estimate of σ_R may be obtained from

$$s_R = \sigma_w \frac{\bar{R}}{d_2}. \tag{4}$$

This can be developed according to the following reasoning. If σ_x is the standard deviation of a population of values of x,

$$\sigma_x = \sqrt{\frac{\sum_i (x_i - \mu)^2}{N}},$$

where N is the size of the population, the standard deviation of a population of values of kx (k a constant) is

$$\sigma_{kx} = \sqrt{\frac{\sum_i (kx_i - k\mu)^2}{N}}$$

$$= k\sqrt{\frac{\sum_i (x_i - \mu)^2}{N}}$$

$$= k\sigma_x .$$

Thus, according to the definition of the relative range

$$w = R/\sigma_x$$

and

$$R = w\sigma_x .$$

Then, since the standard deviation of a distribution of values of w is σ_w, the standard deviation of a set of values of R, σ_R, is

$$\sigma_R = \sigma_w \sigma_x .$$

From this, one can estimate σ_R as

$$s_R = \sigma_w s_x$$

$$= \sigma_w \frac{\bar{R}}{d_2} \qquad (5)$$

and control limits set based on $3s_R$.

From the table, the standard deviation of the distribution of the relative range, σ_w, for samples of five, is 0.864. In order to estimate the standard deviation of the distribution of ranges, σ_R, it is only necessary to set

$$s_R = 0.864 \frac{\bar{R}}{d_2} .$$

Since $\bar{R}/d_2$ is an unbiased estimate of σ_x, in the given example this gives $s_R = 7.9$. Then an R chart may be plotted as in Figure 5–8, using $\pm 3s_R$ limits with the upper control limit

$$UCL_R = 21.1 + 3(7.9)$$
$$= 44.8$$

and the lower control limit

$$LCL_R = 21.1 - 3(7.9)$$
$$= 0$$

since the range cannot be negative.

Figure 5–8

CONTROL CHART FOR RANGE

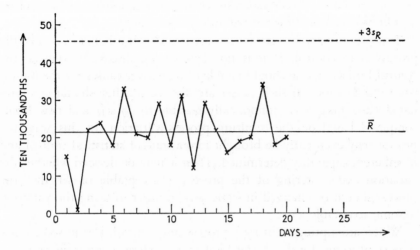

The tables in Appendix II greatly simplify the computation of upper and lower control limits for $\bar{X}$ and R charts. For the $\bar{X}$ chart, since $\sigma_{\bar{x}}$ may be estimated from $\dfrac{\bar{R}}{d_2}$ and $s_{\bar{x}} = \dfrac{s_x}{\sqrt{n}}$, then

$$UCL_{\bar{x}} = \bar{\bar{x}} + 3\frac{\bar{R}}{d_2\sqrt{n}}$$

and

$$LCL_{\bar{x}} = \bar{\bar{x}} - 3\frac{\bar{R}}{d_2\sqrt{n}}.$$

Setting

$$A_2 = \frac{3}{d_2\sqrt{n}},$$

then the $3s_{\bar{x}}$ control limits become

$$\bar{\bar{x}} \pm A_2\bar{R}. \tag{6}$$

If D_4 is defined as $1 + \dfrac{3s_w}{d_2}$ and D_3 as $1 - \dfrac{3s_w}{d_2}$, then the control limits for the R chart become

$$UCL_R = D_4\bar{R} \tag{7}$$

and

$$LCL_R = D_3\bar{R}. \tag{8}$$

Thus, it is only necessary to compute $\bar{x}$ and $\bar{R}$ from preliminary data in order to obtain control limits to begin using these charts. As more data become available, better estimates of the population values σ_x and $\sigma_{\bar{x}}$ should be substituted for the preliminary estimates.

The preliminary limits may be used to test the hypothesis that the process is in control. If it is not (points are discovered outside the control limits), action should be taken to discover causes for the out-of-control indications. If such causes are discovered, they should be eliminated (assuming it is economically feasible to do so) and new limits computed based on the resulting process variation. In this way, the process may eventually be brought into a state of statistical control and its inherent capability determined. Then it may be decided whether the variation and centering of the process is acceptable or whether the process should be changed in some way in order to bring the variation to some acceptable level.

When attempting to bring a process into control, it is in some cases important to test for the existence of "runs." Here, a run is defined as a succession of items of the same class. A run of defective items, a run above or below the average, and a run of increasing or decreasing values may all indicate lack of control even though sample values remain within the control limits. Tests have been devised utilizing the distribution of the total number of runs of a given kind and of the lengths of runs of various kinds.[8]

Simulation of Control Charts in Operation

In order to demonstrate the way in which the above described control charts may be used to institute and maintain control over a process, a computer program has been written (using the FORTRAN IV language) to allow one to experiment in a variety of situations. The program is listed in the Appendix to this chapter together with a description of its functions and operation.

The input is of two kinds. First, a cumulative distribution giving the shape of the expected process output is read in normalized form, that is, with mean 0. and standard deviation of 1. Then the statistics of various possible states of the process in terms of mean and standard deviation as well as the probability that the system will be in that state are entered. The expected state is always given as state 1.

The control chart parameters are entered in terms of deviate, sample size, and appropriate relative range statistics (d_2 and d_3). In addition,

---

[8] See Acheson J. Duncan, *Quality Control and Industrial Statistics* (3d ed.; Homewood, Ill.: Richard D. Irwin, Inc., 1965), pp. 132–37.

provision is made for entering various cost parameters but their use will be explained later. The optimal number of samples per production period is computed in a manner to be explained later and used to set up the simulation. Initial control limits may be based on either the statistics given for state 1 or an initial set of data generated by the computer itself.

As an example of the use of this program consider the following situation. It is desired to produce output conforming to the specification $2.5250'' \pm 0.0005''$ as given previously. It is expected that the process will produce output according to a normal distribution with mean at $2.5250''$ and a standard deviation of $0.0002''$. It is assumed for this demonstration that at any time there is a 10 per cent chance that the process will operate so that its centering is at $2.5254''$, a 3 per cent chance that it will operate at $2.5248''$, and a 2 per cent chance of operating at $2.5260''$. These changes occur at random due to some assignable causes currently operating in the process, but once detected can be traced and eliminated. Thus the statistics for these states are entered as

PROB(J)	XMU(J)	SIGMA(J)	NBIAS(J)
0.85	2.5250	0.0002	0
0.10	2.5254	0.0002	0
0.03	2.5248	0.0002	0
0.02	2.5260	0.0002	0

The meaning of NBIAS(J) is that if 0, changes to any state occur at random among the states. If this is set equal to one, a change to any such state is permanent until detected and the cause removed.

The program in this case will produce a set of initial control limits based on $\bar{X}$ and $\bar{R}$ as given for state 1. Then actual points are compared with these limits based on a given deviate DEVK (in this case set at 3.0). If any out of control points are discovered, the state which gave rise to this is eliminated from the set, the PROB(J)'s recomputed (since they must add to 1.0), and the control limits recomputed based on sample data but eliminating this observation for which presumably an assignable cause has been discovered.

The program continues to operate on a current basis for a set of production periods stipulated by the user or until all states other than the desired state have been detected and eliminated. A partial set of output for the situation described is given in the Appendix to this chapter.

Process Control and Process Capability

As can be seen from the example just given, the capability of a process depends on the relationship between process performance and product specifications. The latter are given to us by the interaction of product and process design systems while the former can be determined only after the process has been brought under control. Control implies both measurement and understanding—measurement in the sense that the degree of conformance of output to specification has been determined quantitatively, and understanding in the sense that assignable causes of variation have been discovered and eliminated where feasible.

A process in a state of statistical control is generating output which can be described by a set of parameters, and only under such conditions can the behavior of the process be related to the desired specifications. Thus in the case just given, it was desired to produce output conforming to the specification that a dimension be $2.5250'' \pm 0.0005''$. For an initial set of 50 samples, it was found to be centered at 2.52503 with a standard deviation estimated as 0.00019. However, these estimates could not be used to judge process capability as it was also observed that the process was out of control at two sample points in the original set of 50.

If one had erroneously assumed these statistics to be predictive of process capability, fraction defective would have been estimated at 0.0094 assuming normality of output. (This assumption places a lower bound on the estimate.) Given that the cause for the out of control condition could be discovered and removed (not a necessary condition for control), then new estimates of the mean and standard deviation would be 2.52501 and 0.0002, respectively. We would then estimate the process fraction defective as 0.0125.

Once control had been established for the process, a capability study could be undertaken since any estimates made would be for a population of stable characteristics rather than one which was subject to changes due to causes which were discoverable and could be corrected.

Control Charts for Fraction Defective

When output is merely classified as to whether it is good or bad, a p chart may be used to show variations in quality. Up to now, inspection has been by *variables,* i.e., the quality characteristic has been measured to determine its value. Now inspection by *attributes* will be considered.

In this kind of inspection, the item is checked merely to see whether it is inside or outside of specifications. If in the long run 2 per cent of output is expected to be defective (based on past experience), then the probability distribution of defects for production over any period of time is given by the binomial distribution:[9]

$$P(c) = \binom{n}{c} p'^c (1 - p')^{n-c}$$

$$= \binom{n}{c} (0.02)^c (0.98)^{n-c},$$

in which

n = number of measurements taken in the period,
p' = the process average,
c = number of defects.

For this distribution the mean number of defects will be np'. What we wish to do is draw a sample from the process, estimate p as the ratio of c to n, and test the hypothesis that the estimate is a random sample drawn from a population for which the fraction defective is some expected value p'.

If this is true the expected number of defects will be $p'n$ and the standard deviation of this distribution of c will be

$$\sigma_c = \sqrt{np'(1 - p')}.$$

The distribution of estimates of p computed as c/n from each sample will tend to be normal and will have a standard deviation of

$$\sigma_p = \sqrt{\frac{p'(1 - p')}{n}}.$$

Based on this, an estimate of p' may be obtained from some initial observations, σ_p estimated and a control chart set up to test the hypothesis that each value of p came from a population with the estimated process average fraction defective.

For example, consider the situation presented below. Table 5–4 shows the results of the production and inspection of 100 castings a day for 30 days. Based on these data, the average fraction defective is $\bar{p} = \dfrac{549}{3,000} = 0.183$, and if the process is under control, this is an estimate

---

[9] $\binom{n}{c}$ is a short form which means the combination of n things taken c at a time.

Table 5–4

Day	No. Defective	Day	No. Defective
1...................	6	16...................	14
2...................	11	17...................	13
3...................	20	18...................	5
4...................	22	19...................	7
5...................	9	20...................	9
6...................	40	21...................	12
7...................	12	22...................	4
8...................	10	23...................	23
9...................	31	24...................	27
10...................	30	25....	31
11...................	33	26...................	33
12...................	39	27...................	16
13...................	25	28...................	14
14...................	18	29...................	11
15...................	17	30...................	7

of the process fraction defective p' and may be taken as the central line on the control chart. Also, $3\sigma_p$ limits can be set by estimating

$$s_p = \sqrt{\frac{0.183(0.817)}{100}} = 0.039 \, .$$

Adding and subtracting $3s_p$ from 0.183, we get 0.300 as the estimated upper limit and 0.066 for the lower. Figure 5–9 is a plot of the

Figure 5–9

CONTROL CHART FOR FRACTION DEFECTIVE

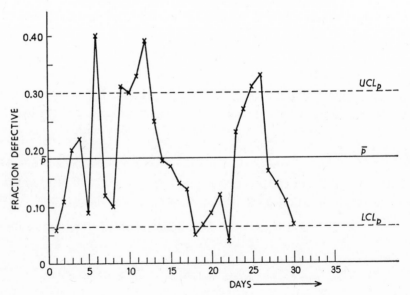

data and shows six points out of control on the high side and three out of control on the low side. The inference is clear that the process is not in a state of statistical control.

Investigation disclosed that on day 6, faulty sand had caused the very poor showing, while two new men had been added to the work force on both day 9 and day 25. On the basis of these assignable causes, data for days 6, 9, 10, 11, 12, 25, and 26 (learning was assumed as the cause of faulty output during the latter 6 days) were eliminated and a new chart (Fig. 5–10) set up with

$$\bar{p} = \frac{312}{2,300} = 0.136$$

$$UCL_p = 0.136 + 3\sqrt{\frac{0.136(0.864)}{100}} = 0.238$$

$$LCL_p = 0.136 - 3\sqrt{\frac{0.136(0.864)}{100}} = 0.034 .$$

This chart is only valid if the assignable causes discovered in the analysis of the original set of data have been eliminated from the process, in this case the cause of the defective sand and inadequate training of new workers. The analysis also suggests that a training program for new workers might eliminate the occurrence of such causes in the future. The chart now shows only two points out of control. This is a consider-

Figure 5–10

REVISED FRACTION DEFECTIVE CONTROL CHART

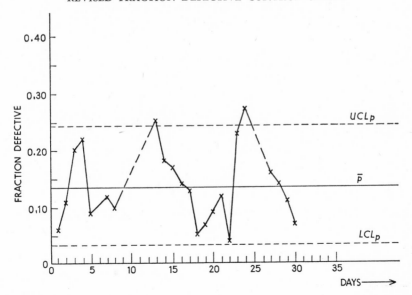

able improvement but indicates that there is, very probably, still trouble in the process.

This last chart could be used as the basis for control, for, say, the next 30 days and then a new average and limits computed as a result of this additional experience. It is to be expected that with effort spent on removing assignable causes of variation, the process will be brought into statistical control. Then, the chart can be used to maintain the process in control which is its primary purpose.

The chart should be used to focus attention on possible process improvement. The removal of assignable causes for poor production will, of course, effect noticeable improvements. The chart should also be watched for out-of-control points or long runs on the low side and causes for especially good showings discovered as clues to future improvement.

In the previous situation, the number of items inspected per time period was constant. If the number inspected varies only slightly (say, no more than 15 per cent), then limits may be computed based on the average number of items inspected. However, if there is wide variation in this number between periods, then one of two courses of action is open as follows:

1. Compute new limits for each inspection period.
2. Convert the deviations into standard deviation units.

Consider the data in Table 5–5 on a production process. Under the first method, the computations shown in Table 5–6 would result in the chart shown in Figure 5–11 (the lower limit is zero for all days except 6 and 10 since p cannot be negative). Days 6 and 10 are out of control and would be investigated for assignable causes of variation. If explana-

Table 5–5

Day	No. Inspected	No. Defective	Day	No. Inspected	No. Defective
1	42	1	11	66	5
2	55	3	12	57	1
3	60	1	13	48	3
4	71	2	14	62	5
5	53	2	15	59	1
6	49	9	16	40	3
7	61	0	17	46	4
8	93	2	18	66	5
9	50	5	19	72	1
10	65	9	20	70	4
				1,285	66

Table 5–6

Day	p	$3\sqrt{\dfrac{\bar{p}(1-\bar{p})}{n}}$	UCL_p	Day	p	$3\sqrt{\dfrac{\bar{p}(1-\bar{p})}{n}}$	UCL_p
1..........	0.024	0.102	0.153	11..........	0.075	0.082	0.133
2..........	0.055	0.090	0.141	12..........	0.018	0.088	0.139
3..........	0.017	0.086	0.137	13..........	0.063	0.096	0.147
4..........	0.028	0.079	0.130	14..........	0.081	0.084	0.135
5..........	0.038	0.091	0.142	15..........	0.017	0.086	0.137
6..........	0.183	0.095	0.146	16..........	0.075	0.105	0.156
7..........	0	0.085	0.136	17..........	0.087	0.098	0.149
8..........	0.022	0.069	0.120	18..........	0.076	0.082	0.133
9..........	0.100	0.094	0.145	19..........	0.014	0.078	0.129
10..........	0.138	0.082	0.133	20..........	0.057	0.079	0.130

$$[UCL_p = \bar{p} + 3\sqrt{\frac{\bar{p}(1-\bar{p})}{n}} = 0.051 + 0.663/\sqrt{n}]$$

Figure 5–11

FRACTION DEFECTIVE CONTROL CHART WITH VARIABLE LIMITS

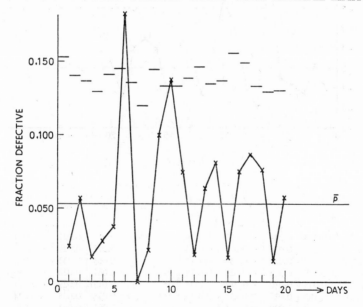

tions could be found, the data would be eliminated, $\bar{p}$ recomputed, and a new set of limits constructed for use in controlling current output.

Stabilized p Chart

These same data may be used to construct a so-called "stabilized" p chart. Here, instead of using the fraction defective, compute and plot:

$$\frac{p - \bar{p}}{s_p} = \frac{p - \bar{p}}{\sqrt{\dfrac{\bar{p}(1 - \bar{p})}{n}}}. \tag{11}$$

This expresses the variation in p in terms of its standard deviation, where s_p differs from sample to sample due to differences in n. Then the limits will be constant at ± 3, as shown in Figure 5–12, plotted from the computations shown in Table 5–7. The plot in Figure 5–12 gives the same indications as Figure 5–11, but it is simpler in its interpretation. Both, however, involve relatively laborious computations compared to the chart for fraction defective when sample size is constant.

Figure 5–12

STABILIZED p CHART

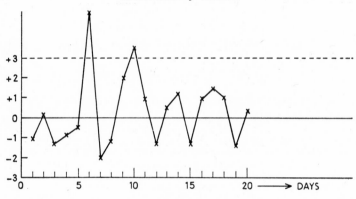

Table 5–7

Day	p	s_p	$p - \bar{p}$	$\dfrac{p - \bar{p}}{s_p}$	Day	p	s_p	$p - \bar{p}$	$\dfrac{p - \bar{p}}{s_p}$
1	0.024	0.034	−0.027	−0.79	11	0.075	0.027	+0.024	+0.89
2	0.055	0.030	+0.004	+0.13	12	0.018	0.029	−0.033	−1.14
3	0.017	0.029	−0.034	−1.17	13	0.063	0.032	+0.012	+0.37
4	0.028	0.026	−0.023	−0.88	14	0.081	0.028	+0.030	+1.07
5	0.038	0.030	−0.013	−0.43	15	0.017	0.029	−0.034	−1.17
6	0.183	0.032	+0.132	+4.13	16	0.075	0.035	+0.024	+0.69
7	0	0.028	−0.051	−1.82	17	0.087	0.033	+0.036	+1.09
8	0.022	0.023	−0.029	−1.26	18	0.076	0.027	+0.025	+0.93
9	0.100	0.031	+0.049	+1.58	19	0.014	0.026	−0.037	−1.42
10	0.138	0.027	+0.087	+3.22	20	0.057	0.026	+0.006	+0.23

Control Chart for Defects per Unit

In the production of many items, it is the defects per unit which is important as an indication of quality. For example, in the weaving of cloth, the number of defects in an inspection unit, say, 20 square yards, could be the variable. Perhaps, defects could be classified as major and minor, each class assigned a value, and the sum of these values for a given area used as the variable. In the production of complicated assemblies such as radios, the number of defects per unit may be used to advantage for control purposes.

Situations such as this involve a universe wherein the *opportunity* for defects is large while the actual occurrence tends to be small. This kind of situation can usually be described by the Poisson distribution, and use will be made of it here. The expression for this is:

$$P(c) = \frac{e^{-m} m^c}{c!}, \tag{12}$$

where

$$c = \text{number of defects in an inspection unit,}$$
$$m = \text{expected number of defects per unit.}$$

The mean and variance of a Poisson distribution are equal so that

$$\sigma_c = \sqrt{m}.$$

The data in Table 5–8 give the number of defects found in the

Table 5–8

Sample No.	No. of Defects	Sample No.	No. of Defects
1..................	1	11..................	2
2..................	4	12..................	5
3..................	4	13..................	9
4..................	1	14..................	8
5..................	6	15..................	4
6..................	3	16..................	2
7..................	5	17..................	7
8..................	10	18..................	2
9..................	7	19..................	6
10..................	3	20..................	4

inspection of samples of 100 yards each of cloth. Here:

$$\bar{c} = \frac{\Sigma d}{n} = \frac{93}{20} = 4.64.$$

As a preliminary estimate of σ_c, from the Poisson distribution:

$$s_c = \sqrt{\bar{c}} = \sqrt{4.64} = 2.16.$$

The control chart using $3s_c$ limits is shown in Figure 5–13 indicating the process is in control. Further data would give better estimates of m

and σ_c for use in continuing control.[10] This kind of chart has uses other than the control of quality, for example, in the charting of accident statistics and of equipment breakdowns.

In the case of c charts, as with p charts, when the sample size is a variable, either varying control limits may be used or the data stabilized by converting it into standard deviation units.

Figure 5–13

CONTROL CHART FOR DEFECTS PER UNIT

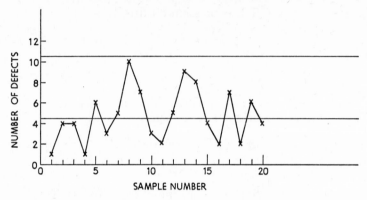

THE SELECTION OF A CONTROL PLAN

The effectiveness of any control plan using the above devices depends on the ability of the chart in detecting the presence of assignable causes of variation. The hypothesis is made that the process is in a state of statistical control and that, therefore, no assignable causes of variation are present. It must be recognized that when a point falls outside the control limits, either of the following may be true:

1. There is an assignable cause of variation present in the process, i.e., the null hypothesis is not correct.
2. There is not an assignable cause of variation present, i.e., the point may just represent an unlikely sample. In this case the null hypothesis is correct.

The probability of the second of these events may be determined in advance. The cost associated with this event is that of looking for trouble in the process when there is none.

---

[10] It is important to recognize when using 3-sigma limits with binomial or Poisson distributions that the probabilities of making the two kinds of errors are not the same as when using $\bar{X}$ and R charts. The normal distribution only gives an approximation of these probabilities when $p'n > 5$.

Also, when a point is inside the control limits, either of the following may be true:

1. There is not an assignable cause of variation present in the process.
2. The process had changed due to some assignable cause.

The probability of the latter event is not known unless the nature and magnitude of the shift in the process is also known. However, if any shift in centering at all occurs, the probability of a point falling outside the limits is increased. The cost of this event is due to not looking for trouble when it is really present.

It is clear that the design of a control plan must in some way balance these two kinds of costs. In order to do so, three factors must be determined as follows:

1. The control limits.
2. The size of sample.
3. The sampling interval.

Consider a situation in which a process is expected to center at 2.5250" and the standard deviation has been estimated from prior data at 0.0002". Production per hour is 1,000 pieces. It has been estimated that the frequency of a process change is once in ten hours and that when this change occurs the process centering shifts to 2.5254". If the tolerance specified is 2.5250" $\pm$ 0.0005", then the process is giving 1.24 per cent defectives before a change assuming a normal distribution of output and 30.9 per cent defectives after a change. It costs $0.10 to inspect a unit of output plus a $10 fixed cost per sample, and an undetected defect costs $5.00 on the average.

If a sample of size r is taken once an hour, the extra loss due to defective output per inspection interval would be

$$1,000(0.3085 - 0.0124)(\$5.00) = \$1,480 .$$

The duration of this loss would depend on the ability of the plan being used to detect a change of this kind. If the control limits are set at $ks_{\bar{x}}$ with $k = 3$, the probability of detecting a shift from 2.5250" to 2.5254" is 0.84 on any sample. This can be determined from Table A, Appendix II. The deviate from 2.5254" to the upper control limit (2.5253") is $- 1s_{\bar{x}}$ since $s_{\bar{x}} = 0.0002/\sqrt{4}$. The number of intervals until the change is detected is, of course, a variable ranging from 1 to ∞, but its expected value is $1/0.84$, or 1.191. This is easy to see as follows. If P_{2j} is the probability of failing to detect a change to the jth state $(1 - 0.84$, or 0.16 in our case), then the expected number of trials r until detection would be:

$$E(r) = 1 + P_{2j} + P_{2j}^2 + P_{2j}^3 + \dots$$
$$= \sum_{r=1}^{\infty} P_{2j}^{r-1}$$
$$= 1/(1 - P_{2j}) \tag{12}$$

If we assume that the number of changes in an interval is proportional to the length of the interval, then on the average we would expect approximately one half an interval to be the duration of production in the new state until the first sample. Then the expected period of production in this state until the change is detected would be (measured in sample intervals):

$$1/(1 - P_{2j}) - 0.5 .$$

The loss from defective production would be the product of the duration and the loss per interval, that is

$$\$1,480(1.191 - 0.5) = \$1,020 .$$

Since the expected number of changes is 0.1 (based on one change in 10 hours), the conditional loss is $102.

The cost of inspection is $10 + $0.10(4) = $10.40 plus the expected cost of error. If a correction in the process incurs a cost of $10, the expected cost of making it unnecessarily through inferring a change when none has occurred is with $k = 3$ about $0.03 giving $10.43 as the total inspection cost per interval. This gives $112.43 as the expected cost per hour for this plan.

If we change the interval to 30 minutes the conditional loss is:

$$500(0.3085 - 0.0124)(\$5.00)(1.191 - 0.5)(0.05) = \$25.55 .$$

As can be seen the effect of decreasing the interval comes in twice. First the production period during which extra defectives are produced is reduced, and second, the expected number of changes is reduced. In general the conditional loss per inspection period would be:

$$\text{Loss} = c_d(P/N_s) \sum_{j=2}^{J} (P_j/N_s)(p_j - p_1)(1/(1 - P_{2j}) - 0.5)$$

in which

c_d = cost of a defect,
P = production rate per period,
N_s = number of samples per period,
j = states of system ($j = 1, 2, \dots J$) with state 1 the desired state,
P_j = probability of change to state j in period,
P_j = fraction defective in state j,
P_{2j} = probability that given plan will fail to detect a change to state j.

If the cost of inspection per sample is

$$\text{Inspection cost} = C_i + nc_i + c_e P_1 \tag{13}$$

in which

C_i = fixed cost of inspection per sample,
c_i = variable cost of inspection per unit,
n = sample size,
c_e = cost of inferring that process has changed when it has not,
P_1 = probability of inferring that process has changed when it has not,

then the total expected cost per production period is

$$TC = \left[c_d P \sum_{j=2}^{J} P_j(p_j - p_1)(1/(1 - P_{2j}) - 0.5) \right] / N_s + N_s(C_i + nc_i + P_1 c_e) . \tag{14}$$

The term in brackets is a constant for any set of values for n and k, and thus the minimum cost sampling interval can be established as

$$TC = B/N_s + N_s C$$
$$\frac{dTC}{dN_s} = -BN_s^{-2} + C$$

Equating this to zero gives

$$N_s = \sqrt{\frac{B}{C}}. \tag{15}$$

In (15), B is the term in brackets from (14) and C is the total cost of inspection per sample given by (13). For the case being considered here

$$B = 5.00(1,000)(0.1)(0.3085 - 0.0124)(1.190 - 0.5)$$
$$= \$102$$

and

$$C = \$10.43 .$$

This gives

$$N_s = \sqrt{\frac{102.00}{10.43}}$$
$$= 3.13$$

or an inspection interval of about 19 minutes. The expected cost for this plan per hour would be

$$TC = 102/3.13 + 3.13(10.43)$$
$$= \$65.21 .$$

Table 5–9

EXPECTED COSTS FOR VARIOUS CONTROL PLANS

n	k	Samples per Period	P_{a1}	P_{a2}	Cost per Sample	Conditional Loss	Total Cost per Period
4	3.0	3.13	0.9973	0.1587	10.427	101.949	65.208
4	2.5	2.84	0.9876	0.0668	10.524	84.622	59.685
4	2.3	2.76	0.9786	0.0446	10.614	80.929	58.618
4	2.0	2.67	0.9545	0.0228	10.855	77.469	57.997
4	1.8	2.62	0.9281	0.0139	11.119	76.109	58.180
4	1.5	2.53	0.8664	0.0062	11.736	74.948	59.316
5	3.0	2.85	0.9973	0.0735	10.527	85.772	60.097
5	2.5	2.71	0.9876	0.0256	10.624	77.910	57.541
5	2.3	2.67	0.9786	0.0158	10.714	76.396	57.220
5	2.0	2.62	0.9545	0.0071	10.955	75.088	57.361
6	3.0	2.72	0.9973	0.0287	10.627	78.400	57.729
6	2.5	2.65	0.9876	0.0082	10.724	75.246	56.814
6	2.3	2.63	0.9786	0.0047	10.814	74.716	56.851
7	3.0	2.66	0.9973	0.0107	10.727	75.627	56.965
7	2.5	2.62	0.9876	0.0026	10.824	74.402	56.757
7	2.3	2.61	0.9786	0.0014	10.914	74.223	56.924
8	3.0	2.63	0.9973	0.0040	10.827	74.621	56.848
8	2.8	2.62	0.9949	0.0022	10.851	74.347	56.807
8	2.5	2.61	0.9876	0.0008	10.924	74.143	56.919

If we reduce k to 2.5, P_{2j} becomes 0.067,

$$B = 5.00(1,000)(0.1)(0.3085 - 0.0124)(1.072 - 0.5)$$
$$= \$84.60$$

and

$$C = 10.40 + 0.0124(10)$$
$$= \$10.52 ;$$

then

$$N_s = \sqrt{\frac{84.60}{10.52}}$$
$$= 2.84$$

and

$$TC = 84.60/2.84 + 2.84(10.52)$$
$$= \$59.70 .$$

Continuing in this way we find that for $n = 4$ the minimum cost deviate is $k = 2.00$, for which $B = 77.47$, $C = 10.86$, and the total cost per production period is \$58.00. The inspection interval is 22.5 minutes, or 2.67 samples per period. At this level the probability of acceptance in state 1 is 0.95450 and in state 2 is 0.02275.

The Control Chart Demonstration Program described and listed in the Appendix to this chapter was used to generate a sequence of values of this kind for various sample sizes with results shown in Table 5–9. Some of the actual output for this case is given in this Appendix.

It can be seen from this table that a minimum cost plan is not difficult to find and that $k = 3.0$ is not always a good choice. The relative flatness of the cost surface in the region of the optimal plan may also be seen in this table. It should be recognized, however, that the arbitrary use of $n = 4$, $k = 3.0$ would entail a cost penalty of over \$8.00 per period (15 per cent) over the best plan of $n = 7$, $k = 2.5$.

SPECIAL CONTROL PLANS

One of the most commonly encountered situations in which a variant of the basic control chart technique already described is required is that in which a defective item can be due to more than one kind of defect and the consequences of each type are different. In an assembled product, for example, one kind of defect might only require a simple part replacement while another might be cause for scrapping the entire unit. Treating these alike in terms of process control may be to misstate the problem quite badly. An alternative is to weight each kind of defective found in accordance with its relative economic importance and base the control chart on the composite.

In some situations it is possible for the centering of a process to change and for one to get quite long runs of sample means whose average behavior is above or below the expected value without ever exceeding the control limit. In the past rules have been devised based on runs above or below the central line,[11] but these tend to be fairly

[11] See Duncan, *op. cit.*, pp. 132–37.

complicated to administer. A recently developed alternative is the cumulative sum chart described briefly below.[12]

Control Charts for Multiple Defects

Consider a situation in which an assembled product may be defective for a large number of reasons ranging from defective components which render the unit inoperable all the way to imperfections in surface finish of the cabinet in which it is housed. Based on economic considerations principally the cost of rectifying each particular defect, these have been classified into three types. Each type is given a point rating as shown below:

Type of Defect	Points
A	60
B	30
C	10

For each assembly in the sample to be inspected, defects found are assigned points as above and the composite defective score computed as the weighted average number of defects per unit. For example, if one type A, three type B, and seven type C defects were discovered, the score would be

$$c = \frac{1(60) + 3(30) + 7(10)}{60 + 30 + 10}$$
$$= 2.20 .$$

This number of defects would be recorded for each unit inspected and a control chart kept just as given on page 189 for a defects per unit situation. The only difference would be, of course, that in this case fractional values of c are to be expected.

Cumulative Sum Charts

As was indicated earlier, the cumulative sum chart is based on the premise that while a small change in process centering may go undetected for a large number of samples, its presence may be detected more rapidly if the effect of the change is cumulated over several samples. If one cumulates the difference between each sample mean obtained and the expected mean, this should turn out to be zero if the process remains stable at the value of the expected mean. Any change in the process, however, would result in a positive or negative value for this sum depending on the direction of the change. If the change persisted, the

---

[12] G. A. Barnard, "Cumulative Charts and Stochastic Processes," *Journal of the Royal Statistical Society*, B, Vol. XXI (1959), p. 239.

sum would increase and thus the fact of a change would be apparent more quickly than by observation of means of independently drawn samples alone. If the change were only of short duration, even then a bias would be built into the cumulative sum during the period of the change and, depending on the criteria selected, might still be detected more reliably than by the standard technique.

The procedure which has been developed calls for the computation of

$$x_m = \frac{\sum_{i=1}^{m} (\bar{x}_i - \bar{\bar{x}})}{s_{\bar{x}}} \tag{16}$$

in which

x_m = cumulative sum of deviations ,
x_i = sample mean ,
$\bar{\bar{x}}$ = expected mean ,
$s_{\bar{x}}$ = standard deviation of means of samples of size n .

This value in standard deviation units is plotted as shown in Figure 5–14 and compared to limits shown as a sliding V-mask. Of course, the sum may be computed without division by $s_{\bar{x}}$ by appropriate choice of a vertical scale. The limits are necessarily increased as the observations are further back in time due to the cumulative character of the plot.

These limits are based on two parameters as follows:

δ = standard expected change in process ,
α = probability of error of the first kind .

If one expects a change of say 3. in a process with a mean of 20 and a standard deviation of 2., the standard expected change would be 3./2.,

Figure 5–14

CUMULATIVE SUM CONTROL CHART

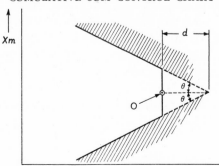

or 1.5. The parameters of the V-mask are (θ, d) with meanings as shown in Figure 5–14. The point "O" is placed over the last plotted point, and lack of control is indicated by any points in the shaded region.

The values for (θ, d) may be computed easily by approximate formulae[13] as follows:

$$\tan \theta = \tfrac{1}{2} \delta \qquad (17)$$
$$d \approx -2\delta^{-2} \ln \alpha . \qquad (18)$$

For example, if d were 1.5 and $\alpha = 0.001$ (corresponding to 3.09 s_x limits for an $\bar{X}$ chart), θ would be 36.9° and $d = 6.14$. This last figure is the average number of samples required to detect a difference of δ_x in the process mean. The corresponding figure for a standard $\bar{X}$ chart is 17.89 giving an indication.of the relative effectiveness of these techniques for the given α. The corresponding figures for $\alpha = 0.005$ are 4.71 and 7.09, but for $\alpha = 0.05$, they are 2.66 and 2.45 indicating a slight disadvantage for the cumulative sum chart at this value of α. Most often in practice so far, these values are determined empirically so that the probabilities of errors of both kinds are acceptable.[14] Experience to date with this technique indicates that for small α (0.001 — 0.005) the chart is considerably more effective for control than the standard $\bar{X}$ chart. Its disadvantages are primarily the greater cost of design and of administration.

SUMMARY

The statistical control concept has wide application in industry wherever it is necessary to institute control over some process whose output is subject to variation, due to some stable system of chance causes. The process could be an actual manufacturing situation where the variable to be controlled is quality of product, or the variable of interest to be controlled could be the time necessary to produce an item. The cost of production, accident rate, labor turnover, absenteeism, and machine breakdown are all output variables of some process over which statistical control could be instituted.

It is important to recognize that once a process has been brought to a state of statistical control, the problem becomes one of maintaining control over the system parameters on a continuing basis. It is not just enough to be able to say that the process is in control at some given

[13] N. L. Johnson, "A Simple Theoretical Approach to Cumulative Sum Charts," *American Statistical Association Journal,* Vol. LVI (1961), pp. 835–40.

[14] G. A. Barnard, "Control Charts and Stochastic Processes," *Journal of the Royal Statistical Society,* B, Vol. XXI (1959), pp. 239–57.

time. Rather, the analyst must make certain that his expectations (and therefore his economic calculations) continue to be valid. In all cases where economic problems are solved using expected values, this provision on the problem solution must be recognized. This holds for all of the methods treated in this book.

The Central Limit Theorem was seen in many cases to provide the necessary predictive ability in order to institute control. The important variations of the control chart are as follows:

1. $\bar{X}$ and R charts for variables control.
2. p and c charts for attributes control.

The economic selection of a control plan, in order to give optimum decisions with respect to the process being controlled, is difficult to attain, but should be approached with all the information available in each situation. The succeeding chapters on statistical method in production will deal with sampling inspection (making decisions based on less than complete information about a process) and industrial experimentation (gathering and analyzing information for decision making in the most efficient manner possible).

REFERENCES

1. *Control Chart Method of Controlling Quality during Production: American War Standard Z1.3,* 1942. New York: American Standards Association, Inc., 1942.
2. DUNCAN, ACHESON J. *Quality Control and Industrial Statistics.* 3d ed. Homewood, Ill.: Richard D. Irwin, Inc., 1965.
3. SHEWHART, W. A. *Economic Control of Quality of Manufactured Product.* New York: D. Van Nostrand Co., Inc., 1931.
4. SIMON, LESLIE E. *An Engineer's Manual of Statistical Methods.* New York: John Wiley & Sons, Inc., 1941.
5. TIPPETT, L. H. C. *Technological Applications of Statistics.* New York: John Wiley & Sons, Inc., 1950.

APPENDIX TO CHAPTER 5

CONTROL CHART DEMONSTRATION PROGRAM

This program consists of a main routine, six subroutines, and a random number generating function. There are two basic modes of operation available, the simulation mode and the expected cost mode. For each of these there are several alternatives available as described in the following material. The basic purpose of the simulation mode is to allow one to observe the behavior of variables control charts under conditions approaching those which might be encountered in an actual operating situation. This could be done as a means of discovering a suitable control plan for an actual situation, as a training device in the use of statistical control plans, or as a research tool for experimenting with processes and specifications in the design of production systems.

If one wishes to simulate the behavior of a quality control system, it is necessary to enter data as shown in the variable dictionary under the column heading simulation. If XDBAR is set to 0. then an initial set of samples (INITNS) each of size N will be taken (subroutine SAMPLE), XDBAR and RBAR estimated, and control limits calculated by subroutines XCHART and RCHART. The initial set will then be checked serially by subroutine COMPAR, and if out of control points are discovered the offending state will be eliminated if NDELET = 1. In this case, the remaining state probabilities will be recomputed, the out of control data eliminated, and new control limits calculated. If NDELET = 0, only a message indicating the out of control condition will be printed. If XDBAR was given a nonzero value at input, this initializing procedure will be skipped and control limits calculated directly based on the desired state.

Then specification limits are compared to process limits for each state and the fraction defective computed. The probability of a type one error is computed and for each state, the probability that the control limits will fail to detect a change to that state is computed and stored as PTWO(J). Based on this data, the costs read in, and using the method described in Chapter 5, the optimum number of samples per period is computed and the total expected cost per production period printed out.

At this point a value is read for NSWCH and a 7-way branch occurs. If NSWCH is 6 or 7, simulation begins by reading the number of production periods which define the run length. If NSWCH is 6, this number of periods will be completed, while if it is 7, the run will terminate when all states other than $J = 1$ have been discovered and eliminated. At the end of the simulation, the actual number of defectives, number of samples, and costs of inspection and defectives will be computed and printed followed by a return to the READ NSWCH statement.

If NSWCH = 4, control will go to the first input statement and an entirely new case may be started. If NSWCH = 3, control will return to read new control chart parameters (DEVK and N), new output directions (KOUT(I)) and a new run made. If NSWCH = 2, new costs will be read followed by control chart parameters as for NSWCH = 3. If NSWCH = 1, a new DEVK is read and expected costs recomputed based on the new optimal sampling interval which results.

Thus if one wished only to compute the expected costs for various values of DEVK with N constant, initial input with XDBAR = 0. and repeated cycles of NSWCH = 1 followed by the desired values of DEVK would accomplish this. Costs could be changed by cycling with NSWCH = 2, while sample size could be changed with NSWCH = 3. It is assumed here that searching for a least cost control plan is most easily accomplished by exploring the parameters in the order implied by the above list. That is, various values of DEVK are explored for each value of N tried. A sample run of this kind with N = 4, 5, 6, and 7 yielded the results shown in Table 5–9 of Chapter 5.

A listing of the main program and the various subroutines follows together with a variable dictionary. Portions of output for several runs are shown together with the input data used. Run 1 is a simulation in which an initial set of 50 samples is used to set up trial control limits, the samples are scanned for out of control points, two are found, control limits are recomputed, and set up for subsequent operations. In this case only one state other than the desired state was present and it was discovered on the initial run.

Run 2 is a simulation run involving four states but with XDBAR = 50. and INITNS = 0 at input. In this case, initial limits are based on the expected values of state 1. As each out of control point is discovered it is eliminated, and control limits computed based on actual sample data. When all states but the desired state have been eliminated, the run will terminate. If NSWCH had been set equal to 6, a run of length determined by the value of PERIOD would have been made. In any case, this will be the maximum run length.

Run 3 is a portion of that which resulted in Table 5–9 in Chapter 5 and only uses the cost evaluation part of the program.

```
      COMMON PROB(50),XMU(50),SIGMA(50),NBIAS(50),PN(400),EX(300),P(50),
     1PEX(300),PIWO(50),MAX,,MAXDST,MADIST,N,DEVK,D2N,D3N,UCLR,LCLR,SN,
     2SIGMAX,UCLX,LCLX,ASUMX,ASUMR,XBAR,R,NDELET,J,KOUT(7),SX(30),
     3AXBAR(200),AR(200),JSTAT(200),TIME(50),ONEOUT,MJ
    4 READ(5,93) XDBAR,XSPEC,XTOL,PRCDX                                       1
      READ(5,96) MAXJ,MXDIST,MAXDST,NEVAL,NDELET,INITNS                       2
      READ(5,92)(PROB(J),XMU(J),SIGMA(J),NBIAS(J),J=1,MAXJ)                   9
      READ(5,95)(PN(I),I=1,MADIST)                                           19
      READ(5,94)(EX(I),PEX(I),I=1,MAXDST)                                    26
    2 READ(5,93)COSTD,COSTE,COSTF,COSTI                                      34
    3 READ(5,92) DEVK,D2N,D3N,N                                              35
      READ(5,96)KCUT                                                         37
      REAL LCLX,LCLR
      ONEOUT = 0.
      MJ = MAXJ
      AN = N
      SN = SQRT(AN)                                                          40
      ASUMX = 0.
      ASUMR = 0.
      IF(XDBAR.NE.0.)GO TO 100
C         BEGIN PRODUCTION
      DO 11 I = 1,INITNS
      CALL SAMPLE(I)                                                         47
      AXBAR(I) = XBAR
      AR(I) = R
      JSTAT(I) = J
      ASUMX = ASUMX + XBAR
   11 ASUMR = ASUMR + R
      XDBAR = ASUMX/FLOAT(INITNS)
      RBAR = ASUMR/FLOAT(INITNS)
C         CALCULATE INITIAL CONTROL LIMITS
      CALL XCHART(XDBAR,RBAR)                                                55
      CALL RCHART(RBAR)                                                      57
      IF(KOUT(2).EQ.1)WRITE(6,98)UCLX,LCLX,UCLR,LCLR                         59
C         CHECK FOR LACK OF INITIAL CONTROL
      INS = INITNS
      DO 200 I=1,INS
      XBAR = AXBAR(I)
      R = AR(I)
      J = JSTAT(I)
      CALL COMPAR(I,INITNS)                                                  69
  200 CONTINUE
      ONEOUT = 0.
      GO TO 50
    1 READ(5,93) DEVK                                                        74
  100 RBAR = SIGMA(1)*D2N                                                    76
      CALL XCHART(XDBAR,RBAR)                                                78
      CALL RCHART(RBAR)                                                      80
      IF(KOUT(2).EQ.1)WRITE(6,98)UCLX,LCLX,UCLR,LCLR
   50 UPPER = XSPEC + XTOL
      XLOWR = XSPEC - XTOL
      DO 10 J=1,MAXJ
      DEVU = (UPPER - XMU(J))/SIGMA(J)
      CALL LOOKUP(DEVU)                                                      88
      DEVL = (XLOWR - XMU(J))/SIGMA(J)
      CALL LOOKUP(DEVL)                                                      92
   10 P(J) = DEVU + (1. - DEVL)                                             97
      IF(KOUT(6).EQ.1)WRITE(6,97)(P(J),J=1,MAXJ)
      KDEV = DEVK*20. + 1.5
      IF(KDEV.GT.MXDIST)KDEV = MXDIST
      PONE = 2.*PN(KDEV)
      DO 20 J=1,MAXJ
      DEVU = (UCLX - XMU(J))/SIGMA(J)
      DEVU = DEVU*SN
      DEVL = (XMU(J) - LCLX)/SIGMA(J)
      DEVL = DEVL*SN
      IDEVU = ABS(DEVU)*20. + 1.5
      IDEVL = ABS(DEVL)*20. + 1.5
      IF(IDEVU.GT.MXDIST)IDEVU = MXDIST
      IF(IDEVL.GT.MXDIST)IDEVL=MXDIST
      PTU = PN(IDEVU)
      PTL = PN(IDEVL)
      PTWO(J) = PTU + PTL
      IF(DEVU.LT.0..OR.DEVL.LT.0.) GO TO 21
      PTWO(J) = 1. - PTWO(J)
   21 IF(PTWO(J).GT.1.) PTWO(J) = 1.
   20 CONTINUE
      IF(KOUT(7).EQ.1)WRITE(6,99)(PTWO(J),J=1,MAXJ)                         138
      FRCDEF = 0.
      DO 30 J=2,MAXJ
      FN = 1. - PTWO(J)
      FN = 1./FN
      FN = FN - .5
   30 FRCDEF = PROB(J)*(P(J) - P(1))*FN + FRCDEF
      CLOSS = PRODX*FRCDEF*COSTD
      CINSP = COSTF + (AN*COSTI) + (COSTE*PONE)
      ARG = CLOSS/CINSP
      SAMPN = SQRT(ARG)                                                     155
      EXCOST = (CLOSS/SAMPN) + CINSP*SAMPN
```

```
      WRITE(6,51)N,DEVK,SAMPN,CINSP,CLOSS,EXCOST                          156
 1000 READ(5,96)NSWCH                                                     157
      GO TO (1,2,3,4,5,6,6),NSWCH
C          BEGIN SIMULATION
    6 READ(5,93)PERIOD                                                    160
      J = 1
      NSAMP = SAMPN*PERIOC + 0.5
      NSAMPD = INITNS
      ICT = 0
      DO 51 JK=1,MAXJ
   51 TIME(JK) = 0.
      DO 60 I=1,NSAMP
      CALL SAMPLE(I)
      ASUMX = ASUMX + XBAR                                                175
      ASUMR = ASUMR + R
      NSAMPD = NSAMPD + 1
      CALL COMPAR(I,NSAMPD)                                               178
      ICT = ICT +1
      IF(MJ.EQ.1.AND.NSWCH.EC.7) GO TO 61
   60 TIME(J) = TIME(J) + 1.
   61 ACTFD = C.
      ASAMP = ICT

      DO 70 J=1,MAXJ
      TIME(J) = TIME(J)/ASAMP
   70 ACTFD = (TIME(J)*P(J)) + ACTFD
      PERIOD = ASAMP/SAMPN
      PRODUC = PRCDX*PERIOD
      XNDEF = PRODUC*ACTFD
      CLOSS = XNDEF*CUSTD
      CINSP = (COSTF + (AN*CUSTI))*ASAMP + ONEOUT*COSTE
      ACTCST = (CLOSS + CINSP)/PERIOD
      IF(KOUT(3).EQ.1)WRITE(6,90)PERIOD,NSAMP,XNDEF,PRCDUC,ONEOUT,ACTCST  200
      GO TO 1000
    5 STOP
   90 FORMAT(1H0,3H INF6.2,8H PERIODSI6,20H SAMPLES WERE TAKEN,F6.0,
     128H DEFECTIVES WERE PRODUCED OFF6.0,12H TOTAL ITEMS/5X,F5.0,
     244H TYPE ONE ERRORS WERE MADE WITH TOTAL COST=$F10.2)
   91 FORMAT(1HC,13H SAMPLE SIZE=I3.4H, K=F5.2,17H, SAMPLES/PERIOD=
     1F5.2/20X,12HCOST/SAMPLE=F8.3/20X,17HCONDITIONAL LOSS=F8.3/20X,
     229HTOTAL COST/PRODUCTION PERIOD=F9.3)
   92 FORMAT(3F10.4,I10)
   93 FORMAT(7F10.4)
   94 FORMAT(5(F7.4,F7.6))
   95 FORMAT(10F7.6)
   96 FORMAT(7I10)
   97 FORMAT(1H0,10X,14HTHE P(J)'S ARE/5X,(10F10.5))
   98 FORMAT(1H0,25H CONTROL LIMITS - - UCLX=F10.4,7H, LCLX=F10.4,7H, UC
     1LR=F10.4,7H, LCLR=F10.4)
   99 FORMAT(1H0,10X,17HTHE PTWO(J)'S ARE/5X,(10F10.5))
      END




      SUBROUTINE SAMPLE(NS)
      COMMON PROB(50),XMU(50),SIGMA(50),NBIAS(50),PN(400),EX(300),P(50),
     1PEX(300),PTWO(50),MAXJ,MAXOST,MXDIST,N,DEVK,D2N,D3N,UCLR,LCLR,SN,
     2SIGMAX,UCLX,LCLX,ASUMX,ASUMR,XBAR,R,NDELET,J,KOUT(7),SX(30),
     3AXBAR(200),AR(200),JSTAT(200),TIME(50),ONEOUT,MJ
      SUMX = 0.
      XMIN = 999999.
      XMAX = 0.
      IF(NBIAS(J).EQ.1)GO TO 30
      RAND = GRN(1.0)                                                      6
      PROBJ = PROB(1)
      DO 20 JK=1,MAXJ
      IF(RAND.GT.PROBJ)GO TO 19
      J=JK
      GO TO 30
   19 PROBJ = PROBJ + PROB(JK+1)
   20 CONTINUE
   30 DO 10 I=1,N
      X = GRN(1.0)                                                         23
      CALL LOOKDN(X)                                                       24
      SX(I) = XMU(J) + X*SIGMA(J)
      IF(SX(I).LT.0.)SX(I) = 0.
      IF(SX(I).LT.XMIN) XMIN = SX(I)
      IF(SX(I).GT.XMAX) XMAX = SX(I)
   10 SUMX = SUMX + SX(I)
      XBAR = SUMX/FLOAT(N)
      R = XMAX - XMIN
      IF(KOUT(1).EQ.1) WRITE(6,99)NS,XBAR,R,J                             45
      IF(KOUT(5).EQ.1) WRITE(6,89)(SX(I),I=1,N)                          47
   99 FORMAT(1H0,11H FOR SAMPLEI5,7H, XBAR=F8.3,4H, R=F8.3,29H, AND THE
     1SYSTEM WAS IN STATEI5)
   89 FORMAT(20X,23H THE SAMPLE VALUES WERE/(27X,F10.4))
      RETURN
      END
```

```
      SUBROUTINE COMPAR(IX,IY)
      COMMON PROB(50),XMU(50),SIGMA(50),NBIAS(50),PN(400),EX(300),P(50),
     1PEX(300),PTWO(50),MAXJ,MAXDST,MXDIST,N,DEVK,D2N,D3N,UCLR,LCLR,SN,
     2SIGMAX,UCLX,LCLX,ASUMX,ASUMR,XBAR,R,NDELET,J,KOUT(7),SX(30),
     3AXBAR(200),AR(200),JSTAT(200),TIME(50),ONEOUT,MJ
      REAL LCLX,LCLR
C           CHECK FOR CONTROL
      IF(XBAR.GT.UCLX.OR.XBAR.LT.LCLX)GO TO 10
      IF(R.GT.UCLR.OR.R.LT.LCLR)GO TO 10
      RETURN
   10 IF(KOUT(4).EQ.1)WRITE(6,97)IX,XBAR,R,J,UCLX,LCLX,UCLR,LCLR          9
      IF(J.EQ.1)GO TO 30
      IF(NDELET.EC.0)RETURN
      IF(IY.EQ.0) RETURN
      IF(PROB(J).EQ.0.) GO TO 21
C           ELIMINATE STATE J
      PROBT = 1. - PROB(J)
      PROB(J) = 0.
      NBIAS(J) = 0
      DO 20 JK=1,MAXJ
   20 PROB(JK) = PROB(JK)/PROBT
      MJ = MJ - 1
   21 ASUMX = ASUMX - XBAR
      ASUMR = ASUMR - R
      IY = IY- 1
      AY = IY
      XX = ASUMX/AY
      RR = ASUMR/AY
      CALL XCHART(XX,RR)                                                 35
      CALL RCHART(RR)                                                    37
      IF(KOUT(2).EQ.1)WRITE(6,98)UCLX,LCLX,UCLR,LCLR                     39
      RETURN
   30 ONEOUT = ONEOUT + 1.0
      RETURN
   97 FORMAT(1H0,25H OUT OF CONTROL ON SAMPLEI5,5X,5HXBAR=F8.4,4H, R=F8.
     14,8H, AND J=I5/10X,5HUCLX=F8.4,7H, LCLX=F8.4,7H, UCLR=F8.4,7H, LCL
     2R=F8.4)
   98 FORMAT(1H0,25H CONTROL LIMITS - - UCLX=F10.4,7H, LCLX=F10.4,7H, UC
     1LR=F10.4,7H, LCLR=F10.4)
      END




      SUBROUTINE RCHART(RR)
      COMMON PROB(50),XMU(50),SIGMA(50),NBIAS(50),PN(400),EX(300),P(50),
     1PEX(300),PTWO(50),MAXJ,MAXDST,MXDIST,N,DEVK,D2N,D3N,UCLR,LCLR,SN,
     2SIGMAX,UCLX,LCLX,ASUMX,ASUMR,XBAR,R,NDELET,J,KOUT(7),SX(30),
     3AXBAR(200),AR(200),JSTAT(200),TIME(50),ONEOUT
      REAL LCLR
      SIGMAR = (D3N*RR)/D2N
      UCLR = RR + DEVK*SIGMAR
      LCLR = RR - DEVK*SIGMAR
      IF(LCLR.LT.0.)LCLR = 0.
      RETURN
      END




      SUBROUTINE XCHART(XX,RR)
      COMMON PROB(50),XMU(50),SIGMA(50),NBIAS(50),PN(400),EX(300),P(50),
     1PEX(300),PTWO(50),MAXJ,MAXDST,MXDIST,N,DEVK,D2N,D3N,UCLR,LCLR,SN,
     2SIGMAX,UCLX,LCLX,ASUMX,ASUMR,XBAR,R,NDELET,J,KOUT(7),SX(30),
     3AXBAR(200),AR(200),JSTAT(200),TIME(50),ONEOUT
      REAL LCLX
      SIGMAX = RR/(D2N*SN)
      UCLX = XX + DEVK*SIGMAX
      LCLX = XX - DEVK*SIGMAX
      IF(LCLX.LT.0.)LCLX = 0.
      RETURN
      END




      SUBROUTINE LOOKON(ARG)
      COMMON PROB(50),XMU(50),SIGMA(50),NBIAS(50),PN(400),EX(300),P(50),
     1PEX(300),PTWO(50),MAXJ,MAXDST,MXDIST,N,DEVK,D2N,D3N,UCLR,LCLR,SN,
     2SIGMAX,UCLX,LCLX,ASUMX,ASUMR,XBAR,R,NDELET,J,KOUT(7),SX(30),
     3AXBAR(200),AR(200),JSTAT(200),TIME(50),ONEOUT,MJ
      DO 10 I=1,MAXDST
      IF(PEX(I) - ARG)20,20,10
   20 IX = 1
      GO TO 30
```

```
10 CONTINUE
   IX = MAXDST
30 IF(IX.EQ.1) GO TO 31
   IXX = IX - 1
   ARG = (ARG - PEX(IX))/(PEX(IXX) - PEX(IX))
   ARG = ARG*(EX(IXX) - EX(IX))
   ARG = EX(IX) + ARG
   RETURN
31 ARG = EX(IX)
   RETURN
   END
```

```
   SUBROUTINE LOOKUP(ARG)
   COMMON PROB(50),XHU(50),SIGMA(50),NBIAS(50),PN(400),EX(300),P(50),
  1PEX(300),PTWD(50),MAXJ,MAXDST,MXDIST,N,DEVK,D2N,D3N,UCLR,LCLR,SN,
  2SIGMAX,UCLX,LCLX,ASUMX,ASUMR,XBAR,R,NDELET,J,KOUT(7),SX(30),
  3AXBAR(200),AR(200),JSTAT(200),TIME(50),ONEOUT,MJ
   DO 10 I=1,MAXDST
   IF(ARG-EX(I))20,20,10
20 IX = I
   GO TO 30
10 CONTINUE
   ARG = 0.
   RETURN
30 IF(IX.EQ.1) GO TO 31
   IXX = IX - 1
   ARG =(ARG - EX(IX))/(EX(IXX) - EX(IX))
   ARG = ARG*(PEX(IXX) - PEX(IX))
   ARG = PEX(IX) + ARG
   RETURN
31 ARG = 1.0
   RETURN
   END
```

RANDOM NUMBER GENERATING FUNCTION

```
GRN     SAVE    1
LDXR    AXT     0,1             LOAD XR1 WITH INITIAL VALUE
        LDQ     SEED
INST1   MPY     RAND8,1
        TOV     *+1
        XCA
INST2   STO     RAND8,1
        ARS     32
        ANA     MASK1
        STA     LDXR            RELOAD ADDRESS OF AXT INSTRUCTION
INST3   CLA     RAND8,1
        ARS     8
        ANA     MASK
        ORA     EXP             GIVES NUMBER EXPONENT
        FAD     EXP             NORMALIZES NUMBER
        RETURN  GRN
MASK1   OCT     7
MASK    OCT     000777777777
EXP     OCT     200000000000
SEED    DEC     273691
RAND1   DEC     16815
        DEC     24369
        DEC     00697
        DEC     62825
        DEC     43997
        DEC     12151
        DEC     25549
RAND8   DEC     71945
        END
```

RAND1-RAND8 MAY BE CHANGED
TO GIVE DIFFERENT SEQUENCES

Input Variables (In Order of Input)	Definition	Input Value (If Any)	
		Simulation Mode	Expected Cost Mode
1. XDBAR	Expected value of process mean (if 0., will be estimated based on an initial production period)	0. or expected value	Expected value
2. XSPEC	Process centering given by product specification	Desired value	Desired value
3. XTOL	Process tolerance (assumed equal on both sides of XSPEC)	Desired value	Desired value
4. PRODX	Production rate of process in units per period with period defined arbitrarily by user	Desired value	Desired value
5. MAXJ	Number of states to be defined by input	Desired value	Desired value
6. MXDIST	Number of points used to define normal distribution used for control charts (70 in this case)	70	70
7. MAXDST	Number of points used to define shape of process distribution	Optional with user	Optional with user
8. NEVAL	Not used by program currently		
9. NDELET	If equal to "one," system states other than the desired states are eliminated when discovered by out of control points	0 or 1	0 or 1
10. INITNS	Number of samples on which initial control limits are to be based	Optional with user but must be 0 if XDBAR 0.	
11. PROB(J)	Probability of state J. Sum of PROB(J)'s must be 1.	Optional with user	Optional with user
12. XMU(J)	Expected value of process mean in state J	Optional with user	Optional with user
13. SIGMA(J)	Standard deviation of process in state J	Optional with user	Optional with user
14. NBIAS(J)	If 1, system will remain in state J from time of change until discovered and eliminated. Otherwise, selection of this state is at random on each sample.	0 or 1	Not used
15. PN(I)	Cumulative unit normal probabilities from mean to + defined by 70 points	See data list	See data list
16. EX(I), PEX(I)	Pairs of values defining cumulative probabilities for process output in normalized form with mean of 0.0 and standard deviation of 1.0. First value is deviate, second is probability.	See data listing for example	See data listing for example
17. DEVK	Number of standard deviations to be used in control chart	Optional with user	Optional with user
18. D2N	Expected value of relative range for given sample size	Values in Table F, Appendix II	Values in Table F, Appendix II
19. D3N	Standard deviation of relative range for given sample size	Values in Table F, Appendix II	Values in Table F, Appendix II

Input Variables (In Order of Input)	Definition	Input Value (If Any)	
		Simulation Mode	Expected Cost Mode
20. N	Desired sample size	Optional with user	Optional with user
21. KOUT(I)	Define output alternatives—output if equal to 1	Optional with user	Optional with user
I = 1	Sample output of $\bar{X}$, R and state of system	0 or 1	Not used
= 2	Control limits based on initial sample	0 or 1	Not used
= 3	Summary output at end of a simulation run	0 or 1	Not used
= 4	Output each time an out of control point is found	0 or 1	Not used
= 5	Sample output giving each process measurement	0 or 1	Not used
= 6	Not used		
= 7	Not used		
22. COSTD	Cost of a defect not discovered	Optional with user	Optional with user
23. COSTE	Cost of a type one error	Optional with user	Optional with user
24. COSTF	Fixed cost of inspection per sample	Optional with user	Optional with user
25. COSTI	Cost per item inspected	Optional with user	Optional with user
26. SAMPN	Number of samples to be taken each production period. May be fractional.	Optional with user	Optional with user
27. NSWCH	Defines program alternatives		
= 1	Expected cost will be recomputed for a new SAMPN		
= 2	Expected cost recomputed for new costs and new SAMPN		
= 3	New run with input from variable 17 (DEVK)		
= 4	New run with input from variable 1 (XDBAR)		
= 5	STOP.		
= 6	Begin simulation by reading variable 28 (PERIOD)		
= 7	Begin simulation by reading variable 28 (PERIOD) and run only until all assignable causes (states other than J = 1) have been deleted		
= 3			
28. PERIOD	Number of production periods it is desired to simulate	Optional with user	Not used

Other System Variables	Definition
29. AR(I)	Sample ranges for initial production period
30. ASUMR	Cumulative sum of sample ranges
31. ASUMX	Cumulative sum of sample means
32. AXBAR(I)	Sample means for initial production period
33. J	Identifies current state of system
34. JSTAT(I)	Sample states for initial production period
35. LCLR	Lower control limit for R
36. LCLX	Lower control limit for $\bar{X}$
37. MJ	Number of states remaining at any time during simulation
38. ONEOUT	Number of type one errors occurring during simulation
39. P(J)	Fraction defective in state J
40. PTWO(J)	Probability of type two error in state J
41. R	Sample range

Ohter System Variables	Definition
42. RBAR	Expected value of sample range
43. SIGMAX	Standard deviation of sample means
44. SX(I)	Sample values from process
45. TIME(J)	Number of sampling intervals system was in each state J
46. UCLR	Upper control limit for R
47. UCLX	Upper control limit for $\bar{X}$
48. XBAR	Sample mean
49. ACTCST	Total cost during simulation
50. ACTFD	Fraction defective actually experienced during simulation
51. AN	Floating point value of N
52. ASAMP	Number of samples actually taken during simulation
53. CINSP	Cost of inspection including type one errors
54. CLOSS	Loss due to defective production
55. DEVL	Standard deviations to XLOWR
56. DEVU	Standard deviations to UPPER
57. EXCOST	Expected cost of control plan per production period
58. FRCDEF	Fraction defective cumulator
59. ICT	Counts samples taken during simulation
60. IDEVL	Normal probability point defined by difference between LCLX and each XMU(J)
61. IDEVU	Normal probability point defined by difference between UCLX and each XMU(J)
62. INS	Saves initial value of INITNS
63. KDEV	Normal probability point corresponding to DEVK
64. NSAMPD	Counts number of samples on which to base recomputation of control limits
65. NSAMP	Number of samples to be taken during simulation
66. PONE	Probability of type one error
67. PRODUC	Number of units actually produced during simulation
68. PTL	Area of normal distribution between LCLX and XMU(J)
69. PTU	Area of normal distribution between UCLX and XMU(J)
70. SN	Square root of N
71. UPPER	Upper specification limit
72. XLOWR	Lower specification limit
73. XNDEF	Number of defectives actually produced during simulation

INPUT FOR RUN #1

```
  0.          50.          5.     1000.
        2            80          70          1              1            50
     .9          50.          2.               0
     .1          54.          2.               0
 .5000   .4801   .4602   .4404   .4207   .4013   .3821   .3632   .3446   .3264
 .3085   .2912   .2743   .2578   .2420   .2266   .2119   .1977   .1841   .1711
 .1587   .1469   .1357   .1251   .1151   .1056   .09680  .08851  .08076  .07353
 .06681  .06057  .05480  .04947  .04457  .04006  .03593  .03216  .02872  .02559
 .02275  .02018  .01786  .01578  .01390  .01222  .01072  .009387 .008198 .007143
 .006210 .005386 .004661 .004025 .003467 .002980 .002555 .002186 .001866 .001589
 .001350 .001144 .000968 .000816 .000687 .000577 .000483 .000404 .000337 .000280
 .000232 .000192 .000159 .000131 .000108 .000088 .000072 .000059 .000048 .000000
 -3.40   .9997   -3.30   .9995   -3.20   .9993   -3.10   .9990   -3.00   .9987
 -2.90   .9981   -2.80   .9974   -2.70   .9965   -2.60   .9953   -2.50   .9938
 -2.40   .9918   -2.30   .9893   -2.20   .9861   -2.10   .9821   -2.00   .9772
 -1.90   .9713   -1.80   .9641   -1.70   .9554   -1.60   .9452   -1.50   .9332
 -1.40   .9192   -1.30   .9032   -1.20   .8849   -1.10   .9643   -1.00   .8413
 -0.90   .8159   -0.80   .7881   -0.70   .7580   -0.60   .7257   -0.50   .6915
 -0.40   .6554   -0.30   .6179   -0.20   .5793   -0.10   .5398   0.00    .5000
 0.10    .4602   0.20    .4207   0.30    .3821   0.40    .3446   0.50    .3085
 0.60    .2743   0.70    .2420   0.80    .2119   0.90    .1841   1.00    .1587
 1.10    .1357   1.20    .1151   1.30    .09680  1.40    .08076  1.50    .06681
 1.60    .05480  1.70    .04457  1.80    .03593  1.90    .02872  2.00    .02275
 2.10    .01786  2.20    .01390  2.30    .1072   2.40    .008198 2.50    .006210
 2.60    .004661 2.70    .003467 2.80    .002555 2.90    .001866 3.00    .001350
 3.10    .000968 3.20    .000687 3.30    .000483 3.40    .000337 3.50    .000233
   5.          10.          10.              .10
   3.          2.059        .880              4
        1            1            1            1            1            1            1
```

PARTIAL OUTPUT FOR RUN #1

```
FOR SAMPLE    1, XBAR=  50.703, R=   3.300, AND THE SYSTEM WAS IN STATE    1
                  THE SAMPLE VALUES WERE
                             49.9978
                             52.2263
                             51.6604
                             48.9263


FOR SAMPLE    2, XBAR=  51.476, R=   2.122, AND THE SYSTEM WAS IN STATE    1
                  THE SAMPLE VALUES WERE
                             50.4785
                             50.7688
                             52.6001
                             52.0561


FOR SAMPLE    3, XBAR=  49.542, R=   5.164, AND THE SYSTEM WAS IN STATE    1
                  THE SAMPLE VALUES WERE
                             49.9427
                             47.0534
                             52.2171
                             48.9567


FOR SAMPLE    4, XBAR=  49.628, R=   1.400, AND THE SYSTEM WAS IN STATE    1
                  THE SAMPLE VALUES WERE
                             49.1522
                             50.1114
                             48.9238
                             50.3241
```

•
•
•

PARTIAL OUTPUT FOR RUN #1—(*Continued*)

```
FOR SAMPLE    13, XBAR=  53.665, R=    4.674, AND THE SYSTEM WAS IN STATE    2
                  THE SAMPLE VALUES WERE
                            54.3482
                            51.2816
                            55.9556
                            53.0753

FOR SAMPLE    14, XBAR=  51.072, R=    4.596, AND THE SYSTEM WAS IN STATE    1
                  THE SAMPLE VALUES WERE
                            51.2401
                            53.7208

                            49.1247
                            50.2010
          •
          •
          •



FOR SAMPLE    25, XBAR=  54.547, R=    1.674, AND THE SYSTEM WAS IN STATE    2
                  THE SAMPLE VALUES WERE
                            54.4789
                            55.3460
                            53.6721
                            54.6900

FOR SAMPLE    26, XBAR=  49.014, R=    6.584, AND THE SYSTEM WAS IN STATE    1
                  THE SAMPLE VALUES WERE
                            44.4261
                            50.3656
                            51.0100
                            50.2536
          •
          •
          •



FOR SAMPLE    50, XBAR=  49.084, R=    4.914, AND THE SYSTEM WAS IN STATE    1
                  THE SAMPLE VALUES WERE
                            51.5401
                            50.0327
                            48.1392
                            46.6256

CONTROL LIMITS - - UCLX=   53.2144, LCLX=   47.4140, UCLR=   9.0853, LCLR=   0.0000

OUT OF CONTROL ON SAMPLE   13     XBAR= 53.6652, R=  4.6739, AND J=    2
                  UCLX= 53.2144, LCLX= 47.4140, UCLR=  9.0853, LCLR=  0.0000

CONTROL LIMITS - - UCLX=   53.1357, LCLX=   47.3560, UCLR=   9.0530, LCLR=   0.0000

OUT OF CONTROL ON SAMPLE   25     XBAR= 54.5467, R=  1.6738, AND J=    2
                  UCLX= 53.1357, LCLX= 47.3560, UCLR=  9.0530, LCLR=  0.0000

CONTROL LIMITS - - UCLX=   53.0809, LCLX=   47.2315, UCLR=   9.1621, LCLR=   0.0000
```

INPUT FOR RUN #2

```
  50.            4.118      1.         50.        5.      1000.
         4            80         70          1          1          50
      .85       50.         2.          0
      .10       54.         2.          1
      .03       48.         2.          1
      .02       60.         2.          1
 .5000  .4801  .4602  .4404  .4207  .4013  .3821  .3632  .3446  .3264
 .3085  .2912  .2743  .2578  .2420  .2266  .2119  .1977  .1841  .1711
 .1587  .1469  .1357  .1251  .1151  .1056  .09680 .08851 .08076 .07353
 .06681 .06057 .05480 .04947 .04457 .04006 .03593 .03216 .02872 .02559
 .02275 .02018 .01786 .01578 .01390 .01222 .01072 .009387.008198.007143
 .006210.005386.004661.004025.003467.002980.002555.002186.001866.001589
 .001350.001144.000968.000816.000687.000577.000483.000404.000337.000280
 .000232.000192.000159.000131.000108.000088.000072.000059.000048.000000
 -3.40  .9997  -3.30  .9995  -3.20  .9993  -3.10  .9990  -3.00  .9987
 -2.90  .9981  -2.80  .9974  -2.70  .9965  -2.60  .9953  -2.50  .9938
 -2.40  .9918  -2.30  .9893  -2.20  .9861  -2.10  .9821  -2.00  .9772
 -1.90  .9713  -1.80  .9641  -1.70  .9554  -1.60  .9452  -1.50  .9332
 -1.40  .9192  -1.30  .9032  -1.20  .8849  -1.10  .9643  -1.00  .8413
 -0.90  .8159  -0.80  .7881  -0.70  .7580  -0.60  .7257  -0.50  .6915
 -0.40  .6554  -0.30  .6179  -0.20  .5793  -0.10  .5398   0.00  .5000
  0.10  .4602   0.20  .4207   0.30  .3821   0.40  .3446   0.50  .3085
  0.60  .2743   0.70  .2420   0.80  .2119   0.90  .1841   1.00  .1587
  1.10  .1357   1.20  .1151   1.30  .09680  1.40  .08076  1.50  .06681
  1.60  .05480  1.70  .04457  1.80  .03593  1.90  .02872  2.00  .02275
  2.10  .01786  2.20  .01390  2.30  .1072   2.40  .008198 2.50  .006210
  2.60  .004661 2.70  .003467 2.80  .002555 2.90  .001366 3.00  .001350
  3.10  .000968 3.20  .000687 3.30  .000483 3.40  .000337 3.50  .000233
       5.           10.         10.         .10
       3.            2.059        .880         10          4
                1           1           1           1          1          1          1
               7
  50.
       5
```

PARTIAL OUTPUT FOR RUN #2

CONTROL LIMITS - - UCLX= 53.0000, LCLX= 47.0000, UCLR= 9.3980, LCLR= 0.

THE P(J)'S ARE
0.01241   0.30850   0.06703   0.99380

THE PTWO(J)'S ARE
0.99730   0.15870   0.84130 -0.

SAMPLE SIZE= 4, K= 3.00, SAMPLES/PERIOD= 4.36
              COST/SAMPLE= 10.42/
              CONDITIONAL LOSS= 198.551
              TOTAL COST/PRODUCTION PERIOD=   91.001

FOR SAMPLE   1, XBAR= 50.703, R=   3.300, AND THE SYSTEM WAS IN STATE   1
              THE SAMPLE VALUES WERE
                   49.9978
                   52.2263
                   51.6604
                   48.9263

PARTIAL OUTPUT FOR RUN #2—(*Continued*)

```
FOR SAMPLE     2, XBAR=  51.476, R=   2.122, AND THE SYSTEM WAS IN STATE    1
               THE SAMPLE VALUES WERE
                         50.4785
                         50.7688
                         52.6001
                         52.0561

FOR SAMPLE     3, XBAR=  49.542, R=   5.164, AND THE SYSTEM WAS IN STATE    1
               THE SAMPLE VALUES WERE
                         49.9427
                         47.0534
                         52.2171
                         48.9567

FOR SAMPLE     4, XBAR=  49.628, R=   1.400, AND THE SYSTEM WAS IN STATE    1
               THE SAMPLE VALUES WERE
                         49.1522
                         50.1114
                         48.9238
                         50.3241

FOR SAMPLE     5, XBAR=  48.496, R=   5.981, AND THE SYSTEM WAS IN STATE    1
               THE SAMPLE VALUES WERE
                         52.8673
                         46.9232
                         46.8865
                         47.3054

FOR SAMPLE     6, XBAR=  50.484, R=   1.843, AND THE SYSTEM WAS IN STATE    1
               THE SAMPLE VALUES WERE
                         50.7569
                         51.4903
                         49.6474
                         50.0415

FOR SAMPLE     7, XBAR=  49.014, R=   3.803, AND THE SYSTEM WAS IN STATE    1
               THE SAMPLE VALUES WERE
                         46.3536
                         49.3975
                         50.1568
                         50.1498

FOR SAMPLE     8, XBAR=  50.942, R=   4.481, AND THE SYSTEM WAS IN STATE    1
               THE SAMPLE VALUES WERE
                         49.3671
                         53.8482
                         50.4896
                         50.0620

FOR SAMPLE     9, XBAR=  49.497, R=   3.483, AND THE SYSTEM WAS IN STATE    1
               THE SAMPLE VALUES WERE
                         47.2644
                         49.3632
                         50.7477
                         50.6137
```

PARTIAL OUTPUT FOR RUN #2—(*Continued*)

```
FOR SAMPLE    10. XBAR=   51.357. R=    4.773, AND THE SYSTEM WAS IN STATE    1
                    THE SAMPLE VALUES WERE
                              52.3619
                              51.4705
                              53.1838
                              48.4111

FOR SAMPLE    11, XBAR=   50.721, R=    4.341, AND THE SYSTEM WAS IN STATE    1
                    THE SAMPLE VALUES WERE
                              52.5140
                              50.6322
                              48.1729
                              51.5656

FOR SAMPLE    12. XBAR=   55.524, R=    4.040. AND THE SYSTEM WAS IN STATE    2
                    THE SAMPLE VALUES WERE
                              55.7573
                              56.1854
                              53.0574
                              57.0971

OUT OF CONTROL ON SAMPLE    12    XBAR= 55.5243, R= 4.0397, AND J=    2
       UCLX= 53.0000. LCLX= 47.0000. UCLR=  9.3980, LCLR=  0.

CONTROL LIMITS - - UCLX=    52.807. LCLX=    47.459. UCLR=   8.379.   LCLR=    0.
```

INPUT FOR RUN #3 IS IDENTICAL TO THAT FOR RUN #2 UP TO THE
THIRD ENTRY FROM END OF DATA (NSWCH = 7) AT WHICH POINT THE
FOLLOWING IS INSERTED:

```
            1
 2.5
            1
 2.3
            1
 2.
            1
 1.8
            1
 1.5
            3
 3.0       2.326     0.864        5
            0       1        1        1        0        1        1
            1
 2.5
            1
 2.3
            1
 2.
            1
 1.8
            1
 1.5
            5
```

PARTIAL OUTPUT FOR RUN #3

```
CONTROL LIMITS - - UCLX=    53.0000. LCLX=    47.0000. UCLR=   9.3980. LCLR=    0.

       THE P(J)'S ARE
     0.01241    0.30850

       THE PTWO(J)'S ARE
     0.99730    0.15870

SAMPLE SIZE=  4, K= 3.00, SAMPLES/PERIOD= 3.13
              COST/SAMPLE=   10.427
              CONDITIONAL LOSS= 101.949
              TOTAL COST/PRODUCTION PERIOD=   65.208

CONTROL LIMITS - - UCLX=    52.5000. LCLX=    47.5000. UCLR=   8.5180. LCLR=    0.

       THE P(J)'S ARE
     0.01241    0.30850

       THE PTWO(J)'S ARE
     0.98758    0.06681

SAMPLE SIZE=  4, K= 2.50, SAMPLES/PERIOD= 2.84
              COST/SAMPLE=   10.524
              CONDITIONAL LOSS=  84.622
              TOTAL COST/PRODUCTION PERIOD=   59.685
```

PARTIAL OUTPUT FOR RUN #3—(*Continued*)

```
CONTROL LIMITS - - UCLX=    52.3000,  LCLX=    47.7000,  UCLR=   8.1660,  LCLR=    0.0700

        THE P(J)'S ARE
     0.01241   0.30850

        THE PTWO(J)'S ARE
     0.97856   0.04457

SAMPLE SIZE=   4,  K= 2.30,  SAMPLES/PERIOD= 2.76
                   COST/SAMPLE=   10.614
                   CONDITIONAL LOSS=  80.929
                   TOTAL COST/PRODUCTION PERIOD=   58.618

CONTROL LIMITS - - UCLX=    52.0000,  LCLX=    48.0000,  UCLR=   7.6380,  LCLR=    0.5980

        THE P(J)'S ARE
     0.01241   0.30850

        THE PTWO(J)'S ARE
     0.95450   0.02275

SAMPLE SIZE=   4,  K= 2.00,  SAMPLES/PERIOD= 2.67
                   COST/SAMPLE=   10.855
                   CONDITIONAL LOSS=  77.469
                   TOTAL COST/PRODUCTION PERIOD=   57.997
```

•
•
•

```
CONTROL LIMITS - - UCLX=    52.2361,  LCLX=    47.7639,  UCLR=   8.9720,  LCLR=    0.3320

        THE P(J)'S ARE
     0.01241   0.30850

        THE PTWO(J)'S ARE
     0.98758   0.02559

SAMPLE SIZE=   5,  K= 2.50,  SAMPLES/PERIOD= 2.71
                   COST/SAMPLE=   10.624
                   CONDITIONAL LOSS=  77.910
                   TOTAL COST/PRODUCTION PERIOD=   57.541

CONTROL LIMITS - - UCLX=    52.0572,  LCLX=    47.9428.  UCLR=   8.6264.  LCLR=    0.6776

        THE P(J)'S ARE
     0.01241   0.30850

        THE PTWO(J)'S ARE
     0.97856   0.01578

SAMPLE SIZE=   5,  K= 2.30,  SAMPLES/PERIOD= 2.67
                   COST/SAMPLE=   10.714
                   CONDITIONAL LOSS=  76.396
                   TOTAL COST/PRODUCTION PERIOD=   57.220
```

•
•
•

PROBLEMS

1. In the manufacture of bowling balls, hardness is the most critical quality characteristic. This characteristic depends on the composition of the original compounds, the mixing of these compounds, the molding temperature and pressure, and the temperature and time in the vulcanizer. One company has determined the optimum range of hardness as 75–85 Rockwell. Below is given a set of data from samples of five balls selected from each day's output of approximately 350.

Day	1	2	3	4	5	6	7	8	9	10
	87	84	90	87	92	80	80	80	91	90
	94	86	93	91	92	91	81	93	90	79
	86	82	87	93	91	89	77	91	91	90
	91	90	83	87	92	92	88	87	78	88
	88	84	89	87	93	82	90	80	91	87

Day	11	12	13	14	15	16	17	18	19	20
	89	81	78	82	85	80	84	79	80	90
	87	84	89	83	90	81	75	90	78	91
	91	80	84	94	84	85	80	90	87	89
	88	88	89	79	84	87	84	93	85	86
	89	87	89	82	83	83	89	93	86	89

a) Construct $\bar{X}$ and R charts using these data.
b) Is the process in control?
c) How well are specifications being met?
d) What recommendations can be made from these data?

2.[15] The data given in Tables 5–10 and 5–11 represent observations of a molding process which had been divided into 7 work elements. Over a period of weeks, two observers took data on a number of workers. The data given here represent only observations taken on one worker. Table 5–10 shows the results of measurement of 80 consecutive cycles by observer R on worker M during the morning of a given day. Table 5–11 gives the results for observer P on the same worker of measurement of 52 consecutive cycles during the afternoon of that same day.

	Table 5–10				*Table 5–11*	
M/R	3/8 A. M.			M/P	3/8 P. M.	
	$\bar{X}$	R			$\bar{X}$	R
1.	229	31		1.	211	12
2.	212	35		2.	216	16
3.	197.5	65		3.	212	35
4.	203	10		4.	216	11
5.	201	25		5.	218	16
6.	206	37.5		6.	221	37
7.	205.9	29		7.	212	15
8.	207.5	15		8.	202	32
9.	211	30		9.	212	62
10.	202	62.5		10.	240	55
11.	197	20		11.	245	47
12.	196	34		12.	215	37
13.	197	24		13.	223	33
14.	200	33				
15.	202.5	24				
16.	201	8				
17.	220	12.5				
18.	200	40				
19.	205	22.5				
20.	215	20				

---

[15] Adapted from Sebastian B. Littauer, "Statistical Quality Control in Industrial Engineering," *6th N. E. Quality Control Conference.*

The data were arranged in subgroups of 4 consecutive observations each, and the averages and ranges of these subgroups are given in the tables. All readings are in hundredths of a minute.

a) Assume that both morning and afternoon data come from the same universe and set up $\bar{X}$ and R charts for the combined data.

b) Comment on the significance of the resulting control charts.

c) Set up a separate set of $\bar{X}$ and R charts for both morning and afternoon data.

d) Is there any significant difference between the morning and afternoon runs?

3. Specifications for a dimension of a manufactured part are $4.0050'' \pm 0.0005''$. Samples of 5 each taken every 15 minutes gave the following results for the first 5 hours of operation (in units of $0.0001''$ above $4.0000''$):

Sample	1	2	3	4	5	6	7	8	9	10
	47	50	47	48	45	50	46	50	54	58
	54	45	55	48	52	46	44	49	54	55
	51	49	49	49	51	49	52	54	49	52
	56	46	55	52	54	52	55	52	50	56
	54	53	55	49	51	53	50	48	50	53

Sample	11	12	13	14	15	16	17	18	19	20
	56	54	47	57	48	51	49	53	56	46
	51	50	50	53	49	51	53	50	52	55
	49	56	50	52	51	45	46	47	52	48
	50	47	47	49	50	54	49	50	50	51
	47	51	51	53	57	44	48	49	55	55

a) Set up $\bar{X}$ and R charts to be used in the control of future production. If any out of control points are found, assume assignable causes are discovered and removed.

b) Set up a chart using sample standard deviation for the control of variability rather than sample range.

4. The data below give mean and range for samples of 5 each taken every 15 minutes from a process whose production rate was 500 per hour and for which the specified tolerance was $1.230'' \pm 0.010''$:

Sample	1	2	3	4	5	6	7	8	9	10
$\bar{X}$.....	1.237	1.232	1.232	1.234	1.235	1.233	1.234	1.234	1.231	1.235
R.....	0.010	0.009	0.008	0.005	0.006	0.010	0.009	0.003	0.002	0·006

Sample	11	12	13	14	15	16	17	18	19	20
$\bar{X}$.....	1.238	1.232	1.236	1.232	1.230	1.237	1.228	1.235	1.236	1.237
R.....	0.007	0.002	0.013	0.005	0.008	0.012	0.006	0.005	0.004	0.006

a) Set up $\bar{X}$ and R charts for control of this process in the future.

b) If the process gives rise to a normal distribution of output, what fraction defective can be expected?

c) If process centering can be set to any level, would you recommend a change? If so, to what level?

5. In Problem 4, what would be the probability of detecting a shift in process average to $1.210''$ on the first sample after the shift? By the third sample?

6. The following data are the results of life tests on 20 samples of 5 fluorescent lamps each. The values are in hours.

Sample	1	2	3	4	5	6	7	8	9	10
$\bar{X}$.....	3,290	3,180	3,350	3,470	3,080	3,240	3,260	3,310	3,640	4,110
R.....	560	410	200	300	90	650	890	410	1120	520

Sample	11	12	13	14	15	16	17	18	19	20
$\bar{X}$.....	3,220	3,590	4,270	4,040	3,580	3,500	3,570	3,560	2,740	3,200
R.....	580	670	480	250	170	670	440	660	560	590

a) Is the process in a state of statistical control?
b) Assuming assignable causes could be discovered and eliminated, what is your best estimate of the capability of this process?

7. The following data are defectives found in samples of 200 items each taken from each days production for one month:

Sample	1	2	3	4	5	6	7	8	9	10
No. def.	25	28	42	16	6	13	3	11	23	16

Sample	11	12	13	14	15	16	17	18	19	20	21
No. def.	5	23	8	9	8	9	5	5	7	15	19

a) Is the process in control?
b) Assuming assignable causes are found for any out of control points, construct a p chart to control future output.

8. The defective items from a manufacturing process are as follows for 25 days' production:

Day	No. Inspected	No. Defective
1..............................	56	2
2..............................	73	5
3..............................	47	4
4..............................	51	3
5..............................	59	6
6..............................	60	2
7..............................	63	2
8..............................	72	4
9..............................	41	3
10..............................	45	0
11..............................	54	2
12..............................	56	4
13..............................	65	7
14..............................	62	5
15..............................	70	4
16..............................	76	3
17..............................	81	6
18..............................	85	8
19..............................	79	8
20..............................	82	5
21..............................	90	10
22..............................	75	4
23..............................	77	3
24..............................	81	6
25..............................	61	4

a) Is this process in control with respect to its fraction defective?

b) Assuming assignable causes for all points out of control, construct a *p* chart to be used in controlling future output.

9. The following shows the number of lost-time accidents per month experienced by a manufacturing firm over a period of two years:

Year	Month	No. of Lost-Time Accidents	Man-Hours (000's)
1	1	2	95
	2	7	97
	3	0	91
	4	9	102
	5	12	106
	6	4	98
	7	8	93
	8	6	110
	9	6	111
	10	1	109
	11	8	84
	12	5	89
2	1	5	92
	2	3	99
	3	8	104
	4	13	110
	5	14	117
	6	5	102
	7	1	101
	8	9	99
	9	9	112
	10	0	122
	11	7	121
	12	10	98

Would you conclude from the above that variations in the accident rate are due to chance alone, or that assignable causes are present?

10. A *p* chart indicates that the current process average is 0.02. If 50 items are inspected each day, what is the probability of catching a shift in process average to 0.04 on the first day after the shift? By the end of the third day after the shift?

11. *a*) A process is to be controlled by a *p* chart with only one chance in 1,000 of exceeding the upper limit, if the process is in control. If you desire the probability of catching a shift in process average from 0.03 to 0.06 to be equal to 60 per cent on the first sample after the shift, what size sample should be taken?

b) What are the control limits?

12. A piston grinding process will be controlled by taking periodic samples of four items and checking the diameter. The allowable tolerance limits are

4.3750 ± 0.0005. In a preliminary study, $s_{\bar{x}}$ was found to equal 0.0001 and is expected to remain constant. $\bar{X}$ changes slowly over time in a random manner.

a) What is the minimum percentage defective the process can be expected to produce?

b) What values should the control limits have if the fact that the process is producing 30.9 per cent defectives or more is to have an 84 per cent probability of getting caught on the first sample after it occurs.

c) With the limits in part (b), what is the chance of looking for trouble when actually the process average has not changed?

13. Solve Problem No. 11, if the shifts to be caught is from 0.01 to 0.10 and the desired first sample chance is 30 per cent. (Hint: $p'n < 5$; the normal approximation will not hold. Use the Poisson chart.)

14. The process of filling 1-pound sugar boxes has been checked, and it is in control. The 3-sigma control limits for means of the contents of four boxes (as a sample) were empirically established at 1.02 pounds and 1.08 pounds. The sugar boxes are labeled as 1-pound boxes which is therefore the legal limit on the low side. A government inspector chooses two boxes at random.

a) What is the probability that the first box is not below the legal limit?

b) What is the probability that neither is below the legal limit?

15. A package filling machine has associated with it acceptable tolerance limits of 2.50 ± 0.04 pounds. Samples of size 4 have revealed $s_{\bar{x}} = 0.01$, and the process is normally distributed.

a) With an actual mean ($\bar{x}$) of 2.51, what percentage of individual boxes do you expect outside the tolerance limits?

b) If the mean ($\bar{x}$) is 2.52, and using 2.50 ± $3s_{\bar{x}}$ limits, what are the chances that by the second sample an out-of-control indication will be given?

c) With the physical variation given in (a), and using the tolerance limits as a separation of rejects from acceptable product, determine the sample size of a per cent defective system where its 3σ limits give the same chances of catching a shift from 2.50 to 2.52 as question (b).

CHAPTER 6

Sampling Inspection

INTRODUCTION

THE concept of statistical control previously discussed was seen to have wide applications in industry to that class of problems where control of some measurable characteristic must be effected in the face of variation, due to the existence of some stable system of chance causes. In the control of quality of manufactured product, this problem is almost universal, and the field of application is wide. In this same area, however, another important class of problems exists which may be analyzed with statistical tools. Apart from the problem of control of measurable quality factors during production, there exists the necessity for making decisions as to the acceptance or rejection of product already past any given control point or from a process over which statistical control has not been instituted.

These decisions are made by a process of comparison of the measurable characteristics of the product with previously determined standards. The result of this inspection process is a body of information concerning the product which forms the basis of the decision as to its acceptability. The decision may be of the simple "yes-no" type based, for instance, on the results of inspection of the diameter of a bored hole with a go or no-go gage.[1] Such a decision may, however, be much more difficult than this to make, as in the case of acceptance or rejection of a jet engine for aircraft use. Here, the decision would be based on a host of information collected during the manufacturing process, and as a result of exhaustive tests after manufacture. Even then a

---

[1] This kind of gage would be a tapered plug whose dimensions at either end corresponded to the specification limits. If the plug could be pushed through the hole, the hole is too large; if it wouldn't go in at all, the hole is too small.

220

"yes-no" type answer usually does not occur, but one which might say to re-do certain work and/or replace certain parts and return for further testing.

A wide variety of specific problems exists within the framework of acceptance inspection in production, but in all cases eventually a decision of either acceptance or rejection must be reached. In many situations, it is not economical or possible to inspect all items from a given process, and decisions must be based on less than complete information about quality of product. In most of these cases, some formal sampling technique is essential so that maximum utility is gained from the information gathered.

The simplest kind of such plans involves the drawing of a random sample of given size, n, from a lot, S; the n items are inspected, and the results of this process compared to some previously determined standard for acceptance. A decision is then made, based on the outcome of this process.

Since only a portion of the items in the lot are inspected before a decision is reached, two kinds of errors are possible with any such plan. First, lots which are in reality acceptable may be rejected, and, second, lots which are in fact bad may be accepted. The objective of any sampling plan is to minimize these two kinds of possible errors subject to the economics of the inspection and production processes.

Sampling plans may in general be based on two different kinds of measurement. Inspection may be performed on manufactured products with only a decision made as to whether each item is acceptable or not acceptable, e.g., measurement of diameter with a snap gage. Inspection may also be accomplished by measuring the degree to which each item conforms to a given standard, e.g., measuring shaft diameters with a micrometer. When related to sampling inspection, the first of these, attributes sampling, can be seen to be generally less expensive per item than the second, variables sampling. However, attributes sampling gives one less information than a sample of the same size inspected by variables.

The Economics of Sampling Inspection

In setting up a lot-by-lot attributes inspection plan, one desires some sampling plan which will economically detect changes in p' (the true fraction defective in submitted lots), so that decisions may be made on a continuing basis as to what constitutes an economic level of inspection. This level may be either 0 per cent or 100 per cent, depending on whether the ratio C_i/C_a is greater than or less than p' ($C_i =$ cost of inspection per unit, and C_d = cost of a defect per unit when it is un-detected).

If, for example, past data indicate that a process is producing defective items 2 per cent of the time, the question of the economic level of inspection may be determined from an examination of the costs involved. With a cost of inspection of $0.10 per item and a loss of $10.00 for every defective item which gets past this inspection point, a decision to inspect all items would be reached. Here, the cost of inspection is $0.10 per item, while the expected loss per item is $0.02 \times \$10.00$, or $0.20. Thus every item inspected results in a net expected gain of $0.10. If, however, the loss per defective item were only $4.00, then the expected loss per item inspected is only $0.08, and no inspection would be called for.

In this latter situation, the rationale for no inspection assumes that the process average fraction defective is known and stable. If the process average changed from 2 per cent to 4 per cent and the change were undetected, a net expected loss of $0.06 for each item not inspected would be experienced until 100 per cent inspection were instituted. Thus, when the economics of a situation call for no inspection, in reality some kind of sampling inspection is called for in order to give assurance as to the stability of the process average and to detect changes in its level.

If $p = c'/n$ (c' = number of defects in a sample of size n) is an estimate of p', it may be equal to p', and then there will be no loss since a correct decision will be made. However, if p incorrectly estimates p', some loss may be incurred. If p' has not changed, and p is greater than c/n, where c is the maximum allowable defects in the sample which will still accept the lot, some cost (C_1) is incurred. This cost results from inferring that p' has changed when, in fact, it has not. The probability that this cost (C_1) will be incurred depends on the number assigned to c and the sample size n. That is,

$$P(C_1) = P[p > \frac{c}{n} \mid E(p) = p'],\qquad (1)$$

where p' is the process average fraction defective from a statistically controlled universe and $E(p)$ is the expected value of p.

If p' has changed and p is equal to or less than c/n, some cost (C_2) will be incurred. This cost results from not taking action based on a conclusion that p' has not changed when, in fact, it has changed to some value p''. That is:

$$P(C_2) = P[p \leq \frac{c}{n} \mid E(p) = p''] . \tag{2}$$

Both equations (1) and (2) assume that the decision criterion is one-sided, that is, costs are incurred only when quality is worse than expected. Two-sided criteria (as in control charts) may certainly be expressed in the same way that (1) and (2) express one-sided criteria.

The expected costs of making these two kinds of errors are equal to their respective probabilities times the costs.

$$E(C_1) = C_1[P(C_1)] \tag{3}$$

$$E(C_2) = C_2[P(C_2)] \tag{4}$$

For a sampling plan to be economic, the sum of $E(C_1)$, $E(C_2)$, and the cost of the sampling plan must be minimized. The cost of the sampling plan will be assumed to consist of fixed and variable costs, so that

$$C_s = C_f + nC_i , \tag{5}$$

where C_s is the total cost of the plan, C_f, the fixed cost of the plan, C_i, the variable cost of inspection per unit, and n the sample size. Then the expression

$$\text{Expected total cost} = E(C_1) + E(C_2) + C_s \tag{6}$$

is to be minimized with respect to n and c. As can be seen from equation (2), this cannot be done without some knowledge of the changes which are likely to occur in p'. If one is completely uncertain as to these changes, no explicit solution to the economic problem is possible. It is technically feasible, however, to set up an economic sampling plan which will guard against the maximum loss which would result from *any* change in p'. But this could very well be uneconomic, if the change which would produce this maximum loss had a very low or no probability of occurrence.

When one guards against the occurrence of some maximum loss in this manner, he is, in effect, playing a game with the machine. Such a game may be characterized as two-person (two opposing players), where the manager chooses some decision rule from among the many available and "nature" chooses some course of action. The manager's decision rule should provide a course of action for each choice made by nature. However, nature has no known objective or strategy, and therefore the payoff for nature is not known. Under such conditions, the outcome of the game is difficult to predict. Some criteria for playing such games have been suggested, and some concrete examples of the selection of a plan, based on economic criteria, will be detailed later in this chapter.

In determining an economic inspection plan, the quality level which can be tolerated at a given inspection point must also be calculated. The ratio C_i/C_d sets this economic limit to the quality level leaving this point. Any level of fraction defective greater than this cannot be tolerated economically, and a product which is received at a level above this ratio must be screened 100 per cent, or returned for supplier action. This kind of reasoning assumes that the cost of producing a unit is constant over the range of fractions defective experienced in each case. If the cost of production decreases as the fraction defective increases (poorer quality costs less to produce), the situation will have to be examined in terms of incremental costs and yields (see Chapter 9) to determine what maximum fraction defective can be tolerated. The cost of 100 per cent inspection may be assumed constant from lot to lot, but if the fraction defective is more than C_i/C_d, then the yield of usable product per lot will be smaller and smaller as the fraction defective increases. At some point the cost of quality will be balanced with the yield of good product. The information just given provides at present only the conceptual outline of what constitutes economic inspection by attributes. A numerical example will be worked out later after the technical derivation of a sampling scheme has been developed.

Thus it can be seen that acceptance inspection procedures revolve around the basic requirement of estimating the quality level of each batch of output submitted for inspection in order to reach a decision as to whether it should be accepted or rejected. The major technique necessary to implement this concept is sampling.

Sampling

Given a box of output from our process, we select at random a unit, compare it with the standard, and classify it as "good" or "bad." The process is repeated until n items have been inspected with c defects found and the fraction defective $\bar{p}$ of the sample is

$$\bar{p} = \frac{c}{n}. \tag{7}$$

This is an estimate of the fraction defective of the process (p) on condition that the sampling process used in inspection was random. For a sampling process to be random, the order of events constituting the outcome of the process is dependent only on the underlying probabilities associated with each possible event (in this case "defective" and "not defective") and in no way on the sequence of events obtained to any point. The sampling may be from a finite or infinite population and may be with or without replacement but there should be no information added as a result of the order of events only. While these conditions may not be met precisely, any departure from this requirement should be evaluated in terms of its impact on the estimating process and significant departures accounted for in the design of the plan.

Operating Characteristic Curve

Any sampling plan may be described in terms of its expected outcomes by means of an operating characteristic curve. As is shown in Figure 6–1, this relates the true (unknown) fraction defective of the lot being inspected with the probability of acceptance. Whatever are the technical attributes of the plan described by Figure 6–1, its operating characteristics are as shown. If the fraction defective of the lot were 0.04, this plan would accept such a lot 31 per cent of the time and reject it 69 per cent of the time. This curve says nothing at all about whether such a lot will ever be submitted to the plan, only describing the consequences for any incoming quality level.

Some standard terminology has been adopted for the statistical attributes of any sampling plan and they are shown also on Figure 6–1. any sampling plan should be designed so as to discriminate among lots which should be accepted without further inspection and those which should be screened for defects or scrapped. The precise manner in which this discrimination should be effected is, of course, an economic question. Thus any plan can be expected to display discrimination around the break-even or indifference quality level. In the simplest case, this may be given as the ratio of the cost of inspection per unit (C_i) to the cost of an undetected defect (C_d).

The probability of acceptance of a lot of this quality would depend on the probability that such a lot would be presented for inspection in the first place. If this were high we would expect the plan to exhibit maximum discrimination at this point.

That level of quality considered "good" and which it is desired to accept most of the time is called the acceptable quality level (AQL). That level considered "bad" and which it is desired to reject most of the time is called the lot tolerance per cent defective ($LTPD$). The probability that a plan will reject AQL lots is called the producer's risk (α) and the probability that a plan will accept bad lots is called the consumer's risk (β). As will be shown, any OC curve may be defined in

Figure 6-1

SPECIFICATION OF SAMPLING PLANS

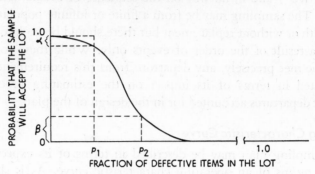

FRACTION OF DEFECTIVE ITEMS IN THE LOT

terms of two points which might be (p_1, P_{a1}) and (p_2, P_{a2}) corresponding to $(AQL, 1 - \alpha)$ and $(LTPD, \beta)$ respectively but do not have to be.

In standard statistical terminology, a simple sampling plan consists of hypothesizing that the lot is acceptable $(H_0{:}p \leqslant C_i/C_d)$ and then taking action based on the following rule:

$$\text{Accept } H_0 \text{ if } c \leq c_a|n$$
$$\text{Reject } H_0 \text{ if } c > c_a|n$$

in which

$$n = \text{sample size},$$
$$c = \text{number of defects in } n,$$
$$c_a = \text{acceptance number}.$$

The *OC* curve gives the probabilities of making errors of the first kind (rejecting the hypothesis when it is true) and errors of the second kind (accepting the hypothesis when it is not true). Of course, the frequency with which errors will be made depends on the fraction defective of incoming lots as well as the attributes of the plan.

Binomial Sampling

Any process which generates output which can be characterized as either "good" or "bad," for which each generating event (trial) is independent in the sense that it is not influenced by prior events and does not influence subsequent events, and which can be described by a single parameter giving the probability of "good" (or "bad") events is called a Bernoulli process. The probability of exactly c "good" (or "bad") events in n trials of such a process for which the parameter is p is given by the binomial distribution

$$P(c) = \binom{n}{c} p^c (1 - p)^{n-c} \tag{8}$$

in which

$P(c)$ = probability of c successes ,
p = probability of success ,
n = number of trials ,
$\binom{n}{c}$ = combination of n events taken c at a time ,
$= \dfrac{n!}{c!(n-c)!}$.

If one generated from such a process 10 units of output and the process was known to be characterized by a long-run fraction defective of 0.05, the probability of exactly 1 defect in 10 trials would be

$$P(1) = \binom{10}{1} 0.05^1 (0.95)^9$$
$$= 10(0.05)(0.63)$$
$$= 0.315 .$$

A problem which we face immediately in attempting to use this theory in acceptance inspection is that the conditions of this application do not fit the assumptions of the theory. First, we are usually dealing with a finite rather than an infinite population. That is, our unit of inspection is a lot rather than a process. The process of interest is that by which the sample is drawn and not that which produced the lot in the first place. Second, such sampling is ordinarily done without replacement; that is, as each item is drawn from the lot it is inspected and set aside rather than being returned to the lot. The outcome of this kind of process is not binomial since the probability of success is not the same from one trial to the next.

If a lot of size S contains in fact d defects then the probability of a defect on the first trial is $p = d/S$. However, on the second trial, the value of p is $(d-1)/(S-1)$ if the first unit was a defect or $d/(S-1)$ if it was not.

If our sample of 10 in the previous example were drawn from a lot of size 20, the probability of a defect on the first draw would be $\frac{1}{20}$ ($p = 0.05$) as before. However, if the first draw was defective, the probability of a defect on the second draw would be 0. If the first draw was not defective, the probability of a defect on the second draw would be $\frac{1}{19}$ ($p = 0.053$) and so on for succeeding draws. In this case, the probability of 1 defect in a sample of 10 would be

$$P(1) = 10 \left(\frac{19}{20} \times \frac{18}{19} \times \ldots \times \frac{11}{12} \times \frac{1}{11} \right)$$
$$= 0.5$$

rather than 0.315 as in the previous case.

If, however, the lot size were 100, the probability of 1 defect in a sample of 10 would be

$$P(1) = 10 \left(\frac{95}{100} \times \frac{94}{99} \times \frac{93}{98} \times \cdots \times \frac{87}{92} \times \frac{5}{91} \right)$$
$$= 0.340 .$$

If the lot size were 1,000,

$$P(1) = 10 \left(\frac{950}{1,000} \times \frac{949}{999} \times \cdots \times \frac{942}{992} \times \frac{50}{991} \right)$$
$$= 0.318 .$$

For a lot size of 10,000, the same calculation gives

$$P(1) = 10 \left(\frac{9,500}{10,000} \times \frac{9,499}{9,999} \times \cdots \times \frac{9,492}{9,992} \times \frac{500}{9,991} \right)$$
$$= 0.315 .$$

Thus it can be easily inferred that as the size of the sample gets smaller relative to the lot size, the change in probability from draw to draw approaches zero. It would follow, then, that binomial probabilities may be used to approximate these hypergeometric probabilities as this condition obtains.

In almost all cases of acceptance inspection, this approximation can be accepted without giving rise to any discernible error. It is important at the same time to recognize that in any sampling process the trials must be individually and collectively random. That is, the selection of any item from a lot must not have been influenced consciously or unconsciously by information either external to the process or as a result of previous draws. If such influence is present in the sampling process, the theories just given and, in fact, all those to follow do not apply. Every reasonable effort must be made to assure conditions of randomness in using the techniques described here.

The Technical Design of Sampling Plans

Any simple sampling plan requires for its operation that sample size and acceptance number be specified. Referring to Figure 6–1, if a lot of p_1 quality is submitted, the probability of acceptance (P_{a1}) will be $(1 - \alpha)$. If a lot of p_2 quality is submitted, P_{a2} will be β. In terms of binomial probabilities

$$1 - \alpha = \sum_{c=0}^{c_a} \binom{n}{c} p_1{}^c (1 - p_1)^{n-c} \tag{9}$$

and

$$\beta = \sum_{c=0}^{c_a} \binom{n}{c} p_2{}^c (1 - p_2)^{n-c} \tag{10}$$

Equations (9) and (10) can be solved for n and c_a subject only to integer restrictions on their value giving us the desired plan.

In cases for which n is large, this is very laborious computationally and, again, approximate methods have been devised. It is known that if the expected number of defects (pn) is small, the Poisson distribution may be used to approximate the binomial. In this case we are assuming that pn is small relative to the size of a lot so that the probability of a defect is very small and a constant unaffected by the results of previous draws.

If p is intermediate in value, the Normal distribution (Table A, Appendix II) may be used to approximate binomial probabilities. In this case, the parameters are

$$E(c) = pn$$
$$\sigma_c{}^2 = pn(1 - p) .$$

For example if $p = 0.2$ and $n = 100$,

$$E(c) = 20$$
$$\sigma_c{}^2 = 16$$

and

$$\sigma_c = \sqrt{16}$$
$$= 4 .$$

From the Normal table, the probability of 16 defects would be

$$P(16) = P(c \geq 16) - P(c \geq 17)$$
$$= P\left(Z = \frac{20 - 16}{4}\right) - P\left(Z = \frac{20 - 17}{4}\right)$$
$$= P(Z = 1.00) - P(Z = 0.75)$$
$$= 0.8413 - 0.7734$$
$$= 0.0679 .$$

The binomial probability is 0.0638.

When p is small (or large), then the Poisson approximation may be used to reduce the computational burden. For example, if $p = 0.05$ and $n = 10$, then the probability of 1 defect is

$$P(c) = e^{-pn} \frac{(pn)^c}{c!}$$
$$= e^{-0.5} \frac{(0.5)^1}{1!} \tag{11}$$
$$= 0.303$$

as contrasted to the binomial value of 0.315. If however, n is 100 and p is 0.02, then

$$P(1) = e^{-2} \cdot \frac{(2.)^1}{(1)!}$$
$$= 0.271$$

and the binomial probability is also 0.271.

For small p, the Poisson approximation improves as n becomes larger. For intermediate values of p, the Normal approximation similarly improves. A chart of the Poisson distribution giving the probability of c or fewer defects for various values of pn is given in Figure 6–2.

Assuming this approximation to the binomial to be valid for most sampling inspection plans, it becomes possible to solve the following for n and c_a

$$1 - \alpha = \sum_{c=0}^{c_a} e^{-p_1 n} \frac{(p_1 n)^c}{c!}$$

$$\beta = \sum_{c=0}^{c_a} e^{-p_2 n} \frac{(p_2 n)^c}{c!}$$

in the derivation of a simple sampling plan.

In the example below, the method for determining a plan where p_1, p_2, α, and β have been specified is demonstrated. Given are the following specifications for a sampling plan: $p_1 = 0.01$, $p_2 = 0.06$, $\alpha = 0.05$, $\beta = 0.10$. This defines a cumulative frequency curve which passes through the points (defined in terms of p and P_a); (0, 1.00); (0.01, 0.95); (0.06, 0.10); and (1.00, 0). The two equations which result from substitutions of the given values in the cumulative Poisson expressions are:

$$(1 - 0.05) = \sum_{c=0}^{c_a} \frac{e^{-0.01n}(0.01n)^c}{c!}$$

and

$$0.10 = \sum_{c=0}^{c_a} \frac{e^{-0.06n}(0.06n)^c}{c!}.$$

These may be solved for n and c_a, and the appropriate plan determined. Since this is often a laborious computation, a method for the determination of n and c_a using the Poisson chart of Figure 6–2 is given below.

From Figure 6–2, we may determine pn for various c_a, where $\alpha = 0.05$ ($P_a = 0.95$) and $\beta = 0.10$ ($P_a = 0.10$) as follows:

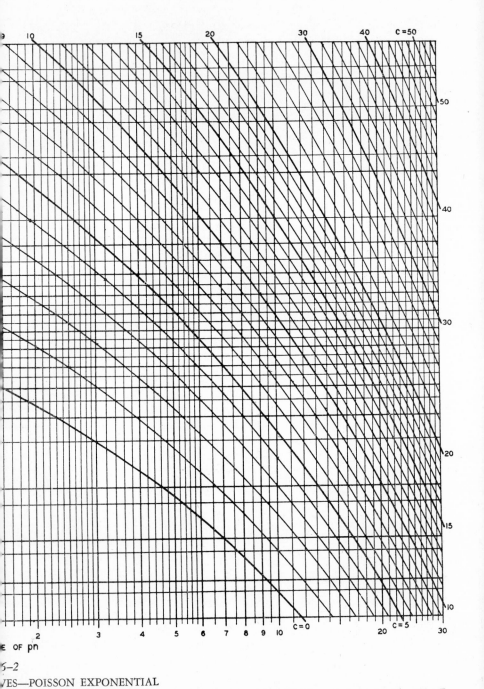

5–2

VES—POISSON EXPONENTIAL

infinite universe in which the fraction defective is p (a modification of chart given by Miss F.
F. Dodge and Harry G. Romig, *Sampling Inspection Tables*, 1944, John Wiley & Sons, Inc.

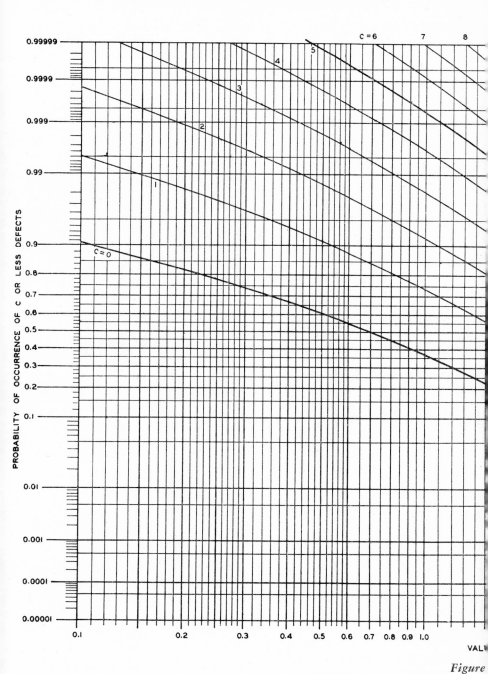

Figure

CUMULATIVE PROBABILITY CUR

For determining probability of occurrence of c or less defects in a sample of n pieces selected from a…

Thorndike *Bell System Technical Journal,* October, 1926). Reprinted with permission from Harold

c_a	$\dfrac{p_1 n}{P_a = 0.95}$	$\dfrac{p_2 n}{P_a = 0.10}$	p_2/p_1
0........................	...	2.30	...
1........................	0.36	3.90	10.8
2........................	0.80	5.35	6.7
3........................	1.36	6.70	4.9
4........................	1.95	8.00	4.1

The ratio of p_2 to p_1 can be readily determined from the second and third columns, since n must be the same in a single plan. The ratio p_2/p_1 for the desired plan is $\left(\dfrac{0.06}{0.01}\right) = 6$, which is between $c_a = 2$ and $c_a = 3$ (since c_a and n must both be integers, this kind of result should be expected). Therefore, the following alternative plans, with the indicated degrees of protection, are possible.

	α	β
1. $n = 80$, $c_a = 2$	0.05	0.14
2. $n = 89$, $c_a = 2$	0.07	0.10
3. $n = 136$, $c_a = 3$	0.05	0.03
4. $n = 112$, $c_a = 3$	0.03	0.10

Plans 1 and 3 are found by holding $\alpha = 0.05$, and determining β and pn from Figure 6–2. Plans 2 and 4 are found by holding $\beta = 0.10$ and reading α and pn from Figure 6–2. Selection of plan 2 ($n = 89$, $c_a = 2$) would, for example, appear to correspond closely with the requirements. If none of these are satisfactory, the probabilities associated with values of n from 81 to 88 where $c_a = 2$ and from 113 to 135 where $c_a = 3$ could be determined and selection made from these values. For example the plan for $n = 85$, $c_a = 2$ yields a P_a of 0.94 at $p = 0.01$ ($\alpha = 0.06$) and P_a of 0.12 at $p = 0.06$. These values may be considered more satisfactory levels of protection than those given in the first set of calculations. However, this method brackets the possibilities for satisfying the protection requirements.

The effect of variation in n and c_a on the discrimination provided by any sampling plan is illustrated in Figures 6–3 and 6–4, given that $n = 200$ and $c_a = 3$, where n is the size of a random sample drawn from the lot of size S and c_a is the acceptance number such that if c_a or fewer defects are found in n the lot will be accepted, while if more than c_a defects are found in n, the lot will be rejected. It is assumed that lot size S is large relative to n. Several points on the OC curve for this plan may be determined from the Poisson chart. When submitted quality is 1 per cent defective, $pn = 0.01 \times 200 = 2$. Moving vertically from $pn = 2$ to $c_a = 3$ curve, the probability of acceptance is found to be

0.86. At $p = 0.02$, it is 0.44; at $p = 0.03$, 0.15, etc. Plotting these points, the OC curve, as shown in Figure 6–3, results.

From this example, it can be seen that the OC curve for any sampling plan gives the probability with which the plan will discriminate between good and bad lots for any level of fraction defective in submitted lots. A plan may be made more discriminating (a steeper OC curve) by increasing the sample size and the acceptance number proportionately. Figure 6–4 shows the OC curve for the plan $n = 1,000$, $c = 15$.

Figure 6–3

OPERATING CHARACTERISTIC CURVE

$n = 200$

$c_a = 3$

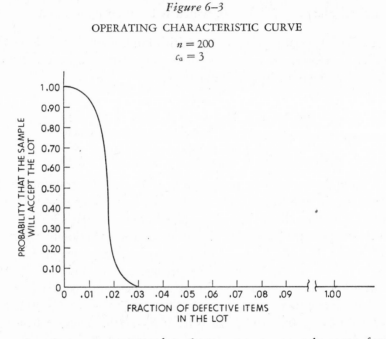

FRACTION OF DEFECTIVE ITEMS
IN THE LOT

Changing the acceptance number alone serves to move the curve farther from or nearer to the origin, as shown in Figure 6–5.

Average Outgoing Quality

Plans may also be specified according to the quality level of lots which leave the inspection point. Of course, if lots which are rejected by a plan are merely shipped back to a supplier, then the plan does not affect the quality level of lots submitted to it, except insofar as defectives found in the samples are replaced. However, where the inspection point is within a production process, rejected lots must either be thrown away or submitted to 100 per cent inspection; the latter, of course, being the normal course. In these cases, the average outgoing quality (AOQ) becomes important in order to give assurance as to the worst

Figure 6–4

OPERATING CHARACTERISTIC CURVE

$n = 1000$
$c = 15$

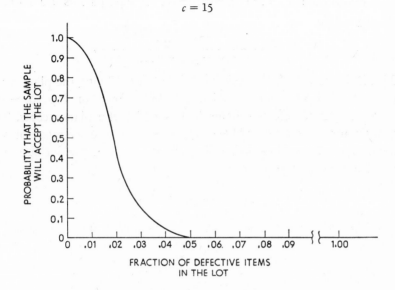

FRACTION OF DEFECTIVE ITEMS
IN THE LOT

Figure 6–5

OPERATING CHARACTERISTIC CURVES

$n = 200$

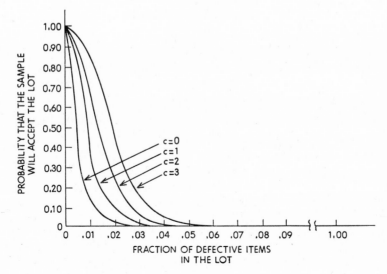

FRACTION OF DEFECTIVE ITEMS
IN THE LOT

average quality which can be expected to leave the inspection point.

If lots of fraction defective p are submitted to a given plan, then, assuming all defectives are discarded and all rejected lots are 100 per cent inspected,

$$AOQ = \frac{P_a p(S - n)}{S - pn - p(1 - P_a)(S - n)}, \tag{12}$$

which is the average fraction defective in all lots leaving the plan, when the submitted lot fraction defective is p. The numerator, $P_a p\ (S - n)$, is the number of defective items in lots which the plan accepts. The denominator, $S - pn - p(1 - P_a)\ (S - n)$ is the average lot size after defectives are discarded. If it is desired to maintain lot size at S, defectives must be replaced, and

$$AOQ = \frac{P_a p\ (S - n)}{S}, \tag{13}$$

assuming replacements are 100 per cent inspected. Under the plan of equation (12), the average number of items inspected per lot will be

$$I = n + (1 - P_a)(S - n)$$
$$= S - P_a\ (S - n),$$

that is, the number in the sample plus remaining items in rejected lots. When the plan of equation (13) is followed,

$$I = n + (1 - P_a)(S - n) + p[n + (1 - P_a)(S - n)] + \cdots$$
$$= [n + (1 - P_a)(S - n)]\ (1 + p + p^2 + \cdots),$$

which gives

$$I = \frac{S - P_a\ (S - n)}{1 - p}. \tag{14}$$

In equation (14), the numerator is the average number of items which will be inspected in lots submitted to the plan (lot size less those passed without inspection), while the denominator is the correction necessary to account for inspection to secure replacements.

This calculation is illustrated below for the plan of Figure 6–3.

Given: $n = 200$,
$c = 3$,
$S = 10,000$,
$p = 0.01$ (lot fraction defective).

From the OC curve of Figure 6–3, $P_a = 0.86$. In the sample n, all defectives will be replaced. In the 9,800 items in each of the rejected lots, all defectives will be replaced, while the 9,800 items in accepted lots will average $0.01\ (9,800) = 98$ defectives. Thus,

$$AOQ = \frac{0.86\,(0.01)(9,800)}{10,000} = 0.0084 \cdot$$

In order to achieve this *AOQ*, the average number of items inspected per lot will be

$$I = \frac{S - P_a\,(S - n)}{1 - p} = \frac{10,000 - 0.86\,(9,800)}{0.99} = 1,588 \cdot$$

If *AOQ* is calculated for various p, Figure 6–6 is obtained. As proportion defective in incoming lots increases, the proportion defective in outgoing lots also increases, until enough lots are rejected and inspected 100 per cent to turn the curve down. The maximum value of *AOQ* represents the worst expected quality which will leave this plan

Figure 6–6

AVERAGE OUTGOING QUALITY

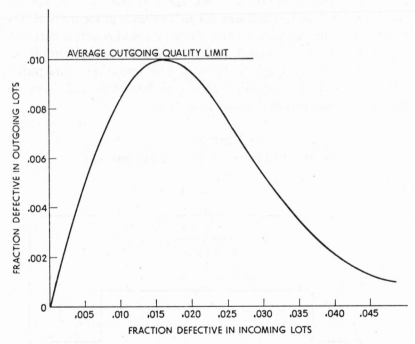

and is called the average outgoing quality limit (*AOQL*). In this case, it occurs where the incoming lot is 0.014 defective and is equal to an expected fraction defective in outgoing lots of 0.0097. Plans may thus be specified in terms of the *AOQL* protection desired as long as (1) the *OC* curve is satisfactory and (2) a good estimate of the process average fraction defective, p', can be obtained. This latter consideration is important in order that the costs of inspection be as small as possible for the desired protection. Sampling tables[2] are available which give plans for any desired $AOQL$ or p_2. These plans have been determined at that point where expected number of items inspected (I) is minimized. It is necessary to know the process average, the lot size, and the desired level of $AOQL$ or p_2 in order to enter these tables; β is assumed at 0.10.

Double Sample Plans

A reduction in the amount of inspection necessary to secure a given degree of protection may often be obtained by a double sampling plan. Such plans are designated by n_1, n_2, c_{a1}, and c_{a2}, where the operation is as shown in Figure 6–7.[3] Here, it should be noted that c_{a2} is an acceptance number for the combined sample ($n_1 + n_2$) and not just for n_2.

For example, if $n_1 = 60$, $n_2 = 80$, $c_{a1} = 1$, and $c_{a2} = 6$, the OC curves for the first and second samples are as shown in Figure 6–8. The region between the acceptance curve for n_1, c_{a1}, and rejection curve for n_1, c_{a2} is an area of no decision, indicating that the second sample, n_2, must be inspected to reach a decision. The operating characteristic curves for this double sampling plan may be determined from the cumulative Poisson exponential of Figure 6–2.

Figure 6–7

DOUBLE SAMPLING INSPECTION PROCEDURE*

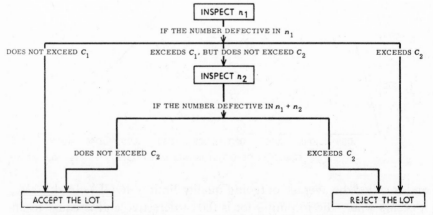

* From H. F. Dodge and H. G. Romig, *Sampling Inspection Tables* (New York: John Wiley & Sons, Inc., 1944), p. 28, with permission of the publishers.

---

[2] Harold F. Dodge and Harry G. Romig, *Sampling Inspection Tables* (New York: John Wiley & Sons, Inc., 1944).

[3] *Ibid.*, p. 28.

The probability of acceptance on the first sample (P_{a_1}) when, for example, $p = 0.04$ may be read from Figure 6–2 as 0.32 $[pn_1 = 0.04$ $(60) = 2.4$ and $c = 1]$. The probability of rejection after n_1 is the probability of 7 or more defects in a sample of 60, which is about 0.01. This is found by computing one minus the probability of 6 or less defects. The probabilities associated with drawing a second sample (2, 3, 4, 5, or 6 defects in n_1) are as follows:

Defects in n_1	Prob. of This No.	No. in n_2 to Accept	Prob. of This No. or Less $(pn_2 = 3.2)$
2.........................	0.25	4 or less	0.78
3.........................	0.21	3 or less	0.60
4.........................	0.13	2 or less	0.38
5.........................	0.06	1 or less	0.18
6.........................	0.02	0	0.04

Then the probability of acceptance after n_2 items have been inspected is:

$$P_{a_2} = 0.25(0.78) + 0.21(0.60) + 0.13(0.38) + 0.06(0.18)$$
$$+ 0.02(0.04) = 0.38 \, .$$

The probability of acceptance for the combined sample is thus $0.32 + 0.38 = 0.70$. Similar values of P_a for other fractions defective may be worked out, and the OC curve for this plan determined.

The average number of items which will be inspected per sample (ASN) will vary with the fraction defective of submitted lots. This number is given by

$$ASN = n_1 (P_{a_1} + P_{r_1}) + (n_1 + n_2) [1 - (P_{a_1} + P_{r_1})] \, . \qquad (15)$$

That is, the number inspected is a function of $(P_{a_1} + P_{r_1})$, which is the proportion of time a decision is reached on the first sample. Somewhat less than this number will be inspected if inspection is curtailed before completing n_2 whenever the number of defective items exceeds c_{a2}.

The average number of items inspected in a lot of size S when rejected lots are inspected 100 per cent would be

$$I = n_1[P_{a_1} + P_{a_2}] + n_2[P_{a_2}] + S[1 - (P_{a_1} + P_{a_2})] \qquad (16)$$

where defective items are not replaced.

A single sample plan with approximately the same OC curve as the final curve for the plan given above is $n = 80$, $c_a = 3$. Whether or not the double sample plan is effective in reducing sample size depends on the kind of lots which are submitted. If most lots are in the range for which probability of acceptance or rejection is high on the first sample, then assuredly, the average sample size will be nearer 60 than 140. If, however, the second sample must be drawn in many cases, average sample size to give the same assurance may be higher with the double sample plan. If inspection is curtailed[4] as soon as a decision is reached, in general the average sample size will always be less for double than that for single sampling.

As was mentioned, the problem of designing a double sample plan is much more difficult than for a corresponding single sample plan. This is due to the fact that specifying two points $[(P_1, \alpha), (P_2, \beta)]$ is not sufficient to give a unique plan since three operating characteristic curves are involved. The usual procedure is to assign a fixed relationship to the ratio of n_1 and n_2 and derive tables which make the determination of a plan easy.[5]

Multiple Sample Plans

Of course, we can continue the process of subdividing the sample to be taken producing multiple schemes such as that shown below:

Sample	n	c_{a1}	c_{a2}
1........	20	...	1
2........	20	0	1
3........	20	1	2
4........	20	2	2

In this case acceptance is not allowed on the first sample while rejection will occur if two or more defects are found. If 0 defects are found in $n_1 + n_2$, the lot will be accepted while three or more are required for rejection and so on. On the final sample in 80 items inspected 2 or fewer give acceptance and more than 2 rejection. A collection of such plans based on their *AQL* may be found in reference 3.

Sequential Sampling

Sequential sampling plans allow the number of items inspected to be determined by the cumulative results of the inspection process. In Figure 6–9, c is plotted against n, and the plan is represented by the two parallel lines. As n increases, c also increases, and inspection is contin-

---

[4] See Irving W. Burr, "Average Sample Number under Curtailed or Truncated Sampling," *Industrial Quality Control*, February, 1957, pp. 5–7.

[5] Acheson J. Duncan, *Quality Control and Industrial Statistics* (3d ed.; Homewood, Ill.: Richard D. Irwin, Inc., 1965), pp. 171–74.

Figure 6–8

OPERATING CHARACTERISTIC CURVES

Double Sampling Plan

$n_1 = 60$ $c_1 = 1$
$n_2 = 80$ $c_2 = 6$

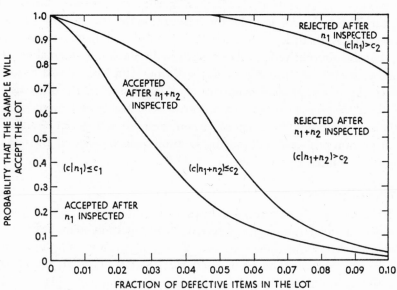

Figure 6–9

SEQUENTIAL SAMPLING PLAN

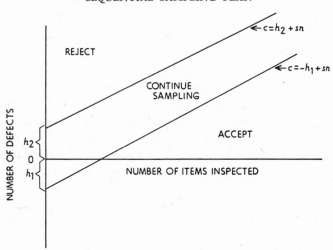

ued until the cumulative number of defects plotted against n puts one in a decision area.

Tables of h_1, h_2, and s for various α, β, p_1, and p_2 are available.[6] The logic of sequential sampling rests basically on determining after each observation the probability of obtaining the observations cumulated thus far. This is done first under the assumption that the null hypothesis is true (that is, that the lot is acceptable) and second under the assumption that the alternative hypothesis is true (the lot is not acceptable). If the ratio of the latter probability to the former (the "likelihood ratio") ever reaches some predetermined level, A, the inspection process stops and the alternative hypothesis is accepted. If it ever falls to some level B, the null hypothesis is accepted. When the ratio is between A and B, the inspection process is continued. The protection afforded by the test is given by α and β, where $A = (1 - \beta)/\alpha$ and $B = (1 - \alpha)/\beta$.

Special Attributes Plans

If the product submitted for inspection is such that it cannot be classified as defective or not defective on an item-by-item basis, e.g., cloth, carpeting, television sets, etc., a defects-per-unit sampling plan may be appropriate. The plans used for fraction defective inspection may be converted to defects-per-unit plans merely by replacing the words "defective units" with "defects" and "fraction defective" with "number of defects per unit." Thus, the plan where $N = 200$, $c = 3$ might mean to inspect 200 square yards of carpeting from each lot with the acceptance number equal to three defects in the sample. Otherwise all computations are carried out exactly as given previously.

A sampling plan for continuous production has been devised by H. F. Dodge.[7] This kind of plan is characterized by two numbers, f and i, which represent, respectively, the proportion of items to be regularly inspected as long as no defects are found and the number of items to be inspected continuously and found free from defects after a defective has been found in f. For example, if $f = 0.05$ and $i = 100$, the plan says that every twentieth item is to be inspected until one defect is found. Then resort to 100 per cent inspection until a run of 100 is found free from defects, at which signal revert to inspecting every twentieth item. The plan will give a stated $AOQL$ protection, where $\beta = 0.10$ according to a graph in f, i, and p_2 available in the source given.

---

[6] Statistical Research Group, Columbia University, *Sequential Analysis of Statistical Data: Applications* (New York: Columbia University Press, 1945).

[7] H. F. Dodge, "A Sampling Plan for Continuous Production," *Annals of Mathematical Statistics,* Vol. XIV, pp. 264–79.

VARIABLES SAMPLING PLANS

So far we have been concerned only with inspection plans based on merely classifying items as "good" or "bad" (attributes plans) rather than on measurements of the *degree* of conformance of output to specifications (variables plans). The advantages of such plans over attributes plans are that fewer items must be inspected to give the same degree of assurance as regards acceptance or rejection, additional diagnostic information is provided as a means of process control, and since the decision criterion is continuous rather than discrete each item is given its proper weight in the lot decision.

The major disadvantages are of course the higher cost of inspection (especially instrumentation), the greater time usually required, and the more complex computations involved. As might be expected, such plans are almost always more economical than attributes plans when inspection is destructive.

As an example of the development of a variables inspection plan, consider a process in which a battery of machines is producing output characterized by a dimension for which the specification is $2.030'' \pm 0.025''$. The output is gathered in boxes of 1,000 each and it is desired to develop an inspection plan to assure conformance of output quality to this specification. The standard deviation of the process (based on machine capability studies to be described later) is known to be $0.010''$ but it is also known that the mean of the various machines drifts so that from lot to lot one may get considerable variation in quality. Given that the distribution of output is normal the *best* that the process can do in terms of fraction defective is $p = 0.0124$ as shown in Figure 6–10 (dimensions given in $0.001''$). It is considered (based on costs as will be discussed later) that a "good" lot is one for which $p_1 = 0.015$ and should be accepted 95 per cent of the time without further inspection ($\alpha = 0.05$) and a "bad" lot is one for which $p_2 = 0.04$ and should be accepted only 5 per cent of the time ($\beta = 0.05$).

The procedure in variables inspection would be to draw a sample of size n, compute a statistic of the sample (in this case the mean), and compare this statistic to an established criterion for acceptance. In this case a range of mean values must be established such that if the sample mean falls within the range the given criterion for acceptance will be satisfied. In order to establish the operating characteristic curve, the relationship between measurements and p_1 and p_2 must be determined. Assuming that the process output may be described in terms of a normal

Figure 6–10
NORMAL DISTRIBUTION OF PROCESS OUTPUT
Abscissa in 0.001 inches

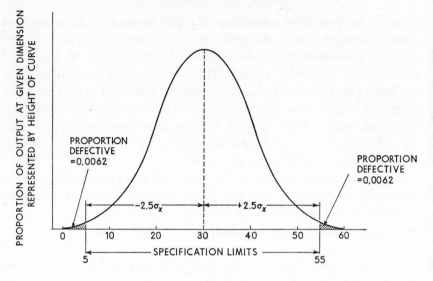

Figure 6–11
SHIFT PRODUCING FRACTION DEFECTIVE = 0.015

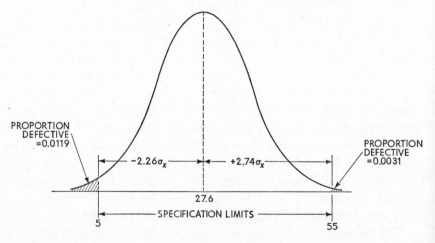

distribution and using the Table in Appendix II, Figures 6–11 and 6–12 can be drawn.

These show the shift down from 0.030″ required to give p_1 and p_2 lots if we assume that the standard deviation of the process remains at 0.010″. Of course, a shift upward to 0.0324″ for p_1 and 0.0374″ for p_2 would have the same effect. If we assume that shifts in either direction can occur it can be seen that any process mean from 0.0276 to 0.0324 will produce lots with fractions defective between 0.0124 and 0.0150. Assuming we wish to have the same protection against shifts up as that for shifts down, α and β will be split equally. Thus it becomes necessary to establish a sample size and a pair of sample means such that acceptance will follow for any actual observation in that range.

Figure 6–12
SHIFT PRODUCING FRACTION DEFECTIVE = 0.04

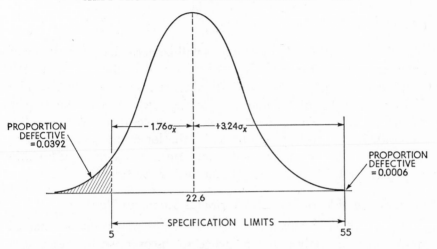

Considering shifts down as shown in Figures 6–11 and 6–12, the following relationship can be established.

$$\frac{\bar{x}_a - 27.6}{10./\sqrt{n}} = -1.96$$

and

$$\frac{\bar{x}_a - 22.6}{10./\sqrt{n}} = 1.96$$

in which

$$\bar{x}_a = \text{lower acceptance limit},$$
$$n = \text{sample size}.$$

The first of these follows from the fact that we would expect 2.5 per cent of the sample means to fall beyond 1.96 standard deviations and thus 97.5 per cent to be between -1.96 standard deviations and $+\infty$. Of course, we can see that 95 per cent of sample means will fall in the interval between -1.96 and $+1.96$ standard deviations if the true mean is 0.0276″ and this is just our acceptance requirement for p_1. The denominator gives us the standard deviation of sample means ($\sigma_{\bar{x}}$) if the standard deviation of the population is 10. and the sample size is n.[8] Similarly the second relationship stipulates acceptance 2.5 per cent of the time, that is 97.5 per cent of the sample means beyond $\bar{x}_a + 1.96\sigma_{\bar{x}}$ and thus considering both downward and upward shifts will assure that the requirement that the probability of acceptance equal β for lots of p_2 quality will be met.

Solving these for $\bar{x}_a$ and n we obtain

$$\bar{x}_a = 0.0251 \,,$$
$$n = 62 \,.$$

Since the distribution of sample means will be normal, considerations of symmetry give us that $\bar{x}_a$ for upward shifts will be 0.0349″. Thus the sampling inspection plan to give the desired assurance would require drawing a sample of 62 items, measuring each item to the nearest 0.0001″, and computing the mean of the sample. If the mean was less than 0.0251″ or greater than 0.0349″, the lot would be rejected and subjected to 100 per cent inspection for defects. If the mean fell within these limits it would be passed without further inspection.

Comparison of Variables and Attributes Sampling Plans

If one wished to obtain the same degree of protection as obtained above but using only a simple guage to discover whether each unit inspected was in or out of the specified tolerance limits, a sampling plan to do this could be derived from the Poisson chart in the manner illustrated previously. The requirements are

$$p_1 = 0.015, \ \alpha = 0.05 \,,$$
$$p_2 = 0.040, \ \beta = 0.05 \,,$$

and p_2n/p_1n should be $0.015/0.040 = 2.67$. At $c_a = 10$, $p_2/p_1 = 2.74$ and at $c_a = 11$, 2.63. If we let $c_a = 11$, then a sample size of 455 would come very close to the desired result. This is more than seven times that required by the previous plan and thus the extra costs of inspection and computation for the variables plan would have to be more than seven times that for this attributes plan for the attributes plan to be justified.

It should also be noted that with a lot size of 1,000 and a sample size of 455, the assumption of a Bernoulli process is almost certainly not valid and binomial probabilities would not be correct. The reader has assuredly noted that up to this point the fact that the lot size was 1,000 played no part at all in the development of the plans. It would have made no difference if it were 2,000 or 5,000 or 10,000 as far as the

---

[8] Those who are not aware of this relationship should refer to page 172 on which a derivation will be found.

assurance given by the plan is concerned. In all of these cases a sample size of 62 for the variables plan would have the identical discriminatory power as between good and bad lots. It is always the *absolute* rather than the *relative* size of a sample which determines its capability. The notion that one should inspect some *percentage* of a lot in order to gain a given degree of reliability is false as the above example demonstrates.

However, the fact remains that if the lot size were 10,000 instead of 1,000, our derivation of the plan $n = 455$, $c_a = 11$ could be accepted without any further questions. Given that the lot size is 1,000, this plan is suspect in that the Poisson probabilities used in its derivation are not likely to be good approximations for the true (hypergeometric) probabilities.

While it should be clear that a complete comparison of variables and attributes plans could not be given due to the very large number of conditions implied by such a comparison, one can always be made for a given situation and this should always be done when attributes inspection itself is expensive. This would be true, for example, when any test involved destruction of the item inspected.

Variables Sampling Plans—σ_x Unknown

When the standard deviation of the population sampled is unknown and must be estimated from the sample, the derivation of a variables sampling plan to give some desired degree of protection is much more difficult. In this case, the appropriate statistic for decision is Student's "t."[9] A sample of size n would be drawn from the lot and estimates of the population mean and standard deviation made according to

$$\bar{x} = \frac{\sum\limits_i x_i}{n}$$

and

$$s_x = \sqrt{\frac{\sum\limits_i^n (x_i - \bar{x})^2}{n - 1}} \, .$$

Then, the decision statistic

$$\frac{\bar{x} - \bar{x}_a}{s_x / \sqrt{n}}$$

---

[9] When sample size is less than 30, the estimate of σ_x from the data does not give good results. The distribution for a normal universe of sample values of the statistic $t = \dfrac{\bar{x} - \mu}{s_x / \sqrt{n}}$ was developed by W. S. Gossett (under the pen name "Student"). This distribution is tabled in Appendix II.

would be computed, where $\bar{x}_a$ is the acceptable quality level, and compared to the "t" deviate exceeded with probability α. The difficulty here lies in the fact that the OC curve, and therefore α and β, is dependent on knowledge of the lot standard deviation. Some judgment must be made as to the expected standard deviation in order to get any idea at all of the risks involved. Also, this judgment is necessary in order to derive a test based on α and β and the corresponding quality levels. Data which will enable one to derive a plan based on such an estimate are available.[10]

If the decision criterion is the fraction defective in the lot submitted, then this number is the proportion of the distribution of values of the characteristic outside the tolerance limits. An inspection plan would be based on acceptance when the sample average falls in the interval $\bar{x} \pm ks_x$, where k is the tolerance limits in standard deviation units (assuming these limits are given as $\pm T$ about some value of the quality characteristic, $k = \dfrac{T - \bar{x}}{s_x}$). The derivation of such plans based on p_1, p_2, α and β is beyond the scope of this book but may be found elsewhere.[11]

ECONOMICS OF SAMPLING INSPECTION

A Quality Control Problem

A process is known to be capable of producing output for which the fraction defective is 0.01. At intervals of 1,000 units produced, the tooling must be replaced and the machine set up again for the next run. If the set up is accomplished correctly and the new tooling has been produced correctly, the fraction defective will again be $p = 0.01$.

All output including any defectives is incorporated into the final product and an extra cost of $1 per unit is incurred at final test for each defective unit replaced. It is possible to run a check on the setup before production begins at an extra cost of $20 and this would ensure that the fraction defective would be at its minimum value of 0.01.

It is easy to see that if the check is not made the cost of defectives would be $1 (1,000p) or $1,000p, while if the check is made it would be $20 + $1(0.01 × 1,000), or $30. If the value of p were 0.05 then the cost without a check would be $50 and the check should always be

---

[10] J. Neymann and B. Tokarska, "Errors of the Second Kind in Testing Student's Hypothesis," *Journal of the American Statistical Association*, Vol. XXXI, pp. 318–26.

[11] Statistical Research Group, Columbia University, *Techniques of Statistical Analysis* (New York: McGraw-Hill Book Co., Inc., 1947), chap. i, pp. 3–93. Tables of k and n where $\alpha = 0.05$ and $\beta = 0.10$ are given for various combinations of p_1 and p_2 on pp. 22–25.

made. The break-even value (the value at which the costs with and without the check are the same) is

$$\$1,000p = \$30,$$
$$\text{Break-even } p = 0.03.$$

The problem facing us is to estimate p by means of some sampling plan. If inspection costs are $0.10 per unit the cost of screening the entire lot would be $100 and this would not be a reasonable alternative since total cost of only $30 would be incurred if the check were always made. If the check is not made and the process turns out 1 per cent defectives, the cost is only $10 per run and we can afford to spend up to $30 — $10 = $20 to estimate the fraction defective.

If we were willing to specify some values for (p_1, α) and (p_2, β), then a plan could be developed. It seems plausible to pick some set such as

$$p_1 = 0.02, \ \alpha = 0.05,$$
$$p_2 = 0.06, \ \beta = 0.10,$$

since p_1 and p_2 bracket the break-even quality ($p = 0.03$) and thus we achieve a high probability of accepting a 0.01 setup and rejecting a setup for which defective costs would exceed $30.

The plan which meets these specifications is $n = 200$, $c_a = 7$, but the cost of this is $20 and this is only what we could afford for perfect discrimination around the break-even level. If we relax the requirements by setting $\alpha = 0.10$ then $n = 154$, $c_a = 5$ is a plan which comes close to satisfying the requirements at a cost of $15.40.

Even if we were to adopt such a plan there is no guarantee that it would be an economical one. For example, if no setups were ever made which produced lots more than 4 per cent defective, the selection of $p_2 = 0.06$ as an objective is not a very good one. It should be clear that in the absence of any knowledge concerning the values of p which might be produced, it is not likely that an economic sampling plan will result.

A Procedure for Least Cost Sampling

If we keep records of the outcome of each setup and observe that 80 per cent of the time the fraction defective turns out to be 0.01 but that 10 per cent of the time it is 0.10 and 10 per cent of the time 0.25, we are justified in assuming the following prior distribution of p:

j	p_j	P_j
1......	0.01	0.8
2......	0.10	0.1
3......	0.25	0.1

Given this and the costs given previously if we select a sampling plan which costs less than $20, say, $n = 100$, $c_a = 5$ the expected cost per run can be developed by the following procedure.

From the Poisson Chart we determine the probability of acceptance for each state (P_{aj}) as shown in Table 6–1, Col. 3. The unconditional

Table 6–1

EXPECTED RESULTS FOR $n = 100$, $c_a = 5$

(1) p_j	(2) P_j	(3) P_{aj}	(4) $P_j \times P_{aj}$	(5) $P_j \times P_{aj} \times p_j$	(7) $P_j \times p_j$	(6) $P_j \times p_1(1 - P_{aj})$
0.01	0.8	0.9994	0.7995	0.007995	0.008	0.000006
0.10	0.1	0.07	0.007	0.0007	0.01	0.00093
0.20	0.1	0.0	0.0	0.0	0.02	0.001
	Σ		0.8065	0.008695	0.038	0.001936

probability of acceptance is $\sum\limits_{j=1}^{j=3} P_j P_{aj}$ that is the sum over all states of the probability of acceptance in each state times the probability of being in that state. This is shown in Table 6–1, Col. 4. Rejection carries with it the requirement that the setup be checked and incurs a cost of $10. Thus the expected cost of checking is $10(1 - 0.8065)$, or $1.935 per run.

The expected cost of undetected defects would be first the fraction defective in accepted runs times the probability of acceptance times the probability of occurrence of such a run summed over all states, that is,

$$\sum_{j=1}^{j=3} P_j P_{aj} p_j \,.$$

Since this only accounts for accepted runs the fraction defective in that proportion of runs that are checked must be added. This would be the probability of rejection of each state times the fraction defective in state 1 (after the check) times the probability of the occurrence of that state, that is,

$$\sum_{j=1}^{j=3} (1 - P_{aj}) p_1 P_j \,.$$

These two quantities are given in Cols. 5 and 6 of Table 6–1 and the sum of the two is 0.010631 which is the average fraction defective which will leave the process in the long run.

Since the sample will be screened for defects leaving only $(S - n)$

or 900 units uninspected per run the expected cost per run can be seen to be

Expected cost = inspection cost + checking cost + cost of defects
= $0.10(100) + $10.(1 - 0.8065) + $1.(900)(0.010631)
= $21.50 .

Expressed in general terms this relationship is

$$\text{Expected cost} = c_i n + c_k(1 - \Sigma P_j P_{aj})$$
$$+ c_d[(S - n)(\Sigma P_j P_{aj} p_j + \Sigma P_j(1 - P_{aj})p_1)] \quad (17)$$

in which

c_i = cost of inspection per unit,
c_k = cost of checking setup,
c_d = cost of defects per unit,
P_j = probability of jth state,
p_j = fraction defective in j^{th} state,
P_{aj} = probability of acceptance in j^{th} state,
S = run size,
n = sample size.

It can be seen that the expected cost of $21.50 per run is less than the $30 which would be incurred if every run were checked and is less than the expected cost of $43 per run if none were checked (the reader should verify this figure). However, there is no assurance that this is the best plan available given the distribution of fractions defective assumed. In order to discover this, (17) would have to be explored for various sampling plans.

A computer program which computes the expected cost per run for any plan is shown in the Appendix to this chapter. This program includes a procedure whereby starting with a given (n, c_a), the sample size is incremented downward as long as the cost is decreasing. As soon as cost turns up, sample size is reset to a higher level, c_a is increased by one and the process continues. When cost is determined to increase for changes in both n and c_a, the program terminates. Thus if one begins with a plan for which cost is higher than the minimum cost, at least a local minimum and in most cases, the minimum cost plan will be determined. The data for the situation just described were input to this program and the results are shown in Table 6–2. The minimum cost plan is $n = 32$, $c_a = 1$ and the cost is $16.60 per run.

A General Procedure for Economic Acceptance Plans

It should be clear at this point that the economic determination of any sampling plan rests critically on some prior knowledge or assumptions as to the kind of lots which will be presented to the plan. One must define in some way the conditions under which the plan will be used if the resulting plan is to have any rational results. We wish now a procedure for determining an economic plan in situations in which rejected lots are screened 100 per cent for defects.

Table 6–2

RESULTS OF COMPUTER SEARCH FOR LEAST COST SAMPLING PLAN

n	c_a	P_{a1}	P_{a2}	P_{a3}	Defect Cost	Total Cost
50	1	0.9098	0.0404	0.0001	9.8468	17.5280
40	1	0.9384	0.0916	0.0005	10.4027	16.8031
36	1	0.9488	0.1257	0.0012	10.7590	16.6414
32	1	0.9585	0.1712	0.0030	11.2416	16.5993
30	1	0.9631	0.1991	0.0047	11.5480	16.6396
75	2	0.9595	0.0203	0.0000	9.4187	19.2225
51	2	0.9848	0.1165	0.0003	10.4911	17.5956
45	2	0.9891	0.1736	0.0010	11.0644	17.4769
43	2	0.9904	0.1974	0.0015	11.3041	17.4823

Let us assume that costs of inspection and costs of defectives are linear, with values c_i and c_d per piece, respectively; and that P_j is the probability that a fraction defective p_j will be presented for inspection. Then the expected cost per lot with no inspection is

$$AC_0 = c_d S \sum_j P_j p_j ,$$

and the cost per lot with 100 per cent screening is

$$AC_{100} = c_i S .$$

The cost of production is not included here since the yield of good pieces is the same in both cases. If AC_{100} is more than AC_0, then no inspection is justified except to guard against changes in the p_j and the question arises as to the cost of a sampling scheme. This can be given as an average cost per lot and is

$$AC = \text{Cost of inspection} + \text{Cost of undetected defects}$$

$$= c_i \left[S - (S - n) \sum_j P_j P_{aj} \right] + c_d (S - n) \sum_j P_j p_j P_{aj} \quad (18)$$

where P_{aj} is the probability of acceptance in the jth state and can be approximated by the Poisson expression

$$P_{aj} = \sum_{c=0}^{c_a} e^{-(p_j n)} \frac{(p_j n)^c}{c!}$$

if n is the sample size and c_a the acceptance number. Thus, (18) could be explored with various plans until the least cost plan were found. In a concrete case, say the following are estimates of prior probabilities and costs:

$$
\begin{aligned}
c_i &= \$0.08 \text{ per piece,} \\
c_d &= \$2.00 \text{ per piece,} \\
P_1 &= 0.95, \ p_1 = 0.02, \\
P_2 &= 0.05, \ p_2 = 0.06, \\
S &= 5,000.
\end{aligned}
$$

Thus it is assumed that there are only two possible states of the world, p_1 and p_2. The cost of no inspection is

$$
\begin{aligned}
AC_0 &= \$2.00(5,000)[0.95(0.02) + 0.05(0.06)] \\
&= \$220 ,
\end{aligned}
$$

and the cost of 100 per cent inspection is

$$
\begin{aligned}
AC_{100} &= 0.08(5,000) \\
&= \$400 .
\end{aligned}
$$

Thus, no inspection is indicated except to provide for detection of changes in expectations as concerns the p_j. If a plan is selected according to "classical" criteria ($\alpha = 0.05$, $\beta = 0.10$) the result is $n = 200$, $c_a = 7$ (giving $\alpha = 0.051$ and $\beta = 0.090$), and the average cost per lot is

$$
\begin{aligned}
AC &= 0.08[5,000 - (4,800)(0.95 \times 0.95 + 0.05 \times 0.09)] \\
&\quad + 2.00[4,800(0.95 \times 0.02 \times 0.95 + 0.09 \times 0.05 \times 0.06)] \\
&= \$227.78
\end{aligned}
$$

and a premium of $7.78 per lot is paid. Exploration of (18) for various plans gives the results shown in Table 6–3. It can be seen that a plan whose total cost closely approaches that of no inspection can be attained and the cost of protection against shifts in fraction defective reduced to near zero. The table shows clearly the effect of decreasing n and holding c_a constant on the probabilities of acceptance and costs. As the minimum cost plan for each c_a is found, c_a is incremented and values of n again searched for a minimum. When the minimum cost for a given c_a indicates we have passed the minimum point for n and c_a together, we infer that the best plan has been found.

It is interesting to observe the results of a search for a least cost sampling plan in a situation in which estimates of probabilities and costs are as follows:

$$c_i = \$0.30,$$
$$c_d = \$8.00,$$
$$P_1 = 0.90, \; p_1 = 0.01,$$
$$P_2 = 0.10, \; p_2 = 0.10,$$
$$S = 1,000.$$

In this case the cost of no inspection is $152 while the cost of 100 per cent inspection is $300, and sampling is indicated. The least cost plan found as shown in Table 6–4 was $n = 55$, $c_a = 2$ with $P_{a1} = 0.9815$ and $P_{a2} = 0.08846$. The fraction defective leaving the plan would be 0.0097 and the total cost of inspection plus undetected defects, $120.52.

Thus, in situations in which there is a great deal to be gained by the detection of "bad" lots (contrast the 0.01 lots with the 0.10 lots) sampling inspection is the *only* economical means to rectify the process fraction defective. In this case the gain over no inspection is over $30 and the gain over 100 per cent inspection is almost $180.

A computer program to carry out this computation is shown in the Appendix to this chapter. This is the same as that used in the previous case with changes in the form of the equation to (18) by setting JCHECK to zero at input. Results for the situation above (Tables 6–3 and 6–4) were obtained with this program.

Table 6–3

AVERAGE COST PER LOT FOR VARIOUS SAMPLING PLANS

n	c_a	P_{a1}	P_{a2}	AOQ	Defect Cost	Total Cost
200	4	0.6288	0.0076	0.0120	$114.9187	$285.3731
150	4	0.8153	0.0550	0.0157	151.8525	250.2801
120	4	0.9041	0.1555	0.0176	172.2156	233.8557
100	4	0.9473	0.2851	0.0189	184.7767	226.3975
80	4	0.9763	0.4763	0.0200	196.5915	222.1540
60	4	0.9923	0.7064	0.0210	207.2048	220.7136
55	4	0.9946	0.7626	0.0212	209.5147	220.6534
50	4	0.9963	0.8153	0.0214	211.6249	220.6595
100	5	0.9834	0.4457	0.0200	196.2188	221.2518
80	5	0.9940	0.6510	0.0208	205.0484	220.5752
75	5	0.9955	0.7029	0.0210	207.0876	220.6078
130	6	0.9828	0.3384	0.0197	191.7707	221.4136
110	6	0.9925	0.5108	0.0204	199.4215	220.5625
105	6	0.9941	0.5582	0.0206	201.3149	220.5455
100	6	0.9955	0.6063	0.0207	203.1811	220.5860
150	7	0.9881	0.3239	0.0197	191.5314	221.0358
140	7	0.9919	0.3987	0.0200	194.8031	220.6965
130	7	0.9947	0.4812	0.0203	198.1339	220.6164
125	7	0.9958	0.5246	0.0205	199.8090	220.6519

Table 6–4

RESULTS OF SEARCH FOR LEAST COST SAMPLING PLAN

n	c_a	P_{a1}	P_{a2}	AOQ	Defect Cost	Total Cost
50	1	0.9098	0.0404	0.0086	65.3025	130.7877
35	1	0.9513	0.1359	0.0099	76.5889	124.7862
30	1	0.9631	0.1991	0.0107	82.7143	124.6927
25	1	0.9735	0.2873	0.0116	90.7490	126.0714
60	2	0.9769	0.0620	0.0094	70.7756	121.0948
55	2	0.9815	0.0884	0.0097	73.4650	120.5206
75	3	0.9927	0.0591	0.0095	70.4911	120.9210
70	3	0.9942	0.0818	0.0098	72.6581	120.7215
65	3	0.9956	0.1118	0.0101	75.3869	120.9224

Economic Acceptance Plans for Destructive Inspection

It may be that yield is affected by inspection as, for example, when inspection is destructive. In such a case, sampling inspection can provide a gain over no inspection and the problem of determining an optimal plan is more critical than in the first case.

Say that the cost of inspection is $C_i + nc_i$, where C_i is fixed cost per lot and c_i is cost/piece. Production costs are $C_p + Sc_p$. Inspection is destructive so if a lot is rejected it is scrapped and its value is Sc_s. The problem is to determine an optimal inspection plan. Since total production is a function of inspection decisions, yield is part of the problem. Assume an undetected defect costs c_d and that there are a priori two possible states of the world, P_1 and p_2. Our estimates of prior probabilities are

$$P(p_1) = 0.90,$$
$$P(p_2) = 0.10.$$

Concretely, assume

$$C_i + nc_i = \$10 + \$0.10n,$$
$$C_p + Sc_p = \$100 + 1{,}000(\$1.00),$$
$$c_s = \$0.10,$$
$$c_d = \$10,$$
$$P_1 = 0.01,$$
$$P_2 = 0.10,$$
$$P(p_1) = 0.90,$$
$$P(p_2) = 0.10.$$

If we do not inspect,

Average cost per lot = $\$1{,}100 + 0.90[10(\$10)] + 0.10[100(\$10)]$
= $\$1{,}290$

and the average yield per lot is

Average yield = $1{,}000[1 - 0.90(0.01) - 0.10(0.10)]$
= 981 good pieces,

or a cost per piece of $1,290/981 = \$1.315$. We cannot inspect 100 per cent, but if we could detect bad lots at no cost and these were scrapped,

$$AC/\text{lot} = \$1,100 + 0.90[10(\$10)] - 0.10[1,000(\$0.10)] = \$1,180;$$

the average cost per lot would be

$$\begin{aligned} \text{Average yield} &= 1,000[1 - 0.90(0.01) - 0.10] \\ &= 891, \end{aligned}$$

and the cost/piece is $1,180/891 = \$1.325$. Thus, we cannot afford to inspect on any basis since there can be no gain from this operation.

However, if the cost of a defect or the value of scrap were higher, then there might be some potential gain from a sampling inspection plan. Say, the cost of a defect is $40 instead of $10. Then the average cost per lot for no inspection is

$$AC/\text{lot} = \$1,100 + 0.90[10(\$40)] + 0.10[100(\$40)] = \$1,860$$

with a cost per piece of $1,860/981 = \$1.896$. With the rejection of bad lots at no cost the average cost per lot is

$$AC/\text{lot} - \$1,100 + 0.90[10(\$40)] - 0.10[1,000(\$0.10)] = \$1,450,$$

and the cost per piece is $1,450/891 = \$1,627$.

Thus we could afford to spend up to $(1.896 - 1.627)$ per unit of good production to screen lots. The maximum inspection cost per lot then is

$$(1.896 - 1.627)891 = \$239.32.$$

but in order for this to be economic it would have to give perfect discrimination between p_1 and p_2 lots. The problem here is to determine a sampling plan which results in an average cost per piece less than $1.896. An optimal plan would be that one which results in a cost per piece closest to $1.627.

If the entire $239.32 were spent, the sample size would be about 220 since the cost of inspection is $10 + \$0.10n$, and as the test is destructive, a production cost (loss) of $(c_p - c_s) = \$0.90/\text{piece}$ is also incurred. Since such a sample would not give perfect discrimination, it is reasonable to try sample sizes of 200 and less to determine the optimal level of inspection.

In general, the expression for average cost per piece produced would be

$$AC/\text{pc.} = \frac{\text{Cost of production} + \text{Cost of inspection plan}}{\text{Number of good pieces produced}}$$

$$= \frac{(C_p + Sc_p) + (C_i + nc_i) + (S - n)\left[c_d \sum P_j p_j P_{aj} - c_s \sum P_j (1 - P_{aj})\right]}{(S - n)\left[1 - \sum P_j p_j P_{aj} - \sum P_j (1 - P_{aj})\right]}$$

since inspection is destructive and thus yield is affected by inspection. The numerator adds the cost of production, the cost of inspecting the sample, and the cost of defects in accepted lots and subtracts the return from scrapped lots. The denominator reflects the fact that of the $(S - n)$ pieces remaining after inspection, on the average, a proportion equal to $\Sigma P_j(1 - P_{aj})$ will be scrapped.

A computer program which carries out this computation and searches as described below for a least cost plan is shown in the Appendix to this

Table 6–5

SEARCH FOR LEAST COST SAMPLING PLAN WITH $c_d = \$40$

n	c_a	P_{a1}	P_{a2}	Average Cost per Piece
219	0	0.1119	0.0000	14.0362
14	0	0.8694	0.2466	1.9070
9	0	0.9139	0.4066	1.8791
4	0	0.9608	0.6703	1.8792
39	1	0.9411	0.0992	1.7975
34	1	0.9538	0.1468	1.7867
29	1	0.9653	0.2146	1.7837
24	1	0.9754	0.3084	1.7898
59	2	0.9779	0.0666	1.7705
54	2	0.9824	0.0948	1.7650
49	2	0.9864	0.1333	1.7633
44	2	0.9898	0.1851	1.7662
74	3	0.9930	0.0632	1.7737
69	3	0.9945	0.0871	1.7707
64	3	0.9958	0.1189	1.7703
59	3	0.9968	0.1604	1.7728

chapter. Results for the case given above for $c_d = \$40$ are shown in Table 6–5. The program sets sample size at the maximum which can be afforded calculated as indicated above. The acceptance number is set to zero and average cost per piece computed. Then sample size is reduced by a preset increment and cost per piece compared with that previously found. This process is repeated as long as cost per piece continues to decrease or until sample size reaches zero. Then c_a is increased by one, n reset to its maximum value, the minimum value of cost per piece found thus far stored, and the process repeated. When c_a is incremented, the minimum for the current value is compared to the minimum for the previous value and if the former is larger, the search is terminated. Table 6–5 shows how this search resulted in the least cost plan shown when the sample size increment was set at five.

SUMMARY

While sampling has been discussed here primarily relative to inspection to assess quality of product, its possible application even in production management is more general than this. Whenever a decision must be reached, based on less than complete information concerning some process, the sampling theory has a part to play. It is the concern of the manager to draw from such incomplete information a preponderance of "correct" inferences. Clearly in the case of a single decision, such an inference can only be either correct or incorrect, but the long-run effect of this kind of a decision process should be in the direction of correct inferences.

In order that such an objective be attained with regard to this kind of a decision process, it is essential that the manager avail himself of some formal sampling technique in order that

1. The right kind and amount of information is gathered, and
2. The best use is made of this information in arriving at a decision.

It is true that the decision can be no better than the information on which it is based, but it can certainly be much worse if the information is not utilized to best advantage.

Sampling plans by variables and attributes are available in considerable variety, depending on the objectives which the plan must fulfill. The operating characteristic curve for any plan portrays the protection afforded by the plan for all input possibilities. The economic justification for sampling inspection should be established in each situation, insofar as this is possible. Then the type of plan best suited to the situation would be selected from among those available. It should be pointed out, however, that it is certainly possible, and in many cases desirable, to design a sampling plan to fit a given situation rather than placing sole reliance on published tables.

REFERENCES

1. BOWKER, A. H., and LIEBERMAN, G. J. *Engineering Statistics.* Englewood Cliffs, N.J.: Prentice-Hall, Inc., 1959.
2. DODGE, HAROLD F., and ROMIG, HARRY G. *Sampling Inspection Tables— Single and Double Sampling.* New York: John Wiley & Sons, Inc., 1944.
3. DUNCAN, ACHESON J. *Quality Control and Industrial Statistics.* 3d ed. Homewood, Ill.: Richard D. Irwin, Inc., 1965.
4. MILNAR, JOHN. "Games against Nature," *Decision Processes* (eds. THRALL, COOMBS, and DAVIS). New York: John Wiley & Sons, Inc., 1945.
5. SCHLAIFER, ROBERT. *Introduction to Statistics for Business Decisions.* McGraw-Hill Book Co., Inc., 1961.
6. STATISTICAL RESEARCH GROUP, COLUMBIA UNIVERSITY. *Sampling Inspection.* New York: McGraw-Hill Book Co., Inc., 1948.
7. TIPPETT, L. H. C. *Technological Applications of Statistics.* New York: John Wiley & Sons, Inc., 1950.

8. WALD, A. *Sequential Analysis.* New York: John Wiley & Sons, Inc., 1947.

APPENDIX TO CHAPTER 6

PROGRAM TO DETERMINE LEAST COST ACCEPTANCE SAMPLING PLAN

This program is designed to search for a single sample plan based on the cost function of equations (17) or (18) of Chapter 6. In general, equation (18) will be used since (17) represents the special case in which a machine setup may be checked at an extra cost if the sample indicates an uneconomic level of fraction defective will be produced. Equation (18) represents the usual lot by lot acceptance problem encountered in process and receiving inspection.

Input

Input values consist first of desired output options as described in the variable dictionary, the number of states defined for the problem, and a switching variable indicating whether equation (17) or (18) is to be used. Relevant costs are entered next followed by data describing the probability of each state and the fraction defective in each. Then the initial values for n and c_a are given together with the amount by which n is to be incremented at each step in the search and the multiplier by which n is to be reset to a higher value each time c_a is incremented by one.

Computations

The expected fraction defective is computed and the cost of no inspection and 100 per cent inspection determined. These are then output if KOUT(1) equals one. For the initial n and c_a, the subroutine POISON computes the probability of acceptance for each state using the standard Poisson expression with some rearrangement to make for speedy computation. In addition the subroutine determines the over-all probability of acceptance by cumulating the products of each value found and the probability of that state.

These values are then used to determine the expected cost per lot of using the given plan and this is printed out if KOUT (4) is equal to one. At this point the cost is compared to the cost of 100 per cent inspection and if it is lower, n is decreased by an increment and the program returns to call subroutine POISON and compute the expected cost per lot as just described.

The Search Procedure

On the next pass, the cost per lot is compared to the value found at the previous step and if lower, n is decreased again and the computations repeated. When the cost is found to increase, the minimum value for that c_a is stored, c_a is increased by one, n is reset by multiplication by a number read in initially, and the entire process repeated.

When on any pass, the minimum cost plan for that c_a is found to be higher than that found for the previous c_a, the entire process terminates and depending on KOUT(7) a new problem is tried, this problem is rerun with a new initial plan, or the program terminates. As a safeguard, KOUT(6) is set initially to a value which puts an upper limit on the number of plans which will be tried no matter what the outcome up to that point of the search procedure. This coupled with the fact that n is always incremented downward and is not allowed to go negative assures a termination to the search procedure.

Following is a listing of the program, a sample set of data, and a portion of the resulting output. A variable dictionary is also given.

```
       COMMON KOUT(7),P(10),PA(10),PROB(10)
80 READ(5,98) KOUT                                                    1
   READ(5,98) JMAX,JCHECK                                             3
   READ(5,99) COSTD,COSTI,FCOSTI,COSTP,FCOSTP,COSTS,S                 6
   READ(5,99)(P(J),PROB(J),J=1,JMAX)                                  7
90 READ(5,98) N,ICA,INC,MULT                                        15
   EFD = 0.
   DO 10 J=1,JMAX
10 EFD = P(J)*PROB(J) + EFD
   ACO = COSTD*S*EFD
   ACI = COSTI*S + FCOSTI
   IF(KOUT(1).EQ.1)WRITE(6,97)ACO,ACI                               28
   ICT = 0
   ATSAVE = ACI
 2 ATCP = ACI
 1 SN = S - FLOAT(N)
   PAJSUM = 0.
   CALL POISON(JMAX,N,ICA,PAJSUM)                                    33
   IF(JCHECK)11,11,12
11 ACSI = COSTI*(S - SN*PAJSUM) + FCOSTI
   GO TO 13
12 ACSI = COSTI*FLOAT(N) +FCOSTI + COSTS*(1.-PAJSUM)
13 EFDC = 0.
   DO 50 J = 1,JMAX
50 EFDC = PA(J)*P(J)*PROB(J) + EFDC
   ACUD = COSTD*SN*EFDC
   IF(JCHECK)14,14,15
15 CHKDEF = 0.
   DO 16 J=1,JMAX
   PR = 1. - PA(J)
16 CHKDEF = PR*P(1)*PROB(J) + CHKDEF
   ACUD = ACUD + COSTD*SN*CHKDEF
14 ATC = ACSI + ACUD
   IF(KOUT(4).EQ.1) WRITE(6,96) N,ICA,EFDC,ACSI,ACUD,ATC            60
   IF(ATC.GT.ATCP) GO TO 60
   ATCP = ATC
   N = N - INC
   IF(N)70,70,17
17 ICT = ICT + 1
   IF(ICT - KOUT(6))1,1,70
60 IF(ATCP.GT.ATSAVE) GO TO 70
   N = (MULT*N)/10
   ICA = ICA + 1
   ICT = ICT + 1
   ATSAVE = ATCP
   IF(ICT - KOUT(6))2,2,70
70 IF(KOUT(7) - 1)100,90,80
100 STOP
99 FORMAT(7F10.4)
98 FORMAT(7I10)
97 FORMAT(1H0,5X,4HACO=F10.4,6H, ACI=F10.4)
96 FORMAT(1H0,7H FOR N=I5,6H, ICA=I3/6H F.D.=F6.4,13H, INSP. COST=F10
  1.4,14H, DEFECT COST=F10.4,13H, TOTAL COST=F10.4)
   END


   SUBROUTINE POISON(JMAX,N,ICA,PAJSUM)
   COMMON KOUT(7),P(10),PA(10),PROB(10)
   DO 20 J=1,JMAX
   PN = P(J)*FLOAT(N)
   PA(J) = 0.
   IF(ICA.EQ.0) GO TO 40
   PAN = 1.
   DO 30 I = 1,ICA
   PAN = (PAN*PN)/FLOAT(I)
30 PA(J) = PA(J) + PAN
40 PA(J) = EXP(-PN)*(PA(J) + 1.)                                     17
20 PAJSUM = PAJSUM + PA(J)*PROB(J)
   IF(KOUT(2).EQ.1) WRITE(6,87)(PA(J),J=1,JMAX)                     25
   RETURN
87 FORMAT(10X,10F10.3)
   END
$DATA
        1         1         1         1         1       200         2
        2         0
  8.        .3        0.        1.        0.        .1      1000.
   .01       .9        .1        .1
        50        1         5        30
        1         1         1         1         1       200         2
        3         1
  1.        .1        0.        0.        0.       10.      1000.
   .01       .8        .1        .1       .25       .1
        50        1         2        25
        1         1         1         1         1       500         0
        2         0
  2.        .08       0.        0.        0.        0.      5000.
   .02       .95       .06       .05
        200       4         5        20
```

16

VARIABLE DICTIONARY

Input Variables (In Order of Input)	Definition	Input Value
1. KOUT(I)	Output instructions	
I = 1	Write average cost of no inspection and 100% inspection	Set equal to 1 for output
2		
3		
4	Write results of computations for each sample	Set equal to 1 for output
5		
6	Sets limit on number of sample points computed	Any positive integer
7	Transfers control to STOP if −1, to read new beginning sample if 0, or new problem if +1	−1, 0, or +1
2. JMAX	Defines number of states to be read for current problem	Optional
3. JCHECK	Defines problem type—if 0, equation (18), Chapter 6; if +1, equation (17), Chapter 6	0 or +1
4. COSTD	Cost of a defective unit	Optional
5. COSTI	Variable cost of inspection per unit	Optional
6. FCOSTI	Fixed cost of inspection per lot	Optional
7. COSTP	Variable cost of production per unit	Not used currently
8. FCOSTP	Fixed cost of production per unit	Not used currently
9. COSTS	Cost of checking setup (only used if JCHECK = 1)	Optional
10. S	Lot size	Optional
11. P(J)	Fraction defective expected in state J	Optional
12. PROB(J)	Probability of state J	Optional
13. N	Initial sample size	Optional (Integer)
14. ICA	Initial acceptance number	Optional (Integer)
15. INC	Increment by which N is decreased at each trial	Optional (Integer)
16. MULT	Multiplier by which N is reset when ICA is incremented expressed in tenths, e.g. for 1.7 enter 17.	Optional (Integer)
Other Variables		
17. ACI	Average cost per lot of 100% inspection	
18. ACO	Average cost per lot of no inspection	
19. ACSI	Average cost per lot of sample inspection	
20. ACUD	Average cost per lot of undetected defects	
21. ATC	Average total cost per lot for current sample plan	
22. ATCP	Average total cost per lot for previous sample plan	
23. ATSAVE	Minimum value of ATC found for (ICA-1). Reset each time ICA is incremented	
24. CHKDEF	Fraction defective if setup is checked. Only used if JCHECK = 1	
25. EFD	Expected fraction defective if no inspection	
26. EFDC	Expected fraction defective for current sample plan	
27. ICT	Counts number of plans evaluated	
28. PA(J)	Probability of acceptance for state J. Calculated by subroutine POISON	
29. PAJSUM	Sum of products of PA(J) and PROB(J) over all J	
30. PR	Probability of rejection. Only used if JCHECK = 1	
31. SN	Number of items in lot after sampling	

INPUT FOR RUN

```
$DATA
        1           1           1           1           1        200          2
        2           0
   8.         .3        0.          1.          0.          .1       1000.
    .01        .9          .1          .1
        50          1           5          30
```

PARTIAL OUTPUT

```
ACO=  152.0000,  ACI=   300.0000
           0.910        0.040

FOR N=   50, ICA=  1
F.D.=0.0086, INSP. COST=   65.4851, DEFECT COST=    65.3025, TOTAL COST=  130.7877
           0.925        0.061

FOR N=   45, ICA=  1
F.D.=0.0089, INSP. COST=   59.8515, DEFECT COST=    68.2408, TOTAL COST=  128.0923
           0.938        0.092

FOR N=   40, ICA=  1
F.D.=0.0094, INSP. COST=   54.1168, DEFECT COST=    71.8987, TOTAL COST=  126.0155
           0.951        0.136

FOR N=   35, ICA=  1
F.D.=0.0099, INSP. COST=   48.1973, DEFECT COST=    76.5889, TOTAL COST=  124.7862


           0.963        0.199

FOR N=   30, ICA=  1
F.D.=0.0107, INSP. COST=   41.9784, DEFECT COST=    82.7143, TOTAL COST=  124.6927
           0.974        0.287

.FOR N=   25, ICA=  1
F.D.=0.0116, INSP. COST=   35.3224, DEFECT COST=    90.7490, TOTAL COST=  126.0714
           0.959        0.020

FOR N=   75, ICA=  2
F.D.=0.0088, INSP. COST=   59.8041, DEFECT COST=    65.4013, TOTAL COST=  125.2054
           0.966        0.030

FOR N=   70, ICA=  2
F.D.=0.0090, INSP. COST=   56.6461, DEFECT COST=    66.8788, TOTAL COST=  123.5249




           0.972        0.043

FOR N=   65, ICA=  2
F.D.=0.0092, INSP. COST=   53.4979, DEFECT COST=    68.6311, TOTAL COST=  122.1289
           0.977        0.062

FOR N=   60, ICA=  2
F.D.=0.0094, INSP. COST=   50.3191, DEFECT COST=    70.7756, TOTAL COST=  121.0948
           0.982        0.088

FOR N=   55, ICA=  2
F.D.=0.0097, INSP. COST=   47.0557, DEFECT COST=    73.4650, TOTAL COST=  120.5206
           0.986        0.125

FOR N=   50, ICA=  2
F.D.=0.0101, INSP. COST=   43.6379, DEFECT COST=    76.8894, TOTAL COST=  120.5273
           0.934        0.000

FOR N=  150, ICA=  3
F.D.=0.0084, INSP. COST=   85.5596, DEFECT COST=    57.1971, TOTAL COST=  142.7566
```

·
·
·

PROGRAM TO DETERMINE LEAST COST ACCEPTANCE SAMPLING PLAN WITH DESTRUCTIVE INSPECTION

This program operates in essentially the same way as the preceding program in order to compute the value of equation (19) of Chapter 6. This gives the average cost per good piece produced of a sampling plan and is the appropriate criterion when inspection is destructive. The major difference with the preceding program is that the initial plan is computed based on the data. The only element in the search procedure which is input by the user is the increment by which sample size is decreased at each step.

The maximum sample size is determined as explained on page 254 in Chapter 6, c_a is set to zero, and the search begins. When a minimum cost is reached or n reaches zero, c_a is increased by 1, n reset to its maximum value, and the process repeated. The process is terminated when the minimum for a value of c_a is above that for the next lower value or the limit set on number of trials by KOUT(6) is reached.

A listing of the program follows together with data for a sample problem and a portion of the output. A variable dictionary is also given.

```
      COMMON KOUT(7),P(10),PA(10),PROB(10)
    1 READ(5,98) KOUT                                                        1
      READ(5,98) JMAX,JGOOD,INC                                              3
      READ(5,99) COSTD,COSTI,FCOSTI,COSTP,FCOSTP,COSTS,S                     7
      READ(5,99)(P(J),PROB(J),J=1,JMAX)                                      8
      JBAD = JGOOD + 1
      CPROD = FCOSTP + S*COSTP
      EFD = 0.
      DO 10 J=1,JMAX
   10 EFD = PROB(J)*P(J) + EFD
      ACL = CPROD + EFD*S*COSTL
      AYLD = S*(1. - EFD)
      ACP = ACL/AYLD
      SCRAP = 0.
      DO 40 J=JBAD,JMAX
   40 SCRAP = PROB(J) + SCRAP
      SCRAP = SCRAP*S
      DEFS = 0.
      DO 50 J=1,JGOOD
   50 DEFS = PROB(J)*P(J) + DEFS
      DEFS = DEFS*S
      ACLO = CPROD + DEFS*COSTD + SCRAP*COSTS
      AYLDO = S - SCRAP - DEFS
      ACPO = ACLO/AYLDO
      IF(KOUT(1).EQ.1)WRITE(6,89) ACP,AYLD,ACPO,AYLDO                       40
      IF(ACPO.GE.ACP) GO TO 4
      ACFIN = 99999999.
      CSAMP = (ACP - ACPO)*AYLDO - FCOSTI
      N = CSAMP/(COSTI + COSTP + COSTS)
      IF(N)4,3,3
    3 LS = S
      IF(N.GT.LS) GO TO 4
      ICA = 0
      NSAVE = N
      ICT = 0
    9 ACMIN = 99999999.
    2 CALL POISON(JMAX,N,ICA,0.)                                            56
      DEFS = 0.
      SCRAP = 0.
      DO 20 J=1,JMAX
      SCRAP = PROB(J)*(1. - PA(J)) + SCRAP
   20 DEFS = PROB(J)*P(J)*PA(J) + DEFS
      FN = N
      SN = S - FN
      DEFS = SN*DEFS
      SCRAP = SN*SCRAP
      GOOD = SN - DEFS - SCRAP
      CINSP = COSTI*FN + FCOSTI
      ACP = (CPROD + CINSP + (COSTD*DEFS) + (COSTS*SCRAP))/GOOD
      IF(KOUT(3).EQ.1) WRITE(6,88) N,ICA,ACP                               69
      IF(ACP.GT.ACMIN) GO TO 30
      ACMIN = ACP
      N = N - INC
      IF(N)8,8,6
    6 ICT = ICT + 1
      IF(ICT - KOUT(6))2,2,4
   30 IF(ACMIN - ACFIN)8,8,4
    8 ACFIN = ACMIN
      ICA = ICA + 1
      N = NSAVE - INC
      IF(N)4,4,7
    7 ICT = ICT + 1
      IF(ICT - KOUT(6))9,9,4
    4 IF(KOUT(7) - 1)5,1,1
    5 STOP
   99 FORMAT(7F10.4)
   98 FORMAT(7I10)
   89 FORMAT(2H0,10X,4HACP=F10.4,7H, AYLD=F10.4,7H, ACPO=F10.4,8H, AYLDO
     1=F10.4)
   88 FORMAT(1H0,5X,6HFOR N=I5,6H, ICA=I3,14H, AVG COST/PC=F10.4)
      END
```

```
$DATA
          1            1            1            1            1         200            1
          2            1            5
        20.          .10          10.           1.         100.          -.1        1000.
         .01           .9           .1           .1
          1            1            1            1            1         200            0
          2            1            5
        40.          .10          10.           1.         100.          -.1        1000.
         .01           .9           .1           .1
```

VARIABLE DICTIONARY

Input Variables (In Order of Input)	Definition	Input Value
1. KOUT(I)	Output instructions	
I = 1	Writes average cost per piece and yield for no inspection and for perfect discriminations	Set to 1 for output
2		
3	Writes current sample plan and average cost per piece	Set to 1 for output
4		
5		
6	Sets limit on number of sample points computed	Any positive integer
7	If negative, run is terminated at end of current problem; if zero or positive, a new problem is read in	Negative or positive integer
2. JMAX	Defines number of states to be read for current problem	Optional
3. JGOOD	Number of last state considered acceptable quality. At least state 1 must be acceptable and any state numbered higher than JGOOD is considered unacceptable	Positive integer
4. INC	Increment by which sample size is to be decreased at each step	Positive integer
5. COSTD	Cost of a defective unit	Optional
6. COSTI	Variable cost of inspection per unit	Optional
7. FCOSTI	Fixed cost of inspection per lot	Optional
8. COSTP	Variable cost of production per unit	Optional
9. FCOSTP	Fixed cost of production per unit	Optional
10. COSTS	Cost of scrap per unit. If scrap has value, COSTS will be negative.	Usually negative value
11. S	Lot size	Optional
12. P(J)	Fraction defective expected in state J	Optional
13. PROB(J)	Probability of state J	Optional
Other Variables		
14. ACFIN	Minimum value of ACP found for each value of ICA	
15. ACL	Average cost per lot if no inspection	
16. ACLO	Average cost per lot if perfect discrimination between good and bad lots at no cost	
17. ACMIN	Average cost per piece which is smallest found so far	
18. ACP	Average cost per piece for current sample plan	
19. ACPO	Average cost per piece if perfect discrimination at no cost	
20. AYLD	Average yield of good pieces per lot if no inspection	
21. AYLDO	Average yield of good pieces per lot if perfect discrimination at no cost	
22. CINSP	Cost of inspection per lot	
23. CPROD	Cost of production per lot	
24. CSAMP	Maximum amount which can be spent per lot on inspection	
25. DEFS	Expected number of defective units per lot	
26. EFD	Expected fraction defective if no inspection	
27. FN	Floating point value of N	
28. GOOD	Expected number of good pieces per lot	
29. ICA	Acceptance number	
30. ICT	Counts number of plans evaluated	
31. JBAD	Lowest numbered state considered unacceptable	
32. LS	Fixed point value of S	
33. N	Sample size	
34. NSAVE	Initial sample size	
35. PA(J)	Probability of acceptance for state J. Calculated by subroutine POISON	
36. SCRAP	Expected number of scrap units per lot	
37. SN	Number of pieces in lot after sampling	

INPUT DATA FOR SAMPLE RUN

```
$DATA
        1           1           1           1           1       200           1
        2           1           5
   20.         .10        10.          1.        100.         -.1      1000.
      .01         .9          .1          .1
        1           1           1           1           1       200           0
        2           1           5
   40.         .10        10.          1.        100.         -.1      1000.
      .01         .9          .1          .1
```

PARTIAL OUTPUT FOR SAMPLE RUN

```
        ACP=      1.8960, AYLD=   981.0000, ACPO=      1.6274, AYLDO=   891.0000
          0.101      0.000

FOR N=   229, ICA=   0, AVG COST/PC=    15.6820
          0.106      0.000

FOR N=   224, ICA=   0, AVG COST/PC=    14.8352
          0.112      0.000

FOR N=   219, ICA=   0, AVG COST/PC=    14.0362

          •
          •
          •


          0.869      0.247

FOR N=    14, ICA=   0, AVG COST/PC=     1.6487
          0.914      0.407

FOR N=     9, ICA=   0, AVG COST/PC=     1.5902
          0.961      0.670

FOR N=     4, ICA=   0, AVG COST/PC=     1.5441
          0.881      0.019

FOR N=    59, ICA=   1, AVG COST/PC=     1.6872

          •
          •
          •


          0.978      0.067

FOR N=    59, ICA=   2, AVG COST/PC=     1.5547
          0.982      0.095




FOR N=    54, ICA=   2, AVG COST/PC=     1.5435
          0.986      0.133

FOR N=    49, ICA=   2, AVG COST/PC=     1.5341
          0.990      0.185

FOR N=    44, ICA=   2, AVG COST/PC=     1.5267
          0.993      0.253

FOR N=    39, ICA=   2, AVG COST/PC=     1.5215

          •
          •
          •
```

```
           0.991      0.045
FOR N=    79, ICA=  3, AVG CUST/PC=    1.7789
           0.993      0.063
FOR N=    74, ICA=  3, AVG CUST/PC=    1.7737
           0.995      0.067
FOR N=    69, ICA=  3, AVG COST/PC=    1.7707
           0.996      0.119
FOR N=    64, ICA=  3, AVG CCST/PC=    1.7703
           0.997      0.160
FOR N=    59, ICA=  3, AVG COST/PC=    1.7728
```

PROBLEMS

1. Find P_{a_1} and calculate P_{a_2} for the double sampling plan where $n_1 = 60$, $n_2 = 80$, $c_1 = 1$, $c_2 = 4$, and the process average is 0.06.

2. Calculate the average number of items which will be inspected per sample under the plan of Problem No. 1.

3. Plot a curve of average number of items inspected per sample against incoming fraction defective for the plan of Problem No. 1.

4. If $S = 2,000$, what is the total number of items which will be inspected under the plan of Problem No. 1, assuming that rejected lots are inspected 100 per cent.

5. Calculate the $AOQL$ of the plan in Problem No. 1.

6. Present a defects-per-unit sampling plan where the inspection unit is 1,000 square yards of canvas and the following is given:

> Allowable defects per unit $= 40$
> Probability of exceeding this number of defects $= 0.10$
> "Good" quality $= 10$ defects/unit
> Chance of rejecting if "good" $= 0.02$

7. Design a single sample plan which satisfies the following operating conditions:

$$p_1 = 0.02, \alpha = 0.05,$$
$$p_2 = 0.08, \beta = 0.10.$$

Construct an AOQ curve for the plan developed.

8. The following procedure represents the sampling plan for a particular product. Test one article from a lot. Pass the lot if the article is satisfactory. Take a second sample of one if the article fails the test. If the second article fails, the lot is rejected; if the second article proves satisfactory, the lot is accepted. Assume the submitted lot is large enough so that the selection of a defective article on the first sample does not make any appreciable change in the probability of getting a defective article on the second sample.

a) Compute the probability of acceptance of a 10 per cent defective lot.

b) Assume that a lot rejected by this sampling plan will be 100 per cent inspected. Write down an expression for the *AOQ* of submitted lots, assuming defectives are not replaced.

9. It is desired to have a single sample plan whose *OC* curve passes through the points (0.01, 0.98) and (0.05, 0.05).

10. If the lot size in Problem No. 5 is 5,000, what will be the average number of items inspected per lot for $p = 0.02$? $p = 0.03$?

11. If the cost of inspecting an item is \$0.25 and the cost if not inspected and later discovered defective is \$5.00, at what process average would the manufacturer be indifferent as to whether he inspected or did not inspect the product?

12. If the process average in the preceding problem is 0.05, what decision concerning inspection should be made? Devise a sampling inspection plan which will with a probability of 0.99 detect a shift in process average to the level where 100 per cent inspection is economical. What proportion of lots 0.02 defective will be rejected by your plan? How can you decrease this proportion while maintaining the given probability of detecting a shift in process average?

13. It is estimated that the following are possible values of p for the process of Problems 11 and 12 together with the probabilities of these lots occurring. Lot size is 2,000 and it is desired to develop an economical sampling plan. Specify "reasonable" values for an *OC* curve (describe your reasoning) and develop a plan which meets these specifications.

j	p_j	P_j
1................	0.02	0.85
2................	0.06	0.10
3................	0.10	0.05

14. Use the computer program described in this chapter to develop a minimum cost plan for the situation of Problem No. 13. Contrast this plan with one based on ($p_1 = 0.02, \alpha = 0.05$) and ($p_2 = 0.10, \beta = 0.10$) in terms of cost.

15. A manufacturer must decide whether or not to have each setup on his machines checked and readjusted by an expert mechanic at an extra cost, or let it run using the setup made by the regular operator. Past experience shows that the fractions defective when *not* checked have been as follows:

p	Relative Frequency	$p \times$ (Rel. Freq.)
0.01	0.02	0.0002
0.02	0.10	0.002
0.03	0.20	0.006
0.04	0.25	0.01
0.05	0.20	0.01
0.06	0.15	0.009
0.07	0.05	0.0035
0.08	0.02	0.0016
0.09	0.01	0.0009
		$E(p) = 0.0432$

The cost of the extra check is $10 while the loss on a day's production amounts to $0.50 per defective piece with production averaging 1,000 per day. If the check is made, experience shows the fractions defective to be as follows:

p	Relative Frequency	$p \times$ (Rel. Freq.)
0.01	0.10	0.001
0.02	0.40	0.008
0.03	0.30	0.009
0.04	0.15	0.006
0.05	0.05	0.0025
		$E(p) = 0.0265$

New runs are set up once per day on the average.

a) Would it pay to have all setups checked by the expert mechanic? Show the expected cost per day if checked and if not checked.

b) If we could estimate p for each operator setup in advance, which lots would it pay to check?

c) Set up a sampling plan for estimating p for the operator setup based on an initial run, so that we can discriminate between runs which should be checked and those which should not. (Select your own risks of making an error.) Show the operating characteristic curve of the plan you select.

16. Use the computer program described in this chapter to develop a minimum cost inspection plan for the situation of Problem No. 15 if inspection costs $0.015 per unit.

17. Specifications require that a certain quality characteristic of a manufactured product have a minimum value of 200 units. This quality characteristic can be tested only by a destructive test. The product is made in batches of several thousand. The past practice regarding acceptance inspection has been to test four articles from each batch. If all four articles met the quality specification of 200, the batch was accepted. If two or more failed, the batch was rejected. If one failed, a second sample of four was taken; with no failures on the second sample, the batch was accepted; otherwise it was rejected.

a) What is the probability that a batch containing 5 per cent of defectives will be accepted by this procedure?

b) Control charts for $\bar{X}$ and R have been plotted from the first samples. These charts indicate that the range stays in statistical control even though the average shifts from batch to batch. The standard deviation of the population appears to be 10 units. The suggestion is made that the acceptance decision be based on the average value computed from a single sample of four, with the batch accepted if the average is 210 or more. Assuming that the standard deviation continues to be at 10 units and assuming a normal distribution of the quality characteristic within a batch, what is the probability of acceptance of a 5 per cent defective lot?

18. Past experience with a manufacturing process indicates that 98 per cent of the time it produces output with an average fraction defective of 0.02 and is in control. However, at random intervals, it goes out of control and produces defective output at an average rate of 0.12. The cost of inspection is $0.20 per unit and is not destructive. In order to get ready to inspect a batch of output a $12 setup charge is incurred. The extra cost of a defective unit which is undetected at this stage and is discovered later after assembly is $10. Output occurs in lots which average 500 units.

a) Determine a sampling plan which minimizes total cost under these conditions.

b) If inspection in the preceding problem is destructive, what sampling plan will minimize total cost, assuming a scrap value of $50 on rejected lots?

19. Devise a single sampling plan which will give the following protection:

$$\alpha = 0.02 \qquad p_1 = 0.01$$
$$\beta = 0.05 \qquad p_2 = 0.05$$

20. What double sampling plan will give the same protection as that afforded by the plan of Problem No. 19?

21. Construct an AOQ curve for the plan of Problem No. 19.

22. If inspection is curtailed for the double sampling plan of Problem No. 20 whenever a decision is reached, construct a curve of the average number of items inspected per sample versus incoming quality.

23. Incandescent lamps are submitted in batches of 1,000 for final inspection. The specified illumination of these lamps is 100 end foot-candles, and it is known that variation in the manufacturing process is such as to give a standard deviation of output at 50 end foot-candles. The mean of the process is known to vary, and it is desired to have a sampling plan which will assure that lots for which $p = 0.01$ are accepted 95 per cent of the time while lots for which $p = 0.05$ are accepted only 10 per cent of the time. Develop a variables plan which will give this result. Find an attributes plan with the same characteristics and compare the sample sizes.

CHAPTER 7

Industrial Experimentation

OBJECTIVES AND METHODS IN INDUSTRIAL EXPERIMENTATION

IT IS often desirable, and in some instances essential, in production management to associate cause and effect in some meaningful way. In the case of an "out-of-control" quality variation revealed through the use of control charts, the "cause" might not be at all obvious. In fact, the number of factors which might contribute to some observed variance could well be very large. An experiment which could pinpoint quantitatively the significant causes of variation with some minimum of expense would be called for in such a situation.

Perhaps, the causes of variation in output of workers, production times, machine breakdown, or any of a large number of items essential to the efficient management of a production operation is in question. Some kind of tool is necessary to isolate the causes of variation and determine their effect. Industrial experimentation has available some quite powerful statistical tools whose nature is best explained as a departure from traditional methods of experimentation.

Traditional Methods

Traditional methods for experimenting in manufacturing situations generally call for a procedure somewhat as follows:

1. Statement of the problem. It might be desired, for example, to determine the way in which production workers would respond in terms of changed output to changes in some of the conditions surrounding their work.
2. Definition of initial conditions. For the given problem, the environment, the job, the equipment, the workers, and their output would have to be defined as they existed at the beginning of the experiment.

270

3. Standardization of conditions. The definitions of part 2 would be carried to the point of standardization, in order that all conditions except those under investigation might be held constant.

4. Change one aspect of working conditions. Here, the effects of this change would be recorded for comparison with the initial conditions and cause (change in working conditions) related to effect (change in output).

5. Repeat 4 with all changes and combinations of changes which it is desired to investigate.

6. Summarize results in terms of the effect of the given changes on output.

Some Difficulties with Traditional Methods of Experimentation

The above outline reveals quite clearly the drawbacks of the traditional method of experimentation as it might be applied to experiments in a factory. Here an attempt is made to standardize all conditions surrounding the work to be done and measure output. Then one factor is deliberately varied and the effect noted. It is then presumed that the effect is explained by the factor change. The most obvious difficulty with such a technique is that the effect may be due to the fact that the two sets of measurements were taken at different times. That is, something else may have changed between period one and period two, and a false association of cause and effect deduced. Elimination of difficulties from this source is best done by the use of a "control" on the experiment. That is, a simultaneous experiment is performed under the same conditions where the factor under consideration is not varied.

A second kind of fallacy which is encountered in industrial experiments is that of drawing too general a conclusion from limited data. The extension of the results of an experiment to a different set of circumstances (what is true for guinea pigs is true for humans) is the commonest example of this kind of reasoning. Thus, a careless experimenter might try to generalize some results of the above kind of experiment, where the job was light assembly work, to explain changes in productivity on the part of maintenance workers in a steel mill. This could only be done with the greatest of care and with evidence as to the correlation of circumstances which existed between the two situations.

A more modern method of experimentation would be to avoid standardization wherever such standardization constitutes an artificial constraint on the experiment. Standardization of working conditions by the use of a laboratory environment for the output experiment outlined above would be an example of artificial constraints. It would certainly not be the intent of the experimenters that small groups of workers should perform this kind of work in a laboratory as normal practice if in fact this was not done in the factory. Deliberate selection and conditioning of the workers might represent another artificial constraint imposed by attempts at standardization. Further, if a factor which has been standardized is really an important source of variation, the experimenter has lost the opportunity of finding this out.

If possible, all factors which are not to be deliberately varied should be randomized. That is, the effect of any factors not under direct consideration in the course of the experiment should occur according to the probability distribution which would, under operating conditions, govern its occurrence. If, for example, materials are selected at random from that received from several suppliers and it is judged that materials are not an important source of variation in the situation under study, then some mechanism should be provided so that during the course of the experiment, materials are randomly assigned. Thus, the experimental error (that part of the observed variation not due to deliberately varied factors) for this factor is representative of that which could be expected in actual practice. If it is suspected that the material from different suppliers causes significant variation, then the material from each supplier could be systematically varied while random drawings of such material could be made from within each suppliers' shipments. This would give rise to a "supplier effect" in the final results.

Modern statistical techniques allow for the deliberate variation of a relatively large number of possible cause factors and the subsequent isolation of the magnitude of the variation due to each. Thus, during the course of an experiment which involved four factors, three of them might be deliberately varied, and the fourth randomized. For example, if it were desired to isolate the cause of some observed variation in the quality of output of a particular production process, then operators, machines, methods, and materials could all contribute to the observed variation. Based on the nature of the process, an experiment could be devised whereby each operator, machine, and method would come together the same number of times, but in some random order, and materials would be supplied according to a scheme whereby each combination of operator, machine, and method had an equal chance of receiving each piece of material used. Then the relative effect of each of the deliberately varied factors could be compared to the experimental error (variation due to materials and all other factors not considered), and a judgment made as to its importance as a source of variation. Here one would estimate the experimental variation holding all factors constant (arithmetically), except one for each estimate. Then this estimate would be tested against the hypothesis that the value obtained could have occurred by chance. Thus, those factors which actually contribute to observed variation in other than a random fashion could be isolated. Also, any interaction which occurred between any of the factors tested could be isolated by specifically allowing for this in the design of the experiment. The possibilities of this kind of experimentation will be explored with a specific example.

AN EXPERIMENT WITH PRODUCTION STANDARDS

In a certain metal fabricating firm, the methods department wished to determine the extent of observed variation in the time necessary to perform a particular machining operation. A series of measurements of this time were taken with the following results in minutes (these are direct measurement of production times taken in sequence with no allowances or corrections made):

4.77	4.43	4.93
4.81	5.47	5.11
4.87	4.80	4.15
4.58	4.71	4.70
4.55	5.44	5.25
4.47	4.61	4.56
4.38	4.51	4.59
4.74	5.48	4.59
4.62	4.80	4.52

This mean time is

$$\bar{x} = \frac{\sum_{i=1}^{n} x_i}{27} = 4.76 \text{ minutes}, \tag{1}$$

and the variance is estimated as

$$s_x^2 = \frac{\sum_{i=1}^{n} (x_i - \bar{x})^2}{n-1} = 0.11, \tag{2}$$

from which an estimate of the standard deviation is

$$s_x = 0.34 .$$

Assuming individual values from the time studies are normally distributed about $\bar{x}$, one would expect 95 per cent of all operating times to fall in the interval $4.76 \pm 2s_x$, or from 4.08 to 5.44 minutes. In the 27 readings taken, two values fall outside this interval which is not too far from our expectation of 1 in 20.

The methods department considered this variation, s_x, too large to allow for accurate scheduling and wished to find out what, if anything, could be done to reduce it. One time-study man maintained that the machines were causing the wide variation since the three being used on this job, while all were of the same make, had been purchased at different times, and had been used differently in the past. They had only been moved to the same location and put on the same job recently. A methods engineer maintained that the operators were primarily at fault, even though they had all been trained at the same time and according to a standard operating procedure devised by the department. He said his observation on the job led him to believe that the mean and variation could both be reduced by better operator training and in one case by a better operator.

Test for Differences between Means

One kind of difference between times could be due to differences in the level of performance on the part of each operator where the effect of all other factors is the same. In order to test for the existence of such differences, the data previously obtained could be regrouped by operators (Table 7–1), assuming all other factors (machines, sup-

Table 7–1

O_1	O_2	O_3
4.77	4.59	4.61
4.43	4.74	4.56
4.93	5.48	4.47
4.58	5.11	4.80
4.71	4.81	4.52
4.70	5.47	4.62
4.38	5.25	4.80
4.51	4.55	4.15
4.59	5.44	4.87
$\bar{x}_1 = 4.62$	$\bar{x}_2 = 5.07$	$\bar{x}_3 = 4.60$
$s_{x_1}^2 = 0.0302$	$s_{x_2}^2 = 0.1466$	$s_{x_3}^2 = 0.0478$

pliers, etc.) are randomized. Now the differences between means may be tested by comparing each observed difference with that which could be expected to occur by chance. The simplest procedure can be used when the standard deviations of the populations are known. If in this case our prior experience revealed a stable standard deviation of 0.34

for all operators, the standard deviation of a distribution of means based on samples of 9 could be immediately computed as

$$\sigma_{\bar{x}} = \frac{0.34}{\sqrt{9}}$$

$$= 0.11$$

and a test set up based on the hypothesis that the observed differences between means in Table 7–1 are due to chance. The statistic

$$Z_{12} = \frac{|\bar{x}_1 - \bar{x}_2|}{\sigma_{\bar{x}_1 - \bar{x}_2}}$$

will have a normal distribution in this case and the value which will be exceeded, say, 5 per cent of the time by chance if there is no difference between the means can be read from Appendix II, Table A and is 1.96. The variance of the sum or difference of two independent variables is the sum of the variances so that

$$\sigma_{x_1 \pm x_2}^{2} = \sigma_{x_1}^{2} + \sigma_{x_2}^{2}$$

and also

$$\sigma_{\bar{x}_1 \pm \bar{x}_2}^{2} = \sigma_{\bar{x}_1}^{2} + \sigma_{\bar{x}_2}^{2}$$

for the distributions of means of two variables. Thus

$$\sigma_{\bar{x}_1 \pm \bar{x}_2} = \sqrt{\frac{\sigma_{x_1}^{2}}{n_1} + \frac{\sigma_{x_2}^{2}}{n_2}}$$

and the test statistic is

$$Z_{12} = \frac{|\bar{x}_1 - \bar{x}_2|}{\sqrt{\sigma_{\bar{x}_1}^{2} + \sigma_{\bar{x}_2}^{2}}}$$

$$= \frac{(4.62 - 5.07)}{\sqrt{(0.11)^2 + (0.11)^2}}$$

$$= \frac{0.45}{0.156}$$

$$= 2.88 \ .$$

Reference to the normal table shows that there are only four chances in 1,000 of a difference this large if, in fact, the performance of both operators is at the same level.

Continuing with the other observed differences

$$Z_{13} = \frac{0.02}{0.156}$$

$$= 0.13$$

$$Z_{23} = \frac{0.47}{0.156}$$
$$= 3.01 .$$

Thus operator 2 is clearly performing at a level significantly above that of operators 1 and 3.

Setting the risk of rejecting the null hypothesis when it is, in fact, true at 0.05 seems primarily to be a matter of statistical convention. This idea has been discussed in the preceding chapter where the value almost always assumed for α was 0.05. This is not to imply that this is always the best course when, in fact, each situation should be judged on its own merits. It is usually assumed here since practice indicates that this generally provides a reasonable test for significance. This is the same kind of convention which sets control limits at $\pm 3s_{\bar{x}}$. This point was discussed in Chapter 5 in developing economic criteria for control plans.

If the population standard deviations are unknown but can be assumed equal, then the appropriate statistic is

$$t = \frac{\bar{x}_1 - \bar{x}_2}{s \sqrt{\dfrac{1}{n_1} + \dfrac{1}{n_2}}} \qquad (3)$$

in which s is an estimate of the population standard deviation. This can be determined from the two sample estimates by

$$s = \sqrt{\frac{(n_1 - 1)s_{x_1}^2 + (n_2 - 1)s_{x_2}^2}{n_1 + n_2 - 2}} .$$

Values of "t" for various values of $(n_1 + n_2 - 2)$ are available in Appendix II, Table C.

For example, consider the data given previously arranged according to different suppliers of material as shown in Table 7–2. It is desired to test the observed difference between suppliers 1 and 3. On the assumption that $\sigma_{x_1} = \sigma_x$ (this can be tested as will be shown later)

$$s_{13} = \sqrt{\frac{8(0.0945) + 8(0.1711)}{9 + 9 - 2}}$$
$$= 0.365$$

and

$$t_{13} = \frac{|4.67 - 4.95|}{0.365\sqrt{\frac{1}{9} + \frac{1}{9}}}$$
$$= \frac{0.28}{0.172}$$
$$= 1.63$$

If we are willing to accept the hypothesis that there is no difference between the means given a 5 per cent chance of observing a difference as large as 0.28, then a value of t larger than 2.120 would be necessary to reject the hypothesis. Thus the hypothesis would be accepted in this case.

If there is no basis on which to assume the variances are equal, or they are known to be different, the Aspin-Welch test can be used.[1]

Tests for Differences between Variances

Another important test is that for differences between variances of sample data. In order to do this, the F-test may be employed. Here one computes the ratio of the variances obtained from the samples and tests this ratio on the hypothesis that a value as large as that obtained (always testing the larger variance against the smaller) could have occurred by chance if the two samples come from the same population. When a universe is normally distributed and samples from this universe are independent, sample values of the ratio of two variance estimates are distributed according to the F (after Fisher) distribution.[2] This ratio is defined as

$$F = \frac{s_{x_1}^2/\sigma_{x_1}^2}{s_{x_2}^2/\sigma_{x_2}^2} .$$
(4)

The hypothesis is made that $s_{x_1}^2$ and $s_{x_2}^2$ are variance estimates from the same population, that is, that $\sigma_{x_1}^2$ is equal to $\sigma_{x_2}^2$. Then a value of F larger than can be expected, due to sampling variation alone, will disprove the hypothesis. In such a test, $s_{x_1}^2$ is an unbiased (corrected for degrees of freedom) estimate of σ_x^2, and $s_{x_2}^2$ is also an unbiased estimate of σ_x^2. Percentage points of the F distribution are given in Appendix II. The distribution depends on the degrees of freedom used to estimate the two variances. Thus, for the values arrayed according to operators:

$$F_{12} [8, 8] = \frac{0.1466}{0.0302} = 4.79$$

$$F_{13} [8, 8] = \frac{0.0478}{0.0302} = 1.58$$

$$F_{23} [8, 8] = \frac{0.1466}{0.0478} = 3.07 .$$

---

[1] See A. J. Duncan, *Quality Control and Industrial Statistics* 3d ed. (Homewood, Ill.: Richard D. Irwin, Inc., 1965), pp. 505–7.

[2] R. A. Fisher, *Statistical Methods for Research Workers* (11th ed.; London: Oliver & Boyd, Ltd., 1950).

Table 7–2

T_1	T_2	T_3
4.77	4.43	4.93
4.59	4.74	5.48
4.61	4.56	4.47
4.58	4.71	4.70
5.11	4.81	5.47
4.80	4.52	4.62
4.38	4.51	4.59
5.25	4.55	5.44
4.80	4.15	4.87
$\bar{x}_1 = 4.67$	$\bar{x}_2 = 4.55$	$\bar{x}_3 = 4.95$
$s_{x_1}^2 = 0.0945$	$s_{x_2}^2 = 0.0374$	$s_{x_3}^2 = 0.1711$

From Table E in Appendix II,

$$F\,[8,\,8]_{0.05} = 3.44\,.$$

Thus, the difference between $s_{x_1}^2$ and $s_{x_2}^2$ is significant, while the other differences must be judged as not significant. A further test may be made by pooling the variances $s_{x_1}^2$ and $s_{x_3}^2$ (since F_{13} was not significant). This is done by treating the values for operators 1 and 3 as if they came from the same universe and obtaining a new estimate of the variance

$$s_{x_{13}}^2 = \frac{(n_1 - 1)s_{x_1}^2 + (n_3 - 1)s_{x_3}^2}{n_1 + n_3 - 2}$$
$$= 0.0367\,.$$

This could also be done by computing the variance of the observations for operators 1 and 3 as a single sample. Then,

$$F_{13.2}\,[8,\,17] = \frac{0.1466}{0.0367}$$
$$= 3.99\,.$$

From the table,

$$F\,[8,\,17]_{0.05} = 2.55\,,$$

and the difference is judged significant at the 0.05 level.

The conclusion to be drawn here is that the variance contributed by operator 2 is significantly greater than that contributed by either of the other two operators. The result, coupled with the results of the tests for differences between means, leads one to conclude that the performance of operator 2 contributes much to the total variation. In fact, the 95 per cent interval for operators 1 and 3 taken together is approximately

$$4.61 \pm 2(0.20)\,,$$

or from 4.21 to 5.01 minutes, a considerable reduction in variation over the interval 4.08 to 5.44 for all three operators.

Variance ratio tests for the distributions according to different suppliers give:

$$F_{12} [8, 8] = \frac{0.0945}{0.0374} = 2.53 ,$$

$$F_{13} [8, 8] = \frac{0.1711}{0.0945} = 1.81 ,$$

$$F_{23} [8, 8] = \frac{0.1711}{0.0374} = 4.58 ,$$

from which $s_{x_2}^2$ and $s_{x_3}^2$ must be judged as from different populations. Again, if $s_{x_1}^2$ and $s_{x_2}^2$ are pooled,

$$s_{x_{12}}^2 = 0.0621 ,$$

and the variance ratio $F_{12.3}$ computed,

$$F_{12.3} = \frac{0.1711}{0.0621}$$
$$= 2.75 .$$

Then, since $F[8, 17]_{0.05} = 2.55$, this result must be judged as significant. By a similar test, $F_{13.2}$ is just at the border line of significance.

Here the conclusion is not so clear as in the case of operators, but the materials from supplier 2 seem superior to those from supplier 3 in the contribution to better performance times.

THE ANALYSIS OF VARIANCE

In many cases in which it is desired to obtain information as to the factors which contribute to some observed variation in a process, considerable efficiency may be obtained through application of the technique of analysis of variance. Consider the situation outlined previously in which machines, operators, and suppliers may each contribute to the observed variability in output and the problem is to determine whether or not they do contribute and, if so, how much.

Assume that there are four machines, three operators, and two suppliers which have been producing output characterized by the measurements shown in Table 7–3. Here the measurements are classified by machines only. The problem is to determine whether the machines all produce output at the same level or whether their outputs are different and thus when mixed produce greater than expected variability. If we assume that the machines produce individually output which comes from the same (normal) population, then the variance may be esti-

Table 7-3

	M_1	M_2	M_3	M_4
	4.77	4.93	4.71	4.38
	4.43	4.58	4.70	4.51
	4.59	5.48	4.81	5.25
	4.74	5.11	5.47	4.55
	4.61	4.47	4.52	4.80
	4.56	4.80	4.62	4.15
$\bar{x}_j$	4.62	4.89	4.81	4.61

mated in three distinct ways, and these should all be estimates of the same thing. First,

$$s_T^2 = \frac{\sum_{ij} (x_{ij} - \bar{\bar{x}})^2}{n - 1}$$

in which

$s_T^2 =$ estimate of population variance based on all observations
$x_{ij} = i^{\text{th}}$ value of x in column j
$\bar{\bar{x}} =$ grand mean of the x_{ij}

is an estimate of the population variance if the hypothesis that all observations come from the same population is true. However, if machine population 1 produces output whose mean value is greater than that of machine 2, this computation is really confounding two populations.
Second,

$$s_{\text{col.}}^2 = \frac{\sum_{j} n_j(\bar{x}_j - \bar{\bar{x}})^2}{c - 1} \tag{5}$$

in which

$s_{\text{col.}}^2 =$ estimate of population variance based on column means
$c =$ number of columns
$n_j =$ number of items in each column
$\bar{x}_j =$ column mean

is an estimate of the population variance also based on the assumption that the machine populations are identical.
Third,

$$s_R^2 = \frac{\sum_{ij} (x_{ij} - \bar{x}_j)^2}{cn_j - c} \tag{6}$$

in which

s_R^2 = estimate of population variance based on within column differences only

is an estimate of the population variance in which differences between column means have been eliminated. If there are no such differences then an F-test of $s_{\text{col.}}^2$ against s_R^2 should result in acceptance of this hypothesis. That is, if (5) and (6) are really estimates of the same population variance, any difference should be due to sampling error. If the hypothesis is rejected, then the inference to be drawn is that the means of the populations are different (the machines are producing at different levels). A value of F which results in acceptance of the hypothesis that all machines are alike may result from two conditions. Either the machines really are alike or the experiment was not sensitive enough to reveal the actual differences. The sensitivity of this kind of test can be increased by reducing the residual variance (s_R^2). As will be shown later, this can be done by developing estimates of the total variance based on other classifications of the data as was done by machines in this case.

The two variance estimates of interest can be made by direct computation. The difference between each column mean and the grand mean is squared and divided by the degrees of freedom for the estimate ($c - 1$) to give an estimate of the variance of column means. This can be used to estimate the total variance if it is remembered that

$$s_x^2 = n s_{\bar{x}}^2 .$$

Thus, in this case, the estimate of variance based on column means is

$$s_{\text{col.}}^2$$
$$= 6 \left[\frac{(4.62 - 4.73)^2 + (4.89 - 4.73)^2 + (4.81 - 4.73)^2 + (4.61 - 4.73)^2}{4 - 1} \right]$$
$$= 0.1178 .$$

The residual variance based on within column differences is

$$s_R^2 = \frac{(4.77 - 4.62)^2 + (4.43 - 4.62)^2 + \ldots + (4.15 - 4.61)^2}{24 - 4}$$
$$= 0.1023 .$$

Then an F-test may be performed (in which one always tests variance estimates against the residual) as

$$F\,[3, 20] = \frac{0.1178}{0.1023}$$
$$= 1.15 .$$

From Table E in Appendix II,

$$F[3, 20]_{0.05} = 3.10 .$$

Therefore, one would conclude that the value of F obtained could have arisen from chance causes and there is no significant variation due to machines. The measurement of variation would have to give a value considerably larger than 0.1178 in order for one to conclude from this experiment that machines are a significant source of variation.

It should be noted that the total variation in the observations can be measured as the sum of the squared differences between individual observations and the grand mean. This total sum of squares is broken into two components, one, the squared differences between column means and the grand mean and, two, the squared differences between individuals and column means. The variance estimates are obtained as the mean of each of these sums. Thus

Total sum of squares = Column sum of squares + Residual sum of squares

$$\sum_{ij}(x_{ij} - \bar{\bar{x}})^2 = \sum_{j}n_j(\bar{x}_j - \bar{\bar{x}})^2 + \sum_{ij}(x_{ij} - \bar{x}_j)^2 \qquad (7)$$

This can be demonstrated by expanding the left-hand side as follows:

$$\sum_{ij}(x_{ij} - \bar{\bar{x}})^2 = \sum_{ij}[(x_{ij} - \bar{x}_j) + (\bar{x}_j - \bar{\bar{x}})]^2$$

$$= \sum_{ij}(x_{ij} - \bar{x}_j)^2 + \sum_{ij}(\bar{x}_j - \bar{\bar{x}})^2$$

$$+ 2\sum_{ij}(x_{ij} - \bar{x}_j)(\bar{x}_j - \bar{\bar{x}})$$

$$= \sum_{ij}(x_{ij} - \bar{x}_j)^2 + \sum_{i}n_j(\bar{x}_j - \bar{\bar{x}})^2 + 0$$

since

$$\sum_{i}(x_{ij} - \bar{x}_j) = 0 .$$

It is not known in advance whether or not the sums of squares thus generated will actually produce true variance estimates. Therefore it is convenient to compute these sums, determine the degrees of freedom for each variance estimate, compute the mean, and make an F-test. A convenient table for this analysis is shown in Table 7–4. The expected value is just the variance estimate obtained by the mean square computation. Under the null hypothesis, both mean squares are estimates of the same population variance, that is, σ_M^2 (machine variance) is zero. If it is not, the F-test should reveal its presence.

Table 7–4

ONE-FACTOR ANALYSIS OF VARIANCE

Source of Variation	Sum of Squares	Degrees of Freedom	Mean Square	Expected Value
Machines (columns)........	0.3533	3	0.1178	$n_j\sigma_M^2 + \sigma_R^2$
Experimental error (residual)	2.0467	20	0.1023	σ_R^2
Total..................	2.4000	23		

The computations necessary to produce Table 7–4 can be shortened by reference to the format shown in the Appendix to this chapter.

Two-Factor Analysis of Variance

In order to increase the sensitivity of the experiment, the same number of readings is taken as before, but now operators are systematically varied as well as machines. Each operator-machine combination occurs twice in the experiment but with all other possible factors randomized. The measurements are shown in Table 7–5. If the number of rows (i)

Table 7–5

OPERATORS	MACHINES					
	M_1	M_2	M_3	M_4	Σx_i	$\bar{x}_i$
O_1	4.77	4.93	4.71	4.38	37.01	4.63
	4.43	4.58	4.70	4.51		
O_2	4.59	5.48	4.81	5.25	40.00	5.00
	4.74	5.11	5.47	4.55		
O_3	4.61	4.47	4.52	4.80	36.53	4.57
	4.56	4.80	4.62	4.15		
Σx_j	27.70	29.37	28.83	27.64		4.73
$\bar{x}_j$	4.62	4.89	4.81	4.61		

is r, the number of columns (j) is c, and the number of observations per combination (k) is g, then the total sum of squares is

$$\sum_{ijk} (x_{ijk} - \bar{\bar{x}})^2 = \sum_{jk} cg(\bar{x}_i - \bar{\bar{x}})^2 + \sum_{ik} rg(\bar{x}_j - \bar{\bar{x}})^2$$
$$+ \sum_{ijk} [x_{ijk} - (\bar{x}_i + \bar{x}_j - \bar{\bar{x}})]^2 .$$

The first term on the right side of the equation is the sum of squared differences between each row mean and the grand mean multiplied by the number of observations per row. The second term is the same sum by columns. The third term is the sum of squared differences between each item and the value expected in each cell if there were no row or column variation. That is,

$$ x_{ijk} - [\bar{\bar{x}} + (\bar{x}_i - \bar{\bar{x}}) + (\bar{x}_j - \bar{\bar{x}})] = x_{ijk} - (\bar{x}_i + \bar{x}_j - \bar{\bar{x}}) . $$

In order to make variance estimates under the null hypothesis, the degrees of freedom associated with each sum of squares must be determined. The between columns estimate is as before based on $(c - 1)$ and similarly the between rows estimate is based on $(r - 1)$. The residual variance (that due to all other effects) is based on rcg items less the number of independent estimates used to produce this sum of squares. There is one degree of freedom lost for each row mean and column mean except that one estimate is redundant since the mean of the column means and the mean of the row means is the same. Thus, the correct number is $rcg - r - c + 1$. The variance estimates of interest are

$$ s_{\text{col.}}^2 = \frac{\sum_{ik} rg(\bar{x}_j - \bar{\bar{x}})^2}{c - 1} , \quad s_{\text{row}}^2 = \frac{\sum_{jk} cg(\bar{x}_i - \bar{\bar{x}})^2}{r - 1} , $$

and

$$ s_R^2 = \frac{\sum_{ijk} [x_{ijk} - (\bar{x}_i + \bar{x}_j - \bar{\bar{x}})]^2}{rcg - r - c + 1} . \tag{8} $$

The basic assumption made by the above interpretation of the meaning of the residual variance is that rows and columns do not "interact" on each other in producing the total variance. That is, in this case, machine and operator bias, if any exists, are independent of each other. If it does make a difference to the outcome of the experiment which operator uses which machine, then this kind of interaction variance will be included in the estimate of the residual. While this interaction could be estimated due to the fact of more than one measurement for each combination of operator and machine, it will be assumed not to exist in the present analysis and treated in the next section.

The null hypothesis in this case states that s_{row}^2, $s_{\text{col.}}^2$, and s_R^2 are all estimates of the universe variance. That is, it is assumed that all variation is due to random effects and that the systematic variation of machines and operators during the course of the experiment will have no effect on the estimates made in these different ways. An F-test will then indicate whether or not the systematic variation introduced had a significant effect on any of the estimates. The rejection of the null hypothesis in the case of either $s_{col.}^2/s_R^2$ or s_{row}^2/s_R^2 indicates that the given characteristic contributed significantly to the observed variation.

Computing according to the above (or using the technique shown in the Appendix to this chapter) results in Table 7–6.

Table 7–6

TWO-FACTOR ANALYSIS OF VARIANCE

Source of Variation	Sums of Squares	Degrees of Freedom	Mean Square	Expected Value
Machines (columns)...........	0.3533	3	0.1178	$rg\sigma_M^2 + \sigma_R^2$
Operators (rows).............	0.8654	2	0.4327	$cg\sigma_0^2 + \sigma_R^2$
Experimental error (residual)...	1.1813	18	0.0657	σ_R^2
Total...................	2.4000	23		

The null hypothesis states that all of the mean squares are estimates of σ_R^2. If machine variance (σ_M^2) or operator variance (σ_0^2) exist at all, this may be tested by the F-test. The ratio of the column mean square to the residual mean square must give a value larger than expected due to random causes alone in order that the null hypothesis be rejected. From Table 7–6 the existence of machine bias may be tested by

$$F\,[3,\,18] = \frac{0.1178}{0.0657}$$
$$= 1.95\,.$$

From Table E in Appendix II,

$$F\,[3,\,18]_{0.05} = 3.16\,,$$

and the null hypothesis is accepted for machines. That is, machines are not judged a significant source of variation based on this experiment. For operators,

$$F\,[2,\,18] = \frac{0.4327}{0.0657}$$
$$= 6.59\,,$$

and from the table,

$$F\,[2,\,18]_{0.05} = 3.56\,.$$

Thus, the null hypothesis is rejected in the case of operators, and they are judged a significant source of variation. In fact, examination of the F table reveals that one would expect a value as large as 6.59 less than once in a hundred such tests if, in fact, operators were not a significant cause of variation.

It should be noted that the value of F for machines obtained in this experiment is relatively larger than that obtained previously. This is due to the fact that the operator bias has been separated out of the residual and the resulting experiment has greater sensitivity than the previous, single-factor experiment.

Interaction in a Two-Factor Analysis of Variance

If the data collected for the preceding analysis had included only one measurement for each combination of operator and machine, it would have been necessary to assume (as was done) that no interaction between operators and machines exists. If (as was the case) more than one value were obtained for each combination, then it is possible to compute a measure of the interaction between the factors considered. This is the variance resulting from differences between factor combination means and the expected value for these if there were no interaction. This expected value can be estimated using row, column, and grand means according to

$$g\sigma_{MO}^2 + \sigma_R^2 = \frac{\sum_{ij} [\bar{x}_{ij} - (\bar{x}_j + \bar{x}_i - \bar{x})]^2}{(r - 1)(c - 1)}, \qquad (9)$$

where g is the number of measurements made for each combination of factors and $\bar{x}_{ij}$ is the mean of the set of values for each factor combination. This should be compared with (8), and it can be seen that the only change in the numerator is to replace each x_{ijk} by each factor combination mean. The degrees of freedom are now the number of items (rc) minus the independent restrictions $(r + c - 1)$. This number of restrictions stems from the fact that the means of the factor combination means for each row and column must equal the row and column sums. With this interpretation, the experimental error (residual variance) is now the result of differences between individual values and the mean of the k values taken for each combination. Thus,

$$\sigma_R^2 = \frac{\sum_{ijk} (x_{ijk} - \bar{x}_{ij})^2}{rc(g - 1)}, \qquad (10)$$

where $\bar{x}_{ij}$ is the mean of the values for each factor combination, and the degrees of freedom are the total number of measurements (rcg) less the number of independent estimates of means used (rc).

Computing the sums of squares according to the numerators of the relationships just shown and determining the appropriate number of degrees of freedom results in Table 7–7. In order for interaction vari-

Table 7–7

TWO-FACTOR ANALYSIS OF VARIANCE WITH INTERACTION

Source of Variation	Sum of Squares	Degrees of Freedom	Mean Square	Expected Value
Machines...................	0.3533	3	0.1178	$rg\sigma_M^2 + \sigma_R^2$
Operators...................	0.8654	2	0.4327	$cg\sigma_O^2 + \sigma_R^2$
Machine-operator interaction...	0.3742	6	0.0624	$g\sigma_{MO}^2 + \sigma_R^2$
Experimental error...........	0.8071	12	0.0673	σ_R^2
Total...................	2.4000	23		

ance to exist at all, the mean square for interaction must be greater than the residual mean square. Since, in this case, it is not, the interaction sum of squares could be pooled with the residual and Table 7–6 obtained from which F-tests could be made as was done previously. If the interaction mean square did exist, then an F-test could be used in an attempt to determine whether or not it was significant. If the null hypothesis were accepted, then this interaction sum of squares could be pooled with the residual and F-tests made for the factor sources. If the null hypothesis were rejected, it could be concluded that operators and machines do interact on each other and some physical interpretation of this sought.

Three-Factor Analysis of Variance

A still more sensitive experiment could be designed in this situation where materials from each of two suppliers was included as a factor for analysis. Here each machine, operator, and supplier comes together once during the course of the experiment, and measurements are taken as previously. The outcome (coded in hundredths of a minute) is shown in Table 7–8. With the data gathered this way, a two-way analysis by

Table 7–8

OPERATORS	SUPPLIERS	MACHINES			
		M_1	M_2	M_3	M_4
O_1	T_1	4	20	-2	-35
	T_2	-30	-15	-3	-22
O_2	T_1	-14	74	8	52
	T_2	1	38	74	-18
O_3	T_1	-8	-26	-21	7
	T_2	-17	7	-11	-58

machines and operators could be performed as just illustrated with the same computations and numerical outcome. Here again the mean square value for machines is an estimate of variance due to machine effect weighted by the number of machine readings taken plus the error variance. An estimate of the interaction between machines and suppliers may be obtained by performing a two-way analysis of variance with machines as columns, suppliers as rows, and operators as factor combination groups. Rewriting the data in this way results in Table 7–9.

Table 7–9

SUPPLIERS	OPERATORS	MACHINES				Σx_i	$\bar{x}_i$
		M_1	M_2	M_3	M_4		
T_1	O_1	4	20	− 2	−35	59	5
	O_2	−14	74	8	52		
	O_3	− 8	−26	−21	7		
T_2	O_1	−30	−15	− 3	−22	−54	−4
	O_2	1	38	74	−18		
	O_3	−17	7	−11	−58		
	Σx_j	−64	98	45	−74	5	
	$\bar{x}_j$	−11	19	8	−12		

Carrying out the computations according to the steps given previously results in the analysis of variance shown in Table 7–10. In this case, an

Table 7–10

TWO-FACTOR ANALYSIS OF VARIANCE

Source of Variation	Sums of Squares	Degrees of Freedom	Mean Square	Expected Value
Machines (columns).........	3,533	3	1,178	$rg\sigma_M^2 + \sigma_R^2$
Suppliers (rows).............	532	1	532	$cg\sigma_T^2 + \sigma_R^2$
Machine-supplier interaction..	3,257	3	1,086	$g\sigma_{MT}^2 + \sigma_R^2$
Experimental error..........	18,407	16	1,050	σ_R^2
Total..................	24,000	23		

F-test on machine-supplier interaction would be performed first, yielding

$$F\,[3, 16] = \frac{1,086}{1,050} = 1.03\,.$$

Since

$$F\,[3, 16]_{0.05} = 3.24\,,$$

this variance component must be judged as not significant. Then this sum of squares may be pooled with that due to suppliers (the supplier mean square is less than the residual mean square, so supplier variance is assumed not to exist) and with the residual to yield a new (and better) estimate of the residual mean square. This gives:

$$\frac{532 + 3{,}257 + 18{,}407}{1 + 3 + 16} = 1{,}110 \; .$$

Then the machine mean square may be tested by

$$F\,[3,\,20] = \frac{1{,}178}{1{,}110} = 1.06 \; .$$

Then from the table,

$$F\,[3,\,20]_{0.05} = 3.10 \; ,$$

and machine variance is again judged as not significant. The interaction mean square for suppliers and operators would be treated similarly.

The computations which would be performed on the three-factor data are shown in the Appendix to this chapter, and the results are summarized in the analysis of variance of Table 7–11.

Table 7–11

THREE-FACTOR ANALYSIS OF VARIANCE

Source of Variation	Sums of Squares	Degrees of Freedom	Mean Square	Expected Value
Machines..................	3,533	3	1,178	$r g \sigma_M{}^2 + \sigma_R{}^2$
Operators.................	8,654	2	4,327	$r c \sigma_O{}^2 + \sigma_R{}^2$
Suppliers.................	532	1	532	$c g \sigma_T{}^2 + \sigma_R{}^2$
$M \times O$ interaction..........	3,742	6	624	$r \sigma_{MO}{}^2 + \sigma_R{}^2$
$M \times T$ interaction..........	3,257	3	1,086	$g \sigma_{MT}{}^2 + \sigma_R{}^2$
$O \times T$ interaction...........	571	2	286	$c \sigma_{OT}{}^2 + \sigma_R{}^2$
Experimental error..........	3,711	6	618	$\sigma_R{}^2$
Total...................	24,000	23		

Calculation of F ratios for the various mean squares shows that only that due to operators is significant compared to the residual mean square. This gives:

$$F\,[2,\,6] = \frac{4{,}327}{618} = 7.00 \; .$$

Since

$$F\,[2,\,6]_{0.05} = 5.14 \; ,$$

the null hypothesis is rejected, and operators are judged the only significant source of variation in this situation, based on this experiment.

Interaction

If, for example, machine-operator interaction had been judged significant, several interpretations are possible. Certainly, it may be presumed that operators are biased differently toward different machines. More precisely, it means that at the time the measurements were taken, the variation from machine to machine and from operator to operator is not the same. This may be due to changes which occur because of the timing of the measurements, and a further experiment taking explicit account of time would have to be designed. It is also possible that there is some interaction between all the factors independent of the machine-operator interaction which is causing this bias to be judged significant. The separation of such interactions is not possible within the scope of this kind of experiment.

If this experiment had dealt with factors (machines, operators, suppliers) which were a random sample of these factors rather than being fixed, the expected values for the mean squares would have been somewhat different. In the case of a random model, the variance components of the mean square for the main factor effects include some interaction components. For example, the expected values for the test of Table 7–11 in the case of a random model would be as follows:

Source	Expected Value of Mean Square
Machines	$rg\sigma_M^2 + r\sigma_{MO}^2 + g\sigma_{MT}^2 + \sigma_R^2$
Operators	$rc\sigma_O^2 + r\sigma_{MO}^2 + c\sigma_{OT}^2 + \sigma_R^2$
Suppliers	$cg\sigma_T^2 + g\sigma_{MT}^2 + c\sigma_{OT}^2 + \sigma_R^2$
$M \times O$ interaction	$r\sigma_{MO}^2 + g\sigma_{MT}^2 + \sigma_R^2$
$M \times T$ interaction	$g\sigma_{MT}^2 + c\sigma_{OT}^2 + \sigma_R^2$
$O \times T$ interaction	$r\sigma_{MO}^2 + c\sigma_{OT}^2 + \sigma_R^2$
Experimental error	σ_R^2

The treatment as far as the significance tests are concerned would be the same as for the fixed model, but separation of the variance components would be made according to the above expectations.

If, say, two of the interaction components could be immediately judged as not significant, the proper procedure would be to pool the sums of squares of these terms with the residual, producing a better (more sensitive) estimate of experimental error. In fact, one should progress from the smallest F ratio to the largest in testing the outcome of an analysis of variance, pooling with the residual all those sums of squares which accept the null hypothesis.

Components of Variance

With the revised estimate of the residual variance, it would then be possible to estimate the factor and interaction variances which did prove significant based on F-tests. The right-hand column of Table 7–11 gives the variance components estimated by the mean square values in the table. It can easily be seen that operator-supplier interaction variance and supplier variance do not exist at all, and these can immediately be pooled with the residual, giving

$$s_R^2 = \frac{3,711 + 571 + 532}{6 + 2 + 1} = 535 .$$

Then machine-operator interaction may be tested against this new estimate of the residual, giving

$$F[6, 9] = \frac{624}{535} = 1.17 .$$

Since from the table,

$$F[6, 9]_{0.05} = 3.37 ,$$

this component is judged not significant and may be pooled with the residual, giving a new estimate,

$$s_R^2 = \frac{4,814 + 3,742}{9 + 6} = 571 .$$

Machine-supplier interaction would then be tested against this residual, giving

$$F[3, 15] = \frac{1,086}{571} = 1.90 .$$

From the table,

$$F[3, 15]_{0.05} = 3.29 ,$$

and this interaction is judged as not significant. Pooling this value with the residual gives:

$$s_R^2 = \frac{8,556 + 3,257}{15 + 3} = 657 .$$

Testing the machine mean square gives:

$$F[3, 18] = \frac{1,178}{657} = 1.79 ,$$

which is not significant at the 0.05 level, and a new estimate of the residual gives:

$$s_R^2 = \frac{11,813 + 3,533}{18 + 3} = 731 .$$

Then, the variances due to operators, which is significant, may be estimated from the mean square value. This can be done since the operator mean square estimates only operator variance times the number of items on which the estimate is based plus the residual variance (both interaction terms shown were judged to be not significant and pooled with the residual). Then,

$$s_o^2 = \frac{4{,}327 - 731}{8} = 450 \ .$$

Converting this into the units of the original data, an estimate of the standard deviation is:

$$s_o = \sqrt{0.0450} = 0.21 \ .$$

Assuming normality in the population from which the items were measured, operator variations may be seen to account for about 38 per cent of the over-all variation observed [$450 \times 100/(731 + 450) = 38\%$].

A word should be added here about the practice followed in this treatment of pooling nonsignificant estimates in order to obtain better estimates of the error variance. This practice has one disadvantage which should be considered; it can lead to bias in the pooled result. If a variation is judged not significant when, in fact, it is, then the pooling process would lead to the introduction of bias in the pooled result. However, if the level at which the test is taken is acceptable for judging significance, then it is probably safe to pool. It should be remembered, however, that it is always correct not to pool, and if the gain by pooling is not judged worth the risk taken that bias will be introduced, then don't pool.

Many variations and extensions of the technique of analysis of variance are possible and certainly to be recommended if called for in a given situation. More factors can be taken into account than those treated here. It is not essential that the same number of measurements be taken for each factor combination. Variations on the basic model used and the technique of calculation are beyond the scope of this presentation but may be found in some of the references listed at the end of the chapter.

The Chi-Square Test

In attempting to determine whether useful data can be generated from some theoretical statistical distribution, we must find out whether any real difference exists between an empirical distribution and the distribution which is assumed to represent it. A procedure based on the chi-square distribution provides such a test. It will indicate whether or not the difference between two distributions—empirical and theoretical —is statistically significant. Where a significant difference does not exist, the statistical distribution can be used as the data-generating function. Although there are many theoretical distributions which might not differ significantly from some given sample, the important point here is that some physical grounds exist for deciding on the particular distribution to be tested. If no such grounds exist, then one has no justification in accepting the results of any statistical test.

The chi-square test is a test for "goodness of fit" and is based on the following relationship:

$$\chi^2 = \sum_{o=1}^{k} \frac{(f_o - f_e)^2}{f_e}, \qquad \text{(See Appendix II, Table B.)}$$

where

$$f_o = \text{observed value}$$
$$f_e = \text{expected value}$$

With the χ^2 value thus calculated, the table of expected values of χ^2 can be entered for the appropriate degrees of freedom[3] to determine whether the difference between observed frequencies and expected frequencies is significant.

An example of the application of chi-square is shown in Table 7–12.

Table 7–12

CALCULATION OF χ^2 FOR ACTUAL DEMAND DISTRIBUTION
AND THEORETICAL POISSON DISTRIBUTION

u = Units Demanded per Day	Frequency of Demand		$f_o - f_e$	$(f_o - f_e)^2$	$\frac{(f_o - f_e)^2}{f_e}$
	f_o = Observed (for 100 Days)	f_e = Expected (per Poisson Distribution)			
0	40	36.8	3.2	10.24	0.28
1	30	36.8	−6.8	46.24	1.25
2	20	18.4	1.6	2.56	0.14
3	10	6.1 ⎫			
4	0	1.5 ⎬ 8.0	2.0	4.0	0.50
5	0	0.3			
6	0	0.1 ⎭			$\chi^2 = 2.17$

$\chi_{0.70}^2(3) = 1.424$
$\chi_{0.50}^2(3) = 2.366$

Here some demand data are tested against the Poisson distribution, the objective being to determine whether there is any statistically significant

---
[3] See below for an explanation of the concept of degrees of freedom.

difference between the reported data and the expected—or Poisson generated—data. Theoretical frequencies according to the Poisson distribution are shown in column 3 of the table. Frequencies for demand of three units through six units are grouped arbitrarily because of observed zero frequencies in the actual experience. Thus, the chi-square comparison or test is among four groups of data, zero, one, two, and three or more units demanded per day. The result of the calculation produces chi-square $= 2.17$. From a table of chi-square values, for degrees of freedom equal to $n - 1$ (3), it is observed that there is more than a 50 per cent probability that the chi-square value larger than 2.17 could occur purely by chance. The statistical interpretation is that no significant difference exists between the actual data and the theoretical or expected data. A word about *degrees of freedom* is appropriate here. This phrase is used to describe the number of variables in a numerical problem which are free to vary. For example, consider the following sums:

a_1	2	-5	24
a_2	5	10	4
a_3	12	4	3
a_4	8	-50	2
a_5	7	75	1
Σa_i	34	34	34

With the total of 34 given, it is possible to change or alter any four of the numbers contributing to this total. However, as soon as the fourth number is determined, the fifth is fixed. In other words, only four degrees of freedom are possible in this summation if the total is taken as fixed.

χ^2 is only an approximate distribution in tests for goodness of fit, and if cell frequencies are too small, the approximation will not be reliable. As a rule, good results can be obtained if $f_e \geqq 5$ and $k \geqq 5$; if $k < 5, f_e$ should be somewhat larger than 5.

It should be noted here that there are also graphical means for testing—in a very approximate and limited way—the similarity between actual and theoretical distributions. For example, cumulative Poisson and normal probability paper can be used effectively to get a first indication of conformity between an empirical distribution of data and either the normal or Poisson distribution. However, these kinds of graphical tests should be used only as a preliminary to determine whether it is profitable to attempt a chi-square test.

Regression and Correlation

It may be that changes in quality level as measured by the degree to which output conforms to requirements is due to some assignable cause which cannot be dealt with in the usual way. For example, if the centering of a process is a function of tool wear, it may not be economical or physically feasible to adjust the tooling each time a unit of output is finished. What is required is to establish the functional relationship between process centering (and/or variability) and units produced so that an economic determination can be made as to the timing of adjustments and tool changes.

In another situation, for example, it is known that the quality of output is affected by the amount of a particular ingredient used in a product. If the manufacturer is free to use this ingredient over a range of values in each application, the particular value to be used is an economic question depending on the cost of the ingredients and the cost of defectives in each case. In order to establish the level at which control is to be exercised on each batch, the relationship between product quality and the amount of this ingredient must be established. For this purpose, least squares *regression* analysis[4] is often useful.

A Regression Model

For the situation just described assume that a set of production runs has been made with the amount of ingredient A in the product as the independent variable. For each of 20 batches records are kept of the fraction defective which resulted as shown in Table 7–13. A plot of these data shown in Figure 7–1 reveals the existence of a pronounced linear trend in fraction defective as a function of the amount of A and it is hypothesized that this can be described by a model of the form

$$y = a + bx \tag{11}$$

in which

$$y = \text{fraction defective}$$
$$x = \text{amount of A}$$

and a and b are the parameters representing the y co-ordinate at $x = 0$ and the slope of the line respectively.

The method of least squares linear regression calls for determining values for a and b such that the sum of the squared deviations between the line and the observations is minimized. The rationale for this

---

[4] A. J. Duncan, *Quality Control and Industrial Statistics* (3d ed.; Homewood, Ill.: Richard D. Irwin, Inc., 1965).

Figure 7–1

REGRESSION GIVING FRACTION DEFECTIVE
AS A FUNCTION OF PER CENT OF "A"

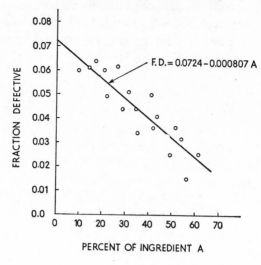

PERCENT OF INGREDIENT A

Table 7–13

DATA FOR REGRESSION MODEL

Sample No.	Ingredient A (x)	Fraction Defective (y)	xy	x^2
1..............	10	0.060	0.600	100
2..............	14	0.061	0.854	196
3..............	17	0.064	1.087	289
4..............	21	0.060	1.260	441
5..............	22	0.049	1.078	484
6..............	26	0.062	1.612	676
7..............	28	0.044	1.232	784
8..............	31	0.051	1.581	961
9..............	34	0.044	1.496	1,156
10..............	35	0.034	1.190	1,225
11..............	41	0.050	2.050	1,681
12..............	42	0.036	1.512	1,764
13..............	43	0.041	1.763	1,859
14..............	46	0.035	1.610	2,116
15..............	49	0.025	1.225	2,401
16..............	51	0.037	1.887	2,601
17..............	54	0.032	1.728	2,916
18..............	54	0.029	1.566	2,916
19..............	56	0.015	0.830	3,136
20..............	61	0.025	1.525	3,721
Σ	735	0.854	27.786	31,423

procedure will not be discussed here and the interested reader is urged to explore the references given for elaboration of these ideas.

In this case these deviations may be defined by first establishing the co-ordinates of the sample points as follows:

$$0.060 = a + 10b$$
$$0.061 = a + 14b$$
$$0.064 = a + 17b$$
$$\cdot$$
$$\cdot$$
$$\cdot$$
$$0.025 = a + 61b$$

The first deviation would be $[0.060 - (a + 10b)]$ and similarly for the remainder. Squaring each deviation and summing we get in general

$$Z = \Sigma[y - (a + bx)]^2 \qquad (12)$$

The minimum of Z may be obtained by differentiating with respect to a and b and setting the result equal to zero giving

$$\frac{\partial Z}{\partial a} = -2\Sigma[(y - a - bx)] = 0$$

and

$$\frac{\partial Z}{\partial b} = -2x\Sigma[(y - a - bx)] = 0 .$$

Reducing gives

$$\Sigma y = na + b\Sigma x \qquad (13)$$

and

$$\Sigma xy = a\Sigma x + b\Sigma x^2 \qquad (14)$$

from which a and b may be computed.

For the data of Table 7–13, the resulting values are 0.0724 and −0.000807 for a and b respectively. Thus the equation for the line of interest is

$$y = 0.0724 - 0.000807x .$$

This gives us an estimate of the fraction defective on the assumption that a straight line is the best approximating relationship. If we had reason to believe that some other functional form would be more appropriate then the equation for that form could be inserted in place of $(a + bx)$ in equation (12) and the same procedure used for that case.

If we wished to hypothesize more than one fit and compare their estimating power or just state the effectiveness of the relationship obtained, the coefficient of correlation would prove useful.

Coefficient of Correlation

The question as to how well the observed facts would have been predicted by the relation obtained is always of interest in regression analysis. The variance of the original data is

$$\sigma_y^2 = \frac{\Sigma(y_i - \bar{y})^2}{n}. \tag{15}$$

In this case, $\sigma_y^2 = 0.000191$. This variance is in part explained by the line whose parameters were just computed. The part explained can be expressed as the variance of each point predicted by the equation, $\tilde{y}_i$, and the mean value, that is

$$\sigma_e^2 = \frac{\Sigma(\tilde{y}_i - \bar{y})^2}{n} \tag{16}$$

in which

σ_e^2 = variance explained by regression line
$\tilde{y}_i$ = points predicted by regression line with observed a's and b's

For the given data, $\sigma_e^2 = 0.000143$. The remaining component measured by differences between observed points and predicted points is not explained by the regression line and is presumed to be residual variance, that is, variance due to all other causes. This component is

$$\sigma_r^2 = \frac{\Sigma(y_i - \tilde{y}_i)^2}{n} \tag{17}$$

and is 0.000048 giving a standard deviation of 0.0069. With this latter figure and the equation of the line, a prediction of process average fraction defective can be made for any amount of ingredient A and the error of this estimate stated.

It should be clear that a measure of the goodness of the prediction obtained could be made by using the ratio of explained to total variance and given other estimating relationships these could be compared relatively by such a measure. This relationship is σ_e^2/σ_y^2 and is called the coefficient of determination, r^2. In this case it is 0.000143/0.000191, or 0.749.

The coefficient of correlation, r, is the ratio of the standard deviations on which r^2 is based and in this case is 0.867. We can see that the line accounts for about 75 per cent of the total variance in the observations and this is a measure of its suitability for any given predictive task. If it is desired to estimate r directly without first obtaining the regression line, this can be done from

$$r = \frac{\Sigma(x_i - \bar{x})(y_i - \bar{y})}{\sqrt{\Sigma(x_i - \bar{x})^2 \, \Sigma(y_i - \bar{y})^2}} \tag{18}$$

This concept can be extended to cases in which the number of independent variables is greater than one and for which the hypothesized predictive forms are more complex than simple linear forms. The interested reader is urged to consult the references given for further help in such cases. A number of very powerful computer programs exist to provide computational aid in complex cases, and it is recommended that the nearest available computer center library be consulted for these.

SUMMARY OF CONCEPTS EMPLOYED IN THE EXPERIMENT

The statistical tools employed in the experiment described are some of the most powerful available to the industrial experimenter. Those employed here fall into three major categories:

1. Tests of differences.
2. The analysis of variance.
3. Parameter estimation.

The analysis of variance, regardless of the number of factors, essentially involves setting up a balanced design within the framework of which data may be generated which will allow for the separation of components of variance according to the factors under direct examination. The remaining factors which contribute to the total observed variance are randomized. Then, each of the factor variances is compared to this residual due to random effects. Since the base for comparison (the residual) is the same for all factors, not only is the significance of the variation determined but also the extent of its effect.

The number of factors included for analysis has no effect on the basic logic of the technique, but considerable effect on the difficulty of computation. The number of interactions which could be important increases faster than the number of factors which are included. It is important to include enough factors so that the residual (experimental error) is reduced to a level low enough so that the relative significance of the factors can be determined. It is also important to include only enough factors to do this, since the computational expense of an additional factor rapidly becomes larger than the value gained from including it.

Tests for differences always involve a comparison of the results of two sets of observations under the assumption that the two were drawn from the same population. The question is asked as to the probability that an observed difference could have occurred under such an hypothesis. An answer can always be found where the experimenter has knowledge as to the general kind of distribution with which he is dealing (normal, binomial, Poisson, etc.).

Analysis of Variance and Control Charts

It has probably been recognized that the analysis of variance technique is quite similar to the use of $\bar{X}$ and R charts. That is, in both cases, the assumption is made that the process under investigation is in some sense "in control." Then a test is designed to accept or reject this hypothesis. The major technical difference between the two procedures is that the analysis of variance is based on the over-all variation among sample means, while the $\bar{X}$ control chart is based on the way in which individual sample means vary. Both, however, tend to indicate the presence or lack of control among sample means.

The advantages of $\bar{X}$ and R charts over the analysis of variance may be summarized as follows:[5]

1. The range chart provides a test for whether or not the within sample variation is in control. The analysis of variance assumes this but does not test the assumption.
2. Control charts are easier to understand.
3. The control chart can be read by those who understand very little of the underlying theory.
4. The control chart tests the null hypothesis from sample to sample.
5. The analysis of variance does not pinpoint those sample means which are out of control.
6. The control chart reveals much more information to the experienced user than the summary table of the analysis of variance.

The major advantages of the analysis of variance over control charts are as follows:

1. More information is obtained from limited data, making it especially effective where data are costly to get.
2. With limited observations, explicit account is taken of the degrees of freedom associated with each estimate, thus making better estimates of the variances.

---

[5] Adapted from Cecil C. Craig, "Control Charts versus the Analysis of Variance in Process Control by Variables," *Industrial Quality Control,* January, 1947, pp. 14–16.

3. The analysis of variance *assigns* variation quantitatively to the factors considered.

This last is usually the most telling advantage when considering the two techniques. If the only objective is process control, then the control chart seems clearly superior, but if it is desirable to assign variation as among possible causes, then the technique of analysis of variance usually becomes superior.

The Role of Experimentation in Production Management

It is hoped that the preceding has given an insight into the value of well-designed experiments in industry. While the situation described is limited in its scope, the principles of design and methods of analysis are quite general. There are many variations on these basic techniques which have been designed to allow for analysis in other and more complex situations. An especially important class of these are sampling models for analysis of variance where the levels of the various factors are drawn at random from a population. The techniques of statistical inference and analysis of variance provide one with powerful tools which may be brought to bear on any problem of measurement and analysis.

Through the use of modern statistical tools, answers may be sought to questions which heretofore were often the subject of intuitive reasoning alone. The important point is the confidence one may gain in data on which to base decisions. Once the manager has a firm confidence in the ability of these tools properly applied to supply desired information, a long step forward in the science of management will have been taken.

REFERENCES

1. BOWKER, A. H., and LIEBERMAN, G. J. *Engineering Statistics.* Englewood Cliffs, N.J.: Prentice-Hall, Inc., 1959.
2. BROWNLEE, K. A. *Industrial Experimentation.* New York: Chemical Publishing Co., 1948.
3. COCHRAN, WILLIAM G., and COX, GERTRUDE M. *Experimental Designs.* New York: John Wiley & Sons, Inc., 1950.
4. DUNCAN, ACHESON J. *Quality Control and Industrial Statistics.* 3d ed. Homewood, Ill.: Richard D. Irwin, Inc., 1965.
5. FISHER, R. A. *Statistical Methods for Research Workers.* 11th ed. London: Oliver & Boyd, Ltd., 1950.
6. MANN, H. B. *Analysis and Design of Experiments.* New York: Dover Publications, Inc., 1949.
7. TIPPETT, L. H. C. *Technological Applications of Statistics.* New York: John Wiley & Sons, Inc., 1950.

APPENDIX TO CHAPTER 7[6]

Computational Technique—One-Factor Analysis of Variance

For the data given, the computations may be considerably reduced by "coding" the data. This is done by rewriting the values as deviations from the mean (or some other convenient number). These data may be rewritten as deviation from 4.73 yielding (in hundredths) data shown in Table 7–14.

Table 7–14

	M_1	M_2	M_3	M_4	
	4	20	− 2	−35	
	−30	−15	− 3	−22	
	−14	74	8	52	
	1	38	74	−18	
	− 8	−26	−21	7	
	−17	7	−11	−58	
Σx_j	−64	98	45	−74	Grand
$\bar{x}_c$	−11	16	8	−12	total $= 5$

Then the total sum of squared deviations between each item and the mean of all the items may be found. In this case, the sum is:

$$\left(4 - \frac{5}{24}\right)^2 + \left(20 - \frac{5}{24}\right)^2 + \left(-2 - \frac{5}{24}\right)^2 + \left(-35 - \frac{5}{24}\right)^2 +$$
$$\left(-30 - \frac{5}{24}\right)^2 + \dots + \left(-58 - \frac{5}{24}\right)^2 = 24{,}000 \, .$$

This sum of squares divided by $(24 - 1)$ gives the total observed variance for these data. The two estimates which must be made in order to test for differences between columns may be found next. First, an estimate of total variation may be made by assuming that the data in all columns come from the same universe. The column mean, then, is assumed to represent each item in its column, and the sum of squares is the difference between the column mean and the grand mean times the number of items in each column summed over all columns. The difference between column mean and the grand mean is multiplied by the number of items in each column, since these deviations are measured from means of samples of six ($s_{\bar{x}}^2 = n s_x^2$). This gives:

$$6\left(-\frac{64}{6} - \frac{5}{24}\right)^2 + 6\left(\frac{98}{6} - \frac{5}{24}\right)^2 + 6\left(\frac{45}{6} - \frac{5}{24}\right)^2 + 6\left(\frac{-74}{6} - \frac{5}{24}\right)^2 = 3{,}533.$$

---

[6] In all cases the computations shown here use the data given in the chapter but coded in hundredths and shown as deviations from 4.73.

The experimental error sum of squares may be computed by adding the squared differences between each item in a column and the column mean and summing over all columns. This also should estimate the total sum of squares under the null hypothesis. That is, if there is no significant difference between columns, the column mean is an estimate of the grand mean. In the present case this gives

$$\left(4 - \frac{-64}{6}\right)^2 + \left(-30 - \frac{-64}{6}\right)^2 + \ldots + \left(20 - \frac{98}{6}\right)^2 + \ldots + \left(-2 - \frac{45}{6}\right)^2$$
$$+ \ldots + \left(-35 - \frac{-74}{6}\right)^2 + \ldots + \left(-58 - \frac{-74}{6}\right)^2 = 20{,}467 .$$

The figures just computed are the numerators of equations (8) and (9). The above computations are somewhat laborious, and a better (though less revealing) method is as follows:

1. Square the column totals and divide by the number of items in each column:

$$\frac{(-64)^2 + 98^2 + 45^2 + (-74)^2}{6} = 3{,}534 .$$

2. Square each item and sum the squares:

$$4^2 + (-30)^2 + (-14)^2 + 1^2 + (-8)^2 + (-17)^2 + 20^2 + (-15)^2 +$$
$$74^2 + 38^2 + (-26)^2 + 7^2 + (-2)^2 + (-3)^2 + 8^2 + 74^2 + (-21)^2 +$$
$$(-11)^2 + (-35)^2 + (-22)^2 + 52^2 + (-18)^2 + 7^2 + (-58)^2 = 24{,}001.$$

3. Sum the individual items, square the sum, and divide by the number of items [this factor will correct (1) for any deviation of the grand total from zero]:

$$\frac{(5)^2}{24} = 1 .$$

4. The column sum of squares is (1) − (3), or $3{,}534 - 1 = 3{,}533$; and the residual sum of squares is (2) − (1), or $24{,}001 - 3{,}534 = 20{,}467$.
5. The total sum of squares is (2) − (3), or $24{,}001 - 1 = 24{,}000$.

From the above, an analysis of variance table may be prepared, giving the sources of variation, the degrees of freedom for each source [the denominators of (8) and (9)], and the mean square value for each source as shown in Table 7–15.

Table 7–15

ONE-FACTOR ANALYSIS OF VARIANCE

Source of Variation	Sum of Squares	Degrees of Freedom	Mean Squares	Expected Value
Machines (columns).........	3,533	3	1,178	$n_j\sigma_M^2 + \sigma_R^2$
Experimental error (residual)..	20,467	20	1,023	σ_R^2
Total................	24,000	23		

Computational Technique—Two-Factor Analysis of Variance

In the two-factor case, computations for columns are carried out as before, and the procedure is repeated for rows. That is,

1. Square the column sums, add, and divide by the number of items in each column:

$$\frac{(-64)^2 + 98^2 + 45^2 + (-74)^2}{6} = 3,534 .$$

2. Square the row sums, add, and divide by the number of items in each row:

$$\frac{(-83)^2 + 215^2 + (-127)^2}{8} = 8,655 .$$

3. Square each item and sum. From the previous calculation this value is 24,001.

4. Sum all items, square the sum, and divide by the total number of items:

$$\frac{(5)^2}{24} = 1 .$$

5. Then the column sum of squares is $(1) - (4)$, or

$$3,534 - 1 = 3,533 .$$

6. The row sum of squares is $(2) - (4)$, or

$$8,655 - 1 = 8,654 .$$

7. The residual sum of squares is $(3) - [(1) + (2) - (4)]$, or $24,001 - [8,655 + 3,534 - 1] = 11,813$.

The analysis of variance table is shown in Table 7–6.

Two-Factor Case with Interaction

In the previous computations, steps (1) through (6) are the same, but now:

7. The residual sum of squares may be computed by summing the items for each factor combination, squaring these sums, adding, dividing by the number of items in each cell, and then subtracting this total from (3):

$$24,001 - \frac{(-26)^2 + (-13)^2 + (-25)^2 + 5^2 + 112^2 + (-19)^2 + (-5)^2}{2}$$
$$\frac{+ 82^2 + (-32)^2 + (-77)^2 + 34^2 + (-51)^2}{} = 8,071 .$$

8. The interaction sum of squares is the sum of the factor combination sums squared and divided by the number of items for each factor combination (as shown above) less the column and row sums of squares corrected for the mean $[(1) + (2) - (4)]$. This gives:

$$15,930 - (3,534 + 8,655 - 1) = 3,742 .$$

Three-Factor Case with Interaction

Table 7–16

THREE-FACTOR ANALYSIS OF VARIANCE

Source of Variation	Sums of Squares	Degrees of Freedom	Mean Square	Expected Value
Machines.................	3,533	3	1,178	$rg\sigma_M^2 + \sigma_R^2$
Operators................	8,654	2	4,327	$rc\sigma_O^2 + \sigma_R^2$
Suppliers................	532	1	532	$cg\sigma_T^2 + \sigma_R^2$
$M \times O$ interaction..........	3,742	6	624	$r\sigma_{MO}^2 + \sigma_R^2$
$M \times T$ interaction..........	3,257	3	1,086	$g\sigma_{MT}^2 + \sigma_R^2$
$O \times T$ interaction...........	571	2	286	$c\sigma_{OT}^2 + \sigma_R^2$
Experimental error...........	3,711	6	618	σ_R^2
Total.................	24,000	23		

1. Sum the items for each machine, square, add over all machines, and divide by the number of items for each machine:

$$\frac{(-64) + 98^2 + 45^2 + (-74)^2}{6} = 3,534 .$$

2. Square the sum of items for each operator, add over all operators, and divide by the number of items for each operator:

$$\frac{(-83)^2 + 215^2 + (127)^2}{8} = 8,655 .$$

3. Square the sum of items for each supplier, add over all suppliers, and divide by the number of items for each supplier:

$$\frac{59^2 + (-54)^2}{12} = 533 .$$

4. Sum the items for each machine-operator factor combination, square, add over all combinations, and divide by the number of values for each combination:

$$\frac{(-26)^2 + (-13)^2 + (-25)^2 + 5^2 + 112^2 + (-19)^2 + (-5)^-}{2}$$

$$+ \frac{82^2 + (-32)^2 + (-77)^2 + 34^2 + (-51)^2}{} = 15,930 .$$

5. Sum the items for each machine-supplier factor combination, square, add over all combinations, and divide by the number of values for each combination:

$$\frac{(-18)^2 + (-36)^2 + 68^2 + 30^2 + (-15)^2 + 60^2 + 24^2 + (-98)^2}{3} = 7,323$$

6. Sum the items for each operator-supplier factor combination, square, add over all combinations, and divide by the number of values for each combination:

$$\frac{(-13)^2 + (-70)^2 + 120^2 + 105^2 + (-48)^2 + (-79)^2}{4} = 9,758 .$$

7. Square each item in the table and sum over all items:

$4^2 + (-30)^2 + (-14)^2 + 1^2 + (-8)^2 + (-17)^2 + 20^2 + (-15)^2 + 74^2 + 38^2 + (-26)^2 + 7^2 + (-2)^2 + (-3)^2 + 8^2 + 74^2 + (-21)^2 + (-11)^2 + (-35)^2 + (-22)^2 + 52^2 + (-18)^2 + 7^2 + (-58)^2 = 24,001$.

8. Sum all the items, square the sum, and divide by the total number of items:

$$\frac{5^2}{24} = 1 \ .$$

9. The machine sum of squares is $(1) - (8)$:

$$3,534 - 1 = 3,533 \ .$$

10. The operator sum of squares is $(2) - (8)$.

$$8,655 - 1 = 8,654 \ .$$

11. The supplier sum of squares is $(3) - (8)$:

$$533 - 1 = 532 \ .$$

12. The machine-operator interaction sum of squares is $(4) - [(1) + (2) - (8)]$:

$$15,930 - (3,534 + 8,655 - 1) = 3,742 \ .$$

13. The machine-supplier interaction sum of squares is $(5) - [(1) + (3) - (8)]$:

$$7,323 - (3,534 + 533 - 1) = 3,257 \ .$$

14. The operator-supplier interaction sum of squares is $(6) - [(2) + (3) - (8)]$:

$$9,578 - (8,655 + 533 - 1) = 571 \ .$$

15. The residual sum of squares is $(7) - [(9) + (10) + (11) + (12) + (13) + (14) + (8)]$:

$$24,001 - (3,533 + 8,654 + 532 + 3,742 + 3,257 + 571 + 1) = 2,713 \ .$$

PROBLEMS

1. The following is a set of data giving hardness (Rockwell) of forgings produced from steel rods. Four forgings are obtained from each rod. All are placed in a furnace and heated to forging temperature. The first rod is withdrawn, a forging made, and the rod replaced in the furnace. The first forging is made using each rod in turn, and then the sequence is repeated to produce the second, third, and fourth forging from each rod. It is desired to learn whether variation in hardness is attributable to differences between rods or to the order in which forgings are made. Prepare a suitable analysis of variance.

Rod No.	Order of Forgings			
	1	2	3	4
1	60.4	60.4	59.2	60.4
2	62.8	62.8	62.0	62.8
3	61.2	61.6	62.8	64.0
4	59.2	60.4	59.6	61.2
5	60.8	60.4	58.4	60.8
6	59.6	60.0	59.0	59.6
7	61.4	62.2	66.0	68.8
8	60.6	59.2	68.8	61.6
9	58.8	59.0	57.6	60.4
10	59.9	60.1	59.4	61.2
11	59.8	60.4	62.0	62.8
12	60.8	60.8	62.8	63.2
13	58.0	59.2	60.2	60.4
14	58.4	57.6	58.6	59.0
15	61.4	60.4	60.6	60.8
16	61.0	60.4	61.0	61.6
17	61.4	59.2	60.8	61.6
18	60.4	60.6	62.0	61.6
19	62.8	61.4	61.8	61.6
20	62.8	63.6	62.4	60.8
21	61.2	62.0	61.4	63.0
22	59.4	61.2	60.8	61.4
23	58.8	60.0	60.8	61.2
24	59.8	59.6	60.8	60.4
25	58.4	58.8	61.0	61.2

2. A multihead machine is used to bore cylinders in V-8 engines. The following are measurements in order of production of cylinder diameter (given in thousandths of an inch above 3.300″). It is desired to determine if there is any significant difference between heads or sides of this machine.

Head No.	Left Side				Right Side			
	1	2	3	4	5	6	7	8
Engine No. 1	21	20	23	20	28	23	29	27
Engine No. 2	18	15	18	20	26	26	21	22
Engine No. 3	17	21	25	23	17	23	25	32
Engine No. 4	18	18	26	23	20	13	22	19
Engine No. 5	22	19	29	19	27	23	25	27
Engine No. 6	21	21	25	35	13	13	19	22
Engine No. 7	33	26	21	26	43	33	25	22
Engine No. 8	27	21	29	27	29	31	25	23

Present an appropriate analysis of variance. Are there any other experiments which might be recommended for this situation?

3. The following data show the results of an experiment conducted in an attempt to validate a production standard. Three machines producing the same item, three operators, and four time-study men were involved. Data are given in hundredths of a minute over two minutes.

MACHINE	OPERATOR	TIME-STUDY MEN			
		1	2	3	4
1	I	56	27	28	14
	II	84	25	6	14
	III	73	28	6	20
2	I	34	22	20	11
	II	31	25	53	8
	III	11	17	45	17
3	I	78	25	62	14
	II	22	115	14	11
	III	64	56	22	48

Determine which sources of variation are significant.

Can you suggest any other experiments which might be conducted based on the outcome of this analysis?

4. You are given the following results of resistance measurements on two wires:

I	II
2.50 Ω	2.42 Ω
2.57	2.40
2.41	2.50
2.44	2.39
2.51	2.45

Is there a significant difference in the resistances of the two wires?

5. The tensile strength of specimens from each of two successive melts in a cupola gave the following results in pounds per square inch:

Specimen	Melt A	Melt B
I	6,120	6,140
II	6,130	6,110
III	6,110	6,100
IV	6,150	6,120
V	6,190	6,120

Would you conclude that there was any significant difference between the melts?

If there is a difference, state the 0.95 confidence limits for this difference.

6. Distributor brush wear and commutator plate burning has been a costly maintenance problem in the airline industry. After considerable research, laboratory and field testing of different brush materials and spring configurations, United Air Lines[7] conducted a statistically designed and controlled

---

[7] Allan M. Hull, "Optimizing Maintenance Costs through Quality Control," *Industrial Quality Control*, Vol. XII, No. 12:4 (June, 1956) by permission of the author.

service test. However, in actual service, the performance of the new parts appears questionable. The table below gives the number of hours each type of part lasted on twelve different engines:

Engine	Old Part	New Part
1........................	751	751
2........................	751	393
3........................	751	751
4........................	791	491
5........................	85	217
6........................	712	712
7........................	791	791
8........................	791	160
9........................	471	373
10........................	650	394
11........................	650	750
12........................	447	269
	7,641	6,052

On the basis of this data what information can be given to United?

7. During both the month of June and the month of July, average daily production of rivets was 20 million. However for June the standard deviation was 3 million, while during July it was only 1 million. Does the data show a significant difference in rivet production? What is the meaning of this difference (if any)?

8. *a*) A series of numbers are generated by two populations with different means and standard deviations. Tests of the mean and standard deviations of the series were not significant at the 5 per cent level. Does this mean that the two populations are different by too little to be observable?

   b) The differences were significant at the 35 per cent level. What exactly does this fact mean?

9. Two suppliers deliver barrels of apples with the following counts of bad apples in ten successive barrels.

	A	*B*
	2	8
	5	3
	4	1
	7	4
	1	4
	0	9
	8	3
	3	6
	5	5
	2	6
Total........	37	49

Would you say the quality of these suppliers is different?

10. A manufacturer is interested in pinpointing the cause or causes of observed variation in the diameter of a piece turned out by an automatic screw machine operation. He first of all wishes to determine whether the three different machines are different in the way they produce output or whether differences in tooling are important. You propose an experiment and collect the following data on this measurement (coded in thousandths above 2.000″):

Tool Set	Machine		
	1	2	3
1......................	6	5	4
2......................	15	10	8
3......................	15	15	12

a) What can you tell the manufacturer about the problem he presents based on an analysis of variance?

b) Within what dimensional limits do you expect 95 per cent of output to fall?

c) What portion of this variation is accounted for by differences between machines? By differences between tooling?

11. Tolerance specifications for a product are given as $4.50″ \pm 0.05″$. The results of measurements on 25 samples of size 4 give $\bar{x} = 4.49″$ and $\sigma_{\bar{x}} = 0.015$. The process is in control.

a) Given the sampling results as the best estimate of process characteristics, what percentage of the product produced is outside of the specifications?

b) At what level of significance would you say the process (sampled at $\bar{x} = 4.49″$) is different from the nominal specification ($4.50″$)?

SECTION IV

Economic Analysis

A large number of problems in production management are of the type where the question asked is, "how much?," "how many?," "when?," "how long?," "where?," and the like. Essentially the problem requires a single decision which often may be characterized by one number or a range of numbers. Such problems as those which involve inventory levels, scale of operations, number of maintenance personnel, and equipment investment are of this type.

Almost always these problems involve some measure of uncertainty. Methods for analysis of these kind of problems will be developed here under conditions of both certainty and uncertainty.

These problems are first approached by total value analysis where the model expresses the variable of interest as a function of other variables, some of which are subject to manipulation or control by management. Then incremental analysis is presented where the model deals with the incremental or last unit "added" to the solution. Incremental analysis and total value analysis are not necessarily mutually exclusive, but their orientation differs. Equipment investment analysis, a special case of total value analysis, is applied where a major factor in the problem is time preference (for capital) or a flow of income and expenditures over a period of time.

CHAPTER 8

Total Value Analysis

MODELS UNDER CERTAINTY

TOTAL value analysis refers to a diverse group of models. This is the standard method of analysis in the physical sciences, engineering, and some of the social sciences. A variable of interest, the "dependent variable" is expressed as a function of "independent variable(s)," some of which may be capable of management manipulation or control. The mathematical model, which is an abstraction, should yield additional insight into the problem being studied. As the model is an abstraction, "unreal" assumptions will undoubtedly be made. A compromise must usually be made between the demands of model simplicity and real world facts. As was pointed out in Chapter 1, the model is never "true" and, therefore, the pragmatic criterion of usefulness should be the controlling one. (See Chapter 1 for a fuller discussion of these points.)

Economic Lot Size Model

The problem of economic lot size will be first used to illustrate total value analysis. This same problem will be used to illustrate incremental analysis in Chapter 9. When manufacturing to stock, the producer has a decision to make as to the size of the lots he will put into stock periodically. The first step in a problem such as this is to choose a meaningful and measurable objective. Minimum total variable costs per year will be the one used here. The next step is to decide which variables in this problem affect the variable of interest—the measure of effectiveness. On the basis of an examination of the economic nature of the problem, total variable costs (TVC) are held to be a function of lot size (Q), yearly requirements (R), setup costs (S), and carrying cost per piece per year (I), i.e., $TVC = f(Q, R, S, I)$. The next

313

step is to set up the model. A graphical model of the inventory level might look like Figure 8–1.

The setup cost is due to the need in most manufacturing processes to get the equipment ready to produce a particular run of product. The cost may vary from an almost negligible amount to an extremely large expense, such as the new model changeover in the automobile industry. The expenses of carrying inventory include such costs as property taxes, insurance, obsolescence, depreciation, storage, and interest. These costs may be implicit as well as explicit. For instance, an interest charge is not usually part of the accounting record as an explicit cost where the

Figure 8–1

SIMPLIFIED INVENTORY MODEL

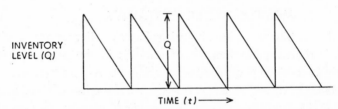

INVENTORY
LEVEL (Q)

Q

TIME (t) ⟶

firm has not borrowed money for inventory purposes. However, even if the company has sufficient funds to carry the inventory, the fact that the funds are tied up in inventory means that they can't be used for other purposes—where they would earn some return. This opportunity cost must be charged to inventory for purposes of making an economic decision. This cost is sometimes treated as a percentage per year of the value of the inventory unit, and must therefore be multiplied by this value to yield a cost per unit per year.[1]

A specific problem will be used as an illustration. The relevant data are as follows:

$$R = 10,000 \text{ units per year,}$$
$$S = \$18 \text{ per setup,}$$
$$I = \$0.12 \text{ per piece per year.}$$

A tabular analysis or "model" will first be used. Different possible lot size decisions will be evaluated and compared as shown in Table 8–1 for lot sizes of 500, 1,000, 2,000, 5,000, 10,000.

Of the choices listed, a lot size of 2,000 units would be most economical. Other choices near 2,000 may be similarly evaluated for a

---

[1] For an extended discussion of the problem of determining these and similar costs, see Billy E. Goetz, *Management Planning and Control* (New York: McGraw-Hill Book Co., Inc., 1949).

more precise choice. If the total number of possible solutions to a problem is small, it may well be possible to evaluate each one of the solutions and pick the best one by inspection. Even when the number of possible solutions is large (as in the present case), evaluation of

Table 8–1

TABULAR ANALYSIS OF INVENTORY PROBLEM

a) Lot Size	500	1,000	2,000	5,000	10,000
b) Number of setups $\dfrac{10,000}{(a)}$	20	10	5	2	1
c) Maximum inventory	500	1,000	2,000	5,000	10,000
d) Average inventory $\frac{1}{2}(c)$	250	500	1,000	2,500	5,000
e) Setup cost 18 (b)	$360	$180	$ 90	$ 36	$ 18
f) Carrying cost 0.12(d)	$ 30	$ 60	$120	$300	$600
g) Total cost (e) + (f)	$390	$240	$210	$336	$618

a few solutions which bracket the wide range of solutions available may yield much insight into the problem. A graphical model of rows *e*, *f*, and *g* is shown in Figure 8–2.

Figure 8–2

INVENTORY COST BEHAVIOR

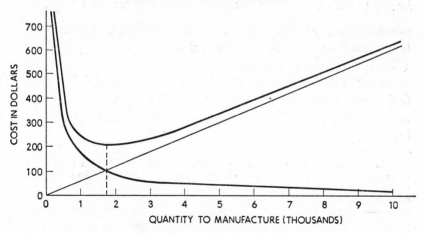

The graphical model shows that carrying costs increase linearly, with an increase in Q. The setup costs decrease at a decreasing rate with an increase in Q. The total variable cost, which is the sum of these two lines, decreases at first with an increase in Q, and then increases. The problem is to find the low point on the TVC line. It happens in this problem (a special case) that the low point is at the quantity at which the two curves cross. A geometrical analysis shows that the low point on the sum line of a rectangular hyperbola and a straight line drawn through the origin is at the point where the two lines intersect. An important related fact is that the lines intersect where their slopes are equal but opposite.

In the preceding paragraphs, both tabular and graphical methods have been used to carry out a total value analysis. A mathematical expression or model which does the same thing as these two previous methods will now be presented using the same notation. The variable of interest, TVC, will be expressed explicitly as a function of other variables (Q, R, I, S).

$$TVC = \frac{Q}{2}I + \frac{R}{Q}S \qquad (1)$$

The total variable cost is the sum of carrying costs and setup costs. $\frac{Q}{2}I$ represents the carrying cost, i.e., $\frac{Q}{2}$ (average inventory in pieces) times I (carrying cost per piece per year). $\frac{R}{Q}S$ represents the setup costs, i.e., $\frac{R}{Q}$ (number of setups per year) times S (cost per setup). This is precisely the way Table 8-1, the tabular approach, was constructed, i.e., line g was the sum of line f (line d times carrying charge) plus line e (line b times setup charge).

After the model, equation (1) has been constructed, it is desirable to find what value of the variable, Q, which is subject to manipulation by management, will minimize the total variable cost. The procedure is as follows:[2]

_____

[2] When given costs and values are substituted in the model, it is possible to chart this model as in Figure 8-2, and see where the low point is. Without the specific costs and values, it is not possible to do this. However, it can be seen from Figure 8-2 that the total cost line, which is the sum of the other two lines, has a slope which is the sum of the slopes of the other two lines. In the left-hand portion of the chart, the setup cost has a very large negative slope (setup cost is decreasing with an increase in quantity), the carrying cost line has a positive (increasing with quantity) slope (constant throughout the chart), and the total variable cost line has a fairly large negative slope, i.e., costs are decreasing. As the quantity, Q, is increased, the magnitude of the negative slope of the setup cost line decreases. At one point it has decreased to the same magnitude as the carrying cost line (slopes equal and opposite) so that when they are totaled, the slope of the total line is zero. The total variable cost curve has a zero slope $\left(\frac{\Delta TVC}{\Delta Q} = 0\right)$ when it is a minimum. It is desirable to establish an equation of condition in order that by solving it the conditions which make it true may be determined. The operation of differentiation from the calculus, or determining the derivative, makes this possible. To differentiate is to determine the rate of change of one variable with respect to another. The derivative expresses this ratio.

$$TVC = \frac{Q}{2}I + \frac{R}{Q}S \qquad (1)$$

$$\frac{d(TVC)}{dQ} = \frac{I}{2} - \frac{R}{Q^2}S \qquad (2)$$

When[3]

$$\frac{I}{2} - \frac{R}{Q^2}S = 0, \qquad (3)$$

$$Q = \sqrt{\frac{2RS}{I}}. \qquad (4)$$

Differentiating equation (1) gives equation (2), which expresses the rate of change of TVC with respect to a change in Q $\left[\frac{d(TVC)}{dQ} \right.$ being the limit of $\frac{\Delta(TVC)}{\Delta Q}$ as ΔQ approaches zero $\left. \right]$. This expression is the slope of the total variable cost curve. Equation (3) is the equation of condition which makes it equal to zero. Equation (4) is the solution of equation (3) and is the condition which makes equation (3) true.

The square root expression for Q is the answer to the problem posed. As in this case, for many models which can be minimized by differentiation, solutions for specific values may also be determined by a tabular or graphical approach. The use of the calculus, however, should yield a quicker solution and a more general solution, which normally means a more useful solution. Probably the major advantage of the more general calculus solution is that a better grasp of deductions from the model is permitted. However, the part of the total effort required to analyze a complex production problem given to model manipulation is normally a minute one.

Only a very small proportion of the millions currently spent for research goes into model-making. Even when the scientists are well paid, most of the money goes into the process of collecting data.[4]

Though the lot size problem has been used for illustration, its importance should not be magnified unwarrantedly. However, several modifications of the problem will be included in this discussion to illustrate the rapid transition possible with a model such as equation (1).

---

[3] $\dfrac{d^2(TVC)}{dQ^2}$ can be checked to assure that this will be a minimum.

[4] I. D. J. Bross, *Design for Decision.* New York: Macmillan Co., 1953.

Variation on Lot Size Model

The cost of an item purchased was not itself included as a part of the model, as it would not vary with the decision being made, i.e., lot size. However, to solve a purchasing problem in which a quantity discount of a certain type is offered, the model may be readily modified. If pricing by the vendor is on the basis of a fixed cost (F), plus a variable cost (v), times the quantity sold, the modification would be as follows:

$$TVC = \frac{Q}{2}I + \frac{R}{Q}S + \frac{R}{Q}(F + Qv), \tag{5}$$

where the last part of the expression represents the vendor's bill; then,

$$TVC = \frac{Q}{2}I + \frac{R}{Q}S + \frac{R}{Q}(F + Qv) \tag{5}$$

$$= \frac{Q}{2}I + \frac{R}{Q}S + \frac{R}{Q}F + Rv$$

$$= \frac{Q}{2}I + \frac{R}{Q}(S + F) + Rv$$

$$\frac{d(TVC)}{dQ} = \frac{I}{2} - \frac{R}{Q^2}(S + F). \tag{6}$$

When

$$\frac{I}{2} - \frac{R}{Q^2}(S + F) = 0, \tag{7}$$

$$Q = \sqrt{\frac{2R(S + F)}{I}}. \tag{8}$$

It can be seen that the fixed cost (F) is analogous to the setup cost or cost of making a purchase (S). In one case it is the purchasing company's fixed cost per purchase, in the second it is the vendor's fixed cost per sale, but in both cases the buyer bears the expense. For purposes of the decision then they may be lumped together.

One additional point should be noted. The carrying cost per piece per year (I) may normally be considered largely an investment cost or an interest charge. In this sense it can be expected to vary with the cost of the piece. Both F and S could also be allocated to each piece for purposes of determining the yearly carrying charges, one of the two major components of the decision. However, for each inventory cycle (one triangle in Figure 8–1), these two costs are invested.

If amortized over the pieces involved, they may be considered invested for the whole period (and every period) at half their values (like the rest of the carrying charge). Note, however, that this investment is entirely independent of the number of pieces purchased in each cycle (Q), and, therefore, is not a part of the decision. This may be demonstrated more forcefully mathematically than verbally. Assume the carrying cost per piece (I) is a fraction of the cost of the piece as follows:

$$I = K\left(\frac{S + F + Qv}{Q}\right),$$

where K is the constant of proportionality, and $S + F + Qv$ is the total cost associated with purchasing the material each inventory cycle, which, divided by the amount purchased (Q), gives cost per piece. Then

$$TVC = \frac{Q}{2}K\left(\frac{S + F + Qv}{Q}\right) + \frac{R}{Q}S + \frac{R}{Q}(F + Qv)$$

$$= \frac{KS}{2} + \frac{KF}{2} + \frac{QKv}{2} + \frac{R}{Q}S + \frac{R}{Q}F + Rv$$

$$= \frac{K}{2}(S + F) + \frac{Q}{2}Kv + \frac{R}{Q}(S + F) + Rv$$

$$\frac{d(TVC)}{dQ} = \frac{Kv}{2} - \frac{R}{Q^2}(S + F).$$

When

$$\frac{Kv}{2} - \frac{R}{Q^2}(S + F) = 0,$$

$$Q = \sqrt{\frac{2R(S + F)}{Kv}} \quad (Q.E.D.).$$

Kv is equivalent to I in the previous example.

When the vendor's billing may not be expressed as a single, continuous function of Q, as in equation (5), an iterative solution may be necessary; for instance, in a step function system of pricing, each step may have to be evaluated and compared.

A second modification of the model may be made for a warehousing cost (W) which varies with the maximum inventory rather than with the average inventory. Many conditions of storage might suggest this revision. In such a case

$$TVC = \frac{Q}{2}I + QW + \frac{R}{Q}S, \tag{9}$$

where the second term (QW) represents this yearly warehousing cost. Rearranging terms gives

$$TVC = Q(\tfrac{1}{2}I + W) + \frac{R}{Q}S$$

$$\frac{d(TVC)}{dQ} = \tfrac{1}{2}I + W - \frac{R}{Q^2}S, \tag{10}$$

which when equated to zero yields

$$Q = \sqrt{\frac{2RS}{I + 2W}}. \tag{11}$$

It is probably well to point out here that small differences in the problems call for small differences in the models. Likewise, large differences in the problems would call for large differences in the models. *The important job is to build a model to fit the problem, not to memorize one that has already been built.*

Scale of Operations Example

The second kind of example used to illustrate total value analysis will be what an economist calls a problem of scale. How large should a particular operation be, e.g., a company, a plant, a warehouse territory? This second example will point up a basic difference from the first one given in the way data are secured for the model. In the lot size example, data for the specific cost elements would be determined from the firm's books and operations by essentially a cost accounting and/or engineering approach—building the model from pieces of information. In this scale of operations example, data for the "specific cost elements" are determined by a statistical approach—working from the total picture.

The problem to be illustrated was one of branch warehouse territories.[5] A firm had approximately a dozen warehouses covering New England. The question raised was how large a warehouse territory for this company should be, and therefore how many warehouses were needed to cover this total territory.

After studying the situation, the first problem was to pick a specific objective, a criterion, a measure of effectiveness. For purposes of this decision, company profit maximization was an acceptable objective to management. As sales would not be affected by the decision, cost

---

[5] See E. H. Bowman and J. B. Stewart, "A Model for Scale of Operations," *Journal of Marketing,* January, 1956, pp. 242–47.

minimization was selected as appropriate for framing the problem. The measure of effectiveness chosen was cost (within the warehouse district) per unit (dollar's worth) of goods distributed. Initially, minimum cost per warehouse was considered as an objective. However, this would yield a large number of very small warehouses which would give an inefficient total operation.

Available data were obtained from the company's records. Examination of these data revealed that the cost of the material handled in each warehouse territory appeared to be primarily dependent upon two opposing factors as follows: (1) the volume of business passing through the warehouse, and (2) the size of the area served by the warehouse. The greater the volume handled, the smaller would be the cost per dollar's worth of goods distributed. However, the greater the area served, the greater would be the cost per dollar's worth of goods distributed. It was then necessary to establish the relationship between these two factors and the rate at which their variation affected the over-all economy of the system. This done, it would be possible to predict the cost of distributing goods as the area served by, and the volume handled in, each warehouse changed. More importantly, the systems could be so arranged that total cost would be minimized. Though, it was recognized that variables other than volume and area would affect the measure of effectiveness, it was desirable to keep the analysis fairly simple; and, therefore, only the two factors considered most important were included.

To build the mathematical model, it was necessary to understand the economics of the problem. Warehousing cost per dollar of goods handled tends to decrease with increasing volume. Costs of supervision and other overhead are spread over more units, and labor can usually be used with a lower proportion of idle time. Since distance traveled would be the main factor determining costs associated with area, it followed that this cost would tend to vary with the square root of the area. As concentric rings of equal area are added, rings rapidly become narrower, i.e., *additional* radial distance traveled becomes smaller.

To summarize, it was determined that the cost per dollar's worth of goods distributed (the warehouse efficiency) was equal to certain costs which vary inversely with the volume, plus certain costs which vary directly with the square root of the area, plus certain costs which were affected by neither of these variables. Putting this last factor first, these same variables, arranged as a mathematical expression, are as follows:

$$C = a + \frac{b}{V} + c\sqrt{A}, \qquad (12)$$

where

C = cost (within the warehouse territory) per dollar's worth of goods distributed—the measure of effectiveness;[6]

V = volume of goods in dollars handled by the warehouse per unit of time;

A = area in square miles served by the warehouse;

a = cost per dollar's worth of goods distributed, independent of either the warehouse's volume handled or area served;

b = "fixed" costs for the warehouse per unit of time, which divided by the volume will yield a cost per dollar's worth distributed;

c = the cost of distribution which varies with the square root of the area, that is, costs associated with miles covered within the warehouse district, such as gasoline, truck repairs, driver hours, etc.

A statistical approach such as this attempts to draw inferences about the importance of different variables, some of which may be manipulated by management, from operations already underway or experiments made. The company had more than a dozen warehouses, and it was possible to determine for each the cost per dollar's worth of goods distributed (C), the volume of goods handled by the warehouse (V), and the area served by the warehouse (A). By multiple regression it was possible to use this warehousing experience and to determine mathematically the values of the coefficients or parameters, a, b, and c, which would make the model the closest predictor of the actual cost for all present warehouses using the individual volume and area figures.

Least squares multiple regression minimizes the sum of the squares of the difference between the actual cost and the predicted cost. An expression for this is as follows:

$$\sum_{i=1}^{i=N} [C_i - (a + \frac{b}{V_i} + c\sqrt{A_i})]^2,$$

where C_i, V_i, and A_i indicate actual values in a given (the ith) branch warehouse operation, and the Σ indicates a sum for all (N) warehouses. Actually, a set of three simultaneous equations (partial derivatives equated to zero) are solved for a, b, and c, in order to establish the conditions for a minimum sum of squares of prediction

---

[6] This is a total cost divided by total number of units, and it is therefore an average cost. Totals and averages, though not identical, are essentially interchangeable, and both differ conceptually from incrementals.

error.[7] These equations establish what are called the normal equations.

In order to confirm the accuracy of this model, a cost (C) was computed for each warehouse using the determined values of a, b, and c from the multiple regression calculation, and the warehouses' specific figures for V and A. By comparing these computed costs with the actual warehousing costs, it was possible to see how well the model described the actual situation. This comparison can be made statistically by determining the multiple correlation coefficient for the two sets of figures.[8] The multiple correlation coefficient was found to be 0.89 in this study, indicating a fairly high degree of correlation for such a simple model. The coefficient squared ($r^2 = 0.79$) represents that portion of the total variance explained by the model, i.e., variation in the dependent variable related to variation in the independent variable(s). If the model had not been acceptable at this point, it would have been necessary to expand and/or modify it. If the model is to aid the understanding of the situation and is to be manipulated so that the real world situation may be manipulated in like manner, there

---

[7] $\dfrac{\partial \Sigma}{\partial a} = 0$; $\dfrac{\partial \Sigma}{\partial b} = 0$; $\dfrac{\partial \Sigma}{\partial c} = 0$.

The form of these partial derivatives is as follows:

$$\frac{du^n}{dv} = nu^{n-1}\frac{du}{dv} \text{ and } \frac{d\Sigma u_i}{dv} = \sum_i \frac{du_i}{dv} .$$

Therefore

$$\frac{\partial \Sigma}{\partial a} = \Sigma \frac{\partial}{\partial a} = \sum_i 2[C_i - (a + \frac{b}{v_i} + c\sqrt{A_i})](1) = 0$$

$$\frac{\partial \Sigma}{\partial b} = \Sigma \frac{\partial}{\partial b} = \sum_i 2[C_i - (a + \frac{b}{v_i} + c\sqrt{A_i})] \cdot (\frac{1}{v_i}) = 0$$

$$\frac{\partial \Sigma}{\partial c} = \Sigma \frac{\partial}{\partial c} = \sum_i 2[C_i - (a + \frac{b}{v_i} + c\sqrt{A_i})] \cdot (\sqrt{A_i}) = 0$$

or

$$(\Sigma C_i - a\Sigma 1 - b\Sigma \frac{1}{v_i} - c\Sigma \sqrt{A_i}) = 0$$

$$[\Sigma \frac{1}{v_i} C_i - a\Sigma \frac{1}{v_i} - b\Sigma(\frac{1}{v_i})^2 - c\Sigma \frac{\sqrt{A_i}}{v_i}] = 0$$

$$[\Sigma \sqrt{A_i} C_i - a\Sigma \sqrt{A_i} - b\Sigma \frac{\sqrt{A_i}}{v_i} - c\Sigma (\sqrt{A_i})^2] = 0 .$$

Note that certain terms are common to more than one of the above equations. This has made possible certain computational short cuts. Note that the ability to take partial derivatives in the above manner implies independence of a, b, and c. Graphical methods for regression analysis are also available. See Spurr, Kellogg, and Smith, *Business and Economic Statistics* (rev. ed.; Homewood, Ill.: Richard D. Irwin, Inc., 1961).

[8] $$r = \frac{\frac{1}{N}\Sigma(x - \bar{x})(y - \bar{y})}{\sigma_x \sigma_y}$$

obviously must be similarity between the model and the real world.

There are at least two kinds of reasons why the multiple correlation coefficient differs from 1.00. The first reason is due to the model itself. It does not include all of the variables which influence the measure of effectiveness, and it may not correctly specify the nature of the influence of those variables which are included. The second reason is due to the errors of measurement. Even though the model itself were perfect (extremely unlikely), the measurements of the different variables taken for each observation might be faulty. In the study of the warehouses, this would be particularly true of the costs—the measure of effectiveness. What was the total cost of operating each warehouse during the period studied? The only feasible way of answering this question was on the basis of the costing system the firm had in operation. Because of problems such as allocating costs to time periods, the changing purchasing power of the dollar, and many, many others, any company's costing system will introduce "errors of measurement." It is possible to eliminate some of these errors; it is certainly not feasible to eliminate them all.

Certain cautions concerning the above test should be given. As indicated in Chapter 1 on analysis, a test is considered much stronger if it gives successful prediction rather than successful explanation. If the number of observations (warehouses) had been larger, it would have been preferable to separate them into two groups in a random manner. Then one of the groups could have been used to estimate the parameter values (by least squares) and the other could then have been used to test the model. However, this could not have been done in this analysis because of another problem. The analysis is weakened when the number of variables and associated coefficients is large relative to the number of observations. When a model has five to ten variables but is being fitted to over a hundred observations, this is not a problem. However, consider the case in which the number of variables in the model is equal to the number of observations. Each variable supplies an unknown coefficient; each observation supplies an equation. Without even using a least squares calculation, these equations could be solved simultaneously for the unknown values. The answer would be unique (only one possible set of values). Tested back against the observations, the model would give perfect "predictions," even though the model were nonsensical. Any model would do this. For this reason, adjustments in the correlation coefficient for the relation of numbers of variables to observations, and statements of significance, should be made. Though this will not be given further treatment here, a statistics book should be consulted for a fuller discussion of these ideas.[9]

Before manipulating this warehousing model, it was necessary to convert a part of it in order to allow for minimization. A relationship was found between volume and area for each section of area covered. This sales density (K) in dollar volume per square mile of area is (by definition):

$$K = \frac{V}{A} \tag{13}$$

Therefore, $V = KA$, and it is possible to substitute this expression for V in the original model, giving

$$C = a + \frac{b}{KA} + c\sqrt{A}, \tag{14}$$

where a, b, and c are now specific figures determined from the multiple regression calculation. What was desired was an expression for A, the variable to be manipulated by management, which would make this cost a minimum. Differentiating C with respect to A gives[10]

$$\frac{dC}{dA} = -\frac{b}{KA^2} + \frac{c}{2\sqrt{A}}. \tag{15}$$

Setting the derivative equal to zero

$$-\frac{b}{KA^2} + \frac{c}{2\sqrt{A}} = 0$$

and

$$A = \left(\frac{2b}{cK}\right)^{2/3} = \left(\frac{2b}{c}\right)^{2/3}\left(\frac{1}{K}\right)^{2/3} \tag{16}$$

This expression for the area (A) indicates the area which would yield a minimum cost and is a function of b and c (costs calculated from empirical data) and K (the sales density of the area in question). The expression for A indicates that each area throughout the total territory should not be equal but should vary with the two-thirds power of the sales density. A decision rule has been established by mathematical and statistical investigation. Management judgment will still be necessary in a case such as this, but management's experience in

---

[9] Mordecai Ezekiel, *Methods of Correlation Analysis* (2d ed.; New York: John Wiley & Sons, Inc., 1941).

[10] $\frac{d^2C}{dA^2}$ can be calculated to determine that a minimum has in fact been determined.

warehouse operations will be capitalized upon explicitly and quantitatively, rather than intuitively.

The danger of extrapolating far beyond the conditions of the empirical observations should be pointed out. Had the decision rule called for warehouses four times as large as any of the present ones, little confidence could have been placed in the specific figures recommended because of the complete lack of empirical data at that level.

As pointed out in Chapter 1 on analysis, the segment of the total situation to be scrutinized must be blocked out (perhaps arbitrarily), as it is not feasible to solve all problems at once. The problem analyzed here was that of size. The problem of selecting specific geographic boundaries and warehouse locations was excluded from the analysis described here.

As many business problems can be approached by similar methods of analysis, the particular approach used here may be generalized as a sequence of steps as follows:

1. Following a study to determine the economics of the problem, a measure of effectiveness was selected.
2. A mathematical model of the problem was built around this measure of effectiveness and included those variables which most appeared to influence the measure of effectiveness.
3. The coefficients in the model were chosen by mathematical manipulation (multiple regression) to make the symbolic description as accurate as possible. Present experience was capitalized upon in "particularizing" the model.
4. The model was "tested" by statistical means (multiple correlation coefficient). The test was one of explanation, however, rather than one of prediction.
5. Again, by a mathematical manipulation (differentiation) the cost was minimized with respect to the factor (A) to be used in the decision rule.

Some variations within the same general framework of analysis might be considered as follows:

1. The measure of effectiveness might have been cost per pound of goods distributed, or some other similar criterion.
2. The model might have included more variables, such as warehouse design, etc. For instance, in a somewhat similar case in which the optimum size of branch manufacturing plants and the territories they were to serve was being studied, additional variables such as the mix of product manufactured (M) by the branch plant, the average size of the customer (S) in the territory, and the local labor rates (L) were considered important; and the model appeared as follows:

$$C = L \left(a + \frac{b}{V} + c\sqrt{A} + dM + \frac{e}{S} \right) . \tag{17}$$

3. The coefficients in the model might have been determined from an engineering or cost accounting type of approach. From a chart of accounts and past records and budgets, *a, b, c,* etc., might have been determined. This type of approach is more common in business today than the statistical one. Though the correlation coefficient of the model, with parameter values developed by means other than least squares regression, could have been no higher than the one obtained, such a development would have value as an independent check.

4. A tabular or graphical comparison of costs "predicted" by the model to actual warehouse costs might have been used rather than the correlation coefficient.

5. A tabular, graphical, or trial and error method might have been used to determine the area (A) which minimized the cost expression. However, this would vary with K, the sales density, and therefore it would have been necessary to repeat this procedure for selected values of K.

Multivariable Control

Both of the general problems illustrated in the chapter to this point have been concerned only with one controllable variable. In the inventory problem, the lot size was the variable to be manipulated. In the scale of operations problem, it seemed that both volume and area were to be manipulated. However, it was both possible and necessary to express one of these variables in terms of the other. In reality, then, it was only one of these variables (area) which was being manipulated.

In some problems, such as the sampling problem on page 246 where both n and c are being manipulated, two or more variables may be controllable by management. In this case partial derivatives of the total value function can be taken with respect to the controllable variables. These conditional equations (equated to zero) could then be solved simultaneously for the optimizing values of the controllable variables. This may be expressed symbolically as follows:

$$TVC = f(x, y, z) \, ;$$
$$\frac{\partial f}{\partial x} = 0 \, ; \quad \frac{\partial f}{\partial y} = 0 \, .$$

Multi-item Inventory Models

Consider the problem of managing an inventory consisting of more than one item and with a limited warehouse space. The model of equation (9) would become

$$TVC = \sum_{i=1}^{n} \left[\frac{R_i}{Q_i} S + \frac{Q_i}{2} I_i + W_i Q_i \right] \qquad (18)$$

which would give the same result shown in (11) but no consideration has been given to the space limitation. If K is the cubic content of the warehouse and k_i is the cubic requirement for storage of each unit of the ith item, then the restriction to be observed is

$$\phi(Q_i) = \sum_{i=1}^{n} k_i Q_i - K \leq 0. \tag{19}$$

A new variable λ_w is defined with the following properties:

$$\lambda_w = 0 \quad \text{if} \quad \phi(Q_i) < 0$$
$$\lambda_w > 0 \quad \text{if} \quad \phi(Q_i) = 0.$$

Multiplying $\phi(Q_i)$ by λ_w insures that the function is always equal to zero, and it may be added to equation (18) giving

$$TVC + \lambda_w \phi(Q_i) = \sum_{i=1}^{n} \left[\frac{R_i}{Q_i} S + \frac{Q_i}{2} I_i + W_i Q_i + \lambda_w(k_i Q_i - K) \right].$$

If the partial derivative with respect to the Q_i is obtained and equated to zero,

$$\frac{\partial TVC}{\partial Q_i} + \lambda_w \frac{\partial \phi}{\partial Q_i} = -S \frac{R_i}{Q_i^2} + \frac{I_i}{2} + W_i + \lambda_w k_i = 0.$$

$$Q_i = \sqrt{\frac{2 R_i S}{I_i + 2(W_i + \lambda_w k_i)}} \tag{20}$$

Equations (19) and (20) would be solved for the Q_i and the value of λ_w which yield minimum cost and at the same time observe the storage limitation.

The technique illustrated here is known as the Lagrange Multiplier. It is useful in cases in which some restriction is placed on the values of a set of variables. The procedure is to set up the restricting relationship as a function of value zero when multiplied by a variable and add the product to the original set of equations. One more unknown is introduced, but so is an additional equation. The resulting system is then solved for values of the variable including λ. The resulting set will be optimal subject to the restricting relation as in the case illustrated, i.e., subject to the restriction that the maximum inventory fit into the warehouse. It would have been perfectly feasible to consider the average inventory in this connection, and the only change would have been in the denominator of (20) in which the 2 would become 1.

The multiplier λ_w has an interesting and useful interpretation in this kind of problem. In contrasting (20) with (11) it can be seen that the only change is in the addition of $2\lambda_w k_i$ to the unit carrying cost. This amounts to an increase in the storage cost due to the restriction. Thus it may be interpreted as the price (possibly zero) one pays because no more warehouse space is available. If one more cubic foot were available, total cost would decrease by λ_w. Thus λ_w is the marginal value of warehouse space.

Assume two items with the following characteristics are to be purchased:

$$R_1 = 325 \text{ units/year} \qquad R_2 = 1,000 \text{ units/year}$$
$$S = \$20 \text{ per order} \qquad S = \$20 \text{ per order}$$
$$I_1 = \$2.00 \text{ per unit per year} \qquad I_2 = \$1.00 \text{ per unit per year}$$
$$W_1 = \$0.20 \text{ per unit per year} \qquad W_2 = \$0.40 \text{ per year}$$
$$k_1 = 1 \text{ ft.}^3 \qquad k_2 = 2 \text{ ft.}^3$$

Total cubic content available is 300 cubic feet, and thus the restricting relation is

$$\phi(Q_i) = \sum_{i=1}^{2} k_i Q_i - 300 \leq 0 .$$

Solving (20) for Q_1 and Q_2 assuming $\lambda_w = 0$:

$$Q_1 = \sqrt{\frac{2(325)20}{2 + 2(0.20)}} \quad ; \quad Q_2 = \sqrt{\frac{2(1,000)20}{1 + 2(0.40)}}$$
$$= 74 \qquad\qquad = 149$$

The restriction is exceeded since

$$\sum_{i=1}^{2} k_i Q_i - 300 = 72 .$$

Assume $\lambda_w = 1$ and the solutions to (20) are

$$Q_1 = 54 \; ; \; Q_2 = 83 ,$$

giving

$$\phi(Q_i) = -80 .$$

At $\lambda_w = 0.5$,

$$Q_1 = 62 \; ; \; Q_2 = 103$$

and

$$\phi(Q_i) = -32 .$$

At $\lambda_w = 0.25$,

$$Q_1 = 67 \; ; \; Q_2 = 120$$

and

$$\phi(Q_i) = 7 .$$

330 · Analysis for Production and Operations Management

The value of $\phi(Q_i)$ is zero at $\lambda_w = 0.28$ and

$$Q_1 = 66 \; ; \; Q_2 = 117 \, .$$

This tells us the lot sizes that should be purchased in order not to exceed the available storage space and at the same time tells us the cost savings per year ($0.28) which would result from one more cubic foot being made available. It may well be that our restriction is uneconomic relative to the cost which would be incurred in providing more storage space.

Other kinds of limitations could be placed on this kind of model. For example, if there were an upper limit on the capital available for investment in inventories, this could be expressed as

$$\psi(Q_i) = \sum_{i=1}^{n} \frac{C_i Q_i}{2} - B \leq 0 \tag{21}$$

in which B is the total amount of capital available. Equation (21) could be multiplied by λ_b so as to give a zero-valued function. This would be added to (18) and a minimum cost solution obtained. The interpretation to be placed on λ_b is that it represents the incremental cost which could be saved if there were more capital available for inventory investment. In a similar manner, restrictions due to limited setup time in a production situation or a limited number of orders which could be processed by a purchasing group could be observed.

It has probably been noted that trial and error has been used to solve for the Q_i and λ in these examples. Ordinarily one would solve the set simultaneously, but in this case trial and error is easier due to the fact that the expressions for Q_i are radicals while the restraint equation is linear.

UNCERTAINTY MODELS

The first part of this chapter has dealt with problems where uncertainty is not a major factor to be explicitly considered. Whenever uncertainty is part of the problem to be understood and resolved, sometimes an average or mean figure used for the uncertain variable will suffice. However, many times this kind of treatment will not be acceptable.

Where uncertainty must be handled formally, i.e., whenever probability must be used, at least four possibilities are open as follows:

1. Total value analysis with probability distributions explicitly included in the mathematical model as integrals or sums which may be formally (mathematically) manipulated. This will be demonstrated conceptually in the following section.

2. Total value analysis with probability explicitly considered through a series of tables. A discussion of this method for the "Servicing Problem" will conclude this chapter, with some of the associated mathematics and tables included in an Appendix to this chapter.
3. Incremental analysis with probability distributions explicitly included. This will be demonstrated in the next chapter.
4. Total value analysis with probability distributions explicitly included for purposes of simulation with random numbers. This, the Monte Carlo method, is presented in Chapter 11.

The Inventory Problem

Total value analysis with probability included can be illustrated with the case where a business firm must stock goods for a period during which the demand for these goods may be described by some probability density function as shown in Figure 8–3.[11] Here x represents the number

Figure 8–3
PROBABILITY DENSITY FUNCTION FOR SALES OF PRODUCT

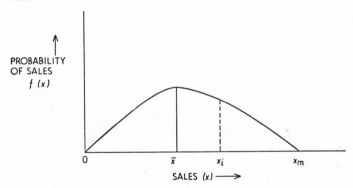

of items which will be sold in the period, and $f(x)\,dx$ the probability of finding x in the interval x to $x + dx$.[12] The expected number to be sold is $\bar{x} = \int_0^{x_m} xf(x)\,dx$, where x_m is the maximum number which can be sold in the period. Let

$$x_s = \text{actual number which can be sold,}$$
$$x_i = \text{number of items stocked,}$$
$$P = \text{profit per item sold in the period,}$$
$$L = \text{loss if not sold in the period.}$$

---

[11] *Notes from M.I.T. Summer Course on Operations Research* (Cambridge, Mass.: Technology Press, 1953).

[12] A continuous distribution is used here as an approximation to the correct discrete distribution to allow for the use of integral equations. As long as x_i is large, no appreciable error is involved.

Then for $x_s < x_i$, the profit would be

$$P(x_s) - L(x_i - x_s) .$$

For $x_s > x_i$, the profit would be

$$P(x_i) .$$

The expected profit is

$$E(\text{profit}) = \int_0^{x_i} [P(x_s) - L(x_i - x_s)] f(x)dx + \int_{x_i}^{x_m} P(x_i)f(x)dx . \quad (22)$$

Maximizing (22) with respect to x_i[13]

$$\frac{d(E)}{dx_i} = P(x_i)f(x_i) - L\int_0^{x_i} f(x)dx + P\int_{x_i}^{x_m} f(x)dx - P(x_i)f(x_i) = 0$$

$$= P - (P + L)\int_0^{x_i} f(x)dx .$$

Thus, the condition for a maximum is

$$\int_0^{x_i} f(x)dx = \frac{P}{P + L} . \quad (23)$$

Stated verbally, this says that one should order x_i units such that the probability of selling the ith unit or fewer is equal to the ratio of the profit per unit sold to the sum of this profit and the loss per unit not sold. This same answer will be demonstrated in the next chapter by incremental analysis.

In the production management type problems discussed here, the objective sought will be the minimization or maximization of an expected value. Several potential drawbacks exist to this criterion. First, alternative outcomes may cover such a wide range of dollar values that

---

[13] The differentiation of an integral containing a parameter in the limit may be accomplished according to

$$F(x_i) = \int_{a(x_i)}^{b(x_i)} f(x_i,x)dx$$

$$\frac{dF(x_i)}{dx_i} = \int_{a(x_i)}^{b(x_i)} \frac{\partial f(x_i,x)}{\partial (x_i)} dx + f(b,x_i)\frac{db}{dx_i} - f(a,x_i)\frac{da}{dx_i}$$

See Hildebrand, *Advanced Calculus for Engineers* (New York: Prentice-Hall, Inc., 1948), p. 352.

the manager's utility scale or preference for dollars may not be presumed to be linear. Second, the decision may be unique in that it will not be repeated even once in the future, much less an infinite number of times consistent with mathematical expectations. However, where many different decisions are being made, none of which involve a major portion of the firm's funds, straightforward mathematical expectation should provide a suitable decision process.

The Servicing Problem in Manufacturing

Whenever service must be provided to meet some demand where the demand is in any way irregular, an economic decision problem exists. The manager must decide on the level at which he is to provide this service. Consider, for example, the problem of supplying maintenance service to a group of machines subject to random breakdowns.

Here, the manager must decide on the level of maintenance service to provide over a relatively long period in advance. If at any time the service is not sufficient to meet the demand, a waiting line of idle machines will form with a consequent decrease in productive capacity. If too much service is made available, then the cost of idle maintenance system time will be excessive. An economic balance must be made between these two kinds of costs.

The ability of the manager to do this depends on his ability to predict that part of the total idle time which is *avoidable* and to determine the cost of this lost time to the firm. The manager can reduce some of this avoidable lost time by increasing the level of maintenance service, but at some point it becomes uneconomic to increase the service level any further.

A similar kind of problem exists when one operator tends a number of automatic machines as, for example, in the weaving of cloth or the winding of coils for electric lamps. Here the machines call for various kinds of service—loading, unloading, adjusting, setup, etc.—at essentially random intervals. An increase in the number of machines assigned to one operator decreases his ability to handle calls as they arrive and may occasion machine waiting time with a consequent loss in productive time. A minimum cost assignment exists, but the waiting time for all possible assignments must be determined in order to make this economic assignment.

This same problem exists when materials-handling service must be provided in the face of some random demand, such as movement of in-process materials from department to department via fork-lift trucks or overhead cranes. Here the problem is one of determining the optimum number of pieces of equipment to provide. The number of machines to provide in a job shop production center presents a similar problem when the arrival of orders is essentially random.

Waiting Time

The servicing time in all such situations may consist of two parts—that time when the unit demanding service is actually receiving it and that time when the unit is waiting for service. The former is necessary and unavoidable, but the latter is avoidable and gives rise to the economic problem. The prediction of the amount of waiting time expected in a given situation depends on the probability of receiving a call for service and the probability that the service facility or facilities are busy with prior calls. In order to determine this time, then, the following must be known:

1. The relationship between the population which demands service and the servicing facility(ies), e.g., one serviceman to a group of machines or a group of servicemen to a group of machines.
2. The priority system which governs the assignment of service facilities to calls for service, e.g., first-come, first-served.
3. The calling interval distribution.
4. The service time distribution.

With this knowledge it is possible, under certain conditions, to develop the waiting time mathematically.[14]

In order to do this, it is necessary to describe, in terms of the given probability distributions, the states in which the system may exist and the ways in which it may go from one state to another. For example, in the case of a group of units serviced by a single facility, the system may be characterized by two parameters A and S, where $1/A$ is the average operating interval between arrivals and A, therefore, is the arrival rate; and $1/S$ is the average service time, S being the rate at which service can be provided. Assuming these parameters completely describe the probability distributions and that the priority system is first-come, first-served, then it is possible to describe in terms of a set of equations all the states in which the servicing system may be over time. All units may be operating or any number of them down at any one time. For any small passage of time, the system may go from a state with n units down to $n + 1$ or $n - 1$ units down or remain in the state with n units down. The probabilities of these transitions are given by the distributions of which A and S are parameters, and the system can be described by a set of differential equations which can be

---

[14] For a fuller development of the waiting-line theory see the Appendix to this chapter.

solved for the probability of any number of units in the system waiting and in service at time t. If this is denoted by $P_n(t)$, then

$$\sum_{n=0}^{\infty} P_n(t) = 1$$

and the expected number of units in the system is

$$E(n) = \sum_{n=0}^{\infty} nP_n(t)$$

while the expected number waiting for service is

$$E(q) = \sum_{n=0}^{\infty} (n - c)P_n(t)$$

in which c is the number of service channels in operation.

Solutions for the $P_n(t)$ have been obtained for a number of different calling and servicing populations, waiting-line behavior, priority systems for handling calls, and physical configurations of service channels.[15] These formulae can be used to compute state probabilities but even in the simplest cases, the computations involved in doing this are quite lengthy if the number of units in the calling population is at all large, and especially so if the economic problem involves trying several alternative servicing policies. Therefore, in most cases, practical results from the use of this probability concept depend on either tables which give general solutions to various waiting time situations or the use of Monte Carlo simulation (see Chapter 11).

Available Tables

Tables which have been computed for general use in servicing situations are generally of two kinds as follows:

1. Those which deal with the case of a calling population assumed to be infinite.
2. Those which deal with a finite calling population.

If the number of units in the calling population is not large, then the fact of a call arriving affects the average rate of arrival. That is, the service facility is faced with a demand which is a function of the number of units which can potentially call. If a unit is waiting or in service, then it cannot call and therefore the probability of a call is only a function of the number of units which are able to give calls.

While this is true regardless of the number of units in the calling

---

[15] For a resumé of these, see T. L. Saaty, "Resumé of Queuing Theory," *Operations Research,* Vol. V (1957), pp. 161–200.

population, as the number in this population gets very large, the effect of the number in service or waiting becomes small and the situation can be characterized by an average calling rate. The major difference of economic consequence between these two situations is that when the calling population is infinite and the service facilities are not sufficient to handle all calls, the waiting time increases without limit. In the case of the small population, however, the waiting time would only increase until, on the average, the number of units waiting had decreased the *effective* population size to that which could be handled by the given servicing facilities.

Tables and graphs, as well as computational forms, for both large and small calling populations under certain given conditions are contained in the Appendix to this chapter. Examples of the use of these will be given next.

An Operator Assignment Problem

The assignment of operators problem (as in a textile mill) will be presented briefly to illustrate the use of tables for waiting time values in the case of a small calling population.[16]

C = total cost of machine operation per time unit per machine
C_m = cost of machine running time per time unit per machine
C_s = cost of service time per time unit per machine (excluding labor)
C_w = cost of waiting time per time unit per machine
C_r = cost of operator per time unit
C_o = cost of output per time unit of machine running time per machine, *the measure of effectiveness* (analogous to cost per unit of output)
m = machine running time per time unit
s = service time per time unit
w = waiting time per time unit
N = number of machines assigned to an operator, *the variable to be manipulated by management*

Then,

$$C = mC_m + sC_s + wC_w + \frac{Cr}{N}. \tag{24}$$

Assuming that output occurs only during (m), the cost of this output is the expected total cost divided by the expected output

$$C_o = \frac{C}{m}. \tag{25}$$

Combining equations (24) and (25):

---

[16] See R. B. Fetter, "The Assignment of Operators to Service Automatic Machines," *Journal of Industrial Engineering*, September–October, 1955, pp. 22–29.

$$C_o = C_m + \frac{s}{m} C_s + \frac{w}{m} C_w + \frac{1}{mN} C_r$$

$$= C_m + \frac{s}{m} C_s + \frac{wC_w + C_r/N}{m}. \tag{26}$$

Now $\dfrac{s}{m}$, the ratio of service time (fixing, not waiting) to machine operating time is a constant (k) for a given type of equipment. It has nothing to do with the amount of time waiting for service (w), ($w + s + m = 1$, by definition).

The measure of effectiveness (C_o) is to be minimized by the proper value for N, the number of machines to assign to each operator (operators not to work on other than their assigned machines in this case). The first and second terms ($C_m + \dfrac{s}{m} C_s$) do not vary with N and therefore may be ignored for the analysis. The last term, $\dfrac{wC_w + C_r/N}{m}$, is to be minimized with a proper choice of N. However, w and therefore m ($w + m + s = 1$; $\dfrac{s}{m} = k$) vary with N. The mean waiting time per time unit (w) is the variable for which probability equations must be solved, and for which tables have been, and are being, developed. The basic nature of the problem here is that a whole series of state probabilities must be considered. For each state of the problem (length of line), the probability of the state changing (line increasing or decreasing) must be formulated. This is done with a series of differential equations.[17] Before using the tables for w, a number of things must be known or assumed as follows:[18]

1. The distribution of the calls for service.
2. The distribution of the service times.
3. Whether the calling universe is small or large.
4. The ratio of $\dfrac{s}{m}$, i.e., k, for the particular equipment.

The following information is given as an illustrative example corresponding to the above list:

---

[17] See T. C. Fry, *Probability and Its Engineering Use* (New York: D. Van Nostrand, Co., Inc., 1928); and W. Feller, *An Introduction to Probability Theory and Its Applications* (New York: John Wiley & Sons, Inc., 1950), pp. 379–83, for the nature of the calculations.

[18] Information such as that all arrivals in the line stay in the line will not be discussed but are also necessary.

338 · Analysis for Production and Operations Management

1. Completely random, i.e., exponential distribution.
2. Completely random, i.e., exponential distribution.
3. Small calling population.
4. $k = 0.08$.
5. $C_w = \$10/\text{hour}$; $C_r = \$2.00/\text{hour}$.

Table 8–2 presents this information in tabular form where:

Column 1 is the variable to be manipulated;
Column 2 gives values of w developed from probability theory, and selected from tables given in the Appendix to this chapter;
Columns 3–6 are solutions for terms from equation (26);
Column 7 is the measure of effectiveness to be minimized.

Table 8–2

TABULAR ANALYSIS OF MACHINE ASSIGNMENT PROBLEM

(1) N	(2) w	(3) wC_w	(4) C_r/N	(5) (3) + (4)	(6) m	(7) (5)/(6)
1.	0.000	$ 0	$2.00	$2.00	0.926	$2.16
2.	0.005	0.05	1.00	1.05	0.921	1.14
3.	0.012	0.12	0.67	0.79	0.915	0.86
4.	0.019	0.19	0.50	0.69	0.909	0.76
5.	0.027	0.27	0.40	0.67	0.901	0.74
6.	0.035	0.35	0.33	0.68	0.893	0.76
7.	0.045	0.45	0.29	0.74	0.884	0.84
8.	0.057	0.57	0.25	0.82	0.873	0.94
9.	0.070	0.70	0.22	0.92	0.861	1.07
10.	0.085	0.85	0.20	1.05	0.848	1.24

It can be seen that five machines is the optimum assignment. Also, if, for example, twelve machines are to be operated, the optimum set of assignments can be readily determined from the table (i.e., 5, 5, 2; 4, 4, 4; 5, 4, 3; 6, 6; etc.).

SUMMARY

It was not intended to emphasize any of the particular problems used here as examples. Rather, it is hoped the reader has gained some appreciation of the general model building procedure in problems where some measure of effectiveness may be minimized or maximized. The procedure in these cases is as follows:

1. Pick the measure of effectiveness.
2. Determine the important variables.
3. Determine the relationship of these variables to the measure of effectiveness, i.e., build the model. Probability may or may not be a major factor.
4. Determine the values of the parameters. This determination may be a statistical or a cost accounting and/or engineering approach.

5. Test the model. Steps (2) through (5) are repeated until a satisfactory model is constructed.
6. Manipulate the model for purposes of determining a useful decision rule.

Three special cases of this general approach, incremental analysis, simulation, and equipment replacement analysis are presented in the following chapters.

REFERENCES ON TOTAL VALUE ANALYSIS

1. BAUMOL, W. J. *Economic Theory and Operations Analysis.* Englewood Cliffs, N.J.: Prentice-Hall, Inc., 1961.
2. BUFFA, E. S. *Models for Production and Operations Management.* New York: John Wiley & Sons, Inc., 1961.
3. EILON, S. *Elements of Production Planning and Control.* New York: Macmillan Co., 1962.
4. FELLER, WILLIAM. *An Introduction to Probability Theory and Its Applications.* New York: John Wiley & Sons, Inc., 1950.
5. HANSMANN, F. *Operations Research in Production and Inventory Control.* New York: John Wiley & Sons, Inc., 1962.
6. HOLT, C. C.; MODIGLIANI, F.; MUTH, J.; and SIMON, H. A. *Planning Production, Inventories, and Work Force.* Englewood Cliffs, N.J.: Prentice-Hall, Inc., 1960.
7. MANNE, A. S. *Economic Analysis for Business Decisions.* New York: McGraw-Hill Book Co., Inc., 1961.
8. SCHLAIFER, ROBERT. *Introduction to Statistics for Business Decisions.* McGraw-Hill Book Co., Inc., 1961.
9. THUESEN, H. G., and FABRYCKY, W. J. *Engineering Economy.* 3d ed. Englewood Cliffs, N.J.: Prentice-Hall, Inc., 1964.

APPENDIX TO CHAPTER 8

WAITING-LINE THEORY

A waiting-line model is designed to describe a situation where congestion of some kind may occur in a system due to either random input or output, or both. In such a situation units arrive at a "gate" in some way, are processed through the system, and leave. If any part of this process is random, i.e., may be described by a probability distribution, a congestion problem exists and a waiting line may form. Under certain conditions, it is possible to develop models which will describe the behavior of such a system. The basic information necessary is as follows:

1. The distribution of intervals between arrivals
2. The distribution of clearing times
3. The priority system in effect governing the order in which arrivals will be cleared
4. The relationship between arrivals and processing facilities

Two basic types of treatment are required. The first occurs where the population which gives rise to arrivals is infinite (or can be assumed so), and the second where this population must be treated as finite. The assumption will be made throughout that arrivals are individually and collectively at random.

The Probability of an Arrival

The probability of an arrival from a unit in the population in question may be worked out by postulating an event space as shown in Figure 8–4, [3], [4], [7] (see references to this Appendix).

Figure 8–4

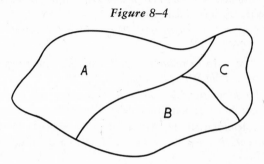

In Figure 8–4, A is the probability that an arrival occurs between 0 and t, B is the probability of an arrival after $t + dt$, and C is the probability (small) of an arrival during dt. Then we define the following functions:

$$p(t) = \frac{C}{A + B + C}$$
$$= \text{probability of an arrival during } dt$$

$$P(t) = \frac{A}{A + B + C}$$
$$= \text{probability of an arrival between 0 and } t$$

$$Z(t) = \frac{C}{B + C}$$
$$= \text{probability of an arrival during } dt, \text{ given that the}$$
$$\text{arrival did not occur between 0 and } t\,(A = 0)$$

Since the sum of A, B, and C must be unity,

$$p(t) = C$$
$$P(t) = A$$

and

$$Z(t) = \frac{C}{1 - A}$$
$$= \frac{p(t)}{1 - P(t)}. \tag{1}$$

Since

$$p(t) = \frac{d[P(t)]}{dt},$$ (2)

then

$$Z(t) = \frac{\dfrac{d[P(t)]}{dt}}{1 - P(t)}$$ (3)

and integrating

$$\int_0^t Z(t)dt = -\ln\,[1 - P(t)]\,.$$ (4)

The probability given by $[1-P(t)]$ is the probability that the unit in question will not require service until at least t. This, then, is the probability of no arrivals between 0 and t. Calling this $P_0(t)$,

$$P_0(t) = e^{-\int_0^t Z(t)dt}\,.$$ (5)

If the unit or set of units is given service each time it arrives, the system will reach a state of statistical equilibrium and the arrival rate $Z(t)$ will be a constant A. Then,

$$P_0(t) = e^{-At}\,.$$ (6)

Thus the probability of a unit or set of units not arriving in at least t is exponential, and the mean time between arrivals is $1/A$.

The probability of no arrival occurring during dt is

$$1 - Z(t) = e^{-Adt}$$

and

$$Z(t) = 1 - e^{-Adt}\,.$$

Expanding,

$$1 - e^{-Adt} = 1 - (1 - Adt + \frac{(Adt)^2}{2!} - \frac{(Adt)^3}{3!} + \ldots)$$
$$= Adt - \frac{(Adt)^2}{2!} + \frac{(Adt)^3}{3!}\,.$$

Neglecting higher order terms,

$$Z(t) = Adt.$$ (7)

Then the probability of no arrival between 0 and t and one arrival during dt times the probability of no arrival between 0 and t is

$$P_0(t)\,[Z(t)] = e^{-At}\,(Adt)\,,$$

and thus

$$p(t) = Ae^{-At}dt , \qquad (8)$$

which is the density function which describes the condition of interest, the fact of an arrival in exactly t.

The Distribution of Clearing Times

In order to determine waiting time, it is also necessary to know something about one's expectation as to the duration of clearing times, since waiting time occurs when a unit has arrived, and the clearing time interval for units which gave prior calls is such that no clearing facility is available. If the same assumptions could be made about the distribution of clearing times as was made about calls, that is, that at any time the probability of a clearing interval ending (call arriving) was not dependent on how long the clearing interval (running interval) had lasted until that time, then

$$P_s(t) = Se^{-St}dt , \qquad (9)$$

where $P_s(t)$ is the probability of a clearing time of exactly t, and $1/S$ is the average clearing time.

While the assumption that clearing times are distributed individually and collectively at random does not seem plausible, since the amount of time until a unit is cleared is certainly in some way dependent on how long it has been in the system, yet in many situations an exponential distribution seems to describe the data quite well. If this distribution holds, then the problem of determining waiting time is not nearly so difficult as for any other case, including that of a constant service time. In any case, a knowledge of the shape of the clearing time distribution is essential to the determination of waiting time.

Single Channel—Infinite Universe

The simplest servicing situation involves one servicing facility handling calls from an infinite universe without help. Units are serviced in the order in which they arrive, and each arrival is cleared without interruption. Further, it is assumed that arrival intervals can be described by an exponential distribution (6), and, therefore, the probability of an arrival in dt is Adt. Also, it is assumed that clearing times are exponentially distributed, and, therefore, the probability of clearing in dt is Sdt.

Then, the probability of no units in the system during the interval from t to $t + dt$ is given by

$$P_0(t + dt) = P_0(t) (1 - Adt) + P_1(t)Sdt . \qquad (10)$$

That is, the probability of no units in the system in the interval $t + dt$ is the probability of no units in the system at t times the probability of no arrivals during dt plus the probability of one unit in the system at t times the probability of one departure during dt. Similarly,

$$P_1(t + dt) = P_1(t)(1 - Sdt - Adt) + P_2(t)Sdt + P_0(t)Adt$$
$$P_2(t + dt) = P_2(t)(1 - Sdt - Adt) + P_3(t)Sdt + P_1(t)Adt$$

.

.

.

$$P_n(t + dt) = P_n(t)(1 - Sdt - Adt) + P_{n+1}(t)Sdt + P_{n-1}(t)Adt . \quad (11)$$

Thus a set of equations (infinite) which describe the system can be generated. Equation (11) is differentiated with respect to t in order to get the probability of each change of state which may occur.

Since it is the long-run behavior of the system which is desired, the first derivative of (11) with respect to t may be set equal to 0 to get the steady state behavior of the system. The rate of change of $P_n(t)$ with respect to t during dt is by definition:

$$\frac{dP_n(t)}{dt} = \frac{P_n(t + dt) - P_n(t)}{dt} .$$

Then from equation (10),

$$\frac{P_0(t + dt) - P_0(t)}{dt} = -AP_0(t) + SP_1(t) ,$$

and from equation (11),

$$\frac{P_n(t + dt) - P_n(t)}{dt} = -(A + S)P_n(t) + SP_{n+1}(t) + AP_{n-1}(t) . \quad (12)$$

For equilibrium,

$$\frac{dP_n(t)}{dt} = 0 ,$$

giving

$$-AP_0(t) + SP_1(t) = 0$$
$$P_1(t) = \frac{A}{S} P_0(t) ,$$
$$-AP_1(t) - SP_1(t) + AP_0(t) + SP_2(t) = 0$$
$$P_2(t) = \left(\frac{A}{S}\right)^2 P_0(t) ,$$

and, by iteration,

$$P_n(t) = \left(\frac{A}{S}\right)^n P_0(t) . \quad (13)$$

With (13), the probability of any number of units in the system may be found in terms of $P_0(t)$, and since

$$\sum_{n=0}^{\infty} P_n(t) = 1 , \quad (14)$$

the state probabilities are completely determined. That is,

$$P_0(t) + P_0\left(\frac{A}{S}\right) + P_0\left(\frac{A}{S}\right)^2 + \ldots P_0\left(\frac{A}{S}\right)^n + \ldots P_0\left(\frac{A}{S}\right)^\infty = 1 \,.$$

Since

$$1 + x + x^2 + x^3 + \ldots x^n + \ldots x^\infty = \frac{1}{1-x} \,.$$

Then

$$P_0 \frac{1}{1 - A/S} = 1 \,,$$

and

$$P_0 = 1 - \frac{A}{S} \,. \tag{15}$$

If it is desired to find the expected number of units in the system (length of waiting line including the unit in service), then this can be done by summing over all states the number in each state times the probability of that state. Thus,

$$E(n) = \sum_{n=0}^{\infty} nP_n \tag{16}$$

$$= \sum_{n=0}^{\infty} n\left(\frac{A}{S}\right)^n \left(1 - \frac{A}{S}\right)$$

$$= \left(1 - \frac{A}{S}\right) \sum_{n=0}^{\infty} n\left(\frac{A}{S}\right)^n \,.$$

Since

$$\sum_{n=0}^{\infty} nx^{n-1} = \frac{1}{(1-x)^2} \,,$$

then

$$E(n) = \left(1 - \frac{A}{S}\right)\left(\frac{A}{S}\right) \frac{1}{\left(1 - \frac{A}{S}\right)^2}$$

$$= \frac{A}{S-A} \,. \tag{17}$$

The expected waiting line is given by the expected number of machines waiting for service in each state summed over all states where waiting can occur. Thus, in this case,

$$E(w) = \sum_{n=2}^{\infty} (n-1)P_n(t) \,, \tag{18}$$

and substituting (13) in (18) gives

$$E(w) = \left(\frac{A}{S}\right)\left(\frac{A}{S-A}\right) \,. \tag{19}$$

Multiple Channels—Infinite Universe

If more than one channel is utilized to clear arrivals under the same assumptions as for the previous case, then the probability of a departure in dt is not Sdt but $nSdt$ for $n < r$ and $rSdt$ for $n > r$, where n is the number of items in the system and r the number of channels. Then equation (12) must be written as:

$$\frac{dP_n(t)}{dt} = -(A + nS)P_n(t) + AP_{n-1}(t) + (n+1)SP_{n+1}(t) \quad n < r$$

$$\frac{dP_n(t)}{dt} = -(A + rS)P_n(t) + AP_{n-1}(t) + rSP_{n+1}(t) \qquad n \geq r$$

(20)

Setting $dP_n(t)/dt = 0$,

$$P_n(t) = P_0(t)\frac{\left(\dfrac{A}{S}\right)^n}{n!} \qquad n < r$$

$$P_n(t) = P_0(t)\frac{\left(\dfrac{A}{S}\right)^n}{r!r^{n-r}} \qquad n \geq r$$

(21)

From (21) each value of $P_n(t)$ can be found in terms of $P_0(t)$. Since

$$\sum_{n=0}^{\infty} P_n(t) = 1 ,$$

all the $P_n(t)$ can be evaluated. The expected waiting line is

$$E(w) = \sum_{n=r+1}^{\infty} (n - r)P_n(t) .$$

(22)

Other priority systems than first-come, first-served have been treated analytically, notably where the arrival with the shortest clearing time goes to the head of the line [1][19]. For a given channel to calling unit ratio, this system will minimize the waiting time, regardless of the shapes of arrival and clearing time distributions.

Finite Universe Model

When the number of units in the calling universe is finite, an average arrival for the population cannot be used. Rather, it is necessary to give A in terms of a unit in the population. Thus, A might be one breakdown per running hour per machine or one call per hour per department. Then the arrival rate facing the clearing process would be given by NA when no units of the population of size N were in service or waiting and $(N - n)A$ when n units were in the system. It is only necessary to modify equations (12) and (20) by these values in order to get the finite universe model. The resulting equations are more difficult to evaluate computationally, but,

---

[19] Numbers in brackets refer to references at the end of this Appendix.

in general, there will be fewer equations to handle in each situation ($N+1$ rather than an infinite set). However, in this case there are no general expressions for expected waiting time or number in line. Each situation must be solved for its state variables in order to get these values.

Tables of Waiting Time Values

Fortunately, some tables are available for the finite case where the arrival interval distribution is exponential and where the clearing time distribution

Table 8–3

TABLES OF WAITING TIME AND MACHINE AVAILABILITY FOR SELECTED SERVICING CONSTANTS*†
(Values expressed as percentages of total time where m + s + w = 100%)

k = 0.01

n	(a) w	(a) m	(b) w	(b) m
1	0.0	99.0	0.0	99.0
10	0.1	99.0	0.1	98.9
20	0.1	98.9	0.2	98.8
30	0.2	98.8	0.4	98.6
40			0.6	98.4
50			0.9	98.1
60			1.3	97.8
70			1.8	97.2
80			2.7	96.3
85			3.4	95.7
90			4.2	94.9
95			5.2	93.8
100			6.7	92.4
105			8.5	90.6
110			10.7	88.4
115			13.4	85.8
120			16.3	82.9
121			16.9	82.3
122			17.5	81.7
123			18.1	81.1
124			18.8	80.4
125			19.4	79.8
126			20.0	79.2
127			20.6	78.6
128			21.2	78.1
129			21.8	77.5
130			22.4	76.9
131			22.9	76.3
132			23.5	75.7
133			24.1	75.2
134			24.6	74.6
135			25.2	74.1
136			25.7	73.5
137			26.3	73.0
138			26.8	72.5
139			27.3	71.9
140			27.9	71.4
141			28.4	70.9
142			28.9	70.4
143			29.4	69.9
144			29.9	69.4

k = 0.02

n	(a) w	(a) m	(b) w	(b) m
1	0.0	98.0	0.0	98.0
5	0.1	98.0	0.2	97.9
10	0.2	97.8	0.4	97.6
15	0.4	97.7	0.7	97.4
20	0.6	97.5	1.1	97.0
25	0.8	97.2	1.6	96.5
30	1.2	96.9	2.2	95.9
35			3.1	95.0
40			4.3	93.8
45			6.1	92.0
50			8.7	89.5

k = 0.02 (cont.)

n	(a) w	(a) m	(b) w	(b) m
51			9.3	88.9
52			10.0	88.3
53			10.7	87.6
54			11.5	86.8
55			12.3	86.0
56			13.1	85.2
57			14.0	84.3
58			14.9	83.4
59			15.9	82.5
60			16.8	81.5
61			17.9	80.5
62			18.9	79.5
63			19.9	78.5
64			21.0	77.5
65			22.0	76.4
66			23.1	75.4
67			24.2	74.4
68			25.2	73.3
69			26.2	72.3
70			27.2	71.3
71			28.2	70.4
72			29.2	69.4

k = 0.03

n	(a) w	(a) m	(b) w	(b) m
1	0.0	97.1	0.0	97.1
5	0.2	96.9	0.4	96.7
10	0.5	96.6	1.0	96.2
15	1.0	96.2	1.8	95.4
20	1.6	95.5	3.0	94.2
25	2.8	94.4	4.7	92.5
26	3.1	94.1	5.2	92.1
27	3.4	93.7	5.7	91.6
28	3.8	93.4	6.2	91.1
29	4.3	92.9	6.8	90.5
30	4.8	92.4	7.4	89.9
31			8.1	89.2
32			8.9	88.5
33			9.7	87.7
34			10.6	86.8
35			11.6	85.9
36			12.6	84.9
37			13.7	83.8
38			14.9	86.8
39			16.1	81.4
40			17.4	80.2
41			18.8	78.9
42			20.1	77.5
43			21.6	76.2
44			23.0	74.8
45			24.4	73.4
46			25.9	72.0
47			27.3	70.6
48			28.7	69.2

k = 0.04

n	(a) w	(a) m	(b) w	(b) m
1	0.0	96.2	0.0	96.2
2	0.1	96.1	0.2	96.0
3	0.2	96.0	0.3	95.9
4	0.2	95.9	0.5	95.7
5	0.3	95.8	0.7	95.5
6	0.5	95.7	0.9	95.3
7	0.6	95.6	1.1	95.1
8	0.7	95.5	1.3	94.9
9	0.8	95.4	1.5	94.7
10	1.0	95.2	1.8	94.4
11	1.1	95.1	2.1	94.1
12	1.3	94.9	2.4	93.8
13	1.5	94.7	2.8	93.5
14	1.8	94.5	3.2	93.1
15	2.0	94.2	3.6	92.7
16	2.3	94.0	4.0	92.3
17	2.6	93.6	4.5	91.8
18	3.0	93.3	5.1	91.3
19	3.4	92.9	5.7	90.7
20	3.9	92.4	6.4	90.0
21	4.5	91.8	7.1	89.3
22	5.2	91.2	8.0	88.5
23	6.0	90.4	8.9	87.6
24	6.8	89.6	9.9	86.7
25	7.9	88.6	11.0	85.6
26	9.0	87.5	12.2	84.5
27	10.4	86.2	13.4	83.2
28	11.9	84.7	14.8	81.9
29	13.6	83.0	16.3	80.5
30	15.5	81.3	17.9	79.0
31			19.6	77.4
32			21.3	75.7
33			23.0	74.0
34			24.8	72.3
35			26.6	70.6
36			28.4	68.9
37			30.1	67.2

k = 0.05

n	(a) w	(a) m	(b) w	(b) m
1	0.0	95.2	0.0	95.2
2	0.1	95.1	0.2	95.0
3	0.2	95.0	0.5	94.8
4	0.4	94.9	0.7	94.5
5	0.5	94.7	1.0	94.3
6	0.7	94.6	1.4	94.0
7	0.9	94.4	1.7	93.6
8	1.1	94.2	2.1	93.3
9	1.4	93.9	2.5	92.9
10	1.6	93.7	3.0	92.4
11	2.0	93.4	3.5	91.9
12	2.3	93.0	4.1	91.4
13	2.7	92.6	4.7	90.8
14	3.2	92.2	5.4	90.1
15	3.8	91.7	6.2	89.3

k = 0.05 (cont.)

n	(a) w	(a) m	(b) w	(b) m
16	4.4	91.0	7.1	88.5
17	5.2	90.3	8.1	87.6
18	6.1	89.5	9.1	86.5
19	7.1	88.3	10.4	85.4
20	8.4	87.3	11.7	84.1
21	9.8	85.9	13.1	82.7
22	11.5	84.3	14.7	81.2
23	13.4	82.5	16.5	79.6
24	15.5	80.5	18.3	77.8
25	17.8	78.2	20.2	76.0
26	20.3	75.9	22.2	74.1
27	22.8	73.6	24.3	72.1
28	25.3	71.2	26.4	70.1
29	27.9	68.8	28.5	68.1

k = 0.06

n	(a) w	(a) m	(b) w	(b) m
1	0.0	94.3	0.0	94.3
2	0.2	94.2	0.3	94.0
3	0.4	94.0	0.7	93.7
4	0.6	93.8	1.1	93.3
5	0.8	93.6	1.5	92.9
6	1.1	93.3	2.0	92.5
7	1.4	93.1	2.5	92.0
8	1.7	92.7	3.1	91.4
9	2.1	92.4	3.7	90.8
10	2.6	91.9	4.5	90.1
11	3.1	91.4	5.3	89.4
12	3.8	90.8	6.2	88.5
13	4.5	90.1	7.3	87.5
14	5.4	89.2	8.4	86.4
15	6.5	88.2	9.7	85.2
16	7.8	87.0	11.2	83.8
17	9.3	85.6	12.8	82.3
18	11.1	83.9	14.6	80.6
19	13.2	81.9	16.5	78.8
20	15.6	79.7	18.6	76.8
21			20.8	74.7
22			23.1	72.5
23			25.5	70.3
24			27.9	68.0
25			30.3	65.8

k = 0.07

n	(a) w	(a) m	(b) w	(b) m
1	0.0	93.5	0.0	93.5
2	0.2	93.2	0.4	93.1
3	0.5	93.0	0.9	92.6
4	0.8	92.7	1.4	92.1
5	1.1	92.4	2.0	91.6
6	1.5	92.1	2.7	91.0
7	1.9	91.7	3.4	90.3
8	2.4	91.2	4.3	89.5
9	3.1	90.6	5.2	88.6
10	3.8	89.9	6.3	87.6

* All tables assume random calls for service. Column (a) is for constant servicing time and column (b) for an exponential distribution of servicing times. It is hoped that the missing values in column (a) can be secured by approximation in the near future.
† Where no entry appears in column the figures were not available.

Table 8–3—(Continued)

TABLES OF WAITING TIME AND MACHINE AVAILABILITY FOR SELECTED SERVICING CONSTANTS*† (continued)

k = 0.07 (cont.)

n	(a) w	(a) m	(b) w	(b) m
11	4.7	89.1	7.5	86.4
12	5.7	88.1	8.9	85.1
13	7.0	86.9	10.4	83.7
14	8.6	85.4	12.2	82.1
15	10.4	83.7	14.1	80.3
16	12.6	81.6	16.2	78.3
17	15.2	79.3	18.5	76.2
18	18.1	76.6	21.0	73.9
19	21.1	73.7	23.5	71.5
20	24.4	70.7	26.2	69.0
21			28.9	66.5

k = 0.08

n	(a) w	(a) m	(b) w	(b) m
1	0.0	92.6	0.0	92.6
2	0.3	92.3	0.5	92.1
3	0.6	92.0	1.2	91.5
4	1.0	91.7	1.9	90.9
5	1.4	91.2	2.7	90.1
6	2.0	90.8	3.5	89.3
7	2.6	90.2	4.5	88.4
8	3.4	89.5	5.7	87.3
9	4.3	88.6	7.0	86.1
10	5.4	87.6	8.5	84.8
11	6.7	86.4	10.1	83.2
12	8.4	84.8	12.0	81.4

k = 0.08 (cont.)

n	(a) w	(a) m	(b) w	(b) m
13	10.4	83.0	14.2	79.5
14	12.8	80.8	16.5	77.3
15	15.6	78.2	19.0	75.0
16	18.8	75.2	21.8	72.4
17	22.2	72.0	24.6	69.8
18	25.7	68.8	27.6	67.1
19	28.2	66.5	30.5	64.4

k = 0.09

n	(a) w	(a) m	(b) w	(b) m
1	0.0	91.5	0.0	91.7
2	0.4	91.4	0.7	91.1
3	0.8	91.0	1.4	90.4
4	1.3	90.6	2.3	89.6
5	1.9	90.0	3.3	88.7
6	2.6	89.4	4.5	87.7
7	3.4	88.6	5.8	86.5
8	4.5	87.6	7.3	85.1
9	5.7	86.5	9.0	83.5
10	7.3	85.0	10.9	81.7
11	9.3	83.2	13.1	79.7
12	11.7	81.0	15.6	77.5
13	14.5	78.4	18.3	75.0
14	17.8	75.4	21.2	72.3
15	21.5	72.0	24.2	69.5
16	25.3	68.5	27.4	66.6
17	29.2	65.0	30.6	63.7

k = 0.10

n	(a) w	(a) m	(b) w	(b) m
1	0.0	90.9	0.0	90.9
2	0.4	90.5	0.8	90.2
3	1.0	90.0	1.8	89.3
4	1.6	89.5	2.8	88.3
5	2.3	88.8	4.1	87.2
6	2.2	88.0	5.5	85.9
7	4.4	86.9	7.1	84.4
8	5.8	85.7	9.0	82.7
9	7.5	84.1	11.2	80.8
10	9.7	82.1	13.6	78.5
11	12.4	79.8	16.3	76.1
12	15.6	76.8	19.3	73.4
13	19.2	73.4	22.5	70.4
14	23.3	69.8	25.9	67.4
15	27.4	66.0	29.4	64.2
16	31.5	62.0		

k = 0.15

n	(a) w	(a) m	(b) w	(b) m
1	0.0	87.0	0.0	87.0
2	0.9	86.2	1.7	85.5
3	2.1	85.1	3.6	83.8
4	3.9	83.8	6.0	81.8
5	5.5	82.2	8.7	79.4
6	8.0	80.0	11.8	76.7
7	11.2	72.2	15.4	73.5
8	15.2	73.7	19.5	70.0
9	20.1	69.5	23.8	66.2
10	25.5	64.8	28.4	62.3
11	31.0	60.0		

k = 0.20

n	(a) w	(a) m	(b) w	(b) m
1	0.0	83.3	0.0	83.3
2	1.5	82.0	2.7	81.1
3	3.6	80.4	5.9	78.4
4	6.3	78.1	9.8	75.2
5	10.0	75.0	14.2	71.5
6	14.7	71.1	19.2	67.4
7	20.6	66.2	24.6	62.8
8	27.3	60.6	30.3	58.1
9	32.6	56.1		

k = 0.30

n	(a) w	(a) m	(b) w	(b) m
1	0.0	76.9	0.0	76.9
2	3.0	74.6	5.1	73.0
3	7.4	71.3	11.1	68.4
4	13.3	66.7	18.0	63.1
5	21.1	60.7	25.4	57.4
6	29.9	53.9	33.0	51.6

k = 0.40

n	(a) w	(a) m	(b) w	(b) m
1	0.0	71.4	0.0	71.4
2	4.8	68.0	7.5	66.0
3	11.8	63.0	16.3	59.8
4	21.2	56.3	25.6	53.1
5	31.9	48.6	34.9	46.5

is (a) constant [1] and (b) exponential [7]. These are given in Table 8–3. Values for the infinite universe case are also available where the arrival and clearing time distributions are exponential. Figure 8–5 is a plot of A/S versus mean length of line, $E(n)$, for channels from 1 to 20.[20]

REFERENCES

1. ASHCROFT, H. "The Productivity of Several Machines under the Care of One Operator," Royal Statistical Society Journal (B), Vol. XII (1950), pp. 145 ff.

2. COBHAM, ALAN. "Priority Assignment in Waiting Line Problems," Journal of the Operations Research Society of America, February, 1954, pp. 70–76.

3. DAVIS, D. J. "An Analysis of Some Failure Data," Journal of the American Statistical Association, Vol. XLVII (June, 1952).

4. FELLER, W. An Introduction to Probability Theory and its Applications. New York: John Wiley & Sons, Inc., 1950.

5. FETTER, R. B. "The Assignment of Operators to Service Automatic Machines," The Journal of Industrial Engineering, September–October, 1955.

6. Notes from M.I.T. Summer Course on Operations Research. Cambridge, Mass.: Technology Press, 1953.

7. PALM, C. "Arbetskraftens fördelning vid betjäning av automatmaskiner," Industritidningen Norden, Vol. LXXV (1947).

---

[20] T. A. Mangelsdorf, "Waiting Line Theory Applied to Manufacturing Problems," in E. H. Bowman and R. B. Fetter (eds.), Analyses of Industrial Operations (Homewood, Ill.: Richard D. Irwin, Inc., 1959).

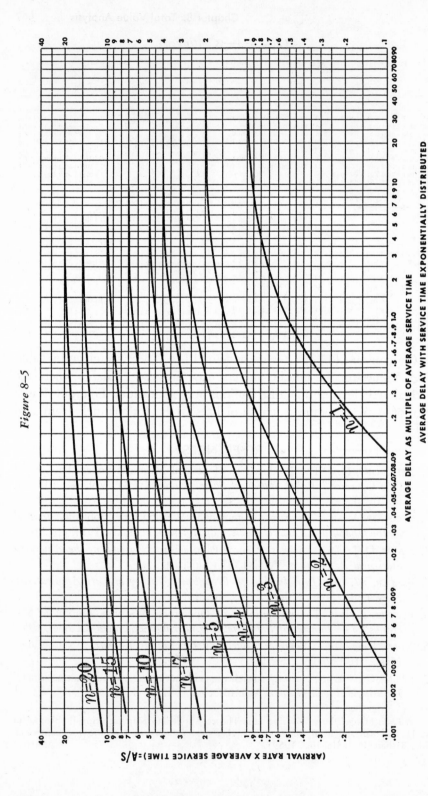

Figure 8-5

AVERAGE DELAY AS MULTIPLE OF AVERAGE SERVICE TIME

AVERAGE DELAY WITH SERVICE TIME EXPONENTIALLY DISTRIBUTED

(ARRIVAL RATE X AVERAGE SERVICE TIME)=A/S

PROBLEMS

1. A manufacturer has become interested in the manufacturing interval of his plant. Manufacturing interval is defined as the total time from the time an order is started on the plant floor until it is ready for shipment. The following data have been accumulated on 20 past orders.

Order Number	Manufacturing Interval (Shop Hours)	Designated a Rush Order	Number of Pieces in Order	Number of Operations
1.....................	153	no	100	6
2.....................	192	no	35	11
3.....................	162	yes	127	7
4.....................	240	no	64	12
5.....................	339	yes	600	5
6.....................	185	yes	14	16
7.....................	235	yes	96	11
8.....................	506	no	257	13
9.....................	260	yes	21	9
10.....................	161	no	39	8
11.....................	835	no	426	14
12.....................	586	no	843	6
13.....................	444	no	391	8
14.....................	240	yes	84	13
15.....................	303	yes	235	9
16.....................	775	no	520	12
17.....................	136	yes	76	8
18.....................	271	yes	139	11
19.....................	385	yes	165	14
20.....................	451	no	304	10

What can you tell the manufacturer about his manufacturing interval?

2. In the *Production Handbook* by Alford and Bangs, page 400, is given Norton's economic lot size formula:

$$Q = \sqrt{\frac{S}{k}}$$

$$\text{where } k = \frac{(B + I)C + 2A\left(1 - \dfrac{U}{P}\right)}{2NU}$$

A = storage cost/piece/year—$\$$
B = taxes, insurance, etc., on inventory—%/year
C = material, direct labor, overhead/piece—$\$$
I = desired return on capital—%/year
U = pieces used/day
P = pieces made/day
N = days worked/year
S = total preparation cost/lot—$\$$

What are the conditions of the problem and assumptions required for this model?

3. The Midwest Supply Corporation is a manufacturer of plastic products.

In January, Midwest received an order from a manufacturer of electrical apparatus for 300 pieces of a special part. The customer furnished information concerning certain electrical and strength characteristics which were needed in the item, but left the choice of a particular plastic compound up to Midwest.

After studying the problem, the Midwest engineers determined that the customer's specifications could be met with 12 pounds per piece of any compound commonly referred to in the company as the "1500 series" compounds. These compounds consist basically of two ingredients (shortened from their complex names to simply "S" and "N") in different relative amounts. Ingredient N varies from 0 per cent to 50 per cent; ingredient S makes up the remainder. The number of specific mixes is infinite.

The cost of any of these compounds is directly related to the related amounts of N and S in the composition. Ingredient S costs $0.10 per pound and ingredient N costs $0.60 per pound when used in the No. 1500–50 compounds.

The company has had extensive manufacturing experience with these compounds. The detailed quality control records maintained reveal that the fraction of N in the compound affects the average fraction defective, p, that can be expected in the manufacturing process. The following data are a sample from several recent orders (the mixing may be continuous, though these samples differ by units of 10 per cent):

Compound	$\bar{p}$	Compound	$\bar{p}$	Compound	$\bar{p}$
No. 1500	0.25	No. 1525	0.16	No. 1530	0.10
No. 1500	0.23	No. 1525	0.15	No. 1540	0.09
No. 1510	0.22	No. 1525	0.14	No. 1540	0.08
No. 1510	0.20	No. 1525	0.12	No. 1540	0.08
No. 1510	0.18	No. 1530	0.13	No. 1550	0.05
No. 1520	0.17	No. 1530	0.12	No. 1550	0.04
No. 1520	0.15	No. 1530	0.11	No. 1550	0.03
No. 1520	0.15				

The quality control section also has determined that the inherent variability of the manufacturing process causes the actual fraction defective for any compound to be normally distributed around $\bar{p}$ with a standard deviation equal to 0.02.

Besides affecting $\bar{p}$, the function of N also is known to influence the forming and processing costs per piece according to the following expression (where P_N is the fraction by weight of N):

$$M = 3 + 80(P_N - 0.3)^2 \ \$/\text{piece}$$

No matter which compound was used, the costs involved in setting up for the job totaled $500.

Since the piece ordered was a special one, additional good pieces over the 300 ordered were not salable as such, and they were valueless, the same as rejects.

a) Determine which compound should be used (within 1 per cent).

b) Determine how many pieces should be scheduled. (For purposes of simplification, consider questions (*a*) and (*b*) as independent.)

4. In the weaving of cotton cloth, there are two principal kinds of service which the looms require. The duties of a weaver include such things as servicing warp stops, filling stops, and miscellaneous stops; cleaning lint and slugs from warp; doffing cloth; repairing fabric damage; and inspection and patrol. The fixer handles all mechanical breakdowns of the looms. These two classes of labor usually have different machine assignments. Calls for service for both weavers and fixers occur individually and collectively at random.

Assuming that mechanical breakdowns are under control at some steady rate, the following data is given for weavers:

a) Calls for service occur at random at an average interval of 60 minutes per loom.

b) Weaver's service times are of random duration (exponential distribution), but average 2 minutes per call.

c) Cloth is produced at the rate of 5 yards/running hour/loom.

d) The mill works 40 hours/week, 250 days/year.

e) Weavers are paid an average of $1.80/hour.

f) All cloth that can be produced can be sold with $0.10/yard profit.

Find the optimum machine assignment for a weaver, using the tables for waiting time values which are in the Appendix to this chapter. (Set up the problem symbolically and then put in the proper numbers.)

5. For a group of Swiss screw machines, service times for tool setters is exponentially distributed with a mean value of 34 minutes. Calls for service occur at random, and the average interval between calls on any one machine is 7 hours. If the cost of lost production due to waiting is reckoned at $10/hour, and the labor cost for a toolsetter is $2.00/hour, compute the optimum number of toolsetters (operating on assigned machines without collaboration) to assign to a group of 50 machines.

6. In a job shop, it is desired to determine the number of machines to operate each week under varying production loads. Orders come in essentially at random intervals (from an infinite population), but the average load can be predicted with considerable accuracy. The firm does not know how much it costs to have an order wait, but wants to operate sufficient machines so that orders are delayed no more than one day between machining operations. The length of time necessary to process an order through any one of the machine groups was ascertained to have an exponential distribution.

The three machine groups and their characteristics are as follows:

	Arrival Rate (Orders/Hour)	Machine Time per Order (Hours)
1. Vertical millers	0.525	13.3
2. Engine lathes	0.450	11.7
3. Spindle drills	0.475	14.4

Machines may be operated two shifts (16 hours) each day. What is the smallest number of machines that should be provided in each group if the given delay criterion is to be satisfied? What average delays will be experienced? If the production load increases by 20 per cent, how many machines must be provided in each group? (See Appendix to this chapter.)

7. In a garment factory, 400 sewing machines are operated 8 hours a day, 5 days a week. The management is interested in the proper number of mechanics and standby machines to have available in order to minimize costs. Mechanics wages are $2.50/hour, additional machines may be rented for $2.00/day, and downtime costs $10/hour in lost profits. Studies indicate machines break down at random intervals, but the average running time between breakdowns is 16 hours. Service times are exponentially distributed and average 30 minutes.

    Set up this problem for solution and include a statement of the cost function to be minimized in the case of:
    a) Group servicing (r men for u machines)
    b) Individual servicing (one man per n machines)

8. For Problem 7, Chapter 9, set up the total cost expression which can be used to determine the number of pieces to start.

9. Set up a total cost expression for Problem 8, Chapter 9.

10. Given the analysis of the scale of operations problem, pages 320–27, how does the optimum warehouse territory vary with the sales density of the area? Why? On one chart, for a series of values of b/c, plot optimum area as a function of sales density (k).

11. In the operator assignment problem, pages 336–38, what does it mean that $\frac{s}{m}$, the ratio of service time to machine operating time, is a constant (k) for a given type of equipment? Why? For what time period is this true?

12. For the operator assignment problem, page 338, Table 8–2, plot the optimum machine assignment as a function of k (i.e., keeping everything the same but letting k vary from 0 to ∞).

13. Compute the economic lot size for the following problem:

    Yearly requirements.........................87,000
    Carrying cost.............................$0.08/piece/year
    Setup cost................................$27

    What effect would an error of $0.02 either way in the estimate of the carrying cost have on the total yearly cost in this problem?

14. A company has 24 identical machines which are operated 24 hours/day, 360 days/year. The average interval between breakdowns is 5 days (exponential distribution), and the average repair time is 12 hours (exponential distribution). Repairmen get $2.00/hour and work 8 hours/day. A machine not

repaired results in a loss in profits of $2.00 per hour (expected production rate × profit/piece).

a) What is the optimum number of repairmen if one man is assigned to a group of machines?

b) What is the machine utilization (available machine time) at this optimum assignment?

15. The following data are a sales forecast, initial inventory and production, and cost functions in a situation for which it is desired to make least cost production rate decisions.

Sales by period (must be satisfied):

$$S_1 = 30$$
$$S_2 = 10$$
$$S_3 = 40$$

Initial inventory, $I_0 = 12$.
Production in period 0, $P_0 = 15$.
Inventory required at end of period 3, $I_3 = 10$.
Costs:

$$\$100 \, (P_t - P_{t-1})^2$$
$$\$20 \, (10 - I_t)^2 \text{ per period}$$

Required are P_1, P_2, P_3 which minimize cost.

a) Set up the problem for mathematical solution and indicate how it would be solved.

b) Solve the problem as a total value problem, using a tabular—i.e., numerical—approach (an approximate solution).

16. It is required to plan operations in a situation in which initial conditions, costs, and requirements are given as follows:

$P_0 = 2,000$, production rate in previous period,
$W_0 = 600$, work force in previous period,
$I_0 = 300$, inventory at end of previous period,
$K = 3$, production units per worker per period in regular time.

Costs:

$$\$200 \, (W_n - W_{n-1})^2$$
$$\$50 \, P_n$$
$$\$25 \, (P_n - KW_n)^2$$
$$\$20 \, (500 - I_n)^2$$

Requirements:

$$S_1 = 3,000, \text{ sales in period No. 1}$$
$$S_2 = 1,800$$
$$S_3 = 2,400$$

Back ordering is permitted.
The management desires to make those plans which will result in lowest operating costs for meeting the above requirements.

a) Express system objective function mathematically.

b) Solve for an optimum schedule.

c) What is the meaning of each of the cost components?

CHAPTER 9

Incremental Analysis[1]

CERTAINTY MODELS

WHEN determining how much of a factor of production (labor, machinery, material, etc.) to use or bring into a production scheme, a manager must appraise both the cost of bringing it in and the gain from bringing it in. Under one approach to this problem, the *total* cost may be compared with the *total* gain, or, virtually the same thing, both totals may be divided by the number of units and the average cost may be compared to the average gain. A comparison of this type may be useful in making a rough check as to whether a current scheme is economically justified. However, of more use is a comparison of *incremental* cost to *incremental* gain.

Given a number of units (of men, for instance), if one more unit (man) is added to this production scheme, there will be an increase in cost. This increase in cost is the incremental cost. It is the difference between total cost before the unit is added and total cost after the unit is added. The addition of one unit (man) to the production scheme should also have some associated benefit. For instance, production rejects might be decreased, or overtime reduced, or idle machine time eliminated. This gain, or increase in gain, associated with the additional unit is the incremental gain. Incremental gain in the analysis of production management problems will normally be due to a reduction in a set of costs. That is, because a unit of some factor of production has been added, certain costs have decreased.

A comparison of the incremental cost with the incremental gain will

---

[1] The analysis presented here is somewhat akin to the marginal analysis of standard economic theory. The main difference is that marginal analysis concentrates equally on revenues procured in the market place and costs. The incremental analysis presented here concentrates essentially on two kinds of costs, and the term *incremental* is purposely used so as not to confuse the problem with demand analysis of economic theory.

354

reveal the net contribution due to the additional unit. If the cost of this unit is less than the gain attributable to this unit, it is certainly worth while having it in the production scheme. The essence of incremental analysis is that units are added to the scheme as long as incremental costs are less than incremental gains. When incremental costs are greater than incremental gains, too many units have been added. The difference between the incremental cost and gain is a net contribution to profits. When costs are less than gains, this net contribution is positive and profits are increased. When costs are greater than gains, net "contribution" is negative and profits are reduced. As a logical extension of this idea, then, units are added to the scheme until incremental cost ($\triangle C$) equals incremental gain ($\triangle G$), that is, until

$$\triangle C = \triangle G.$$

Until this point is reached, profits have been increased; after this point, profits would be decreased. Actually, of course, the unit for which $\triangle C = \triangle G$ exactly may or may not be added. This unit is an indifference unit; if added it won't affect profits either way. However, if the number of units which might conceivably be applied in the production scheme is large, finding the unit for which $\triangle C = \triangle G$ is not a matter of indifference but the nub of the problem.

The whole problem of incremental analysis centers around the need to get expressions which accurately represent incremental cost and incremental gain in terms of the number of units added. Once these expressions are built from an analysis and understanding of the problem, then the statement of the condition $\triangle C = \triangle G$ defines the answer. That is, $\triangle C = \triangle G$ is an equation of condition. It is not necessarily true. It is true only at the point of maximum profits or minimum costs, and if the expression is properly set up and solved, it will reveal this optimum number of units which makes $\triangle C = \triangle G$.

In a sense, of course, incremental analysis is a special case of total value analysis as the equations of condition are identical for the same problem. If both are valid for the given assumptions, this must be the case. Though technically incremental analysis starts with the first derivative from total value analysis, operationally this is not the case. The difference centers about the nature of the model which is being constructed, and the stage at which formal mathematical deduction takes over. In one case, a total value model is constructed, at which point the mathematical deduction of taking a derivative can be followed with no attention to the economic problem. In the second case, an incremental model is constructed directly from the economic problem itself, at which point the mathematical deduction of solving for the value of the variable in question is followed. As a generalization, it may be added that incremental analysis is more difficult to formulate, but the resulting mathematical expression easier to manipulate, while total value analysis is easier to formulate, with the mathematical expression more difficult to manipulate. This is particularly true when probability distributions are involved.

Incremental cost and incremental gain may be plotted as a function of the number of units. The shape of the curves formed will, of course, differ with different problems. In a hypothetical case in which the curves do not intersect, either no units will be added ($\Delta C \geqq \Delta G$) or an infinite number of units will be added ($\Delta C \leqq \Delta G$). In the common case, which calls for analysis, the incremental gain is initially greater than the incremental cost, and at some point (to be determined) the curves cross. A very common case will have a horizontal line for incremental cost (cost per unit is constant) and an incremental gain curve which slopes downward to the right, due essentially to decreasing marginal returns.[2]

Economic Lot Size Example

The economic lot size problem may be used to illustrate the concept of incremental analysis. This is the same problem used to introduce total value analysis in the previous chapter. When a manufacturer produces goods to stock, he periodically produces a batch of goods and stores it, meeting his sales requirements out of the storage. The problem arises as to how large a quantity to manufacture and put into storage at one time.

The factors considered pertinent to this problem are the following:

Q = quantity to manufacture in one lot,
R = sales requirements per year (or other time period),
S = setup costs (per order),
I = interest and carrying cost including storage all expressed per piece per year.

A simplified picture of the inventory situation is shown in Figure 9–1. The solid line represents the inventory level, over time, with a given lot size (Q). The dotted line represents the same thing with an incremental increase in lot size ($Q + \Delta Q$). The nature of incremental analysis is the consideration of the effects upon costs and gains of adding an incremental unit to the operation. The question to be answered

---

[2] In the unusual case where these curves cross more than once, certain total calculations must be made to determine the economic quantity. Normally, as long as the incremental gain exceeds the incremental cost for each unit, regardless of the shape of the curves, it pays to add units.

Figure 9–1

INVENTORY MODEL

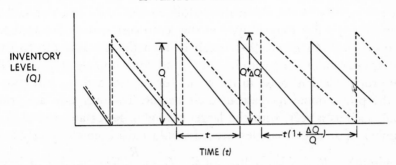

INVENTORY LEVEL (Q)

TIME (t)

is: What are the incremental costs and what are the incremental gains?

The first step in incremental analysis is to establish the equation:

$$\triangle C = \triangle G. \tag{1}$$

This equation is an "equation of condition." Incremental cost is not necessarily equal to incremental gain. But when they are equal, an optimum quantity has been chosen. The quantity is optimum because at this point profits are maximized (or costs are minimized). What has been done is to set up an equation of condition in order to find out, by solving the equation, what conditions make this possible.

Working from $\triangle C = \triangle G$, the equation of condition, an expression is substituted for each side of the equation. The question to be asked is: If a small increase ($\triangle Q$) were to be made in Q, the quantity to be manufactured, what would be the incremental cost? If Q is increased, the amount of inventory in storage will be increased as can be seen in Figure 9–1. During the year (or appropriate time period), with one manufacturing cycle following another, the average inventory on hand is $\tfrac{1}{2}Q$. This follows from the simplifying assumptions that the lot is manufactured instantaneously (the line representing increase in inventory is vertical) and that sales are at an even (and known) rate during the period. This gives a series of triangles of height Q, and the average height of a triangle is one half the maximum height. A further assumption in this problem as it has been developed is that inventory carrying charges are a function of the average inventory. The incremental cost then is equal to the increase in average inventory

$$\left(\frac{Q + \triangle Q}{2} - \frac{Q}{2} = \frac{\triangle Q}{2} \right)$$

times the inventory charge, I, or $\dfrac{\triangle Q}{2} I$.

The nature of the incremental gain in this problem is that with larger quantities to be manufactured, each lot will last longer, given the same rate of sales. From this it follows that the larger lot will be manufactured less frequently, and the setup cost will be incurred less frequently. From Figure 9–1 it can be seen that because the two triangles are similar (one with height Q, and one with height $Q + \triangle Q$), the proportional increase in their base, or depletion time, is the same as the proportional increase in their height. To cover the same time span, such as a year, with the larger triangles, fewer are needed. The number of smaller triangles needed would have been the yearly sales requirement, R, divided by the lot size Q, or $\dfrac{R}{Q}$. The number of larger triangles needed would be

$$\frac{R}{Q + \triangle Q} .$$

The incremental revenue is then the difference in number of setups

$$\left(\frac{R}{Q} - \frac{R}{Q + \triangle Q} \right)$$

times the setup cost (S), or

$$\left(\frac{R}{Q} - \frac{R}{Q + \triangle Q} \right) S ,$$

which reduces to

$$\left(\frac{\triangle Q}{Q + \triangle Q} \right) \left(\frac{R}{Q} \right) S .$$

It is now possible to make the substitution shown in equation (2) below. From this is developed algebraically the standard equation for economic lot size shown in equation (3)[3]

$$\triangle C = \triangle G$$

$$\frac{\triangle Q}{2} I = \left(\frac{\triangle Q}{Q + \triangle Q} \right) \left(\frac{R}{Q} \right) S \tag{2}$$

$$\frac{I}{2} = \left(\frac{1}{Q + \triangle Q} \right) \left(\frac{R}{Q} \right) S$$

$$\frac{I}{2} = \frac{RS}{Q^2 + Q \triangle Q}$$

---

[3] This same equation has been developed by total values analysis in Chapter 8, which is the conventional and probably easier approach to the problem.

Then as $\triangle Q$ approaches zero,

$$Q = \sqrt{\frac{2RS}{I}} \qquad (3)$$

To illustrate the application of this lot size model, consider the following situation:

R = 10,000 units per year,
S = \$18 per setup,
I = \$0.12 per piece per year,

$$Q = \sqrt{\frac{2RS}{I}} = \sqrt{\frac{2 \times 10,000 \times \$18}{\$0.12}} = \sqrt{3,000,000} = 1,000\sqrt{3} = 1,732 .$$

The economic lot size is 1,732, and the lot should be manufactured approximately six times per year $\left(\dfrac{10,000}{1,732}\right)$.

The economic lot size formula has been, and may be, applied to procurement and transportation problems as well as manufacturing problems. In procurement of an item, when price fluctuations are not a major consideration, the same type of problem exists. The larger the individual purchase, the higher will be the inventory carrying charges, but the lower will be the purchase expenses over the course of a year. Equation (3) may also be used for this problem. Similarly, if the transportation of a good is to be undertaken periodically and there are costs which are fixed for each transportation, the same analysis may be applied. Though the kind of problem illustrated here is important, of much more importance is the method of analysis. To give the method more meaning, a second type of problem will be described in the incremental analysis framework.

Plant Warehouse Example

A manufacturer who had one plant and several warehouses was interested in the optimum size territory to serve directly from the warehouse connected physically to his plant. The advantages of direct delivery from the plant warehouse is that the intermediate step of bulk delivery from plant to branch warehouse is eliminated. Delivery was made from the various warehouses to retail stores. The question was how far out from the plant its delivery trucks should serve.

An equation of incremental analysis was used for this problem. It was an expression of distribution cost ($\triangle C$) and savings ($\triangle G$) per piece for the marginal truck load of goods added to the delivery radius. That is, the unit of measure added was one truck load at a particular section of the perimeter. Many, many such truck loads are contained in the total area served by the plant warehouse. As the number of pieces in a truck load which may be delivered within one working day will differ with the distance out the truck must go, the equation must be in terms of cost per piece. $\triangle C$ has this dimension. The objective was to minimize cost per piece. The incremental cost expression developed was as follows:

$$\triangle C = \frac{2T_m \times P_d + T_f + D_h \times \text{hrs./day}}{\text{pcs./hr. (hrs./day} - 2 \times P_d \times \text{hrs./mi.} - D_f)} \tag{4}$$

where

T_m = truck operating cost per mile,
P_d = plant to perimeter delivery distance (a round trip once per day),
T_f = truck fixed cost per day,
D_h = driver cost per hour,
hrs./day = total duty hours per day,
pcs./hr. = number of pieces that could be delivered per hour,
hrs./mi. = hours per mile for the truck,
D_f = driver fixed time per day, such as check in and check out, coffee time, etc.

It can be seen that this incremental cost, the cost of a delivered truck load (only one per day) at the edge of the territory expressed in dollars/piece, is an increasing function of the variable to be manipulated by management, P_d, the distance to the perimeter of the plant warehouse territory (i.e., how large should the territory be?). As this distance (area) was increased, the incremental cost/piece increased. This was for two reasons. The numerator, which is cost per day, increases with P_d, i.e., $2T_m \times P_d$. The denominator, which represents the number of pieces which can be delivered from the truck (and per day), decreases with an increase in P_d, i.e., $-2P_d \times$ hrs./mi.

The incremental gain expression was as follows:

$$\triangle G = \frac{S_l + B_e + 2S_oD_p + S_f + 2S_d \cdot \text{hrs./mi.} \cdot D_p + I_w}{P_s} +$$
$$\frac{2T_mD_b + T_f + D_h \cdot \text{hrs./day}}{\text{pcs./hr. (hrs./day} - 2D_b \cdot \text{hrs./mi.} - D_f)}$$

where the additional notation is

S_l = semi (trailer truck) load and unload costs,
B_e = branch expense per semi,
S_o = semi operating cost per mile,
D_p = miles from plant to branch,
S_f = semi fixed costs per day (an amortization type charge),

S_d = semi driver cost per hour,
I_w = inventory cost per semi,
P_s = pieces per semi,
D_b = miles from branch to delivery.

The expression for incremental gain represents the cost of making the same delivery from a branch warehouse, including the intermediate step of shipment to that warehouse. Therefore it is shown in two steps.[4] It is considered as the incremental gain because a delivery made from the plant does not have to be made from the branch, and as the plant territory is increased, incurring the incremental costs, the deliveries from the branches are saved, providing the incremental gains. This increase (conceptually) in the plant territory is continued as long as the incremental costs are less than the incremental gains, or until $\triangle C = \triangle G$, the equation of condition.

A fuller discussion of the problem is not warranted here, though such a discussion would be necessary to justify the assumptions on which the model was based. Different assumptions would of course give a different model. A real disadvantage to incremental analysis is the great difficulty in testing an equation of condition, however desirable such a test may be. For solution, all values could be inserted into the marginal equation except P_d, the plant perimeter distance. This was the unknown which was to be determined. It should be pointed out here that with a problem which will probably be considered but once, such as this one, it might be just as satisfactory to substitute a series of values for the unknown, P_d, into the expressions for the two choices separately, Plant and Branch, $\triangle C$ and $\triangle G$, and see which value for the unknown makes the two choices equal. However, where many versions of the same problem remain to be solved, such as in the economic lot size problem, a general formula such as the one developed in equation (3) is most useful.

UNCERTAINTY MODELS

The presentation of incremental analysis to this point has been under conditions of certainty, or at least, conditions treated as certain. However, in many economic decision problems, uncertainty is one of the major factors which must be considered.[5]

---

[4] For a fuller description of this problem, see Bowman and Stewart, "A Model for Scale of Operations," *Journal of Marketing,* January, 1956.

[5] See Chapter 5, Statistical Control, for a brief discussion of probability. Further reference to the concepts of probability may be found in the books by Moroney, Munroe, and Schlaifer listed in the bibliography to this chapter.

Relative frequency or probability may be expressed or charted in two different but related ways. For instance, production figures of past years

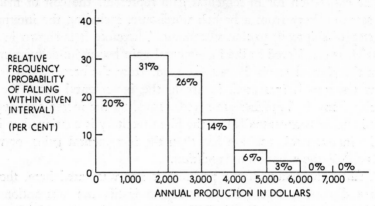

Figure 9–2

HISTOGRAM OF ANNUAL PRODUCTION

may be shown in a frequency distribution, as in Figure 9–2, and listed below:[6]

Intervals	Number of Years	Percentage	Cumulative Percentage
0–$ 999	7	20%	100%
$1,000–$1,999	11	31%	80%
$2,000–$2,999	9	26%	49%
$3,000–$3,999	5	14%	23%
$4,000–$4,999	2	6%	9%
$5,000–$5,999	1	3%	3%
$6,000 and over	0	0	0
	35	100%	

A second way of presenting the same information is as a cumulative probability distribution, as in Figure 9–3.

Here the probability reading on the *y*-axis represents the probability of experiencing production corresponding to the reading on the *x*-axis or higher. For instance, the probability of having production between 0 and $1,000 or higher is 100 per cent, as this covers the full range of experience (negative production here not being possible). The probability of having production of more than $6,000 is zero, i.e., this is impossible according to this chart.

---

[6] Time series problems in forecasting are ignored here.

Figure 9–3

PROBABILITY DISTRIBUTION OF ANNUAL PRODUCTION

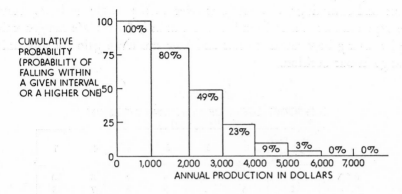

An Inventory Example

The use of probability with incremental analysis will be illustrated with several examples. Consider a simple inventory problem in which a decision must be made each day as to the number of items to stock for use in manufacture. It costs $1.00 per item stocked to handle it into storage and carry it for the day. It costs the firm an additional $1.00 if an item is left over at the end of the day and must be thrown away. The firm loses $5.00 in net revenues if a unit is demanded but not available. If we knew how many would be used each day, then the decision is trivial. If the possible uses are from 0 to 5, then the cost of each possible decision-use combination is shown in Table 9–1. If we knew that

Table 9–1

STOCKING DECISION COST TABLE

Demand \ Stock	0	1	2	3	4	5
0	0	2	4	6	8	10
1	5	1	3	5	7	9
2	10	6	2	4	6	8
3	15	11	7	3	5	7
4	20	16	12	8	4	6
5	25	21	17	13	9	5

2 units would be used today, it is clear that 2 should be ordered. However, if there is some uncertainty about demand today, the goodness of the decision will depend on our ability to estimate this uncertainty.

In Table 9–2, an estimate of the *chance* that any of the possible demands will occur is shown and it is now possible to determine the *expected value* of each possible act and thus the "best" possible act assuming we wish to minimize expected cost of operation. This can be done by multiplying the cost outcome of each event by the chance that it will occur and summing these products over each possible decision. Thus the expected cost of a decision to stock 2 units is $6.50. We can generalize by asking how much it costs and how much we gain for any unit change in our decision.

Table 9–2

EXPECTED COSTS OF STOCKING DECISION

Probability	Demand \ Stock	0	1	2	3	4	5
0.05	0	0	2	4	6	8	10
0.15	1	5	1	3	5	7	9
0.30	2	10	6	2	4	6	8
0.25	3	15	11	7	3	5	7
0.15	4	20	16	12	8	4	6
0.10	5	25	21	17	13	9	5
Expected Cost		12.50	11.40	6.50	5.50	6.00	7.40

The cost of a decision to stock one more unit would be the cost of carrying the unit for one day plus the loss if it is left over at the end of a day. The gain would be a saving of stockout costs if this extra unit was actually demanded. We would be willing to stock this extra unit as long as the cost was less than the saving. As soon as the cost exceeded the saving, no more units would be stocked. This condition for least cost decision can be expressed as

$$E(\Delta C) = E(\Delta G)$$
$$C + LP(x) = D[1 - P(x)]$$

C = carrying cost per unit per day
L = cost per unit left over
D = cost per unit demanded but not available
$P(x)$ = probability that fewer than x units will be demanded.

Solving for the optimal value of $P(x)$, denoted by $P(x)^*$, gives

$$LP(x) + DP(x) = D - C$$
$$(D + L)P(x) = D - C$$
$$P(x)^* = \frac{D - C}{D + L}.$$

It is important to recognize that our model results from asking the question "what do we need to know to make this decision and how is it related to the decision?" We did not consider at all whether we had or could even get certain kinds of information. The first purpose of the model is to give us the answers to these questions.

As illustrations of this process, let us consider two kinds of uncertainty which may exist with respect to the information required in the given problem: first, uncertainty as regards our estimate of a cost, and second, uncertainty as regards our estimate of demand. The questions we want to answer are the following:

1. How important is the information to the decision?
2. How much can we afford to pay (in money, worry, etc.) for getting the information?

Uncertainty of Estimate of a Particular Parameter

In the previous example it was assumed that the cost of an item demanded but not available was known with certainty. Say that the $5.00 used as its value was only the revenue lost when a stockout occurred and that the value of D is larger than this due to such factors as loss of future sales and disruption of production schedules but it is not known by how much. The question of interest which can be examined with our decision model is how good an estimate of D do we really have to have in order to make a good decision. Having decided, based on a value of $D = 5.00, that the best decision is to stock 3 units, what value of D would just cause us to change our minds and stock 4 units. In order for this to be the best decision, it must be true that D is at least large enough so that the optimal value of $P(x)$ turns out to be at least 0.75. If we substitute 0.75 in our decision model and solve for D, we obtain a value of $7.00. This tells us that if D is estimated between the known value of $5.00 and a value of $7.00, the decision to stock 3 is the best decision. But if it is estimated at more than $7.00, the decision should be changed at least to 4. Whether or not it would be profitable to stock 5 units can be assessed by solving for the value of D which would lead to 0.90 as the optimal value of $P(x)$. This turns out to be $19. Now we know that any value of D between $7.00 and $19 will lead to a decision to stock 4 units; any value more than $19 would lead to a decision to stock 5 units. The sensitivity of our decision to errors in estimating D, that is to the uncertainty of such an estimate, has been evaluated. It is not worth anything to us to obtain an estimate within any closer limits than those provided by the above analysis.

Uncertainty of Estimate of Probabilities

Say our forecast calls for a higher rate of production by 40 per cent and we have no experience with usage under these conditions. However, knowledge of plant, personnel, and equipment capabilities plus past experience should enable us to determine a set of reasonable probabilities. We can do this by noting, e.g., that average demand will go from 2.6 to 3.4 and asking what is the probability of a demand of zero under these conditions? The answer is probably less than 0.05 but more than 0.00.

If we pose a game as follows it should provide some insight into the process of estimating probabilities:

A bowl contains 100 chips some of which (an unknown number) are marked 0. You are given the following choice:

1. A ticket carrying a penalty of $100 if a chip marked 0 is drawn from the bowl.
2. A ticket carrying a penalty of $100 if a demand of 0 occurs tomorrow.

What number of chips marked 0 will make you indifferent as to 1 and 2? The number thus established represents one's best estimate as to the probability of a demand of zero occurring. Once this has been established, the same choice can be presented with chips marked one for the first ticket and a demand of one for the second ticket. Continuing the process in this way over all possible demands, a probability distribution for future demand can be established.

Say we get the following:

Demand	Probability
0	0.02
1	0.05
2	0.15
3	0.25
4	0.30
5	0.20
6	0.03

Then, the decision is as follows if $D = \$5.00$:

$$P(x)^* = 0.67$$

and

$$x = 4 .$$

Say we know $D = \$20$, then

$$P(x)^* = \frac{20 - 1}{21}$$

$$= \frac{19}{21} = 0.905 .$$

All we have to determine then is whether demand for 6 is less than or greater than 0.095; if less than, stock 5 (demand for 5 or 6 greater than 0.095); if greater than, stock 6. No more precise estimate is needed. Thus the sensitivity of the decision to errors in the demand forecast can be established.

Consider the consequences of a shift in the demand probabilities to the following:

Demand	Probability
0	0.01
1	0.10
2	0.25
3	0.40
4	0.20
5	0.04

The expected values become

Decision	2	3	4
Expected value	6.82	4.82	5.19

and even though our expectations have shifted considerably, the decision is still to stock 3 units.

In fact, it takes a radical shift in demand to budge us from this decision. Consider the following:

Demand	Probability
0	0
1	0
2	0.25
3	0.40
4	0.20
5	0.15

The expected values for various decisions are

Decision	2	3	4	5
Expected value	8.25	5.75	5.40	6.75

and we are persuaded to change our decision but only to 4 and only with an expected loss of $0.25 per day if the distribution turns out to be the last given one and we make a decision to stock 3 based on assuming the first given distribution.

What we always need in such situations is a way to evaluate the economic effect of errors in estimating uncertainty. How critical does our judgment really have to be? If a standard can be provided against which judgment can be calibrated, we will have gone a long way toward solving our decision problem even though our crystal ball is quite cloudy as far as demand is concerned.

Let's consider the situation given previously without any estimate of demand given. All we know are the costs. We compute

$$P(x)^* = 0.67$$

and now know that all we have to establish is the demand point which includes $2/3$ of demands expected tomorrow. If we estimate that the probability of demand for 5 units is more than $1/3$, we should stock 5.

No more precise estimate is necessary. If we estimate that the combined probability of demands of 4 and 5 is more than $\frac{1}{3}$ while the probability of 5 is less than $\frac{1}{3}$, we should stock 4, and so on.

Our decision can be made with great clarity without great refinement in estimates of demand. The degree to which uncertainty affects our decision has been defined quite precisely in economic terms.

The important thing is to focus judgment in those areas where it is necessary and not to waste time worrying about estimates which will in no way affect the decision at hand.

Simultaneous Incremental Equations

In some economic decisions more than one quantity must be chosen at one time. A case in point, for instance, would be the amount of inventory to stock at several levels or stages in an operation.[7] In such a case as this, for each quantity to be decided a separate incremental equation is established, with the proper expressions substituted for $\triangle C$ and $\triangle G$. This should give a number of equations equal to the number of unknowns. A simultaneous solution is then possible.

In presenting the individual expressions of incremental equality, only one unknown is allowed to "vary" at a time, i.e., the others are considered to be constant for this equation.[8]

Order-Point, Order-Quantity Inventory Models

One important two-variable problem which can be approached using incremental analysis is in deciding when and how much to order to supply a manufacturing demand for some material. Whereas previously in dealing with economic order quantities the assumption has been made that usage and lead time are constant so that stockouts cannot occur, now both usage and lead time will be treated as random variables and thus stockouts are possible. If usage during the interval between placing an order and receipt of the order is measured, a distribution of this variable can be obtained as shown in Figure 9–4. The following notation is used:

u = usage during any lead time,
$P(u)$ = probability of usage greater than u,
r = reorder point in units,
$\bar{u}$ = expected usage during lead time,
π = stockout cost per unit demanded but not available.

---

[7] J. G. Bryan, G. P. Wadsworth, and T. M. Whitin, "A Multi Stage Inventory Model," *Naval Research Logistics Quarterly*, Vol. II, Nos. 1 and 2 (March–June, 1955).
[8] This is analogous to partial differentiation.

If the reorder point r is established, the probability of a stockout occurring is given by $P(u > r)$.

Assuming the economic order quantity, Q, is known from equation (3), then the cost of an additional unit added to the reorder point (ordering earlier) is I and the saving due to this unit is π times the probability that demand will exceed r. If the carrying cost per unit I is at yearly rates, then it must be divided by the number of orders per year D/Q to be comparable with the saving. Thus the condition for optimality is

$$\frac{IQ}{D} = \pi P(u > r),$$

and the optimal stockout probability is

$$P(u > r)^* = \frac{IQ}{\pi D}.$$

Figure 9–4

PROBABILITY DISTRIBUTION OF USAGE DURING REORDER PERIOD

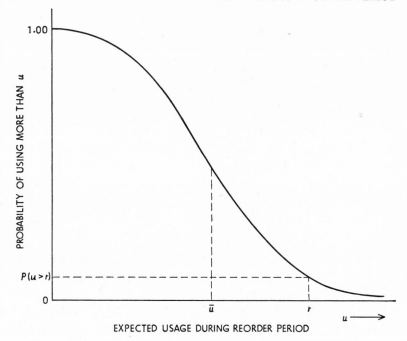

EXPECTED USAGE DURING REORDER PERIOD

The assumption that Q can be computed from (3) has now been shown to be incorrect since stockouts will occur with the probability per order given above. If it is now assumed that the reorder point is known, the expected cost of stockouts per order cycle is

$$E(s) = \pi \sum_{u=r+1}^{u_{max.}} (u - r)p(u)$$

in which $p(u)$ is the probability of a usage equal to u. $E(s)$ is an additional fixed cost per order placed and may be added to S giving as the economic lot size

$$Q = \sqrt{\frac{2R[S + E(s)]}{I}}.$$

One would then proceed to re-evaluate the reorder point using this Q and so on until a consistent set of values (r, Q) was established.

As an example of this consider the following item:

$$R = 325 \text{ units/year,}$$
$$S = \$3.00 \text{ per order placed,}$$
$$I = \$6.00 \text{ per unit per year.}$$

Then

$$Q = \sqrt{\frac{2(325)3}{6}}$$
$$= 18,$$

assuming stockout cost is zero.

Demand and lead time data are tabulated below:

x = Demand/Day			t = Lead Time in Days		
x	%	Σ %	t	%	Σ %
0	20	20	1	30	30
1	40	60	2	50	80
2	30	90	3	20	100
3	10	100			

These data show the kind of variability which has been experienced in the past. In order to use this in predicting the future, two conditions must be met. First, both sets must be demonstrated to be random phenomena, i.e., generated by some stable system of chance causes. Second, it must be assumed that the future as far as is known will be just like the past. Then it is possible from the above to develop the important statistic: *use during lead time.*

This may be done by direct observation, direct computation, or Monte Carlo simulation. The second approach will be used here since the first needs no illustration, and the third will be demonstrated later (see Chapter 11). In order to compute the $p(u)$ where u is use during lead time, a general process is available involving expansion of multinomials but the basic computations are straightforward.

It should be clear that $u_{max.} = 9$. This follows from the fact that a 3-day lead time is the largest value of t and a demand per day of three is the largest possible value of x. The probability of this event is the product of the probabilities of the four subevents necessary to give $u = 9$. That is, we must have a 3-day lead time and a usage of three per day each day in order that $u = 9$. This gives

$$p(u = 9) = 0.20(0.10)(0.10)(0.10)$$
$$= 0.0002 .$$

That is, there are only two chances in 10,000 of this event occurring. The probability that $u = 8$ may be found by determining the number of ways in which this event can occur, computing the probability of each way, and summing over all events. In this case, $u = 8$ can occur in three ways, all of which have the same probability, that is, a lead time of 3 days and demands of 3 on 2 days and 2 on 1 day. This gives

$$p(u = 8) = 3[0.20(0.10)(0.10)(0.30)]$$
$$= 0.0018.$$

The value of

$$p(u = 7) = 3(0.20)[(0.10)(0.30)(0.30) + (0.10)(0.10)(0.40)]$$
$$= 0.0078 .$$

At $u = 6$, a number of possibilities occur. If we get a 2-day lead time, then we must have 3 items per day used, but if we get a 3-day lead time, we could have 0 one day and 3 for 2 days (3 ways), or 1, 2, and 3 on each of the days (6 ways), or 2 on each of the 3 days (1 way). This gives

$$p(u = 6) = 0.50[(10.10)(0.10)] + 0.20[(0.20)(0.10)(0.10)3 +$$
$$(0.40)(0.30)(0.10)6 + (0.30)(0.30)(0.30)]$$
$$= 0.026 .$$

Proceeding in this way the probability of any usage during lead time is obtained, and it will be noted as a matter of interest that the first appreciable value occurs at $u = 6$. The relevant portion of the distribution is as follows:

u	$p(u)$	$P(u) =$ Probability of More Than u
4		0.1042
5	0.0684	0.0358
6	0.0260	0.0098
7	0.0078	0.0020
8	0.0018	0.0002
9	0.0002	0.0000

If an estimate of the cost incurred when an item is demanded but not available is made, the optimal values of r and Q may be determined readily. Say that $\pi = \$20$ represents the extra production cost (loss) incurred if an item is unavailable. Then

$$P(u > r)^* = \frac{IQ}{\pi D}$$
$$= \frac{6.00(18)}{20(325)}$$
$$= 0.0166 \, .$$

In this case $r = 5$ is not quite sufficient while $r = 6$ is more than sufficient. If $r = 6$, then the expected stockout cost is

$$E(s) = \pi \sum_{u=r+1}^{u_{max.}} (u - r)p(u)$$
$$= 20[0.0078 + 2(0.0018) + 3(0.0002)]$$
$$= \$0.24$$

Recomputing

$$Q = \sqrt{\frac{2(325)(3 + 0.24)}{6}}$$
$$= 19$$

and our policy is determined as $r = 6$, $Q = 19$ since recomputing $P(u > r)$ results in 0.0175 which is not sufficient to change r. It should be noted that this policy reduces the expected frequency of a stockout to about once in 6 years since the order frequency is 17 per year and probability of a stockout on any one order is 0.0098. This implies that a stockout might cost as much as $36, computed as follows:

$$\pi = \frac{6.00(19)}{0.0098(325)}$$
$$= \$36$$

However, if one set $P(u) = 0.00358$ by picking $r = 5$, then

$$E(s) = 20[0.0260 + 2(0.0078) + 3(0.0018) + 4(0.0002)]$$
$$= \$0.96$$

and

$$Q = \sqrt{\frac{2(325)\$3.96}{6.00}}$$
$$= 21$$

leaving the decision about r virtually unchanged. Then, the implied stockout cost per unit is

$$\pi = \frac{6.00(21)}{0.0358(325)}$$
$$= \$11 .$$

Thus, while $20 was sufficient to make the decision $r = 6$, any value in the region $\$11 < \pi < \$36$ would have led us to the same decision. It should further be noted that Q is relatively insensitive to π in that $E(s)$ is small relative to S.

Although we have gone to considerable length to illustrate the computation in terms of basic concepts, it should be clear that the actual decision is quite easy to reach as the interaction between Q and r was very small in this case.

If the criterion selected for inventory policy is not given as some explicit value of π, but is stated in terms of a service level, the same approach may be used. If it is required in this case that stockout frequency be less than once in 10 years, the initial value of $Q = 18$ gives 18 orders per year, or 180 orders in 10 years. Thus $P(u)$ must be less than $\frac{1}{180}$ at the optimal value of r. This gives $r = 7, Q = 18$ as the best policy.

SUMMARY[9]

The theory of incremental analysis has been presented here and combined with elementary probability theory. It is likely that the problems presented here and those like them are currently being solved by most managers by incremental analysis. However, the analysis is usually intuitive and implicit rather than explicit. Writing out the analysis formally should throw additional light on the decision-making process.

---

[9] Before leaving incremental analysis, one further point should be made. The allocation of scarce resources to multiple uses should be in line with their incremental gain, according to economic theory. Search theory from operations research reaffirms this same point. Sometimes the analysis may be explicit, but where circumstances do not permit this, this theory should guide the intuition. Where a resource is allocated to several uses, the return from the last unit allocated to each use, however measured, should be equal. If the marginal unit returns more from one use than another, surely the resource should be taken from the latter and given to the former. Where several resources are allocated, if they are allocated in accord with the above theory, it follows that the ratios to each other of the incremental gains of these resources in their different uses will be equal for all uses. For example, if the incremental gain of resource A in each use is 6, and the incremental gain of B in each use is 5, then the ratio of these returns to each other is 5/6 in all uses. Where the resources may be substituted for each other in the different uses, these ratios of return should also be constant. Finally, even though the returns from the different uses may not be compared, the ratios of incremental gains of the resources in each use should be equal whenever substitution is possible.

Though subjective judgment will still be required in determining the values of some of the separate variables, the deductions from the incremental analysis model may be objective (mathematical). It may be well to point out that a bad model can be worse than no model at all. However, even the attempt to build an incremental model, though unsuccessful, may well help the necessary analysis for decision making.

REFERENCES

1. FETTER, R. B., and DALLECK, W. C. *Decision Models for Inventory Management.* Richard D. Irwin, Inc., 1961.
2. MORONEY, M. J. *Facts from Figures.* Baltimore: Penguin Books, 1953.
3. MUNROE, M. E. *Theory of Probability.* New York: McGraw-Hill Book Co., Inc., 1951.
4. SCHLAIFER, ROBERT. *Introduction to Statistics for Business Decisions.* McGraw-Hill Book Co., Inc., 1961.
5. WHITIN, THOMSON, M. *The Theory of Inventory Management.* Princeton: Princeton University Press, 1953.

PROBLEMS

1. The Rollo Ball Bearing Company believes in maintaining constant employment regardless of work load. At present, the total cost of direct labor and all overhead for the entire company is $200,000 per month, and production is 16,000,000 bearings per month. The manufacturing cost, not including materials of each ball bearing made by the company, is approximately the same

   Normal plant capacity is 20,000,000 bearings per month, and for each million over that, total cost increases by 10 per cent of the previous total in discrete steps. Material costs for a bearing are 0.13 cents.

   a) What is the lowest price for which Rollo will accept an order for an additional 3,000,000 bearings per month?

   b) If bearings sell for 2.1 cents, how many will Rollo produce per month to maximize profits?

2. The Metal Products Company has vacant space in their plant which they are considering leasing. The shortest term lease that they can get a renter to accept is one year. The amount of space the company will need next year is uncertain but can probably be approximated by the following:

   Probability of needing x or more square feet $= e^{-\frac{x}{150,000}}$

   The space will rent for $0.30 a square foot. If Metal Products needs more space than is available, the loss in contribution to profit and overhead per year is $0.80 a square foot. If the vacant space in question is 200,000 square feet, how much should be rented?

3. The Admiral Tire Company plans to carry inventory into their peak sales period, as their sales will exceed their regular time capacity to manufacture

tires. If they do run short of tires during their peak sales period, they can manufacture tires utilizing overtime. To put each 100 tires into storage for the peak sales cost $10. To manufacture 100 tires in overtime costs (in addition to the regular manufacturing cost) $50.

Admiral estimates their probable sales during the peak period, in addition to regular time production capacity, to be represented by the following cumulative probability distribution:

Probability											
of at least	1.000	0.90	0.80	0.70	0.60	0.50	0.40	0.30	0.20	0.10	0.00
	600	800	1,000	1,100	1,200	1,300	1,400	1,600	1,800	2,000	2,200

a) Showing your method, determine the number of tires to store, which in the long run will minimize storage and overtime costs. Determine the expected cost of this optimum solution.

b) If Admiral followed their usual procedure of aiming at the average sales peak (to be determined from the above distribution) in determining inventory, what would be their expected cost?

4. Your purchasing agent has told you that he calculates economic lot sizes according to a standard formula, sets his reorder point according to use during the average delivery time, but still seems to have poor control of inventories as evidenced by excessive "stockouts" on many items. You ask him to prepare a distribution of delivery times for one of the worst offenders, and the following is a tabulation of the results of 100 orders of this item:

Working Days after Ordering	Number of Deliveries	Working Days after Ordering	Number of Deliveries
1	0	9	14
2	0	10	18
3	0	11	18
4	0	12	14
5	0	13	11
6	1	14	6
7	3	15	4
8	8	16	2
		17	1

Other data on this item are as follows:
Unit cost = $1.50.
Annual use = 100,000 (use rate is quite stable).
Interest on investment in inventory = 10% (annual rate).
Deterioration and obsolescence are estimated at 5% annually.
Taxes and insurance = 2% per year.
Storage charges = $0.01 per unit per year (on maximum inventory).
Ordering cost = $10 per order.
The cost of running out of stock is estimated at $100 per day.
The company works 250 days during the year.

Assuming that your objective is to minimize the cost of supplying this item, find:

a) The economic lot size.

b) The reorder point.

c) What minimum stock level do you expect?

5. Find the economic lot size under the following circumstances:

a) Annual consumption = 2,000.

No minimum stock is to be maintained (i.e., stock can go to zero).

Acquisition cost = $5.00.

Annual carrying cost (not including storage) = 10% of value of average inventory.

Annual storage cost = $0.05/piece of average inventory.

Direct cost per piece = $2.00.

b) Where vendor's bill = $2.00/piece plus $15.

c) Where purchase cost = $2.00 piece,

but 5% discount for 50 pieces and over

additional 4% discount for 100 pieces and over

additional 3% discount for 200 pieces and over

additional 2% discount for 400 pieces and over

additional 1% discount for 800 pieces and over

d) Where purchase cost = $2.00 but storage cost = $0.13/piece/year for maximum inventory.

6. Consider the Cleveland Steel Company's problem. It must store iron ore from Minnesota for use during the winter while the lakes are frozen and lake traffic is not possible. The amount of iron ore necessary to supply the winter's needs is uncertain for two reasons: (1) the season of ice is a variable, and (2) the amount of iron ore consumed per unit time is also a variable.

If too much iron ore has been stored during the winter, unnecessary storage costs have been incurred. If too little iron ore has been stored during the winter, it is necessary to bring the needed ore in by train, a substantially more expensive operation than by boat.

Develop an expression for determining the amount of ore to store at the beginning of the winter. Use the following notation for costs:

Transport a ton of ore by ship $= s$

Transport a ton of ore by train $= t$

Hold a ton of ore for the whole winter $= h$

7. A job shop gets a special order for 40 units of a part. The blueprint is supplied with the order, and they do not expect a reorder for the part. The raw material for each part started costs $8.00. The manufacturing operation costs $9.00 per unit to do. The operation costs $65 to set up. The average reject rate in the operation is 10 per cent. The distribution of rejects may be approximated by the Poisson distribution. (This distribution is tabulated on Fig. 6–2 in Chapter 6 on sampling inspection.) If the number of good pieces resulting from the process is less than the number ordered (40), the process must be set up again and run. In the operation the entire

lot is done simultaneously, and a setup is required for each lot. This particular industry has the accepted convention of allowing a 5 per cent overrun to be shipped and billed. That is, the customer must accept a shipment which may range from the number ordered to the number ordered plus 5 per cent of this number. Consider that the customer pays for any overrun at the rate of the variable or out-of-pocket cost.

The problem is to develop the number of pieces to start which maximizes the expected profit on this order.

Solve this problem by an iterative incremental analysis. That is, solve for the incremental cost and the incremental gain or "revenue" at successive sizes of the number to schedule.

8. A greeting card manufacturer is faced by the problem of how many Christmas cards he should stock to meet his demand. The cards are all produced before orders start to arrive. During the time orders for Christmas cards are arriving, the capacity of the plant is completely occupied by other lines. Each card costs 5 cents to produce and is sold for 7 cents in wholesale lots. Cards not sold must be carried in inventory until the next year at an average cost of 1.3 cents per card. Previous experience indicates that any number of sales between 1,000,000 and 2,000,000 is equally likely. How many cards should be manufactured?

9. Assume that in Problem No. 8 the manufacturer can also print up sheets of cards but not cut or fold them. The annual cost of storing a card in sheet form is 0.5 cents. However only 60 per cent of the dealers will wait for the cards to be made up. The rest cancel their orders.

a) How many complete cards should be stocked?

b) How many should be held in sheet form?

Hint: The point at which the expected value of stocking cards is equal to the expected value of stocking sheets is the point after which cards will no longer be stocked. The point after which sheets will no longer be stocked is found as in Problem No. 8.

10. The Jones Company wishes to use some analytical procedure to determine the economic order quantity on 5 h.p. gasoline motors. Each motor costs $100. Storage and capital costs are 16 per cent. Annual usage occurs at a constant rate and totals 3,000 per year. The purchasing department will be writing around 125 orders per month next year, not including 5 h.p. motors. Operating records for the purchasing department are as follows:

Period	Orders Processed	Total Direct and Overhead Costs
1........................	130	$2,229
2........................	5	2,000
3........................	75	1,997
4........................	200	3,000
5........................	97	2,002
6........................	350	3,500

What is the economic order quantity for 5 h.p. motors?

11. In a large machine shop, the demand for grommets is quite steady at 1,000 per day, 250 days per year. The purchasing agent wishes to adopt an ordering policy which will be most economical. Grommets can be purchased in lots of 1,000 for $10.00 per lot, or in lots of 10,000 for $95 per lot. The cost of ordering is $5.00 per order, and the carrying cost for inventory is 20 per cent per year. Storage charges are considered negligible.

a) What is the most economical ordering policy?

b) The demand for grommets is expected to change for the next few years from a constant 1,000/day to 600/day 60 per cent of the days and 1,600/day 40 per cent of the days. The distribution as between these days is at random. What is the average demand? What is the most economical ordering policy based on this average demand?

c) Under the conditions of part (b), if it always takes 3 working days to get delivery (nobody including deliverymen works on week ends), what is the reorder point based on average usage? How many times during the year do you expect to run out of stock? How many times during the year do you expect to run out of stock if the reorder point is increased by 1,000 grommets?

12. A company manufactures metal parts on semiautomatic equipment. The metal blank from which the parts are made may contain a continuously varying amount of silver which may be specified upon purchase of the blank.

The blank cost varies with the silver content. The machining costs appear to be a function of the silver content, and the following averages have been obtained from past records:

Silver Content	Machining Cost	Purchase Cost
25%.	$0.80/unit	$0.55/unit
80.	0.25/unit	1.10/unit
50.	0.40/unit	0.80/unit
10.	2.00/unit	0.40/unit
60.	0.37/unit	0.90/unit
40.	0.50/unit	0.70/unit
68.	0.29/unit	0.98/unit

Through small adjustments of the equipment, almost an infinite variety of sizes and shapes of the metal part can be manufactured. Most orders for the part are special orders. An average of 5,000 parts of this type are made each year.

The rate of rejects produced by the machine (which is independent of the silver content in the blank) may be shown in the following probability table:

% reject rate range	0 − 2	2 − 4	4 − 6	6 − 8	8 − 10	10 − 12	12 →
% probability	30	50	10	5	3	2	0

a) Determine what proportion of silver in the blank to purchase by total value analysis (total cost as a function of silver content, etc.).

b) For an order of 100 parts, how many should be started in the schedule? Solve this by marginal analysis, given:

(1) Set up cost $25, and if enough good pieces are not obtained on first run, then the job has to be set up again.

(2) Extra good pieces are disposed of for scrap value at half the blank purchase price.

13. The following are data on the costs, price, and demand for an item which must be supplied to a manufacturing process. The rate of use is steady from day to day, and it always takes 10 working days to get an order.

> Annual demand = 10,000
> Working days/year = 250
> Order cost = $10 per order
> Carrying charges = 25% per year on average inventory
> Storage charges = $0.02 per unit per year (must be charged on maximum inventory)

Price schedule:

Quantity	Price/Unit
0–99	$1.00
100–999	0.96
1,000–	0.95

a) Determine the reorder point and order quantity which will result in supplying the year's requirements at minimum cost.

b) Consider the above situation with the use rate and delivery time as variable, all other data the same. Investigation has shown that the distribution of use during any delivery time is a normal distribution with a mean of 400 and a standard deviation of 80. Assuming the order quantity calculated in part (a) is correct, what is the reorder point which will reduce the probability of a stockout to 0.02 for any one order? What is the total cost of supplying one year's demand with this reorder point if the cost of a shortage is $100?

14. In scheduling the production of a lot of a given item, the production manager desires to allow for rejects so that the expected cost is a minimum. Currently the process is running at 5 per cent defective and is in control. The schedule calls for 200 good pieces. If 200 are not obtained, rejects can be repaired at a cost of $10 per unit to make up the schedule. The variable cost of production is $4.00 per unit.

a) What is the optimal number to schedule?

b) What is the probability that more than five rejects will have to be repaired?

15. A tabulation of use during lead time for a purchased material gives the following results:

Units Used	Relative Frequency
0	0.05
1	0.10
2	0.20
3	0.25
4	0.15
5	0.10
6	0.07
7	0.05
8	0.02
9	0.01

The item costs $100 per unit in quantities of 1 to 9 and $95 per unit for 10 or more per order. It is estimated that 100 will be used next year. The management has directed that inventory policy must be such that stockouts occur on the average only once in 5 years or more. Other relevant costs are as follows:

Ordering cost = $20 per order placed

Carrying charges = 20% per year (this includes interest on investment, taxes, insurance, depreciation and deterioration)

Storage charges = $5.00 per unit per year (this must be charged on the maximum inventory since space cannot be used for anything else)

a) Determine the least cost order quantity and reorder point to satisfy management's stockout criterion.

b) What stockout cost per unit would cause you to *decrease* the reorder point?

c) Compute the *total* cost of supplying this item for one year using the results of part (a).

CHAPTER 10

Equipment Investment Analysis

ONE kind of problem faced by manufacturing firms which is susceptible to total value analysis is that of making decisions concerning investment in capital equipment. Here, management is spending money in the expectation that it will produce revenue in the future. A sum of money is "sunk" in a machine, for example, and the machine is used up over a period of years in the production of goods from which the firm derives some revenue.

THE EQUIPMENT INVESTMENT PROBLEM

The economic problem faced by any firm in making decisions as to investment in production equipment is often one of maximizing the return on such investment. This return arises from the use of the equipment in the production of goods. The sale of these goods (where the customer may be the next step in the production process) gives rise to a stream of revenue over time. Associated in time with this stream of revenue is a corresponding stream of operating and maintenance expenses necessary to the production of these goods. The difference between these streams represents the return on investment before deducting capital costs.[1]

If a firm wishes to maximize the return on its total investment, the problem is not simply one of maximization of return on a machine by machine basis, but such maximization for the group of machines which constitutes the production unit.

---

[1] Alfred Marshall in his *Principles of Economics,* 1890, called this difference the quasi-rent of equipment. Revenues are calculated before depreciation is deducted, i.e., expenses do not include depreciation and interest on investment. Therefore, the difference is the net cash inflow resulting from the investment.

381

A decision model for replacement of equipment should portray the basic economic problem in such terms that the parameters may be evaluated with generally available business data. At the very least, it must be economically feasible to secure the required data. Also, the model should be capable of modification to fit the requirements of as wide a range of situations as possible. The model should portray, symbolically, the economic problem involved in selecting the best course of action given some alternatives regarding the acquisition of production equipment. The model should first aim at economic soundness, and then be modified in order to

1. Allow for the use of data which it is economically feasible to secure, and
2. Be reasonably easy to use by those who have the responsibility for making such decisions.

This second condition does not mean that necessary economic soundness should be sacrificed merely for computational ease. Rather, it must be recognized that modern business machines can make relatively short work of what might formerly have been considered insurmountable computational difficulties. The basic criterion for the model should be that of both economic soundness and of understanding on the part of those who must use such decision models.

A MODEL FOR PROFIT MAXIMIZATION

In constructing an economic model for the comparison of investment alternatives facing any firm, a distinction must be made between the two general kinds of equipment which firms use, i.e., "diminishing efficiency" and "constant efficiency" types. The concern here is with equipment of the "diminishing efficiency" type, that is, durable goods whose lifetime can be extended almost indefinitely if their various parts are replaced or repaired as necessary. These kinds of equipment tend to decline in productivity and/or increase in maintenance cost as they are used over time. The other major type of capital goods is the "constant efficiency" type. These are goods which produce some output at a constant level until their productive life suddenly comes to an end, as, for example, an electric light bulb. The economic problem connected with replacement decisions about this latter type of durable good is quite different from that for the "diminishing efficiency" type. With constant efficiency, the probability distribution for length of life of an item (e.g., an electric light bulb) may be determined from life tests and investment action taken based on this expectation. Various alternative courses of action may be evaluated using such a distribution, but there is no cost of declining efficiency to reckon with, and any problem can usually be reduced to a comparison of expected values, incremental or total.

If a piece of production equipment earns revenue according to some function $R(t)$, and in doing so incurs operating and maintenance expenses according to some function $E(t)$ (this includes all expenses except depreciation and interest on investment), then the value of the investment to the firm may be given by[2]

$$V = \int_0^T [R(t) - E(t)]e^{-it}dt + S(T)e^{-iT} - B, \qquad (1)$$

where

$V =$ present value of the investment,
$B =$ installed cost of equipment,
$T =$ life of the equipment,
$S(T) =$ salvage value at T,
$e =$ 2.71828 (the base of natural logarithms),
$i =$ annual rate of interest.

The Discounting Process

Multiplication of a function by e^{-it}, where i is some annual rate of interest, "instantaneously" discounts the dollars given by the function to their present worth. Thus, if some function $Q(t)$ expresses the way in which an investment would earn money in the future, and if both the function and the interest rate are in equivalent terms (usually given in annual rates), then each bit of earnings is discounted *at the time it is earned* to a present worth. The usual bank method, which is discrete rather than continuous, is to accumulate the money which would be earned or paid over a period and discount for the entire period. This may be done by $Q_t/(1+i)^t$, where Q_t is the earnings for the period represented by t. This is the opposite case to that of a sum of money earning compound interest. Dividing by $(1+i)^t$ yields a figure which if it were to grow at the compound interest rate would just equal the value being discounted. If the discount period is made small and earnings expressed as annual rates, then the limit is

$$\sum_{t=1}^{T} \frac{Q_t}{(1+i)^t} \longrightarrow \int_0^T Q(t)e^{-it}dt,$$

---

[2] G. A. D. Preinreich, "The Economic Life of Industrial Equipment," *Econometrica* 1940.

where

Q_t = annual earnings,
$Q(t)$ = annual rate of earnings,
i = annual rate of interest,
T = period over which it is desired to measure earnings.

Both sides of this equation represent the present worth of a stream of earnings. The primary reason for using the continuous form is the great convenience afforded by the integral equation. Furthermore, income and expense streams are continuous, not discrete. Of course, the period used could be any which was appropriate, although annual rates are the most widely used and readily understood.

Thus, equation (1) gives the present value of a piece of equipment as the sum over its useful life $(0,T)$ of the discounted difference between revenues and expenses plus the discounted value of the machine at T, less its first cost. The economic life, T, may be determined by setting the first derivative of (1) with respect to T equal to 0, which gives[3]

$$\frac{dV}{dT} = [R(T) - E(T)]e^{-iT} - iS(T)e^{-iT} + S'(T)e^{-iT} = 0 \,,$$

from which

$$R(T) - E(T) = iS(T) - S'(T) \,. \tag{2}$$

Conceptually, equation (2) may then be solved for T. This T would be substituted in (1), and the appropriate value of V determined.

The present worth of the capital value in excess of the installed cost of the piece of equipment represents return on investment in addition to that specified by the given rate of interest. An entrepreneur would continue to invest in equipment until the present worth of the difference between revenues and expenses was just equal to the cost of the investment, i.e., until $V = 0$, assuming that the given interest rate was the minimum rate acceptable to the firm. In comparing available mutually exclusive alternatives, an entrepreneur would select that alternative which yielded the greatest present worth of return on investment (V). This assumes that capital is available in the amount re-

---

[3] Differentiation of a function with respect to a parameter where this parameter is in the limits may be found in Hildebrand, *Advanced Calculus for Engineers* (New York: Prentice-Hall, Inc., 1948), p. 352. See footnote 13, Chapter 8. The sign of the derivative of $S(T)$ is negative, but since $S(T)$ declines over time, the derivative itself will be negative and a positive expense results.

quired at the interest rate used. This does not mean that one should necessarily use the same interest rate for all investments which are to be compared, unless the amount of each investment is the same or the amounts are such, relative to the firm's total available capital, that the interest rate is not affected by the decision. Thus, if investments of $1,000,000 and $1,000 are being compared and the cost of money is different for these amounts (as would usually be the case), then the interest rate must be adjusted for this difference or else the V's which result are not directly comparable.

With little loss in accuracy, the continuous expression of equation (1) may be converted to a discrete equation as

$$V = \sum_{t=1}^{T} \frac{R_t - E_t}{(1+i)^t} + \frac{S(T)}{(1+i)^T} - B,$$ (3)

where $R_t =$ revenue for a given period (usually taken as one year), and $E_t =$ operating and maintenance expenses incurred during the corresponding revenue period. Equation (3) is amenable to maximization by a tabular solution. In either case, the condition of equation (2) is repeated.

To illustrate, assume the following information for a given machine:

B = $5,000
$R(t)$ = $3,000 (1 − 0.01t), where $3,000 is the beginning annual rate of revenue
$E(t)$ = $1,000 (1 + 0.14t), where $1,000 is the beginning annual rate of expenses
i = 0.10

An estimated schedule for end-of-year salvage values is as follows:

T	1	2	3	4	5	6	7	8	9	10	11
$S(T)$	3,500	2,800	2,400	2,000	1,600	1,300	1,000	800	600	500	500

(These data may be approximated by $S(T) = 5,000e^{-\frac{T}{4}}$).

The linear form for $R(t)$ and $E(t)$ is assumed for simplicity of presentation. However, many real situations may be approximated by linear forms. Substituting in equation (2), trial and error yields $T = 10.88$.

Substituting in equation (1) and evaluating the integral,

$$V = \int_0^{10.88} [3{,}000 - 30t - 1{,}000 - 140t]e^{-0.10t}dt + 500e^{-0.1(10.88)} - 5{,}000$$

$$= \int_0^{10.88} (2{,}000 - 170t)e^{-0.10t}dt + 500e^{-1.088} - 5{,}000$$

$$= \$3{,}378 \ .$$

A tabular solution using average annual values for revenues and expenses yields a maximum V at $T = 11$. If a decision were to be made among several alternatives, the one yielding the greatest V would be chosen, assuming the interest rate reflected the cost of the capital represented by each B.

A Chain of Machines

The model of equation (1) assumes that the firm uses a machine for some kind of production until the end of its life, T, and then sells it for $S(T)$, and never again engages in production of this kind. The more usual situation is that the firm intends to continue the given kind of production over an indefinite future period and will consider the acquisition of a chain of equipment to do this. When the chain is infinite, the capitalized value of all future income will be constant and the lifetimes of the machines in the chain will be the same. In this case[4]

$$V = \left[\int_0^T [R(t) - E(t)]e^{-it}dt - B + S(T)e^{-iT} \right] (1 + e^{-iT} + e^{-2iT} + \ldots)$$

$$= \left[\int_0^T [R(t) - E(t)]e^{-it}dt - B + S(T)e^{-iT} \right] \frac{1}{1 - e^{-iT}} \qquad (4)$$

---

[4] The sum of n terms of a geometric progression in which the nth term is ar^{n-1} is

$$\sum_n ar^{n-1} = a\left(\frac{r^n - 1}{r - 1} \right) \ .$$

Thus when $|r| < 1$

$$\sum_n^\infty ar^{n-1} = \frac{a}{1 - r} \ .$$

The first derivative of V with respect to T when equated to zero yields the condition

$$[R(T) - E(T)] = iS(T) - S'(T) +$$

(5)

$$\frac{i}{1 - e^{-iT}} \left[\int_0^T [R(t) - E(t)]e^{-it}dt - B + S(T)e^{-iT} \right]$$

Equation (5) indicates that each machine in the chain will be kept until that time when the earnings of the machine (the left-hand side) just cover interest on its salvage value plus decline in salvage value plus interest on the present worth of all future earnings of machines in the chain. With knowledge of revenue and expense functions and the appropriate rate of interest, T may be determined from (5), and the optimum replacement time determined.

Equation (4) may be expressed in discrete form as

$$V = \left[\sum_{t=1}^{T} \frac{R_t - E_t}{(1 + i)^t} - B + \frac{S(T)}{(1 + i)^T} \right] \left[1 + \frac{1}{(1 + i)^T} + \frac{1}{(1 + i)^{2T}} + \cdots \right]$$

$$= \left[\sum_{t=1}^{T} \frac{R_t - E_t}{(1 + i)^t} - B + \frac{S(T)}{(1 + i)^T} \right] \frac{(1 + i)^T}{(1 + i)^T - 1}$$

(6)

for which the decision criterion is the same as before. That is, the equipment should be kept until that period when it just earns enough to cover interest on the salvage value plus decline in salvage value plus interest on the capitalized value of all future return of revenue less expenses. Various alternatives for a given investment may be compared by determining the present worth of their capital values in excess of equipment cost from either (4) or (6) and selecting that alternative which yields the largest return.

Assuming the same data as in the previous example, the condition of equation (5) yields $T = 5.71$.[5] Substituting this value in (4) gives

$$V = \left[\int_0^{5.71} [(3,000 - 30t) - (1,000 + 140t)]e^{-0.10t}dt + \right.$$

$$\left. 500e^{-0.571} - 5,000 \right] \frac{1}{1 - e^{-0.571}} = \$5,950 ,$$

---

[5] The lower value for T when a *chain* is contemplated as compared to a single machine results from the fact that a newer and "better" machine is always waiting to displace the current machine. As each machine "ages," the next machine in the chain seeks to displace it, and does so under the condition of equation (5).

as the maximum present value of the return expected from the use of this machine when it is replaced approximately every 6 years. This is equivalent to saying that for this kind of a replacement cycle such a series of investments would (1) pay for themselves, (2) earn a 10 per cent return, and (3) yield a cash income whose present worth is $5,950. The total rate of return may be determined by setting $V = 0$ in the above equation and solving for i (an exceedingly difficult computation by hand but not too difficult using a set of interest tables).

A tabular solution using average annual values for revenues and expenses in equation (6) is shown in Table 10–1. This table reveals a 6-year replacement cycle as optimum, but also shows a relatively flat value curve stretching from 4 to 8 years.

Difficulties with a Profit Maximization Model

The decision models which make use of a basic present worth formula such as those just presented require that the following be known:

1. A revenue function and
2. A corresponding expense function (or a profit function in place of 1 and 2)
3. The salvage value for all conditions of age
4. The proper rate of interest

The revenue function may be ascertainable for a firm which uses only a single piece of equipment in its production process. Here, all sales revenue may be attributed to the single machine. However, if the firm's production process consists of a series of operations, each requiring a different piece of equipment, then, in order to use capitalization models, the sales revenue must be distributed back to each piece of equipment. The problem of distributing such joint revenue in order to determine that portion due to each piece of equipment is one which has perplexed economists and accountants for a long time.[6] Before general use can be made of this kind of model, ways will have to be found to determine revenue functions for machines. Actually, the marginal revenue and marginal cost curves for various production rates would be satisfactory, since the difference between these at the appropriate production rates over time is the cash income of the machine. Although total revenue and total cost functions would necessarily yield the same difference, the determination of these functions for a single machine in a process consisting of a sequence of different

---

[6] F. and V. Lutz, *The Theory of Investment of the Firm* (Princeton, N.J.: Princeton University Press, 1951).

Table 10–1

TABULAR SOLUTION OF EQUIPMENT INVESTMENT PROBLEM

	1	2	3	4	5	6	7	8	9	10	11
T	R_t	E_t	$R_t - E_t$	$\dfrac{1}{(1+i)^t}$	$\dfrac{R_t - E_t}{(1+i)^t}$	$\displaystyle\sum_{t=1}^{T}$	$-B$	$\dfrac{S(T)}{(1+i)^T}$	$6+7+8$	$\dfrac{(1+i)^T}{(1+i)^T - 1}$	V 9×10
1	$2,985	$1,070	$1,915	0.9091	$1,740	$1,740	$5,000	$3,180	$ -80	11.00	$ -880
2	2,955	1,210	1,745	0.8264	1,440	3,180	5,000	2,315	495	5.762	2,860
3	2,925	1,350	1,575	0.7513	1,182	4,362	5,000	1,803	1,165	4.021	4,685
4	2,895	1,490	1,405	0.6830	960	5,322	5,000	1,366	1,688	3.155	5,320
5	2,865	1,630	1,235	0.6209	755	6,077	5,000	995	2,072	2.638	5,451
6	2,835	1,770	1,065	0.5645	600	6,677	5,000	734	2,411	2.296	5,540
7	2,805	1,910	895	0.5132	459	7,136	5,000	513	2,649	2.054	5,449
8	2,775	2,050	725	0.4665	338	7,474	5,000	373	2,847	1.874	5,348

machines is a difficult problem, and such data are not usually available in a firm.

The expense function is, in most cases, much easier to determine than the revenue function. The operating and maintenance costs of a piece of equipment in current use are often available from accounting records. There are, of course, many difficulties connected with the allocation of various fixed and semivariable expenses to the production of a single machine. However, the problem of estimating an appropriate expense function is not nearly so difficult as that of estimating revenue. It must be remembered that the expense function includes *all* expenses associated with the given kind of production, except depreciation and interest on investment. Expense estimates for equipment whose purchase is being contemplated are, of course, more uncertain than estimates for equipment currently in use. Information must usually be secured from the equipment manufacturer and/or firms which have had experience using that kind of equipment.

Determining expected salvage values for various periods of use of a piece of equipment is a problem in prediction which is certainly hazardous. However, some knowledge of the market for used equipment of the type in question can often provide clues to these figures. Furthermore in many cases, the timing of the decision is not very sensitive to errors in the magnitude of this figure, as can be demonstrated by computing results over a range of functional forms for $S(T)$.

The selection of an appropriate rate of interest for use in any investment decision model presents problems which neither businessmen nor economists have yet completely resolved. Various concepts have been presented which aim at making this determination, but no satisfactory theory exists. It is possible, of course, in an equation such as (1), to set the present worth of capital value V equal to zero, and solve the equation for i. The rate of interest determined in this manner has been called the "internal rate of return" by Kenneth Boulding.[7] The models for an infinite chain of replacements may be solved for this rate, and selection made of those alternatives which yield the highest rates. Such a procedure does not answer the question as to what constitutes an optimum total investment for a given firm, but only allows the selection of the most profitable investments up to some capital limit determined by other criteria. If i represents the minimum rate of return for a firm, all investments yielding a positive V would be chosen.

---

[7] Kenneth Boulding, "The Theory of a Single Investment," *Quarterly Journal of Economics,* May, 1935.

In comparing a given set of alternatives, a firm may use an interest rate, determined by that rate which the next best alternative investment would earn. This is often approximated in practice by assuming that each investment must earn at least that return which is earned on capital invested in the business as a whole. Some firms use so-called industry rates of return which have been developed through experience. None of these procedures take account of the differing risks of the alternatives; for example, the replacement of a general-purpose machine with a special-purpose machine. (A good recommendation to determine i in practice is to begin with the general rate earned by the capital already invested in the firm and adjust this upward for differing degrees of risk and expected obsolescence for each alternative.)

A COST MINIMIZATION MODEL

In view of the difficulties just described, it is necessary to make some modifications in the basic model in order to cover the majority of situations actually encountered. Since the objective is one of comparing alternatives, if the revenue which the various alternatives are to produce over time is the same, then it may be assumed a constant in the comparison, and the problem turned into one of cost minimization. If there are significant differences in revenue production for the alternatives, and these *differences* can be estimated, they may be treated as additions to, or subtractions from, expenses and included in the expense function. Under these special conditions, the cost is given by

$$C = [B - S(T)e^{-iT}] + \int_0^T E(t)e^{-it}dt \qquad (7)$$

for a firm whose future is limited to the acquisition and use of a single machine. If, as is usual, a chain of replacements is contemplated and equation (7) is repeated to infinity by multiplication by the series

$$(1 + e^{-iT} + e^{-2iT} + \ldots) = \frac{1}{1 - e^{-iT}}, \qquad (8)$$

the cost is

$$C = \left[(B - S(T)e^{-iT}) + \int_0^T E(t)e^{-it}dt\right]\frac{1}{1 - e^{-iT}}, \qquad (9)$$

and the condition for a minimum is

$$E(T) + iS(T) - S'(T) = \frac{i}{1 - e^{-iT}} \left[(B - S(T)e^{-iT}) + \int_0^T E(t)e^{-it}dt \right]. \quad (10)$$

That is, a machine should be replaced in that period when its expenses plus interest on its salvage value plus decline in salvage value just equal interest on the present worth of all future costs. Given the expense function $E(t)$, equation (10) may be solved for T and the minimum cost of the investment found from (9). The minima for the various alternatives may then be compared, and that one selected which yields the least cost for the given use.

Equation (9) may also be expressed in discrete form for use with periodic data. The sum of capital costs and expenses is

$$C = \left[B - \frac{S(T)}{(1 + i)^T} + \sum_{t=1}^{T} \frac{E_t}{(1 + i)^t} \right] \frac{(1 + i)^T}{(1 + i)^T - 1} \quad (11)$$

and the condition for a minimum is the same as that stated previously. Replacement in kind will occur in that period during which expenses plus interest on salvage value plus decline in salvage value just equal interest on the present worth of all future expenses. In terms of incremental analysis, the left-hand side of equation (10) represents the additional cost of keeping the equipment for an additional period and the right-hand side represents the incremental gain. Equation (11) may be solved without too much difficulty by use of a bond table wherein will be found enumeration of the interest formulas contained in (11) for various i and T. Since the solution of the first difference of (11) with respect to T must be by trial and error, it is often simpler to understand and more informative to prepare a tabular solution of (11) in order to determine the optimum life. When alternatives are to be compared, the minimum costs for each should be determined and that one selected which yields the least cost.

Using the same data as in the previous example, the expense function must be modified to account for the given revenue loss over time. This may be done by postulating $E(t) = 1,000(1 + 0.17t)$, where $1,000 is the yearly expense rate when the machine is new. Equation (10) may then be solved for the optimum replacement period giving $T = 5.71$ years, which is the same as with equation (5). This result should be expected since the rate of change of expenses is the same as the rate of change in the cash income in the previous example. Substituting in (9) gives[8]

$$C = \left[\frac{5,000 - 1,385e^{-0.10(5.71)} + \int_0^{5.71} (1,000 + 170t)e^{-0.10\,t}dt}{1 - e^{-0.10(5.71)}} \right]$$

$$= \$24,090 \,,$$

which is the present worth of the cost of using this machine, according to a 5.71-year replacement cycle. Using the same data on an annual cost basis, equation (11) yields Table 10–2. It should be noted that the E_t's are average values since they must represent expenses for the entire period rather than annual rates at any given point in time as in the continuous expression. This solution gives a 6-year replacement cycle, but again the result shows a rather large area of indifference, beginning at about the fourth year.

The total costs obtained in this way may be compared for the alternative equipment choices and that equipment with the least cost chosen. It may be more appropriate to convert this cost figure to a uniform annual equivalent which may be done by multiplication with the rate of interest. In this case, the average annual cost would be $2,441. This operation takes the present worth of all future costs and spreads them back into the future as an annuity.

The expense functions contained in equations (9) and (11) are not the same as those in (4) and (6). In the cost minimization model, this function is capable of several definitions, depending on the circumstances of the situation. It must first be pointed out that costs which are the same with respect to the use of the equipment in question would play no part in the minimization process. However, all costs

---

[8] The solution of the integral for $E(t) = E + Gt$, where G is the annual rate of change in expenses is

$$\int_0^T E(t)e^{-it}dt = \int_0^T (E + Gt)e^{-it}dt$$

$$= E\int_0^T e^{-it}dt + G\int_0^T te^{-it}dt$$

$$= E\left[-\frac{1}{i}e^{-it} \right]_0^T + G\left[\frac{e^{-it}}{i^2}(-it - 1) \right]_0^T$$

$$= E\left[-\frac{1}{i}e - it - E\left(-\frac{1}{i}\right) \right] + G\left[\frac{e^{-it}}{i^2}(-iT - 1) + \frac{1}{i^2} \right]$$

$$= E\left[\frac{1 - e^{-iT}}{i} \right] + G\left[\frac{1 - e^{-iT} - iTe^{-iT}}{i^2} \right]$$

Table 10–2
TABULAR SOLUTION FOR COST OF EQUIPMENT

T	1 E_t	2 $\dfrac{1}{(1+i)^t}$	3 $\dfrac{E_t}{(1+i)^t}$	4 $\sum\limits_{t=1}^{T}$	5 B	6 $\dfrac{S(T)}{(1+i)^T}$	7 $(5)-(6)+(4)$	8 $\dfrac{(1+i)^T}{(1+i)^T-1}$	9 C 8×7
1	$1,085	0.9091	$ 987	$ 987	$5,000	$3,180	$2,807	11.00	$30,877
2	1,255	0.8264	1,038	2,025	5,000	2,315	4,710	5.762	27,180
3	1,425	0.7513	1,070	3,095	5,000	1,803	6,292	4.021	25,250
4	1,595	0.6830	1,089	4,184	5,000	1,366	7,518	3.155	24,650
5	1,765	0.6209	1,096	5,280	5,000	995	9,205	2.638	24,450
6	1,935	0.5645	1,091	6,371	5,000	734	10,637	2.296	24,410
7	2,105	0.5132	1,081	7,452	5,000	513	11,939	2.054	24,530
8	2,275	0.4665	1,053	8,505	5,000	373	13,132	1.874	24,600
9	2,445	0.4241	1,038	9,543	5,000	254	14,289	1.736	24,790
10	2,615	0.3855	1,009	10,552	5,000	193	15,359	1.628	25,000

which are different for each alternative must be included in order to allow comparison of the various minima.

If some gain in revenue is achieved by the use of any of the alternatives (e.g., increased quality or quantity of output), this should be accounted for in the expense function. Increased quantity of output may be considered as a cost saving only if it is contemplated that such output can be sold. Then, either the present equipment's costs may be modified upward as necessary to secure such increased output or the *additional* income due to the higher output deducted from the alternative's expenses. The basic requirement is that the expense functions reflect accurately those costs which are different for the alternatives.

When major overhauls which constitute capital additions occur or are contemplated during the life of the equipment, the basic cost expressions may be modified by the addition of a term to account for this. Equation (11), for example, would read:

$$C = \left[B - \frac{S(T)}{(1+i)^T} + \sum_{t=1}^{T} \frac{E_t}{(1+i)^t} + \frac{M_{T}'}{(1+i)^{T'}} \right] \frac{(1+i)^T}{(1+i)^T - 1} \quad (12)$$

where M_{T}' is the overhaul cost at time T'. If a series of overhaul costs is contemplated, each at some definite period (such as every third year), then the sum of such terms (appropriately discounted) would be inserted in the expression. In any case, such costs must be accounted for in the same manner as the other capital and operating expenses.

The Average Annual Cost of Equipment

From the standpoint of business practice, there is one interesting variation in computation made possible by the form of equations (9) and (11). The cost which is determined in these expressions is the present value of the sum of all future costs associated with the acquisition of an infinite chain of machines of like kind (if some definite length of time may be assigned to the duration of the firm's intention to continue in the kind of production in question, then the series in equations (4), (6), (9), and (11) may be stopped at the appropriate term). If it is desired to express the results in terms of an average annual cost (or an average cost for the period used in the equation if other than one year), it is only necessary to multiply (4), (6), (9), or (11) by the rate of interest. If uniform annual equivalents are more meaningful in a given situation, this modification may be easily made. Multiplication by the rate of interest, of course, has no effect on the minimization process.

Comparison with Some Present Methods

It is interesting to compare the model of equations (9) and (11) with some presently used methods for equipment replacement analysis. Equation (9) may be readily converted to the so-called $MAPI$[9] approach[10] by setting $E(t) = gt$ and multiplying the entire expression by i. The definition given to g is that it is the annual rate (linear) at which a machine is accumulating "operating inferiority" relative to its next best alternative. This gradient, therefore, represents the opportunity cost of keeping the present machine as against what could be obtained if a new one were purchased. If, for example, a machine's operating and maintenance expenses come to $3,000 in a given year, while those of a new machine to do the same job (the next best alternative for the given purpose) are $2,400 and the machine currently in use is 5 years old, g is equal to $\dfrac{3,000 - 2,400}{5} = \$120$. This $120 is the rate at which the present equipment has accumulated operating inferiority relative to its next best alternative, and this rate is assumed to continue in the future.

The rationale for this linear assumption seems to rest primarily on the premise that nothing better can be suggested by any available evidence. Further, within this framework, revenue differences between present and next best may be accounted for. If the piece of equipment presently in use has as its next best alternative a new model capable of higher production, and it is assumed that this production will be used, then g may be modified to include this. With the same costs as given above, but increased revenues of $250 over the presently used model, g becomes $\dfrac{3,000 - 2,400 + 250}{5} = \$170$ per year. This corresponds to the example given for equation (9), and the minimum cost life is 5.71 years. The average annual minimum cost would be $24,090 \times 0.10 - \$1,000 = \$1,409$. This solution is equivalent to the one obtained previously where the starting point for the gradient increase is 0 rather than $1,000. Various minima computed in this way may be compared, and the lowest of these selected. The chain thus selected is assumed to continue indefinitely by purchase of the indicated next best alternative every T years until a comparative analysis reveals that a change to a new chain would result in lower costs.

---

[9] Machinery and Allied Products Institute.

[10] G. Terborgh, *Dynamic Equipment Policy* (New York: McGraw-Hill Book Co., Inc., 1949).

The method of "engineering economics" as given by various authors[11] is analogous to the basic model as given in equation (11), where expenses per year are those which are different, as between the various alternatives, and where some T is assumed as appropriate to the given situation. The usual stipulation placed on the selection of T is that the capital invested

$$B - \frac{S(T)}{(1 + i)^T}$$

should be recovered by savings in expenses in this period, and in addition, earn a return i. Having set up such a criterion, the annual costs for each alternative may be computed and compared. In this computation, one must be careful to see that each alternative to be compared has the same production potential or else the comparison is not valid. That is, a machine which can turn out 100 pieces per day should not be compared with one capable of 150 pieces per day, unless appropriate adjustments in expenses are made.

The engineering economy method often involves the selection of some T which is assumed to be the service life based on experience with equipment of the same kind as that under consideration. Where this is the case, the assumption is made that the expenses which are explicitly considered, plus the decline in salvage value, are not sufficient to prevent the equipment from becoming uneconomic in this use by the end of the stated period.

If, in the previous example, a 3-year payoff requirement had been imposed on the investment, the average annual cost (present worth) can be found in Table 10–2 by multiplying the figure found opposite $T = 3$ under C by the rate of interest, in this case, 0.10. The result gives a cost of $2,525 per year, which figure may be compared with other average annual costs similarly computed for alternatives which have the same production capacity. The payoff criterion cannot produce equipment decisions for which costs (in the sense given previously) are a minimum unless the correct T is assumed (a purely fortuitous event). However, it is often used as a device which forces conservatism in the use of a firm's stock of capital. It might be better if a rate of interest in keeping with the investment risk were assigned for each computation and the minimum cost computed as shown in the example.

---

[11] E. L. Grant, *Principles of Engineering Economy* (New York: Ronald Press Co., 1938). P. T. Norton, *The Selection and Replacement of Manufacturing Equipment*, Bulletin No. 32 (Blacksburg, Va.: Virginia Polytechnic Institute, 1934). H. G. Thuesen, and W. J. Fabrycky, *Engineering Economy*, 3d ed. (New York: Prentice-Hall, Inc., 1964).

A widely used method for evaluating specific investment proposals is to calculate the payoff period. This is defined as the ratio of the cost of the investment to its annual earnings before deducting depreciation. That is,

$$P = \frac{B}{R_t - E_t},$$ (13)

where P is the period required to "pay off" the investment. If the salvage value is likely to be significant, the numerator of (13) should be $B - S(T)e^{-iT}$ (although often in practice the salvage value is not discounted or is assumed zero, regardless of its possible magnitude). Also, the denominator of (13) would have to be average figures for revenues and expenses, unless these were assumed constant from year to year. If any discounting at all is done in (13), solution would be by trial and error. A basic shortcoming of this method is that it ignores the useful life of the equipment. The simple payoff period (13) is an estimate of the rate of return reciprocal of the investment as has been shown recently.[12] It is, however, a satisfactory estimate only when the life of the equipment is considerably longer than the payoff period.

Model Sensitivity

In order to explore the sensitivity of the model to some general functional forms and parameter values, computer models can be very useful. Carrying out the computations of (9) and (10) via digital or analog computer is a fairly simple process. The results of a study using an analog device are reproduced here.[13] In this study $E(t)$ was set equal to $E + Gt$ and $S(T) = Be^{-kT}$. Then the parameters $i, k,$ and G were varied systematically over a wide range in order to obtain a set of solutions for equation (10). The values used for i were 0.10, 0.20, 0.30, and 0.50. The values used for k were 0.250, 0.091, and 0.033, giving the following salvage functions:

$$S(T) = Be^{-0.250T}, \qquad S(T) = Be^{-0.091T}, \qquad S(T) = Be^{-0.033T}.$$

These salvage functions are plotted in Figure 10–1. During the actual operation of the analog, for each combination of i and $S(T)$, G (expressed as a proportion of B) was varied from that value giving a mini-

[12] Myron J. Gordon, "The Payoff Period and the Rate of Profit," *The Journal of Business,* January, 1955, pp. 253–60.

[13] Robert B. Fetter and Thomas P. Goodman, "An Equipment Investment Analog," *Operations Research,* Vol. V, No. 5 (October, 1957), pp. 657–69.

mum cost at 1 year to that value giving a minimum beyond 15 years. Since the effect of varying any parameter could be determined in 15 seconds (the time required for the analog to plot a solution representing 15 years), it was possible to choose the ranges of the parameters during the course of obtaining solutions. In cases where the minimum occurred at more than 15 years, this time appeared sufficient (as judged by eye

Figure 10–1

SALVAGE FUNCTIONS USED IN ANALOG COMPUTER STUDY

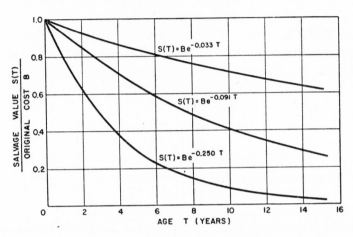

from the ink trace) for costs to have approached to within 2 per cent of their minimum value. Cost curves with a minimum at or beyond 15 years were uniformly flat, indicating a large area of indifference as to minimum cost life in these cases.

Tabulation of Results

The plots of Figure 10–2 were taken directly from the solution curves and show expense gradient G as a fraction of original cost B against the time T in years for which the cost C is a minimum. While it can be seen that the minimum cost life becomes more and more sensitive to changes in expense gradient as this gradient decreases, it is also true that the cost curves become flat very rapidly as the expense gradient approaches zero. As the interest rate increases, the curves become more steep, i.e., the minimum cost life becomes less sensitive to changes in expenses. The minimum cost life for any set of conditions within the limits considered may be determined from these curves.

The plots of Figure 10–3 enable the determination of the actual minimum cost in dollars for the minimum points given by Figure 10–2.

Solution in dollars for a given set of conditions would proceed as follows:

1. Given $B = \$5,000$, $S(T) = Be^{-0.25T}$, $E(T) = \$1,000 \,(1 + 0.20 \,t)$, $i = 0.20$.
2. From this, $G = \$200$ which is $0.04B$. Entering Figure 10–2b, we get $T = 7$ years; and from Figure 10–3b, $C - E/i = +1.78B$.
3. Then $C = \$1,000/0.20 \times 1.78 \,(\$5,000) = \$13,900$.
4. If the average annual cost is desired, multiplication by i gives $AAC = \$13,900 \,(0.20) = \$2,780$.

Figure 10–2

ANALOG COMPUTER RESULTS: MINIMUM COST LIFE

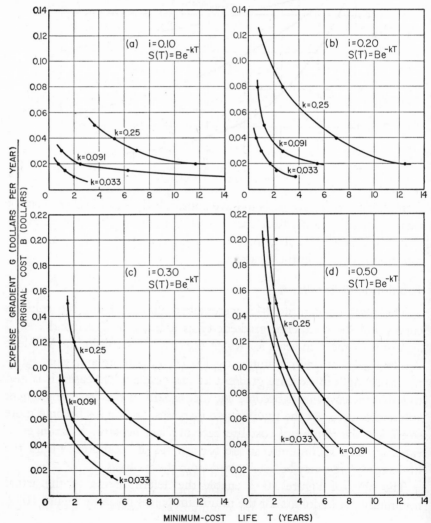

Figure 10–3

ANALOG COMPUTER RESULTS: MINIMUM COST

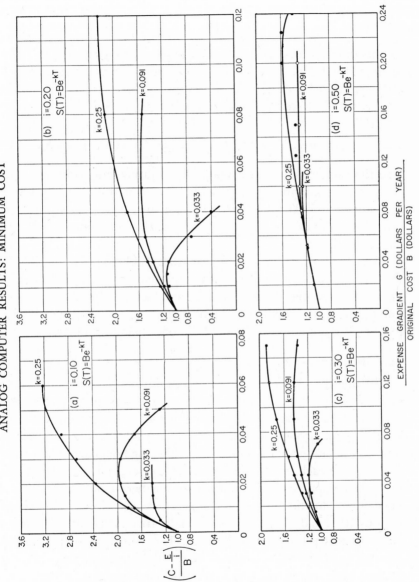

If a solution according to the MAPI method is desired, this may be accomplished in the same manner with $E = 0$ and $G = g$, the "operating inferiority" gradient. Using the costs given for the previous MAPI example, but with increased revenues of $250 over the presently used model, g becomes $[(\$3,000 - \$2,400 + \$250]/5 = \$170$ per year. If the installed cost B is $5,000 and the salvage function $S(T)$ is assumed to be $Be^{-0.25T}$, then the operating inferiority gradient g is $0.034B$. From Figure 10–2a (assuming $i = 0.10$), the optimum life is approximately 6 years. From Figure 10–3a, $C - E/i$ is found to be $3.97B$. Thus

$$C = E/i + 3.97B = 0/0.10 + 3.97 \ (\$5,000) = \$19,850.$$

The time-adjusted annual average of operating inferiority and capital cost (adverse minimum) may be obtained by multiplying this result by i, giving $1,985. This result may be compared with adverse minima for other alternatives and selection made of that equipment yielding the least annual cost.

Two results of importance appear from this kind of calculation. First, for a given kind of equipment, the replacement cycle which results in minimum cost may be ascertained; and, second, by a comparison of minimum costs for various equipment chains, decisions may be made as to when it is economical to move from one chain to another.

Sensitivity Analysis

The ranges of values of the parameters that were considered here are sufficient to give considerable insight into the sensitivity of replacement decisions to both changes and errors of estimate with respect to these. While the major value of such a technique as this would certainly come from its operation within a firm in establishing boundary values that are important in each specific decision, some general guides may be gained from the computations tabulated here. Further, it has been found that good approximations for many real situations can be obtained from Figures 10–2 and 10–3. This is especially true where the MAPI formulation of this problem is to be used. The sensitivity of the model to changes in parameter values may be readily discerned from these plots.

Expense Gradient. There must be some increase in the expenses over time associated with some given revenue production, or else it would never be economical to replace a machine. This increase in expenses can come about from a lessened productive capacity, poorer quality of output, increased maintenance costs, or some combination of the above. When the gradient (measured as a fraction of original cost per year) is small, the minimum cost life is very sensitive to minor changes. For example, an increase from $0.01B$ to $0.02B$ reduces minimum cost life from 14 years to 2.5 years for $i = 0.10$ and $S(T) = Be^{-0.091T}$ (Fig. 10–2a). However, as the gradient becomes small, the cost curves become flat and the annual cost becomes quite insensitive to any error of estimate. That is, for small gradients (whose values may be determined in each case from the end points of the plots in Fig. 10–2) the manager would be relatively indifferent to when he replaced any given piece of equipment and only concerned with comparisons of first cost.

As the gradient increases, the cost of keeping the equipment increases but (because of discounting) at a slower rate, and then drops as the minimum cost replacement cycle speeds up. Points at or near the peak of the curves of Figure 10–3 are extremely important relative to replacement decisions. Under the conditions given by these points, the replacement cycle is short and the total (or annual) cost quite sensitive to changes in the expense gradient. Where the cost begins to drop sharply, the minimum cost life has decreased to a point which must be considered as unimportant, involving as it does a durable asset of very short economic life.

Interest Rate. As the required rate of return on investments increases, both minimum cost life and total cost become quite insensitive to changes in the values of the other parameters. When $i = 0.50$, for example, T is 3 years for an expense gradient of $0.08B$ and $S(T) = Be^{-0.033T}$ while if $S(T) = Be^{-0.091T}$, it is 4 years, and has only increased to 5.5 years at $S(T) = Be^{-0.25T}$. The lower the expense gradient the greater this difference, but at the same time, the less is the cost difference. For expense gradients from 0 to $0.08B$ (where the greatest sensitivity to minimum cost life is shown), no discernible cost difference can be found at $i = 0.50$. Thus, an interest rate at this level "swamps" all other effects and the decision is quite insensitive to changes in values of the other parameters.

For any one salvage function, the sensitivity of the minimum cost life to changes in the discount rate is striking. When the decline in salvage value is rapid, the effect is most pronounced in the region from $i = 0.10$ to $i = 0.30$. At $G = 0.06B$ and $S(T) = Be^{-0.25T}$, for example, $T = 2$ years at $i = 0.10$, 5 years at $i = 0.20$, 6.5 at $i = 0.30$, and 7.5 at $i = 0.50$. However, at $S(T) = Be^{-0.033T}$ and $G = 0.03B$, $T = 0.5$ years at 0.10, 1 year at 0.20, 3 years at 0.30, and 7 years at 0.50. Thus, it can be seen quite clearly the regions wherein these variables become respectively more and less important to the replacement decision.

When the required rate of return is low ($i = 0.10$), large expense gradients (above say $0.08B$) lead to nonsense results regardless of the salvage function. This is so because with any reasonable salvage value, expenses accumulate so fast that the replacement cycle is necessarily short. This kind of situation is one that involves short life, "throw away" type goods. That is, the kind of equipment that has no or little salvage value when installed and that wears or is "used up" quickly.

Salvage Value. Changes in salvage value may be seen to be quite important to the investment decision over a wide range of the values given here. This is true both from the standpoint of minimum cost life and total cost of the investment. For all interest rates, investments whose realizable value declines slowly with use should be replaced sooner than those whose value declines rapidly in use. For example, Figure 10–2b shows that for $S(T) = Be^{-0.033T}$ and an expense gradient of $0.02B$, $T = 1.7$ years, while for $S(T) = Be^{-0.25T}$, $T = 12.5$ years. This salvage value effect decreases as the interest rate changes but is still quite pronounced, for the lower values of G at $i = 0.50$. Again, in the cost sensitive regions (those areas where the cost curves peak in Fig. 10–3), the differences due to different rates of decline in salvage value are striking for all but the highest interest rates.

SUMMARY

The models given here represent specific applications of the general mathematical model, for investment by a firm, to problems of equipment selection and replacement. These models are purposely stated in as general terms as possible, in order that their area of application be wide. It is perfectly feasible to modify them according to the dictates of a particular situation, and, in fact, this is clearly the most desirable course of action. All knowledge available and pertinent to the investment problem under investigation should be included in the model so long as it remains computationally feasible.

Actually, models such as those given here allow for the comparison of any investment alternatives, but it is certainly not necessary to use them for all investments. An improvement in an operation, for example, usually involves constant returns in the future, and the discounted savings may be easily totaled for comparative purposes. Also, if the period of use for the investment is short, the discounting process becomes much simpler and sometimes may even be neglected when comparing alternatives. Investment in inventories could also be considered using such models and compared, for example, with investments in more equipment, if these are feasible alternatives.

The important point here, as throughout this book, is that the model is a means to a decision, and it is the decision which is important. Usefulness is the proper criterion for choosing a model, and if it isn't useful, the best advice is to get another model. The simplest effective model which can be designed to aid in making a given kind of decision should always be used. The best course of action is to design a model based on the given situation.

REFERENCES

1. BUFFA, E. S. *Models for Production and Operations Management.* New York: John Wiley & Sons, Inc., 1963.
2. DEAN, JOEL. *Capital Budgeting.* New York: Columbia University Press, 1951.
3. GRANT, EUGENE L. *Principles of Engineering Economy.* 3d ed. New York: Ronald Press Co., 1950.
4. LUTZ, F. and V. *The Theory of Investment of the Firm.* Princeton: Princeton University Press, 1951.
5. MORRIS, W. T. *The Analysis of Management Decisions.* Rev. ed. Homewood, Ill.: R. D. Irwin, Inc., 1964.
6. TERBORGH, GEORGE. *Dynamic Equipment Policy.* New York: McGraw-Hill Book Co., Inc., 1949.
7. THUESEN, H. G., and FABRYCKY, W. J. *Engineering Economy.* 3d ed. Englewood Cliffs, N.J.: Prentice-Hall, Inc., 1964.

APPENDIX TO CHAPTER 10

The following is a listing of a computer program which performs the tabular analysis shown in Tables 10–1 and 10–2 of this chapter. It is written in FORTRAN II-D, and in this form was executed on an IBM 1620 computer. The data and results shown are for the cases given in the tables referred to above with an interest rate of 0.20 added to show this effect. It can be seen that the maximum value (or minimum cost) life extends from 6 to 8 years given this change. The additional problems shown involve only turning on the switch (NOSTOP) which terminates the computation when the maximum (or minimum) has been reached.

Input Variable Dictionary (In Order of Input)

NT	—number of periods for which data is provided
Q(I)	—net revenue or cost per period
S(I)	—end of period realizable value
PROB	—problem identification number
RHO	—interest rate

VC   —value or cost model switch. Must be −1. for value model and +1. for cost model

B   —amount of initial capital investment

NOSTOP —if equal to 0, all results for NT periods will be printed; if equal to any other integer, results will be printed only to one period past maximum or minimum.

NCAS   —switch to read in new problem. If equal to −1, computer will stop; if 0, new data will be read from beginning of program; if +1, only new parameter card (statement 1) will be read.

PROGRAM TO COMPUTE COST OR VALUE AT AN INVESTMENT ALTERNATIVE

```
      DIMENSION Q(40),S(40),DF(40),COST(40)
    2 READ 905,NT
      READ 902,(Q(I),I=1,NT)
      READ 902,(S(I),I=1,NT)
    1 READ 901,PROB, RHO,VC,B,NOSTOP,NCAS
      PRINT 904,PROB,RHO
      SUM = 0.
      DF(1) = 1. + RHO
      DO 10 I=1,NT
      IT = I + 1
      DF(IT) = DF(I)*DF(1)
      SUM = SUM + (Q(I)/DF(I))
      COST(I) = SUM + VC*(B-(S(I)/DF(I)))
      COST(I) = COST(I)*(DF(I)/(DF(I)-1.))
      PRINT 903,I,COST(I)
      IX = I - 1
      IF(NOSTOP)8,10,8
    8 IF(IX)9,10,9
    9 TEST = COST(I) - COST(IX)
      TEST = VC*TEST
      IF(TEST)10,10,11
   10 CONTINUE
   11 IF(NCAS)12,2,1
   12 STOP
  901 FORMAT(4F10.4,2I10)
  902 FORMAT(7F10.4)
  903 FORMAT(10X,I4,3X,F10.3)
  904 FORMAT(/17H THIS IS PROBLEM F6.2,23H, THE INTEREST RATE IS F6.4/10
     1X,5H YEAR,15H  COST OR VALUE)
  905 FORMAT(I5)
      END
```

INPUT DATA

10							
1915.	1745.	1575.	1405.	1235.	1065.	895.	
725.	555.	385.					
3500.	2800.	2400.	2000.	1600.	1300.	1000.	
800.	600.	500.					
1.	.10	−1.	5000.	0	1		
1.1	.20	−1.	5000.	0	1		
1.2	.20	−1.	5000.	1	1		
1.3	.10	−1.	5000.	1	0		
10							
1085.	1255.	1425.	1595.	1765.	1935.	2105.	2275.
2275.	2445.	2615.					
3500.	2800.	2400.	2000.	1600.	1300.	1000.	
800.	600.	500.					
2.0	.10	1.	5000.	0	1		
2.1	.20	1.	5000.	0	1		
2.3	.20	1.	5000.	1	1		
2.3	.10	1.	5000.	1	−1		

```
THIS IS PROBLEM  1.00, THE INTEREST RATE IS  .1000
       YEAR  COST OR VALUE
         1     850.001
         2    2864.284
         3    4702.869
         4    5337.889
         5    5503.670
         6    5574.479
         7    5477.033
         8    5369.736
         9    5176.818
        10    4993.173
```

```
THIS IS PROBLEM   1.10. THE INTEREST RATE IS  .2000
        YEAR  COST OR VALUE
          1    -2925.000
          2     -811.364
          3      256.318
          4      697.577
          5      896.113
          6     1029.939
          7     1079.882
          8     1112.921
          9     1106.290
         10     1095.454

THIS IS PROBLEM   1.20. THE INTEREST RATE IS  .2000
        YEAR  COST OR VALUE
          1    -2925.000
          2     -811.364
          3      256.318
          4      697.577
          5      896.113
          6     1029.939
          7     1079.882
          8     1112.921
          9     1106.290

THIS IS PROBLEM   1.30. THE INTEREST RATE IS  .1000
        YEAR  COST OR VALUE
          1     -850.001
          2     2864.284
          3     4702.869
          4     5337.889
          5     5503.670
          6     5574.479
          7     5477.033

THIS IS PROBLEM   2.00. THE INTEREST RATE IS  .1000
        YEAR  COST OR VALUE
          1    30850.000
          2    27135.713
          3    25297.128
          4    24662.108
          5    24496.327
          6    24425.518
          7    24522.962
          8    24630.259
          9    24823.179
         10    25006.825

THIS IS PROBLEM   2.10. THE INTEREST RATE IS  .2000
        YEAR  COST OR VALUE
          1    17925.000
          2    15811.363
          3    14743.680
          4    14302.421
          5    14103.885
          6    13970.059
          7    13920.115
          8    13887.075
          9    13893.707
         10    13904.542

THIS IS PROBLEM   2.30. THE INTEREST RATE IS  .2000
        YEAR  COST OR VALUE
          1    17925.000
          2    15811.363
          3    14743.680
          4    14302.421
          5    14103.885
          6    13970.059
          7    13920.115
          8    13887.075
          9    13893.707

THIS IS PROBLEM   2.30. THE INTEREST RATE IS  .1000
        YEAR  COST OR VALUE
          1    30850.000
          2    27135.713
          3    25297.128
          4    24662.108
          5    24496.327
          6    24425.518
          7    24522.962
STOP
```

PROBLEMS

1. The Rome Foundry has just received a 2-year contract to manufacture 6,000 items of a casting per month for the "Ready Robert" rocket. Since this rocket style will be obsolete by the end of the contract, no additional orders are expected. Some old casting equipment which has no foreseeable use in the future is being stored by Rome at an estimated cost of $200 a year because no one wanted to spend money to have it hauled away. This equipment can be rebuilt to produce the rocket casting at a cost of $6,000. It will require $600 per month of direct labor and maintenance to produce the 6,666 parts needed to get 6,000 acceptable parts. Defective parts are melted back down. At the end of the 2 years the machine can be sold for the cost of hauling it away.

A new centrifugal casting machine can be bought for $30,000 and will produce 500 parts/day at a cost of $30 a day for direct labor and maintenance. The machine is expected to produce about 2 per cent defectives. During the first year no other use for the machine exists, but during the second, idle time can be subcontracted at a total charge of $65 per day. The company works 22 days per month. At the end of the 2 years the machine can be sold for $15,000.

At present most of Rome's work is in highly speculative lines. Management, therefore, feels that only projects which are expected to yield 25 per cent or more per year are worth undertaking. The government contract was taken because it was a sure thing and would help stabilize the business. Which alternative should be followed in producing the castings?

2. The Grid Department of the Howey Electronic Company has a number of highly specialized and very delicate machines which are used to wind grids for the KKK series electronic tubes. When these machines are no longer useful, the company is dropping this method of manufacturing. Over time, the quality of output from the machines deteriorates even when the machines are well maintained. The following information has been collected on the machines:

Installed cost of the machine = $17,300
Yearly revenue produced by a machine of age T(years) = $10,000e^{\frac{T}{5}}$
Yearly expense of producing the revenue = $500T$
Salvage value of the machine = $15,000 (e^{-\frac{T}{4}})$
Expected rate of return for company investments = 10%

If, at present, all the machines are new, at what date should the operation be discontinued?

3. a) Solve Problem No. 2 for an interest rate of 5 per cent and for one of 15 per cent. How sensitive is the model to interest rate changes?
   b) Solve No. 2 for $S = 15,000 (e^{-\frac{T}{10}})$. Is the model sensitive to salvage value changes?
   c) Solve Problem No. 2 for $E(T) = 250T$.

4. The Elbridge Company has a number of 50-ton punch presses. A new press can be purchased and installed for $100,000. These presses are expected to last for 40 years and have zero salvage value at that time. Resale value of a

brand new machine is $80,000, and deprecition from then on is assumed to be straight line. When the presses are new, revenue is $30,000 per year for each press and decreases approximately $300 per year due to increased spoilage, lower speeds, etc. Operating expenses per press run about $1,500 a year for a brand new press and increase gradually by $700 per year. The company at present makes 10 per cent on capital invested and intends to stay in the same business in the future.

The accounting department believes the presses should be used for 40 years, the production department believes that 20 years is long enough, and the plant manager is in favor of 30 years. What is your recommendation?

$$\text{Note:} \qquad \int e^{ax} dx = \frac{1}{a} e^{ax}; \qquad \int x e^{ax} dx = \frac{e^{ax}}{a^2} (ax - 1)$$

5. *a*) If in Problem No. 4, Elbridge did not plan to replace the presses when they had ended their useful life, what is the length of the optimum life in this case?

b) What is the value which results from using a press for its optimum life?

6. A specially designed safety device to shut off motive power in the event of an interruption of the power supply is being contemplated for installation on particular machines. The installed cost for the device is $5,000; the estimated life for the device is 10 years.

In the event of an interruption, damage to product will amount to approximately $1,000 if the device is not installed; if it is installed, damage will amount to $200. Interruptions occur about three times every 5 years. Maintenance and upkeep costs for the device are estimated at $50 per year.

With a minimum required return of 20 per cent, what are the expected costs with and without the safety device?

7. A firm engaged in the manufacture of rubber covered machine rollers must decide whether or not to replace a rubber milling machine (used to mix rubber stock) that is giving unsatisfactory service. The present mill (with single-speed drive) had been installed 6 years ago, but was now deemed unsatisfactory for two reasons:

a) A flaw had developed in one of the rollers and was affecting the quality of output.

b) The increasing use of synthetic rubbers, which are heat sensitive and liable to be incompletely mixed by a constant-speed machine, called for greater variable-speed machine capacity.

The company made estimates of the capital costs of the two available courses of action. To strip the old mill, repair the roller, install a variable-speed drive, and put the mill into first-class condition would require an expenditure of $13,500. To purchase a new mill, complete with controls and four-speed drive, would cost $22,150. Installation costs would be $4,500, and transportation charges were estimated at $600. An extremely good offer of $9,000 had been received for the old mill, as it stood, making the net cost of the new machine $17,250.

Since the new machine would have a larger capacity than the old, operating costs are not directly comparable. The foreman in charge of milling operations estimates that the new mill would be able to handle one third more output than the old, while producing as good, or better, quality than would be turned out by the old mill revamped. The old mill, he said, would be capable of doing adequate work for about 10 more years. Its salvage value at the end of that period would be about $2,000. The new mill, however, might well last about 20 years, and would end up with about the same salvage value. Operating costs would be about the same for both machines, but maintenance costs would necessarily be higher for the revamped machine. In 4 or 5 years, that annual maintenance cost might well be $1,000. On the new machine, costs would rise rapidly at first, begin leveling off at about $700, then mount more slowly towards the $1,000 mark as it approached the end of its useful life. It is expected by the management that the increased capacity would gradually be used as business continued to expand. Operations are always at or near full capacity in this department now.

The company's cost accounting, which does not allocate costs by departments, will not give any machine cost figures. It is not possible to determine the profit from the contribution of the mills to finished products. The operating costs for the two machines are estimated to be the same. Both will require one operator, a mill man, paid at $2.00 per hour. The company's books reveal that earnings have averaged about 10 per cent of invested capital, and this is considered the minimum return necessary for any investment.

a) On what basis may these alternatives be compared?

b) Formulate a specific decision rule for this situation.

c) Which alternative should be followed?

8. The Connolly Fan Company in 1955 is considering the purchase of a boring mill to replace a milling machine and lathe now being used in a production operation. If the boring mill is purchased at an installed cost of $17,600, the milling machine and lathe will be moved to the maintenance shop where they are needed only occasionally. The maintenance shop has indicated that they consider it necessary to have the miller, but not essential that they acquire another lathe. The current secondhand market for similar machines indicates the lathe could be sold for $800, and the milling machine for $1,200, both less the cost of removal estimated at $50 per machine.

The new machine will have a capacity of 150 per cent of the current output which fully utilizes the existing machines. The present machines are operated by two men whose wages are $2.20/hour. Only one man at the same rate will be required for the new machine. Maintenance expense records on the milling machine show $100 of preventive maintenance has been carried out every year since it was purchased and the following emergency maintenance:

1945	$ 36	1950	$170
1946	0	1951	410
1947	80	1952	204
1948	120	1953	185
1949	75	1954	290

New milling machines of this type may be purchased for $4,000. The lathe requires $80 per year of preventive maintenance, and has incurred additional maintenance costs as follows:

1945............$ 90		1950.............$143	
1946............ 65		1951............. 86	
1947............ 22		1952............. 314	
1948............ 160		1953............. 209	
1949............ 120		1954............. 127	

This machine was bought used for $2,200, and similar prices prevail today. It is estimated that the new machine will require approximately $300/year preventive maintenance. Figures are not available for emergency maintenance, but management believes that experience will probably be proportional to that for the present milling machine.

There are some qualitative differences in output between these alternatives. The shop superintendent says it is becoming increasingly difficult for the current machines to hold to specifications and cites the increase in rejected output from 2 per cent to 3 per cent since the installation of a quality control program in 1950. He estimates rework and scrap cost at $15,000 last year for this 3 per cent of defective output. The new machine is expected to maintain fraction defective at 0.02 or lower.

The company requires any investment to earn 20 per cent, although investments have been made where the anticipated return was less. Local property taxes are figured at 1½ per cent of appraised value (fairly close to market value), and insurance currently costs 0.3 per cent of market value. Present a rational basis for decision in this situation.

The management of the Brant-Gordon Gear Company maintains the following policies regarding capital investments:

a) Investments in any one year cannot exceed the depreciation reserve set aside the preceding year.

b) All proposals which are submitted must earn 6 per cent interest (or the company's current rate of interest on bank loans if higher) and pay for themselves out of savings in at least 2 years.

c) Investments made for purposes of expansion in capacity must have a demonstrated annual earning potential of at least 20 per cent (using the company's P and L accounting procedures).

Two proposals are currently before the board of directors. The first requests the purchase of a new gear shaper to replace an obsolete model whose output fails to meet most specifications imposed by customers. The shop superintendent estimates that the new machine will save at least $2,000 a year in material cost (scrap) over the current machine, and will, in addition, even out the production load by making it possible to allocate any job to any machine rather than using the current machine on only loose tolerance work. The savings here are estimated to be at least $2,000 in labor cost plus better delivery performance.

The new shaper will cost $10,000 installed, and the old machine can only be sold for scrap (approximately $100). The new machine will be about one third under utilized at present production levels, but the shop superintendent feels quite strongly that the investment is justified primarily because of his inability to meet schedules and difficulty in evening out the work load with the present machine.

  a) What decision should the board of directors reach based on their current policy?

  b) What policy changes, if any, would you recommend?

  c) What decision would be reached, based on these changes in policy?

10. The following are data on two alternatives currently being considered for use in a production process:

	Present Machine	Potential Machine
Price	$20,000	$80,000
Age	6 years	Zero
Book value	$ 8,000	——
Yearly labor expenses	$35,000	$10,000

Yearly maintenance expenses:

		Present Machine	Potential Machine
Probability of average	20%	2,000	5,000
yearly expenses for	70%	4,000	10,000
machine life	10%	6,000	15,000

Quality and rework expenses...$10,000 + $1,000$t$ (age); $8,000 + 600t$ (age)

Secondhand market value equals 80 per cent of previous year's value starting with price. (Ignore all tax considerations.)

Machines will be replaced by identical models at 10 years' age. If investment return criteria (before taxes) is 20 per cent, would this new machine be considered favorably? Why (quantitative)?

11. The usual operating speed of wire weaving looms is 300 r.p.m. and at this speed the looms have a life expectancy of 5 years, average annual maintenance costs of $60 ($36 the first year increasing to $84 during the fifth year), and annual power costs of $70. The machines cost $3,200 and have a scrap value of $100. Space charges are $170 per year per machine. Operators are paid 1.60/hour, and each operator runs four machines regardless of the speed 8 hours/day, 250 days/year. Experiments have given the following data:

r.p.m.	Life Expectancy (Years)	Average Annual Maintenance Cost	Annual Power Cost
250	7.2	40 (1st yr.—$32)	60
300	5	60 (" —$36)	70
350	3.7	80 (" —$48)	80
400	2.8	100 (" —$60)	90
450	2.2	120 (" —$72)	100

What is the most economical speed at which to operate the equipment? What is the average annual cost of operating a machine if the required return on investment is 20 per cent?

SECTION V

Simulation and Heuristics

Many management problems for which some analysis is desired as a prelude to decision do not lend themselves to the kind of formal analysis which has been presented so far. This can be true for a variety of reasons, but these generally fall into two basic categories. First, the numerical complexity which must be dealt with in implementing a formal model may make its use economically not feasible. This complexity of the formal model may be purely relative to some less than formal but "satisfactory" approach, where satisfactory has the meaning that the results provided are sufficient for the purposes of management.

Second, it may be that the problem structure itself is only vaguely understood by the manager, the analyst, or both, and that no formal deductive mathematical approach is possible. This can be true with respect to criteria or relationships between criteria and variables.

In either basic case or some variant, a simulation and/or some heuristic approach may be possible. The construction and use of simulation models with or without accompanying heuristics explicitly included has been increasing in business and industrial operations analysis at a rate faster than that of other approaches. We have attempted in the material which follows to provide a basic framework from which such work may proceed. Given the conditions stated above under which one would use such methods, it is difficult to generalize in this area. We believe its increasing importance warrants inclusion in any course in analytical methods for management.

CHAPTER 11

Simulation

MOST of the problems which have been dealt with thus far have been relatively simple in structure. It is easy to see that many business problems in reality are extremely complex in structure. From an analytical point of view, the important property is whether or not the analysis needs to deal with this complexity in order to obtain useful results. In a large number of situations, the focus is sufficient to give one useful insight into the decision problem. However, there are many situations in which a mathematical formulation may not be feasible or possible. Consider, for example, a complex production and distribution system which has been modeled as a linear programming problem.

Two kinds of difficulties can arise which impede the analysis. First, the number of variables and constraining relationships may be so large that technical and/or economic considerations make it computationally not feasible to pursue such analysis. Second, the model may be, from one or more points of view, such a large departure from the reality of the situation that no confidence can be placed in the results of computations. This later situation might obtain, for example, if the actual objective function were highly nonlinear consisting of both fixed and variable elements or if some of the important structural relationships were not linear as assumed by the model. In short, a system of interest may have been modeled, but techniques do not exist for its solution.

Another kind of difficulty arises in those situations in which a model has been constructed, but its behavior under the environmental conditions of interest cannot be observed. For example, we might have constructed a decision model to be used in purchasing items for use in manufacturing. The model constructed along the lines indicated in earlier chapters calls for the determination of reorder points and order quantities on the assumption that the demand distribution is stable in time. In the actual environment, in which it is proposed that the model be used, however, both the mean and the variance of the demand distribution is known to change over time. What is needed is a way of testing the effectiveness of the static model as it might be used in this dynamic environment. We require the capability of observing the *effect* of using the model without *actually* using it in the real situation.

A further kind of situation not considered thus far is that in which a prediction has been made based upon some theoretical model and it is desired to test this prediction. Ordinarily, one would require that the situation be altered to conform to the theoretical requirements and that the behavior of the system be monitored in order to test the prediction. However, for technical or economic considerations, this may not be possible. Consider, for example, a situation in which our analysis has indicated that the addition of a given production location to an existing system would have the effect of lowering operating costs by some given amount. Putting this prediction to a test by actually constructing the facility and observing its behavior in operation might well be disastrous if there is any flaw in the theory on which the prediction was originally based. It would be very desirable in such a situation to have a laboratory in which the proposed change in the system could be made experimentally and results predicted by tracing a "history" of operations under these altered conditions.

Finally, it may just be in some situation that no way can be discovered in which even to formulate the problem in some closed analytical form. That is, we just don't know enough to set down some set of equations which is representative of the situation in which analysis is required. If we were, for example, interested in predicting the change in effectiveness due to a change in the organization of a maintenance staff assigned to a complex manufacturing facility, we might well be in some difficulty in attempting a purely mathematical formulation of this situation. Difficulties arise both in describing the demands on the system, that is, the complexity of calls for service of various kinds arising from different kinds of equipment (the interaction of scheduled and unscheduled work) as well as the behavior of different mixes of skills and personnel capabilities, in dealing with these demands. Similarly, if we are attempting to evaluate the effect of a change in scheduling policy in a job-oriented manufacturing facility, our ability to describe and deal mathematically with the complexities encountered is severely limited. This is not to say that such limitations on our knowledge and ability will continue to exist but just that we have not yet developed mathematical methods capable of coping with these situations.

For any or several of these reasons, system simulation may be used in developing the vehicle which allows one to pursue analysis in the face of these difficulties. The notion of simulating a system in order to better understand it has gained wide acceptance in recent years and has made increasing contributions to the analysis of management problems.

THE NATURE OF SIMULATION

The definition ordinarily given to simulation is to duplicate the essence of a system or activity without actually obtaining the reality. Simulation takes a real system—technological, human, economic—and in some sense duplicates it. However, the duplication uses paper and pencil, computers, symbols, and words for the real phenomena. This is not the only departure from reality. Because the simulation focuses on certain characteristics of the system, by implication it largely ignores others. This of course is true of any model or theory, and of the methods of science in general.

To be able to simulate a system, either an actual one or one not yet in existence, a fairly good knowledge of the parts or components of the system and their characteristics is required. The desire is to understand, explain, and predict the dynamic behavior of the system—the sum total of these parts. Adequate knowledge of the parts of the system in no sense guarantees adequate knowledge of the system behavior. A mathematical model which is solved may provide this knowledge. Simulation, on the other hand, usually involves a mathematical model which is "run" rather than solved. Some types of simulation, however, involve very little mathematical modeling.

One of the major differences between one simulation and another is the amount of human decision making and participation during the simulation. At one extreme there is no human decision making during the simulation. The problem is entirely structured before the simulation is run. This is the type of simulation which may be entirely carried out by a computer. It is this type of simulation which receives attention in this chapter.

Engineering simulators have a relatively long history. For example, for many years chemical engineers have used analogue devices to simulate the behavior of chemical plants, and electrical engineers to simulate the behavior of motors and flows in networks. Recently there has been considerable interest in the simulation of missile guidance systems. Of course, flight simulators and other such training devices are quite familiar to all of us. The use of an electrical analogue in simulating economic systems was illustrated in the preceding chapter in the case of an equipment investment model. However, because of the complexity of the kinds of problems just enumerated, the use of such devices in business situations is quite limited. Here we are interested in three basic kinds of simulation: Monte Carlo, model sampling, and operational gaming.

Monte Carlo Simulation

Monte Carlo originally referred to analysis in a situation in which a difficult nonprobabilistic problem was to be solved and for which a stochastic process could be invented whose parameters satisfied the

Figure 11–1

ESTIMATING THE AREA OF AN IRREGULAR SURFACE

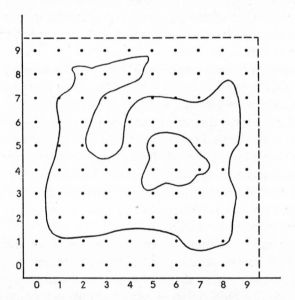

requirements of the original problem. Consider, for example, the problem of determining the area of an irregularly shaped surface as shown in Figure 11–1. One way of doing this would be to superimpose a rectangle of known area and to assign a lattice of points using integer co-ordinates. Then the number of points which fell within the boundaries of the area to be measured would be counted, the area being estimated by the following relationship: $X = A(n/N)$ in which X equals the area to be estimated, A equals the area of the superimposed rectangle, n equals the number of points falling within the area to be estimated, and N equals the total number of points in the superimposed rectangle. Since forty of the points shown in Figure 11–1 fall within the shape whose area is to be estimated, if the area of the superimposed rectangle is 50 square feet, X, the area to be estimated, is estimated as 20 square feet. The precision is, of course, a function of the number of points defined in the rectangle of known area. If it were desired to estimate a large area with considerable precision, then the number of points on each co-ordinate would have to be large. If it were, say, 1,000, then the entire lattice work would consist of 1,000,000 points and the task of counting the points enclosed by the surface to be estimated would be considerable.

One might, however, devise an experiment along the following lines in order to accomplish the estimating task. Assign to each of the grid points along each co-ordinate the numbers 000–999. Place in a bowl a set of chips containing these same numbers. The draw of two chips with replacement and mixing between draws is sufficient to establish a point in the grid. It is then recorded whether a point falls inside or outside the area. A sample of any size (N) is drawn and the area is estimated using the relationship shown above in which n is the number of points which fell in the surface to be measured. This is a true Monte Carlo experiment in which the nonstochastic problem is solved by means of an invented stochastic process.

However, the term Monte Carlo has come to be used to describe any chance process used to solve a problem. A central role is played in this process by random numbers.

The random numbers are used in the following manner. The data of interest (not the random numbers) are plotted or tabulated as a cumulative probability distribution function, i.e., the probability P of x or more, or of x or less "successes" against x on the horizontal axis as in Figures 9–3 and 9–4 in Chapter 9. These data might be number of absences on a given day, number of rejects in a given batch, number of hours between machine breakdowns, and so forth.

Each random number or sequence of numbers which is "generated" is used as a decimal value of the cumulative probability. The number in the "data of interest" corresponding to this cumulative probability value in the chart or table is then obtained.

An example of this process should make the procedure clearer.[1] Suppose the inventory control system of a firm is being analyzed and the sales pattern for 12 days is needed. Suppose also that it has previously been determined that the distribution of sales is random (or that this

---

[1] *Notes from M.I.T. Summer Course on Operations Research* (Cambridge, Mass.: Technology Press, 1953), p. 106.

assumption has been made because no data were available, and it seemed reasonable). The expected (or average) number of sales per day is five. The cumulative probability is determined from the Poisson distribution as[2] $[P(s|m = 5)$ = Probability of s or fewer given 5 as the mean$]$.

$$P(s|m = 5) = \sum_{c=0}^{c=s} \frac{5^c}{c!} e^{-5}$$

In tabular form this gives:

	0	1	2	3	4	5	6	7	8	9	10	11
$P(s,5)$	0.01	0.04	0.12	0.26	0.44	0.62	0.76	0.87	0.93	0.97	0.99	1.00
RN	01	02–04	05–12	13–26	27–44	45–62	63–76	77–87	88–93	94–97	98–99	00

Plotted as a cumulative frequency distribution form this gives Figure 11–2.

Then by the use of a random number (RN) generator (such as a table of random numbers[3]), a sales pattern can be established as follows using the random numbers assigned to events shown above:

Figure 11–2

CUMULATIVE FREQUENCY DISTRIBUTION

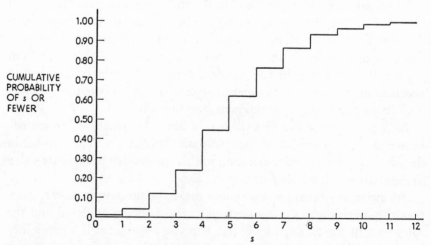

Day	1	2	3	4	5	6	7	8	9	10	11	12
RN	0.57	0.71	0.73	0.70	0.16	0.53	0.43	0.26	0,06	0.66	0.35	0.09
s	5	6	6	6	3	5	4	3	2	6	4	2

Thus a set of random numbers has been used to generate sequences of numbers which have the same statistical character as the actual experience which it is desired to simulate. In this way an inexhaustible fund of simulated experience is available which can usually be secured at much lower cost than further actual experience. So long as the statistical model continues to represent the facts of the situation, the simulated experience is safely usable for a wide variety of purposes.[4]

The Use of Random Numbers

Several points may be further clarified, i.e., how to obtain and use the random numbers, and why to use a cumulative probability distribution. Random numbers may be read from a random number table in any order or sequence (with the obvious restriction that the order not be chosen on the basis of the numbers themselves). The point corresponding to the random number (one at a time) is established on the probability chart or table. Assume for the moment that only random numbers from one through ten (zero excluded) are to be used, and the variable of interest can take only six values (2, 3, 4, 5, 6, 7). This distribution may be plotted two ways, as follows:

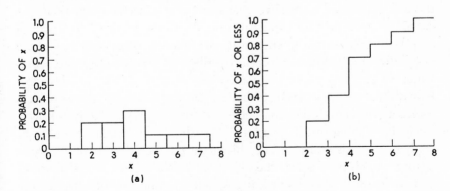

(a)   (b)

Notice in chart (a) the random number 2 may correspond to three values of the variable of interest, i.e., 2, 3, and 4. The random number 8 corresponds to no value. On the other hand, in chart (b) each random

---

[4] *Notes from M.I.T. Summer Course on Operations Research*, p. 109.

number corresponds to only one value of the variable of interest adopting the convention that reading across the chart, the first line met is the corresponding number, e.g., 7 corresponds to 4. This convention is of no help in chart (a). Thus, in the chart correspondence of a random number representing probability to the variable of interest is unique. Notice also that the value for x of 4, for instance, has three such random numbers corresponding to it, i.e., 5, 6, and 7. With random numbers, these three will be drawn an expected 30 per cent of the time, corresponding to the probability of $x = 4$, shown in chart (a).

The rationale behind the use of the cumulative probability distribution and the random numbers is that each number (from the data of interest) will come up with about the same relative frequency in this synthetic process as in the "real world," but their arrangement will be randomized.

With the use of a table or a graph, it is not even necessary to choose a mathematical distribution such as the Poisson, normal, binomial, etc., to represent the process being simulated. The empirical distribution itself constructed from the actual data may be used as the cumulative frequency distribution against which the random numbers are compared. One problem which must be solved is to pick the idealized model which represents the "real world," and the empirical distribution itself may not be as true a model of the population as one of the mathematical distributions which approximate it. The same problem in selecting a distribution to represent the events in the real world exists here as it does in the problems described in Chapter 8, Total Value Analysis. If there is no reason to believe that the process is changing, then the distribution can be built explicitly around past experience. The distribution or histogram of the empirical data may be used. The larger the sample from which the empirical distribution is built, the more representative of the present population or universe it will tend to be. However, if there is reason to believe from the nature of the process itself (a priori) that the data generated from it will probably follow a particular mathematical distribution, it should be tested against that mathematical distribution. The chi-square test would probably be satisfactory for this purpose.[5] If the difference between the two distributions —mathematical and empirical—is not statistically significant, the mathematical distribution should be used. If there is reason to believe that the process is changing or will change, it will be necessary to modify the distribution derived from past experience in accord with the

---

[5] See Chapter 7.

nature and the magnitude of the expected change. A full treatment of the problem of forecasting is beyond the scope of this book.

A schematic diagram[6] of the process (Fig. 11–3) might consist of a

Figure 11–3

THE MONTE CARLO PROCESS

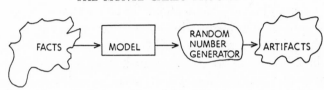

jagged, roughly rectangular figure representing the collection of facts as observed from which an idealized model is derived. The idealized model is represented by a normal rectangle. This model, used with the random number generator, produces an artificially jagged figure, representing the simulated experience. An advantage for Monte Carlo relative to the use of actual data is that the latter may be used repeatedly, introducing the possibility that meaningless, repeated fluctuations may appear in the results. Even when using a random number table, one must be careful not to repeat the use of the same sequences.

It may be that there are several variables present, each of which has an effect on the economic picture. If this is so, all the necessary variables must be generated from their proper distributions. For instance, number of absentees, work load, and reject rate might all be important variables in the problem. All of these would be generated independently by the Monte Carlo.

In some problems the mean value is as useful as the particular sequences that make it up. If such is the case the Monte Carlo is probably not needed. The Monte Carlo technique is helpful only when the particular sequence of the variables is important, or where the particular relation among several variables is important. In each problem analyzed, it will probably be necessary to think through the validity of a solution using means rather than distributions. Actually, a solution using means is usually a good place to start the analysis, as the Monte Carlo will probably call for several solutions to be evaluated and the use of means should at least suggest the neighborhood of possible solutions.

If there are nonrandom components in the data, such as time series, these should be removed and used separately. For example, if rejects

---

[6] *Notes from M.I.T. Summer Course on Operations Research.*

vary with the time of day, then the different periods during the day should be treated independently, each having its own distribution.

Building the Model for Monte Carlo

When using Monte Carlo to solve production problems, it is necessary, after analyzing the problems, to set up a total value function or model which represents the situation. When only one arrangement of a situation is being considered, this means that only one model is necessary with which data are generated by the use of Monte Carlo. However, when Monte Carlo is being used to choose one solution to a problem from several or many, then several or many models should be established for purposes of evaluation and comparison. Some of the models might of course be of the same type but with different values inserted, e.g., three men versus five. Monte Carlo may be used for evaluating one model, as would be more often the case in physics or mathematics, or for evaluating several models for purposes of comparison, which is the more common case in manufacturing analysis.

When several models (or modifications of one model) are to be compared by Monte Carlo, there is no "automatic" way of determining this series of models or solutions. A thorough analysis of the problem and the nature of the environment in which it is found is still necessary in the choice of potential solutions. The job of building the model which represents the real situation always exists. Schematic models might contribute to the understanding required. In some cases theoretical solutions to the type of problem may have been treated in disciplines such as economics or operations research. If this were the case the particular values of the parameters which would "best" handle the specific problem would be sought.

It is well to keep in mind at this point that each model or potential solution added to the list causes added work in the mechanical phase of carrying through the method. Though the consideration would probably be intuitive, the incremental cost of the added calculations should be related to the expected contribution of the incremental model. As it is possible to handle the Monte Carlo technique on computing equipment, this point might not be important if such equipment is available.

As data of interest are generated by Monte Carlo, the costs and revenues associated with these data are recorded. As more and more experience is simulated and economically evaluated, it should be possible to choose the most economic from the potential solutions.

Monte Carlo has one very interesting advantage. In addition to being useful in problems for which no "analytical" solution exists, it is useful to an analyst who can't handle an existing solution. Some of the more elegant solutions to complex problems are beyond the mathematical training of many people. Without tables to help, waiting line problems often fall into this category. In cases such as these Monte Carlo methods of picking a solution to the problem are possible.

Confidence

As a guide, it may be pointed out that the accuracy associated with the method only improves as the square root of the amount of data (the number of trials).[7] If several solutions are quite similar, from an economic standpoint it might take much synthetic experience to assure the proper choice of solutions. Of course the more similar the solutions the less important it is to choose the "best." If the solutions are economically dissimilar, this should become obvious more quickly. The stability of the relative attractiveness of the solutions may be inferred from observing periodically as Monte Carlo is run the relation between the cumulative economic positions (profit, cost, revenue, etc.) of the different solutions. An additional point to be made is that it is probably not advisable to stop the Monte Carlo analysis when the mean of the data of interest synthetically generated differs appreciably from the empirical mean. As an example, if coin tossing is being used to generate two equally likely numbers, the analysis should hardly be stopped after twenty trials with 15 heads and 5 tails having been generated. The real world is not expected to operate with this divergence ad infinitum, and the solution called for might be the wrong one.

For each trial of Monte Carlo, with the associated model evaluation, a number corresponding to the measure of effectiveness may be computed. It is this number which is of interest. Assume two models are being evaluated in order to determine which has the lower cost. As Monte Carlo is run, these two sets of numbers corresponding to the measures of effectiveness will be generated. For some trials one model may be cheaper, for others the second may be cheaper. At any given number of trials, the cumulative cost or the average cost for the two models may be computed. Except in the unusual case where they might be equal, one will have some economic advantage. However, the trials are only a sample which represents experience from a universe. What can be said about the true means of the measures of effectiveness?

This is a statistical problem in estimation and confidence. If the distribution of the measures of effectiveness corresponds to a mathemat-

---

[7] *Notes from M.I.T. Summer Course on Operations Research,* p. 106.

ical distribution such as the normal, then by computing an estimate of the standard deviations, s_x, statements about the band within which the true mean falls may be made with a given degree of confidence. Significant differences between means may be inferred from a comparison of these bands. The bands of the measures of effectiveness of two or more models may be compared at different stages in the Monte Carlo process, with the significantly poorer models at each stage being eliminated. (Chapter 7 on experimentation presents a fuller discussion of these ideas.)

A PROBLEM OF MAINTENANCE POLICY

An example will be presented to illustrate the Monte Carlo method of analysis. A chemical company has a series of high-pressure injection pumps operating under similar conditions and wishes to determine a proper maintenance policy.[8] The pump valves are subject to failure, and their routine maintenance costs about 9,500 man-hours per year. Each pump has three intake valves and three exhaust valves. When a valve fails, it is necessary to shut down the pump and prepare it for maintenance. Each set of valves is covered by a manifold which must be removed after shutdown in order to expose either the three intake valves or the three exhaust valves. There is no down-time cost as the firm has stand-by pumps to be used during maintenance on the valves.

The company is interested in and wants to evaluate four maintenance procedures which it considers practical:

I) Repair a valve only when it fails.
II) Repair all three exhaust values if one exhaust valve fails, or all three intake valves if one intake valve fails.
III) Repair all six valves (three exhaust and three intake valves) whenever a pump must be shutdown to repair one valve.
IV) Repair the valve that fails plus all valves which have been in use more than the estimated average service life (560 hours).

The company supplied the following data for the analysis:

MAINTENANCE COST (EXPRESSED IN MECHANIC'S TIME)

Operation	Time (Hours)
Shutdown, prepare for maintenance	$\frac{1}{2}$
Remove manifold (either intake or exhaust)	$\frac{2}{3}$
Disassemble one valve	$\frac{1}{3}$
Overhaul one valve	$1\frac{1}{4}$
Assemble one valve	$\frac{1}{3}$
Replace manifold (either intake or exhaust)	$\frac{2}{3}$

---

[8] From an unpublished master's thesis by Paul R. Haas, Jr., *The Application of the Monte Carlo Method in the Solution of Production Problems*, M.I.T., 1955.

The cumulative probability distribution for valve service life, Figure 11–4, was constructed from empirical data supplied by the company. Valve life itself, of course, is not a function of the procedures listed above, assuming the valve remains in use until it fails. Figure 11–4 is the cumulative probability distribution against which random numbers, representing decimal values of the probability, are applied in order to simulate experience.

Figure 11–4

VALVE FAILURE DATA

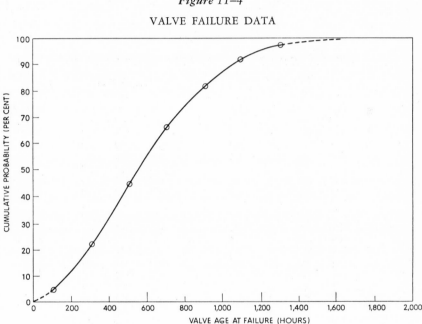

The company analysts felt that valve failure (length of life) followed a normal distribution. A chi-square test was used to check the null hypothesis that the valve age at failure is from a normal distribution. The probability that the data supplied actually came from a normal distribution was evaluated to be 24 per cent or less. Though this is not usually a low enough probability to reject a null hypothesis, the empirical distribution itself was used in this case.

Using a table of random numbers, each number representing a decimal probability along the y-axis in Figure 11–4, a set of valve lives to the nearest 10 hours was generated. Table 11–1 shows this information in table form. The numbers in the *RN* rows are random numbers; the numbers in the lettered rows are valve life in hours.

For instance, the random number for the first valve in the first trial is

705. Treat this as 70.5%, and pick this point on the y-axis, the probability axis in Figure 11–4. Now read across to the line in the chart. Corresponding to a cumulative probability of 70.5% is a valve life, on the x-axis, of 740 hours. All other figures in the table were constructed in the same manner. What is now represented in this table is a series of valve lives, if the valve remains untouched until failure, corresponding to each valve. For instance, valve 5 would last until failure, successively, 820 hours; 1,000 hours; 960 hours; 380 hours; etc. With an overhaul before failure, the next valve life is commenced. That is, if valve 5

Table 11–1

GENERATION OF VALVE LIVES BY MONTE CARLO

Trials	Intake Valves			Exhaust Valves		
	1.	2.	3.	4.	5.	6.
RN	705	872	396	366	776	478
a	740	970	440	420	820	510
RN	548	759	376	354	895	007
b	570	800	430	410	1,000	30
RN	036	479	961	106	864	448
c	80	510	1,200	170	960	490
RN	892	581	486	647	318	439
d	1,010	600	520	670	380	480
RN	442	681	672	676	865	741
e	480	690	700	700	960	780
RN	249	580	141	261	047	963
f	320	600	210	330	100	1,230
RN	330	145	533	167	244	563
g	390	210	560	240	310	580
RN	326	836	648	692	237	965
h	380	900	680	720	310	1,220
RN	874	057	380	994	619	525
i	980	110	430	1,420	640	540
RN	104	022	054	653	349	571
j	170	60	560	680	400	590

during its first life is overhauled at 500 hours, then it would last 1,000 hours from then. However, if overhauled again after 500 hours, it would then last 960 from the time of the second overhaul.

This simulated experience from Table 11–1 is plotted separately for each of the four alternative maintenance policies in Figure 11–5. It can be seen that because of the different policies, the operations take place at different points in time. A vertical line represents a valve overhaul, or set of 3 in II, or set of 6 in III, or a varying number in IV according to the number over the average age of 560 hours.

In case I, each valve life is completely independent of each other valve, as only one valve at a time is overhauled. In Table 11–1, therefore, each valve operates until failure and is then repaired, starting

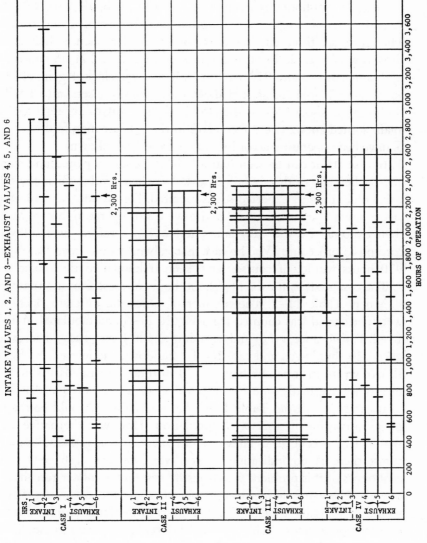

Figure 11–5

SIMULATED VALVE FAILURE EXPERIENCE

INTAKE VALVES 1, 2, AND 3—EXHAUST VALVES 4, 5, AND 6

its next life. For instance, opposite valve 5 is plotted the same lives previously listed, i.e., 820; 1,000; 960; and 380 hours.

Case II will be explained to show the nature of the other charts (and their associated costs). The first valve to fail in the intake manifold was valve 3, at 440 hours. According to procedure two, all three valves, 1, 2, and 3, within the intake manifold are disassembled and repaired. Therefore, all three end their first lives and commence their second lives, row (b) Table 11–1. It can be seen that valve 3 again fails first at 430 hours, or at about 870 (440 + 430) on the clock. Again, all three valves are repaired and started anew. In the third life set, valve 1 fails at 80 hours, or about 950 on the clock, all three valves are repaired, and again started anew. The three valves in the exhaust manifold, 4, 5, and 6, have been operating according to the experience shown.

In case III, it can be seen that all six valves are repaired and started anew when any of the six fail. In case IV when a valve fails, any other valve older than its expected life is repaired. For instance, at 740 on the clock, valve 1 failed. Valves 2 and 5 were still operating but were over their expected lives of 560 hours and were, therefore, overhauled according to procedure IV. The fact that valve 2 would have lasted until 970 hours would, of course, have been unknown to the repair men.

The cost analysis for the first 2,300 hours of these four alternatives is shown in Table 11–2. The number of times the different operations were performed was counted from Figure 11–5 and tabulated in Table 11–2. For instance, up to and including 2,300 hours, case I had experienced 20 shutdowns and case III, 14 shutdowns. However, in case I a shutdown means one overhaul, or 20 in total. In case III a shutdown means six overhauls, one for each valve, or a total of 84 (14 × 6).

It can be seen from Table 11–2 that alternative I would be the best policy according to this brief simulation. However alternative IV is within 10 per cent of it. These are only averages or, rather, cumulative sums; there is no indication of cost variation for each policy. The economics of this problem would justify certainly a longer run than the one used here for demonstration purposes. As the trials are made, it would be advisable to get a cost (in hours of mechanic's time) for each of a set of periods such as every 2,000 hours. From these lists of numbers (costs), the variance inherent in the system could be determined, and some decision reached concerning confidence (statistical or intuitive) in finding the best of the alternatives.

The total value analysis model for this problem has been stated essentially through a series of graphs and tables. Conceivably the state-

Table 11–2

ANALYSIS OF ALTERNATIVE MAINTENANCE POLICIES

OPERATION	HRS./OP.	I No.	I Time	II No.	II Time	III No.	III Time	IV No.	IV Time
Shutdown................	½	20	10	13	6½	14	7	17	8½
Remove intake manifold....	⅔	9	6	6	4	14	9⅓	8	5⅓
Remove exhaust manifold...	⅔	11	7⅓	7	4⅔	14	9⅓	12	8
Disassemble valves.........	⅓	20	6⅔	39	13	84	28	24	8
Overhaul valves...........	5⁄4	20	25	39	48¾	84	105	24	30
Assemble valves...........	⅓	20	6⅔	39	13	84	28	24	8
Replace intake manifold....	⅔	9	6	6	4	14	9⅓	8	5⅓
Replace exhaust manifold...	⅔	11	7⅓	7	4⅔	14	9⅓	12	8
Total time............			75		98⁷⁄₁₂		205⅓		81⅙

ment could be in a more explicit algebraic form, but eventually the tabular approach would probably be used for purposes of convenience.

Model Sampling

A special case of Monte Carlo simulation, known as model sampling, is useful in those situations in which there is some complicated stochastic process too difficult to analyze by standard statistical procedures. In such situations, repeated application of the Monte Carlo process may enable one to collect a set of case histories concerning the system and to estimate its statistical properties. Consider, for example, the problem of determining the distribution of demand during lead time given the basic data as shown on page 370 in Chapter 9. On the assumption that we have a process for generating random decimal digits, say a ten-sided die we could assign decimal digits to the events of interest as shown in the table below:

X	$P(X)$	RN	T	$F(T)$	RN
0	0.2	0,1	1	0.3	0,1,2
1	0.4	2,3,4,5	2	0.5	3,4,5,6,7
2	0.3	6,7,8	3	0.2	8,9
3	0.1	9			

Since the random numbers are by definition equally likely, estimates of the probability of any demand during any lead time may be obtained by simulating the process according to the probabilities above.

The simulation would proceed as follows: (1) generate a random number, (2) determine the lead time event assigned to this number, (3) for each day of the lead time, generate a random number, (4) determine the demand events assigned to each random number generated in step three, (5) add the demand events determined in step four, and (6) record the specific occurrence of the variable defined as demand during lead time. If this process were repeated, say 100 times, the frequency of occurrence of each of the possible values of this variable, ranging from 0 through 9 in this case, would constitute estimates of the probability of these events. A tabulation of a set of events generated according to the above procedure is shown in Table A–1 with the resulting estimate of probabilities in Table A–2 of Appendix III.

A flow chart of a computational routine designed to execute this process is shown in Appendix III, Simulation Languages, together with a FORTRAN program capable of executing this routine. The input and output for a sample case are shown in this Appendix.

Operational Gaming

A third major area of simulation, that called Operational Gaming, is distinguished primarily by the notion of play, involving at some point the intervention of people. In this kind of simulation, the analytical structure is even less well defined than in the previous types. If one were using, say model sampling, to design a maintenance system in a factory, the analysis might well proceed as follows. First, one would construct a model of the system which would be capable of estimating those properties of the system necessary to an economic evaluation of cost structure. One would test the model by determining whether or not it could reasonably simulate reality with respect to economic and technical factors of interest. One would experiment in order to determine the errors associated with properties estimated by the model. Finally, over some predetermined range of facilities, one would estimate the operating characteristics of the maintenance system, extend these by the costs and thus determine by this process the minimum cost configuration of facilities and/or operating policies. In this kind of situation, the structure of the economic analysis is well defined. The difficulty lies in obtaining estimates of the parameters of the system to be priced.

In contrast to the above, consider a situation in which it is desired to determine a satisfactory strategy for loading machines with customers' orders in a factory. In such a situation, it is ordinarily not even possible to define a clear and unambiguous objective function, much less to enumerate the set of alternatives which would with high probability include the "best" in terms of this objective function. Thus, the problem is to discover some strategy which over a complex domain of criteria will be acceptable in operations.

As a first step in this process, a model would be constructed which would load machines with customer orders according to some given strategy on the part of the analyst. A "good" model will allow the analyst to alter his strategy over a fairly wide range of parameter values and to observe the resulting operating characteristics of the system with respect to all factors deemed by the management important in judging its effectiveness. "Play" would proceed to a selection of a strategy or a set of strategies by the analyst, the simulation of the operating effect of implementing such strategies using the system model, estimation of the operating characteristics of the system via the model, and economic and/or judgmental evaluation of the results of play.

A PRODUCTION-INVENTORY SIMULATOR

The purpose of the simulation model to be described is to allow one to experiment with a variety of decision rules for setting production rates under a fairly wide range of demand and technical environments. Basically, two major elements are present. *First,* a general decision model is used to prepare forecasts of demand and compute production rates according to a rule proposed by the experimenter. *Second,* a simulation model acts on the decisions made by the first model and keeps records of the outcome of the application of this rule.

The Forecasting Model

Forecasting is accomplished by the method of exponential smoothing using a model which incorporates both seasonal and trend effects.[9] Records are kept of actual sales experienced, and at the end of each period the smoothed sales rate is calculated as

$$\tilde{S}_t = A(S_t/F_{t-N}) + (1 - A)\tilde{S}_{t-1} \qquad 0 \leq A \leq 1 \qquad (1)$$

in which

$\tilde{S}_t$ = smoothed sales rate at end of period t.
S_t = actual sales during t.
F_t = seasonal factor for period t (ratio of actual sales to smoothed sales).
N = number of periods in the seasonal.
A = smoothing parameter.

Seasonal factors are updated according to

$$F_t = B(S_t/\tilde{S}_t) + (1 - B)F_{t-N} \qquad 0 \leq B \leq 1 \qquad (2)$$

in which B is the seasonal smoothing parameter. Trend is accounted for linearly, and the trend factor is updated by

$$R_t = C(\tilde{S}_t - \tilde{S}_{t-1}) + (1 - C)R_{t-1} \qquad 0 \leq C \leq 1 \qquad (3)$$

---

[9] Peter R. Winters, "Forecasting Sales by Exponentially Weighted Moving Averages," *Management Science,* Vol. VI, No. 3 (1960), pp. 324–42.

in which

$$C = \text{trend smoothing parameter,}$$
$$R_t = \text{trend factor.}$$

Given an initial set of values for $\tilde{S}_t$, R_t, and the F_t's, the system is easy to maintain and forecasts may be produced for any period τ in the future by

$$\hat{S}_{t+\tau} = (\tilde{S}_t + \tau R_t)F_{t+\tau-N} \qquad (4)$$

This method is incorporated into the decision model and it is required to specify A, B, C and the initial values listed above.

The Decision Rule

The form of the decision rule is based upon the notion that a desirable mode of behavior for a production manager is to specify an inventory position in which he would like to find himself at the point in time nearest to the present and still in his control and then make a decision which will come as close as possible to this position subject to any technical constraints on change in rate.

For example, consider a situation as depicted in the time scale of Figure 11–6.

Figure 11–6

PRODUCTION RATE DECISION FOR ONE PERIOD LEAD TIME

TIME →

	I_0	I_1	$I_2{}^*$	I_3	I_4	I_5	I_6
	P_0	P_1	P_2	P_3	P_4	P_5	P_6
	S_0 ↑ $\hat{S}_1$	$\hat{S}_2$	$\hat{S}_3$	$\hat{S}_4$	$\hat{S}_5$	$\hat{S}_6$	

$$I_t = \text{inventory}$$
$$S_t = \text{sales} \, (\hat{S}_t = \text{forecast sales})$$
$$P_t = \text{production}$$

The arrow indicates current time and I_0 current inventory. Based on S_0, forecasts $\hat{S}_1$ through $\hat{S}_6$ are made using the model described previously. The production rate for the current period (P_1) was set previously and is not affected. The problem is to set P_2 and can be seen to be

$$P_2 = \hat{S}_1 + \hat{S}_2 - I_0 - P_1 + I_2{}^* \qquad (5)$$

or in general

$$P_{t+\tau} = \sum_{i=t}^{t+\tau} \hat{S}_i - \sum_{i=t}^{t+\tau-1} P_i - I_{t-1} + I_{t+\tau}{}^* \qquad (6)$$

That is, the requirements to be met are the sales forecast and the inventory at the end of period 2. The resources already available are current inventory and production planned for the current period. Thus, when one has established a desirable value for I_2^*, the desired production rate is fixed.

The rule used for calculating this desired inventory is simple in form but flexible in its outcome. It is

$$I_{\tau+1}^* = \alpha \left[\sum_{i=\tau+2}^{\tau+1+\gamma} S_i \right]^{\beta} \tag{7}$$

in which

τ = production lead time,
α = inventory factor,
β = forecast damping factor,
γ = forecast horizon.

Thus, one could specify a simple rule such as "maintain inventory at one-half month's expected sales by $\alpha = 0.5$, $\beta = 1.0$, and $\gamma = 0$. If it were desired to respond to the square root of sales $\beta = 0.5$ and an appropriate α, given the units involved, would do this.

When the desired inventory has been established, a preliminary value for the production rate is given by (6). Then this rate is checked against any absolute upper and lower limits which may have been specified and reset if exceeded. Finally, the rate is checked against any relative upper and lower limits specified as a percentage of the previous rate set and reset if exceeded. The rate finally determined is stored to be put into effect in the simulator during the appropriate period.

The Simulation Model

The actual simulation proceeds to generate demands for each specified subperiod of the current production period (these would ordinarily be days of the current month). The demand generation is under the control of the experimenter in that a specific set of seasonals and trends can be specified as well as a fraction by which demand will randomly depart from these factors. Thus, the goodness of forecasting can be varied so as to determine the effect of this on the form of the decision rule.

Each "day" production is credited and demand is subtracted (production and demand days do not have to be the same, e.g., production could occur on week ends with no sales). Back orders are recorded and filled from production as available. Average inventory is recorded, and demands are cumulated. At the end of each period, control is given to the decision model for a new rate to be set.

Sample Output

The program listing is included as an Appendix at the end of this chapter and the sample input data are those which produced the output shown in this example. In this form the program was executed on an

Figure 11–7

RESULTS OF PRODUCTION-INVENTORY SIMULATIONS

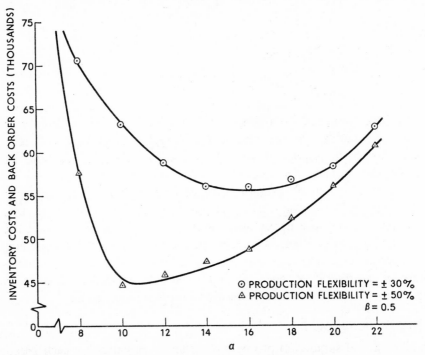

IBM 1620/1311. The results of several simulations are shown in Figure 11–7 in which cost of inventory plus cost of back orders are plotted against values of a. In these runs β was held at 0.5 (a square root response to demand) and production rate changes were limited to $\pm$ 30 per cent and $\pm$ 50 per cent per month. The cost of carrying one unit of stock for one year was assumed to be \$0.0545/lb./day while the cost of a unit stockout was assumed at \$1.100/lb./day.

As can be seen if greater production flexibility is purchased lower variable costs result with a lower value of a required to minimize costs. One is in a position with such output to evaluate the decision to purchase this greater production flexibility.

No claim is made that Figure 11–7 represents an optimal solution to such situations. It is known that the "best" model is only in part a function of costs but also a function of forecasting ability. The demand generator in the simulation model allows one to control error in forecasting so that the effect of this on the model can be predicted. In the case shown here, forecasting ability was good (coefficient of variation of the distribution of forecast errors was 0.05) and one would expect a value of β near 1.0 to be better than a value close to zero. Experimentation with such models would allow one to "fit" a decision rule of this form to a given situation according to a cost and/or service criterion.

THE ART OF SIMULATION

Simulation then refers to a process by which information useful in the analysis of complex operating problems is generated by constructing and observing the operation of models which in some sense are "just like" the situation under analysis. The simulation model is in effect a reproduction of those features of an operating environment which allow one to observe the response of the environment to alternative management actions. We are rarely interested in the environment as such, but rather as a means of determining in a controlled way the outcome of some decision.

In order to allow for the effective practice of this art, computer programs must constitute our core tool. The prodigious numerical problem posed by simulation requires this kind of capability for processing. To this end various languages have been developed which allow one to model with more or less directness the situation of interest and estimate its properties under conditions proposed by the analysis. In Appendix III are described some of these languages together with examples of their use.

REFERENCES

1. BONINI, C. P.; JAEDICKE, R. K.; and WAGNER, H. M. *Management Controls: New Directions in Basic Research.* New York: McGraw-Hill Book Co., Inc., 1964.

2. CONWAY, R. W. "Some Tactical Problems in Simulation Method" (RM-3244-PR), The RAND Corporation, Santa Monica, California, 1962.

3. FORRESTER, JAY W. *Industrial Dynamics.* Cambridge, Mass., and New York: The M. I. T. Press and John Wiley & Sons, Inc., 1961.

4. MARTIN, E. WAINRIGHT, JR. *Electronic Data Processing: An Introduction.* Rev. ed. Homewood, Ill.: Richard D. Irwin, Inc., 1965.

5. ORCUTT, G. H.; GREENBERGER, M.; KORBEL, J.; and RIVLIN, A. H. *Microanalysis of Socio-Economic Systems.* New York: Harper & Row, 1961.

6. TOCHER, K. D. *The Art of Simulation.* Princeton, N.J.: Van Nostrand Co., Inc., 1963.

APPENDIX TO CHAPTER 11
PRODUCTION-INVENTORY SIMULATION PROGRAM

PRODUCTION-INVENTORY SIMULATION PROGRAM

```
      DIMENSION G(12),SHAT(12),PF(12),WD(12),PR(6),SALES(100),FACT(12)
      DIMENSION SFCAST(12)
      COMMON FACT,SALES,G,SHAT,PF,WD,PR,PVC,TRP,URP,A,B,C,SLAST,RLAST
      COMMON JA,KA,MA,ALP,AUP,CBO,COI,PWR,ESF,AH,SBOS,Z11,Z12,Z13
      COMMON ANV,SS,NYMX,NSALE,TRFT,UL,TL,DAYST,BOST,BCOST,NO,MO,LPT
      COMMON DPR,SFACT,COSI,SQER,SLES,SSLES,BORDR,NDWK,SFCAST
      DO 31 I = 1,12
   31 SHAT(I) = 0.
   60 CALL INTIAL
      READ 100,RDAY
   30 READ 100,PVC,URP
      ACCEPT 100,PWR,ESF,AH
      URP = URP + 1.
      TRP = 2. - URP
      DPR = PR(1)/WD(1)
      ANV = 0.
      BOST = 0.
      BCOST = 0.
      DAYST = 0.
      COSI = 0.
      SBOS = 0.
      BORDR = 0.
      SQER = 0.
      SLES = 0.
      SSLES = 0.
      SFCAST(1) = SLAST*G(1)*RDAY
      NDWK = 1
      DO 10 I = 1,NYMX
      MO = 0
   20 CALL PROD
      CALL FCAST
      IF(MO - 12)20,10,10
   10 CONTINUE
      CALL REPORT
      PAUSE
      IF(SENSE SWITCH 1)60,40
   40 STOP
  100 FORMAT(7F10.0)


      SUBROUTINE INTIAL
      DIMENSION G(12),SHAT(12),PF(12),WD(12),PR(6),SALES(100),FACT(12)
      COMMON FACT,SALES,G,SHAT,PF,WD,PR,PVC,TRP,URP,A,B,C,SLAST,RLAST
      COMMON JA,KA,MA,ALP,AUP,CBO,COI,PWR,ESF,AH,SBOS,Z11,Z12,Z13
      COMMON ANV,SS,NYMX,NSALE,TRFT,UL,TL,DAYST,BOST,BCOST,NO,MO,LPT
      COMMON DPR,SFACT,COSI,SQER,SLES,SSLES,BORDR,NDWK,SFCAST
      READ 100,NYMX,JA,KA,MA,NO,NSALE
      READ 101,ALP,AUP,CBO,COI,UL,TL,SFACT
      READ 101,A,B,C,SLAST,RLAST,TRFT
      READ 102,(SALES(I), I = 1,NSALE)
      READ 101,FACT
      READ 101,G
      READ 101,PF
      READ 101,WD
      READ 101,PR
      Z11 = 1.-A
      Z12 = 1.-B
      Z13 = 1.-C
      LPT = MA - 1
      SS = 0.
  100 FORMAT(10I5)
  101 FORMAT(7F10.0)
  102 FORMAT(13F6.0)
      RETURN
      END
```

```
      SUBROUTINE PROD
      DIMENSION G(12),SHAT(12),PF(12),WD(12),PR(6),SALES(100),FACT(12)
      DIMENSION SFCAST(12)
      COMMON FACT,SALES,G,SHAT,PF,WD,PR,PVC,TRP,URP,A,B,C,SLAST,RLAST
      COMMON JA,KA,MA,ALP,AUP,CBO,COI,PWR,ESF,AH,SBOS,Z11,Z12,Z13
      COMMON ANV,SS,NYMX,NSALE,TRFT,UL,TL,DAYST,BOST,BCOST,NO,MO,LPT
      COMMON DPR,SFACT,COSI,SQER,SLES,SSLES,BORDR,NDWK,SFCAST
   60 MO = MO + 1
      NMD = WD(MO)
      DO 5 NDAY = 1,NMD
      DAYST = DAYST + 1.
      IF(NDWK - 7)15,15,20
   20 NDWK = 1
   15 GO TO(10,10,10,10,10,30,30),NDWK
   10 NDWK = NDWK + 1
      R = GRN(1.)
      I = R*SFACT + 1.
      IF(R - .5)100,100,110
  100 R = GRN(1.)
      RATIO = (1. +(R/UL))*FACT(MO)
      GO TO 120
  110 R = GRN(1.)
      RATIO = (1. -(R/UL))*FACT(MO)
  120 R = GRN(1.)
      TREND = (1. - (R/TL))*DAYST*TRFT
      S = SALES(I)*RATIO + TREND
      GO TO 70
   30 S = 0.
      NDWK = NDWK + 1
   70 ANV = ANV + AH + .5*DPR
      IF(SENSE SWITCH 4)80,90
   80 PRINT 200,S
   90 BCOST = BCOST + SBOS*CBO
      BORDR = BORDR + SBOS
      AH = AH + DPR
      COSI = COSI + AH*COI
      AH = AH - SBOS
      IF(AH)600,601,601
  600 SBOS = -1.*AH
      AH = 0.
      GO TO 602
  601 SBOS = 0.
  602 SS = SS + S
      AH = AH - S
      IF(AH)12,5,5
   12 SBO = -1.*AH
      BOST = BOST +SBO
      SBOS = SBOS + SBO
      AH = 0.
    5 CONTINUE
   50 RETURN
  200 FORMAT(F6.0)
      END
```

```
      SUBROUTINE FCAST
      DIMENSION G(12),SHAT(12),PF(12),WD(12),PR(6),SALES(100),FACT(12)
      DIMENSION SFCAST(12)
      COMMON FACT,SALES,G,SHAT,PF,WD,PR,PVC,TRP,URP,A,B,C,SLAST,RLAST
      COMMON JA,KA,MA,ALP,AUP,CBO,COI,PWR,ESF,AH,SBOS,Z11,Z12,Z13
      COMMON ANV,SS,NYMX,NSALE,TRFT,UL,TL,DAYST,BOST,BCOST,NO,MO,LPT
      COMMON DPR,SFACT,COSI,SQER,SLES,SSLES,BORDR,NDWK,SFCAST
    6 IF(MO-12)25,26,26
   26 SUMG = 0.
      DO 110 M=1,12
  110 SUMG=SUMG+G(M)
      DO 120 M=1,12
  120 G(M)=G(M)*(12./SUMG)
   25 SCUR=A*SS/G(MO)+Z11*(SLAST+RLAST)
      IF(NO)39,39,38
   38 FCUR=B*SS/SCUR+Z12*G(MO)
      G(MO)=FCUR
   39 RCUR=C*(SCUR-SLAST)+Z13*RLAST
      RLAST = RCUR
      DO 130 M=1,5
  130 PR(M)=PR(M+1)
      DK = 0.
      DO 606 KANT = 1,KA
      ISUB = MO + KANT
      IF(ISUB-12)44,44,43
   43 ISUB=ISUB-12
   44 DK = DK + 1.
      SHAT(ISUB)=(SCUR+DK*RCUR)*G(ISUB)
      SLAST = SCUR
  606 CONTINUE
      ISUB1 = MO
      IF(ISUB1-12)900,901,901
  901 ISUB1 = 0
  900 SFCAST(ISUB1 + 1) = SHAT(ISUB1 + 1)
      AIC=0.
      DO 610 M=1,MA
      ISUB=MO+M
      IF(ISUB-12)611,611,612
  612 ISUB=ISUB-12
  611 AIC=AIC+SHAT(ISUB)
  610 CONTINUE
      ANC=0.
      DO 607 J=1,JA
      ISUB=MO+MA+J
      IF(ISUB-12)608,608,609
  609 ISUB=ISUB-12
  608 ANC=ANC+SHAT(ISUB)
  607 CONTINUE
      ANC = ESF*(ANC**PWR)
      AIC=AIC+ANC
      ABC=AH
      DO 620 I=1,LPT
  620 ABC=ABC+PR(I)
      AIC=AIC-ABC
      ISUB=MO+MA
      IF(ISUB-12)617,617,614
  614 ISUB=ISUB-12
  617 PR(MA) = AIC
      IF(PR(MA))301,302,302
  301 PR(MA)=0.
  302 UP=AUP*PF(ISUB)
      IF(PR(MA)-UP)801,801,802
  802 PR(MA)=UP
  801 PL=ALP*PF(ISUB)
      IF(PR(MA)-PL)803,804,804
  803 PR(MA)=PL
  804 PCU=PR(MA-1)*URP
      PCD=PR(MA-1)*TRP
      IF(PR(MA)-PCU)805,805,806
  806 PR(MA)=PCU
  805 IF(PR(MA)-PCD)807,808,808
  807 PR(MA)=PCD
  808 ISUB=MO+1
      IF(ISUB-12)615,615,616
  616 ISUB=ISUB-12
  615 DPR=PR(1)/WD(ISUB)
      SQER = SQER + (SS - SFCAST(MO))**2
      SLES = SLES + SS
      SSLES = SSLES + SS**2
      SS = 0.
  100 FORMAT(I4)
  101 FORMAT(F10.4)
      RETURN
      END
```

```
      SUBROUTINE REPORT
      DIMENSION G(12),SHAT(12),PF(12),WD(12),PR(6),SALES(100),FACT(12)
      DIMENSION SFCAST(12)
      COMMON FACT,SALES,G,SHAT,PF,WD,PR,PVC,TRP,URP,A,B,C,SLAST,RLAST
      COMMON JA,KA,MA,ALP,AUP,CBO,COI,PWR,ESF,AH,SBOS,Z11,Z12,Z13
      COMMON ANV,SS,NYMX,NSALE,TRFT,UL,TL,DAYST,BOST,BCOST,NO,MO,LPT
      COMMON DPR,SFACT,COSI,SQER,SLES,SSLES,BORDR,NDWK,SFCAST
      AVGBO = BORDR/DAYST
      AINV = ANV/DAYST
      YEAR = NYMX
      PPVC = PVC*YEAR
      TCOST = BCOST + COSI + PPVC
      DIV1 = DAYST
      DIV2 = 12.*YEAR
      SMEAN = SLES/DIV1
      S2 = SLES**2
      STDEV = ((SSLES - S2/DIV1)/(DIV1 - 1.))**.5
      RMSE = (SQER/DIV2)**.5
      COEFV = RMSE*DIV2/SLES
      TACOST = TCOST/YEAR
      URP = URP - 1.
      PRINT 100,NYMX
      PRINT 109,URP
      PRINT 101,SMEAN,STDEV
      PRINT 102,RMSE,COEFV
      PRINT 103,AINV,AVGBO
      PRINT 104,COSI
      PRINT 105,BCOST
      PRINT 106,PPVC
      PRINT 107,TCOST
      PRINT 108,TACOST
  100 FORMAT(/8HNYEAR = ,I2)
  101 FORMAT(/20HMEAN DAILY DEMAND = F6.0,5X,10HSTD DEV = F6.0)
  102 FORMAT(/16HRMSE OF FCAST = F10.0,5X,8HCOEFV = F7.4)
  103 FORMAT(/10HAVG INV = ,F8.0,5X,18HAVG BACK ORDERS = F10.0)
  104 FORMAT(/26HTOTAL INV CARRYING COST = F10.0)
  105 FORMAT(/24HTOTAL BACK ORDER COST = F10.0)
  106 FORMAT(/28HCOST OF PROD LEVEL CHANGE = F10.0)
  107 FORMAT(/13HTOTAL COST = F10.0)
  108 FORMAT(/25HTOTAL AVG COST PER YEAR = F10.0)
  109 FORMAT(/19HPROD LEVEL CHANGE =,F5.2)
      RETURN
      END
```

VARIABLE DICTIONARY FOR PRODUCTION-INVENTORY SIMULATION

A	Weighting factor for updating de-seasonalized current mean monthly sales, SLAST
AH	Current inventory
ALP	Absolute lower limit of monthly production rate
ANV	Cumulative unit days of inventory
AUP	Absolute upper limit of monthly production rate
B	Weighting factor for updating seasonal factor, G(I)
BCOST	Total back order cost
BORDR	Cumulative number of back order days
BOST	Total number of back orders
C	Weighting factor for updating trend factor, RLAST
CBO	Cost of back orders—$/unit/day
COI	Cost of carrying inventory—$/unit/day
COSI	Total inventory carrying cost
DAYST	Cumulative days at any time during the simulation
DPR	Daily production rate
ESF	Factor which determines fraction of smoothed forecasted demand to be included in the target inventory
FACT(I)	Factor used to vary actual demand for the ith month
G(I)	Seasonal factor used in forecasting for ith month
GRN(1.)	Random number between 0 and 1.
JA	Number of months over which forecasted sales are to be summed to calculate target inventory
KA	JA + MA

LPT	Lead time in months
MA	Lead time minus 1 month
MO	Number of the current month, i.e., January = 1, February = 2, etc.
NDWK	Number of the day of the week, i.e., Sunday = 1, Monday = 2, etc.
NO	Switch used to control updating of seasonal factors. If NO = 0, seasonal factors are not updated. If NO > 0, seasonal factors are updated.
NSALE	Maximum size of array, SALE(I)
NYMX	Total number of years simulation is run
PF(I)	Production factor for i^{th} month
PR(I)	Monthly production rate for i^{th} month
PVC	Cost of production rate change \$/year
PWR	Exponent used to dampen or smooth forecast demand in calculating target inventory
RDAY	Ratio of actual working days per week to 7.
RLAST	Current trend factor
SALES(I)	Probability distribution of daily sales
SBOS	Current number of back orders
SFACT	Total size of array, SALES(I)
SFCAST(I)	Forecasted sales for one month into the future. Used to calculate root mean square error of forecast.
SHAT(I)	Forecasted sales for i^{th} month
SLAST	Current de-seasonalized average monthly sales
SLES	Sum of actual monthly sales
SQER	Sum of difference between forecasted and actual monthly sales squared
SS	Total monthly sales
SSLES	Sum of actual monthly sales squared
TL	Reciprocal of maximum fraction by which trend factor departs from mean value of TRFT × DAYST
TRFT	Trend factor in units/day for actual sales
TRP	Lower limit of relative production rate change from one month to the next
UL	Reciprocal of maximum fraction by which actual seasonal factors depart from forecast seasonal factors.
URP	Upper limit of relative production rate change from one month to the next
WDI	Working days in i^{th} month

INPUT DATA FOR PRODUCTION-INVENTORY SIMULATION

```
NYMX  =  30

JA    =  1

KA    =  3

MA    =  2

NO    =  1

NSALE =  100

ALP   =  4000.

AUP   =  30,000.

CBO   =  1.1

COI   =  0.0545

UL    =  20.

TL    =  1.X10^8

SFACT =  100.

A     =  0.2

B     =  0.3

C     =  0.0
```

```
SLAST = 14,000.

RLAST = 0.

TRFT = 0.

SALES(I), I = 1, 2, 3, ... 100
580.  590.  590.  590.  600.  600.  600.  600.  600.  610.  610.  610.  610.
610.  610.  610.  610.  610.  620.  620.  620.  620.  620.  620.  620.  620.
620.  620.  620.  620.  620.  630.  630.  630.  630.  630.  630.  630.  630.
640.  640.  640.  640.  640.  640.  640.  640.  640.  640.  640.  640.  640.
640.  640.  640.  650.  650.  650.  650.  650.  650.  650.  650.  650.  650.
650.  660.  660.  660.  660.  660.  660.  660.  660.  660.  660.  670.  670.
630.  630.  630.  630.  630.  630.  630.  690.  690.  700.  640.  640.  640.
670.  670.  670.  670.  670.  680.  680.  680.  680.
```

FACT(I)

I = 1   2   3   4   5   6   7   8   9   10   11   12
  1.233 1.061 .824 1.270 1.057 .815 .971 .915 1.160 1.034 .927 1.075

G(I)

I = 1   2   3   4   5   6   7   8   9   10   11   12
  1.233 1.061 .824 1.270 1.057 .815 .971 .915 1.160 1.034 .927 1.075

PF(I) =   1.   for   I = 1 to 12

WD(I)

I = 1   2   3   4   5   6   7   8   9   10   11   12
  31. 31. 30. 31. 30. 31. 31. 31. 30. 31. 30. 31.

```
PR(1)   = 16800.

PR(2)   = 14000.

RDAY    = 0.7143
```

PROBLEMS

1. A plant has 10,000 "automatic" producing units (enough so that the number down has no appreciable effect on the average breakdowns). Breakdowns occur at random with an average interval between breakdowns of 5 minutes (use Poisson distribution in the chapter). Breakdowns are indicated by a flashing red light over the equipment, and it takes virtually no time for a maintenance man to get to a breakdown. However, sometimes all maintenance men are busy, and the breakdowns must wait. Fifty-seven per cent of the breakdowns are of a standard type and take one minute to fix. The time to fix the rest of the breakdowns follows a random pattern which may be approximated by a Poisson distribution with an average of five tenths of an hour.

   Related data:
   Maintenance men on day rate get $2.00/hour.
   Down time costs 20 cents/minute.
   The first man free takes the next job in line (and can't get any help).
   Breakdowns cost money not only when being fixed but also when waiting to be fixed.

   a) How many maintenance men should be hired on a long-term basis?

   b) What is the total cost of the "best" program?

   c) Given that a maintenance man receives $2.00/hour, and your answer to question (*a*), at what lower hourly pay rate (for all men) would you estimate that it would be economic to add an additional man?

d) If each man is assigned a given number of machines and repairs only his own machines, how many men are needed? What is the cost of the best program? If the number of men found in (*a*) are hired on this new basis, what is the total cost?

2. See the Cleveland Steel Company's problem described in Problem No. 6, Chapter 9, Incremental Analysis. Carry through a Monte Carlo solution for determining the number of tons of ore to store.

$$\text{Let: } s = \$3$$
$$t = \$10$$
$$b = \$1$$

Probability distribution for number of weeks in the ice season:

Probability	0%	8%	47%	31%	11%	2%	1%	0%
Weeks	11	12	13	14	15	16	17	18

Probability distribution for average ore demand (in tons) per week during the winter season:

Probability	0%	4%	16%	42%	21%	9%	4%	2%	1%	1%
Tons	7,800	8,000	8,200	8,400	8,600	8,800	9,000	9,200	9,400	9,600

3. In the rejects planning illustration given in Chapter 9, Incremental Analysis, determine by Monte Carlo, the economic schedule with an order of 40, using the distribution given, and including the possibility of having to set up more than once.

4. In the waiting-line maintenance illustration given in Chapter 8, Total Value Analysis, both the arrival rate (of jobs) and the servicing time were random variables (Problem No. 7). Determine, by Monte Carlo, the economic machine assignment if, in this case, the servicing time were a constant equal to the average of the distribution given.

5. For Problem No. 9, Chapter 9, find the expected value of the optimum stocking policy by Monte Carlo.

6. A group of r maintenance men service 8 machines. Each machine calls for service at random (exponential) at an average of once every 4 hours. Service times are also random with an average of one hour. When more than one machine is waiting, the one with the shortest repair time is serviced first. Calculate by Monte Carlo the waiting time for $r = 2$ and $r = 3$.

7. Two women work on a subassembly line. The first woman performs her operation and then pushes the part on to the second woman. The times required for both operations are normally distributed with a mean of 10 minutes and a standard deviation of one minute. The first woman stops working at random to talk to a friend for exactly 5 minutes. On the average she stops every 30 minutes. What is the mean expected number of subassemblies produced in an 8-hour day?

8. The Norton Generator Company is considering using an overhead crane to move heavy assemblies. The main building contains three departments arranged in a line. Calls for crane service come at random (exponential distribution) and may be for interdepartment or intradepartment service.

Dept.	Total Calls per 8-Hour Day	Internal	Probability That Call Will Be—		
			Dept. 1	Dept. 2	Dept. 3
1..........	5	—	—	1.00	—
2..........	17	0.40	0.25	—	0.35
3..........	12	0.90	—	0.10	—

Service time is also random (exponential) except for interdepartment travel time.

Dept.	Mean Service Time	Travel Time to Department		
		1	2	3
1..............	20 min.	X	1 min.	2 min.
2..............	5 min.	1 min.	X	1 min.
3..............	9 min.	2 min.	1 min.	X

How long will the average wait for service be if the crane is installed?

9. A job shop schedule is required. Times required in hours are included in the following table. The shop runs on an 8-hour day, and a 5-day week. Start Monday.

Jobs

Equipment		W	X	Y	Z
	A	7	3	9	6
	B	13	6	4	7
	C	9	2	5	4
	D	6	8	11	10
	E	4	5	12	1

Required operation order:
  W—B, A, C, D, E
  X—E, D, A, B, C
  Y—C, B, A, D, E
  Z—A, B, D, E, C
  a) What schemes are possible for obtaining a schedule?
  b) What schedule takes the fewest number of calendar days?

10. An assembly line is to be set up ("balanced"). The operations required, their times required in minutes, and the ordering constraints (e.g., *a* before *b* and *c*; *b* before *d* and *e*; etc.) are shown below:

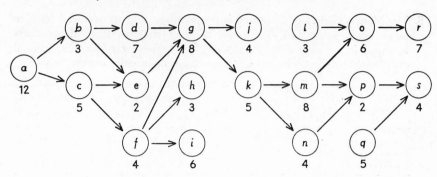

Each of these operations will be performed one at a time, on the assembly line. The operations cannot be split between work stations on the line, that is, they must be wholly contained within one work station. One work station may of course do more than one operation if time permits.

a) If four assembles are required per hour, what is the minimum number of work stations required?

b) If three assembles are required per hour, what is the minimum number of stations required?

c) What schemes are available for solving this type of problem?

11. Production in a given time period (P_t) is to be a function of sales forecasts for future time periods ($\hat{S}_i$), work force in the previous time period (W_{t-1}), and inventory at the end of the previous time period (I_{t-1}):

$$P_t = \sum_{i=t}^{i=t+n} a_i\hat{S}_i + bW_{t-1} + c - dI_{t-1}.$$

Similarly the work force decision rule is a function of the same variables:

$$W_t = \sum_{i=t}^{i=t+n} e_i\hat{S}_i + fW_{t-1} + g - hI_{t-1}.$$

Beginning inventory is 300 units.
Beginning employment is 80.
One worker in regular time within a month produces 6 units.
Sales (and their forecasts) are:

Jan.	Feb.	Mar.	Apr.	May	June	July	Aug.	Sept.	Oct.	Nov.	Dec.
400	300	400	500	550	400	300	300	400	500	600	400

Use the following decision rule coefficients:

$a_t = 0.5$; $a_{t+1} = 0.2$; $a_{t+2} = 0.1$; $b = 0.9$; $c = 150$; $d = 0.5$; $e_t = 0.019$; $e_{t+1} = 0.012$; $e_{t+2} = 0.008$; $f = 0.7$; $g = 2$; $h = 0.01$.

a) Work out the fluctuations in production, work force, and inventory for the year (assume sales next year will duplicate this year's sales).

b) Work through the rules again for the year, using the above sales forecast again, but this time let actual sales be 50 per cent above or below the forecasted figures, flipping a coin each month to determine the direction of the forecast error. Comparing results of (b) with (a), are any effects of forecast errors suggested?

c) How would costs be worked into this analysis?

12. A major material used in production by the X company can only be purchased in quantities of 2,000 or any multiple of 2,000 (greater than 1). Ordering costs (marginal) are estimated at $4.00, and carrying and storage costs are 30 per cent per year based on average inventory. The following discount scale applies:

Quantity	Price/Unit
2,000	$0.900
4,000	0.895
10,000	0.890

A table of delivery times gives the following experiences:

Delivery Time (Days)	% of Total Experience
1	0
2	0
3	5
4	10
5	20
6	40
7	15
8	5
9	3
10	2

If this item is unavailable at any time, the company estimates the probable loss to be $100/day.

a) Assuming demand is steady at 500 per day (250 working days per year), what is the best inventory policy to follow?

b) Demand per day is a variable according to the following distribution:

Demand	No. of Days/Year
0	100
400	50
800	40
1,200	25
1,600	15
2,000	10
2,400	5
2,800	3
3,200	2

Set up this situation to find the best inventory policy by Monte Carlo simulation. Record results for the policies you select until one order has been placed and received for at least one of the policies (use random number table, Appendix II, Table G, in textbook).

13. The following is a tabulation of demand experience for a spare part (the plant works 360 days per year):

No. of Units Demanded	No. of Days
0	80
1	60
2	40
3	30
4	15
5	5

Replenishment time has varied according to the following:

No. of Days to Receive Order	No. of Orders
5	10
6	40
7	25
8	15
9	7
10	3

The part costs $50, and carrying charges are 25 per cent per year. Ordering cost is figured at $30 per order placed due to high fixed receiving costs per lot. If the part is unavailable when needed, the company estimates a cost of $150/day/outage.

a) What is the least cost reorder point and order quantity?

b) If the manufacturer will give you a 10 per cent discount on orders of 50 or more, will it pay to take advantage of this lower price?

c) Set up a Monte Carlo routine for determining the answer to part (a). Show how you would generate experience, how you would keep books on inventory policy, and how the results of the simulation would be used to determine optimum policy.

14. A group of machinists, A, B, C, and D, share an expensive tool and pass it between themselves rather than returning it to the toolroom. The table below shows the per cent probabilities that a given machinist will have passed the tool to the corresponding man in the table at the end of the hour.

		To			
		A	B	C	D
	A	40	10	35	15
From	B	65	0	20	15
	C	30	20	50	0
	D	5	5	10	80

a) Simulate the location of the tool in order to determine the percentage of the time each machinist has the tool.

b) What confidence do you have that the machinist shown by the simulation to have the tool the largest percentage of the time, in fact is the individual who has the tool the largest percentage of the time?

15. Given the analysis of the valve problem as presented in Figures 11–4 and 11–5, and Tables 11–1 and 11–2, what confidence limits would you place on the total time estimate of the cheapest policy—the next cheapest policy? What statement can you make about the number of hours of simulation advisable for this problem?

16.[10] A chemical company desires to minimize the sum of production and inventory costs for one of its products. Demand for the product is highly seasonal. Monthly sales may fluctuate by as much as ± 25 per cent. No sales are made on Saturday, Sunday, or holidays.

The product is produced 365 days per year. Yields are better in the winter than in the summer. Consequently, in planning production, each month is assigned a production factor which is a ratio between the actual production and theoretical maximum production. These factors are listed on the data sheet. In planning production, a lead time of one month is necessary. This means that at the end of December, for example, February's production is set. January's production was set at the end of November and cannot now be changed. Using a one month's lead time allows the production department ample time to make the manpower and equipment changes that are necessary for a corresponding change in the production rate. These manpower and equipment changes are expensive and consequently, a cost penalty is assigned for various ranges (expressed as per cent of change from one month to the next) of changes in the production rate. These penalties are shown on the attached data sheets.

Previously, the target inventory has been one-half month of sales. The cost of carrying inventory is shown on the attached data sheets. When a back order occurs, it must ultimately be filled, and all back orders carry a daily cost penalty which is shown on the data sheet.

A computer program has been written which simulates the activities described above. The demand distribution is simulated using a Monte Carlo technique. At the end of each month, the program forecasts monthly sales using an exponential forecasting model and uses this sales forecast to set a target inventory. It also simulates daily production and sales, and maintains records of the current inventory level and number of back orders. When the simulation is completed, the program calculates (1) the mean and standard deviation of the daily demand, (2) the root mean square error of the forecast and the coefficient of variation, (3) the average inventory and average number of back orders, (4) the total cost of carrying inventory, back orders, and production level change, (5) the sum of the three costs listed in (4), and (6) the total average cost per year.

Target inventories are calculated using the following relationship:

$$\text{ANC} = \text{ESF} \times \left(\sum_{i=3}^{\text{MA}+\text{JA}} \text{SALES}_i \right)^{\text{PWR}} \tag{1}$$

---

[10] The program given in the Appendix can be used for this problem and requires in the form given there an IBM 1620/1311 for execution. Since it is in FORTRAN, it may be modified for execution on other machines. The data shown in the Appendix is that which should be used for this problem.

in which

ANC = target inventory for 2 months into the future.
ESF = factor which determines the fraction of monthly sales forecasts to be included in the target inventory.
$SALES_i$ = forecast of monthly sales i months into the future.
PWR = exponent to dampen or smooth effect of changes in monthly forecasts.
MA = lead time + 1 month.
JA = 1 (may be increased if a longer forecasting period is desired).

This target inventory is for the end of the second month into the future. Once the target inventory has been established, the production rate for 2 months into the future is calculated and is

$$PR_2 = \sum_{i=1}^{2} SALES_i + ANC - AH - PR_1 \qquad (2)$$

in which

PR_2 = production rate for two months into the future.
AH = inventory at the end of this month.
PR_1 = production for next month (already set at the end of the previous month)
$SALES_i$ = same as in (1).
ANC = same as in (1).

Turning on the sense switches produces the following additional data:
Sense Switch #1   On for multiple runs.
Sense Switch #2   The total sales for each month. The production rate for the next two months.
Sense Switch #3   The sales forecasts for the next 3 months.
Sense Switch #4   The daily sales. This switch is also used to correct errors when typing in data. It *must* be off when data is being inserted on the typewriter. If a mistake is made in typing, turn the switch on and press release and start. Then turn off the switch and type the data again.

The program will halt in manual mode after processing the number of years of data specified by the user. (For this problem all runs will be three years in length.) To process additional data, turn on Sense Switch #1 and press the start key on the console.

The following data must be provided by the user at time of execution.
a) Cost of production level change.
b) Value of production level change expressed as a decimal.

You must punch this data yourself with format 2(F10.0) in the order listed above and insert this card at the end of the data deck.

c) Values of PWR, ESF, and ANC in that order must be read in on the typewriter with format 3(F10.0). (Note: use values of PWR to the nearest two tenths and do not carry ANC to a decimal.)

(1) Determine the total average cost per year resulting from using the current rule.

(2) Determine a new rule which reduces the current total average cost per year by at least 55 per cent.

(3) After you have selected a rule which satisfies (2) above, test your rule with an increased value of forecasting error (decrease variable UL in the program).

(4) From the results of (3) above, what effect upon the optimum inventory rule you have selected will decreasing the accuracy of the forecasts have? Why?

DATA

Production Data

Maximum production rate = 30,000 lb./mo.
Minimum production rate = 4,000 lb./mo.
January production   = 19,000 lb./mo.
Production Efficiency Factors

Jan.	0.95	July	0.91
Feb.	0.90	Aug.	0.78
Mar.	0.70	Sept.	0.90
Apr.	0.73	Oct.	0.80
May	1.00	Nov.	0.86
June	0.72	Dec.	0.84

Plant operates 365 days per year.
One month production scheduling lead time.

Inventory Data

Current inventory: To be established.
Old rule inventory goal: $\frac{1}{2}$ month's supply.

Demand Data

Average monthly demand: 14,300
Sales forecast at end of December: Jan. 17,578
                                   Feb. 14,930
                                   Mar. 11,595

Cost Data

±10% rate change from one month to the next $ 5,000/yr.
±30% rate change from one month to the next $15,000/yr.
±50% rate change from one month to the next $32,000/yr.
Inventory: $0.0545/lb./day on average inventory
Back order: $1.10/lb./day of stockout

CHAPTER 12

Behavior and Heuristics

To THIS point this text has focused on the building of mathematical models as an aid to decision making for problems in operations management. The earlier chapter on simulation has moved the reader away somewhat from the concept of optimization. This chapter continues in that direction, while maintaining the spirit of analysis. An analytical extension beyond mathematical models for optimization must take place for at least three reasons:

1. The complexity of some problems is so extensive that even though the essence of the problem may be stated in a mathematical framework, the computation required even on the largest computers is quite infeasible.
2. Some problems are so amorphous that a mathematical model cannot capture their most important characteristics. This is especially true of most policy type problems with which top managers must grapple.
3. Even where a mathematical model may be successfully employed, the prelude to the model and the work subsequent to the modeling must be of a less formal nature.

Fortunately it is possible to present some research results addressed to aspects of all of these problem areas. While this text has addressed itself largely to a normative approach, that is how problems *should* (might) be solved, much of this applicable research has dealt with *descriptions* of decision-making behavior. The people doing the research have felt that useful insights, even from a normative standpoint, may be gained by studying actual problem-solving behavior. Very often these studies have taken place in either an experimental setting, or what might be thought of as a special setting. Chess playing is a good example of this.

As the reader is probably aware, chess is a rather complex game to play well, but an easy game to play poorly. The basic *rules* of chess can be learned in five minutes, while some people virtually devote their whole lives in an attempt to understand how the game should be played. Though the rules are easily specified, the number of choices of play to be made in one game are so large that it is completely impossible to specify a complete game. Formal algorithms are unavailable for winning the game. Yet some people play excellent chess. Therefore the approach taken in the research mentioned has been to study the chess playing (problem solving) behavior of particular chess players. They were asked, as they played in particular situations, to verbalize their thoughts—what was it that they were taking into consideration. From these protocols (written descriptions of thoughts and thought processes) came essentially two outcomes. At the specific level, the researchers were able to write computer programs which would play a fairly good game of chess and play in much the same style as the players studied.

At a more general level (the stronger test of good research) the kinds of heuristics which these problem solvers used could be set forth. Heuristic is a word now commonly used in this regard but difficult to define well. It can be thought of as a method for searching the solution space. Though the method should be helpful and may save time, it has no assurance of finding *the* answer in the sense that an algorithm does. In the vernacular, a heuristic method has been called a rule of thumb.

Administrative Man

Before a more detailed picture is given of heuristic methods in operations management, a wider selection of the decision-making behavior literature should be described. The books of Simon, March, and Cyert have set the tone of much of this work. From the earlier book of Simon, *Administrative Behavior*,[1] through the March and Simon book, *Organizations*,[2] to Cyert and March's, *A Behavioral Theory of the Firm*,[3] the work has moved from a conceptual level toward very specific descriptive models of decision making, with Simon's later book, *The New Science of Management Decision*,[4] being a brief and useful summary of this work.

The main point of departure taken in this work is that decision

---

[1] H. A. Simon, *Administrative Behavior: A Study of Decision-Making Processes in Administrative Organization* (2d ed.; New York: Macmillan Co., 1957).

[2] J. G. March and H. A. Simon, *Organizations* (New York: John Wiley & Sons, Inc., 1958).

[3] R. M. Cyert and J. G. March, *A Behavioral Theory of the Firm* (Englewood Cliffs, N.J.: Prentice-Hall, Inc., 1963).

[4] H. A. Simon, *The New Science of Management Decision* (New York: Harper & Bros., 1960.)

making and problem solving is *the* useful and scientific view of an organization.

What is the scientifically relevant description of an organization? It is a description that, so far as possible, designates for each person in the organization what decisions that person makes, and the influences to which he is subject in making each of these decisions.[5]

The concept of economic man is dismissed as a myth, and a not very useful one. Economic man is presumed to have three properties.[6] He is (*a*) completely informed, (*b*) infinitely sensitive, and (*c*) rational. All of these characteristics are questionable, and Simon particularly questions rationality.[7]

Actual behavior falls short, in at least three ways, of objective rationality. . . .
1. Rationality requires a complete knowledge and anticipation of the consequences that will follow on each choice. In fact knowledge of consequences is always fragmentary.
2. Since these consequences lie in the future, imagination must supply the lack of experienced feeling in attaching value to them. But values can be only imperfectly anticipated.
3. Rationality requires a choice among all possible alternative behaviors. In actual behavior, only a very few of all these possible alternatives ever come to mind.

In place of economic man, administrative man is put forward as a more realistic model. Administrative man has *intended* but *bounded* rationality. "Administrative theory is peculiarly the theory of intended and bounded rationality—of the behavior of human beings who 'satisfice' because they have not the wits to maximize."[8] Administrative man is looking for answers to his problems which are "good enough." What is good enough and how he searches for these answers are part of the developing theory.

Cyert and March in *A Behavioral Theory of the Firm*[9] have developed these ideas into a relatively extensive picture of decision making and problem solving within and by organizations. They build their theory around four concepts:

1. Quasi resolution of conflict: In order to circumvent the problems of conflicting goals between organization parts and members, organizations treat goals as independent constraints, factor problems and treat them inde-

---

[5] Simon, *Administrative Behavior, op. cit.*, p. 37.

[6] D. W. Taylor, "Decision-Making and Problem-Solving" in J. G. March (ed.), *Handbook of Organizations* (Chicago: Rand McNally & Co., 1965), p. 50.

[7] Simon, *Administrative Behavior, op. cit.*, p. 81.

[8] *Ibid.*, p. 24.

[9] Cyert and March, *op. cit.*, p. 116.

pendently, use acceptable-level (satisficing) decision rules, and attend to different goals at different times.

2. Uncertainty avoidance: Rather than facing uncertainty from long range planning, organizations provide short-run responses to short-run feedback. "They solve pressing problems rather than develop long-run strategies." In addition, they negotiate with their environment, explicitly and implicitly—customers, suppliers, competitors—to ameliorate an otherwise uncertain fate.

3. Problemistic search: Search is activated by a problem, and depressed by a problem solution. This search tends to be simple minded and mechanical, only becoming extended as needed.

4. Organizational learning: With experience, both goals (aspiration levels) and search rules are modified.

Figure 12–1 is a summary of these concepts and process.

An extension of the concept of problemistic search has been reported by Pounds.[10] Here problems are defined as differences—differences between an existing situation and a desired situation or model. Four classes of models are defined:

1. Historical Models: A difference appears between the historical trend and current actual (e.g., scrap is up compared to last month).

2. Planning Models: A difference appears between the planned and the actual (e.g., profit is below that budgeted).

3. Other Peoples' Models: Someone defines a problem for the manager (e.g., the personnel manager mentions low departmental morale).

4. Extra-organizational Models: Relative to some other organization, this one appears to be performing badly (e.g., a competitor brings out a new model).

As may be apparent then, models including those presented in this book are not only means for solving problems but also means for finding problems (to be solved). Operations Research models might be considered a special type of extra-organizational models for problem finding.

In addition to problem *finding,* there are a number of other aspects of the application of mathematical modeling which can benefit from future behavioral research. Some of these are:

1. The problem will seem to have characteristics which are not provided for in the model which is presented in the literature. The model must be extended and/or the problem must be simplified.

2. The problem will be tied into other problems with no clear separation between them—the world is full of interrelated systems. Bounds to the analysis must be supplied.

---

[10] W. F. Pounds, "The Process of Problem Finding," *Working Paper 148–65,* Alfred P. Sloan School of Management, M.I.T.

Figure 12–1

ORGANIZATIONAL DECISION PROCESS IN ABSTRACT FORM

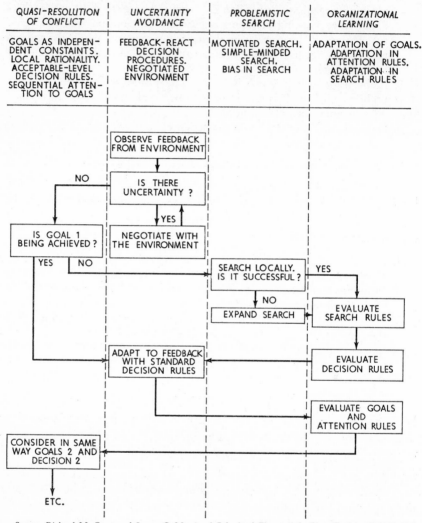

Source: Richard M. Cyert and James G. March, *A Behavioral Theory of the Firm* (Englewood Cliffs, N.J.: Prentice-Hall, Inc., 1963). Reprinted by permission of Prentice-Hall, Inc., Englewood Cliffs, N.J.

3. Data required for the model may be unavailable and/or expensive to obtain or conversely available in such detail and quantities that data aggregation is called for.

4. The validity of many models is extremely difficult to justify. A certain amount of circularity can usually be found in most validations.

5. Because the analyst is often not the decision maker, problems of influencing the decision by the analysis often exist.

The research described to this point has been almost entirely "positive" or descriptive. The attempt has been to explain how managers in organizations actually solve problems. Attention has not explicitly been paid to how problems should be solved (the normative viewpoint). A philosophic point to be made here is that anyone really interested in improving the problem solving ability of an organization is well advised to add to his understanding of actual problem-solving processes.

Lindblom in "The Science of Muddling Through"[11] makes the case that the administrator *must* rely on these informal methods of decision making, especially for the large and important problems, and that it is therefore useful from a normative standpoint to formalize the (descriptive) process. He labels the process of economic man as "Rational-Comprehensive (Root)," and that of administrative man as "Successive Limited Comparisons (Branch)," and makes the following side by side comparison of the two methods:

Rational-Comprehensive (Root)	*Successive Limited Comparisons (Branch)*
1a. Clarification of values or objectives distinct from and usually prerequisite to empirical analysis of alternative policies.	1b. Selection of value goals and empirical analysis of the needed action are not distinct from one another but are closely intertwined.
2a. Policy-formulation is therefore approached through means-end analysis: First the ends are isolated, then the means to achieve them are sought.	2b. Since means and ends are not distinct, means-end analysis is often inappropriate or limited.
3a. The test of a "good" policy is that it can be shown to be the most appropriate means to desired ends.	3b. The test of a "good" policy is typically that various analysts find themselves directly agreeing on a policy (without agreeing that it is the most appropriate means to an agreed objective).
4a. Analysis is comprehensive: Every important relevant factor is taken into account.	4b. Analysis is drastically limited: i) Important possible outcomes are neglected. ii) Important alternative potential policies are neglected. iii) Important affected values are neglected.
5a. Theory is often heavily relied upon.	5b. A succession of comparisons greatly reduces or eliminates reliance on theory.

[11] C. E. Lindblom, "The Science of Muddling Through," *Public Administration Review*, Vol. XIX, No. 2 (Spring, 1959).

Lindblom's main point is that for complex decisions, rather than comparing alternative policies to some abstract standard (composed of a weighted set of values), the alternative policies must be compared directly to each other, and then only the marginal differences between the set of values need be considered.

Perhaps the issue between the supporters of economic man and the supporters of administrative man can be resolved pragmatically. Only when a problem is sufficiently explicit and constrained, or can be made so by the experienced analyst, can quantitative models be usefully employed. Hitch in a sense is quoted to this effect:[12]

I would make the empirical generalization from my experience at RAND and elsewhere that operations research is the art of sub-optimizing, i.e., of solving some lower level problems, and that difficulties increase and our special competence diminishes by an order of magnitude with every level of decision-making we attempt to ascend. The sort of simple explicit model which operations researchers are so proficient in using can certainly reflect most of the significant factors influencing traffic control on the George Washington Bridge, but the proportion of the relevant reality which we can represent by any such model or models in studying, say, a major foreign policy decision, appears to be most trivial.

What should be remembered along with this realism (and to some extent pessimism) is that the boundary lines of effective explicit model building are being continually pushed out and its domains expanded.

Decision Making as Information-Processing

Much work of explicit model building of what on the surface appear to be informal and amorphous decision processes has recently been carried out. These models incorporate many heuristics, or rules of thumb, and most of them are sufficiently detailed, and therefore lengthy, that they are expressed (and tested) as computer programs. They explicitly consider the problem solver as an information processing system. Most of this work can be placed into one of two categories:[13] (1) the simulation of cognitive processes, and (2) artificial intelligence.

While both categories include human-like steps in their decision processes, the first attempts to be descriptive in the sense that a replication of the human decision maker is accomplished, the test being the difficulty of distinguishing between the output of the computer program and the man when both are supplied the same input parameters. The

[12] C. Hitch, "Operations Research and National Planning—A Dissent," *Operations Research*, October, 1957.

[13] E. A. Feigenbaum and J. Feldman (eds.), *Computers and Thought* (New York: McGraw-Hill Book Co., Inc., 1963).

second category, artificial intelligence, attempts to build a problem-solving process, which, though it may employ the same types of heuristics used by a man, is not an attempt to duplicate a particular man's output—in fact a better output is sought.

Assembly Line Balancing

An early example of artificial intelligence in the area of operations management was Tonge's[14] work in assembly line balancing. Where a product, such as a refrigerator, is assembled along a continuous production line, the many individual operations (perhaps a hundred) must be grouped into work stations (perhaps twenty). This grouping is, of course, constrained by factors like required assembly sequence. For a given rate of output, the problem is basically to use the fewest work stations (and operators)—this requires the work time at each station to be as close to the cycle time as possible. If work time at each station equaled the cycle time, this would be a perfectly "balanced" line.

Tonge's work supplies a heuristic procedure (and computer program) to accomplish this job of line balancing. He has this to say about some common characteristics of existing heuristic procedures:[15]

1. *Factorization* of the problem into a number of "smaller" problems and subproblems (often through means-end analysis), with a corresponding goal-subgoal organization of behavior. For example, the "Chess Machine" might realize that it cannot play P-K4 because it would lose an exchange on that square, and consequently sets up the subgoal of first bringing another man to bear on its K4.
2. Use of *cues in the environment* to determine the particular behavior evoked from a wide set of possible alternatives available to the program. That is, a high degree of interdependence between the specific problem (from a more general class) being considered and the particular problem-solving methods used. Thus, the methods used by the assembly line balancing program for choosing elements to shift between groupings depend on the particular characteristics of those groupings.
3. Use of *recursive procedures* to bring to bear on problems the same repertoire of problem-solving techniques used on the original problem. Thus, the "Logic Theorist" can use the same "bag of tricks" to prove a derived expression as to prove the initial statement from which the derived expression was produced.
4. *No guarantee* of a satisfactory solution or, often, of any solution. For example, the "Chess Machine," because of time and space limitations, may not be able to consider some promising continuations, including the a posteriori optimum one.

---

[14] F. M. Tonge, *A Heuristic Program for Assembly Line Balancing* (Englewood Cliffs, N.J.: Prentice-Hall, Inc., 1961).

[15] F. M. Tonge, "Summary of a Heuristic Line Balancing Procedure" in Feigenbaum and Feldman, *op. cit.*, pp. 172–73.

5. Because a heuristic procedure substitutes the effort reduction of its short cuts for the guaranteed optimal solution of an exhaustive method, the *justification* of such a program as a problem-solver must be in terms of the number of cases successfully solved and the relative amount of effort involved.

The computer program which was developed for the assembly line balancing problem was written in a list processing language or symbol manipulation language. This is in contradistinction to a number manipulation language—the more commonly used type of computer language. In addition to the computer storage space required for the language program itself, the assembly line balancing program required about 6700 machine locations. This heuristic program recursively used the following general scheme:[16]

Phase I constructs a hierarchy of increasingly simpler line balancing problems by aggregating groups of elements (operations) into a single compound element. Each of these compound elements is itself a member of this same class of line balancing problems, since it is made up of elements requiring a given operation time and among whom partial ordering relationships exist.

Phase II solves a simple (small number of elements) line balancing problem by assigning groups of available workmen to elements and then taking as subproblems those compound elements (simple problems in themselves) which have been assigned more than one man (work station). This approach requires heuristics for aggregating groups of elements into compound elements, for solving the simplified problems thus created and for reintroducing the detail of the original problem when the simplified version does not yield a solution.

A third phase of the problem-solving process, utilizing virtually the same heuristics as already required, involves "smoothing" the final work load (assigned time) among work stations.

While the main thrust of this ground-breaking research was exploratory (rather than efficiency), the heuristic program developed was able to solve the problems with about the same results as experienced industrial engineers.

Paper Mill Scheduling—The Trim Problem

A further example of heuristic decision rules, or artificial intelligence, is given by Pierce's[17] work on paper mill scheduling. While there are a number of important levels of this problem—jobs on a machine, machines in a plant, plants in a system—the most basic and the one having received the most attention in the literature is that of jobs on a

---

[16] *Ibid.*, p. 173.

[17] J. Pierce, *Some Large-Scale Production Scheduling Problems in the Paper Industry* (Englewood Cliffs, N.J.: Prentice-Hall, 1964).

machine, the so-called trim problem. As paper is manufactured in wide continuous strips, the problem is to map the jobs or orders onto this continuous strip so as to minimize the scrap or trim loss, where the sum of the order widths do not equal the process width of the paper strip. There are additional complications which can be added to the problem but this is sufficient.

The problem can be thought of as a very large linear programming problem, so large as to defy solution in its straightforward format. Because of this Pierce takes two other approaches. One is to decompose the linear program (a form of mathematical analysis which supplies an algorithm which guarantees a solution, i.e., an optimum schedule), while the other is to supply a heuristic decision rule which supplies "good" solutions quickly (on a large-scale computer).

These (heuristic) procedures are based on the simple notion of enumerating trim combinations until a "good" one is discovered, determining the maximum number of production rolls of this combination whose production is consistent with customer demand, and then reducing net customer demand by this production. The criterion of a good process in these procedures takes the form of a maximum amount (or per cent margin) of trim loss incurred per roll for the process. Besides this margin, the decision variables for these procedures include the ordering of customer widths and the specification of the set of widths to be searched before "giving up" and taking the best (minimum trim loss) combination discovered so far.[18]

Because Pierce had the unusual advantage in his study of having also developed a clever algorithm (the decomposed linear program), he was able to compare for a wide variety of empirical situations the schedule effectiveness produced by this heuristic decision rule to the optimum schedules. In many cases the heuristic did in fact produce the optimum schedule—in some it did not (it always produced a "good" *feasible* schedule). In all the cases, the heuristic used less computer time than the algorithm did, so Pierce was able to make some generalizations *at least for these problems* as to the economics of using the heuristic. The ability in most instances to generalize about the use of heuristics is highly limited, and in most problems of this magnitude there is no algorithm to use as an alternative, or as a basis of comparison.

Job Shop Scheduling—Sequencing Problem

Another example of heuristics with a strong normative orientation is Carroll's[19] work on job shop scheduling. This problem has been worked

---

[18] *Ibid.,* p. 10.

[19] D. C. Carroll, "Heuristic Sequencing of Single and Multiple Component Jobs," M.I.T. Ph.D. Thesis, unpublished, 1965.

on by many researchers as it is a good example of a large combinatorial problem which is dynamic and is a common one found in industry. The scheduling problem in its most simple form consists of a number of jobs to be done on a number of machines, each job having a number of operations to be performed by the various machines *in a specified sequence.* What feasible schedule covers the least total time?[20] At any point in time there will tend to be a number of jobs waiting to be processed at most machines. At each machine, which job is to be processed next and which ones are to wait further?

While work on formal mathematical approaches to this problem has been undertaken, the problem in its real dimensions is not only too large to be handled this way, but it is constantly changing with time, and in ways which cannot be anticipated. In other words, what seems to be called for is a real-time heuristic decision system using all available information. This is precisely what Carroll developed with the help of a computer, both for calculation of the heuristic decision rule and for maintenance of the data base, i.e., status of all jobs and all machines at all times.

Most heuristic decision rules to determine priority in the waiting line which have been developed are centered on two key variables: (1) processing time for the job on the machine, and (2) cost of delay of the job. Carroll tested a number of rules centered on these variables under a wide variety of experimental conditions and found that the heuristic decision rule which he termed "COVERT" was almost always superior in its performance. COVERT stands for C over T (C/T), where C is a cost of delay, based essentially on the total remaining processing times for all machines on the job compared to the job's due date, and T is the processing time for the job on the particular machine for which the job waits.

While much work had to be done to determine and demonstrate the superiority of the COVERT heuristic, it can be seen that the essential idea is quite simple. As is often the case, other equally plausible and simple heuristics had to be checked out to validate the superiority of the one heuristic described.

The Management Coefficients Heuristic

A somewhat different approach to artificial intelligence was used by Bowman in the problem of master production scheduling (see Case 16, page 802, in this book for a fuller description of this work). Rather

---

[20] E. H. Bowman, "The Schedule-Sequencing Problem," *Operations Research,* Vol. VII, No. 5 (September–October, 1959), p. 621.

than construct a process much like that used by a manager, as in the case of Tonge or Pierce, the decision outputs (not process) of the manager were analyzed in comparison with the relevant variables in the problem, and decision rules were constructed with the coefficients supplied by regression from the managers' own decisions. This type of artificial intelligence will now be explained more fully in the context of a study which Gordon did.[21] Gordon's study combines (1) simulation of cognitive processes (a program which replicates the actual planning process), (2) artificial intelligence (Bowman's management coefficients approach), and (3) operations research (the model of Holt, Modigliani, Simon and Muth, which is presented as Case 6 in this book, page 608). These three approaches might also be characterized as (1) descriptive, (2) heuristic, and (3) normative. A study of these three model types in some detail in one industrial context is presented here in order to give the reader some feel for what these approaches entail.

The actual decision modeled by Gordon was the development of the master production plan, by weeks, for a complete operating year. The production planning decision studied in this instance relates to the scheduling of production quantities and work force in the bottling operation of a major beverage producer. Although the total operation involved the manufacture, packaging and distribution of the product, the packaging segment was essentially the only one sensitive to the trade-offs between hiring and firing, overtime, and inventory. Two levels of managerial decision making were identified, one in the production control office of each of a number of branch plants and one in the head office planning department. Although both of these decision activities were analyzed in the actual study, only the head office planning models will be reported in detail here. The chronological procedure followed in this study was to develop a descriptive computer model of the actual decision procedure first, then two management coefficients models based on past planning decisions, and finally a normative or prescriptive model which purported to minimize the total relevant costs. Each of these models is described and their performance over a simulated test period is evaluated.

Descriptive Model

Through detailed examination of the information flows and repetitive interviewing of the planning personnel, a verbal description of the planning procedure was developed. The central office planning proce-

---

[21] John R. M. Gordon, "A Multi-Model Analysis of an Aggregate Scheduling Decision," M.I.T. Ph.D. Thesis, unpublished, 1966.

dure employed relates primarily to determining the number of line-shifts which will be operated during each week of the fiscal year. Given the sales forecast and the line-shift productivity and schedule, all other information follows through straightforward bookkeeping extensions. The determination of the line-shift schedule and the production per week will be referred to as Master Production Planning. The Master Production Planning procedure will be described verbally, then presented as a network and finally represented in flow chart form.

The primary input to the plan is the sales forecast for the fiscal year. This forecast shows the sales in thousands of cases which the Plant is expected to meet each week. The other basic input to the plan is a productivity function which relates the number of line-shifts operating to the production in thousands of cases. This function is determined from the previous year's actual performance in terms of production and line-shifts. This function, because of its averaging effect, incorporates a weighting for product mix and actual lines operated, both of which influence the actual productivity of the lines. These productivity values are determined for line-shift integers in the range two through eight.

Plant inventory is not considered in the development of the plan and is assumed to be held constant at one week's sales. This value is considered ideal for the purpose of absorbing random fluctuations of actual shipments with respect to planned shipments and to buffer individual products so that reasonably long production runs can be achieved with respect to change-over considerations.

The next variable considered in the planning procedure is the field inventory. This variable is viewed in aggregate for the total system served by the Plant and the acceptable range for planning purposes is from two to three and a half week's sales. This range of one and a half week's sales represents a restriction on inventory as a factor to absorb sales fluctuations in the planning stage.

The actual procedure assumes that production will remain at the present level and that field inventory at the end of the previous fiscal year is the starting inventory level. Inventory is computed at the end of each week assuming that production continues at the present level of the line-shifts and that sales occur as forecast. As long as the projected week-end inventory remains within the acceptable range, the line-shift level of production is not changed. If the week-end inventory falls below the acceptable minimum, the number of line-shifts is increased by one and the procedure repeated. If the week-end inventory rises above the acceptable maximum, the number of line-shifts is decreased by one and the procedure repeated. This basic projection of sales and production to obtain week-end inventories which are checked against an acceptable range, is repeated for each week of the fiscal year.

The plan now consists of the number of line-shifts to be operated each week during the fiscal year. This plan or profile of production activity over the year, is reviewed in terms of the number of different levels and frequency of change. The ideal profile is viewed as having only two changes during the year and having only two levels of operations. If the profile achieved during the initial pass does not have these characteristics, it is reviewed in detail from the point of view of achieving this ideal profile. To accomplish this, the acceptable inventory range is widened by half a week's sales in either direction thus making it one and a half to four week's sales. Using this increased inventory range, the procedure is repeated for those portions of the year where changes in level occur. The new line-shift plan, which still may have more than two changes, will be used but will be subject to close surveillance during the year as actual sales and production figures become available.

Figure 12–2 is a network diagram of the planning procedure employed to determine the line-shift schedule for the fiscal year.

The procedure as described is summarized in the flow chart shown in Figure 12–3. This form of presentation of the procedure indicates that it is relatively routine and could in fact be performed as a clerical task given the appropriate parameters. The key parameters of the procedure are the productivity function, the sales forecast, the acceptable inventory range, and the ideal production profile.

As will be described next, this flow chart was translated into a computer program in order to test, in a predictive sense, how accurately it represents the actual procedure used in the Central Office.

The flow chart of Figure 12–3 has been translated into a FORTRAN program of the procedure used in the Central Office to plan production for the fiscal year. The listing of the program is given in Figure 12–4.

The program represents the integration of a number of elemental discrimination nets as identified through observation of the actual process. The basic contention is that each of these elements has a one-for-one correspondence with an element in the actual procedure. By linking these elements together in the proper sequence and relationship, the output of the program should be the same as the output of the actual procedure assuming the same input.

The actual test that was used was as follows. The Plan for a given fiscal year contains the sales forecast as well as the production plan and thus forms the basic input and output test. Using the production results for the fiscal year immediately preceding, a scatter diagram was drawn

Figure 12–2

DISCRIMINATION NETS IN PLANNING PROCEDURE

(a) Determining Line-Shift Levels

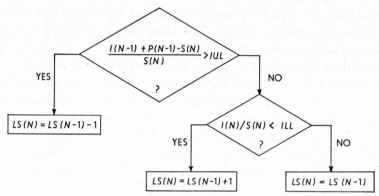

(b) Adjusting Profile

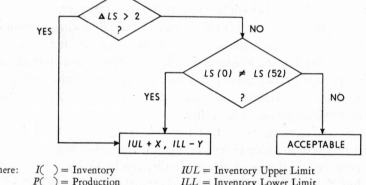

where:

$I(\ )$ = Inventory		IUL = Inventory Upper Limit	
$P(\ )$ = Production		ILL = Inventory Lower Limit	
$S(\ )$ = Sales Forecast		N = Period	
$LS(\ )$ = No. of Line-Shifts		X = Parameterized increment (eg. 0.5)	
		Y = Parameterized decrement (eg. 0.5)	

and a linear production function developed to give the number of cases produced by integer line-shifts from two to six. Finally, the acceptable inventory range was set at the same levels as indicated by the protocol of the procedure—namely, two or three and one-half week's sales.

With these parameters set, the sales forecast for the year was processed by the program to produce the essential elements of the Plan. The key variable considered in evaluating the accuracy of the model, was the line-shifts specified for each week. This was therefore a profile comparison in terms of the number of changes in levels, when they occurred, and what the magnitude of the change was. The initial output was not satisfactory in that although the magnitude and number of changes was

Figure 12–3

FLOW CHART OF PLANNING PROCEDURE

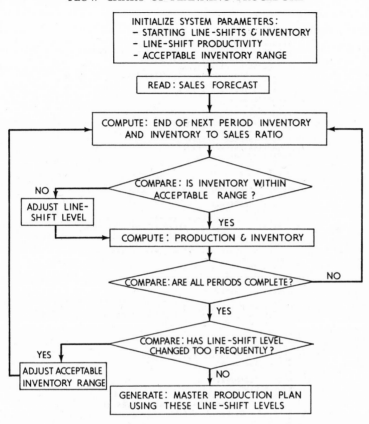

almost identical, the timing was not. Reassessment of the program as a reflection of the procedure and further discussion with the personnel involved in the actual procedure led to some modifications which produced virtually perfect correspondence between the two outputs.

The critical factor which emerges from attempting to capture and model this procedure is the trade-off which occurs implicitly between shelf-life and production profile in the planning process for the Plant.

Management Coefficients Models (Heuristic)

For the heuristic decision rule approach relatively simple models were developed to relate the decision variables, production and work force, to two sets of independent variables. The first set of independent variables were to be the classic economic variables of aggregate scheduling normative models such as sales forecast and present inventory and work force. The second set of independent variables were to be those which were revealed by the descriptive model and which might be more

Figure 12–4

PROGRAM LISTING

```
ZZ      JRM GØRDØN
ZZXEQ FØRTGØ
C  C   JRM GØRDØN
C      PRØDUCTIØN PLANNING SIMULATIØN
       DIMENSIØN SALES(60),BLS(60),CINV(60),PRØD(60)
       DIMENSIØN RINV(60),P(10),PER(60)
C      SET PLANNING PARAMETERS
       READ 10, NTØT, BLS(1), CINV(1), CIUL, CILL, X, Y
    10 FØRMAT(I8, 2F8.0, 4F8.2)
       READ 15, (P(I), I = 2, 6)
    15 FØRMAT(6F8.0)
       NUM = NTØT + 1
       NUMB = NTØT + 4
C      ENTER SALES FØRECAST DATA
       DØ 18 N = 2, NUMB
       READ 20,SALES(N),PER(N)
    20 FØRMAT(8X,F8.0,8X,F8.0)
    18 PER(N)=PER(N)/100.
C      INITIALIZE
       J = 0
    21 M = 0
       DØ 60 N = 2, NUM
       ISW = 0
       BLS(N) = BLS(N-1)
       K1 = BLS(N)
C      END ØF PERIØD INVENTØRY AT PRESENT LEVEL
    25 CINV(N) = CINV(N-1) + PER(N)*P(K1) - SALES(N)
       RINV(N)=4.*CINV(N)/(SALES(N)+SALES(N+1)SALES(N+2)
      1+SALES(N+3))
C      CHECK INVENTØRY AGAINST ACCEPTABLE RANGE
C      AND SET L-S LEVEL
       IF(RINV(N)-CILL)30,34,34
    30 IF(K1-6)28,50,50
    28 M=M+1
       BLS(N)=BLS(N)+1.
       K1 = BLS(N)
       PRØD(N)=P(K1)*PER(N)-10.
       CINV(N) = CINV(N-1) + PRØD(N) - SALES(N)
       RINV(N) = CINV(N)/SALES(N)
       GØ TØ 60
    34 IF(K1-6)35,36,36
    35 IF(CIUL-RINV(N))40,50,50
    36 IF(2.-RINV(N))40,50,50
    40 IF(2-K1)38,50,50
    38 M=M+1
       BLS(N)=BLS(N)-1.
       K1 = BLS(N)
       PRØD(N)=P(K1)*PER(N)+10.
       CINV(N) = CINV(N-1) + PRØD(N) - SALES(N)
       RINV(N) = CINV(N)/SALES(N)
       GØ TØ 60
C      CØMPUTE TØTALS
    50 K2 = BLS(N)
       PRØD(N) = P(K2)*PER(N)
       CINV(N) = CINV(N-1) + PRØD(N) - SALES(N)
       RINV(N) = CINV(N)/SALES(N)
    60 CØNTINUE
       IF(J-1) 65, 90, 90
C      CHECK FREQUENCY ØF LINE SHIFT CHANGES
    65 IF(M-2) 70, 70, 80
    70 IF(BLS(1)- BLS(NUM)) 80, 90, 80
C      ADJUST ACCEPTABLE RANGE
    80 CIUL = CIUL + X
       CILL = CILL - Y
       J = J + 1
       GØ TØ 21
C      PRINT PRØDUCTIØN PLAN
    90 PUNCH 100, NTØT
   100 FØRMAT(22H  PRØDUCTIØN PLAN FØR I2, 8H PERIØDS/)
       PUNCH 110, CILL, CIUL
   110 FØRMAT(29H  ACCEPTABLE INVENTØRY RANGE F3.1,
      1 3H - F3.1, 6H WEEKS)
       IF(J-1) 115, 120, 120
   115 PUNCH 116
   116 FØRMAT(38H     NØ ADJUSTMENT NECESSARY TØ SMØØTH/)
   120 PUNCH 121
   121 FØRMAT(35H     ADJUSTMENT NECESSARY TØ SMØØTH/)
       PUNCH 125, M
   125 FØRMAT(25H NØ. ØF LEVEL CHANGES = I2/)
       PUNCH 130
   130 FØRMAT(2X,6HPERIØD,5X,11HLINE-SHIFTS,5X,5HPRØD.,
      16X,5HSALES5X,7HINVENT.,5X,5HRATIØ/)
       PUNCH 140,(N,BLS(N+1),PRØD(N+1),SALES(N+1),
      1CINV(N+1),RINV(N+1),N=1,NTØT)
       END
```

natural to the actual scheduling environment. The primary source of the data necessary was the Master Production Plan for the years 1963–65. The information contained in the Master Production Plan is subdivided between plan and actual. The planned values relate to decisions made by the Central Office prior to the commencement of the year while the actual values represent decisions made by the Production Control office sequentially during the course of the year.

Using a standard computer program for regression analysis, it was possible to attempt a number of different formulations of intuitively appealing models and then evaluate their appropriateness. Typically this involved a model with a large number of independent variables which would be reduced on the basis of the coefficient of multiple determination and the significance of the individual regression coefficients. In two cases where an actual decision rule is proposed the resulting model was a simple linear function which explained more than two thirds of the variance of the dependent variable.

The data used in the regression analysis were essentially that available to the decision-makers at the time of the decisions and could quite reasonably be available in an operative system using these decision rules. The independent variables used were those which form the basis of the linear decision rules of Holt, Modigliani, Muth, and Simon (in this text see Case 6, page 608) namely sales forecast, and present inventory and work force. The dependent variables were production and work force for the next period although in the case of the Central Office model, production was the only active dependent variable as the work force was assumed by the planning staff to be a direct function of the production rate and a productivity factor conversion.

The first model developed which proved appropriate as a decision rule was that based on the planning decisions made in the Central Office. These decisions were with respect to the number of cases to be produced in a week and were assumed to be dependent upon the present inventory and work force and the sales forecast for a number of weeks into the future. Initially a four-week horizon was assumed but the regression results indicated that the fourth week did not contribute significantly to the model. This was in general agreement with the descriptive model of the Central Office planning procedure which indicated a much shorter horizon than anticipated. The form of the decision rule was:

$$P(t) = -14.80 + 35.64 \, BLS(t-1) - 0.08 \, I(t-1)$$
$$(8.99) \qquad (3.33)$$
$$+ \, 0.36 \, O(t) - 0.21 \, O(t+1) + 0.27 \, O(t+2)$$
$$(3.94) \qquad (1.88) \qquad (3.15)$$

470 · Analysis for Production and Operations Management

where:

$$P = \text{production,}$$
$$BLS = \text{line-shifts,}$$
$$I = \text{inventory in the Distributor system,}$$
$$O = \text{sales forecast,}$$
$$t = \text{week.}$$

and the numbers in parentheses are the t values for the corresponding regression coefficients. The coefficient of multiple determination (R^2) for this model was 0.95.

The second model developed which proved appropriate as a decision rule has been called the Detailed Schedule Management Coefficients model because it was based on the *actual* production achieved and the work force employed (rather than the *plan,* as in the first model). The Production decision was in terms of the number of cases produced per week and the Work Force decision was in terms of the average number of employees on the payroll during the week. Again the independent variables hypothesized to be relevant were sales forecast, and present inventory and work force. A horizon of four weeks was assumed for the initial regression but the results indicated that only the sales forecast for the following week was significant in the linear model. Again this corresponded with the observations made during the detailed analysis of the actual procedure employed by the scheduler at the Plant who prepared the detailed schedule on the basis of the orders he had just received for the following week. The form of the decision rules was:

$$P(t) = 6.98 + 1.66\,W(t-1) - 0.12\,I(t-1) + 0.44\,O(t+1)$$
$$\quad\quad\quad (4.76) \quad\quad\quad\quad (1.80) \quad\quad\quad\quad (2.55)$$

and

$$W(t) = 4.20 + 0.63\,W(t-1) + 0.17\,O(t+1)$$
$$\quad\quad\quad (6.94) \quad\quad\quad\quad (3.62)$$

where:

$$P = \text{production,}$$
$$W = \text{work force,}$$
$$I = \text{inventory in the Distributor system,}$$
$$O = \text{sales forecast,}$$
$$t = \text{week.}$$

and the numbers in parentheses are the t values of the corresponding regression coefficients. The coefficient of multiple determination (R^2) for the production rule was 0.66 and for the work force rule it was 0.79.

It should be pointed out that in the Central Office model the number of line-shifts was used rather than the number of workers as an independent variable in the production rule. This corresponded to the variable which the planning staff actually used in their own procedure and therefore seemed more appropriate. It is possible to make a direct conversion from line-shifts to number of workers and the regression coefficients in the two models for the work force available are approximately in the same ratio as the number of workers per line-shift.

Two heuristic decision rules then have been developed, one based essentially on the descriptive study and model of the planning process in the Central Office (using these plans to estimate the decision rule coefficients), and the second based on the actual production results which were influenced by the local plant management (using these results to estimate the decision rule coefficients).

Normative Model

The prescriptive or Operations Research approach to the aggregate scheduling problem was based on an economic criterion—the minimization of costs. In an analysis such as this one it is helpful to think of at least three cost structures. First, the true cost structure of the situation which we attempt to model but will never capture completely. Second, the analyst's model of the cost structure which represents his perception of the economic environment. This may or may not be a mathematically tractable function but it should be explicit to the degree that it can be used to evaluate various alternative schedules. Finally, for the purpose of analysis the perceived cost function is approximated to make it tractable while still retaining the essential features of the environment.

No matter what ultimate formulation results, the following costs are involved in aggregate scheduling. Direct labor costs enter the scheduling decision in terms of both regular time which is implied by the work force decision and overtime which is the result of asking for more production than can be obtained during regular time with the work force size. Work force size above a certain level may imply second shift operation with the resultant shift premium. Changes in the size of the work force from week to week will result in costs of hiring and firing such as training, inefficient production and unemployment compensation. Finally, the use of inventory implies carrying costs in terms of capital, handling and risk. These costs were determined through a combination of engineering/cost analysis and managerial judgment. In addition to these costs, certain system parameters were considered essential in a specification of the economic environment. One of these is the productivity of the work force. The other was the ideal inventory level. For a detailed discussion of this cost structure see the article by Holt, *et al.*, page 608. Following the formulation in this article the model proposed for the plant bottle shop was:

Regular payroll costs (C_{RP}):   188.00 $W(t)$
Hiring and layoff costs $(C_{H\& L})$: 1.60 $(W(t) - W(t-1) - 10.0)^2$
Overtime costs (C_{OT}):   5.0 $(P(t) - 1.96\, W(t))^2$
Inventory costs (C_I):   0.0222 $(I(t) - 150.0 - 3.0\, S(t))^2$

where:

W = work force in men,
P = production in 1,000's of cases,
I = inventory (total) in 1,000's of cases,
S = sales in 1,000's of cases.

subject to the restraints

$$I(t-1) + P(t) - S(t) = I(t)$$

minimize $E(C_T(T))$
where:

$$C(T) = \sum_{t=1} (C_{RP} + C_{H\&L} + C_{OT} + C_I)$$

and $T = 52$

The analytical solution of this model involves the minimization of the expected value of the total cost function with respect to the decision variables production and work force. Essentially this is accomplished by differentiating the cost function partially with respect to W and P and equating the results to zero. This results in a set of linear equations which may be solved for W and P in terms of I, $W(t-1)$ and $S(t)$. These equations have become known as the linear decision rules and prescribe optimum performance (with respect to the quadratic cost function).

The derived rules were as follows:

$$
\begin{aligned}
w(t) = \ &+0.1173\ S(t) &&+0.5088\ W(t-1) - 0.0823\ I(t-1) \\
&+0.1175\ S(t+1) \\
&+0.0984\ S(t+2) \\
&+0.0727\ S(t+3) &&+9.9471 \\
&+0.0479\ S(t+4) \\
&+0.0276\ S(t+5) \\
&+0.0129\ S(t+6) \\
&+0.0034\ S(t+7)
\end{aligned}
$$

$$P(t) = +0.2487\ S(t) \qquad\qquad +0.9708\ W(t-1) - 0.1703\ I(t-1)$$
$$+0.2427\ S(t+1)$$
$$+0.2000\ S(t+2)$$
$$+0.1459\ S(t+3) \qquad\qquad +30.2931$$
$$+0.0948\ S(t+4)$$
$$+0.0537\ S(t+5)$$
$$+0.0242\ S(t+6)$$
$$+0.0055\ S(t+7)$$

where:

W = work force in men,
S = sales forecast in 1,000's of cases,
I = total inventory in 1,000's of cases,
P = production in 1,000's of cases,
t = week.

The relatively short time horizon indicated by the weighting on the sales forecast in the rules is a reflection of the limited use that can be made of inventory to absorb fluctuations and the fact that changes in the work force can be accomplished without much advance notice. This is not significantly different from actually observed management practice. There is no significant difference in the relative weighting between the work force and the production rule in terms of the emphasis given to the future. The totals of the weights are approximately in the ratio of one to two which is the same ratio of the average work force to average production.

Comparison of Results

For purposes of comparison, we now have one descriptive rule, two heuristic rules, and one normative rule. Comparing these to the actual schedule produced in a test period will then give five resultant schedules to be evaluated:

1. LDR, Linear Decision Rule, the normative rule.
2. ACT, The actual situation in the test period.
3. COMC, Central Office Management Coefficients, the heuristic based on the central plan.
4. DSMC, Detailed Schedule Management Coefficients, the heuristic rule based on actual plant behavior.
5. DM, Descriptive Model.

The procedure used in the evaluation of the various decision rules was essentially to simulate the behavior of the production system under the rules for the test period. This implied generating production and work force decisions for the sales forecast inputs for the entire operating cycle. The actual sales realized during each week of the cycle were then used to generate the resulting inventory at the end of the week. Thus for a 52-week cycle with sales forecast and sales realized as inputs, it was possible to trace the behavior of the system in terms of production, work force, inventory, and overtime for each of the decision models.

The results of these evaluations are shown in Table 12–1 which gives a complete summarization of the economic results of the evaluation of the performance of the different models. The top portion of the table expresses all the results as a percentage of the corresponding linear decision rule cost. The bottom portion of the table indicates the percentage composition of the total cost of each of the five classifications of cost for each of the models.

As can be seen from Table 12–1, the two heuristic rules (COMC and DSMC) give performance which is somewhere between the normative/optimizing rule (LDR) and the actual behavior (ACT), and its simulation (DM). This would normally be the case. Heuristic rules in the same sense as Simon's Administrative Man exhibit intended but bounded rationality. For many real problems, this is as good as the analyst and manager can hope to accomplish.

Table 12–1

COMPARATIVE COST EVALUATION OF SIMULATED AGGREGATE SCHEDULES

Expressed as a Percentage of the LDR Costs

Model	Payroll	Overtime	Inventory	Work Force Change	Inventory* Adjustment	Total
LDR	100.0	100.0	100.0	100.0	100.0	100.0
ACT	117.0	41.0	82.6	189.2	48.1	110.8
COMC	110.6	6.9	123.9	84.9	107.8	107.0
DSMC	117.4	12.5	80.9	77.8	24.4	107.1
DM	117.6	1.0	108.5	158.4	59.3	111.2

Expressed as Percentage Composition of Total Cost for Each Model

LDR	84.7	3.7	5.9	1.9	3.8	100.0
ACT	89.4	1.4	4.4	3.2	1.6	100.0
COMC	87.6	0.3	6.9	1.4	3.8	100.0
DSMC	92.9	0.4	4.5	1.3	0.9	100.0
DM	89.6	0.1	5.7	2.6	2.0	100.0

The total cost base for these calculations is approximately $700,000.

* Because the level of inventory at the end of the test period differed from plan to plan, and from the beginning inventory, an asset adjustment due to imbedded value must be made.

SUMMARY

The purpose of this chapter has been to expose the reader to some of the newer research which has been undertaken in the areas of behavior and heuristics in decision making. It seemed necessary to make some incursions into this field of organization theory because of the influential school of thought which basically equates the study of decision making with the study of organizations. While much of organization theory focuses on decision making by organizations, our major interest is on decision making essentially by individuals, though this line is drawn with difficulty. Brief descriptions have been given of heuristic decision systems in several problem areas of operations management, and then an extended presentation was made of three approaches to aggregate production scheduling—descriptive, heuristic, normative.

REFERENCES

1. CYERT, R. M., and MARCH, J. G. *A Behavioral Theory of the Firm.* Englewood Cliffs, N.J.: Prentice-Hall, Inc., 1963.

2. FEIGENBAUM, E. A., and FELDMAN, J. (eds.). *Computers and Thought.* New York: McGraw-Hill Book Co., Inc., 1963.

3. MARCH, J. G. (ed.). *Handbook of Organizations.* Chicago: Rand McNally and Co., 1965.

4. MARCH, J. G., and SIMON, H. A. *Organizations.* New York: John Wiley & Sons, Inc., 1958.

5. POLYA, G. *How to Solve It.* Princeton: Princeton University Press, 1945.

6. SIMON, H. A. *Administrative Behavior: A Study of Decision-Making Processes in Administrative Organization.* 2nd ed. New York: Macmillan Co., 1957.

7. SIMON, H. A. *The New Science of Management Decision.* New York: Harper & Bros., 1960.

PROBLEMS

1. Develop a heuristic procedure in flow chart form to construct the Gantt Chart for Problem No. 5, page 73, Chapter 2.

2. Develop a heuristic procedure in flow chart form to construct the Gantt Chart for Problem No. 6, page 74, Chapter 2.

3. Develop a heuristic procedure in flow chart form which will provide a "good" feasible solution to the problem used to introduce the reader to the simplex method of linear programming, Chapter 3, pages 77–99. Provide the input parameters of the problem as given in order to calculate the specific schedule and objective function value which your procedure produces.

4. Develop a heuristic procedure in flow chart form which will provide a "good" feasible solution to Problem No. 1, page 108, Chapter 3. Provide the input parameters of the problem as given in order to calculate the specific answer which your procedure produces.

5. Develop the flow chart for the heuristic procedure labeled the "mutually preferred method" in Chapter 4, pages 119–20.

6. Develop the flow chart for the heuristic procedure labeled the "Northwest Corner Rule" in Chapter 4, page 120.

7. Develop a flow chart for a heuristic procedure to handle the "degeneracy problem" in the transportation method of linear programming as described in Chapter 4, pages 130–32.

8. Develop a heuristic procedure in flow chart form which will provide quickly a good feasible solution to the package problem used to introduce the reader to dynamic programming in Chapter 4, page 137. Provide the inputs given there in order to calculate the heuristic procedure's answer.

9. Develop a heuristic procedure in flow chart form which will provide quickly some feasible answer to the procurement problem used to illustrate dynamic programming in Chapter 4, page 143. Emphasize a small number of steps rather than "goodness" as measured in economic terms.

10. Develop a flow chart to replicate the procedure described in Chapter 6, page 231 which determines the values of n and c for a sampling plan to meet the required specifications.

11. Develop a heuristic procedure in flow chart form which will start with and then improve the solution as given by the tabular analysis of the inventory problem, Table 8–1, page 315, Chapter 8. Calculate the answer provided by your procedure.

12. *a*) Provide a heuristic decision rule which will answer question (*a*), Problem No. 3, Chapter 8, page 350 (the plastic compounding problem).
    b) Provide a heuristic decision rule which will answer question (*b*), Problem No. 3, Chapter 8, page 351 (the plastic parts scheduling problem).

13. *a*) Develop a heuristic procedure in flow chart form to solve the job shop scheduling problem given in Chapter 11, page 445, Problem No. 9. How long does the schedule require using your heuristic procedure?
    b) Apply the COVERT decision rule (your version of measures for "C") developed by Carroll and described on pages 461–62 of this chapter to the job shop scheduling problem given in Chapter 11, page 445, Problem No. 9. How long does your version of Carroll's heuristic rule require for the schedule?

14. Emphasizing fewness of steps rather than efficiency of assembly line, develop a heuristic procedure in flow chart form for balancing the assembly line as presented in Chapter 11, page 445, Problem No. 10. How many work stations does your procedure require?

SECTION VI

Case Studies in Production and Operations Management

The cases which follow represent applications of the methods which have been described previously to real problems. The most effective way to learn these methods and to be able to apply them effectively is by experience, or if necessary by vicarious experience, i.e., example. In this sense, the material presented here is more akin to a law school casebook rather than a business school casebook. That is, not only is the problem presented, but also its analysis. The student learns by studying critically the professional work of others. This type of material can be an integral part of the education and background of the industrial manager or administrator. Although the manager might not have time to do this work himself, he will understand and appreciate it so that (a) he can insist on this type of analysis where appropriate, (b) he can contribute effectively to the study, (c) he can evaluate the work as it progresses, and (d) he can use the analysis when it is completed.

In a sense, the ideal article for this book is an empirical study, formally or quantitatively analysed, of an industrial operating problem. While it is important for the student (academic or industrial) to understand the methods of analysis available to him, it is equally important that he understand something of the problems of their application. It is hoped that the study of the articles included here will give some insight into the simplifications, assumptions, method modifications, need for data, difficulties, action, and results associated with this work.

The material seems best used following completion of a course or part of a course based on Chapters 1–12, but it certainly can be used along with these chapters. One alternative is to have each case session of one and a half to two hours duration and one student assigned primary responsibility in leading the case discussion. The students should be encouraged to evaluate critically the work reported in the case and to present alternatives to the approaches taken. The instructor serves basically as a resource person and in addition as a participating member of the seminar discussion. Each paper in the book is preceded by some material designed to stimulate critical reflection and discussion of the article.

Case Studies in Production and Operations Management

CASE 1

Applications of Linear Programming in the Oil Industry[1]

W. W. GARVIN, H. W. CRANDALL, J. B. JOHN, and R. A. SPELLMAN[2]

Some points of special interest in this paper are:[3]

  a. The fixed set-up charge constraint in the model of a producing complex and the indicated cut-and-try approach. What might be the nature of this approach?
  b. The treatment of by-product return as negative cost in the Incremental Product Costs problem.
  c. Some of the problems encountered and a method for solving a problem out of a larger system in the Incremental Product Costs example.
  d. The ability to combine various fictitious parts in the problem of Cut-Points in order to include the effect of nonlinearities.
  e. Modification of the linear programming solution of the refinery problem based on management's experience.
  f. What appear to be new or novel special treatments with each of the cases.
  g. The complexity of the distribution problems considered.

SUMMARY

This paper is the result of a survey made during the summer of 1956. It is a progress report on applications of linear programming by a

---

[1] *Management Science,* July, 1957. Reprinted by permission.

[2] California Research Corporation, La Habra, California; Standard Oil Company of California, San Francisco, California; and California Research Corporation, Richmond, California, respectively.

[3] The "points of special interest" at the beginning of each paper have been inserted by the editors.

number of oil companies. Examples are presented of applications to a variety of problems arising in the areas of Drilling and Production, Manufacturing, and Marketing and Distribution. The examples were selected to illustrate both the power and the limitations of present linear programming methods when applied to actual problems.

INTRODUCTION

Plans were made during early 1956 for a symposium on industrial application of linear programming to be presented at the Fall Meeting of the Institute (of Management Sciences). As the theme of that meeting was "A Progress Report" and some of the earliest applications of linear programming were made in the oil industry, it seemed fitting to include in the program a progress report on what the oil industry had been able to accomplish thus far in this field.

We were requested by George Dantzig to present such a review and to include in it not only some of our applications but, if possible, applications by other oil companies as well. With this in mind, about a dozen major oil companies were contracted by us and were invited to contribute linear programming applications or studies they had made which were of general interest and of nonconfidential nature. The response was most encouraging. Because of limited time available arrangements were made to visit personnel of six oil companies for the purpose of discussing their work and ours in the linear programming field.

The oil industry became aware of linear programming through the pioneering work of Charnes, Cooper, and Mellon[4] and the work of Gifford Symonds.[5] We owe a great deal to these gentlemen and to Alan Manne[6] for pointing out to us that linear programming has a place in our business. A few years ago, there were few people indeed in the oil industry who had ever heard of such things as "basic solution" or "convex set." Today, these terms are much more familiar and as a result much less frightening to some. What is involved here is an educational process, and educational processes are notoriously slow. It is amazing, therefore, to see how much has been done in such a comparatively short time.

---

[4] A. Charnes, W. W. Cooper, and B. Mellon, "Blending Aviation Gasolines," *Econometrica*, Vol. XX (April, 1952), pp. 135–59; "A Model for Programming and Sensitivity Analysis in an Integrated Oil Company," *ibid.*, Vol. XXII (April, 1954), pp. 193–217.

[5] G. H. Symonds, "Linear Programming for Optimum Refinery Operations," paper presented at the IBM Petroleum Conference, October 26, 1953.

[6] A. S. Manne, *Scheduling of Petroleum Refinery Operations* (Cambridge: Harvard University Press, 1956).

As technology advances and improves, problems become more inter-woven and complex. The problems of the oil industry are no exception. They can logically be grouped into categories according to the different phases of our business as shown in Figure 1. An integrated oil company must first of all carry out exploration activities to determine the spots where oil is most likely to be found. The land must then be acquired or leased and an exploratory well or "wildcat" as it is called is drilled. If luck is with us, we hit oil. Additional wells are drilled to develop the field and production gets under way. The oil is transported by various means to the refinery where a variety of products are manufactured from it. The products in turn leave the refinery, enter the distribution system and are marketed.

Figure 1

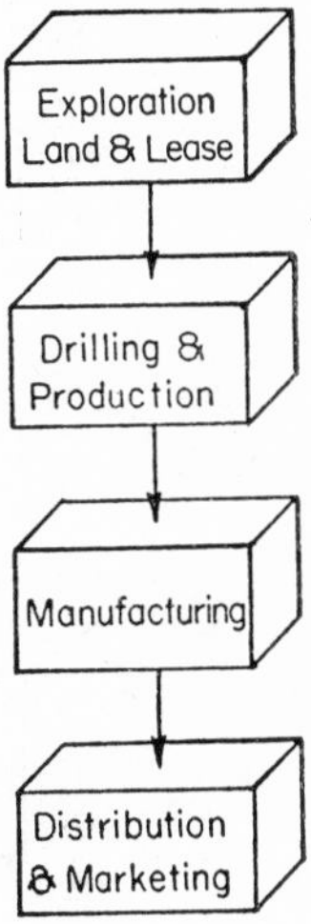

Needless to say, each of the areas shown in Figure 1 is full of unanswered questions and problems. Different methods exist for exploring the oil potentialities of a region. How should they be combined for maximum effectiveness? An oil field can be produced in many different ways. Which is best? The complexity of a modern refinery is staggering. What is the best op-erating plan? And what precisely do we mean by "best"? Of course, not all the problems in these areas lend themselves to linear programming but some of them do. What we would like to do is to pick out a few representative *LP* type problems from each area, show how they were formulated and in some cases, discuss the results that were obtained.

We had hoped to find applications in all four of the areas shown in Figure 1. Unfortunately, we were successful only in three. We did not find any nonconfidential applications in the field of exploration. Exploration is one of the most confidential phases of our business and it is for that reason that oil companies are not very explicit about their studies in this field. We can state, however, from personal experience, that a number of applications to exploration are under investigation.

Let us therefore turn our attention to the remaining three areas of Drilling and Production, Manufacturing, and Distribution and Market-ing. Figure 2 shows an outline of the applications that will be discussed. Out of the Drilling and Production area the problem of devising a model for a producing complex was selected. In the case of Manufactur-ing, the selection was difficult because historically this was the first area of application and much work has been done in this field. The problems shown were selected because they either illustrate an important concept or because they illustrate a peculiar twist in mathematical formulation. The problem of incremental product costs illustrates the technique of parametric programming and also shows what can happen if too many simplifications are introduced. The methods developed for handling tetraethyl lead and variable cut points illustrate how, under certain conditions, nonlinearities can be introduced into the system. The problem of cost coefficients will illustrate the need for realistic refinery costs. Finally, three problems out of the area of Distribution and Marketing were selected—a bulk plant distribution problem having to do with the shipment of products from refineries to bulk plants in an expanding

Figure 2

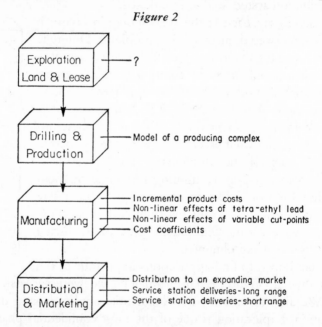

market and the problem of devising long-range and short-range delivery schedules from bulk plants to service stations.

MODEL OF A PRODUCING COMPLEX

Let us now turn our attention to the first problem on the list—a model of a producing complex. We are indebted to the Field Research Laboratory of Magnolia Petroleum Company and to Arabian American Oil Company for contributing this application. This problem will be discussed in more detail in a forthcoming publication by A. S. Lee and J. S. Aronofsky of Magnolia. Consider N oil fields or reservoirs ($i = 1$, $2 \ldots N$), as shown in Figure 3, which are producing at rates $Q_i(t)$

where t is the time. The total production of the N reservoirs is to be adjusted to meet a commitment $Q_c(t)$ (such as keeping a pipe line full or a refinery supplied). An outside source of crude oil is also available. Let the profit realizable per barrel be $c_i(t)$ and consider that the operation is to be run on this basis for a period of T years. Production limitations exists which require that the $Q_i(t)$ do not exceed certain values and that the pressures in the reservoirs do not fall below certain values. These limits may be functions of the time. We shall consider the case where these fields are rela-tively young so that develop-ment drilling activity will oc-cur during the time period under consideration. The prob-lem is to determine a schedule of $Q_i(t)$ such that the profit over T years is a maximum.

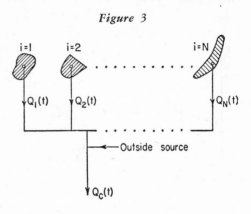

Figure 3

By splitting up the period T into time intervals ($j = 1, 2 \ldots K$) and bringing in the physics of the problem, it can be shown that the condition that the field pressures are not to fall below certain minimum values assumes the form:

$$\sum_{j=1}^{K} (f_{i,K-j+1} - f_{i,K-j})Q_{ij} \leq P_{i0} - P_{i\,min} \tag{1}$$

for all i and K. The f's describe the characteristics of the fields and are known. The right-hand side is the difference between the initial and the minimum permissible pressure of the ith field. The variable is Q_{ij} which is the production rate of the ith field during the jth period. Additional constraints on the Q_{ij}'s are that the total producton for any time period plus the crude oil possibly purchased from the outside source, Q_j, be equal to the commitment for that time period:

$$\sum_{i=1}^{N} Q_{ij} + Q_j = Q_{cj}, \qquad j = 1, 2 \ldots K \tag{2}$$

Furthermore, production limitations exist such that:

$$Q_{ij} \leq Q_{ij\,max} \tag{3}$$

which are simple upper bound constraints. The objective function expressing profit over the time period considered is:

$$\sum_{j=1}^{K}\sum_{i=1}^{N} c_{ij}Q_{ij} + \sum_{j=1}^{K} c_{j}Q_{j} = \text{max} \qquad (4)$$

which completes the formulation of the linear programming problem. The coefficients c_{ij} and c_j are the profit per barrel of the ith reservoir at time j and correspondingly for purchased crude oil.

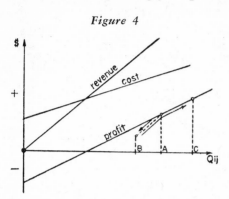

Figure 4

Thus far, everything has been rather straightforward. But now, the time has come to clutter up the theory with facts. Let us take a closer look at the coefficients c_{ij}. If we plot revenue versus a particular production rate Q_{ij}, we get a straight line passing through the origin as shown in Figure 4. Cost versus Q_{ij} is also more or less a straight line which, however, does not pass through the origin. The cost function is discontinuous at the origin, corresponding to a set-up charge such as building a road, a pipe line or harbor facilities or installing a gas-oil separator. It drops to zero when $Q_{ij} = 0$ because this corresponds to not yet developing the field. Also shown on Figure 4 is profit versus Q_{ij} which is the difference between revenue and cost. The profit function thus is the straight line shown plus the origin. Hence, we can say that profit from Q_{ij} production is $c_{ij}Q_{ij} - s_{ij}$ where s_{ij} is zero if Q_{ij} is zero and s_{ij} is a constant if $Q_{ij} > 0$. This is a particularly difficult constraint. No general methods are available for handling this except a *cut-and-try approach.* This type of fixed set-up charge constraint occurs in many practical problems and we shall meet it again later on.

One other complicating feature should be mentioned. Consider that during a certain time period, Q_{ij} was at level "A" as shown in Figure 4 and that in the succeeding time period $Q_{i,\,j\,+\,1}$ has dropped to level "B." The profit at level "B" is not obtained by following the profit line to operating level "B" but rather by following a line as shown which is parallel to the revenue line. The reduction in level from "A" to "B" involves merely turning a few valves and essentially does not entail any reduction in operating costs. If, on the other hand, we go from "A" to "C" in succeeding time periods, then we do follow the profit line because an increase in production necessitates drilling additional wells assuming that all the wells at "A" are producing at maximum economic capacity. If we should go from "A" to "B" to "C" in succeeding time periods and if "A" was the maximum field development up to that time, then in going from "B" to "C" we would follow the broken path as shown in Figure 4.

This state of affairs can be handled by building the concept of "production capacity" into the model and requiring that production capacity never decreases with time. But this can be done only at the expense of enlarging the system appreciably.

There exist other factors and additional constraints which must be taken into account. As is so often the case, we are dealing here with a system which on the surface looks rather simple but which becomes considerably more complex as we get deeper into it to make it more realistic. Nevertheless, the simpler system or modest extensions of it enables an entire producing complex to be studied thus providing a good basis upon which to build more realistic models.

INCREMENTAL PRODUCT COSTS

Let us now leave the problems of petroleum production behind us and venture into the petroleum refinery. As was indicated before, a great deal of work has been done in this area. The few problems we shall discuss will be illustrative of what is going on in this field.

We shall consider at first a simple but nevertheless instructive example. We are indebted to Atlantic Refining Company for contributing this application.[7] A refinery produces gasoline, furnace oil and other products as shown in Figure 5. The refinery can be supplied with a fairly large number of crude oils. The available crude oils have different properties and yield different volumes of finished products. Some of these crudes must be refined because of long-term minimum volume commitments or because of requirements for specialty products. These crudes are considered fixed and yield gasoline and furnace oil volumes V_G and V_F respectively. From the remaining crudes and from those crudes which are available in volumes greater than their minimum volume commitment must be selected those which can supply the required products most economically. These are the incremental crudes. Denote the gasoline and furnace oil volumes which result from the

---

incremental crudes by ΔV_G and ΔV_F and the total volumes (fixed plus incremental) by V_{GT} and V_{FT}. The problem is to determine the minimum incremental cost of furnace oil as a function of incremental furnace oil production keeping gasoline production and general refinery operations fixed.

The formulation of this problem is straightforward:

$$\sum_1^N a_{Gi} V_i = V_{GT} - V_G = \Delta V_G \tag{5}$$

$$\sum_1^N a_{Fi} V_i = V_{FT} - V_F = \Delta V_F \tag{6}$$

$$V_i \leqq V_{i\,max} \tag{7}$$

$$\sum_1^N c_i V_i = min \tag{8}$$

where a_{Gi} and a_{Fi} are the gasoline and furnace oil yields of the ith crude, V_i and $V_{i\,max}$ are the volume and availability of the ith incremental crude and c_i is the cost of producing incremental gasoline plus incremental furnace oil per barrel of the ith crude. This cost is made up of the cost of crude at the refinery, the incremental processing costs and a credit for the by-products produced at the same time.

Figure 5

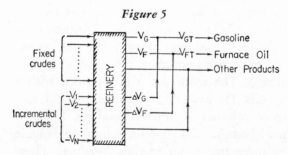

The procedure now consists of assuming a value for ΔV_F and obtaining an optimal solution. The shadow price of equation (6) will then be equal to the incremental cost of furnace oil because it represents the change in the functional corresponding to a change of one barrel in ΔV_F. The incremental cost thus obtained, however, is valid only over ranges of variation of ΔV_F which are sufficiently small so that the optimum solution remains feasible. Beyond that permissible range of ΔV_F the basis must be changed with a resulting change in the shadow price. For problems of this type, the so-called "parametric programming" procedure can be used. This procedure has been incorporated into the IBM 704 LP code. It starts with an optimal solution and then varies in an arbitrary but preassigned manner the constants on the righthand side until one of the basic variables becomes zero. The computer then prints out the optimal solution which exists at that time, changes the basis to an adjacent extreme point which is also optimum, and repeats this process until a termination is reached.

An actual problem was run with the model shown on Figure 5. Thirteen incremental crudes were available and incremental gasoline production was fixed at 14,600 barrels daily. The results are shown in Figure 6 which shows the minimum total incremental cost as a func-

Figure 6

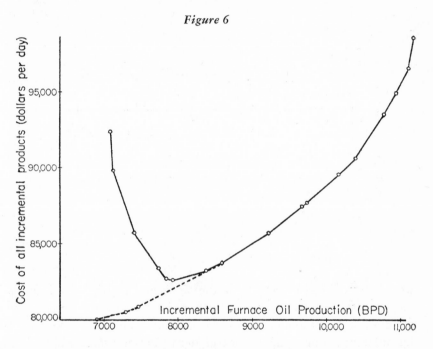

tion of incremental furnace oil production. Ignore the dashed line for the moment. The circles represent points at which the optimum basis had to be changed. The functional is a straight line between these points. It turned out that incremental furnace-oil production was possible only in the range from about 7100 bpd to about 11200 bpd. Between the two extremes, the functional exhibits a minimum at about 8000 bpd. The reason for the minimum is to be found in the fact that near the two extremes of furnace oil production, little choice exists in the composition of the crude slate. Volume is the limitation and economics plays a secondary part. Away from the two extremes, however, we have greater flexibility in crudes run and thus have the freedom to pick the cheapest crude combination. Figure 7 shows the incremental cost of furnace oil as a function of furnace oil production. It is a staircase type function because the shadow price remains unchanged as long as the optimum basis remains feasible and jumps discontinuously whenever the basis is changed. At low levels of incremental furnace oil production, the incremental cost becomes negative because in that region it is *more* expensive to make *less* furnace oil.

If we now were to show our model and our results to the refiner, he

Figure 7

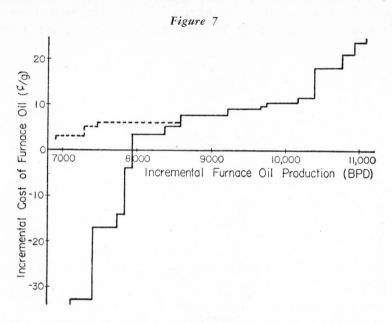

would immediately detect a fly in the ointment. The negative incremental cost at low furnace oil production runs counter to his intuitive feeling for the problem. He would point out, and rightly so, that the formulation of our model is not complete. Common sense would dictate the making of the larger volumes of furnace oil at lower cost and disposing of the excess furnace oil in some manner. For example, this excess can be mixed into heavy fuel production. If all the heavy fuel that is made can be sold, the net cost of the furnace oil overproduction would be the negative of the value of heavy fuel indicating a credit we receive for increasing heavy fuel production.

We are tempted, therefore, to try the formulation shown in Figure 8 where we permit the diversion of some furnace oil to heavy fuel. The equation for gasoline production remains unchanged but the furnace oil equation now reads:

$$\sum_1^N a_{iF}V_i - s_1 = \Delta V_F \qquad (9)$$

and the objective form is:

$$\sum_{1}^{N} c_i V_i - v_{HF} s_1 = \min \tag{10}$$

where s_1 is a slack variable indicating the volume of furnace oil diverted to heavy fuel and v_{HF} is the value per barrel of heavy fuel. It is not possible, however, to divert unlimited amounts of furnace oil into heavy fuel without violating heavy fuel's specifications. The upper limit on how much furnace oil can be mixed into heavy fuel depends on the volume of heavy fuel produced which in turn is related to the crude

Figure 8

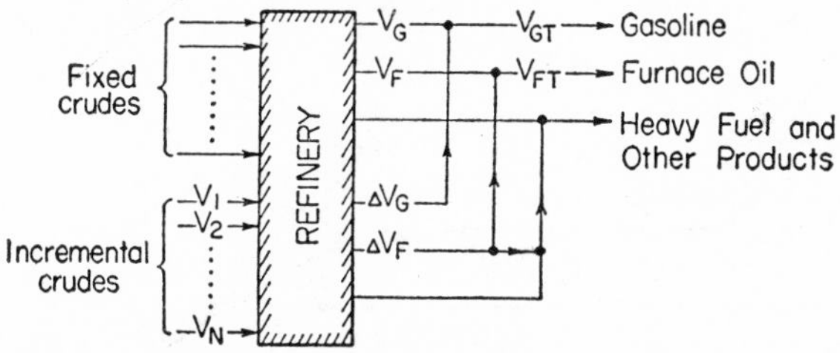

slate, and would depend also on the specifications of heavy fuel. Furthermore, if we bring heavy fuel into the picture explicitly, the cost coefficients used before must be modified. The problem is beginning to become more complex. To take these effects into account would form the basis of an entirely new study. For purposes of the present illustration, however, the situation can be handled roughly as follows. It turns out from experience and by considering the volumes involved that the excess furnace oil production should be less than or at most equal to about 15 per cent of the incremental furnace oil production if all the excess is to go to heavy fuel and specifications on heavy fuel are to be

$$\sum_{1}^{N} a_{iF} V_i + s_2 = 1.15 \Delta V_F \tag{11}$$

met. Therefore, the additional constraint was added to the system where s_2 is a slack variable. This constraint insures that no undue advantage is taken of the freedom introduced by excess furnace oil production.

The results for this second formulation of the problem are shown by the dashed lines in Figures 6 and 7. The abscissa now refers to that part of incremental furnace oil production which leaves the refinery as furnace oil. Excess furnace oil is produced below incremental furnace oil production of about 8600 bpd. Above that level, it is not economic to produce more furnace oil than required and, consequently, there is no difference between the two formulations of the problem. Constraint (11) is limiting for incremental furnace oil production below about 7500 bpd. Figure 9 shows the composition of the optimum crude slate for the second formulation as a function of incremental furnace oil production. This is useful information to have on hand. Note that no

Figure 9

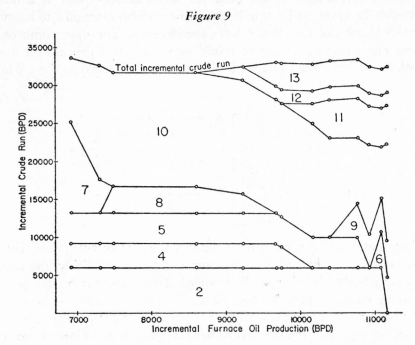

changes occur in the range of incremental furnace oil production from 7500 to 8600 bpd. In this range, actual incremental furnace oil production remains fixed at 8600 bpd with any excess going into heavy fuel.

The modern refinery is a complicated system with strong interdependence among the activities within it. The example just described illustrates this point and shows the importance of the refiner's experience in correctly isolating portions of the refinery which can be separately considered.

NONLINEAR EFFECT OF TETRA-ETHYL LEAD

The next two applications are concerned with partially nonlinear systems. One of the most common types of nonlinearity encountered in refinery operations is connected with the effect of tetra-ethyl lead (TEL). TEL is added to gasoline to increase the gasoline's octane number. The increase in octane number, however, is not a linear function of the TEL concentration. The first cc of TEL has a pronounced effect on octane number, the second cc, however, has a smaller effect, and for the third cc the effect will be still smaller. The maximum concentration permitted in motor gasoline is 3 cc per gallon.

A great deal of work has been done in the past few years on gasoline blending by linear programming. The problem is to blend the different stocks coming out of the refinery into gasolines having specification properties and to do it at mini-mum cost. In addition to octane number, other properties such as vapor pressure and various distillation points must be con-sidered. All the important properties blend linearly on a volume basis except for the effect of TEL. To get around the TEL difficulty, it was usually assumed in setting up the linear programming model that the gasoline was shipped out at maximum TEL level of 3 cc per gallon or the TEL level was arbitrarily set at some lower value. In any event, TEL did

Figure 10

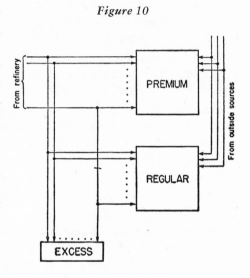

not enter the system as a variable and thus was not permitted to seek its own level as determined by minimum cost. To get a feeling for the order of magnitude of money involved here, consider an average TEL concentration of 2 cc per gallon. At a price of TEL of about $2 per liter, a TEL bill of about $180,000 results for each million barrels of gasoline produced. Many companies produce of the order of tens of millions of barrels per year. Thus, even a reduction of only a few per cent in lead concentration begins to look big when translated into money savings.

Consider now the general blending problem shown in Figure 10. The streams coming out of the refinery are split three ways—to Pre-mium grade gasoline, to Regular grade gasoline or to temporary stor-age. Additional stocks may be purchased from outside sources to go into gasoline. TEL is one such stock. The gasoline blends must satisfy a variety of quality specifications such as vapor pressure, distillation points and octane number.

In setting up this problem in linear programming language, we have first of all the usual types of linear constraints which relate the properties of the stocks and the fraction of their volumes to the desired properties of the blended gasoline. There is no difficulty here until we get to the octane condition. The relation we have is that:

$$\frac{\Sigma ON_{ci}V_i}{\Sigma V_i} + \Delta ON \geqq ON_s \tag{12}$$

where ON_{ci} is the "clear" octane number of the ith stock (its octane number with no TEL in the stock), V_i is its volume, ON_s is the specified minimum octane number and ΔON is the octane increase due to lead. The first term on the left represents the "clear" octane number of the blend under the assumption of linear blending. Actually, clear octane numbers do not always blend linearly, but by using so-called "blending" octane numbers instead of actual ones, a sufficiently close linear approximation can be obtained.

Let us now take a closer look at the ΔON term. If, for a specified octane number of the blend, we plot the difference between the clear octane number of the blend and the specified octane number as a function of TEL concentration required to bring the blend up to specification, we obtain a family of curves as shown in Figure 11 where the parameter is a characteristic called "lead susceptibility." It is a measure of the ability of the blend to respond to TEL. Lead susceptibility can be considered to blend linearly with respect to volume. The curves are concave because of the saturation effects previously mentioned.

From past experience, it is usually possible to estimate within reason-

Figure 11

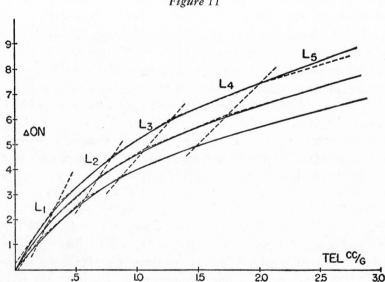

able limits what the lead susceptibility of the blend is going to be. We can then construct curves as shown in Figure 11 for the estimated lead susceptibility and for susceptibilities deviating from that value by, say, ± 10 per cent. Data are available to do this. Let us now imagine that we split up the curves into, say, five bands as shown such that the curves within each band can be approximated by parallel and equidistant straight lines. This will always be possible by considering a sufficiently large number of bands and a sufficiently small range in lead susceptibility. The situation shown in Figure 11 was considered sufficiently accurate by us for our purposes. The bounding lines between bands are not required to be parallel. The bands can be interpreted in the following manner. Instead of having only one type of TEL, we have, in this case, five fictitious types—TEL 1 through TEL 5. Each band corresponds to one type of lead. These fictitious leads have two important properties: they do not saturate, i.e., their effect on octane number is linearly related to the amount of each lead present, and the effect of lead susceptibility on ΔON is independent of the TEL concentration. They are not all equally effective, however, as far as increasing the octane number is concerned. In view of the concavity of the function, lead 1 is much more effective than lead 5. We can thus write:

$$\Delta ON = a + b \frac{\Sigma S_i V_i}{\Sigma V_i} + \frac{\Sigma m_j L_j}{\Sigma V_i} \qquad (13)$$

where S_i is the lead susceptibility of the ith stock, L_j is the amount of lead of type j present in the blend and a, b, and m_j are constants determined from the curves. Also, we know that:

$$m_{j+1} < m_j. \qquad (14)$$

To insure that the fairy tale of the fictitious leads corresponds to reality, we must impose availability restrictions on the L_j's for otherwise we would satisfy the octane restrictions with L_1 because octane-wise it is cheapest and, as a result, get way off the curve. As the straight lines within each band are equidistant, the maximum amount of each lead that can be put into the blend can be represented as a linear function of susceptibility, corresponding to the bounding straight lines between the bands. Hence, we can write:

$$\frac{L_j}{\Sigma V_j} \leq d_j + e_j \frac{\Sigma S_i V_i}{\Sigma V_i} \qquad (15)$$

where d_j and e_j again are constants determined from the curves. Substituting the expression for ΔON into equation (12) and multiplying through by ΣV_i, we obtain a system of linear relations which can be incorporated in the over-all linear programming formulation.

We are not yet quite through, however. Each grade of gasoline has two octane requirements which are called the F-1 and F-2 octane specifications. As we have two gasoline grades, this means that we have four octane specifications that must be met. Therefore, we have in reality four families of curves similar in shape to those shown in Figure 11, and all four must be represented by the procedure just discussed and added to the system. We must also distinguish not only among different TEL types but also between TEL going into Premium or Regular to meet the F-1 or F-2 octane requirement. If five fictitious leads are used for each gasoline grade and each octane, then we have a total of 20 fictitious leads which, as far as the matrix is concerned, are separate activities. From a physical point of view, we must impose two additional constraints because the fictitious leads are not completely independent. The total amount of TEL used in Premium to meet or exceed F-1 must be the same as the total amount of TEL used in Premium to meet or exceed F-2 because these two leads are physically identical. They were separated in the matrix for mathematical reasons only. The same type of constraint applies to Regular. Hence, we must stipulate:

$$\Sigma L_j \text{ Premium } F\text{-}1 = \Sigma L_j \text{ Premium } F\text{-}2 \qquad (16)$$

$$\Sigma L_j \text{ Regular } F\text{-}1 = \Sigma L_j \text{ Regular } F\text{-}2 \qquad (17)$$

Finally, the objective will be of the form:

$$\ldots + c_L \Sigma (L_j \text{ Premium } + L_j \text{ Regular}) + \ldots = \min \qquad (18)$$

where c_L is the unit cost of TEL and the dots indicate other terms whatever they may be.

It is clear that the optimum solution will make physical sense only if the fictitious leads for the limiting octanes are involved in the solution in a physically realizable way. Consider the situation where, let us say, lead 1 and 2 are at the upper bound, while lead 3 and 4 deviate from their upper bound and lead 5 is zero. This is not a physically realizable situation because of the gap existing between lead 3 and 4. This, however, could never occur in an optimal solution because of the concavity of the TEL response curve and because we are aiming to use as little TEL as possible. If a gap exists between L_j and L_{j+1}, it will always be more economic to reduce the level of L_{j+1} and push L_j up to its upper bound because L_j is more effective octane-wise than L_{j+1}. Therefore, we have the assurance that the fictitious leads for the limiting octanes always will be involved in the optimal solution in a physically realizable way. This will not necessarily happen, however, for those leads which belong to the nonlimiting octane specifications. As we have two octane specifications for each grade, there will in general be one octane in each grade which is limiting while there is give-away on the other two. The computer will have no incentive to meet or exceed physically realizably the octane rating for which there is give-away. It cannot make any money by it because the total amount of TEL already is fixed by the octane rating which is limiting as required by constraints (16) and (17). The computer simply picks that octane which is limiting, works on it to meet it most economically and lets the chips fall where they may, as far as the other octane rating is concerned. The optimal solution will still be perfectly satisfactory because the exact value of the give-away for the nonlimiting octane does not affect the solution.

Let us now briefly discuss the results for a case where this approach to the TEL problem was tried. The data were based on an actual situation that existed in one of our refineries a few years ago. In this case, gasoline production was fixed at a given level. The objective was to minimize cost of TEL minus credit for excess stocks. Two solutions of the same problem were available to which the linear programming solution could be compared. One was the solution that was actually used which was calculated in the refinery at the time when the problem arose. This solution, as is often the case, was prepared under severe time limitations. The availability of new blend stocks added to the difficulty of the problem. The other solution to the identical situation was obtained later by allowing sufficient time for a thorough analysis of the problem. In both these solutions, conventional hand blending procedures were used. Table I gives a comparison of TEL levels between these two solutions and the one obtained by linear programming. The reduction in TEL is clearly evident. The solutions should, of course, not be compared merely on the basis of lead savings. As can be seen from the objective function,

Table 1

TEL CONTENT IN CC/GAL. OF BLENDS

	Hand Blend No. 1	Hand Blend No. 2	Linear Prog. Blend
Premium	2.96	2.65	1.51
Regular	0.31	0.56	0.72

the credit for excess stocks must also be considered. The net savings of the linear programming solution still were substantial.

NONLINEAR EFFECTS OF VARIABLE CUT POINTS

In the blending problem just discussed, the volumes and properties of the stocks coming out of the refinery were given and the problem was to blend these stocks to make certain end-products in the most economical way. The refinery as a whole was fixed and the optimum blending solution gave us little or no information about what the optimum refinery operation should be. This, of course, is a tremendous problem because the refinery abounds with nonlinearities and all types of mathematically peculiar constraints. One interesting step toward the over-all refinery optimization was discussed recently by Schrage[8] where linear programming was combined with the method of steepest ascents.

Figure 12

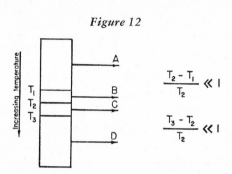

$$\frac{T_2 - T_1}{T_2} \ll 1$$

$$\frac{T_3 - T_2}{T_2} \ll 1$$

The next application we would like to discuss is an attempt to reach back into the refinery just a little way and optimize with respect to gasoline blending a few of the operating conditions. The conditions we shall consider are the re-run still cut points. A re-run still is a unit within the refinery which separates a stock into light and heavy components. The operating temperature of the unit determines the "cut point" between the two components. The volumes and the properties of the "cuts" are nonlinear functions of the cut point. The cut point can be varied within limits and the question arises as to where the optimum cut point should be for any given gasoline blending situation.

One way of handling this problem is to introduce fictitious stocks as shown symbolically in Figure 12. We assume that instead of having only one cut point we have, say, three cut points corresponding to temperatures T_1, T_2, and T_3 which yield small fictitious cuts "B" and "C" and major segregations "A" and "D". The volumes and properties of the fictitious cuts are determined such that when they are combined linearly with the major segregations, correct volumes and properties result. Consequently, the fictitious cuts sometimes have abnormal properties when considered by themselves.

The major segregations and the fictitious cuts are now made available

[8] R. W. Schrage, "Optimizing a Catalytic Cracking Operation by the Method of Steepest Ascents and Linear Programming," paper presented at the meeting of the American Institute of Chemical Engineers, September 9–12, 1956.

to the gasoline blend just as if they were actual stocks coming out of the refinery. The resulting optimal solution then is examined to see what happened to the fictitious cuts "B" and "C" in the shuffle. A number of things can occur as shown in Figure 13.

Figure 13

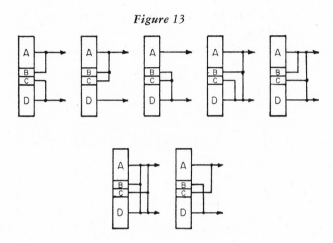

Because of the natural variation in properties with distillation temperature of the stock, it usually happens that in the optimum solution "A" goes entirely to Premium and "D" goes entirely to Regular. If "B" goes to Premium and "C" goes to Regular, we can conclude that the cut point should be at T_2. If both "B" and "C" go to Premium, the cut point should be at T_3 or at a higher temperature; if they both go to Regular, it should be at T_1 or at a lower tempreature. There is nothing in the program that prevents "B" and "C" from splitting. If "B" splits and "C" goes to Regular, the cut point should be between T_1 and T_2. If "C" splits and "B" goes to Premium, the cut point should be between T_2 and T_3. These five situations are the normal ones encountered most of the time because of the normal progression to a higher sulfur content and lower octane as the cuts get heavier. Occasionally, however, it may happen that both "B" and "C" split in such a way that the fraction of "C" going into Premium is greater than the corresponding fraction of "B" or that "B" goes entirely to Regular and "C" goes entirely to Premium. These are situations which are not realizable in practice because we have only one cut point in reality. To prevent such situations from occurring, additional constraints are imposed on the system which stipulate that the percentage of "B" going into Premium should be greater than the corresponding percentage of "C". These constraints will insure that the optimal solution will be physically realizable without too much trouble.

COST COEFFICIENTS

Before leaving the field of refining, let us consider the effect of cost coefficients on optimum gasoline blending. If the objective is an economic one, costs or values have to be determined for some of the stocks that are produced. This can be a complicated problem. In the case of the blending example discussed previously, the objective was to minimize lead costs minus credit for the excess stocks. This meant that a value had

Figure 14

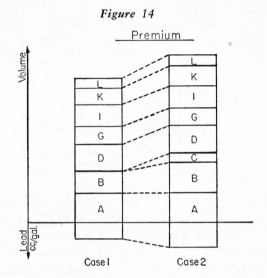

to be determined for each stock which was not required to be used up. The situation was complicated further by the fact that some excess stocks were earmarked for shipment to another refinery. This meant that their values had to be the values to that refinery which in turn depended on the local situation existing there during the time period of interest. These costs can be determined but they must be realistic for the solution to have meaning and a great deal of judgment and experience should go into their making.

As an illustration of the effect of the cost coefficients on the optimal solution, consider a hypothetical blending problem where the volumes of Premium and Regular are allowed to vary but their ratio is fixed. The objective was to maximize value of gasoline plus value of excess stocks minus TEL cost while meeting full quality requirements. Two cases were run which were identical in all respects except that in the second case the unit values of Premium and Regular were increased by a small amount. Stocks A through L were available for blending. The results are shown on Figures 14 and 15 where the composition, volume, and

TEL content of the gasolines are compared for the two cases. As expected, the optimum gasoline production increased for case 2. Changes in composition also occurred. As far as Premium is concerned, it contains more B than before and contains C which did not enter Premium for case 1. Regular loses its B content and part of C and absorbs F which was not utilized at all in case 1. The gross effect of the change in the price structure is a shift of all of Regular's B and part of its C to Premium and extensive utilization of F in Regular. As the change in

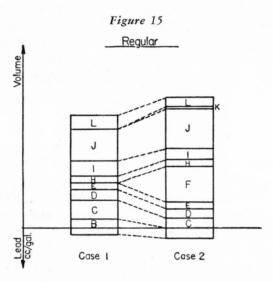

Figure 15

Regular

gasoline value was not drastic, it can be seen that we are dealing here with a system which is rather sensitive to the price structure.

DISTRIBUTION TO AN EXPANDING MARKET

Leaving the refinery with all its problems behind us we shall now turn to the area of marketing and distribution which has problems of its own. The classic example of a problem in this area is the transportation problem. A great deal of work has been done on this, particularly by oil companies. The first application of linear programming that we would like to discuss in this area is a type of transportation problem which, however, has some complicating features. We are indebted to Atlantic Refining Company for contributing this application.

Consider m refineries ($i = 1, 2 \cdot \cdot \cdot m$) and n bulk terminals or distribution centers ($j = 1, 2 \cdot \cdot \cdot \cdot n$) as shown in Figure 16. At the present time, the refineries are producing at levels P_i and the demands at the bulk plants are D_j. We may consider the sum of the P_i's to be equal to the sum of the D_j's so that all the demands are met.

Assume now that we find ourselves in an expanding market. Projections are available for what the demand at the different bulk plants is going to be, say, five years from now. Denote these projected demands by D_j'. To try to meet the increased demands, we must expand refining capacity. Denote the increased production by $P_i + e_i$ where e_i is a variable denoting the amount of expansion. We must also increase the capacity of our bulk plants. The expansion of refining and bulk plant capacity costs money and an upper bound exists on how much can be spent on over-all expansion. This upper bound is such that it is impossible to meet the demand at all the distribution centers. The problem now is to determine which refinery and bulk terminal to expand, and by how much, so as to maximize the net return. The maximization of net return may not necessarily be the best objective but we shall use it here for purposes of illustration.

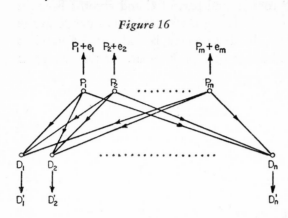

Figure 16

This problem can be formulated as follows: The total production leaving the ith refinery must be equal to the old production plus the expansion. Hence:

$$\sum_{j=1}^{n} x_{ij} = P_i + e_i, \qquad i = 1, 2, \ldots, m \tag{19}$$

where x_{ij} is the amount shipped from i to j. The amount received at the jth bulk plant must be less than or can at most be equal to the projected demand in that area. Hence:

$$\sum_{i=1}^{m} x_{ij} \leqq D_j', \qquad j = 1, 2, \ldots, n \tag{20}$$

If c_{iR} is the unit cost of expanding refinery capacity at i, then the total cost of refinery expansion is $\Sigma\, c_{iR} e_i$. In considering the cost of bulk plant expansion, we must take account of the fact that the shipments to some bulk plants may actually be reduced while others expand so as to be able to take full advantage of shifts in the market with the limited amount of expansion capital. The expansion of a bulk plant does require capital but a "contraction" does not because it simply means that shipments to the bulk plant are reduced. To handle this situation, we add the relation

$$\sum_{i=1}^{m} x_{ij} - D_j = s_j^+ - s_j^-, \qquad j = 1, 2, \ldots, n \tag{21}$$

to the system where s_j^+ and s_j^- are nonnegative variables. We also stipulate that:

$$\sum_{i=1}^{m} c_{iR} \ell_i + \sum_{j=1}^{n} c_{jB} s_j^+ \leqq M \tag{22}$$

where c_{jB} is the unit cost of bulk plant expansion and M is the maximum expansion capital available. The term on the left of (21) is the difference between the new shipments to j and the old shipments. If this difference is positive, then j expands, if it is negative then j "contracts". It can be shown that either s_j^+ or s_j^- but not both will be involved in the optimum basis. Hence, if j expands, then s_j^+ will be in the basis and there will be an expansion cost in view of the last constraint. If j "contracts", then s_j^- will be in the basis and there will be no expansion cost.

Finally, the objective function is:

$$\sum_{i=1}^{m} \sum_{j=1}^{n} c_{ij} x_{ij} - \sum_{i=1}^{m} c_{iR} \ell_i - \sum_{j=1}^{n} c_{jB} s_j^+ = \max \tag{23}$$

where c_{ij} is the profit per barrel shipped from i to j.

This formulation is satisfactory as long as the new shipments to the "contracted" bulk terminals do not fall below a certain value (they may even go to zero). This is a situation which is analogous to the one encountered in discussing the model of a producing complex. The plot of profit at the jth bulk plant as a function of shipments to the bulk plant is again a straight line displaced from the origin because of a fixed overhead. The actual profit function is again the straight line plus the origin. Thus, our objective function should really be:

$$\sum_{j=1}^{n} \left(\sum_{i=1}^{m} c_{ij} x_{ij} - \alpha_j \right) - \sum_{i=1}^{m} c_{iR} \ell_i - \sum_{j=1}^{n} c_{jB} s_j^+ = \max \tag{24}$$

where:

$$\alpha_j = \begin{cases} 0 \text{ if } \sum_i x_{ij} = 0 \\ \\ \text{const. if } \sum_i x_{ij} > 0 \end{cases} \tag{25}$$

but no general method exists for handling situations of this type. However, if it turns out in the optimal solution that none of the bulk plant volumes contract by substantial amounts the solutions will be useful.

SERVICE STATION DELIVERIES—LONG RANGE

Having considered the link of refinery to bulk terminal, let us now consider the last link in the chain—the flow of products from bulk terminal to service stations. Consider the situation shown in Figure 17. We are given the location of service stations and the roads connecting them. The small circles are the service stations, while the large circle denotes the bulk plant which supplies them by truck. Each service station, k, requires a delivery of D_k gallons of gasoline (for simplicity, let us assume only one grade of gasoline). Different truck types, denoted by the index s, are available for making the deliveries. The trucks differ in regard to carrying capacity and operating characteristics. We have a number of trucks of each type available for the operation. The problem is to devise a delivery schedule such that the transportation cost is minimized.

Figure 17

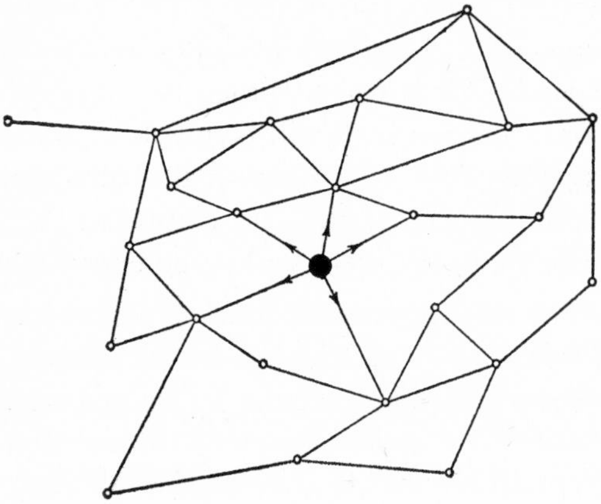

We are actually dealing here with two different types of problems depending on whether we look at this operation from the long-range or the short-range point of view. Let us consider the long-range point of view at first.

Assume that we look at this operation over an extended period of time so that the D_k represent total demands at the service stations during the period under consideration. Assume, furthermore, that the ratios of the D_k's to the gallon capacity of each of the trucks is sufficiently large so that many deliveries have to be made to each station during that period in order to meet the demand. Under these conditions, the problem becomes a transportation type problem with transshipment of goods. The transshipment feature comes about through the fact that if a truck leaves the bulk plant and makes deliveries to, say, service stations 1, 2, and 3 in that order, then the gasoline destined for station 2 is transshipped via station 1 and the gasoline for station 3 is transshipped via stations 1 and 2.

Some work has been done on the transshipment problem[9] in connection with aircraft scheduling and communication networks. Our problem here is slightly different but the general approach is the same. The key to the mathematical formulation lies in the use of triple indices. Adopt the convention that the first index refers to the point of departure, the second index to the intermediate destination and the third index to the ultimate destination. If y_{ijk} denotes the number of gallons shipped from i to j destined for k, then we can write:

$$\sum_i y_{ijk} = \sum_u y_{juk}, \quad \text{all } j, k \text{ but } j \neq k \tag{26}$$

$$\sum_i y_{ikk} = D_k, \quad \text{all } k \tag{27}$$

$$\sum_k \sum_j y_{0jk} = \sum D_k \tag{28}$$

The left side of (26) is the sum of what arrives at j from all points but destined for k while the right side is the sum of what leaves j for all points destined for k. These two must be equal because we do not wish to accumulate anything at j destined for k. Equation (27) states that the sum of what arrives at k from all points and is destined for k must be equal to the demand at k. Equation (28) states that the sum of what leaves the bulk plant (indicated by the index zero) must be equal to the total demand. These three conditions insure that we deliver the proper number of gallons where they are required and that they all originate at the bulk plant.

If x_{ijs} is the number of truck runs per period from i to j in the s-type truck (the index s denotes the type of truck and not ultimate destination), then we must also specify that:

$$\sum_i x_{ijs} = \sum_u x_{jus}, \quad \text{all } j, s \tag{29}$$

---

[9] A. S. Manne, "Air Cargo Transport Scheduling," RAND Report P–533, June 11, 1954. R. E. Kalaba and M. L. Juncosa, "Optimal Design and Utilization of Communication Networks," *Management Science*, Vol. III (October, 1956), pp. 33–44. P. S. Dwyer and B. A. Galler, "The Method of Reduced Matrices for a General Transportation Problem," paper presented at the meeting of the Association for Computing Machinery, August 27–29, 1956. A. Orden, "The Trans-Shipment Problem," *Management Science*, Vol. II (April, 1956), pp. 276–85.

which means that the number of s-type trucks which arrive at j is equal to the number of s-type trucks that leave j.

To insure that we have enough carrying capacity available for each i–j route, we must stipulate that:

$$\sum_k y_{ijk} \leqq \sum_s g_s x_{ijs}, \qquad \text{all } i, j \tag{30}$$

where g_s is the carrying capacity of the s-type truck. The left side represents the actual number of gallons of gasoline that are hauled from i to j, while the right side represents the maximum number that can be hauled. The slack in this relation is indicative of the fact that the trucks may have to run partially full or empty some of the time.

If we denote the time required by the s-type truck to go from i to j by h_{ijs} and let h_s be the time that an s-type truck can be used per period, then we have the additional constraint:

$$\sum_i \sum_j h_{ijs} x_{ijs} \leqq h_s, \qquad \text{all } s \tag{31}$$

which insures that the trucks are not run longer than possible during the time period under consideration.

The objective is:

$$\sum_i \sum_j \sum_s c_{ijs} x_{ijs} = \min \tag{32}$$

where c_{ijs} is the cost per trip of operating an s-type truck over the link i–j. Having determined the x's and y's a schedule can then be constructed from them.

For any actual problem, the number of constraints represented by equations (26) to (32) is rather frightening and can be beyond the capacity of even the largest computers if the standard Simplex procedure is employed. Fortunately the matrix involved here exhibits a great deal of structure. Efforts are under way in a number of places to exploit this structure (as the structure of the ordinary transportation problem was exploited) so as to reduce the computational labor.

The problem considered here represents a simplified situation but the type of analysis employed is representative of what is done for more sophisticated models. In any actual problem, the x's are limited to integral values so that the nonintegral optimal solution must be adjusted to integral x's. If, as we assumed in the beginning, many trips are necessary to meet the demand, this imperfection may not be too serious.

Unfortunately, no general methods exist at present for handling linear programming problems in which some or all of the variables are constrained to be integers.

SERVICE STATION DELIVERIES—SHORT RANGE

The problem just discussed permits us to look at the over-all situation on a long-range basis. From a short-range point of view, however, the problem is somewhat different and much more complicated. It becomes similar in type to the so-called "clover-leaf problem" or "farmer's daughter problem" which in turn is related to the classic problem of the traveling salesman. In the traveling salesman problem, we have a number of towns which the salesman desires to visit in a sequence such that the total distance traveled is a minimum. In the farmer's daughter problem, we have the same situation plus the additional constraint that the salesman wishes to return to, let us say, town "A" before a certain maximum time has elapsed. In the traveling salesman problem, the solution consists of a single loop; while in the farmer's daughter problem, the solution consists of a number of loops, each originating and terminating at town "A". The farmer's daughter, of course, is at "A".

Returning now to our delivery problem and examining it from the short-range point of view, it turns out that it is similar to the farmer's daughter problem except for some additional complications of its own. On a daily basis, the dispatcher at the bulk terminal has a list of service stations to which deliveries of certain amounts must be made *today* because the service stations are on the verge of running out of gasoline. As before, he has trucks of different types at his disposal and his problem now is to devise routes for the trucks so that the deliveries are made at minimum transportation cost. These routes, of course, originate and terminate at the bulk plant. Thus, the bulk plant is equivalent to the farmer's daughter; but instead of having only one boy friend, she has as many as we have different types of trucks on the road. One of the important differences between the long-range formulation of this problem and the formulation on a daily basis is that in the former the individual trucks lose their identity except for the type to which they belong, while in the latter, each truck must be considered as an entity.

The Operations Research Group at Atlantic became interested in devising means for handling this problem on a daily basis. With the assistance of George Dantzig, a method was devised that is not guaranteed to lead to the optimum solution but will usually yield a solution rather close to it.

CONCLUSION

We have attempted in this paper to discuss some oil industry problems and to indicate how linear programming was or can be used to solve them. There can be no doubt that linear programming has made a place for itself in the oil industry, particularly in the manufacturing phase. It is beginning to be appreciated by management as an important help in making complicated decisions. It must be realized, however, that not everything in this world is linear and that occasionally we come across constraints which are mathematically pathological types. This is good in a way because if ever a method is devised that solves all problems, life would become rather dull. Much still remains to be done. We need a great deal more basic research on optimization methods in the universities and industrial research laboratories.

It should be pointed out that the successful application of linear programming to practical problems was made possible by the advent of large, high-speed computers and by the existence of an efficient linear programming code. If digital computers were nonexistent, the answers would be many years too late. We would like to express our thanks to William Orchard-Hays and Leola Cutler of the RAND Corporation and to Harold Judd of IBM for the excellent code which they developed for the IBM 704, and made available to industry.

We would like to thank the management and personnel of Magnolia Petroleum, Esso Research and Engineering, Atlantic Refining, Arabian American Oil, Richfield Oil and Shell Development for their assistance and cooperation in the preparation of this paper.

CASE 2

Application of Linear Programming to Investments in the Electric Power Industry[1]

P. MASSÉ and R. GIBRAT[2]

Some points of special interest in this paper are:

a. The method employed for handling uncertain variables. What was the economic consideration here?
b. The constraints placed on the solution.
c. The assumptions made regarding linearity and additivity of costs.
d. The use of present value concepts for handling investment with operating costs.
e. The concept and use of joint products.
f. The assumption that plants within a class are "homogeneous."
g. The (national) rate of interest (8 per cent).
h. The varying rates of return on incremental capital revealed by the analysis.
i. Graphical versus simplex methods for this problem.
j. The problem of explaining one's results to "nonspecialists."

LINEAR PROGRAMMING TECHNIQUE INTRODUCED

In France, the investment operations in basic industries, notably in the railroad, coal, electricity, and gas sectors, are submitted for approval of the government and the parliament.

---

[1] *Management Science,* January, 1957. Reprinted by permission. Translated from the French by George B. Dantzig and edited by William W. Taylor.

[2] The electric power industry in France is nationalized and operated by the "Electricité de France." Dr. Massé is the Executive Vice President. Dr. Gibrat is a private consultant.

507

The authors of these programs have thus to determine the most economical solution of problems and then to enlighten and persuade the authorities in charge of approving operations.

Towards the end of 1954 and the beginning of 1955, in the course of undertaking these tasks we found ourselves independently faced with remarkably similar problems.

One of us, who had worked on many studies on the economical management of resources, had to obtain official approval of the plan for a very important reservoir project in the French Alps (Roselend). This approval ran afoul of the objection that the cost of the investment in relation to the kilowatt hours producible in an average year was about three times higher for Roselend than for a hydroelectric plant without a reservoir. It is clear to the discerning that this difference in cost is accompanied by a difference in value—for the energy accumulated in the reservoirs can render much more service than can the fleeting energy of rivers. But this difference in value, due to the flexibility in exploitation of reservoirs, was insufficiently understood.

The other of us, who had devoted a good part of his life to the study of tidal power plants and had contributed to reducing their cost and to increasing their efficiency, sought to specify the place to be given in a national program to this characteristically new source of energy The latter appeared endowed indeed with even more flexibility than river reservoirs, thanks to the combinations of cycles rendered possible by the ebb and flow of tides and by the utilization of a new technique of "bulbs —groups."[3]

The heart of the problem, in one case as well as the other, is that electrical investment serves to create not a unique product, the kilowatt hour, but a group of related products. The linear programming technique came to be introduced at the time in a wholly natural way in the investigations of the two authors. Indeed, they discovered one day, not without amusement, that, separately, they had come to the same conclusion; such a coincidence was not astonishing because what one planned for reservoir plants, the other had in mind for tidal plants. The details of this meeting of minds have served as the theme for one of us in his inaugural address as the president of the "Société Française des Electriciens."[4]

---

[3] Each turbine generates electricity during both the ebb and flow of the tide.

[4] R. Gibrat, "La joie de comprendre," *Bulletin de la Société Française des Electriciens,* Mars, 1956.

METHODS AND PROCEDURES

Before starting the detailed exposition of the methods and results, we will indicate generally the lines which we have followed in our researches, considering the principal economic characteristics of the production of electricity.

Optimizing a Given Objective

It is known that optimizing problems can be viewed from two aspects:

—Maximization of profit under assumed price factors (for production) and final products, but not the quantities to employ or to produce.

—Minimization of cost under assumed price factors (for production) and assumed quantities to be produced but not the price of these products.

This second class coincides in principle with that adopted by Tjalling C. Koopmans in *Activity Analysis of Production and Allocation* ("The Best Allocation of Limited Means towards Desired Ends"). We ourselves have chosen it because it represents, in a more realistic manner than the first, the situation of a producer enjoying a quasi-monopoly for the sale of his services, and yet being on the other hand sufficiently small in proportion to the market for each factor required for production that unlimited quantities of each can be acquired at their corresponding given prices.[5]

These two points of view were discussed, as the point at issue in a meeting of one of us, with Mr. Allais,[6] who would have preferred to see, as the given point of departure, the price of products and not the quantities to be produced. It was replied to him that, in the context of the French economy, the given point of departure had been established by the requirements, but that once the solution had been found, we undertook a calculation of the break points in order to verify that the net return of the final solution would not call for a revision of the assigned requirements with regard, in particular, to the net price *arrived at* for joint products.

Elimination of Uncertainty

In the matter of electric production, the uncertainty of the future affects at once the supply and the demand; it is necessary to take account

---

[5] P. Samuelson, *Foundations of Economic Analysis,* chap. iv, p. 58.

[6] P. Massé, "Le problème des investissements à l'Electricité de France," *Nouvelle Revue d'Economie Contemporaine,* Février, 1955.

of the joint variability of the consumption, of the water levels and of machine availability.

In the present study, as in those previously made at headquarters of the Electricité de France, the economy of uncertainty is converted into an economy of certainty by the use of safety margins over and above the probable values:

—The designated demand requirement is 5 per cent higher than the probable demand; it coincides with the highest quartile that would be estimated from the probability distribution of demand, according to the outline of the general goals of economic activity held by the planning commission.

—The parameters representative of the production of an electric plant (which are, we shall see, its average power output for daylight hours during the middle of winter, its peak point, and its annual output) are less than their probable value. For example, the average daylight hourly output during the middle of winter of a hydroelectric plant is taken to be equal to its value at the time of a standard 1948–49 low water level, estimated to happen only about three times in a century; for a steam-generated electric plant, it is taken at 85 per cent of its net continuous output (the allowance of 15 per cent is accounted for by the unavailability of material).

—The probable value of the costs of investments is overestimated by a sum set up to cover the exceptional happenings.

—The costs of operations, repeating themselves a great number of times, are estimated at their probable value.

Estimation of Costs

The costs of investments considered are based on the evaluations of the "Services de Electricité de France." Similarly, the outlays for maintenance and operations conform to accepted norms.

The cost of combustibles can be treated by following a number of schemes:

The simplest scheme consists in placing in juxtaposition to the entirely new consumption C, the wholly new capacities of hydroelectric production H or steam-generated production T (where C, H, T represent probable values). The probable steam-generated electric production is thus C-H, according to the conservation postulate (the dams have no overflow losses).

A scheme a little more complex consists in supposing that C is added to a pre-existent consumption and H and T are added to pre-existent production capacities. Thus the new steam plant capacity furnishes its full production T and the excess $T + H - C$ of the new product over the new consumption, sets to restrict the use of older and consequently more obsolete electric groups.

This more complex scheme, moreover, can be extended in time. The 30-year life and occasionally secular duration of investments lead to the establishment of estimated operating accounts for a long period and the reducing of the successive costs to a common measure by a present value calculation. During the long time span, the technical and economical data are called upon to vary under conditions which are supposedly known in advance, notably those that concern the prices, the specific assumption of combustibles and the characteristics of the steam plants. (It is this third scheme that is utilized by the Department of Equipment of Electricity of France.)

The important point is that, in all the studies made up to the present, including ours, the *linearity of costs* relative to the size of the plants, and the *additivity of costs* for various plants are taken for granted even though this hypothesis is only rigorously exact in the case of infinitesimal changes in the amount of equipment or of homogeneous thermal production.

Definition of Joint Products

Electricity is nonstockable—the kilowatt is a unit of energy but not an economic unit. The kilowatt hours from high water differs profoundly from kilowatt hours at the peak of winter. The producer fabricates and sells joint products which electricians call the load curve.

The question arises at this time of the choice of parameters to represent this load curve. The initial studies of the Department of Equipment, made in the period which followed the creation of the "Electricité de France" (1946), rested on the postulate which, stated a little boldly, is as follows: "A system with production convenient for the average daylight power needs of midwinter (period of maximum consumption and minimum water levels for hydroelectric power[7]) will be superabundant from any other point of view." Otherwise stated, "With regard to service rendered, the load curve characteristic of the electricians can be represented by a unique parameter A."

Then, each hydroelectric plant with cost of investment D can be compared to a standard steam plant having the same average daylight power output in midwinter (called *guaranteed output*). One can thus calculate the increase in value, E, brought about by the substitution of the first for the second, and from this deduce its coefficient of value $V = 1 + E/D$.[8] If it were not for the limitation of total funds for invest-

---

[7] Because of the preponderant influence of plants in the Alps whose supply is reduced in winter by the cold.

[8] R. Giguet, "The Programming of Electric Equipment Considered from the Point of View of Applied Economics," *Economique Appliquée* No. 1, 1951.

ment, the programs would have been determined by taking plants in decreasing order of coefficients of value until the assigned objective A_0 for midwinter daylight power output was obtained. If, as was the case, there intervenes a limitation of total funds for authorized investment, D_0, one proceeds to a new classification of plants by a compromise between those which have the largest coefficients of value and those which carry the largest guaranteed output per franc invested.

However, it was not long before a second criterion was imposed by the Electricité de France: *the peak output*. From that time on one hydroelectric plant became no longer substitutable in terms of equal service to a unique standard steam plant, but rather to a combination of a standard steam and a peak steam (since there must be as many elements in the characterizing combination as there are criteria in the definition of consumption).

It has thus come to us that this idea of extension could be pursued. Moreover, the possibility occurred to one of us one day that our system of production, at least theoretically, would become severely limited in summer if we fill too much reservoirs; that is to say, if we augmented too much our reserves for winter at the expense of our availabilities for summer. This concern leads to the introduction in the definition of consumption of a third criterion—for example, the annual energy. But there is no theoretical reason to limit to three the multiplication of requirements (for example, one-fourth requirement can be a ceiling to the expense of investment)—from which arose the idea of a more general theory allowing m requirements.

It is well to see that this most general notion is contained implicitly in the preceding approaches: these consider only the limiting requirements, and admit only one differential modification of the system within existent freedom relative to other requirements. The equivalence of service rendered is evaluated relative to the limiting requirements. It is not affected by the variation within the freedom relative to the other requirements *so long as this margin of freedom exists*. But it is precisely this which one is not sure of beforehand when one works up a program which is far from being infinitesimal. (It is the essence of the objection mentioned earlier against reservoirs.)

A five-year plan which represents an increase of 40 per cent in the capacity of a system is very far from being infinitesimal. The question arises of finding a guaranteed method for authors of a program which applies even when all surpluses disappear.

In this framework, it seems better to introduce at the start of the calculation m requirements attainable with or without a margin of freedom; doing this gives reliability to the results if the requirements have been well chosen. This new method of presentation calls for the *mathematics of inequalities* whose rapid development conveys the importance of the notions of thresholds and bottlenecks in a great number of economic processes. At the same time it is to our interests to modify our language somewhat and no longer speak of *equivalent solutions* in service rendered, but of admissible solutions relative to an objective (requirements) of *m* parameters. Among these admissible solutions, the optimal solution is that of least cost.

Hypothesis of Groups of Homogeneous Plants

In order to go further, we have made for our purposes a bold hypothesis, which consists in simplifying the definition of the system of production and in supposing that the *m* requirements are to be met from *n* groups of homogeneous plants. The plants are classified into groups by distinguishing in a little vague but well-known way between plants with no reservoir, plants with a small reservoir (daily), plants with a large reservoir (seasonal), and finally tidal plants. We will criticize this hypothesis later on. Let us limit ourselves for the moment to showing its origin. Towards the end of 1954, it was held that the economical advantage of reservoir plants was at times doubtful. It was feared that they were lacking in energy in summer. It was also repeatedly said that, since we were poor in capital and were committed by this fact to making much use of steam power, we had to make the best of a bad situation; that is to say, to get all the energy we could from plants without reservoirs, whose net price per kilowatt hour was sensibly lower than that of plants with reservoirs, and to entrust their regularization to steam plants that we had been obliged to construct anyhow. This opinion was confuted by certain methods of the time, which gave to some reservoir plants a satisfactory coefficient of value. Between a vague reason and a precise calculation, there was no room for hesitation. Nevertheless, the method of coefficient of value, by its very compactness, did not permit the better understanding of the underlying reason of things. It did not with sufficient clarity point up the error of considering the production of electricity from the viewpoint of only kilowatt hours and not from that of joint products. It is then from this aspect that it appears to us necessary to insist on using the technique of inequalities, that is to say, that of linear programming.

The desired purpose being to explain and to persuade, we must simplify. We would be willing to demonstrate that, if an unlimited quantity of "good" steam plants and "good" hydroelectric plants with no reservoir were possible to construct, it would nevertheless be necessary to reserve a place in our program for reservoir plants and also tidal plants. *A fortiori* must it be so if the hydroelectric plants with no reservoir become less and less good as their number increases.

The Assumptions

At the end of 1954, the problem posed at Electricité de France consisted in determining a program of equipment performing the required service at the least cost—the requirements to be met at the end of five years were as follows:

A_0 (guaranteed power output)   1692 MW
B_0 (peak power output)   2307 MW
C_0 (annual power output)   7200 GWh

(1 MW = 1,000 kilowatts, 1 GWh = 1 million kilowatt hours). The ratios $B_0/A_0 = 1.36$ and $C_0/A_0 = 4.3$ are graphed on Figure 1 by the point Ω_2.

It is convenient to observe that the above requirements take into account any prior commitment for certain steam and hydroelectric plants with no reservoir. For the complete plan, the ratios B_0/A_0 and C_0/A_0 would have been 1.27 and 6.4, respectively. (Point Ω_1 of Figure 1.)

Furthermore, the authorized funds for investment had been fixed at

$$D_0 = 271 \text{ Billions of Francs.}$$

To meet these requirements, we presumed to have at our disposal five groups of homogeneous plants:

1. Steam plants (T)
2. Hydroelectric plants with no reservoir (F)
3. Hydroelectric plants with a large reservoir (R)
4. Hydroelectric plants with a small reservoir (E)
5. Tidal plants (M)

where letter in ( ) symbolizes the type.

The supplied quantities in each group will be designated by the letter x, the unit contributions to the requirements by the letters a, b, c, d, the costs of operation by the letter f, the total present value or discounted cost by the letter g, each letter having an index of the group considered.

One will find in Figure 1 the points T, F, R, E, M representing for each group the ratios for the systems of the coordinates $\left(\dfrac{b}{a}, \dfrac{c}{a}\right), \left(\dfrac{g}{a}, \dfrac{g}{b}\right),$ $\left(\dfrac{g}{a}, \dfrac{g}{c}\right), \left(\dfrac{g}{b}, \dfrac{g}{c}\right).$ The consideration of the ratios $\dfrac{b}{a}, \dfrac{c}{a}, \dfrac{d}{a}, \dfrac{d}{b}, \dfrac{d}{c}$ makes evident, in an illuminating fashion, the diversity of the energy and economic properties of the five groups. Thus their classification by order of "merit" is very different depending on the criterion chosen.

Figure 1

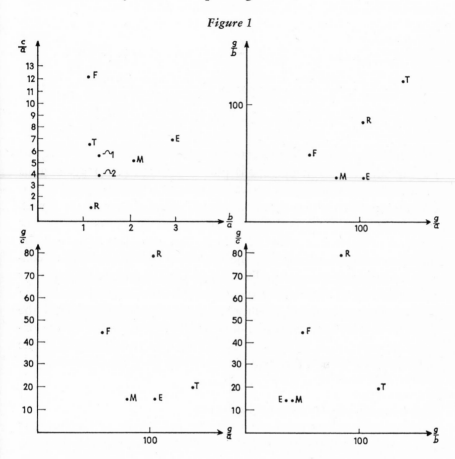

T = Steam plants.
F = Hydroelectric with no reservoir.
E = Hydroelectric with a small
   reservoir.

R = Hydroelectric with a large
   reservoir.
M = Tidal
Ω_1 = Consumption 1954
Ω_2 = Consumption of 2nd plan.

Ranked by peak output per guaranteed output:

E, next M, then R, T, F nearly equivalent $\left(\dfrac{b}{a} \text{ varies from 3 to } 1.15\right)$.

Ranked by energy output per guaranteed output:

F, next E and T almost equivalent, M, then R $\left(\dfrac{c}{a} \text{ varies from } 12.6 \text{ to } 1.3\right)$.

Ranked by investment costs per guaranteed output:

$$T, R, M, E, F \left(\frac{d}{a} \text{ varies from 97,000 to 420,000 fr/KW} \right).$$

Ranked by investment costs per peak power output:

$$T, M, E \text{ and } R, F \left(\frac{a}{b} \text{ varies from 84,500 to 381,000 fr/KW} \right).$$

Ranked by investment costs per annual energy output:

$$T, F, M, E, R \left(\frac{d}{c} \text{ varies from 13.8 to 100 fr/KWh} \right).$$

The introduction of the present value of total costs (that is to say, of the capitalized costs of operations plus investment costs) again turns topsyturvy the ranking and one is not able to escape the study of the complete problem, however complicated it may appear at the outset.

According to our hypothesis the discounted total costs are a linear function of the size of different groups. This total cost consists of the initial costs of investment and the successive operating expenses converted to their present value. The method applies whatever be the law for computing the operating expenses and permits notably taking into account the improvements in efficiency of steam plants. However, in the interests of simplicity, we will limit ourselves here to the case of constant operating costs f, the total discounted cost corresponding to the unit size being then of the form

$$g = d + kf$$

where k is a coefficient of capitalization.

Some observations on the calculation of expenses for combustibles are interesting. In the hypothesis of a plan departing from zero, the probable steam production is

$$C_0' - c_2'x_2 - c_3'x_3 - c_4'x_4 - c_5'x_5$$

(C_0' and the c_i' are probable values and are different from C_0 and the c_i defined earlier which are probable values with a safety margin). The cost of coal is proportional to the above expression.

In the case of a plan augmenting an older homogeneous production system the new steam facilities furnish $c_1'x_1$ and the reduction of the older steam production is

$$c_1'x_1 + c_2'x_2 + c_3'x_3 + c_4'x_4 + c_5'x_5 - C_0'$$

Calling γ_0 the specific consumption of the older central steam plants and γ_1 that of the new, the cost of combustion is

$$-c_1'x_1(\gamma_0 - \gamma_1) - \gamma_0(c_2'x_2 + c_3'x_3 + c_4'x_4 + c_5'x_5) + C_0'\gamma_0.$$

One sees, thus, the expense of production includes a constant term, $C_0\gamma_0$, and terms proportional to x_i with a negative coefficient (zero for x_1 if $\gamma_1 = \gamma_0$).

We give below the numerical values which we have utilized,[9] where we reduced to unity the guaranteed power output. It will be noticed that the economy of coal surpasses the costs of hydraulic plants for maintenance and operation ($f_i < 0$).

	a	b	c	d	f	g
Steam....................	1	1.15	7	97	+3.14	136
Hydroelectric–no reservoir......	1	1.10	12.6	420	−29.10	56
Large reservoir...............	1	1.20	1.3	130	−2.35	101
Small reservoir...............	1	3.00	7.35	310	−16.5	104
Tidal.....................	1	2.13	5.47	213	−10.7	79

Whence the following ratios used in setting up Figure 1:

	$\dfrac{d}{a}$	$\dfrac{d}{b}$	$\dfrac{d}{c}$	$\dfrac{g}{a}$	$\dfrac{g}{b}$	$\dfrac{g}{c}$
Steam....................	97	85.4	13.8	136	118	19.4
Hydroelectric–no reservoir......	420	381	33.3	56	51	4.4
Large reservoir...............	130	108	100	101	84	77.5
Small reservoir...............	310	103	42.2	104	35	14.2
Tidal.....................	213	100	38.9	79	37	14.4

(Millions of francs per MW or GWh)

One should be sure to note that the assumed numbers correspond to November 1954 conditions and ought to be currently recalculated because of certain economic changes that have developed since then. The reader is thus requested to regard them only as an example.

With the rate of interest adopted by the Plan ($i = 8$ per cent), the total costs of the plan, that is to say, the series of investments augmented by the capitalized value of the charges, are in the neighborhood, when expressed in billions of francs, of

$$\Sigma g_i x_i + 270$$

---

[9] R. Gibrat, "Les plans de production d'énergie électrique et les usines marémotrices," *Flamme et Thermique*, No. XC, March, 1956; "L'usine marémotrice de la Rance," *Revue Française de l'Energie*, April, 1956. P. Massé, "Le problème des investissements à l'Electricité de France," *Nouvelle Revue d'Economie Contemporaine*, No. LXII, February 1, 1955.

Statement of the Problem

We now precisely state the problem whose genesis and assumptions we have explained above:

a) Let there exist n groups of homogeneous plants in unlimited and continuous supply—steam plants, hydroelectric plants with no reservoir, a small reservoir, a large reservoir, tidal plants, atomic plants, etc. Associating with these plants the positive or zero quantities (x_1, x_2, . . . , x_n), one obtains by linear combinations the characteristic parameters of the system as a whole:

$$A = \sum_1^n a_i x_i, \qquad B = \sum_1^n b_i x_i, \qquad C = \sum_1^n c_i x_i,$$

$$D = \sum_1^n d_i x_i, \qquad F = \sum_1^n f_i x_i$$

where $a_i, b_i, c_i, d_i, f_i,$ are *constants* characterizing each group of plants. The a, b, c are assumed to be positive unless otherwise indicated. It should be noted that the characteristic parameters of the system were equated above to a linear combination of the parameters of each group; *this is a postulate* whose truth should be verified in each problem (the case, for example, of a series of plants on the same river evidently merits such an examination).

b) We say that a solution ($x_1, x_2,$ . . . , x_n) with all x positive or zero, is a feasible program if it meets the requirements A_0, B_0, C_0 exactly or in a surplus, that is to say, if

$$A \geq A_0, \qquad B \geq B_0, \qquad C \geq C_0.$$

Among the class of feasible solutions, the optimal solution will be defined by a condition of minimum cost, this cost being defined by a linear equation

$$G = D + kF$$

where

$$G = \Sigma g_i x_i \text{ with } g_i = d_i + k f_i$$

and where $k,$ the coefficient of capitalization, fixes the weight given today to future expenses relative to investment expenses. This formula completes the linearization of our programming problem; but this condition of linearity of costs is less fundamental than the condition of linearity with respect to objectives, and it is true, as one knows, that rising prices can give rise to serious computational complications. The ideal formula would be $G(D, F_1, F_2, \ldots, F_t, \ldots)$, the problem remaining convex, but nonlinear. In a recent conference,[10] Ragnar Frisch has shown that one can resolve this problem by introducing gradient vectors for the cost function G and for the logarithmic potential:

$$V = \Sigma \log x_i.$$

In summary, our hypothesis renders our problem convex and linear; this defines the entire mathematical apparatus which we are going to use.

One is able to fix in advance other linear conditions, that is to say, to have other requirements. For example, a very interesting condition results from fixing the total investment costs at less than or equal to a given amount, $D < D_0$. Another interesting condition of similar type is brought about by a limitation on the size of one or several of the groups of plants, for example,

$$x_1 \leq x_1^0.$$

It is known that one begins transforming the problem by introducing the surplus variables x_a, x_b, x_c, x_d corresponding to the requirements and by considering $(n + m + 1)$ vectors in total (here $m = 4$):

P_1	P_2	. . . .	P_n	P_a	P_b	P_c	P_d	P_o
a_1	a_2	. . . .	a_n	-1	0	0	0	A_o
b_1	b_2	. . . .	b_n	0	-1	0	0	B_o
c_1	c_2	. . . .	c_n	0	0	-1	0	C_o
d_1	d_2	. . . .	d_n	0	0	0	$+1$	D_o

It is also known that the optimizing solutions involve, in general, r plant variables not zero and $m - r$ surplus variables not zero $(r \leqq m)$.

The application of the simplex method of George B. Dantzig, necessary to obtain rigorous results, is, in general, very long[11] in spite of its mechanical nature, and *it is important to be able to begin with as good an approximation as possible.* Whence the interest in a method which permits the problem to be reduced to the study of "two group struc-

[10] Ragnar Frisch, "La résolution des problèmes de programme linéaire par la méthode du potentiel logarithmique," *C.N.R.S.,* Seminaire d'Économétrie, Séance du 1er, June, 1955.

[11] Translator's note: Undoubtedly the authors have in mind systems much larger than the 4-equation system considered here which could be solved with a desk calculator in under an hour.

tures" whatever be the parameters fixing the requirements and characterizing the plants. One of us has been able to demonstrate some very general results valid for four requirements, of which the limitation of funds D_0 varied from zero to infinity.[12] They permitted the construction of graphs which gave at a glance the optimum solution (if it exists) among the two group structures of plants for a definite value defining the limitation of authorized expenditures. Thus one combination of the two groups (hydroelectric plants with no reservoir + tidal, for example) would be strictly determined from two requirements; letting *a, b, c, d* denote those requirements, guarantee, peak, annual energy, or expenses, that the structure satisfies exactly, we have the six possible combinations of requirements *bc, ca, ab, ad, bd, cd.* In total the ten combinations of two groups furnish 60 distinct structures. We will take up their examination, being however very brief.[13]

The principle of the method is the following. A solution of the structure q, r, s, t is admissible if each of the determinants

$$\| \; P_0 \quad P_r \quad P_s \quad P_t \; \|;$$
$$\| \; P_q \quad P_0 \quad P_s \quad P_t \; \|;$$
$$\| \; P_q \quad P_r \quad P_0 \quad P_t \; \|;$$
$$\| \; P_q \quad P_r \quad P_s \quad P_0 \; \|;$$

has the same sign as the determinant $P = \| \; P_q, P_r, P_s, P_t, \; \|$.

It is *optimum* if each of the determinants

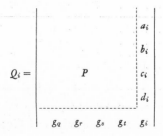

$$Q_i = \left| \begin{array}{cccc|c} & & & & a_i \\ & & & & b_i \\ & & P & & c_i \\ & & & & d_i \\ \hline g_q & g_r & g_s & g_t & g_i \end{array} \right|$$

has the same sign as P.

We take, for example, the structures with surpluses for *b* and *c*, with equality for expenses *d* and for guarantee *a,* and we plot three functions with (d/a) as abscissa and with $g/a, b/a, c/a,$ respectively, as ordinates (Figure 2 on top and to the left).

[12] R. Gibrat, "Les Plans de production d'énergie électrique et les usines marémotrices," *Flamme et Thermique,* No. XC, March, 1956.

[13] The same considerations have inspired, independent of us, Waugh and Burrows, whose article "A Short Cut to Linear Programming" (*Econometrica,* January, 1955), has recently come to our attention.

Each group is characterized by a point on each of the three graphs. The application of the preceding conditions readily permits one to demonstrate that the structure comprising hydroelectric plants with no reservoir and tidal plants (points represented 2 and 5) will be optimal among all possible structures of the type bc if, in the graph g/a, the line (2, 5) fulfills three conditions:

1. It lies below all points representing other groups
2. Its ordinate relative to the origin is positive
3. Its slope is negative

which is certainly the case in Figure 2.

Similarly, one demonstrates easily from the preceding conditions that some structures such as (2,5) will be admissible if the corresponding requirements are defined in the other two graphs by the point with abscissa D_0/A_0 and ordinates C_0/A_0 respectively, situated below the corresponding line (2,5) for the structure studies; it is this which defines the domain where the structure is admissible relative to the requirements and optimal relative to all possible structures of type bc.

Figure 2 (where are shown the values of the second plan B_0/A_0, C_0/A_0, D_0/A_0) shows that the only structures bc which can be optimal besides (2,5) are (1,3) and (3,5) because in the graph g/a the other segments such as (1,5) or (4,5) do not satisfy one of the conditions. On the other hand, (1,3) is not admissible for the second plan because B_0/A_0 is too high (graph b/a, d/a) where the line of ordinate B_0/A_0 is above the line (1,3); structure (3,5), is admissable only for the ratios D_0/A_0 between 188.8 and 213 (points α and 5) because of C_0/A_0; (2,5), is admissible finally for D_0/A_0 between 213 and 367 (points 5 and β), this time because of the value B_0/A_0.

A point of interest regarding this method is that it permits at a glance the picking out of that structure which is probably optimum and fixes limits for the requirements for which it will remain feasible. The study of a new type (nuclear, for example) will be made immediately by the introduction of points which represent it in the graphs, and thus it is easy to see what values of the parameters (a, b, c, d) a new group should have in order to form part of a solution of a given structure type. The examination of the influence of a variation of the energy parameters is also very easy; for example, the raising of the point 5 above the line 32 in the graph of g/a causes the disappearance of the corresponding group (Tidal plants).

Besides structures for two groups of the type bc, there exist analogous structures of type ca and ab. It is sufficient, in order to study them, to make a cyclic permutation of the letters *a, b, c.* One obtains thus the graphs *ab* and *ac* of Figure 2 whose interpretation is also easy.

Finally, the structures for three groups admits of a spatial representation which one can study in an analogous manner by descriptive

Figure 2

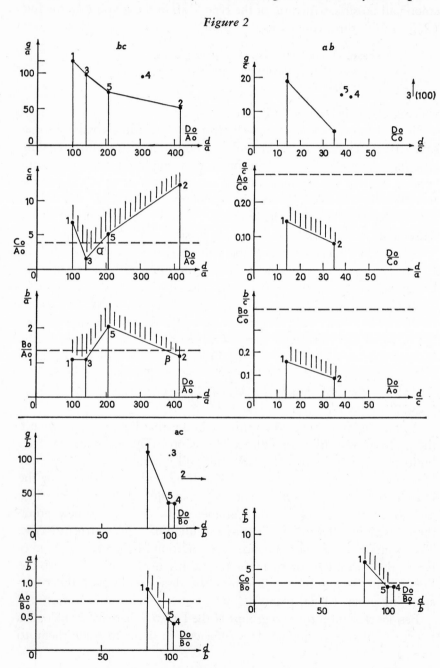

geometry methods. We shall not develop the detail of the study which can be found in a publication by one of us.[14]

Finally, when D_0 varies, one obtains the following succession of optimum structures:

STRUCTURE	D_0 (BILLIONS)	GUARANTEED POWER (MW)				TOTAL DISCOUNTED COST $(G + 270)$	
		1	2	3	5	Billions	%
Impossible	0						
15 *ac*	195	2006	0	0	0	543	100
135 *c*	207	1324	0	0	368	479	88
135 *b*	227	635	0	726	331	456	84
35 *bc*	319	0	0	493	1199	415	76
25 *bc*	360	0	0	0	1692	404	74
25 *cd*	621	0	1259	0	433	375	69
		0	1259	0	433	375	69

Figure 3 shows how one can pass from one structure to another: first of all, the plan is impossible below 195 billion. If this sum is authorized, the solution is uniquely composed of steam plants and its selection is due to the peak load. After one passes this value, the tidal plants are introduced first only with steam plants, then with hydroelectric plants with a large reservoir. After the appearance of the latter ($D_0 = 207$), and for all the higher values of authorized expenses, the system becomes and remains exact for guaranteed output. The triple combination is, at the start, large in annual energy and exact in peak output; where D_0 exceeds 227, the combination becomes large in peak output and exact in annual energy. Moreover, from the start the importance of hydroelectric plants with large reservoirs is increased mainly at the expense of steam plants, but also a little at the expense of tidal plants. When the expenses reach 360, steam plants and hydroelectric plants with big reservoirs disappear, and there remain only the tidal plants. Above this expense, they yield progressively to hydroelectric plants with no reservoir. The tidal plants stabilize at 433 MW of guaranteed power output after the expenses pass 620 billions. The cost decreases when D_0 increases, passing from 543 to 375 between these two extremes. One will note in passing that for the expenses envisioned for the second plan ($D_0 = 271$ billions), the optimum is the combination 135 *b*. The favorable conclusion for large reservoirs, obtained by one of us in making abstractions about tidals,[15] is thus confirmed, even with the introduction of supplementary groups.

[14] R. Gibrat, "Les plans de production d'énergie électrique et les usines marémotrices," *Flamme et Thermique*, No. XC, March, 1956.

[15] P. Massé, "Le probleme des investissements à l'Electricité de France," *Nouvelle Revue de l'Economie Contemporaine*, February, 1955.

Figure 3

SECOND PLAN AT 8 PER CENT RATE OF CAPITALIZATION

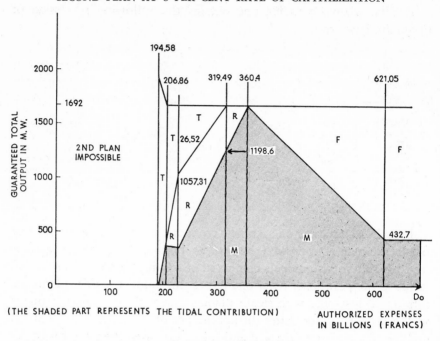

(THE SHADED PART REPRESENTS THE TIDAL CONTRIBUTION)

AUTHORIZED EXPENSES
IN BILLIONS (FRANCS)

LIMITING FACTORS

It is interesting to summarize in a few words the philosophy of the preceding study; for though it would be imprudent to place an absolute value on the numerical results stated throughout under the heading of an example, one can still regard with assurance the order of magnitude and the general tendencies that have been educed.

A first remark is that the admissible solution demanding the minimum expense of investment, the thermal, is heavier in total discounted costs than all which follow it in the table. *Poverty is costly.*

A second remarkable thing, which follows immediately from the first, is the interest to be able to formulate solutions which allow for different groups of plants. The French economy which is possessed of neither rich hydraulic resources, nor rich mine deposits like those of the United States or the Soviet Union, must remedy this relative poverty by the intelligent combination of all its resources. *One hope is variety.*

In the use of this variety there appears the phenomena of *decreasing returns.* An elementary calculation shows that the annual rent rate is in the neighborhood of 50 per cent for 12 billion of supplementary capital which permits the funds for investment to pass from the minimum of 195 billion to 207 billion; 20 billion in supplementary funds permits passage from 207 to 227 billion in investment and a return of 17 per cent, 92 billion permits 11.5 per cent return, the rate of annual rent falls after that to 10 and 9 per cent. It is necessary to remark that above an imprecise threshold a little larger than 300 billion, the demand for power is not sufficient to balance the supply available from hydroelectric plants with no reservoir that have been built, even if steam plants are shut down; hence the phenomena of loss of water over spillways appears; the steam plants and the reservoirs suffice no more to assure the adaptation of the production pattern to the consumption pattern. One concludes that above this threshold, the decrease of returns would be even more pronounced than the figures indicate.

The very important efficiency obtained at the start of the process corresponds to the fact that there are multiple techniques of production for fabricating joint products and that there exists, at the beginning, a bottleneck in the peak load with surplus annual power output and guarantee power output. The return from breaking this bottleneck, by profiting from the surpluses on the other products, is necessarily one of high annual rent (if there exists a technique, tidal, or small reservoir, particularly adapted to fabricating peak output).

We note finally that the graph of G as a function of D_0 (Figure 4) is composed of break points corresponding to a discontinuity in the rent rate during the passage from one type of solution to the following. One other aspect of these sudden mutations is the fact that the optimal solution is indifferent to the choice of the rate of discount in the interior of certain intervals and undergoes a discontinuity at the extremities of the intervals. This phenomenon is accentuated by the hypothesis of groups of homogeneous plants. If each plant had its own peculiar characteristics, and if besides one takes uncertainty into account in a detailed way, one would tend to more classic conclusions (i.e., continuous changes).

The preceding reflections show the richness of the linear programming method in a somewhat schematic application to investments in the production of electricity. It permits a very clear presentation of the problem of fabrication of joint products and makes understandable to nonspecialists considerations which, up to the present, have been accessible only (more or less completely) to experts. It has, thereby, a great value for education and persuasion.

Is it anything more? Does it constitute an innovation susceptible of replacing the methods of definition of an advantageous substitution and the method of composition of an optimal program, surviving to this day in the Electricité de France?

On the first point there is mainly a difference in perspective and language. We will consider here n plants of unknown size ($\geqq 0$) and m requirements attained with unknown surpluses ($\geqq 0$), that is to say, $m + n$ unknowns and m equations; so that, in general, taking some n

Figure 4

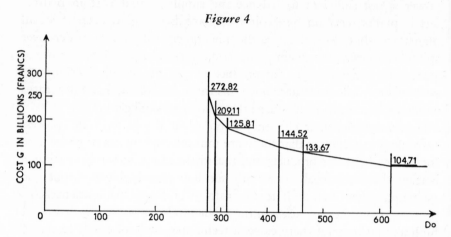

independent unknowns, they ought to satisfy $m + n$ inequalities. In the n-dimensional space of these unknowns the admissible points are "on the positive side" of $m + n$ planes. Whence in the polyhedron of admissible solutions in which each vertex is the intersection of n planes, the optimum point is situated on the plane of least cost. Accordingly, let a vertex, S, be characterized by k surpluses zero and $n - k$ plants zero, that is to say, $m - k$ surpluses not zero and k plants not zero ($k \leqq m$). We move along an edge (i.e., a one-dimensional variety) starting from S and chosen in such a manner that one deviates from the zero plane of a plant. One introduces by this displacement a supplementary plant which is equivalent relative to the requirements to a homogeneous linear combination of m plants and non-zero surpluses. In other terms, the new plant substitutes for a linear combination of older plants, the zero surplus remaining zero and the others remaining positive (at least as long as one is not too far away from S). The elementary operation[16] of our method is thus an admissible substitution relative to requirements (those satisfied exactly remain satisfied exactly), that is to say, in the former language, a substitution rendering equivalent service.

---

[16] Translator's note: There is undoubtedly a close relation between this elementary operation and an iteration of the simplex method which allows a new plant to substitute for a linear combination of other plants and the product surpluses.

The uniqueness of this new point of view is not here however; it is in the hypothesis of homogeneous plants. Its strength is that it permits introduction without difficulty of a synthetic approach with general properties. That is also its weakness because it constitutes in certain cases a schematization which is realistically unacceptable. The hypothesis of plant groupings is approximately applicable for some plants in series on the Rhine or on the Rhone; it is not so for the majority of the hydraulic plants where each has an existence with its own peculiar physiognomy. It is in these, philosophically speaking, that its very profound uniqueness lies. It is this diversity of the sites which has for a long time made the equipment of waterfalls an art irreducible to the law of number and, for the same reason, has made it challenging. Apart from some notable exceptions, water power belongs to the realm of prototype selection rather than group selection.

The new method can, it is true, adapt itself to this situation by multiplying the number of groups and by adding in some inequalities limiting the amount of each of them.[17] It can thereby invoke an illusion of extreme precision in the definition of the energy parameters of the plants relative to the imprecision of others assumed in the calculation.

There is, however, another aspect less negative to which we would like to give consideration in terminating. It is that in France waterfall equipment has not attained its final state but is approaching it. Because of the paucity of energy, the rate of installation of new hydraulic equipment is probably going to be accelerated in the course of future years; nevertheless, one can foresee that, by 1975, it will no longer be able to occupy more than a minor part in our program because almost all the rivers will then be fully equipped. At that time the classic thermal, the gas turbine, the different categories of nuclear reactors, will have to re-enter the solution. From that time on, the linear programming, retaining its simplicity, would become more realistic. It will remain, however, in order to obtain a representation entirely adequate, to elaborate on the nonlinear cost functions, to make progress in the handling of uncertainty and finally to better insert the current (5 year) plan into those that follow or more precisely into the tree of future (5 year) plans.[18]

---

[17] Translator's note: Assuming data for individual hydroelectric plants (that might be constructed) is available, their injection into the model need not complicate the calculation very much when upper boundary techniques of linear programming are used.

[18] P. Massé, "L'optimum de l'intreprise dans un processus économique aléatoire," *Colloque d'Econometrie*, May, 1955.

CASE 3

The Allocation of Aircraft to Routes—An Example of Linear Programming under Uncertain Demand[1]

ALLEN R. FERGUSON and
GEORGE B. DANTZIG[2]

Some points of special interest in this paper are:

a. The objective function chosen.
b. Method used to include demand distribution in the problem matrix.
c. The suggestion to make sensitivity tests by modifying the demand distributions (especially variances). Try the range of a coefficient of variation from zero to one.
d. The natural rates of exchange are not one-for-one in this problem. What arrangements were made to permit a transportation method type of solution?
e. The use of ticket revenue as a measure of lost revenue.
f. The meaning of the "implicit" variables.
g. The meaning of fractional allocations.

SUMMARY

The purpose of this paper is to illustrate an application of linear programming to the problem of allocation of aircraft to routes in order to maximize expected profits when there is uncertain customer demand. The approach is intuitive; the theoretical basis of this work is found in an earlier study. The allocations are compared with those obtained under the usual procedure of assuming a fixed demand equal to the

[1] *Management Science*, October, 1956. Reprinted by permission.
[2] Northwestern University and Stanford University.

528

expected value. The computational procedure is similar to the fixed demand case, with only slightly more computational effort required.

This paper is intended both for readers interested in routing (and analogous resource allocation) problems and for those interested in studying an example of an application of linear programming under uncertainty.

INTRODUCTION

There are many business, economic, and military problems that have the following characteristics in common: a limited quantity of capital equipment or final product must be allocated among a number of final use activities, where the level of demand for each of these activities, and hence the payoff, is uncertain; and further, once the allocation is made, it is not economically feasible to re-allocate because of geographical separation of the activities, because of differences in form of the final products, or because of a minimum lead time between the decision and its implementation. Examples of such problems are (1) scheduling transport vehicles over a number of routes to meet a demand in some future period and (2) allocating quantities of a commodity at discrete time intervals among several storage or distribution points while the future demand for the commodity is unknown. It is assumed, however, that demand can be forecast or estimated as a distribution of values, each with a specified probability of being the actual value.

The general area where the techniques of this paper apply may be schematized broadly as problems where

1. Alternative sets of activity levels can be chosen consistent with given resources
2. Each set of chosen activity levels provides the facilities or stocks to meet an unknown demand whose distribution is assumed known
3. Profits depend on the costs of the facilities, on stocks, and on the revenues from the demand

The general objective is to determine that set of activity levels that maximize profits.

The paper entitled "Linear Programming Under Uncertainty"[3] forms the theoretical basis for the present paper. Our purpose is to illustrate the procedural steps on an example which, in fact, originally inspired the referenced theoretical work in this area. Thus, little in the way of rigorous theory will be attempted, although each step will be justified intuitively.

---

[3] Dantzig, *Management Science*, April–July, 1955.

The method is explained by the use of a model for routing aircraft. Several types of aircraft are allocated over a number of routes; the monthly demand for service over each route is assumed to be known only as a distribution of probable values. The aircraft are so allocated as to minimize the sum of cost of performing the transportation, plus the expected value of the revenue lost through the failure to serve all the traffic that actually developed.

For purposes of month-to-month scheduling, an air-transport operator would, presumably, feel better about having to make an estimate of the range and general distribution of future travel (or shipment) over his routes than about having to commit himself to a single expected value. Indeed, he might feel that the optimal assignment should be insensitive to a wide range of demand distribution, and that an assignment based on expected values (as if these were known fixed demands) would be misleading. It is suggested that the reader make sensitivity tests by modifying the demand distributions given in the illustrative example.

Passenger demand, of course, occurs on a day-by-day, in fact, on a flight-by-flight basis. The assumed number of passengers per type aircraft per given type flight may be thought of as an ideal number which can be increased slightly by decreasing the amount of air freight and by "smoothing" the demand by encouraging the customers to take open reservations on alternative flights as opposed to less certain reservations on the desired flight. In spite of these possible adjustments, traveler preferences and the inevitable last-minute cancellations do cause loss of seat carrying capacity. However, the best way to reflect these effects of the daily variations in demand are beyond the scope of this paper. For our purpose here, either the aircraft passenger capability or the demand may be thought of as adjusted downward to reflect the loss due to daily variations of demand.

The method employed is simple, and the example used can be solved by hand in an hour or two. Larger problems can be solved with computing machines.

In a previously published paper,[4] the method was applied to the same example, assuming the demand on each route to be known,[5] this paper continues the analysis to show how to handle a frequency distribution of demand over each route. A different allocation is found to be optimal in this case.

This paper will describe the problem; briefly indicate the nature of

---

[4] Ferguson and Dantzig, "The Problem of Routing Aircraft," *Aeronautical Engineering Review,* Vol. XIV, No. 4 (April, 1955).

[5] This was equivalent to using the expected value of demand, rather than taking account of the whole frequency distribution, as in this paper.

the solution based on expected values show the method of solving the problem using stochastic values for demand and, finally, compare the two solutions.

REVIEW OF FIXED DEMAND EXAMPLE

The fixed demand example, used to illustrate the method, takes a fixed fleet of four types of aircraft, as shown in (1). These aircraft have differences in speeds, ranges, payload capacities, and cost characteristics. The assumed routes and expected traffic loads (the distribution of demand will be discussed later) are shown in (2).

Since this problem proposes to illustrate the applicability of a method in solving problems in which several realistic elements are considered, it

ASSUMED AIRCRAFT FLEET

Type	Description	Number Available	
A	Postwar 4-Engine	10	
B	Postwar 2-Engine	19	(1)
C	Prewar 2-Engine	25	
D	Prewar 4-Engine	15	

TRAFFIC LOAD BY ROUTE

Route	Route Miles*	Expected Number of Passengers†	Price 1-Way Ticket	
1. N.Y.–L.A. (1 stop)	2,475	25,000	$130	
2. N.Y.–L.A. (2 stops)	2,475	12,000	130	(2)
3. N.Y.–Dallas (0 stop)	1,381	18,000	70	
4. N.Y.–Dallas (1 stop)	1,439	9,000	70	
5. N.Y.–Boston (0 stop)	185	60,000	10	

* *Official Airline Guide*, July, 1954, p. 276. The N.Y.–Los Angeles routes are via Chicago and via Chicago–Denver; the stop en route between New York and Dallas is at Memphis.

† This is the expected number of full one-way trips per month to be carried on each route. If a passenger gets off en route and is replaced by another passenger, it is counted as one full trip.

is assumed that not all aircraft can carry their full loads on all routes, and that the obtainable utilization varies from route to route. Specifically, Type B is assumed to be able to operate at only 75 per cent payload on Route 3, and Type D at 80 per cent on Route 1; whereas Type C cannot fly either Route 1 or Route 3, and Type B cannot fly Route 1. Utilization is defined as the average number of hours of useful work performed per month by each aircraft assigned to a particular route. Utilization of 300 hours per month is assumed on Routes 1 and 2; 285 on Routes 3 and 4; and 240 on Route 5.

The assumed dollar costs per 100 passenger-miles are shown in (3). These costs do not include any capital costs such as the cost of the aircraft and ground facilities. They represent variable costs such as the cost of gasoline, salaries of the crew, and servicing the aircraft.

A second source of "costs" is due to the loss of revenues when not enough aircraft are assigned to the route to meet the passenger demand. In this case, the loss of revenue is the same as the price of a one-way ticket shown in the E row of (3).

Based on the speeds, ranges, payload capacities and turnaround times, passenger capabilities were determined. The resultant potential number of passengers (in hundreds) p_{ij} that can be hauled per month per aircraft type i on route j is shown in (4); see staggered right figure in each box. By multiplying these numbers by the corresponding costs per 100 passenger-miles given in (3), and the number of miles given in (2), the monthly cost per aircraft can also be obtained. This is given in the lower left figure in each box which is the cost c_{ij} in thousands of dollars per month per aircraft type i assigned to the route j. The revenue losses c_{5j} in thousands of dollars per 100 passengers not carried are given in the E row of (4); finally we define $p_{5j} = 1.$[6] The staggered layout of (4) was chosen so as to identify the corresponding data found in Table 1, the latter being the *work sheet* upon which the entire problem is solved.

The basic problem consists of determining the number of aircraft of each type to assign to each route consistent with aircraft availabilities (1) and in determining how much revenue will be lost due to failure of allocated aircraft to meet passenger demand on various routes (2) and (3). Since many alternative allocations are possible, our specific objective will be to find that allocation that minimizes total costs where costs are defined as operating costs plus lost revenues based on the cost factors given in (3).

This may be formulated mathematically as a linear programming problem. Let x_{ij} denote the unknown quantity of the ith type aircraft assigned to jth route where $i = 1, 2, \ldots, m - 1$ and $j = 1, 2, \ldots, n - 1$. If x_{in} denotes the surplus or unallocated aircraft, then (5) states that the sum of allocated and unallocated aircraft of each type accounts for the total available aircraft a_i. If x_{mj} denotes the number of passengers in hundreds turned away, then equation (6) states that the sum of passenger carrying capability of each type aircraft allocated to the jth route, $p_{ij}x_{ij}$, plus the unsatisfied demand accounts for the total demand, d_j. Relation (7) states that all unknown quanti-

---

[6] This will make it easier to form the passenger balance or "column" equations (7).

DOLLAR COSTS PER 100 PASSENGER-MILES

Type Aircraft	ROUTE				
	N.Y. to L.A. 1-Stop	N.Y. to L.A. 2-Stops	N.Y. to Dallas 0-Stop	N.Y. to Dallas 1-Stop	N.Y. to Boston 0-Stop
A	$0.45	$0.57	$0.45	$0.47	$0.64
B	—	.64	.83	.63	.88
C	—	.92	—	.93	1.13
D	.74	.61	.59	.62	.81

(3)

DOLLAR COSTS PER PASSENGER TURNED AWAY*

E	130 (13)	130 (13)	70 (7)	70 (7)	10 (1)

*Figures shown in parentheses are thousands of dollars lost per 100 passengers turned away. (Throughout this paper, passengers are measured in units of hundreds.)

PASSENGER CAPABILITIES AND COSTS PER AIRCRAFT PER MONTH

TYPE AIRCRAFT	ROUTE				
	N.Y. to L.A. 1-Stop	N.Y. to L.A. 2-Stops	N.Y. to Dallas 0-Stop	N.Y. to Dallas 1-Stop	N.Y. to Boston 0-Stop
A Passengers (00) Costs ($000)	$p_{11} = 16$ $c_{11} = 18$	$p_{12} = 15$ $c_{12} = 21$	$p_{13} = 28$ $c_{13} = 18$	$p_{14} = 23$ $c_{14} = 16$	$p_{15} = 81$ $c_{15} = 10$
B Passengers (00) Costs ($000)	*	$p_{22} = 10$ $c_{22} = 15$	$p_{23} = 14$ $c_{23} = 16$	$p_{24} = 15$ $c_{24} = 14$	$p_{25} = 57$ $c_{25} = 9$
C Passengers (00) Costs ($000)	*	$p_{32} = 5$ $c_{32} = 10$	*	$p_{34} = 7$ $c_{34} = 9$	$p_{35} = 29$ $c_{35} = 6$
D Passengers (00) Costs ($000)	$p_{41} = 9$ $c_{41} = 17$	$p_{42} = 11$ $c_{42} = 16$	$p_{43} = 22$ $c_{43} = 17$	$p_{44} = 17$ $c_{44} = 15$	$p_{45} = 55$ $c_{45} = 10$
E (Deficit)	Losses per 100 passengers not hauled				
Passengers (00) Costs ($000)	$p_{51} = 1$ $c_{51} = 13$	$p_{52} = 1$ $c_{52} = 13$	$p_{53} = 1$ $c_{53} = 7$	$p_{54} = 1$ $c_{54} = 7$	$p_{55} = 1$ $c_{55} = 1$.

(4)

ties x_{ij} must be either positive or zero. Finally, if z is total costs, it is the sum of all the individual operating costs of each allocation, $c_{ij}x_{ij}$, plus the revenues lost by unsatisfied demands $c_{mj}x_{mj}$, see equation (8). Any set of x_{ij} satisfying (5), (6), (7) is termed a *feasible solution*, and a feasible choice which minimizes the total cost z of the assignment given by (8) is called an *optimal (feasible) solution*.

Fixed Demand Model

Find numbers x_{ij}, and the minimum value of z such that for $i = 1, 2, \cdots, m$; and $j = 1, 2, \cdots, n$

Row Sums: $\qquad x_{i1} + x_{i2} + \ldots + x_{in} = a_i,$ $\qquad\qquad (i \neq m)$ (5)

Col. Sums: $\qquad p_{1j}x_{1j} + p_{2j}x_{2j} + \ldots + p_{mj}x_{mj} = d_j$ (6)

$$x_{ij} \geqq 0 \qquad (7)$$

$$\sum_{i=1}^{m} \sum_{j=1}^{n} c_{ij}x_{ij} = z \qquad (8)$$

The optimal assignment of aircraft to routes based on fixed demand as developed in the earlier study is shown in Table 1. The values assigned to the unknowns x_{ij} appear in italics in the upper left of each box unless $x_{ij} = 0$ in which case it is omitted; the entire layout takes the form:

The sums by *rows* of x_{ij} entries in Table 1 equated to availabilities yield equations (5). The sums by *columns* of x_{ij} weighted by corresponding values of p_{ij} equated to demands yield equations (6); the x_{ij} weighted by corresponding c_{ij} and summed over the entire table yields (8). As noted earlier, Table 1 is actually the work sheet upon which the entire problem is solved. Later on we shall discuss a revision of this work sheet for solving problems with variable demand. All figures in the table, except for the upper left entries, x_{ij} and values of the so-called "implicit prices" u_i and v_j shown in the margins, are constants which do not change during the course of computation. The values of the variables x_{ij}, u_i and v_j, however, will change during the course of successive iterations of the simplex method as adapted for this problem. For this reason it is customary to cover the work sheet with clear acetate and to enter the variable information with a grease pencil which can be easily erased; alternatively, a blackboard or semitransparent tissue paper overlays can be used. The detailed rules for obtaining the optimal solution shown are given by Dantzig (see footnote 3) and will not be repeated here because a more general set of rules for the uncertain demand case will be given which, of course, could be used for the expected demand case.

In (9) we have a convenient summary serving to identify and define the numerical data entered in Table 1 and to give the test for optimality.

Constants:	a_i = number of aircraft available of type i d_j = expected passenger demand in 100's per month on route j p_{ij} = passenger carrying capability in 100's per month per aircraft type i assigned to route j ($p_{mj} = 1$ by definition) c_{ij} = costs in 1,000's of dollars per month per aircraft type i assigned to route j (c_{mj} is per 100 passengers turned away)	
x_{ij} Entries: Omitted x_{ij} Entries:	x_{ij} = number of aircraft type i assigned to jth route (x_{mj} is 100's of passengers turned away) x_{ij} = 0 if upper left entry in box is missing	(9)
Implicit Prices:	u_i and v_j are determined such that $u_i + p_{ij}v_j = c_{ij}$, ($u_m = v_n = 0$) for (i, j) boxes corresponding to $x_{ij} > 0$, i.e., nonomitted x_{ij} entries	
Test For Optimality:	Solution is optimal if for *all* (i, j) boxes $u_i + p_{ij}v_i \leqq c_{ij}$	

EXTENSION OF EXAMPLES TO UNCERTAIN DEMAND

Up to this point the problem is identical to that described and solved in our previous paper. Now, to introduce the element of uncertain demand, we assume not a known (expected) demand on each route but a known *frequency distribution* of demand. The assumed frequency distributions are shown in (10). Thus on Route 1 (N.Y. to L.A.—1-Stop) it is assumed that either 20, 22, 25, 27, or 30 thousand passengers will want transportation during the month. On the other hand, for the N.Y. to L.A.—2-Stop either 5,000 or 15,000 passengers will want transportation with probabilities 30 or 70 per cent respectively, etc. The assumed traffic distributions are, of course, hypothetical to illustrate our method. The demand distributions on the five routes varied over wide ranges and have different characteristics; Route 1 is flat, Route 2 is U-shaped, Routes 3, 4, 5 are unimodular but have differing degrees of concentration about the mode. Route 4 has a distribution with a very long tail that may reflect a realistic traffic situation.

To illustrate the essential character of the linear programming problem for the case of uncertain demand let us focus our attention on a single route—say, Route 1—with probability distribution of demand as given in (10). Let us suppose that aircraft assigned to Route 1 are capable of hauling 100 Y_1 passengers. The first 200(00) units of this capability are certain to be used and revenues from this source (negative costs) will be 13(000) = k_1 per unit. The next 20(00) units of this capability will be used with probability $\gamma_{21} = .8$. Indeed, 80 per

ASSUMED DISTRIBUTION OF PASSENGER DEMAND

(λ_{hj} = Probability of Demand d_{hj})

Route	Hundreds of Passengers	Approx. Mean (00)	Probability of Passenger Demand	Probability of Equaling or Exceeding Demand
(1)	$200 = d_{11}$		$.2 = \lambda_{11}$	$1.0 = \gamma_{11}$
	$220 = d_{21}$		$.05 = \lambda_{21}$	$.8 = \gamma_{21}$
	$250 = d_{31}$	250	$.35 = \lambda_{31}$	$.75 = \gamma_{31}$
	$270 = d_{41}$		$.2 = \lambda_{41}$	$.4 = \gamma_{41}$
	$300 = d_{51}$		$.2 = \lambda_{51}$	$.2 = \gamma_{51}$
(2)	$50 = d_{12}$	120	$.3 = \lambda_{12}$	$1.0 = \gamma_{12}$
	$150 = d_{22}$		$.7 = \lambda_{22}$	$.7 = \gamma_{22}$
(3)	$140 = d_{13}$		$.1 = \lambda_{13}$	$1.0 = \gamma_{13}$
	$160 = d_{23}$		$.2 = \lambda_{23}$	$.9 = \gamma_{23}$
	$180 = d_{33}$	180	$.4 = \lambda_{33}$	$.7 = \gamma_{33}$
	$200 = d_{43}$		$.2 = \lambda_{43}$	$.3 = \gamma_{43}$
	$220 = d_{53}$		$.1 = \lambda_{53}$	$.1 = \gamma_{53}$.
(4)	$10 = d_{14}$		$.2 = \lambda_{14}$	$1.0 = \gamma_{14}$
	$50 = d_{24}$		$.2 = \lambda_{24}$	$.8 = \gamma_{24}$
	$80 = d_{34}$	90	$.3 = \lambda_{34}$	$.6 = \gamma_{34}$
	$100 = d_{44}$		$.2 = \lambda_{44}$	$.3 = \gamma_{44}$
	$340 = d_{54}$		$.1 = \lambda_{54}$	$.1 = \gamma_{54}$
(5)	$580 = d_{15}$		$.1 = \lambda_{15}$	$1.0 = \gamma_{15}$
	$600 = d_{25}$	600	$.8 = \lambda_{25}$	$.9 = \gamma_{25}$
	$620 = d_{35}$		$.1 = \lambda_{35}$	$.1 = \gamma_{35}$

(10)

cent of the time the demand will be 220(00) or greater, while 20 per cent of the time it will be 200(00); hence, the expected revenues per unit from this increment is $.8 \times 13 = 10.4$ or $10.4 = k_1\gamma_{21}$. On the third increment of 30(00) units (22,001 to 25,000 seats) the expected revenue is $.75 \times 13 = 9.8 = k_1\gamma_{31}$ per unit since there is a 25 per cent chance that none of these units will be used and 75 per cent that all will be used. For the fourth increment of 20(00) units (25,001 to 27,000) the expected revenue is $.4 \times 13 = 5.2 = k_1\gamma_{41}$ per unit. For the fifth increment of 3,000 units (27,001 to 30,000) it is $.2 \times 13 = 2.6 = k_1\gamma_{51}$ per unit. For the sixth increment, which is the number of units assigned above the 30,000 mark, the expected revenue per unit is $.0 \times 13 = 0$ per unit since it is certain that none of these units can be used. It is clear that no assignments above the 30,000 are worthwhile and hence the last increment can be omitted. The index $h = 1, 2, 3, 4, 5$, will be used to denote the 1st, 2nd, . . . , 5th increment of demand.

The number of assigned units in each increment, however, can be viewed as an unknown that depends on the *total* (passenger hauling) capability assigned to Route $j = 1$. Thus if the total assigned is $Y_1 = 210(00)$ then the part of this total belonging to the first increment, denoted by y_{11}, is $y_{11} = 200(00)$ and the part belonging to the second increment, denoted by y_{21}, is $y_{21} = 10(00)$. The amounts in the higher increments are $y_{hi} = 0$ for $i = 3, 4, 5$. To review, the passenger-carrying capacity Y_j is determined by the number of aircraft assigned to route j so that

$$Y_j = p_{1j}x_{1j} + p_{2j}x_{2j} + p_{3j}x_{3j} + p_{4j}x_{4j} . \tag{11}$$

On the other hand, Y_j itself breaks down into five increments

$$Y_j = y_{1j} + y_{2j} + y_{3j} + y_{4j} + y_{5j} \tag{12}$$

for routes $j = 1, 3, 4$, and correspondingly fewer for $j = 2, 5$. Regardless of the total Y_j the amount y_{hj} belonging to each increment is bounded by the total size of each increment which we denote by b_{hj}; the latter, however, is simply the change in demand level so that

$$
\begin{aligned}
0 &\leqq y_{1j} \leqq d_{1j} && = b_{1j} \\
0 &\leqq y_{2j} \leqq d_{2j} - d_{1j} &&= b_{2j} \\
0 &\leqq y_{3j} \leqq d_{3j} - d_{2j} &&= b_{3j} \\
0 &\leqq y_{4j} \leqq d_{4j} - d_{3j} &&= b_{4j} \\
0 &\leqq y_{5j} \leqq d_{5j} - d_{4j} &&= b_{5j} .
\end{aligned}
\tag{13}
$$

The total expected revenue from route j is, therefore,

$$k_j(\gamma_{1j}y_{1j} + \gamma_{2j}y_{2j} + \ldots + \gamma_{5j}y_{5j}) \tag{14}$$

where k_j is revenue (in thousands) per 100 passengers carried on route j and as seen in (10) the probability γ_{ij} of exceeding or equaling demand d_{ij} is related to λ_{ij} the probability of demand by

$$
\begin{aligned}
1 = \gamma_{1j} &= \lambda_{1j} + \lambda_{2j} + \lambda_{3j} + \lambda_{4j} + \lambda_{5j} \\
\gamma_{2j} &= \phantom{\lambda_{1j} + {}} \lambda_{2j} + \lambda_{3j} + \lambda_{4j} + \lambda_{5j} \\
\gamma_{3j} &= \phantom{\lambda_{1j} + \lambda_{2j} + {}} \lambda_{3j} + \lambda_{4j} + \lambda_{5j} \\
\gamma_{4j} &= \phantom{\lambda_{1j} + \lambda_{2j} + \lambda_{3j} + {}} \lambda_{4j} + \lambda_{5j} \\
\gamma_{5j} &= \phantom{\lambda_{1j} + \lambda_{2j} + \lambda_{3j} + \lambda_{4j} + {}} \lambda_{5j}
\end{aligned}
\tag{15}
$$

and the values of λ_{hj} are given in (10). For example, the total expected revenues for Route 1 are

$$13(1.0y_{11} + .8y_{12} + .75y_{13} + .4y_{14} + .2y_{15}) . \tag{16}$$

The most important fact to note about the linear form (16) is the decrease in the successive values of the coefficients, γ_{hj}. Moreover, this will always be the case whatever the distribution of demand since the probability of equaling or exceeding a given demand level d_{hj} decreases with increasing values of demand.

Suppose now y_{11}, y_{21}, . . . , are treated as unknown variables in a linear programming problem subject only to (12) and (13) where the objective is to maximize revenues. Let us suppose further that Y_1 is

---

Uncertain Demand Model

Find numbers x_{ij} and y_{hj} and the minimum value of z such that for $i = 1, 2, \cdots, m; \ j = 1, 2, \cdots, n; \ h = 1, 2, \cdots, r.$

Row Sums: $\quad x_{i1} + x_{i2} + \cdots + x_{in} = a_i$ $\qquad\qquad\qquad\qquad\qquad$ (17)

Column Sums: $\quad p_{1j}x_{1j} + p_{2j}x_{2j} + \cdots + p_{nj}x_{nj} = y_{1j} + y_{2j} + \cdots + y_{rj}$ $\qquad$ (18)

$$x_{ij} \geqq 0, \qquad 0 \leqq y_{hi} \leqq b_{hi} \qquad\qquad (19)$$

Expected costs: $z = \displaystyle\sum_{i=1}^{m}\sum_{j=1}^{n} c_{ij}\, x_{ij} + \left[R_0 - \sum_{j=1}^{n} k_j \sum_{h=1}^{r} \gamma_{hj}\, y_{1j} \right]$ $\qquad$ (20)

---

fixed. It is clear, since the coefficient of y_{11} is largest in the maximizing form (14), y_{11} will be chosen as large as possible consistent with (12) and (13); for the chosen value y_{11}, the next increment y_{21} will be chosen as large as possible consistent with (12) and (13), etc. Thus, we need only specify y_{h1} by restrictions (12) and (13), because *when*

INCREMENTAL BOUNDS, b_{hj}, AND EXPECTED REVENUES $k_j \gamma_{hj}$ PER UNIT OF PASSENGER CARRYING CAPACITY ASSIGNED

	ROUTE 1		ROUTE 2		ROUTE 3		ROUTE 4		ROUTE 5	
Increment h	b_{k1}	$k_1\gamma_{h1}$	b_{h2}	$k_2\gamma_{h2}$	b_{h3}	$k_3\gamma_{h3}$	b_{h4}	$k_4\gamma_{h4}$	b_{h5}	$k_5\gamma_{h5}$
1	200	$k_1 = 16$	50	$k_2 = 13$	140	$k_3 = 7$	10	$k_4 = 7$	580	$k_5 = 1$
2	20	$.8k_1 = 10.4$	100	$.7k_2 = 9.1$	20	$.9k_3 = 6.3$	40	$.8k_4 = 5.6$	20	$.9k_5 = .9$ (21)
3	30	$.75k_1 = 9.8$		*	20	$.7k_3 = 4.9$	30	$.6k_4 = 4.2$	20	$.1k_5 = .1$
4	20	$.4k_1 = 5.2$		*	20	$.3k_3 = 2.1$	20	$.3k_4 = 2.1$		*
5	30	$.2k_1 = 2.6$		*	20	$.1k_3 = .7$	240	$.1k_4 = .7$		*

* Only two increments for route 2 and three increments for route 5 are needed to describe distribution of demand.

the maximum is reached the values of the variables $y_{11}, y_{21}, \ldots$ are precisely the *incremental values* associated with Y_1, which we discussed earlier, (12). Even if passenger capability Y_1 is not fixed, as in the case about to be considered, it should be noted that whatever be the value of Y_1 the values of $y_{11}, y_{21} \ldots$ which minimize an over-all cost form such as in (20) below must maximize (14) for $j = 1$ and hence the incremental values of Y_1 will be generated by $y_{11}, y_{21}, \ldots.$

The linear programming problem in the case of uncertain demand is shown in (17), (18), (19), (20). Thus expected costs are defined as total outlays (first term) plus the expected loss of revenue due to shortage of seats (last two terms), where R_0 is the expected revenue if sufficient seats were supplied for all customers.

For the problem at hand the bounds, b_{hj}, and the expected revenues, $k_j \gamma_{hj}$, per unit for the "incremental variables" y_{hj} can be computed from probability distributions (10) via (13) and (15).

The numerical values of the constants for the stochastic case are tabulated in (21).

RULES FOR COMPUTATION

The work sheet for determining the optimal assignment under uncertain demand is shown in Table 2. The entries in the "x_{ij}" boxes and "y_{hj}" boxes take the form

To form the new row equations (17), the x_{ij} entries are summed to yield the a_i values given in the aircraft available column. To form the column equations (18), the x_{ij} entries are multiplied by p_{ij}, the y_{hj} by -1, and summed down to yield zero.

Step 1. To initiate the computation any set of nonnegative values may be assigned to the unknowns x_{ij} and y_{hj} provided they satisfy the equations and thereby constitute a feasible solution.

Step 2. Circle[7] *any* $(m + n)$ of x_{ij} and y_{hj} entries where $m + n$ is the number of row plus column equations. These circles can be arbitrarily selected except that they must have the property that if the fixed values assigned to the other noncircled variables and the constant terms were *arbitrarily changed to other values* then the circled variables would be determined uniquely in terms of the latter. Such a circled set of variables is called a *basic set* of variables; the array of coefficients associated with this set in the equations (17) and (18) is referred to as the *basis* in the theory of the simplex method.[8]

Note: One simple way of selecting a basic set is shown in Table 3. One x_{ij} entry is arbitrarily selected and circled in each row corresponding to a row

---

[7] Entries referred to as "arbitrarily selected and circled" entries appear in bold face figures in the tables.

[8] G. B. Dantzig, A. Orden, and P. Wolfe, "The Generalized Simplex Method for Minimizing a Linear Form under Linear Inequality Restraints," *Pacific Journal of Mathematics*, June, 1955.

equation, and one y_{hj} is arbitrarily selected and circled in each column corresponding to a column equation. In general, it is suggested that entries be circled that appear to have a chance of having a positive value in an optimum solution; in case of y_{hj} values the last entry in the column that appears likely to be positive in an optimum solution should be circled and other y_{hj} above it in the column be set equal to b_{hj}.

Step 3. Compute for (i, j) and (h, j) combinations corresponding to circled entries, implicit prices u_i and v_j associated with equations by determining values of u_i and v_j satisfying the equations

$$u_i + p_{ij}v_j = c_{ij} \qquad (x_{ij} \text{ circled}) \qquad (22)$$
$$0 + (-1)v_j = -k_j\gamma_{hj} \qquad (y_{hj} \text{ circled}) \qquad (23)$$

There are always $(m + n)$ equations (22) and (23) in $(m + n)$ unknowns u_i and v_j which can be shown always to have a unique solution.[9] They can be solved by inspection, for it can be shown that the system is either completely triangular or at worst contains subsystems—some triangular and some triangular if one unknown is specified.[10]

Step 4. Compute for each box corresponding to x_{ij} or y_{hj}

$$\delta_{ij} = (u_i + p_{ij}v_j) - c_{ij} \qquad (\text{for } x_{ij} \text{ box}) \qquad (24)$$
$$\delta'_{hj} = (0 - v_j) - (-k_j\gamma_{hj}) \qquad (\text{for } y_{hj} \text{ box}) \qquad (25)$$

In practice, one of the δ_{ij} or δ'_{hj} is recorded; the others are computed and compared with it and the largest in absolute value is used. It can be shown[11] that if the x_{ij} or y_{hj} value associated with a noncircled entry is changed to

$$x_{ij} \pm \theta \qquad \text{or} \qquad y_{hj} \pm \theta \qquad \qquad \theta \geqq 0 \qquad (26)$$

the other noncircled variables remaining invariant, and the circled variables adjusted, then the expected costs z will change to z' where

$$z' = z \mp \theta\delta_{ij} \qquad \text{or} \qquad z' = z \mp \theta\delta'_{hj} \qquad (27)$$

Thus it pays to *increase* x_{ij} or y_{hj} if δ_{ij} or $\delta'_{hj} > 0$, unless $y_{hj} = b_{hj}$, its upper bound, in which case no increase in y_{hj} is allowed; also it pays to *decrease* x_{ij} or y_{hj} if δ_{ij} or $\delta'_{hj} < 0$ unless $x_{ij} = 0$ or $y_{hj} = 0$, in which case no decrease is allowed.

Test for Optimality. According to the theory of the simplex method[12] if the *noncircled* variables satisfy the following conditions:

[9] *Ibid.*

[10] This is the analogue for the "generalized" transportation problem of the well-known theorem for the standard transportation problem that all bases are triangular. Its proof is similar.

[11] Dantzig, Orden, and Wolfe, *op. cit.*

[12] Dantzig, "Upper Bounds, Secondary Constraints, and Block Triangularity in Linear Programming," *Econometrica*. April, 1955

(1) they are all at either their upper or lower bounds,

(2) their corresponding δ_{ij} and $\delta'_{hj} \leqq 0$, if they are at their lower bound,

(3) their corresponding δ_{ij} and $\delta'_{hj} \geqq 0$, if they are at their upper bound, then the solution is optimal and the algorithm terminates. Otherwise there are δ_{ij} or δ'_{ij} for which a decrease or increase (depending on whether the sign is negative or positive) in the corresponding variable is allowed; let the largest among them in absolute value be denoted by δ_{rs} or δ'_{rs}.

Step 5. Leaving all noncircled entries fixed except for the value of the variable corresponding to the (r, s) box determined in Step 4, modify the value of x_{rs} (or y_{rs}) to

$$x_{rs} + \theta \text{ (or } y_{rs} + \theta) \text{ if } \delta_{rs} > 0 \text{ (or } \delta'_{rs} > 0) \qquad \text{or to} \qquad (28)$$
$$x_{rs} - \theta \text{ (or } y_{rs} - \theta) \text{ if } \delta_{rs} < 0 \text{ (or } \delta'_{rs} < 0) \qquad\qquad (29)$$

where $\theta \geqq 0$ is unknown and recompute the values of circled variables as linear functions of θ. Choose the value of $\theta = \theta^*$ at the largest value possible consistent with keeping all basic (circled) variables (whose values now depend on θ) between their upper and lower bounds; in the next cycle correct the values of the circled variables on the assumption $\theta = \theta^*$.

Also, if at the value $\theta = \theta^*$ one (or more) of the circled variables attains its upper or lower bound, in the next cycle drop *any one* of these variables (never drop more than one) from the basic set and circle the variable x_{rs} instead. Should it happen that it is x_{rs} that attains its upper or lower bound at $\theta = \theta^*$, the set of circled variables is the same as before; their values, however, are changed to allow x_{rs} to be fixed at its new bound.

Start the next cycle of the iterative procedure by returning to Step 3.

NUMERICAL SOLUTION OF THE ROUTING PROBLEM

For our starting solution we used for values of x_{ij} the best solution of the earlier study, assuming fixed demands equal to the expected values of the distribution.[13] These are shown in Table 3. These x_{ij} will meet the expected demands so that $Y_j = b_j$ except for route 5 where there is a deficit of 100 and $Y_5 = 500$, see (11). These Y_j are broken down into

---

[13] In the humorous parody by Paul Gunther entitled "Use of Linear Programming in Capital Budgeting," *Journal of the Operations Research Society of America,* May, 1955, it will be recalled that Mrs. Efficiency wondered why Mr. O. R. did not start out with a good guess. In this paper you will note that we followed Mrs. Efficiency's suggestion and have started with a guess at the final solution rather than going through the customary use of artificial variables and a phase one of the simplex process.

the successive incremental values shown below the double line, see (12).

Next, one of the variables in each row is circled. The selected variables are x_{11}, x_{22}, x_{35}, x_{43}; each appears likely to be in an optimal solution, however, x_{43} has been circled rather than x_{41}, which may be a better choice. Next, the last positive entry in each column is circled, i.e., the variables y_{31}, y_{22}, y_{33}, y_{44}, y_{15}. In all there are $m + n = 9$ circled variables. The implicit values, u_i and v_j, are determined by solving the nine equations:

$$
\begin{array}{lll}
u_1 + p_{11}v_1 = c_{11} & (p_{11} = 16,\ c_{11} = 18) & (30.1) \\
u_2 + p_{22}v_2 = c_{22} & (p_{22} = 10,\ c_{22} = 15) & (30.2) \\
u_3 + p_{35}v_5 = c_{35} & (p_{35} = 29,\ c_{35} = 6) & (30.3) \\
u_4 + p_{43}v_3 = c_{43} & (p_{43} = 22,\ c_{43} = 17) & (30.4) \\
0 + (-1)v_1 = -k_1\gamma_{31} & (k_1\gamma_{31} = 9.8) & (30.5) \\
0 + (-1)v_2 = -k_2\gamma_{22} & (k_2\gamma_{22} = 9.1) & (30.6) \\
0 + (-1)v_3 = -k_3\gamma_{33} & (k_3\gamma_{33} = 4.9) & (30.7) \\
0 + (-1)v_4 = -k_4\gamma_{44} & (k_4\gamma_{44} = 2.1) & (30.8) \\
0 + (-1)v_5 = -k_5\gamma_{15} & (k_5\gamma_{15} = 1.0) & (30.9)
\end{array}
$$

This permits the computation of δ_{ij} and δ'_{hj}, see (24) and (25). As a check $\delta_{ij} = 0$ and $\delta'_{hj} = 0$ for (i, j) and (h, j) corresponding to circled variables. The largest value of δ_{ij} or δ'_{hj} in absolute value is

$$\delta_{24} = [-76 + 15\,(2.1)] - 14 = -58.5\,,$$

hence a decrease in the variable x_{24} with adjustments of the circled variables will result in a decrease in the expected costs of 58.5 units per unit decrease in x_{24}. If $x_{24} = 6$ is changed to $x_{24} = 6 - \theta$, then in order to satisfy column 4 equations the circled variable $y_{44} = 10$ must be modified to $y_{44} = 10 - 15\theta$ (all other variables in column 4 are fixed). Also to satisfy row equation 2, $x_{22} = 8$ must be modified to $x_{22} = 8 + \theta$, and this in turn causes $y_{22} = 70$ to be changed to $y_{22} = 70 + 10\theta$ in order to satisfy column equation 2. The largest value of θ is $\theta^* = 10/15$ at which value $y_{44} = 0$.

The numerical values of the variables appearing in Table 4 are obtained from those of Table 3 by setting $\theta = \theta^* = 10/15$. The variable x_{24} becomes a new circled variable in place of y_{44} which hit its lower bound, zero; the other variables to be circled remain the same as in Table 3. Computing the new set of implicit prices the largest δ_{ij} in absolute value which can increase or decrease according to sign of δ_{ij} is $\delta_{23} = 23.4$. Changing x_{23} to $5 - \theta$ requires that the variables x_{22}, y_{22}, y_{33} be modified as shown, Table 4. The maximum value of θ is $\theta = \theta^* = 20/14$ at which value $y_{33} = 0$. The new solution in which x_{23} replaces y_{33} as a circled variable is given in Table 5. In Table 5 the decrease in noncircled variable x_{41} causes changes in the variables x_{43}, x_{22}, x_{23}, y_{31}, y_{22}. The largest value of $\theta = 9/16$ at which value y_{22} hits its *upper bound* $b_{22} = 100$.

In the passage from Table 6 to Table 7 we have become a little fancy and have taken a "double" step. The maximum increase is $\theta = 80/29$ at which point y_{15} hits its upper bound $b_{15} = 580$. It is easy to see that if next the incremental variable y_{25} is increased that δ_{32} associated with x_{32} should be changed to $\delta_{32} + 29(\gamma_{15} - \gamma_{25})k_5 = -4.5 + 29(1.0 - .9) = -1.6$; therefore, it is economical to increase y_{25} as well as y_{15}. However, it can be shown that signs of δ_{32} would become positive if the next increment, y_{35}, were considered. The maximum value of $\theta = \theta^* = 100/29$.

In the passage from Table 7 to 8, it will be noted that the variable y_{33} is again brought into solution having been dropped earlier. The maxi-

Table 1

OPTIMAL ASSIGNMENT FOR FIXED DEMAND
(Operating Costs and Lost Revenues = $1,000,000)

Type Aircraft	Route (1) N. Y. to L. A. 1-Stop	(2) N. Y. to L.A. 2-Stop	(3) N. Y. to Dallas 0-Stop	(4) N. Y. to Dallas 1-Stop	(5) N. Y. to Boston 0-Stop	(6) Surplus Aircraft	Aircraft Available	Implicit Prices u_i
(1)A	10 16 / 18	15 / 21	28 / 18	23 / 16	81 / 10	0 / 0	$10 = a_1$	−171
(2)B	**	8 10 / 15	5 14 / 16	6 15 / 14	57 / 9	0 / 0	$19 = a_2$	−51
(3)C	**	7.8 5 / 10	**	7 / 9	17.2 29 / 6	0 / 0	$25 = a_3$	−23
(4)D	10 9 / 17	11 / 16	5 22 / 17	17 / 15	55 / 10	0 / 0	$15 = a_4$	−89
(5)E Deficit	1 / 13	1 / 13	1 / 7	1 / 7	100 1 / 1	0 / 0	**	0
Demand d_j	250	120	180	90	600	**		
Implicit Prices v_j	11.8	6.6	4.8	4.33	1	0		

Table 2

WORK SHEET FOR DETERMINING OPTIMAL ASSIGNMENT UNDER UNCERTAIN DEMAND

Type Aircraft	(1) N.Y. to L.A. 1-Stop	(2) N.Y. to L.A. 2-Stop	(3) N.Y. to Dallas 0-Stop	(4) N.Y. to Dallas 1-Stop	(5) N.Y. to Boston 0-Stop	(6) Surplus Aircraft	Aircraft Available	Implicit Prices u_i
(1)A	x_{11} 15 $p_{11}=16$ $c_{11}=18$	x_{12} 15 21	x_{13} 28 18	x_{14} 23 16	x_{15} 81 10	x_{16} 0 0	10	u_1
(2)B	***	x_{22} 10 15	x_{23} 14 16	x_{24} 15 14	x_{25} 57 9	x_{26} 0 0	19	u_2
(3)C	***	x_{32} 5 10	x_{33} *** 0	x_{34} 7 9	x_{35} 29 6	x_{36} 0 0	25	u_3
(4)D	x_{41} 9 17	x_{42} 11 16	x_{43} 22 17	x_{44} 17 15	x_{45} 55 10	x_{46} 0 0	15	u_4
Increment (1)	$y_{11} \leq 200$ -1 -13	$y_{12} \leq 50$ -1 -13	$y_{13} \leq 140$ -1 -7	$y_{14} \leq 10$ -1 -7	$y_{15} \leq 580$ -1 -1	***	**	0
(2)	$y_{21} \leq 20$ -1 -10.4	$y_{22} \leq 100$ -1 -9.1	$y_{23} \leq 20$ -1 -6.3	$y_{24} \leq 40$ -1 -5.6	$y_{25} \leq 20$ -1 $-.9$	***	**	0
(3)	$y_{31} \leq 30$ -1 -9.8	***	$y_{33} \leq 20$ -1 -4.9	$y_{34} \leq 30$ -1 -4.2	$y_{35} \leq 20$ -1 $-.1$	***	**	0

	$y_{41} \leq 20$		$y_{43} \leq 20$	$y_{44} \leq 20$				
	$y_{61} \leq 30$		$y_{53} \leq 20$	$y_{54} \leq 240$				
(4)	-5.2 -1	***	-2.1 -1	-2.1 -1	***	***	**	0
(5)	-2.6 -1	***	$-.7$ -1	$-.7$ -1	***	***	**	0
Net	0	0	0	0	0			
Implicit Prices v_j	v_1	v_2	v_3	v_4	v_5	0		

**Corresponding row or column has no equation.
***Box not used because aircraft type cannot fly required range or fewer increments are needed to describe the distribution of demand on the route.

Table 3—Cycle 0

WORK SHEET FOR DETERMINING OPTIMAL ASSIGNMENT UNDER UNCERTAIN DEMAND

($\delta_{24} = 58.4$, $\theta = 10/15$, Expected Cost = \$1,666,000)

Type Aircraft	Route (1) N.Y. to L.A. 1-Stop	(2) N.Y. to L.A. 2-Stop	(3) N.Y. to Dallas 0-Stop	(4) N.Y. to Dallas 1-Stop	(5) N.Y. to Boston 0-Stop	(6) Surplus Aircraft	Aircraft Available	Implicit Prices u_i
(1)A	10 16 18	15 21	28 18	23 16	81 10	0 0	10	−139
(2)B	***	8 + θ 5 15 10	5 14 16	6 − θ 15 14	57 9	0 0	19	−76
(3)C	***	7.8 5 10	***	7 9	17.2 29 6	0 0	25	−23
(4)D	10 9 17	5 11 16	5 22 17	17 15	55 10	0 0	15	−91
Increment (1)	200 −1 −13	50 −1 −13	140 −1 −7	10 −1 −7	500 −1 −1	***	**	0
(2)	20 −1 −10.4	70 + 10θ −1 −9.1	20 −1 −6.3	40 −1 −5.6	−1 −.9	***	**	0
(3)	30 −1 −9.8	***	20 −1 −4.9	30 −1 −4.2	−1 − 1	***	**	0

	(4)	(5)	Net	Implicit Prices v_i
	-5.2 (-1)	**-2.6** (-1)	0	9.8
	***	***	0	9.1
	-2.1 (-1)	**-.7** (-1)	0	4.9
$10 - 15\theta$	**-2.1** (-1)	**-.7** (-1)	0	2.1
	***	***	1	1
	***	***	0	0
	**	**		
	0	0		

NOTE: Bold face figures are referred to as circled entries in the text.

Table 4—Cycle 1

WORK SHEET FOR DETERMINING OPTIMAL ASSIGNMENT UNDER UNCERTAIN DEMAND
($\delta_{22} = 23.4$, $\theta = 20/14$, Expected Cost $= \$1,627,000$)

Type Aircraft	Route (1) N.Y. to L.A. 1-Stop	(2) N.Y. to L.A. 2-Stop	(3) N.Y. to Dallas 0-Stop	(4) N.Y. to Dallas 1-Stop	(5) N.Y. to Boston 0-Stop	(6) Surplus Aircraft	Aircraft Available	Implicit Prices u_i
(1)A	10 · 16 / 18	15 / 21	28 / 18	23 / 16	81 / 10	0 / 0	10	−139
(2)B	***	8.7 + θ · 10 / 15	5 − θ · 14 / 16	5.3 · 15 / 14	57 / 9	0	19	−76
(3)C	***	5 / 10	***	7 / 9	17.2 · 29 / 6	0	25	−23
(4)D	10 · 9 / 17	11 / 16	5 · 22 / 17	17 / 15	55 / 10	0	15	−91
Increment (1)	200 · −1 / −13	50 · −1 / −13	140 · −1 / −7	10 · −1 / −7	500 · −1 / −1	***	**	0
(2)	20 · −1 / −10.4	77 + 10θ · −1 / −9.1	20 · −1 / −6.3	40 · −1 / −5.6	−1 / −.9	***	**	0
(3)	30 · −1 / −9.8	***	20 − 14θ · −1 / −4.9	30 · −1 / −4.2	−1 / −.1	***	**	0

(4)	-5.2 $^{-1}$	***	-2.1 $^{-1}$	-2.1 $^{-1}$	***	***	**	0
(5)	-2.6 $^{-1}$	***	$-.7$ $^{-1}$	$-.7$ $^{-1}$	***	***	**	0
Net	0	0	0	0	0			
Implicit Prices v_i	9.8	9.1	6.6	6	1	0		

NOTE: Bold face figures are referred to as circled entries in the text.

Table 5—Cycle 2

WORK SHEET FOR DETERMINING OPTIMAL ASSIGNMENT UNDER UNCERTAIN DEMAND

($\delta_{41} = 56.8$, $\theta = 9/16$, Expected Cost = \$1,594,000)

Type Aircraft	(1) N.Y. to L.A. 1-Stop	(2) N.Y. to L.A. 2-Stop	(3) N.Y. to Dallas 0-Stop	(4) N.Y. to Dallas 1-Stop	(5) N.Y. to Boston 0-Stop	(6) Surplus Aircraft	Aircraft Available	Implicit Prices u_i
(1)A	10 · 16 · 18	15 · 21	28 · 18	23 · 16	81 · 10	0 · 0	10	-139
(2)B	***	$10.1 + 1.6\theta$ · 10 · 15	$3.6 - 1.6\theta$ · 14 · 16	5.3 · 15 · 14	57 · 9	0 · 0	19	-76
(3)C	***	7.8 · 5 · 10	***	7 · 9	17.2 · 29 · 6	0 · 0	25	-23
(4)D	$10 - \theta$ · 9 · 17	11 · 16	$5 + \theta$ · 22 · 17	17 · 15	55 · 10	0 · 0	15	-128
Increment (1)	200 · -1 · -13	50 · -1 · -13	140 · -1 · -7	10 · -1 · -7	500 · -1 · -1	***	**	0
(2)	20 · -1 · -10.4	$91 + 16\theta$ · -1 · -9.1	20 · -1 · -6.3	40 · -1 · -5.6	-1 · -.9	***	**	0
(3)	$30 - 9\theta$ · -1 · -9.8	***	-1 · -4.9	30 · -1 · -4.2	-1 · -.1	***	**	0

(4)	-5.2 -1	***	-2.1 -1	-2.1 -1	***	***	**	0
(5)	-2.6 -1	***	$-.7$ -1	$-.7$ -1	***	***	**	0
Net	0	0	0	0	0	0		
Implicit Prices v_j	9.8	5.5	4	3.6	1	0		

NOTE: Bold face figures are referred to as circled entries in the text.

Table 6—Cycle 3

WORK SHEET FOR DETERMINING OPTIMAL ASSIGNMENT UNDER UNCERTAIN DEMAND

($\delta_{32} = 5.5$, $\theta = 100/29 = 3.45$, Expected Cost = \$1,561,000)

Type Aircraft	(1) N.Y. to L.A. 1-Stop	(2) N.Y. to L.A. 2-Stop	(3) N.Y. to Dallas 0-Stop	(4) N.Y. to Dallas 1-Stop	(5) N.Y. to Boston 0-Stop	(6) Surplus Aircraft	Aircraft Available	Implicit Prices u_i
(1)A	16 / 10 / 18	15 / 21	28 / 18	23 / 16	81 / 10	0 / 0	10	−139
(2)B	***	10 / $11 + .5\theta$ / 15	14 / $2.7 - .5\theta$ / 16	15 / 5.3 / 14	57 / 9	0	19	−40
(3)C	***	5 / $7.8 - \theta$ / 10	***	7 / 9	29 / $17.2 + \theta$ / 6	0	25	−23
(4)D	9 / $9.4 - .3\theta$ / 17	16 / 11	22 / $5.6 + .3\theta$ / 17	17 / 15	55 / 10	0	15	−71
Increment (1)	−1 / 200 / −13	−1 / 50 / −13	−1 / 140 / −7	−1 / 10 / −7	−1 / $500 + 29\theta$ / −1	***	**	0
(2)	−1 / 20 / −10.4	−1 / 100 / −9.1	−1 / 20 / −6.3	−1 / 40 / −5.6	−1 / −.9	***	**	0
(3)	−1 / $25 - 2.7\theta$ / −9.8	***	−1 / 30 / −4.9	−1 / 30 / −4.2	−1 / −1	***	**	0

(4)	-5.2 $^{-1}$	***	-2.1 $^{-1}$	-2.1 $^{-1}$	***	***	**	0
(5)	-2.6 $^{-1}$	***	$-.7$ $^{-1}$	$-.7$ $^{-1}$	***	***	**	0
Net	0	0	0	0	0			
Implicit Prices v_i	9.8	5.5	4	3.6	.8	0		

NOTE: Bold face figures are referred to as circled entries in the text.

Table 7—Cycle 4

WORK SHEET FOR DETERMINING OPTIMAL ASSIGNMENT UNDER UNCERTAIN DEMAND

($\delta_{33} = -.9$, $\theta = 20/22 = .9$, Expected Cost = \$1,542,000)

Type Aircraft	(1) N.Y. to L.A. 1-Stop	(2) N.Y. to L.A. 2-Stop	(3) N.Y. to Dallas 0-Stop	(4) N.Y. to Dallas 1-Stop	(5) N.Y. to Boston 0-Stop	(6) Surplus Aircraft	Aircraft Available	Implicit Prices π_i
(1)A	10 (16) 18	(15) 21	(28) 18	(23) 16	(81) 10	(0) 0	10	−139
(2)B	***	12.8 (10) 15	.9 (14) 16	5.3 (15) 14	(57) 9	(0) 0	19	−40
(3)C	***	4.3 (5) 10	***	(7) 9	20.7 (29) 6	(0) 0	25	−18
(4)D	$8.3 - \theta$ (9) 17	(11) 16	$6.7 + \theta$ (22) 17	(17) 15	(55) 10	(0) 0	15	−71
Increment (1)	200 (−1) −13	50 (−1) −13	140 (−1) −7	10 (−1) −7	580 (−1) −1	***	**	
(2)	20 (−1) −10.4	100 (−1) −9.1	20 (−1) −6.3	40 (−1) −5.6	20 (−1) −.9	***	**	0
(3)	$15 - 9\theta$ (−1) −9.8	***	$+22\theta$ (−1) −4.9	30 (−1) −4.2	(−1) −.1	***	**	0

(4)	-5.2^{-1}	***	-2.1^{-1}	-2.1^{-1}	***	***	**	0
(5)	2.6^{-1}	***	$-.7^{-1}$	$-.7^{-1}$	***	***	**	0
Net	0	0	0	0	0			
Implicit Prices v_j	9.8	5.5	4	3.6	8	0		

NOTE: Bold face figures are referred to as circled entries in the text.

Table 8—Cycle 5 (Optimal)

WORK SHEET FOR DETERMINING OPTIMAL ASSIGNMENT UNDER UNCERTAIN DEMAND
(Minimum Expected Cost $1,524,000)

Type Aircraft	Route (1) N.Y. to L.A. 1-Stop	(2) N.Y. to L.A. 2-Stop	(3) N.Y. to Dallas 0-Stop	(4) N.Y. to Dallas 1-Stop	(5) N.Y. to Boston 0-Stop	(6) Surplus Aircraft	Aircraft Available	Implicit Prices u_i
(1)A	10 — 16 / 18	15 / 21	28 / 18	23 / 16	81 / 10	0 / 0	10	−139
(2)B	***	12.8 — 10 / 15	.9 — 14 / 16	5.3 — 15 / 14	57 / 9	0 / 0	19	−40
(3)C	***	4.3 — 5 / 10	***	7 / 9	20.7 — 29 / 6	0 / 0	25	−18
(4)D	7.4 — 9 / 17	11 / 16	7.6 — 22 / 17	17 / 15	55 / 10	0 / 0	15	−71
Increment (1)	200 — −1 / −13	50 — −1 / −13	140 — −1 / −7	10 — −1 / −7	580 — −1 / −1	***	**	0
(2)	20 — −1 / −10.4	100 — −1 / −9.1	20 — −1 / −6.3	40 — −1 / −5.6	20 — −1 / −.9	***	**	0
(3)	7 — −1	***	20 — −1	30 — −1	−1	***	**	

	(col 1)	(col 2)	(col 3)	(col 4)	(col 5)	(col 6)	(col 7)	(col 8)
(4)	−5.2 **−1**	***	−2.1 **−1**	−2.1 **−1**	*** **−1**	***	**	0
(5)	−2.6 **−1**	***	−.7 **−1**	−.7 **−1**	*** **−1**	***	**	0
Net	0	0	0	0	0	0		
Implicit Prices v_i	9.8	9.1	4.9	6	1	0		

NOTE: Bold face figures are referred to as circled entries in the text.

mum value of θ is 22/20 at which value y_{33} reaches its upper bound, so that the new solution, Table 8, has the same set of circled variables and hence the same implicit values as Table 7. Moreover, the solution is *optimal* since all noncircled variables are either at their upper or lower bounds—those at upper bounds have corresponding $\delta_{ij} \geqq 0$ and those at lower bounds have $\delta_{ij} \leqq 0$.

In comparing this solution (Table 8) with the optimal solution for the fixed demand case (Table 1), it is interesting to note that the chief difference appears to be a general tendency to shift the total seats made available on a route to a *mode* of the distribution rather than to the *mean* of the distribution for those distributions with sharp peaks. The total seats made available to routes with flat distributions of demand appear to be at highest level attainable with the residual passenger-carrying potential.

To compute the expected costs of the various solutions the first step, see (20), is to determine what the expected revenues R_0 would be if sufficient seating capacity were furnished at all times to supply all passengers that show. From (2) or (16) it is easy to see that

$$R_0 = 13(250) + 13(120) + 7(180) + 7(90) + 1(600) = 7300$$

or $7,300,000.

It is seen that the solution presented in the earlier paper,[14] assuming demands to be exactly equal to the expected values of demand has a net expected cost of $1,666,000. [It is interesting to note that if the demands were fixed and equal to expected demands, the costs would only be $1,000,000 (see Table 1). The 67 per cent increase in net cost for the variable demand case is due to 13,400 additional passengers (on the

COMPARATIVE COSTS OF VARIOUS SOLUTIONS

Table	Expected Revenues for Seats Supplied (1)	Expected Lost Revenues* (2)	Operating Costs (3)	Net Expected Cost (Thousands) (2) + (3)	
3	−6534	766	900	1,666	
4	−6574	726	901	1,627	
5	−6607	693	901	1,594	
6	−6638	662	899	1,561	(31)
7	−6641	659	883	1,542	
8	−6659	641	883	1,524	

* Data in column (2) are obtained by subtracting the expected revenues for seats supplied, column (1), from $R_0 = 7300$, the expected revenues if unlimited number of seats were supplied.

---

[14] Ferguson and Dantzig, *op. cit.*

average) being turned away because of the distributions of demand assumed in (10)]. The successive improvements in the solution, Tables 3 to 8, reduced the net expected costs from $1,666,000 to $1,524,000 for the optimal solution.

In the illustration the best solution obtained by pretending that demands are fixed at these expected values has a 9 per cent higher expected cost than that for the best solution obtained by using the assumed distributions of demand. It is also seen that very little additional computational effort was required to take account of this uncertainty of demand.

CASE 4

Linear Programming in Practice[1]

EMIL KAY and ERIC DUCKWORTH[2]

Some points of special interest in this paper are:

a. The treatment of the problem as static (one day at a time).
b. The use of real variables in the initial solution.
c. The physical interpretation of the "slack" vectors.
d. A comparison of the "no experience" solution by linear programming with the results obtained according to past experience.
e. The mention of theoretical difficulties of working with a composite product. Why?
f. The premise that recovered metals "are an inevitable by-product of the manufacturing process (and) therefore the cost of these recovered metals can be set at zero."

INTRODUCTION

Linear programming is a technique used to solve simultaneous equations in which the number of unknowns exceeds the number of equations. Without restrictions this circumstance gives rise to an infinity of solutions. However, by defining that no solution shall be negative and that a given linear function of the solution shall be a maximum (or minimum), the problem can be solved, provided that such a solution does exist.

The linear function which is maximized is often a price or cost func-

[1] *Applied Statistics,* March, 1957. Reprinted by permission.

[2] NAAFI and the Glacier Metal Company Limited, respectively. The authors are very grateful for the assistance of Dr. G. Morton of the London School of Economics; and to Mr. C. A. Marr and Miss L. Sternberg of the Glacier Metal Company for their computational work. Thanks are due to the Glacier Metal Company for permission to publish this paper.

tion of the variables being evaluated, hence the ready application of linear programming to economic problems. The application to be described is one in which linear programming was used in determining the least-cost proportions of new, and of recovered metal to be used in making up alloys to specification.

The computation will not be described in detail. The method used for arriving at the maximizing solution was the so-called "Simplex," due to G. B. Dantzig, which has been described elsewhere.[3] This paper will describe the setting up of the matrices, the simplifications evolved, and the organizational consequences.

THE PROBLEM

Many plain bearings, of the type used in internal combustion engines, consist of a steel shell on the inside of which is cast a thin layer of whitemetal, composed mainly of tin with about 10 per cent of antimony and 4 per cent of copper. Both the surface finish and the thickness of the whitemetal are carefully controlled so that a final machining operation is necessary. The resulting scrap is collected and remelted and is known as "recovered" metal; other sources of recovered metal are scrap bearings from which the whitemetal is melted and surplus whitemetal from other ancillary operations. The recovered metal is collected and cast into batches of ingots. Each batch is given a bin number and stored until it can be used. It can rarely be used directly for casting into bearings because of the alteration in composition which occurs during handling and remelting.

The whitemetal foundry needs an almost daily requirement of whitemetal, and this is provided from a combination of fresh tin, antimony, and copper, and of recovered metal in the correct proportions to give the exact composition of the metal needed when remelted together. As there are fluctuations in the demand for fresh whitemetal and in the supply of recovery melts, the daily requirements may vary from nil to several tons of different specifications and the number of recovery melts available may vary from five to twenty-five. It is clearly desirable to use as much recovered metal as possible in making up fresh melts, but the usage is restricted by the fact that the metal required may differ substantially in composition from the metal available and also that the maximum amount of lead permitted in the whitemetal is 0.2 per cent.

---
[3] A. Charnes, W. W. Cooper, and A. Henderson, *An Introduction to Linear Programming* (New York: John Wiley & Sons, Inc., 1953). T. C. Koopmans (ed.), *Activity Analysis of Production and Allocation* (New York: John Wiley & Sons, Inc., 1951).

Recovered melts are classified into four categories according to their lead contamination:

$$A—\text{less than } 0.35\%$$
$$B—0.35\%–0.50\%$$
$$C—0.50\%–1.00\%$$
$$D—1.00\%–15.00\%$$

Category D is due to the fact that lead-base whitemetals are sometimes produced in close proximity to tin-base ones and contamination is very difficult to avoid.

With the figures for lead contamination in mind and with the realization that a human being with a slide rule cannot juggle with too many figures, a simple rule-of-thumb method of attempting to use 50 per cent recovered metal in each melt was evolved. This method worked tolerably well. Over a period investigated it showed that metal in category D was not used and that the amount of recovered metal available (in the A, B, and C categories) as a proportion of new melts required was 46.2 per cent, and the actual amount of recovered metal used was 42.4 per cent, i.e., 92 per cent of that available. Linear programming was then appled to see if it could do better.

THE DEVELOPMENT OF THE MATHEMATICAL MODEL

If we define economic efficiency in this case as prescribing the makeup of a required alloy in such a way that the cost is at a minimum, we obtain a criterion for minimization, provided that we can attach a cost to the use of the various recovered and virgin metals. Now the cost of one pound of virgin metal is its market price. Any recovered metal in store has in fact two alternative uses: (a) it can be used in the production of alloys, or (b) it can be sold to outside firms such as metal refiners. The price a given recovered metal fetches, when sold outside, depends on its tin content and its lead contamination, and roughly speaking is 93–96 per cent of the market price of tin. Therefore, the function that we have to minimize can be determined.

For a given requirement of a specified alloy on any given day we can choose among the recovered metals available that day, with the restriction that we cannot, of course, use more of any metal than is in fact available. Hence, taking the total amount of each recovered metal available (in pounds) as unity, this restriction yields a set of n inequalities, all of which are of the form $x_i \leqq 1$, where n is the number of recovered metals available and x_i is the amount of the ith recovered metal to be used.

The amounts of tin, copper, antimony, and lead in each recovered metal used, plus the virgin metal needed to add up to the amount required in the specification, furnish three equations and one more inequality.

Thus for tin:

$$t_1x_1 + t_2x_2 + t_3x_3 + \ldots + t_nx_n + x_{(n+1)} = T$$

where t_1 is the amount of tin in the x_1 recovered metal used,

t_2 is the amount of tin in the x_2 recovered metal used,

t_3 is the amount of tin in the x_3 recovered metal used,

t_n is the amount of tin in the x_n recovered metal used,

$x_{(n+1)}$ is the amount of virgin tin added,

T is the total amount of tin required in the alloy.

Similarly for antimony

$$a_1x_1 + a_2x_2 + a_3x_3 + \ldots + a_nx_n + x_{(n+2)} = A$$

for copper

$$c_1x_1 + c_2x_2 + c_3x_3 + \ldots + c_nx_n + x_{(n+3)} = C$$

and for lead

$$l_1x_1 + l_2x_2 + l_3x_3 + \ldots + l_nx_n + 0.0007x_{(n+1)} \leq L$$

The coefficient 0.0007 of $x_{(n+1)}$ is due to the fact that commercial virgin tin contains 0.07 per cent lead.

The function to be minimized is

$$Z = \Sigma(m_ix_i)$$

where m_i is the cost of the ith recovered or virgin metal and x_i the amount of recovered or virgin metal used in the prescription ($0 \leq x_i \leq 1$ except when i refers to virgin metal).

Thus there are three equations, $n + 1$ inequalities, and $n + 3$ unknowns (the amounts of each recovered metal to be used and the quantity of each virgin metal required).

To convert the inequalities into equations in order to apply "Simplex" methods one new variable must be added for each inequality. If these variables are denoted by x_i' the complete set of equations is then as given below:

$$x_1 + x_1' = 1$$
$$x_2 + x_2' = 1$$
$$\cdots\cdots\cdots$$
$$x_n + x_n' = 1$$

$$t_1x_1 + t_2x_2 + t_3x_3 + \ldots + t_nx_n + x_{(n+1)} = T$$
$$a_1x_1 + a_2x_2 + a_3x_3 + \ldots + a_nx_n + x_{(n+2)} = A$$
$$c_1x_1 + c_2x_2 + c_3x_3 + \ldots + c_nx_n + x_{(n+3)} = C$$
$$l_1x_1 + l_2x_2 + l_3x_3 + \ldots + l_nx_n + 0.0007x_{(n+1)} + x'_{(n+4)} = L$$

In general mathematical usage it is not necessary to assign a meaning to the variables added to convert inequalities into equations. In linear programming it is always possible to assign a meaning, and in this example x_i' means *not* to use x_i' of the ith recovered metal and $x'_{(n+4)}$ means *not* to use the full amount of lead allowable. The set of equations describing the restrictions of the problems thus consists finally of $n + 4$ equations in $2n + 4$ unknowns.

There is another way to arrive at this set of equations which makes it easier to obtain the model: namely forming a so-called "activity table." The use of any recovered metal can be considered as a process which has an input, i.e., the recovered metal; and an output, i.e., the various elements which it contains. Using a metal is an "activity"; the various inputs and outputs are "commodities." The activity table is formed by listing all possible activities. It is a convention to enter inputs with negative signs, outputs with positive signs. The nomenclature is a convention derived from economic theory.[4] The activity table which forms our model is shown in Table 1.

If to this table we add a last column, representing the restrictions of the problem, which gives the availabilities of the input commodities and the requirements of the output commodities, the vector so obtained contains all the restrictions of the problem. It is called the boundary or requirements vector, and its usual notation is P_0. If we now imagine equality and/or inequality signs between this vector and the last column of the activity table, and plus signs between each column in each row of the table, we derive the set of equations and inequalities which describe the problem. Again each activity has a known cost m_i, and we wish to find a solution to our set of equations and inequalities in terms of $x_i, i = 1, 2 \ldots (n + 3)$, which minimizes the function Z.

It now remains to show that a "feasible," i.e. nonnegative, solution exists. The first step is to convert the inequalities into equations by the addition of other variables, i.e. by adding activities of a certain form. These new activities, known as disposals, have in our case the meaning *not* to use the recovered metals to which they refer, and the last one (column $P'_{(n+1)}$ of Table 2) means *not* to fulfil the lead requirements, i.e. to have less than the maximum lead contamination allowed. These disposals have zero cost. The system of equations obtained is set out in Table 2.

When in linear programming a set of inequalities is converted into equations by the addition of such disposal vectors, it is always possible

---

[4] See Koopmans, *op. cit.*

Table 1

Notation		P_1	P_2	P_3	...	...	...	...	P_n	$P_{(n+1)}$	$P_{(n+2)}$	$P_{(n+3)}$		P_0
Activity \\ Commodity		Use x_1	Use x_2	Use x_3	...	...	...	...	Use x_n	Use Virgin Tin $x_{(n+1)}$	Use Virgin Antimony $x_{(n+2)}$	Use Virgin Copper $x_{(n+3)}$		Boundary
x_1		-1											$\geq$	-1
x_2			-1										$\geq$	-1
x_3				-1									$\geq$	-1
...														
...														
...														
...														
x_n									-1				$\geq$	-1
Tin		t_1	t_2	t_3	...	...	...	...	t_n	1			$=$	T
Antimony		a_1	a_2	a_3	...	...	...	...	a_n		1		$=$	A
Copper		c_1	c_2	c_3	...	...	...	...	c_n			1	$=$	C
Lead		l_1	l_2	l_3	...	...	...	...	l_n	0.0007			$\leq$	L

Notation
x_i = Amount of ith recovered melt ($i = 1,2,\ldots,n$)
t_i = Tin content of ith recovered melt
a_i = Antimony content of ith recovered melt
c_i = Copper content of ith recovered melt
l_i = Lead content of ith recovered melt

T = Tin content of required alloy
A = Antimony content of required alloy
C = Copper content of required alloy
L = Maximum lead allowed in required alloy
P_i denotes the ith activity

Table 2

NOTATION	P_1	P_2	P_3	...	P_n	$P_{(n+1)}$	$P_{(n+2)}$	$P_{(n+3)}$	P_1'	P_2'	P_3'	...	P_n'	$P'_{(n+1)}$	P_0
Activity / Commodity	Use x_1	Use x_2	Use x_3	...	Use x_n	Use Virgin Tin $x_{(n+1)}$	Use Virgin Antimony $x_{(n+2)}$	Use Virgin Copper $x_{(n+3)}$	DO NOT use x_1'	DO NOT use x_2'	DO NOT use x_3'	...	DO NOT use x_n'	Unused Lead Allowance $x_{(n+4)}$	Boundary
x_1	−1								−1						−1
x_2		−1								−1					−1
x_3			−1								−1				−1
...															...
...															...
x_n					−1								−1		−1
Tin	t_1	t_2	t_3	...	t_n	1									T
Antimony	a_1	a_2	a_3	...	a_n		1								A
Copper	c_1	c_2	c_3	...	c_n			1							C
Lead	l_1	l_2	l_3	...	l_n	0.0007								1	1

Table 3

Notation / Commodity	$P_{(n+1)}$	$P_{(n+2)}$	$P_{(n+3)}$	$P'_{(n+1)}$	P'_1	P'_2	P'_3	...	...	...	...	P'_n
x_1					-1							
x_2						-1						
x_3							-1					
...												
...												
...												
...												
x_n												-1
Tin	1											
Antimony		1										
Copper			1									
Lead	0.0007			1								
Feasible Solution	T	A	C	$L - 0.0007T$	1	1	1	1	1	1	1	1

to assign a meaning to them, though they are not necessarily always of zero cost.

The next step is to find a feasible solution. In this case it is clear that by using virgin metals only for a given required allow a nonnegative solution to the set of equations in Table 2 is obtained. The matrix of coefficients of this solution is given in Table 3.

This solution in explicit form is

$$
\begin{aligned}
x_i &= 0 & i &= 1 \text{ to } n \\
x_i' &= 1 & i &= 1 \text{ to } n \\
x_{(n+1)} &= T \\
x_{(n+2)} &= A \\
x_{(n+3)} &= C \\
x'_{(n+4)} &= L - 0.0007T
\end{aligned}
$$

This matrix must now be inverted, clearly a very simple operation in this case. From this stage onwards "Simplex" computation is used.

We have now shown that our problem is amenable to treatment by linear programming methods, since a feasible solution can be found.

THE TRIAL RUN

The efficacy of the method was tested by a trial run. Prescriptions for the past eighteen months were available, which showed that under the old methods recovered metals in category D tended to accumulate. Ten consecutive weeks were selected at random, and recalculated by the linear programming method. Comparison of the results showed that with linear programming D-category recovered metals again tended to accumulate, e.g., the same type of recovered metal was selected for realloying by both methods, and recovered metals of category D are not suitable for reuse.

The saving due to linear programming was comparatively small and in terms of recovered metal used is shown below. The period investigated was 10 weeks and the amounts are expressed as a percentage of demand.

Usable recovered metal (A, B, C)..........................46.2%
Recovered metal used by old method......................42.4
Recovered metal used by linear programming..............44.6

It should here be pointed out that linear programming did not give prescriptions at the absolute minimum cost (46.2 per cent) because of the practical restriction that the foundry can weigh out metal only to the nearest pound, and that it is impracticable to split a recovered metal into too small quantities.

The percentage of recovered metal used in a prescription by linear programming showed wider fluctuations than the percentage under the old method (Fig. 1). This was to be expected, because the old method tried to use a given percentage, 50 per cent, of recovered metal in each prescription, irrespective of the amount of recovered metal available at the time the prescription was made, whereas linear programming always uses the maximum amount available at any time.

Linear programming speeded up the turnover of recovered metals in the store. This is an advantage when storage space costs money. Table 4 and Figure 2 show the effect of linear programming in accelerating the turnover.

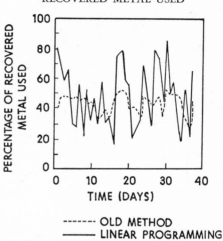

Figure 1

FLUCTUATION IN PERCENTAGE OF RECOVERED METAL USED

------ OLD METHOD
—— LINEAR PROGRAMMING

Linear programming induces greater fluctuations in the demand for virgin tin. This at first sight seems to be a disadvantage, but, in all, less virgin tin is used. In actual working the saving in virgin tin is, up to now, greater than could be expected from the trial run, and the increase in the fluctuation is only of the order of 15 per cent of the standard error.

Finally, whereas under the old method it was practically impossible to consider all the recovered metals available when prescribing, linear programming assures that this is done.

There is a slight theoretical difficulty in applying linear programming. In the model we assumed that at any time any recovered metal

Table 4

"AVERAGE WEEKLY STOCK" OF RECOVERED METALS IN THOUSANDS OF POUNDS
(The figures are coded and represent differences, not actual stocks)

Old Method			Linear Programming		
Category:			Category:		
A	B	C	A	B	C
113	23	82	48	3	44

not in the solution would be sold. In fact such recovered metals remain in store and become available for later prescriptions. Considering, however, that our aim is minimizing cost of prescription, and that in fact we defined cost as opportunity cost, as that definition is used in economic theory, it will be seen that the nonsale of recovered metals not in the solution does not really upset our model. Furthermore, the investigation showed that certain recovered metals (category D) could be sold safely whenever required, since it was not profitable to use them for realloying.

Figure 2

FREQUENCY DISTRIBUTIONS OF THE NUMBER OF DAYS THAT RECOVERED METALS SPENT IN STOCK

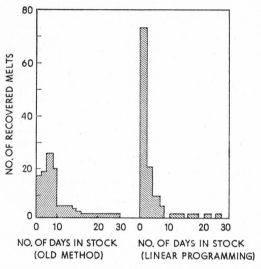

It very often happens that prescriptions for two or more alloys are demanded on the same day. For example, 1,000 pounds of specification A (10 antimony, 5 copper, 0.02 lead, balance tin) and 2,000 pound of specification B (8 antimony, 3 copper, 0.02 lead, balance tin). The model can easily be extended to cover this case, as shown in Table 5. Due to the size of this type of matrix the computation becomes rather prolonged, even for only two alloys. For this reason, and because prescriptions which are demanded at about 10:30 A.M. have to be issued by 4 P.M. to the foundry, the following short cut has been adopted: A new alloy, C, which is the sum of the matrix specifications of A and B, is stipulated, and the program is set up as if only alloy C were demanded (Table 6). After the solution to this has been found, a program of the type illustrated in Table 5 is set up, but only those recovered metals which appear in the solution for alloy C are used. Computing this second program produces the required solution A and B. It must, however, be said that this short cut need not always work, i.e., the second program may turn out a solution to A and B which does not use recovered metals and virgin metals in the same proportion as indicated by the solution to C, and therefore the cost of making A and B is higher than that of making C. Should that happen, A and B would have to be

Table 5

Commodity \ Notation	P_1	P_2	P_3	P_4	P_5	P_6	$\cdots$	$\cdots$	$\cdots$	$\cdots$	$P_{(m-1)}$	P_m
x_1	-1	-1										
x_2			-1	-1								
x_3					-1	-1						
$\vdots$							$\vdots$	$\vdots$	$\vdots$	$\vdots$		
$\vdots$							$\vdots$	$\vdots$	$\vdots$	$\vdots$		
x_n											-1	-1
Alloy A — Tin	t_1		t_2		t_3		$\cdots$	$\cdots$	$\cdots$	$\cdots$	t_n	
Alloy A — Antimony	a_1		a_2		a_3		$\cdots$	$\cdots$	$\cdots$	$\cdots$	a_n	
Alloy A — Copper	c_1		c_2		c_3		$\cdots$	$\cdots$	$\cdots$	$\cdots$	c_n	
Alloy A — Lead	l_1		l_2		l_3		$\cdots$	$\cdots$	$\cdots$	$\cdots$	l_n	
Alloy B — Tin		t_1		t_2		t_3	$\cdots$	$\cdots$	$\cdots$	$\cdots$		t_n
Alloy B — Antimony		a_1		a_2		a_3	$\cdots$	$\cdots$	$\cdots$	$\cdots$		a_n
Alloy B — Copper		c_1		c_2		c_3	$\cdots$	$\cdots$	$\cdots$	$\cdots$		c_n
Alloy B — Lead		l_1		l_2		l_3	$\cdots$	$\cdots$	$\cdots$	$\cdots$		l_n

Table 5 (Continued)

Commodity \ Notation	$P_{(3n+1)}$	$P_{(3n+2)}$	$P_{(3n+3)}$	$P'_{(n+1)}$	$P_{(3n+5)}$	$P_{(3n+6)}$	$P_{(3n+7)}$	$P'_{(n+2)}$	P'_1	P'_2	P'_3	...	...	P'_n	P_0
x_1									-1						-1
x_2										-1					-1
x_3											-1				-1
...												$\vdots$			$\cdots$
...													$\vdots$		$\cdots$
x_n														-1	-1
Alloy A — Tin	1														T_1
Alloy A — Antimony		1													A_1
Alloy A — Copper			1												C_1
Alloy A — Lead	0.0007			1											L_1
Alloy B — Tin					1										T_2
Alloy B — Antimony						1									A_2
Alloy B — Copper							1								C_2
Alloy B — Lead					0.0007			1							L_2

Notation as in Table I, but:

T_1, A_1, C_1, L_1 = Amount of tin, antimony, copper, lead required in alloy A.
T_2, A_2, C_2, L_2 = Amount of tin, antimony, copper, lead required in alloy B.

Table 6

SPECIFICATION FOR ALLOYS; 1,000 LB. OF A AND 2,000
LB. OF B REQUIRED

	Alloy A (%)	Alloy B (%)	Alloy A (Lb.)	Alloy B (Lb.)	Notional Alloy C = A + B (Lb.)
Tin...............	84.8	88.8	$848(T_1)$	$1776(T_2)$	$2624(T_1 + T_2)$
Antimony..........	10.0	8.0	$100(A_1)$	$160(A_2)$	$260(A_1 + A_2)$
Copper............	5.0	3.0	$50(C_1)$	$60(C_2)$	$110(C_1 + C_2)$
Lead..............	0.2	0.2	$2(L_1)$	$4(L_2)$	$6(L_1 + L_2)$

recomputed from the matrix of Table 5, using all the recovered metals available. In practice up to now the short cut method has always worked, but on theoretical grounds there is certainly no reason why it should do so. In actual practice the work of splitting up C into the components of A and B can be done by inspection and a new program is not necessary.

When it was decided to use linear programming for prescribing, another simplification was added. We know from the investigation that recovered metals of categories A, B, C only are usable and that they tend to be used within a very short time from their becoming available. Also they are an inevitable by-product of the manufacturing process. Therefore the cost of these recovered metals can be set at zero. In the function Z which we wish to minimize only those m_i appertaining to virgin metals are different from zero. For the m_i referring to virgin metals the computer can choose any numbers that are found convenient, provided only that their ratio to each other is the same as the ratio of market prices of the corresponding virgin metals. With these simplifications the computing time has been cut down considerably. On the average less than two hours per day are spent on computing prescriptions. The device of using computationally convenient numbers, instead of the actual m_i, can always be used if the actual maximal (or minimal) value of Z is not required. In our case the simplification really means that instead of minimizing the cost function given earlier, the function minimized is the amount of virgin metal used.

A further simplification, suggested recently by S. Babik of the Glacier Metal Company, is that with many alloys where the limiting lead content is reached before the antimony, copper, and tin requirements are satisfied, the function minimized is the cost of reducing $x'_{(n+4)}$ to zero.

ORGANIZATION

The results of applying the linear program do not appear to be spectacular. They represent a use of some 4 per cent more recovered metal. This, together with the more rapid turnover of recovered metal stocks, is a useful advance, however, and well worth the effort. The investigation has provided a reminder that a well-tried rule-of-thumb method in industry can approach the theoretical optimum very closely and it may well be that linear programming tried on a larger scale will result in the same order of useful but marginal improvements.

The initiation of the linear programming presented some practical difficulties which other users of the method may have experienced. Not all the new melt prescriptions asked for were straightforward, and the users of the previous rule-of-thumb method had acquired a skill and an instinct for dealing with unusual situations. It was found desirable to make the transition very gradually so that these skills could be transferred. Where communication with the factory is concerned personal contact is very important, and the transition period helped to establish the new contacts.

The number of recovered melts used for each new prescription had formerly rarely exceeded two; with linear programming it was usually four and could have been as high as seven. This gave rise to some initial handling difficulties. By regulating the receipt of incoming demands the maximum number is kept to four. This results in a slight loss of mathematical efficiency but resolves the handling problems.

CASE 5

A Problem in Optimal Machine Loading[1]

M. E. SALVESON[2]

Some points of special interest in this paper are:

a. The special function of the "control" groups.
b. The objective attained by the machine-loading technique developed.
c. The physical meaning of positive balances after all presses have been assigned.
d. The formulation of the loading problem as a linear programming problem aimed at profit maximization.
e. The problems of attempting to determine some optimal cycle length with sequence restrictions.
f. The stated conflict between independent solutions of economic lot sizes. Does this problem tend to become more or less acute as the number of parts goes from two to a hundred?

SUMMARY

An important managerial problem in manufacturing is to determine the optimum amount and mix of products that can be manufactured from a given set of facilities, such as machine tools. A method is discussed here for handling this problem more effectively in one instance than has been possible. It makes use of several standard procedures, but adapts them and adds others to accommodate the unavoidable difficulty of discreteness in real production situations. The traditional

[1] *Management Science,* April, 1956. Reprinted by permission.

[2] Center for Advanced Management. Prepared while writer was Manager—Business Research, Major Appliance Division, General Electric Company. Sincere appreciation is expressed to W. B. Helgeson, Harlan Mills, and T. T. ·Kwo for their interest and valuable suggestions in connection with this study. The paper was presented originally at the 2nd Annual Meeting of The Institute of Management Sciences, New York, October, 1955.

formulation of the economic lot size is shown to be incorrect in the general case and a preferred formulation is presented for the situation studied here. A method of optimizing the amount of in-process inventory to carry in the circumstances of this study also is given.

INTRODUCTION

The study reported here arose from the need in a sheet metal fabrication center of one of the writer's Company's plants of being able to determine reliably and quickly the number and mix of end products for which fabricated parts could be produced by a given set of heavy presses. The previously used method to make this determination at least approximately was based on an adaptation of the Gantt chart. The engineers planning the production load would endeavor to outline on such chart an assignment of operations for each part on each product to some particular machine tool in such manner as to maximize production of these products, or to determine the maximum production of one product if the production of, say, the two other products were fixed. At the same time they endeavored to plan levels of in-process inventory which would minimize production costs.

In this paper, all illustrative numerical values, names of products, etc., have been disguised in order to protect proprietary information. However, the realistic characteristics of the production problems have been carefully preserved in the formulation and presented in the paper in order that results may be broadly useful.

Before commencing the exposition of the problem analyzed here, it should be commented that this problem is quite limited in scope. It deals only with a computational and conceptual method for loading a set of machine tools in a department of the factory given certain conditions. In the more general case this problem is embedded in a larger, more basic problem of first determining production rates and mixes under conditions of uncertainty as well as the composition and arrangement of the shop. For the purpose of the problem presented here, the basic assumptions included are given narrow limits for some of these rates and mixes. Thus, this technical problem is only part of a larger managerial problem.

Justification for treating this narrow problem is found in two premises. First, it is a problem typical of many shops and hence useful to solve. Secondly, in treating the broader problem in which this one is embedded, there must of necessity follow solutions to functional problems of this character, set within a framework of conditions and boundaries resulting from the larger managerial problem.

TECHNOLOGY

The factory in which the study was made is an integrated manufacturing system producing an assembled electromechanical product. It processes many component parts used in its final products through many fabrication and finishing operations to the finished state. However, other component parts are purchased in the finished state and enter directly into assembly from finished part storage. The basic types of processes which are carried out in the factory include fabrication, finishing and assembly. In general, factory-produced parts enter as raw sheet, unfinished castings, or bar stock, are processed in fabrication, sent to finishing, and thence as finished parts to assembly or subassembly.

There are three principal fabrication sections in the factory: large sheet metal parts, small sheet metal parts, and small machined parts. This study covers only fabrication of the large sheet metal parts. The study was limited to this fabrication area because it then constituted a bottleneck, because it presented a problem which appeared amenable to solution, and because a more general study would presuppose availability of methods for handling such problems as were found in this area. Also, it is likely that methods developed for this area could be generalized to cover the problems involved in the other areas.

The productive equipment in this section is 20 heavy presses, ranging in capacity from 60 tons to 300 tons. These presses can be classified into six categories, according to size and capacity, as follows: Class A, 3 presses; Class B, 5 presses; Class C, 5 presses; Class D, 4 presses; Class E, 1 press; Class H, 2 presses. Each press within any class may be considered as entirely interchangeable with other presses in that class insofar as productive capabilities are concerned, even though there may be certain structural differences between them.

There are 24 different parts which are fabricated or are planned to be fabricated in this section. These range in size from $12'' \times 12''$ up to $36'' \times 36''$. Each part requires a series of operations for its fabrication. In general, each operation is performed on a separate press. Any exceptions to this assumption can be made to fit it by assuming that the two or more operations on one press are only one operation. The number of operations per part ranges from 2 to 13. Each part thus requires a number of presses for its fabrication equal to the number of operations which are required. Each operation on each part must be carried out on a particular class of presses or set of alternative classes. Associated with each operation on each part is a characteristic production rate. This rate is expressed as the number of parts produced per hour. All parts are of such physical dimensions that it is impractical to store large numbers of them between successive operations. Thus, even though the individual operations on any one part may have different rates, it is necessary to carry out all operations on that part simultaneously and to carry them out effectively at the same rate. (There are some minor variations in practice from this statement, but they do not change its essential correctness.) Any combination of presses of the necessary classes may be used to carry out the required operations on any part. A corollary to the two preceding statements is that a part cannot be produced at any given time unless at that time both the required number and classes of presses are all simultaneously available for its production.

The finished parts are assembled into the finished products on a continuous-production conveyorized assembly line[3] which operates and produces at a uniform rate. The rate of assembly is not sufficient, however, to sustain uniform continuous production of each part in fabrication. That is, the rate of parts fabrication is much higher than the rate at which the parts are consumed in assemblying the finished product. Thus, the parts are fabricated intermittently in batches although they are consumed continuously in assembly. The intermittent fabrication permits use of presses on a quasi-job-shop basis using whatever suitable presses are available at the time. Obviously, storage facilities must be provided for the reserve inventory which is required to match intermittent fabrication with continuous assembly. There is a cost for storing and carrying the inventory of the parts. With but one exception, set-up time is required for changing the die in a press when a different part is to be processed.

PRESS CLASSIFICATION AND PARTS ASSIGNMENT

The manufacturing planning instructions yield the (disguised) data shown in Table 1.

On examining the following list, it can be seen that there are characteristic combinations of press types that can accommodate the various parts and their fabrication operations. Explicitly, there are the following groupings or groups of press classes, the members of which can be used interchangeably for one or more operation on one or more parts as illustrated in Table 2.

For example, there are some operations which can be performed on only a Class B press; some may be performed interchangeably on a B or a C press; some on A, B or C, etc.

---

[3] M. E. Salveson, "The Assembly Line Balancing Problem," *Transactions of the ASME*, Vol. LXXVII, No. 6 (August, 1955), pp. 939–48.

Table 1

Part Number	Operation Number	Set-Up Time (Hr.)	Operation Time (Hr./M)	Classes of Presses on Which Operations Can Be Run
1	1	1	3.57	BC
	2	1	4.7	B
	3	1	4.79	EBC
	4	1	4.8	BC
	5	1	5.16	ABC
	6	1	5.56	ABCD
	7		5.56	DH
	8	1	6.25	BC
	9	1	5.83	B
	10	2	6.66	BC
	11	2	5.35	BC
	12	1	5.11	ABC
2	1	1	4.94	BC
	2	1	4.2	BC
3	1	1	3.79	ABCD
	2	1	3.63	ABCD
	3	1	3.36	ABCD
	4	1	4.6	BC
	5	2	4.4	DH
4	1	1	3.62	BC
	2	1	4.83	B
	3	1	5.4	EBC
	4	1	5.32	ABC
	5	1	5.69	BC
	6	1	6.54	BC
	7		6.54	DH
	8	1	5.56	B
	9	3	7.09	BC
5	1	1	5.08	B
	2	1	4.85	BC
	3	1	5.81	BC
	4	1	5.41	BC
	5	1	7.08	BC
	6	1	6.0	BC
6	1	1	4.18	ABC
	2	1	4.44	ABC
7	1	1	4.29	ABC
	2	1	4.31	ABC
8	1	1	5.16	ABC
	2	1	6.18	ABC
9	1	1	3.98	D
	2	1	4.11	D
	3	1	3.99	D
10	1	1	3.89	D
	2	1	4.05	D
	3	1	3.87	D
	4	1	4.73	D
11	1	1	5.17	ABCD
	2	1	6.17	ABCD
	3	1	5.0	ABCD
12	1	2	4.04	ABC
	2	1	3.64	ABCD
13	1	1	4.361	ABC
14	1	1	5.55	ABC

Table 1—Continued

Part Number	Operation Number	Set-Up Time (Hr.)	Operation Time (Hr./M)	Classes of Presses on Which Operations Can Be Run
15	1	1	3.62	BC
	2	1	4.83	B
	3	1	5.4	EBC
	4	1	5.32	ABC
	5	1	5.69	BC
	6	1	6.54	BC
	7	1	7.09	DH
	8	1	5.56	BC
	9	1	7.09	BC
16	1	1	5.08	BC
	2	1	5.82	ABC
	3	1	5.41	BC
	4	1	6.81	BC
	5	1	5.82	BC
17	1	1	3.97	ABCD
	2	1	4.11	ABCD
	3	1	3.97	ABCD
	4	1	3.97	ABCD
18	1	1	4.11	ABCD
	2	1	4.11	ABCD
	3	1	3.99	ABCD
	4	1	4.11	ABCD
19	1	1	4.36	ABC
	2	1	4.88	ABC
20	1	1	4.36	ABC
	2	1	4.36	ABC
21	1	1	4.36	ABC
	2	1	4.36	ABC
22	1	1	5.08	BC
	2	1	5.82	BC
	3	1	5.41	BC
	4	1	6.81	BC
	5	1	5.82	BC
23	1	1	4.08	ABCD
24	1	1	4.58	ABC

From the groups of press classes in Table 2 and from Table 1, we can prepare Table 3, showing the number of presses of each group required for fabricating of each part.

Table 4 gives the number of presses in each class.

The number of presses in each group is shown in Table 5.

These various data on requirements and availabilities now are used in determining what parts can be produced simultaneously with the given set of presses. Recall that when a part is produced, all required presses must be available simultaneously and the several operations carried on concurrently.

Use Part 1 as a beginning illustration of the method for determining

Table 2

GROUPS OF PRESS CLASSES

B
BC
ABC
ABCD
EBC
D
DH

Table 3

PRESS REQUIREMENTS OF EACH PART BY GROUPS OF PRESS CLASSES

Part Number	B	BC	ABC	ABCD	EBC	DH	D
1	2	5	2	1	1	1	
2		2					
3		1		3		1	
4	2	4	1		1	1	
5	1	5					
6			2				
7			2				
8			2				
9							3
10							4
11				3			
12			1	1			
13			2				
14			1				
15	1	5	1		1	1	
16		5					
17			4				
18			4				
19			2				
20			2				
21			2				
22		5					
23				1			
24			1				

Table 4

Type A—3
B—5
C—5
D—4
E—1
H—2

these parts or "assignments." From Table 3 the requirements for presses for Part 1 are as follows:

	B	BC	ABC	ABCD	ABCE	EBC	D	DH	ABCDH	ABCDEH
Part 1	2	5	2	1	0	1	0	1	0	0

Table 5

PRESS GROUPS AND NUMBER OF PRESSES

B—5
BC—10
ABC—13
EBC—11
ABCD—17
ABCE*—14
D—4
DH—6
ABCDH*—19
ABCDEH*—20

* Note: The "control" groups ABCE, ABCDH, and ABCDEH have been added and will be explained later.

That is, Part 1 requires 2 presses of Class B plus 5 of either Class B or C, plus 2 of Class A, B or C, plus etc. In order to determine conveniently what parts can be produced simultaneously, it is necessary to compute the *total* number of presses required in each group of press classes for each part. For example, 2 group B presses are required and 5 group BC. The 2 group B presses must be taken from Class B. However, the 5 group BC presses may be taken from either Class B or Class C. Obviously, the presses which are members of Class B are included in both group B and group BC because they are members of the classes which comprise these groups. Thus, considering only these two press requirements, there would be four possible class assignments ranging in actual use from 2 B and 5 C presses to 5 B and 2 C presses. We need not concern ourselves with making assignments to specific presses. We shall term a selection of parts which can be assigned simultaneously to the presses as a "feasible assignment" and a selection such that no other part can be assigned as a "maximal assignment." Some of the difficulty encountered in handling the assignment problem in practical every day shop planning is that the relations of presses to classes and classes to groups may not be explicitly recognized and used. Two essential points are that in the case of classes we are concerned with interchangeability of classes. However, any press is simultaneously a member of only one class, but any one class a member of more than one group. In order to keep the bookkeeping straight, provision must be made for these relations.

The method of making the assignments which is presented here includes: (1) Enumerate all classes of presses as determined by engineering analysis of the presses and their interchangeability. (2) List all wholly interchangeable presses in the same class. Each press is a member of one and only one class. (3) Enumerate the groups of classes based on analysis of each operation and determination of which classes can be used for it. (4) Compute the number of presses in each group by summing the number of presses in each class which is included in that group. (5) If there are any two groups with one or more classes in common, but one group is not wholly contained in the other, or both are not wholly contained in still a third group which contains exactly those classes, then designate an arbitrary "control" group containing exactly those classes included in the two overlapping groups (for example, groups ABCD and DH require the control group ABCDH in order to assure that the total number of presses assigned from both group ABCD and group DH together do not exceed 19, the total number of presses in Classes A, B, C, D and H). Compute the number of presses in the control groups. (Thus, one obtains columns 5, 9, 10, 11 in Table 6.) (6) For each part compute the number of presses it requires from each group. To illustrate, compute these for Part 1 (assume that the computation begins with Table 3). The required number of presses from a group is obtained by summing the number required

Table 6

Group		B	BC	ABC	ABCD	ABCE	EBC	DH	D	ABCDE	ABCDH	ABCDEH
Total No. Presses		5	10	13	17	14	11	6	4	18	19	20
Part No.	Hr./M	B	BC	ABC	ABCD	ABCE	EBC	DH	D	ABCDE	ABCDH	ABCDEH
1	6.66	2	7	9	10	10	8	1	0	11	11	12
2	4.94	2	2	2	2	2	2	0	0	2	2	2
3	4.6	0	1	1	4	1	1	1	0	4	5	5
4	7.09	2	6	7	7	8	7	1	0	8	8	9
5	7.08	1	6	6	6	6	6	0	0	.6	6	6
6	4.44	0	0	2	2	2	0	0	0	2	2	2
7	4.31	0	0	2	2	2	0	0	0	2	2	2
8	6.18	0	0	2	2	2	0	0	0	2	2	2
9	4.11	0	0	0	3	3	0	3	3	3	3	3
10	4.73	0	0	0	4	4	0	4	4	4	4	4.
11	6.17	0	0	0	3	3	0	0	0	3	3	3
12	4.04	0	0	1	2	1	0	0	0	2	2	2
13	4.36	0	0	2	2	2	0	0	0	2	2	2
14	5.55	0	0	1	.1	1	0	0	0	1	1	1
15	7.09	1	6	7	7	8	7	1	0	8	8	9
16	6.81	0	5	5	5	5	5	0	0	5	5	5
17	4.11	0	0	0	4	0	0	0	0	4	4	4
18	4.11	0	0	0	4	0	0	0	0	4	4	4
19	4.88	0	0	2	2	2	0	0	0	2	2	2
20	4.36	0	0	2	2	2	0	0	0	2	2	2
21	4.36	0	0	2	2	2	0	0	0	2	2	2
22	6.81	0	5	5	5	5	5	0	0	5	5	5
23	4.08	0	0	0	1	0	0	0	0	1	1	1
24	4.58	0	0	1	1	1	0	0	0	1	1	1

for every other group which wholly contains that group. That is, add as follows:

PART NO. 1

NUMBER OF PRESSES WHICH MUST BE FROM:	NUMBER OF PRESSES IN EACH GROUP DUE TO BASIC REQUIREMENTS										
	B	BC	ABC	ABCD	ABCE	EBC	D	DH	ABCDE	ABCDH	ABCDEH
Group B—2.......	2	2	2	2	2	2	0	0	2	2	2
BC—5.....	0	5	5	5	5	5	0	0	5	5	5
ABC—2...	0	0	2	2	2	0	0	0	2	2	2
ABCD—1..	0	0	0	1	0	0	0	0	1	1	1
EBC—1....	0	0	0	0	1	1	0	0	1	0	1
DH—1....	0	0	0	0	0	0	0	1	0	1	1
Total number of presses in each group..........	2	7	9	10	10	8	0	1	11	11	12

The logic of this addition procedure is that the number of presses required in any group is added also to the number required of any other group that wholly contains the first group. By this method, the total number of presses in any group for each part is obtained. For example, in the first row, there is listed the number 2 under all columns whose heading (group) complete contains the group designated by the row index. Specifically, the first row is for group B, and we see that it is wholly contained in the other groups, except D and DH. Hence, "2" is entered in this row under each of these applicable columns, as shown. This process is repeated for all rows and then the columns are summed as shown.

When this process is repeated for all parts, we obtain Table 6.

The next step is to use Table 6 to determine all "maximal" assignments of parts to presses. The procedure for determining all such maximal assignments is a simple exhaustive enumeration procedure. It is carried out, for example, as follows: Select Part 1, subtract the number of presses it requires in each group from the number available in that group. If the result of these subtractions yields no negative difference, try Part 2 in combination with Part 1 by subtracting the number of presses it requires in each group from the remainder in each group after subtracting for Part 1. If, again, the subtraction yields no negative number, try Part 3, etc. until at least one negative number is obtained. Then, drop that last part from the combination and select the next highest numbered part to try, etc., until, at last, all parts have been tried and it has been found that none can be added to that assignment without causing the remainder to have one, or more negative numbers. That assignment is maximal. It is recorded and the next maximal assignment sought by dropping the highest numbered part in the assignment, etc., until the next assignment is found. This procedure is is continued systematically until all maximal assignments have been found. This is a simple routine which can be carried out by a computer.

SELECT MAXIMUM PRODUCTION PROGRAMS

Note in Table 6 that there is a column headed "Hr./M" which indicates the number of hours to produce 1000 of each part. The production rate for each part[4] is entered into the matrix of assignments, Table 7, to designate that the part indicated by the row number is included in the assignment whose number is designated by the column number. For example, the initial assignments generated by the suggested method, would be Table 7.

Table 7

PART No.	ASSIGNMENT No.				
	1	2	3	4	.....
1	150	150	150		
2	202	202	202		
3	217	217	0		
4	0	0	0		
5	0	0	0		
6	0	0	225		
7	0	0	0		
8	0	0	0		
9	0	0	243		
10	0	0	0		
.					
.	—	—	—		
14	180	0	0		
15	0	0	0		
16	0	0	0		
.					
.	—	—	—		
24	0	218	0		

This matrix is used to formulate a mathematical programming problem as follows: Parts 1 to 3 are used in product 1, parts 4 to 14 on product 2, and parts 15 to 24 on product 3. The objective in the problem studied is to make specified amounts of products 1 and 2 and as many as possible of product 3. Thus, the problem can be stated as selecting a combination and amount of assignments such that the required amounts of products 1 and 2 are produced and the maximum amount of product 3 is produced. Of course, the sum of the assignments

---

[4] The production rate for each part equals the reciprocal of Hr./M multiplied by 1000.

must *be equal* to or less than the number of hours available during the work week.

The mathematical problem[5] then is derived as follows:

Let $x_j \geqq 0$, $j = 1, \ldots, m$, be a real number, indicating the number of units of time devoted to the jth assignment. Let (a_{ij}) be the matrix of assignments, Table VII, and any $a_{ij} \geqq 0$ be a real number indicating the number of units of the ith part produced per unit of time by the jth assignment. Let b_1 be the number of units of product 1 which is desired, b_2 the number of product 2, and y be the number of units of product 3 which is to be maximized. Let the number of units of time available be designated by b. Then, the mathematical formulation of the problem can be written:

Equations 1:

Maximize $\quad y$

Subject to

$$\sum_j x_j a_{ij} \geq b_1, \qquad\qquad i = 1, 2, 3$$

$$\sum_j x_j a_{ij} \geq b_2, \qquad\qquad i = 4, \ldots, 14$$

$$\sum_j x_j a_{ij} \geq y, \qquad\qquad i = 15, \ldots, 25$$

$$\sum_j x_j \leq b$$

$$x_j \geq 0, \qquad\qquad j = 1, \ldots, m$$

This can be handled as a straight-forward mathematical programming problem with linear functions and functionals for which standard computational algorithms are available.[6]

It is worth noting at this point that a slightly more general problem can be formulated as follows:

Equations 2:

Maximize $\quad \displaystyle\sum_{k=1}^{n} p_k y_k$

---

[5] I am indebted to Dr. Harlan Mills, General Electric Company, for his original suggestion of this method for selecting from among the possible assignments.

[6] G. B. Dantzig, *Notes on Linear Programming*, Nos. 1 and 2, RAND Corporation, Santa Monica, California, 1954. M. E. Salveson, "Mathematical Methods in Management Programming," Parts I and II, *Journal of Industrial Engineering*, Vol. V, No. 2 (March, 1954), pp. 9–15.

Subject to

$$\sum_j^m x_j a_{ij} \geq y_1, \quad i = 1, \ldots, k_1$$

$$\sum_j^m x_j a_{ij} \geq y_2, \quad i = k_1 + 1, \ldots, k_1 + k_2$$

$$\sum_j^m x_j a_{ij} \geq y_n, \quad i = k_1 + k_2 + 1, \ldots + k_{n-1} + 1,$$

$$\ldots, k_n$$

$$\sum_j^m x_j \leq b$$

$$y_k, x_j \geq 0, \quad j = 1, \ldots, m, k = 1, \ldots, n.$$

where p_k is the profit (in some acceptable sense) on the kth product and k_n is the number of parts in product number $k = n$. This formulation was not immediately useful in the problem studied here because the outputs of the first two products were fixed by management decision and the only information desired was the maximum output of a third, new product from capacity which might be residual in the existing facilities plus certain planned additions.

The purpose in the above method of handling this machine loading problem is to reduce the number of inequalities necessary to represent all relevant restrictions. It "builds-in" a certain amount of the indivisibility inherent in any real production problem where only one product or part can be processed at a time by a machine tool. Of course, the method has its difficulties, notable among which is the size of the combinatorial problem involved in enumerating the assignment matrix. If care is exercised in formulating the assignments, this need not be a serious obstacle, since many techniques can be used for simplifying it. For example, if any part requires more than some predetermined minimum number of hours of production time per week to meet assembly requirements, it is economical to establish a separate production line for fabricating only that part. Thus, that part would no longer share productive time of the presses with the other parts and it could be removed from the problem entirely. Specifically, this occurred for at least Part 1 in this study. If any two or more parts require the same number and kinds of presses, then it is possible to treat all of such parts as one part. Of course, when this is done, it is necessary to make changes in the table of press requirements for that fictitious part. If the production rates of the parts are equal, it is necessary only to add the amounts of each part required to obtain the total amount of the fictitious part. Then, there will be only one such fictitious part in the press requirements matrix. However, in the mathematical formulation, the row for that fictitious part would state that the total number of that part must be equal to or greater than the sum of the number of real parts which it represents.

If the parts which have the same press requirements have different production rates, it is necessary first to adjust the rates to a common rate. This may be done as follows. Say, Part 1 has production rate a_1 and Part 2 has a_2. Say also, that b_1 and b_2 units, respectively, are required. Then, let $a_f = a_1$ be the rate for the fictitious part. b_2 is adjusted according to the ratio $\dfrac{a_1}{a_2}$. Thus the number of units of the fictitious part, b_f, required is: $b_f = b_1 + \dfrac{a_1}{a_2} b_2$. In the more general case where the number of units of each part is to be determined, as in the formulation, equations 2, write $Y_f = y_1 + \dfrac{a_1}{a_2} y_2$ and substitute the right hand side of the equation into the restricting inequality for the fictitious product. Equivalent statements can be derived for the cases in which more than two parts with identical press requirements all are combined into one fictitious part for computational purposes. By this method it is possible substantially to reduce the number of parts to be considered and the size of the combinatorial problem.

In order to illustrate the method of representation and to fix ideas, a very simplified problem is hypothesized and solved. It is used also in the next section to develop further concepts.

Assume we wish to fabricate parts for the manufacture of three products: A, B and C. Product A requires one part, B one part, and C two parts that must be fabricated in one common machine section. We wish to produce at least 9000 per week of product A, 4500 of product B and, with any excess capacity, as many units of product C as are possible. All maximal assignments are given in Table 8.

Table 8

ASSIGNMENT NUMBER

Part No.	1	2	3	4
1........	200	0	200	0
2........	0	200	0	0
3........	100	100	0	100
4........	0	0	100	100

The corresponding mathematical problem is as follows. Let x_1 designate the amount, as yet undetermined, we should use of assignment 1. Let x_2, x_3, x_4 be the equivalent for those assignments. Then we could write the requirements as follows:

Part No. 1	$200x_1 + 0x_2 + 200x_3 + 0x_4 \geq 9000$	—Product A
2	$0x_1 + 200x_2 + 0x_3 + 0x_4 \geq 4500$	—Product B
3	$100x_1 + 100x_2 + 0x_3 + 100x_4 \geq Y$	—Product C
4	$0x_1 + 0x_2 + 100x_3 + 100x_4 \geq Y$	—Product C
5	$1x_1 + 1x_2 + 1x_3 + 1x_4 \leq 450$	—Time available

The "amount" of any assignment is measured in units of time. Hence, the total amount of time used must be equal to or less than the amount of productive time available during the work week, which is assumed to be 450 units. The first four rows or inequalities state the quantity of each part required. For example, row 1 states that the total number of units of Part 1 (which is for product A) that is produced by any selected combination of assignments must be equal to or greater than 9000. In the case of rows 3 and 4, the number must be equal to or greater than Y. It is desired to maximize Y. The last row is the "time-capacity restriction" and states that the total number of hours devoted to any combination of assignments must not exceed the number of hours available during the work period. Although this trivial sized problem is easily solved by inspection, it was used to test a computer routine. The solution obtained is:

$$x_1 = 11.25$$
$$x_2 = 22.50$$
$$x_3 = 33.75$$
$$x_4 = 382.50$$
$$Y = 416.25$$

If these values are substituted back into the algebraic formulation of the problem, they satisfy the requirements with the production of the following number of parts:

Part 1— 9000
Part 2— 4500
Part 3—41625
Part 4—41625

This combination of assignments is termed an "optimal" solution because there is no solution that is better, i.e., that both satisfies our requirements and produces more of both Parts 3 and 4.

Several persons have suggested "various simplifications," to the preceding formulation, such as a mathematical model as follows:

Maximize
$$\sum_i p_i x_i$$

Subject to
$$\sum_i a_{ij}x_i \leq b, \qquad j = 1, \ldots, n$$
$$x_i \geq 0$$

where the x_i are numbers indicating the number of units of the ith product, the p_i indicate a profit measure for the ith product, the a_{ij} are numbers indicating the number of the jth press—group-hours required to produce one unit of the ith product (could include all component parts) and b_j is the number of press group-hours available during the work period. The difficulty with this model is that it admits solutions which are not feasible, as well as solutions which are "better" in fact than can be obtained. The difficulty here arises through the use of the aggregate term "press-group-hours." The model does not exclude (in a mathematical sense) production when there are fewer presses available than operations required. That is, 100 press-group-hours can be obtained with 10 presses for ten hours or with one press for 100 hours. If a part requires 10 simultaneous operations, obviously, a solution based on the latter method of generating press-group-hours (one press for 100 hours) gives a meaningless number. One press will not give $\frac{1}{10}$ the output of 10 presses. Extending this principle for the same 10 operations on the part, 15 presses would not give 150 per cent the output which is achievable with 10 presses.

Another suggestion would be to employ one restricting inequality for each press and use as the restricting term "press hours." This would avoid the ambiguity associated with press-group-hours, but would introduce an even larger combinatorial problem. That is, it would be necessary to include every assignment of every part to every applicable individual press. This would be a much larger number of combinations than merely those involved in assigning to press groups. The loss of specificity in assignments usually is not important in this stage of the calculation.

OPTIMAL CYCLE LENGTH

A solution of the problem as formulated in equation 2 is a statement of the number of units of time which should be devoted to each assignment in order to achieve optimum parts production over the selected interval of time. Such solution does not specify a temporal ordering or sequence in which the assignments are to be carried out, nor does it include the necessary changes in set-up of the presses. For example, at least some dies used in the presses must be changed when production is changed from one assignment to another. The solution easily could be transformed to a set of percentages, each indicating the percentage of any interval of time which must be devoted to that assignment. There is no restriction on the length of this interval. Thus, this section is devoted to methods of handling these three related factors: (1) need for changes in set-up; (2) need for an ordering on the sequence in which the assignments are carried out; (3) need to produce intermittently yet consume continuously.

Changing a set-up introduces periods during which the presses are not used productively. The possibility of different orderings in the sequence of carrying out the assignments introduces the possibility of different amounts of time required for all set-ups in a full sequence. The need to produce any part intermittently while consuming it continuously introduces the need for storing some of it. These three factors together introduce the problem of determining an optimum sequence and lot size for the parts or assignments.

The solution obtained initially is based on the assumption that no set-up times would be required. If the interval of time used in the computation is equal to unity, then the solution is the set of proportions which apply equally to a production period of any length. However, if set-up changes are introduced, then because each set-up consumes a fixed amount of time, whenever required, it is easy to see that: (1) the longer the interval of time between changes in set-up, the smaller the proportion of time and amount of output which are lost while changing dies; (2) some sequences of parts production will require more set-up changes than others; (3) the longer the interval of time between changes in set-up (or equivalently, the longer the production cycle) the more inventory must be stored to supply the continuous demand for parts in assembly.

There are two obvious problems in these three relations. First, there is the problem of determining the least cost sequence of producing the parts, i.e., the sequence which minimizes total set-up time. Second, there is the problem of optimizing the economic lot size—or some variation thereof. There is some relationship between these two problems. However, we will consider it a second order relationship so that the two phases of the problem are considered to be independent. Further, the first, or sequencing, problem is so easily handled in this situation by rule-of-thumb methods that there usually is no need to treat it as a formal mathematical problem. In any case, as is discussed later, there is no real value to computing a minimum set-up because it probably couldn't be used. (Those persons interested in how an analogous problem was handled are referred to the Traveling Salesman Problem.[7] It is sufficient here to say that adequate rules can be used, such as: (1) each part should be produced without interruption during each cycle; (2) if interruption is required, the number should be minimized and each run made as nearly equal in length as is possible; (3) if there is a choice between two or more parts as to which will be produced uninterruptedly and which in two or more interrupted sequences, the one with the largest amount of set-up time should be selected for uninterrupted production. The term "cycle" is defined at this point to denote the repetitive nature of the parts production sequence. One cycle is one full repetition of the selected sequence. Once a representative sequence in which parts are to be fabricated has been selected, the total amount of set-up time required for one full cycle of production is readily computed as the sum of the set-up times required for each change from one assignment to the next.

The set-up cost consists of either the cost of set-up labor plus overhead charges for the amount of time the press is idle or the cost of set-up labor plus the value of production lost while the press is idle for set-up. The cost of storing inventory includes the charges on the investment in the inventory itself, the cost of space, the cost of material handling equipment and insurance, etc. on the inventory. These costs are easily measured or closely estimated. The next step is to determine the optimum lot size or quantity to produce during each cycle.

In order to develop the optimum lot size concept, it is necessary to examine several fundamental relationships which heretofore have been omitted from the conventional economic manufacturing lot size.[8] As early as 1953,[9] this writer pointed out this deficiency, while Moore[10] previously had reported a general trend toward discontinuance of the use of economic lot sizes in manufacturing. In the particular study reported here the planning engineers stated that they had been unable in many instances to obtain useful results from applications of these traditional formulae. The reasons for this difficulty now are discussed

---

[7] G. B. Dantzig, and others, "Solution of a Large Scale Traveling-Salesman Problem," *Journal of the Operations Research Society of America,* Vol. II, No. 4 (November, 1954), pp. 393–411.

[8] Alford and Bangs (eds.), *Production Handbook* (New York: Ronald Press, 1944). F. E. Raymond, *Quantity and Economy in Manufacture* (New York: McGraw-Hill Book Co., Inc., 1931).

[9] Salveson, "Mathematical Theory of Production," *Journal of Industrial Engineering,* Vol. IV, No. 1 (February, 1953), pp. 3–7.

[10] F. G. Moore, *Production Control* (New York: McGraw-Hill Book Co., Inc., 1951).

preparatory to developing an alternative approach to the economic lot size concept and computations for this application.

The fundamental defect in the conventional formulations is that the formulae are designed for minimizing each part's manufacturing cost independently. The formulae do not treat of the circumstances where two or more parts are produced by, or share, a common production facility. Of course, relatively few industrial enterprises manufacture only one part; those that do certainly must manufacture that part continuously so that they have no use for economic lot size formulae. Thus, the economic lot size formulae developed to date are either of no use where they are technically applicable or they are not technically applicable where they may be useful. The desired method when annual production quantity is fixed and when the parts are produced intermittently is to minimize total costs for all parts simultaneously.

Consider the following extremely simple illustration. Assume there are two parts to be produced, there are set-up, storage and direct production costs, and there is one machine tool on which both parts are produced. The desired annual output of each part is fixed and the rate of consumption is uniform. It is desired to compute the economic lot size in which to produce each of these parts. Use the following notation:

a_1 Production rate on Part 1 in Hours/Unit
a_2 Production rate on Part 2 in Hours/Unit
b_1 Set-up time on Part 1 in hours
b_2 Set-up time on Part 2 in hours
c_1 Carrying cost per unit per annum—Part 1
c_2 Carrying cost per unit per annum—Part 2
d_1 Set-up cost on Part 1
d_2 Set-up cost on Part 2
Z_1 Amount of Part 1 in each lot
Z_2 Amount of Part 2 in each lot
P_1 Amount of Part 1 per annum
P_2 Amount of Part 2 per annum
T Total number of productive hours available on the machine tool during the year.
Y Total annual cost of producing Parts 1 and 2.

$$\frac{P_1}{T}, \frac{P_2}{T} \quad \text{uniform usage rates } r_1, r_2$$

The usual economic lot size formula would be in the form of

Equation 3:

$$Z_1 = \sqrt{\frac{2d_1 P_1}{c_1}}$$

There is no formally stated requirement on the solution to equation 3 that it must be consistent with other demands on the machine tool. Yet, it is obvious, for example, that the following inequality must be satisfied.

Equation 4:

$$P_1 a_1 + P_2 a_2 + \frac{P_1 b_1}{Z_1} + \frac{P_2 b_2}{Z_2} \leq 1 \ .$$

Thus, equation 4 is a type of restriction on the lot sizes Z_1 and Z_2 which never has been stated in any of the traditional formulae.

Even if the foregoing restriction is not violated, there is an even more difficult condition which must be satisfied. For example, consider the following very simple case wherein the economic lot size formulae again fail.

Let

$$L_{1_0} = \sqrt{\frac{2d_1 P_1}{c_1}} = 1,000$$

$$L_{2_0} = \sqrt{\frac{2d_2 P_2}{c_2}} = 10,000$$

$P_1 = 10,000$	$b_1 = 500$	$a_1 = 2$
$P_2 = 50,000$	$b_2 = 1000$	$a_2 = 1$
$T = 80,000$		

Clearly although the restriction as expressed by equation 4 above is satisfied, it remains impossible to schedule production of these two parts in such manner as to adhere to their respective lot sizes. Consider the Gantt Chart of one possible schedule of these lot sizes.

If it is assumed that there is a uniform rate of consumption of each part, the periods during which that part is produced must be interspersed in regular cycles of such length that the production equals the consumption. In order to achieve this balance between production and

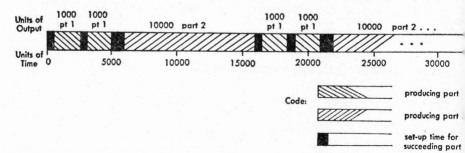

consumption for Part 1, it would be necessary that each lot of 10,000 of Part 2 be split in two and a lot of 1,000 of Part 1 produced between those split lots of Part 2. Otherwise, it would be necessary to produce double lots or two consecutive lots of Part 1 as shown in the chart. Either alternative schedule or cycle would differ from the computed economic lot sizes for Part 1 or Part 2. The obvious defect is that the lot sizes for the two parts were determined independently and without accounting for the interrelation of each part's production on the others. Specifically, for example, it is necessary to account for the fact that as the lot size of Part 2 is increased, the lot size of Part 1 also must be increased, and vice versa. Thus, the cost of Part 1 should include any cost of producing Part 2 which is in excess of its minimum cost and which is due to the need to produce it in lots other than its economic lot size because it otherwise would conflict with Part 1. The reciprocal relation of Part 2 absorbing similar costs due to conflicts with Part 1 also holds. Consequently, the lot sizes for both parts should be determined simultaneously. The two simultaneous equations to be solved in order to find these lot sizes would be obtained from the partial derivatives of the two cost functions:

Equations 5:

$$\frac{\partial Y}{\partial Z_i} = 0 \,, \, i = 1, 2.$$

Of course, these assume that the function for total cost and the interrelation of the lot sizes on total cost are available.

In the problem formulated here, the uniform consumption requirement specifies that the amount of any assignment used (or equivalently, the amount of any part produced) in the cycle must bear a constant relationship to the cycle length, regardless of how the cycle length may vary. Thus, whatever particular permutation is the basis of the cycle, there must be the appropriate constant proportion devoted to each assignment. This requirement states that solution of equations which derive from the partial derivatives, as in equations 5, may not necessarily give answers which can be used in the sense that the lot sizes may not fit into a reasonable repetitive cycle. For example, it would be awkward for a foreman to try to make a practical, sensible schedule and cycle out of a set of lot sizes which could involve, say, multiples of π, $\sqrt{2}$, e, or other irrational numbers, none of which make convenient multiples of any other.

There are at least two methods to follow in developing a schedule and optimum cycle or set of optimum lot sizes.

(1) Hold fixed the permutation of the assignments and the per cent of cycle time devoted to each assignment and take the first derivative of total cost to length, equate to zero and solve for cycle time. This method requires investigating different possible permutations with a simple comparison of total costs at the point at which for each permutation $\dfrac{dY}{d\theta} = 0$, where θ is cycle length.

(2) Solve the equations for the optimum lot sizes, as in equations 5, and attempt to find a permutation of the loss which yields a manageable, repetitive production cycle with minimum total cost.

Of course, it would be optimal to use a method which yields the permutation and the lot size simultaneously. I do not know of the existence of such a method which is itself manageable and I have made no serious effort to find or develop one. My own preference is toward the former method.

In order to fix ideas and to illustrate the implications of a solution to this problem using method (1) above, consider the following (nonoptimal) solution from the earlier example with permutation as follows:

1st position:	Assignment 2	$X_2 = 50$
2nd position:	Assignment 3	$X_3 = 50$
3rd position:	Assignment 4	$X_4 = 325$

Assume set-up, when required, takes place at the beginning of the period during which the part is produced. Also, assume that if a part was in production in some earlier assignment, it requires no set-up in the next period. Thus, a part would require set-up only for the first of any consecutive series of assignments during which it is produced. This is not necessarily true in general, but any exceptions in actual practice easily can be identified and handled. (This nonoptimal solution is used only for convenience. It is easier to draw its inventory history than that for the optimal solution.)

Based on the preceding assumptions, the Gantt Chart of the production cycle is shown in Figure 1.

Figure 1

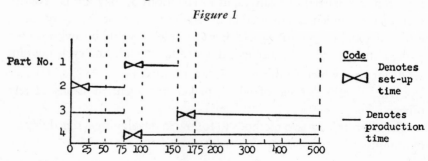

The charts of inventory levels of each part are illustrated in Figure 2. Each chart shows net inventory in units after adjusting for production less consumption. Assume a "minimum" reserve inventory is maintained.

If the cycle length is increased or decreased, the format of the graphs of net inventory will be the same, except that the heights of the peaks will be increased or decreased in proportion to the change in length.

By introducing set-up, a certain amount of time is devoted to nonproductive work; in this case, 50 units of time; thus, productive time is only 450 out of 500 units. The amount of time by which the cycle length is increased, due to set-up, is not simply the sum of all set-up times, but rather the sum of set-up times on the longest chain of parts. The chains in this case are Part 2–Part 4 and Part 1–Part 3. The sum of set-up time in each of these chains is 50 units. The pair of parts (1, 2) does not constitute a chain because the two parts do not span the cycle. Similarly, the pair (2, 3) does not constitute a chain because they are in production simultaneously.

In order to accommodate these new elements in the problem, introduce

θ—a continuous parameter denoting cycle length and measured in units of time. $S(x_j)^0$—total set-up time for the selected permutation of the chosen assignments.

Then, the mathematical problem as stated in equations 1 would become

Equations 6:

Max: y

Subject to:

$$\sum_j x_j a_{ij} \geq r_1 \theta, \qquad i = 1, 2, 3.$$

$$\sum_j x_j a_{ij} \geq r_2 \theta, \qquad i = 4, \ldots, 14$$

$$\sum_j x_j a_{ij} \geq y, \qquad i = 15, \ldots, 24$$

$$\sum_j x_j + S(x_j)^0 \leq \theta$$

$$x_j \geq 0, \qquad = 1, \ldots, m$$

The simple numerical example would become

Equations 7:

Max: y

Subject to: $200x_1 + 0x_2 + 200x_3 + 0x_4 \geq r_1\theta$
$0x_1 + 200x_2 + 0x_3 + 0x_4 \geq r_2\theta$
$100x_1 + 100x_2 + 0x_3 + 100x_4 \geq y$
$0x_1 + 0x_2 + 100x_3 + 100x_4 \geq y$
$S(x_j)^0 + x_1 + x_2 + x_3 + x_4 \leq \theta$
$y, x_1, x_2, x_3, x_4 \geq 0$

Of course, $\theta = 500$, $S(x_j)^0 = 50$ in this case.

Figure 2

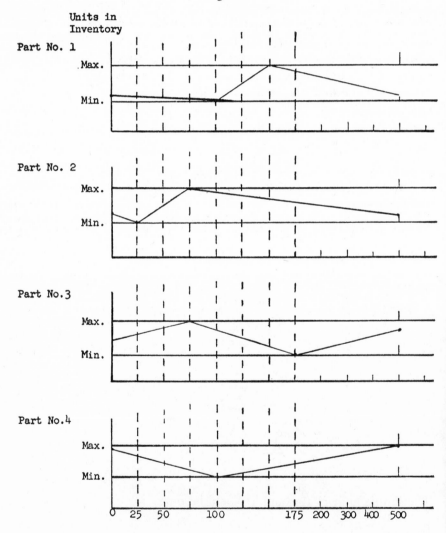

Each of these formulations is acceptable for fixed θ. However, if in equations 7, θ is allowed to vary, then y asymptotically approaches a maximum as θ approaches infinity. Of course, it is not realistic to consider indefinitely long cycle times with the implied indefinitely large storage space as a basis for computing an optimum cycle length. It is necessary, therefore, to introduce cost factors which relate cycle length to total cost. It is simplest to do this for the general case as given in equations 2. These become:

Equations 8:

Maximize:
$$\Phi = \sum_{k=1}^{n} P_k Y_k - \left(c\theta + \frac{d}{\theta} \right)$$

Subject to:
$$\Sigma x_j a_{ij} \geq y_1, \quad i = 1, \ldots, k_1$$
$$\Sigma x_j a_{ij} \geq y_2, \quad i = k+1, \ldots, k_1 + k_2$$
$$\Sigma x_j a_{ij} \geq y_n, \quad i = k_1 + k_2 + 1, \ldots + k_{n-1} + 1, \ldots, k_n.$$
$$\Sigma x_j + S(x_j)^0 \geq \theta$$
$$x_j, y_k \geq 0, \quad j = 1, \ldots, n; k = 1, \ldots, m.$$

where c represents the total carrying costs per annum and d the total set-up costs. p_k is a modified profit concept, probably best expressed as the difference between net sales price and variable costs, such as direct labor and material costs.

The following is a method for finding maximum Φ in equations 8.

(1) Assume values of $\theta = \theta_0$ and $S(x_j)^0 = S_0$. In an active shop, the current values would be appropriate ($\theta_0 > S_0$).

(2) Solve for max $\Phi = \Sigma p_k y_k$ by conventional linear programming methods to obtain $(x_j)^0$. For the $(x_j)^0$ so obtained, determine actual value of $S(x_j)^0$.

(3) Find $\dfrac{d\Phi}{d\theta}$ and solve for θ at $\dfrac{d\Phi}{d\theta} = 0$.

Note that p_k is not a function of θ or S but that y_k is a linear function of θ. Thus, in order to take step 3 above, we express output as a function of cycle length as follows:

Equation 9:
$$y_k = e_k(\theta - S(x_j)^0)$$

where e_k is the number of units of output of k per unit length of the idealized cycle, i.e., as computed from equations 2 in which $b = 1$, then the function for total profit becomes:

Equation 10:*

$$\Phi = \sum_k p_k e_k \left(\frac{\theta - S(x_j)^0}{\theta} \right) T - \left(C\theta - \frac{T \cdot d}{\theta} \right)$$

and we get:

Equation 11:

$$\frac{d\Phi}{d\theta} = \sum_k p_k e_{k_0} - c + \frac{d}{\theta^2} = 0$$

Solving equation 11 yields, of course, the optimal cycle length and economic lot size for the parts under the assumed permutation and product mix.

In the less general formulation, such as equation 5, the preceding method must be altered to allow for possible nonproportional changes in the outpt vector as a function of the cycle length. This could necessitate using a method of successive approximations. For example, below critical values of θ in the sample problem, the assignment vector would include only assignments 2 and 3. This is due to the fact that in equations 5 some of the side constraints represent fixed hyperplanes. Then, of course, as θ is increased, the solution points will move out of the region of the fixed planes, thus causing nonproportional changes in it. This introduces the possibility of local optima. For example, the curves of total value (as some function of y) for the sample problem would be in the form shown in Figure 3.

Curve 1 is for values of $(\theta_0 - S_0)$ less than the critical.
Curve 2 is for values of $(\theta_0 - S_0)$ greater than the critical.

In the general case, in order to select an optimum with respect to both cycle length and mix, it is necessary to take one further step. This is explained, perhaps best, by recourse to a graphic presentation.

---

* T is the number of units of time in the production planning period. If this is taken as unity and all other time measurements as percentages, it can be dropped.

C is a constant for relating cycle length to cost. It is determined as

$$C = \sum_k c_k m_k$$

where c_k is the cost of storing one unit of the kth part and m_k is the average number of units of the kth part stored per unit length of the cycle time. If one wished to be uneconomically exact in computing C, he would include a constant cost term for each part representing the storage cost of the average amount which would be carried during the invariant set-up times. In this instance, this was a second order effect and was dropped for simplicity.

Figure 3

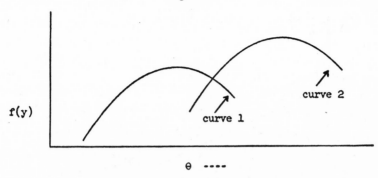

f(y)

curve 1

curve 2

θ ----

Suppose there are only two products, 1 and 2; each requires set-up for its production, and each shares some common productive facility which is available for a finite amount of time. Then, the graph of the family of outputs of these products would be in the form illustrated in Figure 4.

Figure 4

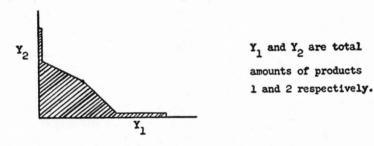

Y_2

Y_1

Y_1 and Y_2 are total amounts of products 1 and 2 respectively.

The horn of the shaded area which lies along the Y_1 coordinate is for $0 \leqq Y_2 < 1$ and vice versa for the horn along the Y_2 coordinate. The length of the horn on the Y_1 is equal to the production rate of product 1 times the amount of time required for set-up for product 2. The reciprocal relation determines the length of the horn on the Y_2 axis.

Of course, production actually is carried out in intermittent cycles. Consider, therefore, the effect of varying the cycle length on the graph of the family of feasible outputs. Let $\overline{Y}_1$ and $\overline{Y}_2$ be the average continuous rate of production respectively of products one and two as obtained from a repetitive cycle in which the products are produced intermittently. Let θ be a parameter which measures the cycle length. Then, the maximum average rate at which each product or both products together could be produced for any given cycle length θ, would be given by a family of curves, each for a particular value of θ and such as is illustrated in Figure 5.

Figure 5

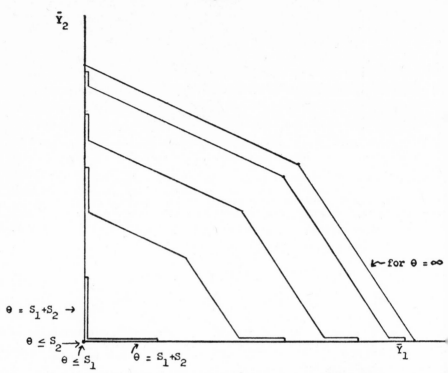

Now, let us define a suitable function in the nature of equation 10 over the space in Figure 5. Then we would have the interpretation of the graph in Figure 6 as follows. The horizontal plane OCF contains the parametric representation of rate of output as given in Figure 5, but without the various representative production curves drawn thereon. The boundary CDF indicates the family of maximum production mixes as obtained with the usual linear programming formulations which do not incorporate set-up times. Shown over this plane are all positive values of the profit function Φ at each value of the parameter θ and product mix. The boundary BLE represents the family of values of Φ for the corresponding production mixes given on CDF. The linear programming solution will select whichever point (or line or hyperplane) BLE is highest. This part of Figure 6 corresponds to Figure IV in "Mathematical Methods in Management Programming."[11]

On the OAC plane there are two curves $G'G\ G''$ and $U'U\ U''$. The higher, $U'U\ U''$, indicates the value of Φ as a function of θ when production is restricted to product 2. $G'G\ G''$ indicates the value of Φ as

---
[11] *Op. cit.*

Figure 6

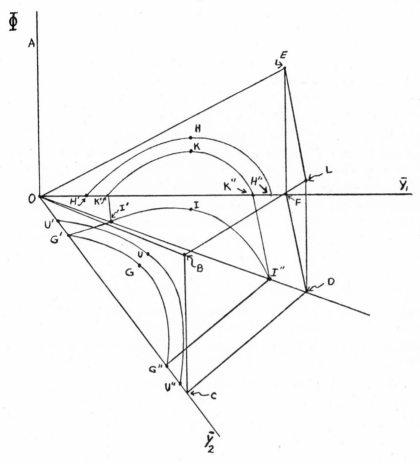

a function of θ but only one unit of product 1 is produced. This latter represents effectively the intersection of the hyperboloid $G'G\,G''\ I'I\,I''$ with the OAC plane. $G'G\,G''$ lies below $U'U\,U''$. $H'H\,H''$ and $K'K\,K''$ represent corresponding functions on the OAF plane.

In this figure, there are three points of interest: U, I, H. U and H each is the highest point on its corresponding curve. Under certain conditions I could be higher than either U or H. Our task is to find whichever point has the highest value of Φ. For problems involving only a few products (but perhaps many parts) this task can be handled as follows: If the linear programming solution indicates that point L is higher than E or B, then there is a possibility that I may be higher than U or K. In this case, it would be appropriate to evaluate Φ at I and compare it against U and K. If the linear programming solution indicates that L is not higher than E or B, then it is necessary to evaluate Φ only at U and H, since I then would not be higher than the higher of these two.

SOME EXTENSIONS

In the general n-product or n-dimensional case, this method would not be very useful, because of the excessively large number of points which must be examined. The number of points increases factorially with the number of products. However, it appears that the number of "production shops" (factories making relatively few products but each in high volume, such as most consumer durable goods factories), is relatively large and that for them the method would be quite useful. Of course, in many instances the range of production rate is specified in large part by marketing considerations quite exterior to the coverage of this formulation. In those instances it is only within that specified range that there is freedom of choice available to factory personnel, and appropriate restrictions must be introduced into the formulation.

Other problems could be studied further. First, c and d must be computed. Although the conventional methods already established probably are adequate for this purpose, they should be refined. For example, it is easy to demonstrate that the following are functions of lot size:

(1) Material handling costs, because the smaller the lot, the more lots to be handled separately, etc.

(2) Clerical production costs, because the smaller the lot the more orders to be prepared and handled, the more dispatcher's time is necessary to handle them, etc..

(3) Capital equipment required, because as lots are smaller more time is spent proportionately on set-up, but the smaller lots are more "schedulable," and as lots are made larger, the set-up time is proportionately smaller but the larger lots are less schedulable into sequences which maintain high equipment utilization.

(4) Indirect equipment costs, such as office, telephone, etc.

A second interesting study would be in the more general case to develop a model and computational algorithm for those instances in which the number of products is too large to handle by the above methods. In those instances, it appears that Monte Carlo methods would be appropriate in order to evaluate the effect of different lot sizes on schedulability. A third problem is that the need for a minimum reserve inventory for any part is due, in part, to the stochastic nature of the production and usage functions. It would be desirable to refine, accordingly, the method of computing minimum reserve inventory. A similar computation should be made to determine a "reserve storage space" so that economic lot sizes can be achieved within predetermined probability limits in those instances in which the production rates are low and usage rates high, or, as one manufacturing engineer said, "What the —— do you do with a fancy schedule in fabrication when 1500 parts go sour in processing and you have to change over suddenly to keep the line going —or, what happens when the line goes down and you've got parts up to your ears in fabrication." Of course, these extreme conditions present interesting problems to the management scientist. A study was undertaken to determine optimum inventory levels and reserve storage spaces for the parts in this regard. It has not been completed. Its completion would require more specific knowledge on the character of the distribution of production and usage rates (or reciprocally, the breakdown or reject rates) at each level of fabrication, processing, and storage. It would require management estimation of the value of insurance against disruptions such as mentioned. The costs, of course, include the obvious direct and easily measured ones, but also the indirect ones such as customer good will on delayed deliveries, etc. Of course, it now can readily be appreciated in the light of the foregoing described stochastic nature of production why so little attention was paid in this paper to minimizing set-up costs in the cycle. The reason, obviously, is that only an "expected" set-up time for the cycle could be used, since perturbation constantly will cause departures during virtually all cycles. Hence, none would have set-up time which would correspond to that minimum.

The output from the basic study reported here and from the various suggested studies is a specification of the *boundary conditions* within which the foreman himself can schedule in some optimal manner. It is not intended to yield a master schedule for the foreman to follow unexceptionally. By establishing storage space requirements consistent with optimum lot sizes, by establishing total output requirements consistent with lot sizes and equipment, capacities, etc., boundary conditions thus are established within which the foreman could use simple rules to schedule in a manner which unexceptionally contributes to over-all business optimality. Thus, a fixed schedule is not computed and enforced but rather the conditions are created for the foreman, easily and efficiently to schedule his production in accordance with the requirements of the whole business.

CONCLUSIONS

A concluding analysis and generalization of the role of the methods presented above are offered relative to certain broader managerial functions and problems. For example, the model used in the loading computation may be adapted also to certain problems in budgeting—both for capital budgets and operating budgets. For capital purposes, it would permit a more exact method of computing the productivity and contribution to be obtained from additions to productive facilities, especially in situations in which a multiplicity of use of the resource is planned, and evaluation of each such use is interrelated to the other uses. For operating purposes the method would permit more exact computation of indirect and overhead costs, as well as direct unit costs and process costs, if desired. In addition, it would provide a method for extending or extrapolating more reliably the cost and operating curves beyond the ranges of previous experience by constructing a model which would be characteristic of new operating levels and ranges, but using basic building blocks for which characteristic parameters have been determined already.

At the level of the general manager of the business, this method—or more correctly, this approach in general—could make even more fundamental contributions. For exmple, it would permit the general manager more accurately and efficiently to explore wholly new regions of outputs, prices and costs. In this regard he would use the model developed here as part of a more general model of the business as a whole to simulate overall operating, production and cost patterns for new regions in the same manner that an engineer uses various analogous physical or mathematical models of systems to explore new ranges of application of these systems or their behavior with new or modified components in the system. Of course, these more fundamental studies which begin at the level of the business as a whole should precede or be carried out concurrently and should provide the orientation for such special studies of components of the business as is reported here. For example, it is not difficult to visualize circumstances within which the detail of the study reported here would be rendered unnecessary for any given plant because entirely different levels of output would permit production methods which transcend the intermittent production involved in this instance.

Of course, the opportunity to use a unified scientific approach for analysis and planning for the business as a whole introduces a whole new range of business and professional opportunities. From the point of view of the business, the opportunities include bringing to the business management a level of scientific application comparable to that characteristic of other fields of human endeavor, such as physics, medicine or other. In this regard, we might extend the analogy suggested by W.

Vatter in *Managerial Accounting*[12] wherein he likened the operation of a business to a continuing experiment. This excellent analogy suggests that the management scientist could assist the managers, not only in the obvious way of assisting in design of the experiment in the statistical sense, but also in the more central tasks such as identifying and characterizing the theory or hypotheses of the "experiment," selecting and designing suitable methods and criteria for measuring the processes and results of the "experiment," for adapting the hypotheses to changes in the environment, etc.

The professional opportunities which arise from this approach to business management are great. Indeed, they are the basis of the management scentist's role in business. It is clear to anyone familiar with these activities that the management scientist must combine a knowledge of the nature and functions of business management with the concepts and methods of science. But such combination of familiarity with the traditionally intuitive process of business management and with the rigorous concepts and methods of science offers an attractive opportunity to increasing numbers of business enterprises and individuals. It especially challenges the university-level schools to offer curricula in the management sciences which will combine education in business processes and institutions with training and experience in the methods of science as applied to these processes and institutions.

---

[12] Prentice-Hall, Inc., New York, 1950.

CASE 6

A Linear Decision Rule for Production and Employment Scheduling[1]

CHARLES C. HOLT,
FRANCO MODIGLIANI and
HERBERT A. SIMON[2]

Some points of special interest in this paper are:

a. The justification of the quadratic cost functions everywhere.
b. The treatment and importance of forecasting errors.
c. The time required on the part of management to operate the rules each time decisions on production and work force are required.
d. The cost functions used to evaluate the company performance vs. the decision rule performance.
e. The plausibility of the decision rules. How sensitive might the results be to errors in the decision rule coefficients?
f. The number of choices required by the manager compared to the time horizon viewed.

[1] *Management Science*, October, 1955. Reprinted by permission. Research undertaken for the project *Planning and Control of Industrial Operations*, under contract with the Office of Naval Research.

The application of this analysis to aggregate production and work force decisions is presented fully in *Planning Production, Inventories and Employment*, by Holt, Modigliani, Muth, and Simon (Prentice-Hall, 1959). This book also extends the analysis to decision rules for individual products, and the mathematical methods are generalized for application to decision problems arising in other areas.

[2] University of Wisconsin, M.I.T., and Carnegie Institute of Technology. The authors wish to express their appreciation for the effective assistance of their colleague, Robert W. Culbertson, and of the following graduate students: John F. Muth, Clyde E. Robertson, Robert F. Byrne, Toshiro Makibuchi, David V. Heebink, William P. Maughan, and Lawrence Schwartz.

Special thanks are due the paint company whose full cooperation with our research made this paper possible.

g. The implied sensitivity of the decision rules to information more than half a year in the future.

h. Generalizations of the mathematical analysis to decision problems other than production and employment scheduling.

INTRODUCTION

The decision problems involved in setting the aggregate production rate of a factory and setting the size of its work force are frequently both complex and difficult. The quality of these decisions can be of great importance to the profitability of an individual company, and when viewed on a national scale these decisions have a significant influence on the efficiency of the economy as a whole. This paper reports some of the findings of a research team that has been developing new methods to enable production executives to make better decisions and to make them more easily than they can with prevailing procedures. With the cooperation of a manufacturing concern, the new methods have been developed in the context of a set of concrete production scheduling problems that we found in a factory operated by the company.

The new method which is presented in this paper[3] involves: (1) formalizing and quantifying the decision problem (using a quadratic approximation to the criterion function) and (2) calculating a generalized optimal solution of the problem in the form of a (linear) decision rule. Like a rule of thumb, an optimal decision rule prescribes a course of action when it is applied to a particular set of circumstances; but, unlike most rules of thumb, an optimal decision rule prescribes courses of action for which the claim can be made that the decisions are "the best possible," the meaning of "best" being clearly specified. The ultimate test, of course, must be whether the new decision methods do or do not outperform prevailing decision methods when full allowance is made for the cost of obtaining the optimal decisions.

In the body of this paper, we explore the problem of setting the aggregate production rate and size of the work force. We describe the particular form that this problem takes in a factory operated by the cooperating company, including a consideration of the various types of costs and intangible penalties that are relevant in making the decision.

---

[3] An earlier version of this paper under the title, "Quadratic Decision Criteria in Production and Inventory Control," was presented at the First National Meeting of The Institute of Management Sciences which was held in October, 1954, at Pittsburgh, Pennsylvania.

Research that served as background for the present work was reported in "Optimal Decision Rules for Production and Inventory Control," by C. C. Holt and H. A. Simon, in *Proceedings of the Conference on Operations Research in Production and Inventory Control*, January, 1954, Case Institute of Technology.

Then, without going into details about the methods used to solve the problem (these are to be reported in a subsequent issue of *Management Science*),[4] we present the solution in the form of the decision rule that is optimal for the type of decision criterion that was used. We found that, once the decision problem of the cooperating company was formalized and quantified, the numerical constants appearing in the decision rule could be computed with a desk calculator in a few hours, or with an electronic computer in a few minutes.

After this decision rule was obtained, it was then applied to the monthly production rate, and labor force decisions that faced the company over a six-year period. Using the decision rule, each of these monthly decisions required only a five-minute calculation. Comparisons are presented of the *actual performance* of the factory with the *hypothetical performance*—the performance that would have been realized if the new methods had been used. These performances are compared also by means of cost estimates.

These analyses indicate a minimum cost saving of 8.5 per cent by the use of the decision rule, and still further savings are possible by improved forecasting. Even for this one-hundred-man paint factory, this saving amounts to $51,000 annually by reducing the total of the following costs: regular payroll, overtime, hiring, training, layoff, and inventory connected costs.

In the opinion of the authors these results are not atypical and the optimal decision rule which is presented in this paper would, in a great many industrial situations, enable production executives to achieve significant improvements in production and employment scheduling and with smaller expenditure of executive time and effort than now goes into such decisions.

The specific decision method that is here applied to a particular factory should be directly applicable to other factories having the same kinds of costs. The general method which has been used in this application may also be adapted readily to factories with types of costs entirely different from those in the example presented. However, until the techniques for applying the method have been further developed, each new application will undoubtedly require some developmental effort.

Ultimately, decision criteria that can be adequately approximated by quadratic functions, and the resulting linear decision rules should prove

---

[4] C. C. Holt, F. Modigliani, J. F. Muth, H. A. Simon, *Planning Production, Inventories, and Work Force* (Prentice-Hall, Inc., 1960).

applicable to a wide range of decision-making problems quite beyond the specific problem of production scheduling.

THE DECISION PROBLEM: SCHEDULING PRODUCTION RATE AND WORK FORCE

It is important at the outset to outline clearly the many facets of the decision problem that faces an executive in setting the aggregate production rate and size of the work force of a factory. A good place to start is to define the variables whose scheduling constitutes the decision problem at hand. By *aggregate production rate* we mean a measure of production per unit of time (per week or per month, for example). Most factories produce many products, rather than just one; hence, a common unit must be found for adding quantities of different products. For example, a unit of weight, volume, work required, or value might serve as a suitable common denominator.[5] The other decision variable, *work force,* refers to the number of employees to whom there shall be a company commitment to supply regular work for one unit of time.

The initial limitation of the problem, to consider these two decision variables only, requires comment. Clearly neither decision can be separated completely from other decisions about product mix, labor mix, and production sequences. For example, the number of workers needed may depend on the number of different products to be produced as well as the aggregate production rate. Although our limitation of the decision problem rules out of consideration certain interactions that will be important for some factories, this limitation appeared reasonable in order to keep the initial research problem within reasonable bounds. In applying the decision rule to the cooperating factory, auxiliary techniques, which will not be described here, have been employed.[6]

The problem is to choose a course of action that will produce the results that are desired. In deciding upon the production rate and the work force of a factory there are three important aspects that contribute sufficient complexity to constitute a formidable problem: (1) How should production and employment be adjusted to *fluctuations in the*

---

[5] The selection of the best unit for aggregation will depend on the particular situation. In general, costs will be associated with each of the above dimensions, and the unit selected for aggregation should be a compromise depending on the relative importance of each type of cost.

[6] See "Some Techniques for the Solution of Dynamic Programming Problems in Production Scheduling," by Herbert A. Simon, Charles C. Holt, and Franco Modigliani, American Society for Quality Control, *10th Annual Meeting Transactions,* Montreal, Canada, June, 1956.

orders received? (2) What provision should be made for *errors in the forecasts* of future orders? (3) What is the implication of the fact that the *current decision is but one of a sequence of decisions* to be made at successive points of time? We consider each of these questions in turn.

The Costs of Responding to Fluctuations in Orders

If the customers of a factory placed their orders in such a way as to call for a constant flow of shipments of finished product, the two decisions under consideration would hardly constitute a problem. In actual fact, orders (or more precisely, ordered shipments) are subject to substantial fluctuation, and the question arises as to how these fluctuations should be "absorbed." That the problem is not trivial may be seen by considering three "pure" alternative ways of responding to such fluctuations.

These alternatives are: (1) to adjust the size of the work force by hiring and firing in exact conformity with the fluctuations in orders; (2) to adjust the production rate into conformity with orders by working overtime or "undertime" with a constant work force; (3) to allow inventory and the backlog of orders to fluctuate while maintaining a constant work force and a constant production rate. Each of these "pure" alternatives has certain costs—interpreting that term broadly to include any tangible or intangible penalty—associated with it:

(1) Under the first alternative, an *increase in orders would be met by hiring, while a decrease in orders would be accompanied by layoffs.* While this procedure is clearly not optimal for the economy as a whole, since the number of workers is constant in the short run, it is nevertheless an admissible alternative for an individual company. However, training and reorganization are usually required when the work force is expanded; and terminal play, bumping,[7] and loss of worker morale frequently occur when the work force is contracted. Since plant and equipment are fixed in the short run, increases in the work force may decrease labor productivity. This cost can be avoided by maintaining the plant and equipment necessary for peak employment, or by paying the premiums involved in second and third shift operation. A similar problem of imbalance may arise when the total work force fluctuates, but some components of the work force, supervision for example, cannot easily be changed. For all these reasons, fluctuations in the work force are costly. From work force considerations alone, the "ideal" work

---

[7] Union seniority rules sometimes require a whole sequence of job transfers when a single job is eliminated.

force would be one of constant size, with an optimum balance of men, machines and supervision.

(2) The second alternative would realize this "ideal" work force situation by *absorbing fluctuations in orders with corresponding fluctuations in overtime work* without changing the size of the work force. However, since there is an upper limit to what a worker can produce by working overtime, the necessity for meeting peak orders would govern the size of the work force. When orders fall to lower levels overtime is eliminated, but with a further fall in orders idle time occurs, i.e., there is not enough productive work to keep the work force busy throughout the regular work week. Hence, this alternative has its limitations. The well-recognized costs of the overtime premium do not require emphasis; the cost of idle time is less obvious. Man-hours paid for with no product output constitute a cost to the factory unless "fill-in" jobs (e.g., maintenance) can be scheduled, or on-the-job leisure has an important positive morale value. Sometimes the cost of idle time can be passed on to the employees by shortening the work week, but even here it is unlikely that the company completely escapes indirect penalties. Thus absorbing fluctuations in orders by overtime and idle time incurs various penalties and costs. From overtime and idle time considerations alone neither "should" be incurred; "ideal" overtime and "ideal" idle time are zero.

(3) Finally, the fluctuations in orders may be absorbed by *allowing the inventory of finished goods to fluctuate* or, lacking a finished inventory, by allowing the backlog of unfilled orders to fluctuate. Big upward swings in inventory necessitate large storage facilities, large amounts of working capital and other direct costs, and create risks such as obsolescence. Big downward swings of inventory, culminating in large order backlogs, impose intangible costs on the company—poor delivery service to customers may lead to loss of sales. Clearly, absorption of order fluctuations by building up or drawing upon inventory (considering an order backlog as a negative inventory) is not altogether a happy answer. If only inventory costs are taken into account the output of the factory should exactly match the shipments to be made; finished inventory "should" be zero!

It is abundantly clear that the fluctuations in customers' orders impose costs and penalties on the supplying company regardless of which policy alternative it may follow in responding to these fluctuations. Because orders fluctuate, these dynamic costs are relevant and important in production and labor force decisions. Or stated differently, when a factory must absorb fluctuations in shipments imposed by its customers' orders, every alternative for absorbing these fluctuations has associated with it a set of costs and penalties for the company. In order to make a good decision, these costs must be weighed to determine what kind of policy will minimize them.

In general, none of the pure alternatives discussed above will prove best, but rather some carefully weighed combination of them. Order fluctuations should, in general, be absorbed partly by inventory, partly by overtime, and partly by hiring and layoffs, and the best allocation among these parts will depend upon the costs in each particular factory. But even for a particular factory, the best allocation is not fixed, but will vary with the frequency of the fluctuations.

Despite the fact that countless production executives are faced daily with this allocation problem, until recently little work[8] has been done to find optimal policies even for the case where fluctuations in orders are predictable, as with seasonal fluctuations. Unfortunately, however, the problem is even more difficult, for fluctuations of orders can seldom be foreseen accurately. This brings us to the problem of forecast errors.

Errors in Forecasting Orders

Any decision setting the production rate and work force of a factory will appear in retrospect to have been a good or poor decision depending upon what orders were in fact received *after* the decision was made. A decision is not good or bad in itself, but only relative to the state of the world during the time in which the influence of the decision is being felt. Of course, the future state of the world—in our case future receipts of orders—ordinarily cannot be known in advance *exactly*. Consequently the decision *must* be made in a setting of uncertainty. At the time a decision has to be made, the outcomes associated with each of the alternatives are uncertain, since they depend partly on the unknown future. The better the future can be forecasted, the less uncertainty is involved in a decision; but uncertainty inevitably enters the decision to some extent, and must be resolved in one way or another.

It is useful to distinguish two aspects of the forecasting problem: (1) With a given forecast, produced by methods whose accuracy in the past is known, how should the decision be reached (i.e., how should decisions be affected by the fact that the forecasts are known to be subject to error)? (2) For any given forecast method, how large are the costs incurred as the direct result of its forecast errors? Knowledge of forecast accuracy usually is important both in using the forecasts and in selecting the forecasting method. However, the most accurate fore-

---

[8] For examples of recent work in this field see the references listed at the end of this paper.

cast method is not always the best, since the cost of obtaining the forecasts may exceed their value in improving the quality of decisions.

The Time Sequence of Decisions

The decisions setting production rate and work force fortunately do not involve a once-and-for-all commitment, but rather permit successive review and revision as the passage of time provides new information. The errors of past forecasts are observed, and new information is obtained that provides a basis for revised forecasts. A decision once taken commits the production executive only until a new decision is made.[9] Although a decision based on an erroneous forecast can to a large extent be offset by subsequent decisions, such oscillations incur the same types of costs as do fluctuations in orders. No one decision is good or bad in itself, but only in its relation to the preceding and following decisions, and the preceding and following orders. Thus it is clear that the time sequence of decisions is an important aspect of the scheduling problem.

Having outlined in a rough way the major components of an important decision problem, and having indicated that the decisions depend upon interacting factors sufficiently complex to make the choice extremely difficult, we next consider a practicable method for finding a solution to this problem.

A QUADRATIC CRITERION FOR THE SCHEDULING DECISIONS IN A PAINT FACTORY

Rather than present the new method in its most general form, we will describe an actual case that we have studied in detail, namely, the paint factory whose scheduling problems supplied stimulus to the development of the method.

A decision-making problem of a business firm may usually be stated formally as a problem of finding a maximum (or minimum) of some criterion. Sometimes profit is the criterion to be maximized; in most cases profit will at least have considerable weight in the criterion function. In the paint factory, we treat the scheduling of production and employment from the point of view of the production manager. We assume that sales volume and price are beyond his control, so that revenue is a given, and the maximization of profits becomes the mini-

---

[9] The selection of the optimal decision period is not studied in this paper, but it is known that the optimal period depends on the size of forecast errors, the cost of forecasting, the time required for enough new information to accumulate to improve forecasts previously made, the cost of making and administering new decisions, and the relative cost of making small decision changes versus making a smaller number of larger changes.

mization of costs. We should emphasize that "costs" are interpreted broadly to include any relevant considerations to which the decision maker chooses to attach importance.

In order to apply the method, all costs, even though some are intangibles, must be reduced to quantitative terms and expressed in comparable units—presumably dollars. We can sometimes attach a dollar value to intangible factors by asking how much the management would be willing to spend outright in order to change these factors. To be sure, difficulties arise in quantifying a criterion function; but no system of rational decision-making can escape the task of assigning weights to the objectives that are desired.

In order to translate the scheduling problem into a mathematical problem of minimizing a cost function, we need a mathematical form that is both sufficiently flexible to approximate a wide range of complex cost relationships, and sufficiently simple to allow easy mathematical solution. From consideration of the kinds of costs that are involved in the scheduling problem it appears that a U-shaped cost curve is required. For example, the cost of inventory is high when inventory is large, and high also at the other extreme when inventory is so small that there are frequent runouts of particular products which cause back orders and a high penalty for delayed shipments to customers. Somewhere between these extremes, the combined costs are at a minimum. With these considerations in view, we decided that the cost function probably could be approximated with reasonable accuracy by a sum of linear and squared terms in the controlled and uncontrolled variables—technically, by a positive definite quadratic form—and we based our analysis on this proposition.

In th following pages we will analyze the costs that are important in the particular paint factory that has been studied, and then show that these can be approximated by a quadratic cost function. Decisions are assumed to be made at regular time intervals (in this case monthly), rather than continuously or intermittently, and the costs are expressed as costs per month. It is convenient to relate these costs to the three alternative ways, discussed earlier, of absorbing order fluctuations.

It should be emphasized again that the following application represents a special case of a method which is itself far more general.

Regular Payroll, Hiring, and Layoff Costs

When order fluctuations are absorbed by increasing and decreasing the work force, the following costs are affected: regular payroll, hiring, and layoff costs.

The size of the work force is adjusted once a month, and setting the work force at a certain level implies a commitment to pay these employees their regular time (as contrasted with overtime) wages for a month. This is shown in Figure 1 by the solid line which may be

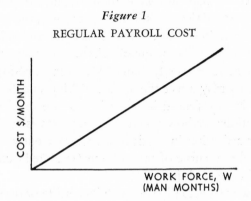

Figure 1

REGULAR PAYROLL COST

Eq. 1)   Regular Payroll Cost $= C_1W + C_{13}$

Figure 2

HIRING AND LAYOFF COSTS

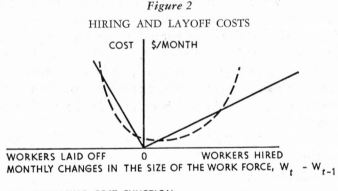

WORKERS LAID OFF   0   WORKERS HIRED
MONTHLY CHANGES IN THE SIZE OF THE WORK FORCE, $W_t - W_{t-1}$

APPROXIMATING COST FUNCTION — — — —

Eq. 2)   Cost of Hiring and Layoffs $= C_2(W_t - W_{t-1} - C_{11})^2$

represented algebraically by the linear cost function, Equation 1. (In the equations that follow, the C's represent constants.)

The fixed cost term, C_{13}, is not changed by the scheduling decisions and hence is irrelevant in their making. For this reason such fixed cost terms will simply be ignored in the other component cost functions. However, the irrelevant fixed cost component, C_{13}, should always be introduced where the quadratic fit will be improved by doing so.

The other labor costs mentioned are associated not with the size of the work force, but with *changes* in its size. The cost of hiring and training people rises with the number hired, as indicated by the solid line plotted in Figure 2. The cost of laying off workers derives from terminal pay, reorganization, etc., and rises with the number of workers laid off. The cost incurred each month depends on the change in the size of the work force between successive months. Since these costs increase both with increases and decreases in the work force, the quadratic curve represented by Equation 2 is a suitable first approximation. It is not required that these costs be symmetrical. Increases in the work force may either be more or less costly than decreases in work force.

Random factors may affect the costs of hiring and firing, e.g., how much difficulty is experienced in a particular case in hiring a man of desired qualifications, or how much reorganization is required in making a particular reduction in work force. Consequently the cost curve should be viewed as a curve of the average (expected) cost of changes of various sizes in the work force.

Whether these costs actually rise at an increasing or decreasing rate is difficult to determine. It can be argued that reorganization costs are more than proportionately larger for large layoffs than for small layoffs; and similarly the efficiency of hiring, measured in terms of the quality of the employees hired, may fall when a large number of people are hired at one time. If this argument holds, then the quadratic curve is especially suitable. But if not, the quadratic still can give a tolerable approximation over a range. The parameters of the function should be set at the values that will give the best possible approximation to the cost curve over the range in which changes in the work force are expected to fluctuate.[10]

In estimating the "costs" of fluctuations in the work force, intangible penalties may, of course, be included as well as the direct costs that are statistically measurable.

Overtime Costs

If order fluctuations are absorbed by increasing and decreasing production without changing the work force, then overtime and undertime costs are incurred. Overtime involves wage payments at an hourly rate that usually is fifty per cent higher than is paid for regular time. Undertime is a waste of labor time that is paid for in the regular payroll, but is not used for productive activities.[11]

---

[10] Note the implied circularity. In order to obtain optimal decisions we need initially to know optimal fluctuation amplitudes of controlled variables. But for practical purposes we need to know only the general range of fluctuations, which can be estimated to a sufficiently close approximation.

[11] It may be possible to perform maintenance activities with labor that would otherwise be wasted. If so, this possibility should be taken into account.

The cost of overtime depends on two decision variables, the size of the work force, W, and the aggregate production rate, P. The simplest form of this cost relation is shown in Figure 3. With a *given* work force, W_1, and an average worker productivity, K, the expression KW_1, is the maximum number of units that can be produced in a month without incurring any overtime. In order to produce at higher rates than KW_1, overtime is required, and its amount increases with increased production.

The relationship shown in Figure 3 can be expected to occur only if

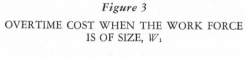

Figure 3

OVERTIME COST WHEN THE WORK FORCE
IS OF SIZE, W_1

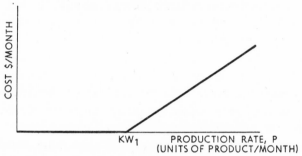

there are no discontinuities and no random disturbances in the production process. However, these are usually present, and should be taken into account. For example, since workers are each somewhat specialized in function, it is likely that a small increase in production would require only a few employees who work in bottleneck functions to work overtime. As production is increased further, more and more employees are required to work overtime until the whole work force is doing some overtime work. The effect of this is to smooth the overtime cost curve of Figure 3 to that shown in Figure 4.

Random disturbances have the same effect of smoothing the overtime curve. For example, *given the number of units* to be produced in a month, the total number of man-hours that will be required is not uniquely determined in advance but will be affected by numerous random disturbances, such as machine breakdowns, quality control problems, productivity fluctuations, etc. Overtime is determined by the excess of the hours that prove to be required by the production target over and above the number of regular-time hours available from the work force in the month. Since the production and employment schedule is made before there is knowledge of the particular disturbances that will occur during the month, estimated overtime costs must depend on an

Figure 4

OVERTIME COST WHEN THE WORK FORCE IS OF
SIZE, W_1 AND RANDOMNESS IS PRESENT

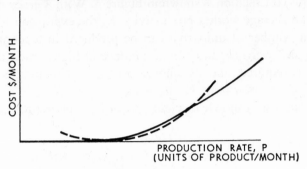

PRODUCTION RATE, P
(UNITS OF PRODUCT/MONTH)

APPROXIMATING COST FUNCTION — — — —

Eq. 4)   Expected Cost of Overtime $= C_3(P - C_4W_1)^2 + C_5P - C_6W_1 + C_{12}PW_1$

estimate of the probabilities that such disturbances will occur. This probability distribution smooths the curve of expected overtime cost shown in Figure 4. The higher the production target with a given size work force, the greater is the probability that some disturbance will occur that will necessitate overtime work to get out the specified production.

In setting the production rate and the work force for a month, it is not certain in advance whether overtime or idle time will occur. In order for the scheduling decision to minimize costs, the cost of having a larger work force than might prove to be needed must be weighed against the cost of having a smaller and cheaper work force, but then perhaps finding it necessary to pay for considerable overtime.

The quadratic curve that approximates the expected cost of overtime for a given size, W_1, of work force, and for different production rates is shown by Equation 4.[12] As production, P, exceeds C_4W_1, a level set by the size of the work force, overtime costs increase. The linear terms, C_5P and C_6W, and the cross product term, $C_{12}PW$, are added to improve the approximation.

The foregoing discussion was premised on a given work force, W_1, but clearly the size of the work force can change. Hence there is a whole family of cost curves similar to that shown in Figure 4, one for each size

---

[12] If production falls to a very low level relative to the work force, the overtime cost which is predicted by the quadratic curve rises and the approximation to the original cost curve becomes poor. Nonetheless, the quadratic may be a quite adequate approximation *in the relevant range.*

of work force. This family of overtime costs curves is obtained by substituting other values for W_1 in Equation 4.

Actually this equation is sufficiently flexible to accommodate other cost components in addition to overtime. For example, the gradual decrease in labor productivity as plant capacity is approached may be reflected in the cost function.

Inventory, Back Order and Machine Setup Costs

When order fluctuations are absorbed by inventory and back order fluctuations other costs are incurred. Increased inventory increases the costs of interest, obsolescence, handling, storage, etc. The decrease of inventory to avoid these costs increases the probability of running out of individual products, thereby incurring the penalty of delaying customer shipments and possibly losing sales. Also, as aggregate inventory is reduced, the average production batch size should be decreased in order to maintain a balanced inventory; consequently, the cost of additional machine setups is incurred. An analysis of the total of these costs will indicate the optimal level of aggregate inventory at which these costs are minimum.

Production decisions in the paint factory are to be made monthly, and prior to each decision the aggregate inventory position should be observed. In formulating the cost function, we assume that the inventory and back order position at the end of each month is representative of the average inventory and back-order positions during the month, and consequently may reasonably be used to estimate the costs related to inventory that were incurred during the month.[13] If this assumption is not tenable, it probably indicates that production decisions should be made more frequently than once a month. Production that is scheduled for a month is assumed to be completed during the month.[14]

In order to have a simple relation between a month's production and the inventory at the end of the month, it is convenient to use the variable, *net inventory,* defined as inventory minus back orders. Net inventory is increased by production, regardless of whether the paint is added to physical inventory or shipped out to decrease the number of back orders. The paint factory usually ships immediately upon receipt of an order, and orders not so shipped are treated as back orders. Conse-

[13] The average of the positions at the beginning and at the end of each month would be even more representative of the average positions during the month. However, this refinement in the cost function would have a very small effect on decisions and would have the disadvantage of being slightly more complex.

[14] Production processes requiring several decision periods to complete may be accommodated in the mathematical model, but this was not necessary in the paint factory.

quently, net inventory is affected immediately upon receipt of an order.[15]

Familiar lot size formulas[16] may be used to determine the optimal production batch size for each paint and the optimal safety stock to protect against its running out while a new batch is being produced. These formulae rest on plausible assumptions about the costs of holding inventory, the cost of back orders, and the probability of errors in forecasting orders for the particular paint. By adding, for each paint, the optimal average safety stock to one-half the optimal batch size we obtain its optimal average inventory.

Then by adding together these optimal average inventories for all the paints that are stocked, we obtain an optimal aggregate inventory for the whole factory. To convert this optimal aggregate inventory to the corresponding optimal *net* inventory, we need to subtract the total back orders for all paints that would be expected to occur, on the average, when the inventory is at its optimal level.

From lot size formulas it is known that both the optimal batch size and the optimal safety stock increase roughly with the square root of the order rate of the individual paint. Thus the optimal aggregate inventory must increase with increased aggregate order rate (total shipments ordered per month). The total expected back orders corresponding to any given size of inventory must also increase with an increased aggregate order rate. By combining these two relationships it appears that optimal *net* inventory increases with the aggregate order rate. The relationship between optimal net inventory and aggregate order rate may be approximated[17] over a range by a function of the form: optimal net inventory $= C_8 + C_8 O$ where the C's are constants, and O is the aggregate order rate.

When actual net inventory deviates from the optimal net inventory $(C_8 + C_9 O)$ in either direction, costs rise as shown in Figure 5. If net inventory falls below this optimal level, then the safety stock and batch

[15] For many factories a lead time is allowed between the receipt of an order and the shipping date requested by the customer. In such a case an order would not affect net inventory until the ordered shipping date. However, the receipt of an order supplies vital information by enabling a perfect forecast to be made of future shipments over a lead time horizon.

[16] See T. M. Whitin, *The Theory of Inventory Management* (Princeton, 1953); and K. J. Arrow, T. Harris, J. Marschak, "Optimal Inventory Policy," *Econometrica,* Vol. XIX (July, 1951), pp. 250–72.

[17] Since back orders will generally be small relative to inventory, the square root relation between aggregate inventory and order rate dominates the relationship between *net* inventory and order rate. Over a limited range a square root function can be approximated by a linear one.

sizes of individual paints must be reduced. We assume that these reductions are optimally distributed over the individual paints by some procedure for scheduling the production of individual products within the constraint of the aggregate production decision.[18] The rise in costs

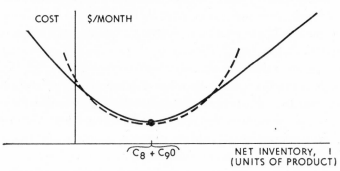

Figure 5

INVENTORY, BACK ORDERS AND MACHINE SETUP COSTS

APPROXIMATING COST FUNCTION — — — —

Eq. 5)   Expected Inventory, Back Order, and Setup Costs

$$= C_7[I - (C_8 + C_9 O)]^2$$

I = Net Inventory = Inventory − Back Orders
O = Order Rate (Units of Product whose Shipment was Ordered during the Month)

as net inventory declines can be estimated by costing the increased number of machine setups, the increased back orders and the decreased inventory. A similar cost calculation can be made for the situation in which net inventory is above the optimal level. In this way the relation, which is shown by the solid line in Figure 5, between expected costs and net inventory, can be determined. Over a range, the curve of inventory-related costs may be approximated adequately by a quadratic of the form shown in Equation 5 in which cost rises as the square of the deviation of net inventory from the optimal level, $(C_8 + C_9 O)$.

The Cost Function for the Paint Factory

Having examined the individual cost components we can now construct the complete cost function for production and employment scheduling. Since the objective is to schedule production and employ-

---

[18] Methods for scheduling the production of individual products have been studied. For example, see "Decision Rules for Allocating Inventory to Lots and Cost Functions for Making Aggregate Inventory Decisions," *Journal of Industrial Engineering,* Vol. IX, No. 1 (January–February, 1958), pp. 14–22.

ment in such a way as to minimize costs, we need a cost function that adds together all the component costs that have been discussed above. Since each month's decision has cost implications that extend over an appreciable length of time, this cost function must span a sufficient time to include virtually all of the cost implications of the decision. The first requirement is met by adding all of the costs attributable to each month; and the second, by adding all of these monthly costs over an extended period of time. The discounting of costs that occur at different points of time by means of an interest rate factor is neglected as an unessential refinement.[19]

Since future costs depend on future sales they are, of course, uncertain. This problem is met by calculating what the costs would be for each combination of forecast errors and taking a weighted average of these costs, using probability weights. This expected cost is to be minimized. No consideration is given to the variability of costs, but only their long-term total. The decision problem can now be stated formally. Find the decisions that minimize $E(C_N)$, where

Eq. 6) $\quad C_N = \sum_{t=1}^{N} C_t$, and

Eq. 7) $\quad C_t = [(C_1 W_t) + C_{13}$

$\qquad + C_2 (W_t - W_{t-1} - C_{11})^2$

$\qquad + C_3 (P_t - C_4 W_t)^2 + C_5 P_t - C_6 W_t + C_{12} P_t W_t$

$\qquad + C_7 (I_t - C_8 - C_9 O_t)^2]$,

| Regular Payroll costs from Eq. 1 |
| Hiring and Layoff costs from Eq. 2 |
| Overtime costs from Eq. 4 |
| Inventory connected costs from Eq. 5 |

subject to the restraints,

Eq. 8) $\qquad\qquad I_{t-1} + P_t - O_t = I_t, \qquad t = 1, 2, \ldots N.$

The optimal production and employment decisions are those that minimize the expected value of total costs, C_N. This cost is the sum of the costs attributable to N months as shown in Equation 6. The total cost attributable to one month, C_t, is shown in Equation 7 to be the sum of the component costs that have previously been discussed. Note that the time subscript, t, has been added to indicate that the variables may take

---

[19] Even without interest discounting, the future beyond a twelve-month forecast horizon is shown in Equations 10 and 11 to have a negligible influence on the current decisions of the paint factory. For periods of this duration, interest discounting would certainly have a negligible influence on the optimum decisions. However, other factories with different costs might have a forecast horizon of several years in which case the neglect of interest discounting should be reconsidered.

on different values at different points of time. The relationship between inventory at the beginning of the month, production during the month, sales during the month, and the month-end inventory is shown by Equation 8. This relationship, of course, applies to each month and must be taken into account in minimizing costs.

The cost function[20] above can be applied to the scheduling decision of a great many factories simply by using the appropriate numerical values for the cost parameters: $C_1, C_2, \ldots, C_{13}$. When we insert the numerical values that we estimated for the paint factory, Equation 9 is obtained. These numerical values are derived from statistical estimates based on accounting data together with subjective estimates of such intangible costs as delayed shipments to customers. In the interest of simplicity, the influence of the order rate on the optimal inventory level was neglected, i.e., C_9 was set equal to zero, and the irrelevant fixed cost C_{13}, was omitted.

Eq. 9)
$$C_N = \sum_{t=1}^{N} \{[340W_t] + [64.3(W_t - W_{t-1})^2]$$
$$+ [.20(P_t - 5.67W_t)^2 + 51.2P_t - 281.W_t]$$
$$+ [.0825(I_t - 320)^2]\}$$

Where C_N is the total cost for N months expressed in dollars, W_t is the work force for month t expressed in men, P_t is production in gallons (a pseudo unit used to disguise company cost data) per month, and I_t is net inventory in gallons.

Since estimates of the cost parameters are subject to many sources of error, it is reassuring that the factory performance proves not to be critically dependent on the accuracy of the cost function. Even if substantial errors are made in estimating the parameters of the cost function, the factory performance measured in cost terms will not suffer seriously.[21]

In obtaining the above cost function for the paint factory it should be remembered that the quadratic form of the cost function is an approximation to the "true" cost function. The adequacy of the quadratic

---

[20] Cost terms that are constants may be added to any of the above cost expressions without having any effect on the optimal decisions. Costs that are constant or, more precisely, costs that do not change with scheduling decisions are irrelevant in making these decisions and hence may be ignored.

[21] An exploratory analysis of the effects of errors in estimating the parameters of a simple quadratic cost function showed that overestimating cost parameters by 100 per cent or underestimating them by 50 per cent—in both cases estimates were incorrect by a factor of two—led to decision rules whose cost performance was approximately 11 per cent above the costs which would occur with correct estimates of cost parameters.

approximation cannot, however, be judged simply in terms of "goodness of fit." Rather, it must be judged by whether the decisions to which it leads are better than the decisions made by alternative decision methods.

Having translated the decision problem into a precise mathematical problem, we can proceed directly to solve for the best scheduling decisions. Without going into the mathematics involved we will now examine the solution that is obtained. This material will be presented in the sequel article, "Derivation and Computation of Linear Decision Rules for Production and Employment Scheduling" by Charles C. Holt, Franco Modigliani, and John F. Muth.[22]

THE OPTIMAL DECISION RULES FOR THE PAINT FACTORY

Once the parameters of the cost function are estimated, the decision rule solution may be obtained by differentiating with respect to each decision variable. We obtain a set of linear equations, and then invert the matrix of these equations to obtain the decision rules. Fortunately, the results of this procedure can be reduced to a formula, requiring only a routine computation. It can be proved, once and for all, that the decisions yielded by the optimal decision rule are the best possible for the given cost function.[23] On the basis of the cost estimates that were made for the paint factory the necessary computations were performed to obtain the optimal decision rules for the factory.

There are two decision rules to be applied at the beginning of each month: one rule sets the aggregate production rate, the other determines the work force. The first rule, shown in Equation 10, incorporates a weighted average of the forecasts of future orders (in this case for a twelve-month period starting with the forthcoming month, t). Since the forecasts of future orders are averaged, production is smoothed, so that there is an optimal response to the fluctuation of forecasted orders. The weight given to future orders declines rapidly as the forecast extends farther into the future. This occurs because, taking into account the cost of holding inventory, it is not economic to produce currently for shipment in the too remote future. One implication is that there is little point in forecasting orders very far into the future since these orders will have little effect upon optimal current production. For the particular costs of the paint company, the forecasts of orders for the forthcom-

---

[22] Holt, *et. al., op. cit.*

[23] A complex mathematical analysis involving the uncertainty of forecast errors and the successive revision of forecasts with the passage of time is required to prove the optimality of this decision rule. "Dynamic Programming under Uncertainty with a Quadratic Criterion Function," H. A. Simon, *Econometrica,* January, 1956, presents this proof.

ing and the two successive months are the major determinants of production as far as orders are concerned.

No information is required about the probability distribution of errors in the forecasts of orders.[24] However, the average forecast error should be zero, i.e., the forecasts should be unbiased.

The second term of Equation 10 ($.993\ W_{t-1}$) reflects the influence on the scheduled production rate of one of the initial conditions at the time the decision is made—specifically, the number of workers that were employed at the end of the preceding month. The more workers that are on the payroll at the beginning of the month, the greater should be the production scheduled for the month, since any large decreases in the size of the work force would be costly, as would an unused work force.

The next two terms in the decision rule may be considered together: ($153. - .464\ I_{t-1}$). If net inventory at the end of the previous month is large, then the negative term will exceed the positive one, and production will be decreased in order to lower inventory. Similarly, if

Eq. 10)
$$P_t = \begin{Bmatrix} +.463\ O_t \\ +.234\ O_{t+1} \\ +.111\ O_{t+2} \\ +.046\ O_{t+3} \\ +.013\ O_{t+4} \\ -.002\ O_{t+5} \\ -.008\ O_{t+6} \\ -.010\ O_{t+7} \\ -.009\ O_{t+8} \\ -.008\ O_{t+9} \\ -.007\ O_{t+10} \\ -.005\ O_{t+11} \end{Bmatrix} + .993\ W_{t-1} + 153. - .464\ I_{t-1}$$

Eq. 11)
$$W_t = .743\ W_{t-1} + 2.09 - .010\ I_{t-1} + \begin{Bmatrix} +.0101\ O_t \\ +.0088\ O_{t+1} \\ +.0071\ O_{t+2} \\ +.0054\ O_{t+3} \\ +.0042\ O_{t+4} \\ +.0031\ O_{t+5} \\ +.0023\ O_{t+6} \\ +.0016\ O_{t+7} \\ +.0012\ O_{t+8} \\ +.0009\ O_{t+9} \\ +.0006\ O_{t+10} \\ +.0005\ O_{t+11} \end{Bmatrix}$$

Where:

P_t is the number of units of product that should be produced during the forthcoming month, t.

---

[24] The mathematical analysis indicates that only the expected values of the distributions of orders are relevant to making optimal decisions (where optimality is defined in terms of minimizing expected costs). The variance and all other higher moments of the distributions have no effect on the decisions under a quadratic criterion. Unbiased forecasts are treated in making decisions exactly as if they were perfect forecasts. Proofs of this point have been made by C. C. Holt for unrevised forecasts in the unpublished manuscript, "Superposition Decision Rules for Production and Inventory Control," and by H. A. Simon for the general case of revised forecasts in the reference above.

W_{t-1} is the number of employees in the work force at the beginning of the month (end of the previous month).

I_{t-1} is the number of units of inventory minus the number of units on back order at the beginning of the month.

W_t is the number of employees that will be required for the current month, t. The number of employees that should be hired is therefore $W_t - W_{t-1}$.

O_t is a forecast of number of units of product that will be ordered for shipment during the current month, t.

O_{t+1} is the same for the next month, $t + 1$, etc.

the initial net inventory is small, the negative term will be small and an increase in production will be called for. Not only does this term determine how the optimal production rule responds to any given initial inventory situation, but it has the special significance of indicating how the rule will take account of past forecast errors, since their effect is to raise the net inventory above, or lower it below, the desired level.

The second decision rule, shown in Equation 11, is used to determine the size of the work force. Again, a term appears which is a weighted average of forecasts of future orders, but in this second rule the weights extend farther into the future before they become negligible in size. Thus the forecasts of orders in the more distant future are relevant in making employment decisions, even though they have little influence on the production decision.

The next term of the employment rule ($.743 \ W_{t-1}$) indicates that the work force on hand at the beginning of the month will influence employment during the following month, because of the costs associated with changing the work force.

The next two terms in the employment rule ($2.09 - .010 \ I_{t-1}$) incorporate the effect of net inventory on the employment decision. A large net inventory will lead to a decrease in the work force while a small net inventory will tend to require an increase in the work force. Net inventory has a much smaller effect on employment than it has on production. Some general comments can now be made about how these two rules operate in concert.

There is a fairly complex interaction between these two decision rules. The production of one month affects the net inventory position at the end of the month. This in turn influences the employment decision in the second month which then influences the production decision in the third month. Thus there is a continual dynamic interaction between the two decisions.

The influence of net inventory on both the production and employment decisions produces a feedback or self-correcting tendency which eventually returns net inventory to its optimal level regardless of whether or not sales have been forecasted accurately.

The weights that are applied to the sales forecasts and the feedback factors in the two decision rules determine the production and employment responses to fluctuations of orders and thereby indicate how much of these fluctuations should be absorbed by work force fluctuations, overtime fluctuations, and inventory and back order fluctuations in order to minimize costs. The work force responds only to fairly long-term fluctuations in orders, but production responds strongly to the orders in the immediate future and to the inventory position. Thus it appears that short-run fluctuations in orders and the disturbances that are caused by forecast errors are absorbed largely by overtime and undertime fluctuations. Extremely sharp fluctuations in orders are absorbed almost entirely by inventory and back order fluctuations.

Implicit in these optimal decision rules is the answer to a question which is frequently raised: How should production be varied when orders follow a predictable seasonal fluctuation? The decision rules are designed to minimize costs despite predicted and unpredicted fluctuations of orders—predictable seasonal fluctuations are no exceptions.

The appearance of negative weights for forecasted future orders in some terms of the production decision rule is surprising. One would expect to prepare for forecasted future orders by increasing production and accumulating inventory. Evidently the response of the rules to a forecast of, for example, increased future orders is to prepare early by building up the work force at a slow rate of increase. In this way the work force build-up is accomplished economically and the increased work force then gradually causes the production rate to increase.

One limitation of the mathematical analysis is that no bounds have been placed on the variables. Specifically, no formal restriction has been set up to avoid negative production and negative work force. This limitation of the formal analysis is not thought to be of practical importance since orders will be positive. (Negative orders imply a net shipment from customers back to the factory.) Positive orders constitute a continual drain on inventory so that the decision rules will call for positive production and employment—except under extraordinary circumstances.

If the numerical constants in the cost function of the paint factory should change, the numbers in the above decision rules would need to be recomputed in order to obtain new decision rules applicable to the changed circumstances. However, the algebraic forms of the decision rules would remain unchanged.

For procurement or other reasons it may be desirable to know what the production and employment levels are likely to be in subsequent months. Plans for *future* decisions may readily be obtained by applying the decision rules to forecasts that extend farther into the future. Of course, when the time comes, the actual decisions may prove to be different from those that had been planned.

COMPARISON OF DECISION PERFORMANCES BY THE FACTORY AND THE DECISION RULES

The decision rules we have described were obtained by finding a mathematical optimum for the decision problem on the basis of specific formal assumptions. In addition, the decision rules have been tested by making a hypothetical application and observing their performance characteristics. The production and employment decisions that the paint company had made over a six-year period were analyzed in detail. With this knowledge of the decision problems that had confronted the paint factory, the decision rules were applied *ex post* to simulate the decisions that would have been made if the new decision rules had been used during this period.

Before this hypothetical performance could be calculated, it was necessary to obtain for each point in time a set of forecasts of future orders (in order to calculate the corresponding employment and production decisions for each point in time). Since no explicit forecasts had been recorded by the company, it was impossible for us to operate with the same forecast information that had been available to the factory management at the times when their decisions were made. As a substitute, two different sets of forecasts were computed which, in terms of accuracy, would necessarily bracket the forecasts that were available to the company. The first set of forecasts is the data on orders which were in fact received. Such a Perfect Forecast is of course limited to "forecasting" a known past, and consequently is not of practical usefulness. However, the Perfect Forecast gives a good basis for comparison since, by its use, an upper limit of decision performance is obtained. The second set of forecasts is obtained by assuming that future orders are predicted by a Moving Average of past orders. The total of orders for the coming year is forecasted to be equal to the orders that had been received in the year just past. This forecast is then converted to a monthly basis by applying a known seasonal adjustment. We now have a basis for a three-way comparison of decision performance: (1) the actual performance of the factory (2) the performance of the optimal decision rule with Perfect Forecasts whose accuracy cannot be exceeded, and (3) the performance of the optimal decision rule with Moving

Average forecasts whose accuracy represents a practical minimum below which there is little excuse for falling.

History of Factory Operations under Alternative Decision Methods

The extreme variability of the orders received by the paint factory is shown in Figure 6. The depressed business conditions of 1949 are clearly reflected in the data. The effects of inventory speculation by distributors and dealers brought on by the Korean War is shown in the high orders of later 1950 and early 1951, and the subsequent rapid decline of orders in the second half of 1951. Hence, the time covered by

Figure 6

ORDERS RECEIVED

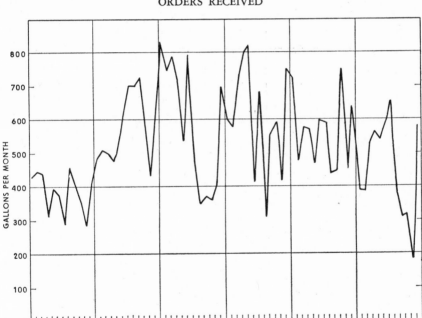

this study includes a period of extreme order fluctuations as well as periods of more moderate fluctuations. The severity of the fluctuations of orders gives some assurance that the decision rules will be subjected to a test of substantial severity. Although not readily observable by eye, there is a significant seasonal pattern in the receipt of orders.

An examination of Figure 7 shows that the production fluctuations of the factory are considerably sharper on a month-to-month basis than

Figure 7

PRODUCTION

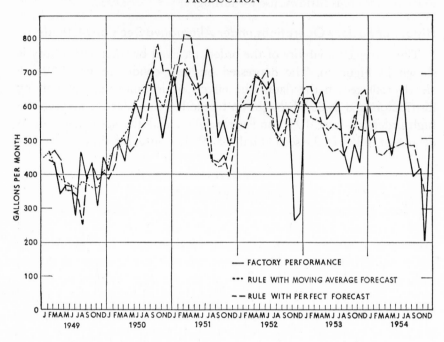

Figure 8

WORK FORCE

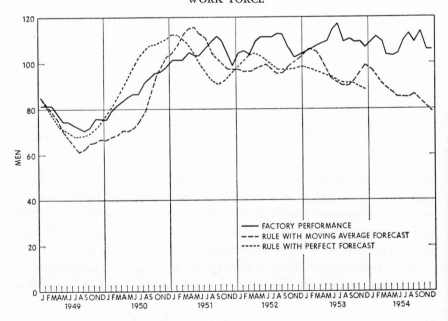

those called for by the decision rule with either Moving Average or Perfect Forecasts.[25] With a Perfect Forecast the decision rule avoids, almost completely, sharp month-to-month fluctuations in production, but responds to fluctuations of orders that have a duration of several months.

The decisions scheduling the size of the work force are shown in Figure 8. Again, the decision rule makes smoother changes and avoids sharp month-to-month fluctuations in work force. The fluctuations in work force with the Perfect Forecast, while substantial in size, are actually occasioned by the severity of order fluctuations and the desire to avoid costly accumulations of inventory and back orders. The additional work force fluctuations that are observed under the Moving Average Forecast are entirely attributable to forecast errors. For example, an erroneous forecast of high sales leads the decision rule to build up the work force. The combination of low sales and large work force causes an accumulation of inventories which in turn necessitates a reduction of the work force in order to lower inventory to the optimal level. The differences which are shown in Figure 8 between the fluctuations of the work force under the Perfect Forecast and the Moving Average Forecast when the same decision rule is used in both cases illustrate the importance of accurate forecasts to the stability of employment.

As would be expected, the Perfect Forecast foresaw the increased "Korean" orders and increased the size of the work force sharply in 1950. Using the Moving Average Forecasts, the decision rule increased the work force about six months later. While the factory actually started its employment buildup as early as the decision rule did using Perfect Forecasts, its rate of buildup was considerably lower; consequently its peak of employment occurred in late 1951 at the time when, as it happened, orders declined sharply. Evidently the decision rule when using the Moving Average Forecast worked tolerably well even under such severe circumstances as the outbreak of war.

Overtime hours are plotted in Figure 9 to show the comparisons in performance between the factory and the decision rule. The inadequacies of the Moving Average Forecast appear clearly in 1950, when the sudden war-induced increase in orders, which, of course, were not foreseen by the backward-looking forecast, led to a large amount of overtime.

Performance in the control of inventory is shown in Figures 10 and

---

[25] For the factory no adjustment was made for the fact that the number of working days varies somewhat from month to month. This accounts for part of the production variability.

Figure 9

OVERTIME HOURS

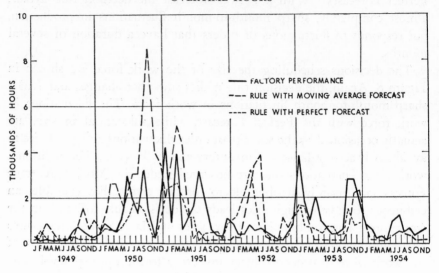

Figure 10

INVENTORY

At End of Month

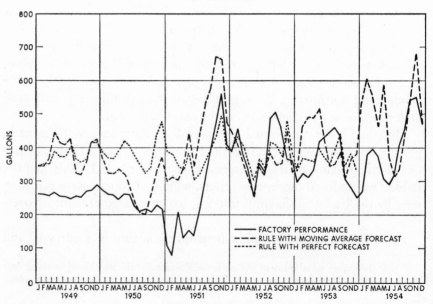

11, which show separately the two components of net inventory; actual physical inventory and back orders. The decision rule operating with the Perfect Forecast displays in Figure 10 the ability to hold inventories quite close to the lowest cost level. Deviations from this optimal level do occur, but they are not of large amplitude. In contrast, the decision rule operating with the Moving Average Forecast allows inventories to fall substantially during the sudden increase in "Korean" sales, and later, when orders decline, inventory rises sharply. However, inventory

Figure 11

BACK ORDERS

At End of Month

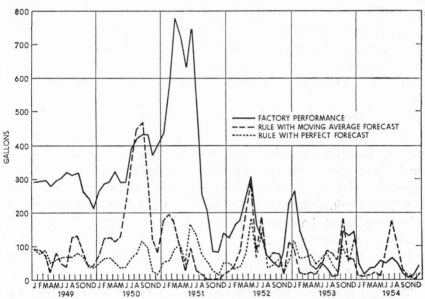

recovered from its low point much earlier with the Moving Average Forecast than the factory actually did. In the winter of 1951–52 when orders declined sharply, the decision rule using the Moving Average Forecast was able to bring down the resulting excess inventories about as quickly as this was in fact achieved by the factory.

The penalty that accompanies low inventory appears clearly in the plot of back orders in Figure 11. With the Moving Average Forecast, back orders rose sharply during the Korean spurt of demand, but these back orders were liquidated by the end of 1950. For the actual factory performance, back orders did not return to their normal level until the second half of 1951. When high orders are speculative in nature as was the case during this period, it is difficult to judge how much weight should be attached to the poor service to customers evidenced by large back orders. The decision rule "took" these back orders seriously and responded accordingly.

Cost Comparisons under Alternative Decision Methods

One test of a decision-making process is its performance in terms of the criteria that serve as the basis for the decisions. To the extent that the minimization of the types of costs which occur in the cost function constitutes the goal of the production executives of the paint factory, the comparison between the cost performances of the factory and of the decision rule calculated on this basis is significant. However, the production executives have been concerned during this six-year period with the accomplishment of other goals in addition to the minimization of the particular types of costs with which the statistical decision analysis is concerned; pursuit of these other goals would undoubtedly raise these costs. Hence performance comparisons based exclusively on the types of costs that are included in the cost function do not tell quite the whole story.

Because the reconstruction of a quantitative history of factory operations for six years constitutes in itself a substantial research job involving in this case the allocation of costs between paint and other products, the indirect calculation of certain information that had never been recorded, and the estimation of nonaccounting costs, the figures that have been obtained must be presented with a certain tentativeness. The estimates of what the costs would have been, *if* things had been done differently, are particularly subject to limitations in accuracy.

In spite of their limitations, the cost differences to be presented are, in the opinion of the authors, highly significant.

To evaluate the cost performance of the decision rules, including the adequacy of the fit of the quadratic cost function, we used, so far as possible, the nonquadratic cost structure that originally had been estimated from the factory accounting and other data.

A cost comparison is shown in Figure 12, for 1949–53, the longest period in which cost figures are available for a complete three-way comparison. The year 1954 could not be included, because, at the time of writing, the authors could not produce the Perfect Forecast of 1955 orders which would be required.

The decision rule with Perfect Forecasts had lower costs than with the Moving Average Forecasts by 10 per cent, or $59,000 per year on the average. Since the identical rule is being used with both sets of forecasts, this difference in cost performance is *entirely attributable to better forecasting.* The decision rule when operating with the obviously modest forecasting ability of the Moving Average gave a cost saving compared to the factory performance of $173,000 per year on the average. The limitations of this comparison which were mentioned above should be noted.

It is striking that the cost saving attributable to the decision rule is greater than the cost saving attributable to the complete elimination of forecast errors. Perhaps forecasting future orders accurately isn't as important as has commonly been thought by production people. Judging by this particular factory and period, making optimal use of crude forecasts is more important than perfect forecasting.

Figure 12

COSTS (THOUSANDS OF DOLLARS)	COMPANY PERFORMANCE	DECISION RULE	
		MOVING AVG. FORECAST	PERFECT FORECAST
REGULAR PAYROLL	$ 1940	$ 1834	$ 1888
OVERTIME	196	296	167
INVENTORY	361	451	454
BACK ORDERS	1566	616	400
HIRING & LAYOFFS	22	25	20
TOTAL $	4085	3222	2929
COST %	139%	110%	100%

Since scheduling production and employment in a period of recession and war is so difficult a problem because of the large and unpredictable fluctuations of orders, it is understandable that the potential savings through improved decision techniques should be large. However, the Korean War period by some may be considered unrepresentative of attainable cost savings in hoped-for times of "normalcy." Also difficult problems in estimating an appropriate penalty cost for back orders arise during such a period. Cost comparisons for shorter periods that exclude the war years should be more representative of "normal" times. However, in posing an easier scheduling problem, these years, of course, offer smaller opportunities for improved performance.

If we drop out the Korean year, 1950, and compare the Perfect Forecast cost performance with that of the Moving Average for the years 1949, 1951, 1952 and 1953, we find that the imperfect forecasting raises costs 5 per cent, or $28,000 per year on the average. While a

5 per cent savings is small in percentage terms, it should be remembered that this is 5 per cent of an amount that is the total of several large costs including the payroll. How much of this saving can actually be achieved by substituting more refined forecasting methods for the moving average is as yet unknown. Obviously a perfect forecasting method is unattainable. Presumably the expenditure of some thousands of dollars for improved forecasts would more than pay for itself in decreased production costs even for this small factory.

Although the expected size of forecast errors for a particular forecasting method does not affect optimal decisions based on its forecasts, the cost performance certainly *is* affected by the size of the forecast errors. Since the cost function is quadratic, the costs of forecast errors rise roughly with their square. Hence it is desirable to find a forecasting method that does not often make large errors[26]—small errors can be forgiven because their cost penalty is low.

The plot of actual factory inventory in Figure 10 shows that the factory in its control of inventories acted *as if* the cost of back orders relative to the cost of holding inventories had increased during this six-year period. The cost structure that we estimated is more nearly in line with the implicit back order and inventory costs of the later three-year period. Consequently, cost comparisons from the later period *may* be more significant than cost comparisons covering the whole six years.

The objection might be made that our estimates of the factory cost structure may be in error which would mean that the factory performance is being judged by an erroneous criterion. Such errors clearly are possible, but it should be remembered that the decision rule is designed to minimize a given cost function. If the cost parameters were changed, the costing of factory performance would be different, but also a new decision rule would be calculated whose decision behavior would be different. Consequently if changes were made in the cost structure that would reduce the estimated cost of the factory performance, the relevant comparison would then be with the cost performance of a decision rule changed to be optimal under the new cost function.

---

[26] An unpublished paper, "Superposition Decision Rules for Production and Inventory Control" by Charles C. Holt, presents a partial analysis of the cost of forecast errors. In an analysis of production scheduling (not considering employment) on the basis of an unrevised forecast of orders that will occur in one future period, the expected cost of forecast errors was found to be proportional to the variance of the distribution of forecast errors. The constant of proportionality is the square of one of the decision rule weights (that are applied to order forecasts) corresponding to the time spanned by the forecast. Not only do forecasts of future orders have less influence on decisions when they are more remote in the future, but the cost implications of forecast errors attenuate even faster (as the square of the weight) as the forecast reaches farther into the future.

To compare the cost performances of the factory, and the decision rule with Moving Average Forecasts we chose the period 1952–54— the latter year is available for this comparison since the Moving Average Forecasts require no unattainable data on 1955 orders. As shown in Figure 13, the actual factory cost performance exceeded that of the decision rule with Moving Average Forecasts by 8.5 per cent, or $51,-000 per year on the average. Economies were achieved by the decision rule as follows: The overtime costs under the decision rule were higher, but the regular payroll costs were enough lower to make a net saving.

Figure 13

COSTS (THOUSANDS OF DOLLARS)	COMPANY PERFORMANCE	DECISION RULE MOVING AV. FORECAST
REGULAR PAYROLL	$1256	$1149
OVERTIME	82	95
INVENTORY	273	298
BACK ORDERS	326	246
HIRING & LAYOFFS	16	12
TOTAL COST	$1953 108.5%	$1800 100%

The inventory holding costs were higher under the decision rule, but the back order penalty costs were enough lower to make a net saving. The hiring and layoff costs were lower under the decision rule. It appears that the cost savings during this period of "normal" paint sales were attained by the decision rule through a combination of several different kinds of cost savings and not through a single simple improvement that might be "hit upon" by casual judgmental analysis.

CONCLUSION

On the basis of the foregoing comparisons between the actual decision performance of an operating factory and the hypothetical performances of the decision rule, the following conclusion seems justified. If the optimal linear decision rule which is introduced in this paper were to be applied using forecasts that are practically obtainable, it would render a performance that would be a considerable improvement in cost terms over that obtainable by the traditional judgmental methods that have been used by the factory. Furthermore, this improved performance probably could be obtained with a smaller expenditure of executive time and effort than now goes into such decisions.

It would be rash of the authors to generalize these conclusions to all firms. However on the basis of their knowledge of the decision techniques that are now in general use, it is their opinion that the decision performance of the paint factory is not atypical, and that the type of decision rule presented in this paper would enable production executives to achieve a substantial improvement in their production and employment scheduling in a great many industrial situations.

Even though a production executive may be aided by adopting this new decision technique, there is still critical need for his judgment, both in the estimation of the original cost function, especially the intangible components of it, and in the application of the decision rule when factors become important that are not explicitly included in the statistical decision analysis. By relieving the executive of the recurring need to consider and analyze the complex interacting cost factors that are taken into account by the decision rule (i.e., regular payroll, overtime hiring, layoff, inventory, back order and machine setup costs), the executive will be left with more time to devote to important nonroutine special factors and unusual situations.

Even though it is possible to prove mathematically that, where the cost function is quadratic, the linear decision rule here presented cannot be surpassed on its average cost performance, and even though a simulated application based on historical data gives highly encouraging results, there is still need for further tests under actual operating conditions before the new method can fully prove its usefulness. For the last year, the paint factory has been carrying out an application of the rule (and an earlier version of it) to the actual scheduling of its production in order to test the rule under operating conditions with available forecasts. The results have been gratifying. The average inventory and average back orders have both decreased, and this was accomplished with smaller fluctuations in the aggregate production of those paints that were included in the experiment.[27]

In summary, we may say that this paper has presented a technique which is designed to facilitate the scheduling of the aggregate production rate and the size of the work force of a factory. This decision

---

[27] A report on this operating test is in preparation for publication in the *Naval Research Logistics Quarterly*. This test also involves the application of decision rules for scheduling the production of individual products as well as the rules that have been the subject of this paper for scheduling aggregate production.

analysis takes explicit recognition of (1) the dynamic costs which are incurred as the result of order fluctuations, (2) the fact that the future, specifically future orders, is relevant to current decisions but can be forecasted only with considerable uncertainty, and (3) the fact that each decision is but one in a time sequence of interrelated decisions. The solution to this complex decision problem is obtained in the form of a decision rule by means of which the decisions that will give the lowest costs in a particular situation can be easily determined by a five-minute computation. The technique may be applied to any factory in which the relevant costs may be approximated adequately by the quadratic cost function.

Since it is anticipated that the decision method discussed in this paper will be applicable in its present form to a good many other factories, a sequel article will show the derivation of the conditions for minimum cost and the formulas for obtaining the final decision rules for scheduling production and employment.

Other factories will need to include different types of cost terms in their cost functions and this will preclude using the rule in the form in which it has been presented. However, the general method of obtaining a linear decision rule from a quadratic criterion function can be extended by the application of straightforward mathematics to a wide variety of other production and inventory control decision problems, and, of equal significance, to decision problems from entirely different fields, the automatic control of chemical processes for example.

REFERENCES

1. BELLMAN, RICHARD. *An Introduction to the Theory of Dynamic Programming.* Santa Monica, Calif.: Rand Corporation, 1953.

2. ———. "Decision-Making in the Face of Uncertainty—I," *Naval Research Logistics Quarterly* (June, 1954), pp. 230–32.

3. ———; GLICKSBERG, I.; and GROSS, O. "The Theory of Dynamic Programming as Applied to a Smoothing Problem," *Journal of the Society for Industrial and Applied Mathematics* (June, 1954), pp. 82–88.

4. CHARNES, A.; COOPER, W. W.; and MELLON, B. "A Model for Optimizing Production by Reference to Cost Surrogates," *Econometrica* (July, 1955), pp. 307–23.

5. DANTZIG, GEORGE B. "Optimal Solution of a Dynamic Leontief Model with Substitution," *Econometrica* (July, 1955), pp. 295–302.

6. DVORETZKY, A.; KIEFER, J.; and WOLFOWITZ, J. "The Inventory Problem," *Econometrica* (April, 1952), pp. 187–222; (July, 1952), pp. 450–66.

7. HOFFMAN, A. J., and JACOBS, WALTER. "Smooth Patterns of Production," *Management Science* (October, 1954), pp. 86–91.

8. HOLT, CHARLES C., and SIMON, HERBERT A. "Optimal Decision Rules for Production and Inventory Control," *Proceedings of the Conference on Operations Research in Production and Inventory Control* (January, 1954), Case Institute of Technology, pp. 73–89.

9. MAGEE, J. F. *Studies in Operations Research 1: Application of Linear Programming to Production Scheduling.* Cambridge, Mass.: Arthur D. Little Inc., unpublished.

10. MODIGLIANI, F., and HOHN, F. "Solution of Certain Problems of Production Planning over Time Illustrating the Effect of the Inventory Constraint," *Econometrica* (January, 1955), pp. 46–66.

11. SIMON, HERBERT A. "On the Application of Servomechanism Theory in the Study of Production Control," *Econometrica* (December, 1952), pp. 247–68.

CASE 7

Production and Inventory Control in a Chemical Process[1]

RUSSELL L. ACKOFF[2]

Some points of special interest in this paper are:

a) The treatment of demand information.
b) The use of schematic flow charts.
c) The cost equation developed from the diagrammatic model.
d) The choice of scheduling period.
e) Safety factors built into the model.
f) The use of "extreme" cases in order to understand the process.
g) The several approaches to solution and their rationale.
h) The application of statistical control techniques to inventory and production decisions.

A great deal of research effort has been directed towards the construction of mathematical models for representing the cost of production in terms of pertinent variable factors. But having the model does not guarantee that it is economical, or even feasible, to use it for control purposes. This paper describes how a model was constructed for a complex chemical process, and why the use of the model was abandoned in favor of a simple operating scheduling rule.

The company that sponsored this project is a chemical producer with average annual gross sales of approximately 55 million dollars. Their production is centered in seven plants spread around the country. The

[1] *Operations Research,* August, 1955. Reprinted by permission. This paper was presented to the Symposium on Operations Research in Business and Industry, sponsored by the Midwest Research Institute, April 8 and 9, 1954 in Kansas City, Missouri, and was published in the *Proceedings* of the Symposium (July, 1954).

[2] University of Pennsylvania.

company employs approximately 2,500 persons. Their products are numerous and varied and involve bacteriological as well as chemical processing.

In 1953, a company representative contacted the OR Group at Case to inquire as to the possibility of the company's fruitful use of OR. This contact led to a preliminary discussion at the company site of several problems that might serve as a jumping-off point. Company interest centered as much in self-education in OR as in the solution to a particular problem.

The production and inventory problem to be discussed in this paper was selected because (1) inventory of the products involved had been subject to severe fluctuations in the preceding three years and hence had required emergency process changes and not infrequent "crash" activity; (2) the process involved was similar to a number of others in the company and hence a study of it could serve as a prototype for similar studies of the other processes and (3) the product was subject to considerable variations in demand and hence presented a scientific challenge because there was no readily available method for handling the problem. This problem provided an opportunity to the Case Group to become engaged in some fundamental research, which is an important incentive to a group associated with an educational institution.

The company's OR interests came from the Production, Development, and Quality Control Division of the Production Department. This is a staff division which reports directly to the Vice President of Production. This division has responsibility for product, process, cost, and inventory control. One man from this division, a section head who was a Ph.D. in chemistry, joined two members of the Case OR Group to form the OR team. In addition, an advisory and review committee was established which consisted of the manager of the division, the manager of the plant in which the products involved were produced, and the inventory and cost control member of the division. Additional assistance was obtained by frequent meetings of the team with the full force of Case's OR Group. The team and advisory committee met frequently during the project. These meetings brought important factors to the attention of the team, factors which might otherwise have been overlooked. Furthermore it permitted those who would eventually have to evaluate and use the results of the project to assimilate its findings in small doses. This meant that eventual implementation of the final results involved practically no transition-confusion. In effect, the final report was an anticlimax; the results had already been assimilated and were being put to use by the time the report appeared.

In addition to those already mentioned, other members of the division were frequently called upon to assist the team. Out of those company personnel who worked with and on the OR team, several were eventually selected to form the company's own OR team. Of these, two were sent to Case's OR Short Course and to several Conferences to supplement their "on-the-job" training. Consequently, at the end of the project about to be reported, the company was in a position to conduct its own OR activity on a modest scale, with only occasional outside assistance and advice.

The development of an efficient procedure for scheduling a production process requires an intimate knowledge of the details of the process. No detailed description of the production process involved in this study was available at the time the project began. A detailed study of the process was made and a flow diagram was prepared which showed all the operations in the production process and the capacity at each stage. The diagram also showed the alternative ways of producing each of the three interrelated products which will be referred to as Finished Q, Crude Q, and R. Also shown were possible recycling channels which could be used for increasing the amounts of Crude or Finished Product Q, and the process times for each operation.

PROCESS FLOW ANALYSIS

The process involves approximately fifty distinct chemical operations. This number makes it impractical (from both the accounting and the mathematical point of view) to construct a cost equation for the process in which the cost of each operation is treated separately. It was decided, therefore, to construct a less complex diagram to describe the process, a diagrammatic analysis which grouped operations around the points at which the process is controlled. This diagram (Fig. 1) was also designed to group the operations so as to permit acquisition of cost data in a convenient way and yet show all possible channels of production.

The symbols $(1, 2, 3, 4 Q_1,$ etc.) shown in Figure 1 represent the following groups of operations, or process-phases:

Symbol	Process-Phase
1	Preparation of seed
2	Setting up fermentors
3	Fermentation
$4Q_1$	Crude Q conversion
$4Q_2$	Crude Q conversion
$4Q_3$	Crude Q conversion

$4R$	Crude R conversion
$5Q_1$	Crude Q drying
$5Q_2$	Crude Q inventory
$5R$	Crude R inventory
$6Q_1$	Finished Q conversion
$6Q_2$	Finished Q drying
$6Q_3$	Finished Q grinding
$6Q_4$	Finished Q blending
$6R$	Finished R conversion

The discs in Figure 1 indicate points at which there is a division of material on the basis of its usability. At such separation points, some material may be suitable only for the R processes, some may be suitable both for the Q and R processes, and some may have to be disposed of as

Figure 1
FLOW DIAGRAM—FIRST SIMPLIFICATION

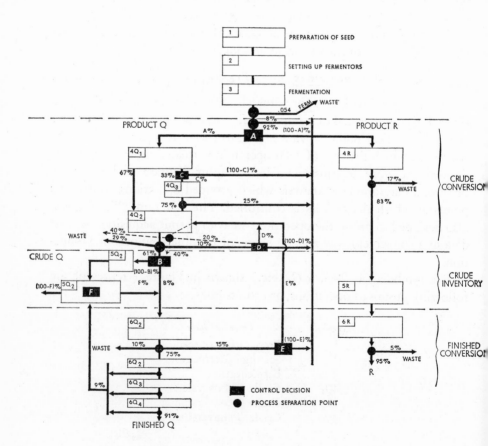

waste. Waste, as it is shown on each of the charts, includes material sewered (because it is uneconomical to reprocess) and process losses resulting from each operation. At each separation point in the Q process a portion of the material is suitable for R processing, but it requires further processing or recycling to be suitable for Q. The small dark rectangles in Figure 1 indicate where control decisions regarding the allocation of usable materials to various channels must be made by those in control of the process. Then, in addition to the decision as to how many fermentors to set, there are six control decisions involved in the production process (shown in Fig. 1 as A through F):

Control Decision Symbol	Control Decision
A	Determination of the portion of materials suitable for both Q and R production that is to be sent through the Q process.
B	Determination of the portion of the materials suitable for the Finished and Crude Q production that is to be sent to the Finished Q production.
C	Determination of the portion of the materials suitable for R production that is to be sent to special process $4Q_3$ which eventually makes more material available for Q processing.
D	Determination of the portion of the materials suitable for R production or recycling that is to be recycled after the Crude Q conversion process.
E	Determination of the portion of the materials suitable for R production or recycling that is to be recycled after the Finished Q conversion process.
F	Determination of the portion of the Crude Q inventory that is to be recycled through the Finished Q conversion process.

PROCESS YIELDS AND RECYCLING

With the information shown in Figure 1 it was possible to construct an equation for the processing cost of the product. The total cost of processing was, of course, dependent on the number of fermentors set up and the value of each of the six control decisions. This same equation could easily be adapted to determine the yield of each product for any combination of control decisions and for any quantity set up in the fermentors.

An analysis was made to determine how the control decisions affected the yield of the process. Six extreme cases were defined. In the first case all suitable material is sent to Finished Q at every control decision; the material not suitable at B is sent to Crude Q, and what is not suitable at

$C, D,$ and E is sent to R processing and no Crude Q is reprocessed. (That is, $A = 1, B = 1, C = 0, D = 0, E = 0,$ and $F = 0.$) This and the other five cases are shown in Table 1, as well as the yields of each product expressed as percentages of the fermentation yield (X).

Table 1 shows that the more material recycled the greater is the waste. Specifically, a comparison of no recycling with complete recycling for daily settings of one or two fermentors, after allowance for nonrecoverable fermentors has been made, shows that there is 6.2 per cent (38.7 per cent — 32.5 per cent) more fermentor yield available for processing from the same amount of raw material. For a maximum

Table 1

USABLE PRODUCT EXPRESSED AS A PERCENTAGE OF FERMENTATION
YIELDS (X) FOR VARIOUS CONTROL DECISIONS

CONTROL DECISIONS, PERCENTAGES					FERMENTOR YIELDS						
					Finished Q		Crude Q		R		Waste*
A	B	C	D	E	Per Cent of X	Per Cent of Finished Product	Per Cent of X	Per Cent of Finished Product	Per Cent of X	Per Cent of Finished Product	Per Cent of X
100	100	0	0	0	25.7	38	2.5	4	39.3	58	32.5
100	100	100	0	0	35.2	56	3.4	5	24.8	39	36.6
100	100	100	100	0	37.5	60	3.6	6	21.3	34	37.6
100	100	100	100	100	39.7	65	3.8	6	17.8	29	38.7
†73.8	100	0	0	0	20.2	29	2.0	3	48.1	68	29.7
†73.8	100	100	100	100	31.2	49	3.1	5	29.0	46	36.7

* This quantity is the total of the expected losses in the system consisting of the process-phase losses plus unusable quantities which are sewered. In addition to this waste, there is also an expected waste of 0.054 fermentors per day at the fermentation stage.

† Since the number of fermentors that can be sent to Q processing per day is limited by the nature of the process if the maximum number of daily settings is made, A can be no greater than 73.8 per cent.

daily setting of fermentors, 7.0 per cent (36.7 per cent — 29.7 per cent) more fermentor yield is available.

The fact that recycling decreased yield was known to management. But the amount of this decrease was not known. This large potential increase in yield suggested that it would be very desirable to consider possible difficulties associated with the elimination of recycling.

First, a study was made to determine how the reduction of waste through the elimination of recycling would affect total production costs and income. In order to use the cost equation to obtain this information, it was necessary to obtain costs for the raw materials and processing costs associated with each phase of the production process.

The cost of each process-phase is made up of two components, one fixed and one variable. The variable component depends on the quantity of material entering the process and the fixed costs includes overhead and some operating costs. Considerable study was required to find the values of these components. This study yielded a cost estimate for each process-phase in the following (linear) form:

Fixed cost + (Variable cost per unit) (Number of units entering process).

The cost estimates obtained from this study were checked in the following way. Comparisons were made between (1) the accounting department's computation of costs for a ten-month period and (2) the team's cost estimates for the same period. Very satisfactory agreement was found.

Using the cost equation and the process-phase cost estimates, costs

Table 2

RECYCLING COST ANALYSIS

Control Decisions					Fin-ished Q Units	Crude Q Units	R Units	Total Units	Proc-ess Cost, $	In-come, $	Re-lated Net In-come, $	Per Cent
A	B	C	D	E								
1	1	0	0	0 a	17.0	1.7	22.9	41.6	2247	3939	1692	100.0
				b	39.1	3.9	92.7	135.7	4638	13062	8424	100.0
1	1	1	0	0 a	23.3	2.3	13.3	38.9	2294	3588	1294	76.5
				b	53.6	5.3	70.6	129.5	4732	12255	7523	89.3
1	1	0	1	0 a	18.2	1.8	20.5	40.5	2273	3814	1514	89.5
				b	41.7	4.1	87.1	132.9	4658	12750	8092	96.1
1	1	0	0	1 a	18.0	1.8	20.7	40.5	2305	3816	1511	89.3
				b	41.4	4.1	87.6	133.1	4694	12773	8073	95.9
1	1	1	1	1 a	27.2	2.7	5.0	34.9	2305	3137	832	49.2
				b	62.5	6.2	51.6	120.3	4744	11219	6475	76.9

Processing:
a Minimum fermentor setting per day.
b Maximum fermentor setting per day.

were computed for various degrees of recycling and for various fermentor settings. These are shown in Table 2. The income was computed by assuming that all material produced is sold at the average market prices. The difference between income and process cost is defined as a related net income. (Note that this is *not* a net profit.)

Table 2 shows that compared with complete recycling, production without recycling yields twice as much related net income for minimum fermentor settings, and one and one-third times as much for maximum fermentor settings.

That production economy results from eliminating recycling was firmly substantiated by these results. It was then necessary to determine whether sales requirements could be met if recycling were eliminated.

Table 3

MAXIMUM ANNUAL YIELDS WITHOUT RECYCLING COMPARED
WITH ANNUAL SHIPMENTS

Product	Annual Yield $A = 0.738$		Annual Shipments		
	$B = 0.5$	$B = 0.95$	1950	1951	1952
Finished Q.............	3.6	7.4	1.0	1.8	7.0
Crude Q...............	5.6	1.2	5.3	1.2	1.0
R.....................	16.6	16.4	6.6	13.4	11.0
Total...............	25.8	25.0	12.9	16.4	19.0

A comparison of annual process capacity with shipments for 1950, 1951, and 1952 was made. The results are shown in Table 3, where 1950 shipments for Finished Q are equated to 1 and are used as a base. All other figures are expressed as multiples of this figure.

Table 3 shows that enough of each product could have been produced to meet annual sales requirements in 1950, 1951, and 1952. This is not conclusive, however, for it does not show whether sales requirements could have been met on a day-to-day basis. To determine whether shortrun requirements could be met, and to determine the cost of so doing, it was necessary to develop a detailed procedure for controlling the production process without recycling.

SIMPLIFICATION OF THE PROCESS

First a flow chart of the simplified process was prepared. This is shown in Figure 2. The symbolism used in Figure 2 corresponds to that used in Figure 1 with the following additions:

n = date (specific hour) at which fermentors are set up
X' = number of fermentors set up
X = number of fermentors set up minus the average number of nonrecoverable fermentors
a = number of units of Finished Q yielded by the process
β = number of units of Crude Q yielded by the process
γ = number of units of R yielded by the process

The primes appearing on the β's and the γ's are used to indicate different times of arrival at various levels in a process. The subscripts on the symbols A, B, and X are used to designate the starting times of the batches on which these quantities were determined.

THE GENERAL COST EQUATION

Using the information shown on Figure 2 a general cost equation was constructed which expressed the total cost of the product as a function of a set of variables used to describe completely the production and inventory processes. The production process was described in the simplified model in terms of a series of steps from seeding, set-up, and fermentation (1, 2, and 3) to finished conversion (6). There is a cost corresponding to each of these steps for each of the three major types of products. In addition to the total cost of production, K_{1-6}, there is the

Figure 2
FLOW DIAGRAM—FINAL SIMPLIFICATION

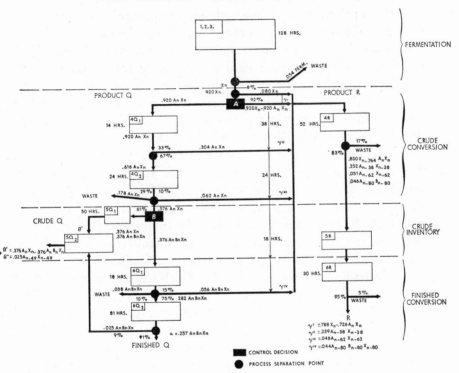

in-process inventory cost, K_7, and the cost of finished inventory, K_8. The total cost K_T may then be expressed in its simplest form as follows,

$$K_T = K_{1-6} + K_7 + K_8.$$

The expansion of the total-cost equation into a computational form involves a detailed mathematical analysis that we need not consider here. The cost of production,[3] K_{1-6}, appeared as follows:

---

[3] This method of computing costs had a value outside of this study. For the first time it made possible the computation of production cost by product type as a function of quantities processed and the mix. A standard form was designed to facilitate rapid computation of these costs.

$$K_{1-6} = \frac{0.788 - 0.350A - 0.119AB}{0.788 - 0.063A - 0.050AB} K_{123}(X + 0.054) + \frac{0.376 - 0.119B}{0.663 - 0.050B} K_{4C1}$$

$$+ \frac{0.376 - 0.119B}{0.424 - 0.050B} K_{4C2}(0.616AX) + 0.79K_{6C1}(0.376ABX) + $$

$$(0.920AX)$$

$$0.91K_{6C2}(0.282ABX)$$

$$+ K_{5C1}(0.376AX - 0.376ABX) +$$

$$K_{4F}(0.788X - 0.726AX + \text{Constant})$$

$$+ K_{6F}(0.788X - 0.726AX + \text{Constant}) + \text{Constant}[4]$$

The inventory terms were considerably more complex. They would easily fill a printed page. The length and complexity of the general cost equation raised critical analytical and practical problems.

The usual procedure for minimizing the total cost (defined by the function developed) would yield the necessary values of the control variables to minimize the total production cost (providing the equation defines a minimum value of the total cost). Such a procedure did not turn out to be feasible in this problem for several reasons. First, the distribution of orders did not lend itself to a convenient mathematical expression. But even if it did, a second difficulty would have remained. The equation was of a form that did not feasibly permit an exact solution. Exploration of methods of approximating a solution showed that even these approximate methods would yield a production-planning procedure too complex to be used by company personnel. Further study indicated that not even the use of automatic computing equipment would make such a scheduling procedure feasible.

The complexity of the equations on which scheduling would have to be based (if the procedure described were used) is caused primarily by the fact that inventory costs were expressed as a function of the distribution of sales. It occurred to the team, then, that it might find another property of sales (other than the distribution of quantities) on which to base scheduling. Attention was first turned to the possibility of using sales forecasts provided by the marketing department.

Sales forecasts in this company covered relatively long periods of time, that is, three or four months. These forecasts for each product were converted into monthly estimates by dividing the amount forecast by the number of months covered in the forecast.

The differences between actual sales and forecast sales for this period were converted into a percentage of the forecast quantity. The means and standard deviations of these percentages, covering the period from May 1952 to March 1953 are as follows:

---

[4] The "Constant" refers to material carried over from previous processings, the quantity of which is known.

Product	Mean, %	Standard Deviation, %
Finished Q	−2.6	37.9
Crude Q	+16.8	87.0
R	−34.1	9.0

These results indicate that approximately 95 per cent of the estimates based on sales forecasts would be expected to yield percentage differences that would lie within the following ranges:

Finished Q	−78.4 to	73.2 per cent
Crude Q	−160.0 to	191.0 per cent
R	−52.1 to	−16.1 per cent

The computations indicate that estimates of future sales for short periods based on sales forecasts for long periods are too unreliable for use in scheduling.

Attention was next turned to a study of changes in sales from period to period and the distribution of these changes.

THE SCHEDULING PERIOD

To study changes in sales some base period was required. Hence, it was necessary first to determine what the frequency of scheduling should be.

A scheduling system is related to a production process and inventory in much the same way that a thermostat is related to a furnace and room temperature. To keep a house at a desired temperature level, the thermostat takes continuous readings of the actual temperature and adjusts the furnace accordingly. If the thermostat took only one reading and made only one adjustment per day, the temperature of the house would tend often to be too high or too low. If it took the readings every week, variations from a desired temperature would be even greater. The efficiency of a thermostat, then, depends on how much of the available information on temperature it uses to adjust house temperature. A scheduling procedure's control of inventory similarly depends on how frequently it takes readings of the actual state of inventory and adjusts the production process to keep inventory close to a desired level. The less frequently the scheduling program takes a reading of inventory and makes an adjustment, the more inventory is apt to vary from a desired level.

The thermostat's adjustment of a furnace brings about a change in temperature in a relatively short time. In the case of production planning, the adjustment can take place only as frequently as a production cycle is begun. Thus, a scheduling procedure for a production process with, say, a month's cycle, requires a month to adjust for a current deviation of inventory from a desired level. But in that month, further changes in inventory will take place because of sales and replenishment of stock by goods previously scheduled. Hence, the scheduling procedure must take these replenishments and sales into account.

Those who schdule usually know with accuracy how much additional goods will become available during the month. Sales, however, can only be estimated. The problem can be put symbolically as follows. Let S represent the amount desired in inventory, and s represent the amount actually in inventory. Let a represent the amount of goods that will become available between t_0 (the time of scheduling) and t_1 (the end of the production cycle beginning at t_o). Let $\bar{O}$ represent the estimated sales in the period $t_0 - t_1$. Then the scheduler would ask the plant to produce the following quantity, Q:

$$Q = S - (s + a - \bar{O}).$$

The advantage of as frequent scheduling as possible can be put in more technical language as follows. The amount scheduled depends on $\bar{O}$, the expected sales volume between scheduling periods. The variance of such estimates of $\bar{O}$ generally increases monotonically as the period of time covered by the estimate increases. Hence, the longer is the scheduling period, the larger is the safety factor that must be added to avoid shortages; consequently, the longer is the scheduling period, the larger must be the inventory cushion against shortages. In general then, inventory increases with increases in the scheduling period.

How frequently should a production process be adjusted? That is, be rescheduled? To allow only the minimum deviations from desired inventory level, adjustments should take place every time a production cycle begins. In this case this would mean every day. This was not feasible in this case, however, for the following reasons.

Though a production cycle begins every day, the level of production cannot easily be changed every day because of the costs associated with these changes. Changes in level of production involve a cost. Again, theoretically, it is possible to weigh this cost against the cost of greater variations in inventory resulting from less frequent adjustments of inventory, and thus to derive an optimum scheduling period. The required data were not available for such an analysis, but discussions with production personnel at the company were directed towards establishing what, in their judgment, is the shortest possible practical period between adjustments. The result was a decision to use the length of the average production cycle as the length of a scheduling period. This decision has been marked for further study.

A study of process times for production without recycling showed that the average process cycle is approximately 10 days, and hence it was decided that scheduling should, if possible, be performed at least every 10 days. This required scheduling three times per month, say on the first, eleventh, and twenty-first days.

DISTRIBUTION OF CHANGES IN SALES

Extensive sales data were collected and arranged according to these three ten-day periods in each month. *Changes* were expressed in amounts sold as a multiple of a standard based on past sales. One can, for example, express sales in any period as some multiple of the sales in the immediately preceding period or some other preceding period. Or, one can express sales in a period as a multiple of the highest or lowest sales in any of a specified number of preceding periods. With a view to the development of a scheduling procedure, it is reasonable to consider use of the highest sale in the preceding periods, because scheduling based on this previous high will tend to minimize shortages.

The next question was: How many previous periods should one take into account?

To examine this problem, a study was made of the ratios obtained by dividing each monthly sale for each of the three products by the highest sale in the previous two, three, four, and five months. Because of the lack of independence in the computed ratios for the different base periods, the distributions appeared to be quite similar. It was observed that not more than 7.3 per cent of the ratios exceeded 2.0 in any of the distributions.

The distribution of the previous "three-month sales ratios" for each product was found to have the least variance and to be approximately normal (slightly skewed to the right). Consequently, three months was selected as the base period and various values around 2.0 were tried as possible scheduling factors.

THE SCHEDULING PROCEDURE

These safety factors (f) were incorporated in the scheduling procedure. In developing such a procedure, it was necessary to take into account the interval between the time of scheduling (t_0) and the time at which the product scheduled at t_0 becomes available (t_1). The interval ($t_0 - t_1$) had been established as being ten days.

The scheduling procedure was developed as follows:

(1) At the time of scheduling (t_0) the amount of each product in stock $(S_{0\alpha}, S_{0\beta},$ and $S_{0\gamma})$ is determined.

(2) The highest ten-day sale of each product in the preceding nine ten-day periods $(X_\alpha, X_\beta,$ and $X_\gamma)$ is determined. Then the estimates of sales for the intervals $(t_0 - t_1)$ and $(t_1 - t_2)$ are $fX_\alpha, fX_\beta,$ and fX_γ.

(3) Then, the amounts of stock desired at t_1 (S_1) are also $fX_\alpha, fX_\beta,$ and fX_γ.

(4) The quantity of each product to be scheduled for production during $(t_0 - t_1)$, $Q_\alpha, Q_\beta,$ and Q_γ is found by adapting the equation,

$$Q = S - (s + a - \bar{0}),$$

as follows:

$$Q_\alpha = S_{1\alpha} - (S_{0\alpha} + a_{0\alpha} - \bar{0}_\alpha). \tag{1}$$

Since $S_{1\alpha} = fX_\alpha$, and $\bar{0}_\alpha$ is estimated to be fX_α, by substitution in equation (1) we get

$$Q_\alpha = fX_\alpha - (S_{0\alpha} + a_{0\alpha} - fX_\alpha) = 2fX_\alpha - S_{0\alpha} - a_{0\alpha}. \tag{2}$$

Q_β and Q_γ are similarly determined.

Suppose, for example, that 25 units of a product are in stock at t_0 (i.e., $S_0 = 25$), and that 75 units were scheduled during the last period and will become available during $(t_0 - t_1)$ (i.e., $a_0 = 75$). Suppose further that the highest sale in the previous nine ten-day periods was 35 units (i.e., $X = 35$). Assume that a safety factor of 2 is used (i.e., $f = 2$). Then the number of units to be scheduled (Q) is determined as follows:

$$Q = (2)(2)(35) - (25) - (75) = 40.$$

To aid in scheduling, a table was prepared to show the yields of the three products for various levels of fermentation in a ten-day period. Thus, by scheduling for Finished Q, certain amounts of Crude Q and R would become available. By using this table, the expected yield of the products could be determined, knowing only the flow of materials from each fermentor. A work sheet was also prepared to aid in scheduling for each ten-day period.

In the first scheduling program using this simple plan, no attempt was made to limit the change in number of fermentors set up from one scheduling period to the next scheduling period. The results of applying this scheduling program retrospectively to the period beginning January, 1950, and ending December, 1952, were as follows: no shortages occurred; Finished Q average inventory was decreased by 58 per cent; Crude Q average inventory was decreased by 63 per cent; and R average inventory was decreased by 56 per cent as compared to actual average inventories of the three-year period being studied. Also, these reductions were reflected in the reduced total number of fermentors required. In the three-year period a reduction of 17 per cent of fermentors processed was obtained. Thus, both inventory costs and production costs would have been reduced by this method.

Other studies have shown that the carrying cost of money invested in finished products, storage, supervision, obsolescence, deterioration, etc., amounts to about 2 per cent of the cost of the finished product per month. On the basis of the 2 per cent per month figure, an approximate cost of inventories for the three-year period was computed. The first scheduling attempt reduced the average monthly cost of inventories by 42 per cent. This, of course, does not include the increase in net income resulting from the elimination of recycling that would have occurred, but which could not be calculated due to the lack of necessary information concerning the actual scheduling used during the three years studied.

Comparison of a wide variety of scheduling factors revealed that 2 was the lowest factor for which no shortages would occur.

STABILIZING EMPLOYMENT

These results were very encouraging. But the resulting schedule had a major difficulty. The level of production was subjected to frequent and severe fluctuations. The resulting procedure required frequent changes in the number of work crews employed. Such changes were unacceptable to the company because of the labor problems that would have arisen out of hiring and laying off men as production fluctuated.

The company that was under study has a plant seniority system in which any one personnel change in the plant making the product involved might require five different personnel changes in other plants. This system requires that if a man is needed in that particular plant, he can be drawn from another job that, in turn, can pick a man from a lower ranking job, according to the company's seniority system. This system requires in all a possible shift of five different people, because of the five different levels of seniority. Such an arrangement could result in increased training costs and in delays in the increase of production. For these reasons, an acceptable scheduling program had to be accompanied by labor stabilization; that is, it must require only a minimum number of transfers either into or out of the plant involved. Data were obtained to show the labor force that would be needed within the plant to handle various production levels.

The *average* fermentation rate of all scheduling programs examined was at a level requiring three crews. This raised the question: If three crews had been employed during these three years (1950–52), and if production had varied from the minimum to the maximum for the three crews, what inventories would have developed, and what shortages would have existed? The same basic scheduling method was then used to schedule over the three-year period, with the imposed limitations of a three-crew operation. The resulting schedule met all sales demands over the three-year period, and it resulted in the following average inventory reductions: Finished Q, 39 per cent, Crude Q, 57 per cent, and R, 57 per cent, or a decrease in inventory costs of about 40 per cent. Also, the number of fermentors needed to be set could have been reduced by as much as 18 per cent.

This scheduling method in its revised form was subsequently applied to the first eight monthly sales in 1953. All sales demands were met. When the program of scheduling was applied to this 44-month period, the following results were obtained:

1. Reduced inventories.
2. No shortages.
3. Increased stability of employment.
4. No recycling, hence lower unit production costs.
5. Ease in using scheduling procedure.

CONTROL OF THE SCHEDULING PROCEDURE

As indicated above, the scheduling procedure described was evaluated by applying it retrospectively to the last three years of operation. The results speak for themselves, but they raise two serious questions:

1. Why does this scheduling procedure work?
2. What assurance is there that it will continue to work? Or, more constructively, how and when can modifications be made in the procedure to keep it working effectively?

This scheduling procedure is designed around two basic characteristics of sales:

1. In general, the amount sold in any one scheduling period did not exceed twice the largest sale in any of the scheduling periods in the preceding three months.
2. The average ten-day sales requirements could be met by a three-crew operation, with no recycling.

To assure the continued usefulness of this scheduling procedure, it is necessary to check these two characteristics to detect changes in them. Furthermore, it is necessary to have methods of determining when and how to change the scheduling procedure, if these characteristics change. First, let us consider the scheduling factor.

The following ratio for each product was plotted for a period of forty-one months:

$$\frac{\text{Actual sales of the month}}{\text{Highest monthly sales in the preceding three months}}.$$

In Figure 3, the results for Finished Q are shown. The results for the other products were quite similar.

It will be noted that the ratios tend to fall in the range from 0.5 to 1.5 with an estimated mean of 1.0. Further studies showed that a scheduling factor of 2 is needed for ratios that fall in this range to avoid shortages during the period studied. For example, when a factor of 1.75 is used, shortages do occur.[5]

The chart shown in Figure 3 can be used for control purposes. As

Figure 3

CONTROL CHART FOR FINISHED Q SCHEDULING FACTOR (RATIO OF ACTUAL SALES TO HIGHEST MONTHLY SALE IN PRECEDING THREE MONTHS)

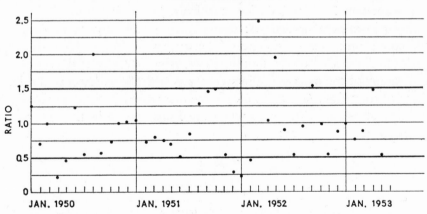

long as the ratios fall within these bands, it will be safe in general to use a scheduling factor of 2. If points regularly fall below 0.5, a re-examination of the system should be made with a view to reducing the scheduling factor. Similarly, if points fall above 1.5, an examination of sales data is called for to avoid possible shortages. If points fall above 1.5 regularly, then the sales data should be re-examined with a view to increasing the scheduling factor.

---

[5] By such computations it was possible to show the company how much it would cost to avoid various numbers of shortages.

Now let us consider the question of crew level. Let O_h represent the highest monthly sales in the preceding three months. Then, according to the scheduling plan, $\frac{2}{3} O_h$ would be scheduled for availability during the first ten-day period. At the end of each month, the ratio

$$\frac{\text{Average monthly inventory}}{\text{Total monthly sales}}$$

could be computed, where the average monthly inventory is the sum of the inventory at the start of each scheduling period divided by three. This may be compared with upper and lower limits expected for this ratio, on the assumption that the scheduling factor 2 remains in control. The calculation of approximations to these limits is made as follows:

In accordance with use of a scheduling factor of 2, actual sales for a month should not be more than $1.5 \, O_h$, nor less than $0.5 \, O_h$; that is, not more than $\frac{1}{2} \, O_h$ nor less than $\frac{1}{6} \, O_h$ for a ten-day period. Scheduling operates by ten-day periods, and production planning takes into account actual sales as they become known. Using the limits associated with a scheduling factor of 2, 0.5, and 1.5, the *upper* limit and *lower* limit for the ratio of average inventory to actual monthly sales are found to be approximately 2.33 and 0.63 respectively. These latter approximate limits are computed as follows: If O_h represents the highest sale in the preceding three months, then, on the assumption of equal sales during each ten-day period of the month, $\frac{1}{3} \, O_h$ may be taken as the highest sale in any of the preceding nine ten-day periods. Scheduling would be directed toward producing $\frac{2}{3} \, O_h$ for the first period in the new month. Table 4 shows what happens when the lowest value in the expected range of sales is obtained:

Table 4

UPPER LIMIT CALCULATIONS

10-Day Period	Inventory (production + "left-over")	Expected Sales
1.	$\frac{2}{3} O_h$	$\frac{1}{3}(0.5 \, O_h)$
2.	$\frac{2}{3} O_h + \frac{2}{3} O_h - \frac{1}{6} O_h = \frac{7}{6} O_h$	$\frac{1}{3}(0.5 \, O_h)$
3.	$\frac{2}{3} O_h + \frac{7}{6} O_h - \frac{1}{6} O_h = \frac{5}{3} O_h$	$\frac{1}{3}(0.5 \, O_h)$
Total.	$\frac{7}{2} O_h$	$\frac{1}{2} O_h$

Average inventory $\frac{7}{2} O_h / 3 = \frac{7}{6} O_h$
Average inventory/total monthly sales $= (\frac{7}{6} O_h)/(\frac{1}{2} O_h) = 2.33$

Similarly, Table 5 shows what happens when the highest value in the expected range of sales is obtained:

In Figure 4, the ratios of average total monthly inventory (over all product types) to total monthly sales are plotted. The upper and lower control limits (2.33 and 0.63) are also shown. When a plotted ratio goes over the upper limit, it indicates inventory is becoming too large, and hence it should alert schedulers to the possibility of reducing the number of crews operating. Actually, one such point would not be sufficient ground for reducing crews. If a significantly long series of consecutive points should happen to fall above the upper limit, careful consideration should also be given to future sales to see if there is any

Table 5

LOWER LIMIT CALCULATIONS

10-Day Period	Inventory (production + "left-over")	Expected Sales
1..............................	$\frac{2}{3}O_h$	$\frac{1}{3}(1.5\,O_h)$
2..............................	$\frac{2}{3}O_h + \frac{2}{3}O_h - \frac{1}{2}O_h = \frac{5}{6}O_h$	$\frac{1}{3}(1.5\,O_h)$
3*............................	$O_h + \frac{5}{6}O_h - \frac{1}{2}O_h = \frac{4}{3}O_h$	$\frac{1}{3}(1.5\,O_h)$
Total.....................	$\frac{17}{6}O_h$	$\frac{3}{2}O_h$

Average inventory $17\,O_h/(6 \times 3) = \frac{17}{18}\,O_h$

Average inventory/total monthly sales $= (\frac{17}{18}\,O_h)/(\frac{3}{2}\,O_h) = \frac{17}{27} = 0.63$

* At the beginning of the second period (when the schedule for production of goods that becomes available during the third period), the first period's sales are known. In this case it is assumed to be $\frac{1}{3}(1.5\,O_h)$. The forecast demand for the third period, then, is $2[\frac{1}{3}(1.5\,O_h)] = O_h$.

Figure 4

CONTROL CHART FOR CREW OPERATION (RATIO OF AVERAGE MONTHLY INVENTORY TO TOTAL MONTHLY SALES)

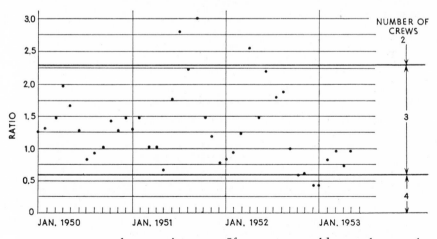

reason to expect them to increase. If so, one would not change the number of crews. If, on the other hand, forecasts indicate continued low sales, the crews should be reduced.

Corresponding remarks relative to increasing the number of crews are applicable when points are observed to fall below the lower limit.

The graphic device, Figure 4, cannot be used alone. Sales forecasts must be taken into consideration when deciding whether crew levels should be changed. The device does, however, show clearly when operations at a three-crew level begin to build too large or too small inventories. It is important to note, however, that its use assumes that the scheduling factor is in control. If the scheduling factor is not in control, the inventory sales ratio will probably also go out of control, but the trouble may be with the scheduling factor and not the crew level.

These two control devices require supplementation by good judgment and knowledge of general and special business conditions. No automatic application of them can be made.

FUTURE STUDIES

No research project is ever completed in the sense that all loose ends have been tied. This project was no exception—but it reached a stage where the results could be applied with confidence in the attainment of production and inventory economies. Furthermore, the approach to production and inventory control described is applicable to other chemical processes, and in particular to fermentation processes. Adaptation to other processes can be made easily by company personnel, with only occasional outside consultation.

Many phases of the study presented here could stand further analysis. Among those that hold some promise of resulting in further significant economies are:

1. In the discussion of the scheduling period it was pointed out theoretically that scheduling should be performed every day. The possibility of decreasing the scheduling period from a practical point of view should eventually be considered.
2. Lack of flexibility in crew levels prevents maximum reductions of production and inventory costs. Such flexibility itself involves costs. These costs should be studied to determine the maximum frequency of crew level changes that can be tolerated. Ways of gaining flexibility other than hiring and firing should also be investigated. In fact, there is a possibility that maintaining the maximum number of crews even when they are not needed, in order to gain maximum production flexibility, may be economically desirable and hence worth further study.
3. This study shows that production costs are extremely sensitive to product mixes and quantities, and this fact suggests that pricing policies and sales effort might be designed so as to stimulate a sales pattern which maximizes net return on production investment.
4. The control devices applicable to this scheduling procedure are the result of only preliminary study. Further study should uncover more effective control devices.

CASE 8

The Determination of Requirements for Warehouse Dock Facilities[1]

DONALD H. SCHILLER and
MARVIN M. LAVIN[2]

Some points of special interest in this paper are:

   a) The derivation of a service time distribution, especially, the combination of exponential distributions.
   b) The methods used to modify the data collected so it could be used in evaluating the proposed system.
   c) The way in which peak season adjustments were made.
   d) "The final optimization, incorporating cost and policy factors, was re-served for the company management."
   e) "The . . . problem, although conceptually simple, contained sufficient mathematical complexity that no theoretical solutions existed; . . . only simulation methods appeared to offer an economical avenue of solution."
   f) The amount of detailed information accumulated in order to simulate the problem.
   g) The implication that the problem is being solved for a peak (and brief) season.

One of the characteristic problems undertaken by operations research is a prediction of the extent of new facilities required to meet contem-

[1] *Operation Research,* April, 1956. Reprinted by permission.

[2] Caywood-Schiller, Associates.

The authors wish to express their indebtedness to Mr. S. J. Fosdick, Vice President, Wieboldt Stores, Inc. and to Mr. F. L. Moore, General Service Manager, for their assistance during the study and for their permission to publish the materials of this article; the authors also wish to acknowledge the considerable assistance of Mr. E. Mentzer of Caywood-Schiller, Associates.

plated changes in a company's business operation. Such a problem—recently presented to Caywood-Schiller, Associates by Wieboldt Stores, Incorporated of Chicago—is the subject of this article.

Wieboldt Stores operates a chain of large department stores in the Chicago area and, at the time of the initiation of the study (spring, 1955), the company was employing three warehouse locations for the storage of consumer merchandise. Two of the warehouses were operated in conjunction with retail stores at the same locations; the third was used for storage exclusively. A number of factors—including lease terminations, obsolescence, and a changing consumer market pattern—led Wieboldt management to consider the consolidation of all warehouse facilities at a single one of these locations.

The problem presented to us was concerned with the extent of new truck-dock facilities that would be required to handle the volume of truck traffic formerly accommodated at the three separate locations augmented by that occasioned by the anticipated openings of several new stores.

If the number of trucks arriving each day were precisely predictable, if their times of arrival could be scheduled, and if their servicing times could be anticipated, then the problem of planning the most economical dock facilities would scarcely require the application of operations research. In actuality, however, the number of daily truck arrivals, the instants of arrival, and the servicing times have a chance character that precludes an elementary arithmetical analysis of the problem.

One immediately recognizes the essential waiting-line nature of this problem of estimating requirements for warehouse docks: the number of truck docks would directly affect the length of wait for service after the arrival of a truck. Since the trucks were, in part, rented by the company on a daily basis for delivery service to the retail stores, there would be out-of-pocket costs immediately derived from time lost awaiting service facilities. Furthermore, an excessive waiting line of trucks would aggravate traffic conditions in a public alley and street. On the other hand, additional service docks would involve significant outlays for their construction and manning. Thus, the factors to be considered by management were in economic conflict, and a waiting-line analysis would be the key to a decision.

The Wieboldt management asked us to study the potential consequences of operating with various amounts of service facilities at the consolidated warehouse being planned. The final optimization, incorporating cost and policy factors, was reserved for the company management. Notwithstanding this limitation in the scope of the formal operations-research investigation, the study provides an informative example of a practical waiting-line problem to which the limited amount of waiting-line theory presently available to the analyst was not applicable.

THE GENERAL APPROACH

The approach taken in the study of the Wieboldt waiting-line problem is reflected in the organization of this article. The following paragraphs summarize the sequence of analysis; the analysis itself is described in more detail in the remaining sections: .

1. To provide an accurate quantitative picture of existing truck-traffic conditions, a complete survey of truck arrivals at the three warehouses was made during a seven-week period. The survey data enabled the truck arrival rates to be determined. (The magnitude of these arrival rates was, of course, related to the existing pattern of traffic flow among the three warehouses and the retail stores.) On the basis of the modified truck-traffic pattern expected to occur under the centralized warehouse scheme, the truck arrival rates obtained for the existing system were factored, adjusted, and recombined to apply to the system under planning. In addition to data on arrival rates, the survey provided evidence from which the variations in truck servicing time could be established.

2. An investigation of available warehouse records was made to measure the extent of seasonal fluctuations in truck-traffic volume; this information, in turn, permitted the properties of the survey-period traffic to be projected to the peak periods of the year.

3. At this juncture, the inputs to the waiting-line problem were largely at hand. Next, applicability of available waiting-line theory to the Wieboldt problem was assessed. If such theory had been previously developed, the results of interest to management might have been obtained directly from formulas. However, the Wieboldt problem, although conceptually simple, contained sufficient mathematical complexity that no theoretical solutions existed; furthermore, only simulation methods appeared to offer an economical avenue of solution. Hence, the truck-docking operations were programmed for simulation on a high-speed computing machine, using a "Monte-Carlo" technique to be described later. The results of the Monte-Carlo analysis included, among other things, estimates of the probability that waiting lines of stated length would occur at various times during the day at the peak period of the year, as a function of the extent of service facilities Wieboldt management might provide.

DETERMINING THE EXISTING TRUCK-ARRIVAL RATES

As indicated above, the first task was one of obtaining an accurate quantitative understanding of the operations of the existing warehouse-docking system. To this end, Wieboldt personnel conducted a traffic survey during a sample period of seven weeks during the spring of 1955. A tally card was prepared for every truck arriving at each of the three warehouse locations; on this card was recorded such information as arrival and departure times, loading and unloading times, type of truck, cargo size and disposition, etc.

There were 4,612 trucks tallied during the complete survey, with noteworthy variation occurring in the daily arrival totals. A first consideration was to establish whether the arrival totals were related to the days of the week, to the weeks of the month, and to the specific warehouse. On the basis of well-known statistical tests, it was concluded that there were no significant differences among the days of the week and among the weeks of the month; on the other hand, one of the three

Figure 1

COMPARISON OF A THEORETICAL CURVE WITH EMPIRICAL DATA OF TRUCK ARRIVALS AT A WAREHOUSE DURING A DAY

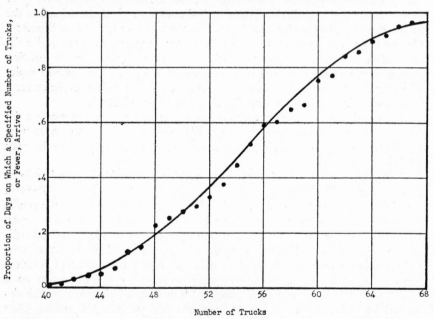

Number of Trucks

warehouses did have a significantly lower average than the other two for the daily arrival totals.

After it had been established that heavy or light arrival traffic did not favor any day or week of the survey period, it was natural to test if the variation in the daily arrival totals appeared to be governed by the same set of chance factors from day to day. If this proved to be the case, then one would have reason to expect that the pattern of this variation would follow a well-known mathematical law; this would be tantamount to finding that the daily variation in total truck arrivals was essentially predictable. Figure 1, which displays the truck arrival data for both warehouses having the same average daily arrival traffic, indicates that the chance factors responsible for the variation did maintain constancy during the survey period. The mathematical law known as the Poisson probability distribution provides a theoretical curve corresponding closely to either set of empirical data.

Once the total truck arrivals were seen to have the same expected magnitude each day, but with chance variability about this amount, the next matter to be investigated concerned the traffic-arrival pattern during the day. Tests of the empirical data showed that the division of

Figure 2

COMPARISON OF A THEORETICAL CURVE WITH EMPIRICAL DATA OF TRUCK ARRIVALS AT A WAREHOUSE DURING HALF-HOUR INTERVALS

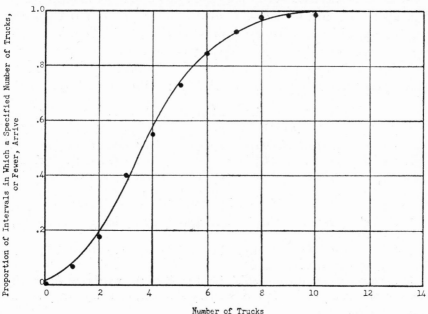

Number of Trucks

arrivals between the morning and afternoon could be assumed constant with approximately 65 per cent of the truck arrivals occurring in the morning. Since the morning period contained one less hour than the afternoon, the morning average arrival rate was larger than the afternoon rate by more than a factor of two. Hence morning was significantly more critical for the formation of excessive waiting lines, and major attention was concentrated on this period.

Next, it was found that the arrival rates at the three warehouses were not significantly different among the half-hours of the morning—each half-hour having (contrary to the intuition of warehouse personnel) the same expected number of truck arrivals. Furthermore, as Figure 2 indicates, the variation of the morning half-hourly arrivals followed a pattern closely corresponding to the Poisson law, that is to say, the structure of chance factors affecting the instants of arrival of trucks appeared to maintain a constant character throughout the morning. (A similar analysis of the afternoon arrival traffic indicated the same property to be present.)

PROJECTING ARRIVAL RATES AT THE CONSOLIDATED WAREHOUSE

The truck arrival rates determined in the survey did not directly apply to the new consolidated warehouse system. In order to make these data applicable, it was necessary to decompose them into elements which could be identified as being present or absent in the new operational scheme, and then to recombine the relevant elements appropriately. The decomposition led to fourteen significant categories of truck arrivals, based on the following classification:

TRUCK TYPE

1. *Vendor trucks*—which delivered merchandise from outside sources to the warehouses or to the retail stores sharing premises with the warehouses.

2. *United Parcel Service (UPS) trucks*—which were rented by Wieboldt Stores to deliver merchandise from the warehouse to the retail stores.

CARGO MOVEMENT

1. *Central movement*—which involved delivery by vendors to a warehouse, or pickup by UPS from a warehouse.

2. *Local movement*—which involved delivery by either vendors or UPS to a retail store on warehouse premises.

3. *Central-local movement*—which involved both the warehouse and retail store on the same premises in a delivery by a vendor, or in a delivery and a pickup by UPS.

LOCATION

1. *Warehouse A*—which was the location of both a warehouse and a retail store, and would be the site of the consolidated warehouse.

2. *Warehouse B*—which was the location of both a warehouse and a retail store, the warehousing function to be eliminated under the new system.

3. *Warehouse C*—which was a warehouse only and would be eliminated by the consolidation.

When each of the fourteen categories of truck arrivals was viewed in the light of consolidated warehouse operations, some disappeared, others were altered. To illustrate:

Warehouse B, Vendor, Local Category. This category was made up of truck arrivals delivering merchandise (e.g., foodstuffs) which did not pass through the warehouse system. These arrivals would continue at this location under the new system, but would not contribute to the dock requirements at the consolidated warehouse.

Warehouse B, UPS, Central-Local Category. In this category were UPS trucks delivering merchandise from warehouses *A* and *C* to the retail store on the warehouse *B* premises and also loading merchandise from warehouse *B* for other retail stores. In this instance, only the loading activities would be transferred to the consolidated warehouse.

In addition to the arrival traffic at the consolidated warehouse arising from the foregoing modifications to the existing fourteen traffic categories, there would be arrivals having no counterpart in the existing categories. For example, merchandise which moved by hand truck from warehouse *B* to the retail store on the same premises was not involved in truck-arrival data obtained in the survey. Under the consolidated warehouse system, movement of this merchandise would augment the need for docking facilities at the warehouse. Estimates of truck arrival traffic for this and other new categories were made, principally on the assumption that the traffic would be proportional to expected future dollar volume of the retail stores involved.

As a result of this analysis of arrival activity, there was obtained the following simplified picture of truck arrival traffic at the consolidated warehouse:

1. Truck arrivals would occur at random times—with the probability of arrival at a particular instant during the morning period being the same as at any other instant, and similarly during the afternoon.

2. The expected number of trucks arriving in the morning would be 105; the number of afternoon arrivals would average 35 per cent of the day's arrivals.

3. Vendor trucks would unload only; UPS trucks would load only.

DETERMINING EXISTING TRUCK-SERVICING TIMES

The second major feature of the waiting-line evaluation was concerned with servicing times. It was to be expected that significant individual variations would occur in the amount of time trucks spent at a dock, and the survey data showed this to be the case. Differences between loading and unloading operations were one source of this variation; differences in the size and character of cargos were another. The task was one of identifying the (possibly) several classes of trucks having distinctly different servicing-time properties, and then characterizing the servicing-time variation of each of these classes in a way which would lend itself to mathematical treatment and to projection to circumstances other than the survey period.

That UPS and vendor trucks should be separated on the matter of required servicing times became quickly apparent. Figure 3 shows the empirical data for the unloading times required by vendor trucks, together with a theoretical curve shown by the broken line that is based on a mathematical law known as the "exponential holding-time" law. The latter law, which has been found to have wide practical applicabil-

Figure 3

COMPARISON OF TWO THEORETICAL CURVES WITH EMPIRICAL DATA OF
VENDOR-TRUCK UNLOADING TIMES

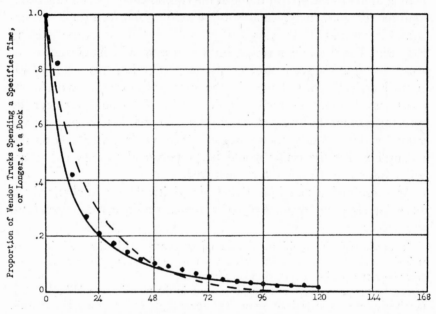

Unloading Time [in minutes]

ity, would apply if the probability that servicing of a particular truck ends at any specific instant is constant throughout the servicing operation. The broken curve in Figure 3 does not have a satisfactory correspondence with the empirical data; on the other hand, the solid curve, which results from the assumption that the vendor trucks were made up of two classes, each having servicing times described by the exponential holding-time law, but with different average servicing times, provides a good representation of the data. More specifically, 75 per cent of the vendor trucks, requiring an average servicing time of 10 minutes, comprised one class; the remaining 25 per cent of the vendor trucks averaged 45 minutes at the loading docks.

In the instance of the UPS trucks being loaded, it was found (as shown in Figure 4) that the exponential holding-time law matched the survey servicing times closely, after a truck had first spent some 18 minutes at the dock. An investigation, suggested by this result, revealed that this 18-minute period was not involved with actual loading, but with certain essential paper work and preloading cargo assembly (which would also be present in the consolidated warehouse).

The servicing-time phenomena observed during the survey period thus required only two simple mathematical expressions for their de-

Figure 4

COMPARISON OF A THEORETICAL CURVE WITH EMPIRICAL
DATA OF UPS TRUCK-SERVICING TIMES

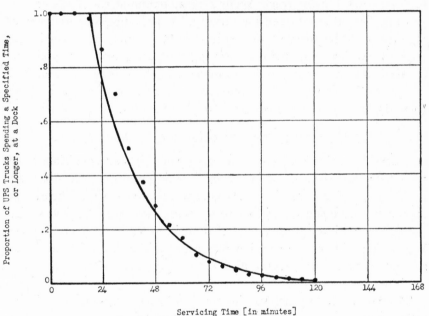

Servicing Time [in minutes]

scription, the first relating to the two classes of unloading times discovered to apply to vendor trucks and the second representing the amount of time spent at freight docks by the UPS trucks undergoing loading. Such factors as warehouse location, time of the day, day of the week, etc. were not found to affect servicing times significantly.

PROJECTING TO THE PEAK SEASON

It was anticipated that the judgment of the Wieboldt management on docking facilities at the consolidated warehouse would be founded preponderantly upon the degree of congestion during the peak (pre-Christmas) season. A suitable basis was needed, therefore, to project the results of the analysis of the survey period to this season. For this purpose, summaries were available for previous years giving the number of vendor shipments received, the number of UPS pickups made, and the number of individual pieces (i.e., containers) processed at the warehouses. An unexpected finding to Wieboldt personnel was that, in the presence of the heavy warehouse congestion preceding Christmas, the weekly warehouse truck arrivals were scarcely 5 per cent higher during the peak season than during the spring. By contrast, however, the number of pieces processed was nearly 50 per cent higher in the peak season than in the spring. It became apparent that the pre-Christmas situation involved approximately the same number of trucks as the survey period, but the trucks spent a greater time at the docks on the average. The information of the survey tally cards suggested that servicing time could be assumed proportional to the number of pieces in the cargo. A sensible basis for transforming the survey results to apply to the peak season appeared to be an increase of the average truck arrival rate by 5 per cent and an increase of the average unloading and average (actual) loading times by approximately 50 per cent.

SIMULATING THE DOCKING OPERATIONS

Judged by the waiting-line structures for which mathematicians have provided practical formulas for use in obtaining solutions, the Wieboldt problem contained formidable mathematical complexity. Theoretical approaches were considered, but these seemed too costly to develop by comparison with the employment of simulation methods; hence, for the Wieboldt problem, the solution was accomplished by a Monte-Carlo simulation procedure programmed for a high-speed digital computing machine.

The Monte-Carlo procedure involved, for each "arriving truck," the assignment of a time of arrival and an amount of servicing time; these two quantities were obtained by random selection from stocks of numbers (that is, frequency distributions) which reflected the properties which the study had shown the arrival times and servicing times to have. For each specified number of service docks, it was then possible to simulate the movement of the trucks through the docking system, and to compute the length of waiting line and the amount of wait until service each time a truck arrived. In this fashion, a day of simulated operations was run. Repeated simulations of the day's operations and a suitable averaging of the results led to the desired description of the waiting-line situation which would result for each selected number of service docks.

The simulation method described above would have been time-consuming and prone to error if performed manually (for example, a hand-computed simulation of a day's docking operations at a 15-dock warehouse required 8 man-hours to perform). Accordingly, it was essential to program the method for a high-speed digital computer. A survey of available machines indicated that the Datatron computer made by the Electrodata Corporation would be best for the purpose.

The program was prepared for the Datatron, and the warehouse docking operation was repeatedly simulated for facilities with 12, 15, 18, and 21 docks, since preliminary analysis had shown this to be the range of interest. The total machine computing time did not exceed 3 hours. The results recorded were the arrival time, the length of waiting line, and the amount of wait until service for each truck arrival.

PRESENTING THE RESULTS

The results obtained from the runs of a day's simulated docking operations offered many alternative ways of describing the waiting-line situation associated with a specified extent of service facilities. The form of description most useful to management would depend upon the form in which cost and policy information was most readily expressible. The

Figure 5

AVERAGE AND EXTREME WAITING-LINE LENGTHS OBSERVED IN TEN
TYPICAL DAYS OF SIMULATED OPERATION OF AN 18-DOCK FACILITY

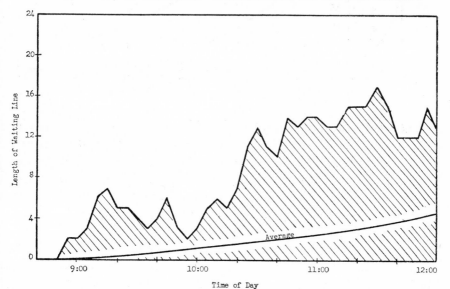

following materials illustrate the presentations chosen for the report to Wieboldt management.

Figure 5 shows one means of summarizing the expected variability of daily docking operations. Here is depicted both the average and the most extreme length of waiting line found in a typical set of ten runs which simulated the operation of an 18-dock facility.

The results of the Monte-Carlo runs also enabled the preparation of charts such as Figure 6, which present estimates of the relative fre-

Figure 6

PROBABILITY DISTRIBUTION OF WAITING-LINE LENGTH, 11:00 A.M. TO 12:00 NOON, PEAK SEASON

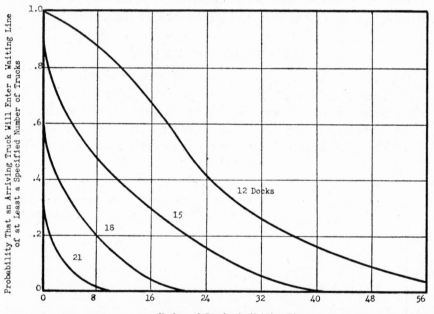

Number of Trucks in Waiting Line

quency (i.e., the probability) with which a truck arriving between (say) 11:00 and 12:00 A.M. on a day of the pre-Christmas season would enter a waiting line of at least a specified number of trucks. Similarly, Figure 7 contains estimates of the probability that this truck would have to wait at least a specified number of minutes before reaching a service dock. As an example of the interpretation of Figure 6, it is found that the probability is approximately one chance in ten that an arriving truck will enter a waiting line of at least 28 trucks if 15 servicing docks are provided. The magnitude of this probability might be of special interest to management if a line of 27 trucks were, for example, the longest line not interfering with traffic at a public street intersection. From Figure 7, when 18 docks are provided, the probability is approximately one chance in five that an arriving truck must wait at least 15 minutes before reaching a service dock.

Figure 7

PROBABILITY DISTRIBUTION OF WAITING TIME, 11:00 A.M. TO 12:00 NOON, PEAK SEASON

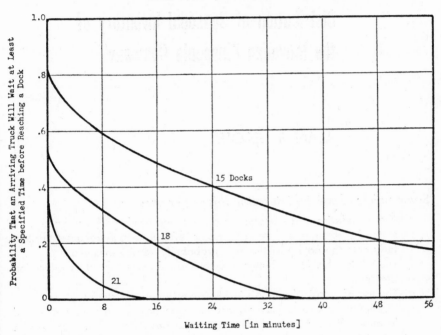

APPLYING THE STUDY TECHNIQUE TO OTHER PROBLEMS

The Wieboldt truck-docking problem is similar to many others from widely diverse business operations. Essentially the same technique of treatment has been applied to study the operation of ticket- and baggage-servicing counters of a major airline. The structure of the latter problem differs from the Wieboldt situation in several interesting respects: a number of parallel waiting lines are present; arrivals sometimes appear in groups; and arrivals are assumed to enter the line of shortest length. No essential difficulties are encountered, however, in generalizing the Monte-Carlo program for the Datatron computer so that it will apply to the airline problem.

CASE 9

Distribution of Seasonal Inventory of the Hawaiian Pineapple Company[1]

ALAN R. EAGLE[2]

Some points of special interest in this paper are:

a) The boundaries of the analysis, e.g., size and number of warehouses.
b) Method used to determine buffer stock level at each warehouse. Particularly note the nature of the joint probability density involved.
c) The relationship of the buffer inventory to the excess inventory allocation problem.
d) The use of marginal analysis in allocating the excess stock.
e) "Company practice of never allocating more (inventory) to any mainland location than will be sold before the next peak season . . . assume on adequate turnover of fresh supplies." In addition, what might happen in the system?
f) The feasibility of the allocation method was checked by a simulation of inventory fluctuations over a hypothetical year of operations.
g) Assigning responsibility to a company officer for incorporating the allocation procedures in company operations.
h) Alternative formulations of the excess inventory allocation problem, e.g., as a dynamic or linear programming problem.

This paper describes a program developed for the Hawaiian Pineapple Company, Ltd., to reduce inventory costs incurred in the distribution of canned pineapple products. The Dole plantations harvest about 75 per cent of their total annual crop during the five summer months, thus creating large canned goods inventories. These inventories are stored in the Company's

[1] *Operations Research*, June, 1957. Reprinted by permission. Presented at the Third Annual Meeting of The Institute of Management Sciences, Los Angeles, California, on October 19, 1956.

[2] *Stanford Research Institute.*

676

Honolulu warehouse and at commercial warehouses on the U.S. mainland. The mainland warehouses store a portion of the seasonal inventories and also provide forward supply points for the Company's buyers, but at considerable expense. An inventory-control model was developed to determine the required inventory at each warehouse for specified protection against an out-of-stock condition. A procedure was developed for allocating inventories in excess of those needed for immediate sales requirements among the available storage points to minimize the total annual warehousing cost. The procedure takes into account the different storage, handling, and tax costs at the various locations and all relevant operating requirements. The principles involved are explained by a graphical approach, which is easy to understand and which facilitates changing the allocation rules in response to changes in operating conditions. The program has been adopted by the Company's management and steps are in progress to incorporate the recommendations in the Company's inventory distribution operations.

Late in 1955, the Hawaiian Pineapple Company, Ltd., approached the Stanford Research Institute with a cost-control problem of growing concern to the Company's management. Over the period of a few years, increases in the Company's sales volume and changes in marketing practices in the pineapple industry had caused a substantial increase in the costs of distributing pineapple to the U.S. market. Of prime concern were the costs involved in handling and storing the large inventories required in the Company's operations. A team was assigned from the Industrial Operations Research staff at Stanford Research Institute to evaluate alternative means of reducing these costs.

A Seasonal Product

The Hawaiian Pineapple Company grows pineapple on a mass basis in the Hawaiian Islands. As many as 500 million pineapple plants may be in the ground at any one time, with a growth cycle four to five years in length. Pineapple harvesting is a highly seasonal operation, and, since the fruit has to be packed immediately after picking, this seasonality extends into the packing operations. Pineapple is transported by barge and truck to the Company's cannery in Honolulu where it is packed into forty different canned items, including different cuts, can sizes, syrup weights, etc.

The seasonality of packing operations is shown in Figure 1. The monthly pack amounts (dashed line) and the cumulative pack as a per cent of the total year's pack are shown for the past three years.[3] The per cent of the total year's pack produced during the five months of summer harvest is also indicated. The sharp peak in canning operations creates

---

[3] Scales incorporating information of a confidential nature have been removed from several of the charts.

large storage requirements following the harvest season. Inventories of canned pineapple products are stored at the cannery in Honolulu and at commercial warehouses on the U.S. mainland.

Figure 1

MONTHLY AND CUMULATIVE PRODUCTION OF
PINEAPPLE AND JUICE, 1953 THROUGH 1955

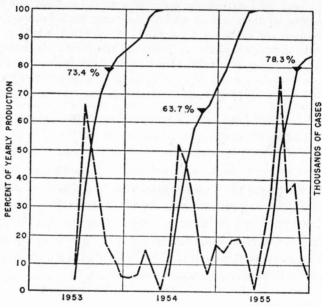

Limitations on Storage in Honolulu

Storage of cased goods inventories in Honolulu is limited by the amount of space available and by the necessity for sharing space with cannery supplies and empty cans. The latter two items are stocked in advance of the pack season and consumed as the season progresses. Because of difficulties in predicting the rate and timing of the pineapple harvest (which is greatly affected by weather factors) provision must be made for large day-to-day fluctuations in storage requirements. Shipping space during the pack season must be requested well in advance of sailing dates. Since pineapple products have a limited shelf life in regions of high temperature, a fast turnover of Honolulu inventories must be maintained. The movement of inventories between Honolulu and the mainland must be planned with these requirements in mind.

An important factor affecting long-range storage planning is the vulnerability of the Hawaiian Islands to interruptions in shipping schedules. The Company is entirely dependent on a free flow of products between Honolulu and the mainland, and shipping tieups at either end of this supply line can have a serious effect on operations. For this reason, Company management is reluctant to make capital investments in additional warehouse facilities in Honolulu. Existing space is used for storage to the fullest extent compatible with operating restrictions, but no new warehousing facilities are contemplated.

A Changing Market

Marketing conditions in the pineapple industry have changed considerably during the past few years. Pineapple was in short supply imme-

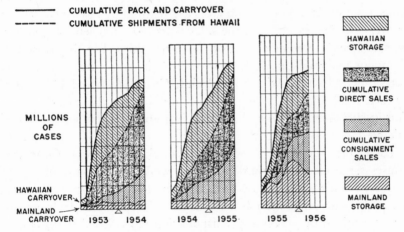

Figure 2

CUMULATIVE PACK, SHIPMENTS, SALES, AND HAWAII AND MAINLAND STORAGE FOR LAST THREE FISCAL YEARS

diately after the war, and all sales were supplied by direct shipment from Honolulu to the Company's buyers. Now, however, pineapple is in a buyer's market. Buyers are cautious of forward buying and want to obtain a major portion of their supplies on an immediate delivery basis. Thus, in addition to storing seasonal inventories, the Company's mainland warehouses serve as forward supply points providing fast service to buyers.

Figure 2 shows the cumulative pack, shipments and sales, and Hawaii and mainland storage over the last three fiscal years. The top line of Figure 2 represents cumulative pack and carryover. The dashed line represents cumulative shipments from Hawaii. Shipments from Hawaii are either moved directly to the customer (direct sales), sold to the customer via a mainland warehouse (consignment sales), or become an addition to mainland inventory. Cumulative direct sales and cumulative consignment sales are shown by shaded areas on the chart. The total inventory at mainland warehouses is represented by the lower hatched portion of the chart. Note the heavy bulge in Hawaiian storage that occurs each year during the pack season. Also note the large increase in mainland storage that has occurred over the past three years, with an accompanying rise in warehousing costs.

Location of Mainland Warehouses

Pineapple sales are billed f.o.b. Honolulu; customers, therefore, specify shipment over the route providing the lowest total transportation cost (water and rail charges combined). The shipping rate is the same from Honolulu to any point on the East or Gulf Coast; similarly, the rate from Honolulu to any point along the West Coast is the same. Thus, the lowest transportation costs are realized by having warehouses at every coastal point where the sales volume is sufficient to justify the port as a regular point of call of the cargo ships. For this reason, the Company maintains inventories at commercial warehouses at seventeen ports on the Pacific, Atlantic, and Gulf Coasts. Although there would be certain advantages in having fewer warehouses, the resulting reduction in customer service and increase in transportation costs cannot be tolerated in today's competitive market.

Each port warehouse serves a local market and most of the warehouses serve an inland market area as well. Buyers naturally specify delivery from the warehouse providing the lowest transportation costs. Hence boundaries of the market area served by a particular warehouse are determined by prevailing transportation rates. Small changes in the rail or water rates may shift large segments of demand from one warehouse to another, altering the sales throughput at the warehouses affected. Sales forecasts by warehouses are thus subject to change with any modification in the transportation rate structure.

Costs of Mainland Warehousing

Competitive conditions require that the Company deliver products from mainland port warehouses at prices approximately the same as those for direct shipments from Honolulu. All costs of storage and handling at these warehouses, plus any transshipments between warehouses, must be borne by the Company. These costs are of four types: warehouse charges accrued on a case-month basis, costs of handling in and out of the warehouses, waterfront cartage costs, and inventory tax levies. The charges vary greatly from location to location and also are subject to change from time to time.

The pattern of warehousing costs at a particular time is shown in Figure 3. In-and-out handling and waterfront cartage costs are combined in the figure since both charges are based on warehouse throughput. Inventory tax levies are based either on the average inventory stored over a year's time or on the inventory level on a specified date (the tax date differs between locations). Note that at several locations the tax assessment is equal to the cost of several months storage. Hence tax levies must be included in inventory cost considerations even though the manner in which they are accrued complicates the problem of warehousing cost control.

Objectives of the Project

The large increase in mainland warehousing requirements over the past three years is highlighted in Figure 2; the unit costs involved are shown in Figure 3. Over the past decade, the total annual cost of mainland warehousing has risen from practically zero to a figure that represents a sizable portion of the Company's net profit, with most of the increase occurring in the last three years. The major objective of the

Figure 3

HANDLING, STORAGE, AND TAX COSTS AT MAINLAND PORT WAREHOUSES

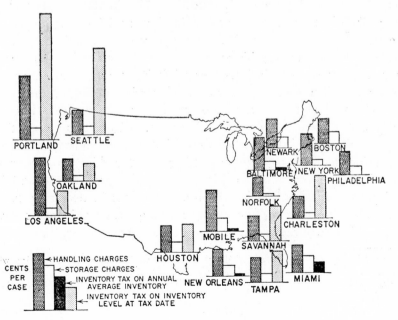

operations-research project was to devise a program for controlling and reducing these costs.

Several alternatives were considered. For one thing, the economics of Company-owned warehouses at the locations of highest throughput were investigated. However, since throughput has to be divided among so many warehouse locations, the savings that can be realized from changes applicable to any one location are small compared with the total warehousing cost. This indicates the need for a system-wide approach to the problem of warehousing cost control.

Total annual warehousing costs are sensitive to (a) the amount of finished-product inventory stored in Honolulu, and (b) the distribution of inventories among the mainland warehouses. In Honolulu, storage space is Company-owned and inventories are not taxed, so there are no out-of-pocket costs accrued on a case-month basis. However, extra materials-handling costs are incurred in using certain marginal warehouse areas in Honolulu, and these costs must be compared with the resulting savings in mainland warehousing charges. One objective of the project was a schedule for optimum use of Honolulu storage space within the operating restrictions discussed above. This schedule has a direct effect on costs in Honolulu and also is important in determining how much inventory must be stored on the mainalnd.[4]

Since charges and taxes differ considerably among the commercial warehouses on the mainland, the total warehousing cost over a year's time depends on how much is stored at which locations and for how long. Therefore a program for allocating inventories among the available storage points can provide the system-wide approach needed for warehouse cost control. This program must meet several requirements. It must be based on principles that minimize total warehousing costs, taking into account the different types of warehouse charges, the different methods by which charges are accrued, and the different amounts charged at the various warehouse locations. All operating restrictions (such as the limited shelf life of pineapple products) must be observed. The principles must be incorporated in a set of working procedures for planning inventory allocations in advance of a pack season and for revising these allocations in response to changes in operating conditions. The development of a program meeting these requirements was a major objective of the operations-research project.

---

[4] A schedule for optimum use of Honolulu storage was developed in cooperation with operating personnel in the Islands. Space does not permit discussion of this phase of the work.

DEVELOPMENT OF A PROGRAM FOR
INVENTORY DISTRIBUTION

It is helpful to consider the inventory at each mainland warehouse as consisting of two portions. One portion is stock needed to satisfy current sales calling for immediate delivery from forward supply points; this stock is called the buffer inventory. The other portion of the inventory (all stock over the buffer amount) represents excess inventory created by the seasonal nature of pack operations. To maintain the current level of customer service, the Company must stock the required buffer inventories at all mainland warehouses regardless of warehousing charges. However, inventories in excess of the buffer amounts can be allocated among the available storage points to minimize total annual warehousing costs. The problem now becomes twofold:

1. Determine the required buffer stock levels at each major mainland warehouse.
2. Devise a procedure for allocating mainland inventories in excess of buffer quantities among the available storage points to minimize costs.

Determining Buffer Stock Levels at Mainland Warehouses

As market changes over the past few years increased the need for forward stocks on the mainland, Company personnel charged with controlling these inventories developed a series of guides to determine the proper stock levels to meet sales requirements at each location. As a check on these operating guides, the research team developed an inventory-control model to describe operation of a mainland warehouse to satisfy current sales requirements in its territory, exclusive of the function of storing excess stock. The basic features of the inventory-control model are presented in Figure 4.

The inventory at the warehouse declines in response to sales and rises on receipt of a shipment. Each time a ship is scheduled for departure for the mainland warehouse under consideration, the inventory at that warehouse is reviewed and an amount ordered that is expected to return the inventory to the buffer level upon receipt of the shipment. Between the time of placing an order and its receipt at the warehouse, another ship departs with another order for the same warehouse. This reflects the fact that, at most warehouses, the time between ship departures is less than the ship-enroute time.

The buffer inventory level is represented in Figure 4 by a dashed line. Although order quantities are estimated to return the inventory to the buffer level upon receipt of a shipment, actual inventory levels after receipts will fluctuate about the buffer level as indicated on the chart. This is due to random variations in ship-departure dates, enroute times, and sales demand. It is assumed that these factors vary in the same manner as independent observations on normally distributed random variables.

Figure 4

INVENTORY FLUCTUATIONS IN RESPONSE TO SALES AND SHIPMENTS. PROBABILITY DISTRIBUTION OF RUN-OUT TIME AND TIME BETWEEN SHIP ARRIVALS ARE ALSO SHOWN

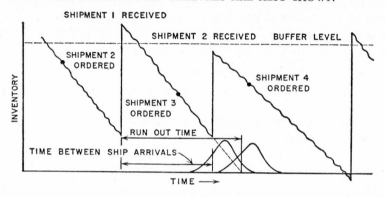

The number of time units from receipt of a shipment until stock depletion, assuming no further shipments are received, is called the run-out time. It can be shown that, if demand is assumed to be normally distributed, run-out times will also be normally distributed. Similarly, if the times between ship departures and the ship-enroute times are normally distributed, the time between ship arrivals are normally distributed. Ordinarily, the *average* run-out time will be greater than the *average* time between ship arrivals, but the probability density functions associated with these factors will overlap, as shown in Figure 4. As the amount of this overlap increases, there is a corresponding increase in the likelihood of a short run-out time occurring in conjunction with a long time between ship arrivals. Such an event means that stock is out and backordered, as shown in the last cycle of Figure 4.

The degree of overlap between the two probability-density functions can be controlled by the buffer-inventory level. The higher the buffer level the longer the average run-out time and the smaller the likelihood of occurrence of a warehouse out-of-stock condition. Mathematical manipulation of the inventory-control model produced an equation relating the buffer-inventory level with the expected fraction of time that an out-of-stock condition will occur. This equation is in terms of the average sales demand, the variance in sales demands, the average time between ship arrivals, and the variance in times between ship arrivals.

Translating model results into inventory requirements at a particular warehouse required estimates of the real-life counterparts of the quantities used in the inventory-control model. These estimates were derived from Company records giving historical data of sales and ship arrivals at each warehouse. A curve was made for each major warehouse showing the buffer-inventory levels corresponding to fractions of time out-of-stock in the range 0 to 2.5 per cent. Four of these curves are presented in Figure 5.

Figure 5

BUFFER INVENTORY LEVELS FOR SPECIFIED PROTECTION
AGAINST A WAREHOUSE OUT-OF-STOCK CONDITION
AT SELECTED PORT WAREHOUSES

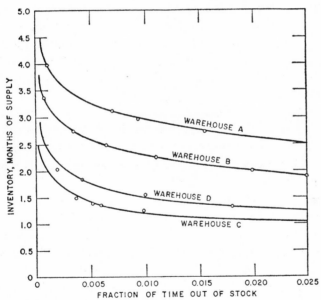

The results from the analytical model were compared with the guides for basic stock requirements at the mainland warehouses currently used in Company practice. It was found that at all major mainland warehouses the stock levels specified by the Company guides provide an expected out-of-stock condition in the range 0.5 per cent to 2.5 per cent. Company marketing personnel considered this an acceptable range. Persons responsible for controlling mainland inventories apparently have developed an accurate feel for the factors involved; their experience indicated the inventory levels that would satisfy service requirements and that can be maintained by the regular shipping schedule. The inventory-control model served to verify stock level guides developed by this experience.

Allocating Excess Inventories among Mainland Port Warehouses

We next consider the problem of allocating inventory amounts in excess of the basic stock levels needed to satisfy current sales requirements. These excess inventories are to be allocated among the mainland storage points as they are produced to minimize the total of the warehousing charges at all points over a year's time. To see how this can be done, consider an idealized case.

Suppose it were possible to decide the destination of each case of excess inventory as it came off the packing line. Cases are then sent, one at a time, to that mainland warehouse where they will receive the lowest total warehousing charge. In other words, each time a decision is made on an individual case, the expected tax and warehousing charges against that case at each warehouse is determined, taking into account the warehouse rate, the inventory tax, and the expected length of stay at each location. The case is then sent to the warehouse that offers the lowest combined cost.

Under this idealized allocation program, excess cases are first sent to the warehouse that has the lowest storage charge per case-month. As the inventory level at this warehouse builds up, the expected length of stay of additional cases increases until the cost of storage equals that at the warehouse with the next lowest storage charge. Additional cases are then allocated to both warehouses until their costs exceed that of the warehouse with the next lowest charge, and so forth. This procedure is continued until all excess cases are allocated. Under this approach the warehousing cost of the last excess case allocated to each location will be equal to the warehousing cost of the last excess case allocated to every other location. The total of the relevant warehousing charges for the last excess case allocated to a warehouse is called the *warehouse marginal unit cost.*

An idealized allocation procedure, which directs each excess case to a point of minimum cost, will result in a minimum total cost for all excess cases taken together. Such an allocation procedure results in equal marginal-unit costs at all warehouses. Of course, in practice it is not possible to determine the destination of each case individually, but the same results that are possible by making decisions on individual cases can be achieved by applying the equal-marginal-unit-cost concept to an allocation of the *total* excess inventory. For any given number of

·excess cases to be allocated, what is required is an allocation that yields equal marginal-unit costs at all warehouses and that accommodates the required number of cases.

In determining such a distribution, it is helpful to express the number of excess cases on hand at a particular warehouse in units of months of sales demand. This approach relates the excess inventory on hand at a

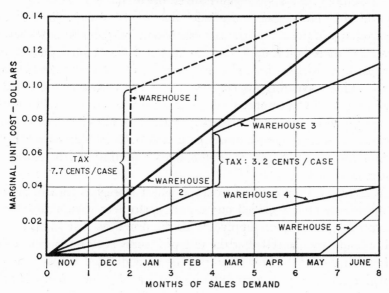

Figure 6
MARGINAL UNIT COST VERSUS NUMBER OF MONTHS OF SALES DEMAND STORED ON NOVEMBER 1 AT SELECTED PORT WAREHOUSES

warehouse with the expected length of stay of an additional excess case. For example, if the excess inventory on hand at a particular warehouse is equal to five months of sales demand, and if stock is handled on a first-in, first-out basis, then an additional excess case allocated to that warehouse will incur the warehousing charges of five months of excess storage. At the end of five months, this case becomes part of the buffer stock and is no longer counted as an excess case.

The procedure discussed here is illustrated in Figure 6. This figure shows a method of allocating excess stock requirements on November 1 against future sales among five hypothetical mainland warehouses (the necessity for dating the chart is explained later). Cases of excess stock on hand on November 1 are expressed in months of sales demand and are plotted along the horizontal axis. The horizontal scale thus represents the expected length of time that the last excess case will incur warehousing charges before it becomes part of the buffer stock. The cost of storing the last excess case for the specified number of months, including inventory tax costs where applicable, is plotted along the vertical axis. This is the marginal-unit cost for excess cases allocated to the warehouses shown on the chart.

The slope of each line in Figure 6 is equal to the storage charge per case-month at the hypothetical warehouse. The abrupt jump in the cost of the last excess case stored at Warehouse 1 when the inventory level there builds up to two months of sales demand reflects a 7.7 cents per case inventory tax assessed against inventory on hand on January 1 (two months after November 1, the index date of the chart). Similarly, the abrupt jump in the cost of the last case stored in Warehouse 3 when the inventory there builds up to four months of demand reflects a 3.2 cents per case inventory tax incurred on March 1 (four months after November 1). Since inventory tax charges at certain warehouses are based on the inventory levels on specific dates, it is necessary to index Figure 6 to inventory allocations as of a particular date. Similar charts were drawn for the first of each month in the pack season. These differ from Figure 6 in location of the jumps in the lines reflecting the inventory tax charges.

Warehouse 5 represents a situation where storage is leased at a fixed monthly rate for a specified number of square feet (assumed sufficient to store $6\frac{1}{2}$ months of supply), with the provision that storage above this amount will be billed at the rate of 2 cents per case-month. Under this arrangement the cost of storage of an additional excess case (the marginal unit cost) is zero until all the leased storage space is filled. After that, the line representing Warehouse 5 slopes upward at the rate of 2 cents per month (there is no tax charge). One of the advantages of the graphical approach is its flexibility in handling warehouses with storage charges and tax assessments accrued in a variety of ways. The chart also has the advantage of being easily altered to reflect changes in warehouse rates, and is easier to explain than an equivalent solution based on linear-programming techniques.

Using the Chart to Determine Inventory Allocations

You will recall that the criterion for a minimum cost allocation is that the cost of the last excess case be equal at all the warehouses. Figure 6 provides a means of determining such an allocation among the five warehouses shown. Suppose there is some quantity of excess stock on hand on November 1, to be allocated among the five warehouses. Select some value of marginal-unit cost, say 8 cents a case, and read from the chart the amount of excess stock at each warehouse that will result in the last case costing 8 cents at all locations. This would be 2-months' sales at Warehouse 1, 4.3-months' sales at Warehouse 2, 4.8-months' sales at Warehouse 3, and 7-months' sales at Warehouses 4 and 5. In the case of the last two warehouses, it is necessary to assign more than 7-months' demand to achieve an 8 cent marginal-unit cost, but here there is a restriction because of the limited shelf life of pineapple products. The chart incorporates the Company practice of never allocating more to any mainland location than will be sold before the beginning of the next pack season on June 1. This assures an adequate turnover of fresh supplies even at the lower-cost warehouses, which would otherwise have large carryover stock from one pack season to the next.

The allocation amounts, expressed in months of demand, are multiplied by sales forecasts by warehouses to yield an allocation expressed in cases. The sum of these case amounts over all warehouses is the amount of excess stock which can be allocated at a marginal unit cost of 8 cents. If this sum is less than the total cases of excess stock to be accommodated, select a larger marginal-unit cost figure and repeat the procedure. If the total allocated is greater than the excess cases to be accommodated, select a smaller marginal unit cost figure and repeat the procedure.

Figure 6 and the trial-and-error allocation procedure just discussed are presented to illustrate the basic principles involved. The sloping lines indicate warehouse-storage costs as being accrued on a continuous basis. Actual billings are based on inventory levels at the first of each month, which are billed for a full month's storage (the practice varies among the warehouses). The sloping lines must be replaced by a series of stepped lines indicating storage-cost jumps at appropriate invervals. If this were done and all warehouses included, the resulting charts would be unreadable. Therefore the charts (corrected to reflect actual billing practices) were converted into a set of tables, one table for the first of each month.

Column headings in the tables are in marginal-unit costs (corresponding to the vertical axis on Figure 6). A row in the table is provided for each of the seventeen major port warehouses. Entries along a row give the number of months of sales demand to be allocated to the relevant warehouse for the marginal-unit-cost figures at the top of each column (these entries correspond to numbers read off the horizontal axis of Figure 6). The table entries are first converted into case amounts by multiplying by sales forecasts by warehouses. Column totals in the converted table give the total number of excess cases accommodated for the marginal-unit-cost figure in the column heading. Entries in the column show the number of excess cases to be allocated to each warehouse to provide a minimum cost result.[5]

The allocation tables can be used in programming allocations of excess inventories month by month in advance of a pack season. The tables can also be used during a pack season to determine corrected allocations necessitated by changes in operating conditions. Each corrected allocation will provide the lowest cost possible under the new circumstances. A set of written procedures for each of these uses was prepared to make the application as straightforward as possible. The procedures take into account additional operating practices and restrictions not explicitly covered in this discussion.

Simulating the Allocation Procedures

Feasibility of the allocation method was checked by a simulation of inventory fluctuations over a hypothetical year of operations. Pack rates, Honolulu storage build-up, and sales patterns representative of normal operations were used as inputs to the simulation. Inventory distribution was computed in accordance with the allocation procedure, and the level at each major warehouse was plotted throughout the fiscal year. Four of these plots are presented in Figures 7 and 8; they illustrate how

Figure 7

INVENTORY FLUCTUATIONS AT SELECTED WAREHOUSES FOR
A SIMULATED YEAR OF OPERATIONS

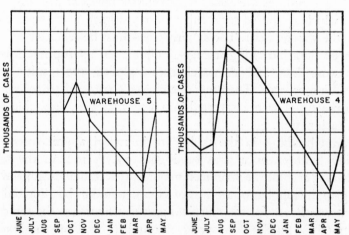

---

[5] This is the *total* number of cases to be assigned a warehouse. The total must be divided among the individual items stocked in proportion to the relative sales rates of the various items in the area served by the warehouse.

the allocation procedure discriminates between warehouses with different storage rates and tax assessments.

Warehouse 5, where a fixed amount of space is leased, is the first warehouse filled. Inventory there is maintained at the leased level until October, at which time it becomes economical to use additional space at extra cost. After October the inventory is allowed to run down until just before the next pack season, when it is refilled by shipments from Honolulu. These shipments reduce Hawaiian storage to the desired

Figure 8

INVENTORY FLUCTUATIONS AT SELECTED WAREHOUSES FOR
A SIMULATED YEAR OF OPERATIONS

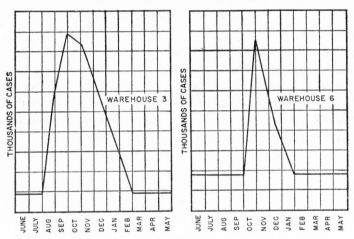

level going into the next pack season. Warehouse 4, which has the lowest monthly storage rate, is filled by shipments during August to a level that will satisfy all demand until the following June. Neither of these locations is subject to inventory tax; and, since they are the lowest cost storage points, their inventories never decline to the buffer level.

Warehouse 3 (Figure 8) also has a low storage rate, but here there is a tax on March 1. This warehouse is maintained at buffer level in June and July, filled by shipments in August and September, and is back to the buffer level by tax date. Warehouse 6 has a high storage charge coupled with a tax based on the average annual inventory. It is maintained at buffer level until October, when the high inventories throughout the system warrant its use. The inventory is sold down to buffer level by February and is maintained there for the remainder of the year. Being a high cost warehouse, it is used for storage of excess stock only for four months of the year.

From inventory plots similar to those of Figures 7 and 8, it was possible to compute the warehousing cost over a year's time at each location. These were totaled to yield the cost over the whole distribution system, using the proposed allocation program under simulated operating conditions. This total cost was substantially less than actual costs incurred in the Company's inventory distribution operations in recent years. The simulation demonstrated the savings potential of the proposed allocation program.

Company Follow-up on the OR Project

The results of the operations-research project were presented to the Company in a written report followed by an oral presentation to top management. The recommended program was adopted and one of the Company's officers assigned responsibility for incorporating the allocation procedures in Company operations. Since this is a new method of approach affecting several operating departments, experience in its implementation is required before maximum savings can be expected. With the continued support of management and operating personnel there is every cause for confidence in the long-range benefits to be expected from the new inventory-distribution program.

CASE 10

On the Determination of Optimum Reserve Generating Capacity in an Electric Utility System[1]

E. LEONARD ARNOFF and JOHN C. CHAMBERS[2]

Some points of special interest in this paper are:

a) Analogy of the basic problem to the inventory problem.

b) Transforming "What is the optimum reserve generating capacity?" into the operational question, "When should generating capacity be added to the system?"

c) The joint problems of optimum time to add generating capacity and economic size of unit.

d) Methods used to forecast customer demand.

e) Methods available for determining the probability of an outage.

f) "Since a system would require an infinitely large amount of generating capacity in order to provide no shortages whatsoever, management must decide upon a certain risk of shortage which is 'acceptable' from a practical, operating point of view."

g) The adjustments made in the demand forecast.

h) The use in the analysis of several levels for a number of different variables. Is the approach basically numerical analysis or mathematical deduction? Is there any difference?

---

[1] This paper was presented by Dr. Arnoff at the Conference on Operations Research sponsored by the Society for Advancement of Management, September 29–30, 1955, in New York, N.Y., and was published in the *Proceedings* of the Conference. It appeared in *Operations Research*, August, 1956, with certain additional data added. Reprinted by permission.

[2] Case Institute of Technology.

For any electric utility system, a prime requirement is the ability to be able to fulfill customer demands for power with some prescribed measure of reliability. Since future customer demands can only be estimated and since generators and auxiliary equipment (boilers, turbines, etc.) are subject to forced outages (i.e., breakdowns), a utility system is required to maintain a reserve of installed generating capacity in the form of "extra" turbo-generator units. An important problem area, then, is that associated with the determination of a proper (or optimum) installed reserve generating capacity. Failure to have a sufficient reserve (sufficient, as measured by some criterion) leads to customer shortages with resulting customer dissatisfaction and loss of revenue, both direct and indirect. On the other hand, a surplus of generating capacity means additional "inventory" costs—costs associated with direct charges on idle or unnecessary capital equipment.

The "reserve" problem, then, is to determine the best balance between these two costs, the cost of a shortage and the cost of excess inventory. The determination of this optimum balance point then determines when a new unit should be added to the line and, hence, gives the best reserve policy for the particular system.

In the electrical utility industry, the reserve question is usually phrased in terms of "What is the optimum reserve generating capacity?" wherein the existence of one single reserve percentage is implied. For example, a rule of thumb in the industry is that the reserve capacity should generally be no less than 15 per cent of the system capacity. However, as will be seen later in this paper, there is no *one* optimum percentage, since the optimum varies with the size of the generators in operation. Furthermore, since the reason one seeks to determine the optimum reserve is to know when additional capacity is required, it seemed much more reasonable to rephrase the research question in terms of "When should generating capacity be added to the system?" Then, having answered this question, one can readily determine the optimum reserve capacity for any given generating system.

An associated problem, and one for which the answer is, in a sense, already implied in the determination of the optimum reserve policy, is that of determining the optimum size of unit to be added to the system. Varying the size of the unit affects coal costs, maintenance costs, labor costs, holding costs, and so forth. Here, in considering large versus small units, one seeks a "best" balance between installation-cost savings, coal savings, and labor and maintenance savings, on the one hand, and increased costs of investment, on the other hand.

This paper presents, first, a method for answering the first question—

that of determining the optimum time to add generating capacity to a system. Then, the second problem, that of determining the most economic size of unit, is considered, subject to restrictions stated later in this paper. The methods described in this paper were developed in a study recently completed for a utility company.

DETERMINATION OF OPTIMUM RESERVE GENERATING CAPACITY

Analysis of the company system showed that the following factors affect the determination of the optimum time for acquiring generating capacity and, hence, must be taken into account:

1. *Available Capacity*
    a) The number and sizes of the generating units now in the system.
    b) The size of new generating units to be added to the system.
    c) The amount of additional power available from (1) interconnections and, to a much lesser extent, from (2) voltage drops, (3) drop-off of customers whose contracts permit reductions in power, and (4) large industries within the system area that have their own generating units.

2. *Requirements* (consumption of power or of power-generating capacity)
    a) Customer demand. Since this is not known, it must be forecast and errors due to forecasting must also be taken into account.
    b) Scheduled, or preventative, maintenance.
    c) Unscheduled, or emergency outages due to breakdowns.

3. *Costs*
    a) Purchase price of the generating equipment.
    b) Installation cost of the generating equipment.
    c) Operating cost of the generating equipment: (1) coal, (2) labor, and (3) maintenance.
    d) Fixed charges on capital equipment: (1) cost of money, (2) income tax, (3) real estate and personal property taxes, (4) depreciation, and (5) miscellaneous.
    e) Costs due to shortages[3] (or, maximum allowable risk of shortage).

Certain of these factors had fixed values and could be determined immediately: for example, the number and sizes of the existing units in the generating system. Additionally, the scheduled maintenance program is an established one and, thus, it is safe to assume, at least for the moment, that it will be continued in its present form during the period of time under study. (A variation of the scheduled maintenance program is also evaluated in a later section of this paper). Finally, the costs

---

[3] A shortage occurs whenever the sum of customer demand, forced outages, and scheduled outages (due to maintenance) exceeds the total system capabilities.

associated with installation and operation of the generators are also known.[4]

Certain other factors could be assigned values, but these values were not unique. Such factors are:

1. *The probability of forced outage* (that is, the probability that a generating unit would not be available owing to a breakdown). Studies conducted on a national scale by the Edison Electric Institute showed that the national average for forced outages, for week-days only, for all types of generating equipment is approximately 2 per cent (or 0.02). Roughly, this means that one can expect generating equipment to be out of commission approximately 2 per cent of the time because of an emergency, or forced, outage, either because of turbo-generator or boiler trouble.

Analysis of the company system showed that forced outages were being experienced only 1 per cent of the time. Accordingly, both figures were used in the study. Using both the 1 and 2 per cent figures also enables management to measure the value of its excellent preventative maintenance program, inasmuch as forced outrages are affected by the rigidity (that is, frequency and nature) of the preventative maintenance program.

2. *The amount of additional power available* to an electric utility company is largely dependent upon contractual arrangements with interconnecting companies. Inasmuch as this amount can vary with respect to the future, several varying amounts of additional power were assumed, namely, 100, 200, and 400 megawatts (MW). Not only does this enable us to provide answers to the reserve question, but it also serves to measure the value of the interconnection and the amount of power that one should contract for from the interconnection.

3. Since a system would require an *infinitely large amount of generating capacity* in order to provide for no shortages whatsoever, management must decide upon a certain risk of shortage which is "acceptable" from a practical, operating point of view.

In the electric utility industry, a "rule of thumb" exists as to a *maximum acceptable risk of shortage*. This, of course, assumes much as to the homogeneity, from one system to another, of the type of customer, sizes of units in the system, costs of shortage, cost of holding excess inventory, and so forth. Within the industry, however, this shortage policy is not too well defined. Accordingly, several shortage policies were assumed and evaluated with respect to total expected cost. In particular, three policies were considered and evaluated. These assumed the *maximum* allowable risk of shortage to be: (*a*) one day in two years, (*b*) one day in five years, and (*c*) one day in ten years.

4. Inasmuch as the research study also included the determination of the optimum size of new units to be added to the system, the alternatives of adding distinct *sizes of generating units* were studied. In particular, two systems were studied, involving the addition of units of 240-MW and 340-MW size.

5. Since the purchase price of new generators will vary with time, study was also made of the effect of various levels of incremental *costs of purchase*. Thus, for a comparison of the addition of 340-MW units with the addition of 240-

---

[4] Since the purchase price of any generating unit will vary with time, this factor was treated essentially as a variable and results were obtained for various price levels.

MW generators, cost differentials[5] of 0, 1, 2, 4, and 8 millions of dollars were considered.

Finally, there were the following factors whose values had to be established. These were: (a) the probabilities of forced outages of varying amounts for the system as a whole, and (b) the determination of expected customer demand. From these two factors and the known scheduled maintenance requirements (as well as the system capacity, etc.) one must then determine (c) the probability of a shortage. Finally, since there will be errors due to forecasts of customer demand, one must determine (d) the amount of reserve capacity required to provide for various levels of protection against forecasting errors.

Determination of Customer Demand

In the determination of expected customer demand, one is normally interested only in the determination of expected daily peak demands, inasmuch as the ability to satisfy customer requirements at peak loads implies the ability to satisfy off-peak demands as well. Furthermore, inasmuch as week-end and holiday peak loads are only 50 to 75 per cent of the normal week-day peak loads, it is assumed that, for all practical purposes, shortages will not occur on these week-ends and holidays. Hence, in the analyses to follow, only peak loads occurring during week-days are considered.

To determine the distribution of peak loads, a method was developed that is based upon the company's forecast of annual kilowatt-hour (KWH) consumption. A study of this annual KWH consumption, by month, revealed a consistent variation in monthly demands. Furthermore, study also revealed that the distribution of daily peak loads within any given month was also predictable.

Therefore, by means of statistical analyses, one is able to obtain the distribution of daily peak loads within each month, and hence, the nature of customer demand for each month. An example of such a distribution of daily peak loads for a sample month is given herewith.

Determination of Probabilities of System Outages

Methods of calculating probabilities of outages for a given system range from the rigorous method of Calabrese[3, 4] to the approximation method of Lyman[7, 10]. For a system such as that discussed here, where unit sizes vary over a very large range, a rigorous computation of system probabilities of outages would require the use of a large electronic computer. Accordingly, the following device was employed. The actual system under study was represented by a system of generating

---

[5] These cost differentials include incremental installation costs.

units whose sizes (i.e., capacities) are multiples of 25 MW. This yields a model of the system whose joint probabilities are then easily calculated. Care was taken so that any errors due to this simplification would be in the direction of increasing reserve requirements.[6]

SAMPLE MONTH

Peaks (MW)	Expected Number of Days	Peaks (MW)	Expected Number of Days
1230	0.32	1310	2.31
1240	0.57	1320	2.00
1250	0.84	1330	1.68
		1340	1.28
1260	1.28	1350	0.84
1270	1.68		
1280	2.00	1360	0.57
1290	2.31	1370	0.32
1300	2.35		

Determination of When Units Are to Be Added to the System

Once having determined (1) expected customer demand, (2) expected frequency and amount of forced outages, and (3) scheduled maintenance requirements, these three factors can then be combined to yield the total expected demand on the system for each month.[7] Such a combination led to the type of table of total expected monthly demands shown in Table 1. Then, having determined the total expected monthly demand on the system, this demand is associated with total system capabilities and maximum allowable risks of shortage so that, finally, one is able to determine when new generating units should be added to the system. The procedure for doing so may best be explained by means of the following example.

Example:

Assume the following conditions to be true:

1. Maximum allowable risk of shortage: 1 day in 5 years. (That is, the system is permitted to have a shortage no more frequently than 0.2 days per year.)

2. Internal system capacity: 1725 MW.

3. Additional capacity (e.g., from interconnection): 100 MW. (Therefore, it is assumed that the total system capacity is 1825 MW.)

---

[6] Since the results obtained from the model of the system are assumed to represent the actual system, several models were tried and the results compared with observed (historical) values, from which the 'multiple of 25 MW' system was selected.

[7] Treating the expected forced outages as a demand on the system is a very useful device which enables one to consider the capacity of the system as fixed.

Assume that we are considering the month depicted in Table 1. Then, referring to Table 1, we see that, for this month, one can expect a demand of 1850 MW or more to occur at the rate of 0.576 days per year (Column 4). Since the total system capacity is only 1825 MW, this number (0.576) represents the expected number of days per year that the system will be short. Then, since 0.576 exceeds the maximum allowable shortage of 0.2 days per year, one must add more generating capacity during this illustrative month.[8]

Table 1

TOTAL EXPECTED DEMANDS FOR "TYPICAL" MONTH

Total Demand Including Forced Outages (1)	Expected No. of Days for Month (2)	Expected No. of Days for Month Indicated Demand or Greater (3)	Expected No. of Days for Year, Indicated Demand or Greater (12 × Col. 3) (4)
1400	1.282	21.000	252.0
1425	1.361	19.718	236.616
1450	3.521	18.357	220.284
1475	4.400	14.836	178.032
1500	2.949	10.436	125.232
1525	2.511	7.487	89.844
1550	1.746	4.976	59.712
1575	0.854	3.230	38.760
1600	0.688	2.376	28.512
1625	0.508	1.688	20.256
1650	0.319	1.180	14.160
1675	0.228	0.861	10.332
1700	0.197	0.633	7.596
1725	0.147	0.436	5.232
1750	0.097	0.289	3.468
1775	0.073	0.192	2.304
1800	0.047	0.119	1.428
1825	0.024	0.072	0.864
1850	0.018	0.048	0.576
1875	0.012	0.030	0.360
1900	0.007	0.018	0.216
1925	0.005	0.011	0.132
1950	0.003	0.006	0.072
1975	0.001	0.003	0.036

Thus for each month one determines a table of total expected demand on the system by combining: (1) expected customer demand, (2) expected frequency and amount of forced outages, and (3) scheduled maintenance requirements. Then, by comparing the expected number of days per year that the system will be short with the maximum allowable risk of shortage, one can determine when (i.e., in which month) additional generating capacity is required.

---

[8] Were the expected number of days short less than 0.2, the system is deemed sufficient and one would then pass on to the next month.

Such an analysis was conducted for combinations of the following values of the factors:

1. Probability of a unit outage: 1 and 2 per cent.
2. Additional power available from the interconnection, etc.: 0, 100, 200, and 400 MW.
3. Maximum allowable risk of shortage: 1 day in 2 years, 1 day in 5 years, and 1 day in 10 years.

The results are summarized in Table 2 which shows, not only when

Table 2

INSTALLATION DATE FOR NEXT UNIT

PROBABILITY OF OUTAGE, %	ADDITIONAL POWER	RISK OF SHORTAGE					
		1 Day/ 10 Yrs	% Res.	1 Day/ 5 Yrs	% Res.	1 Day/ 2 Yrs	% Res.
1	0 MW	Dec. 57	22.0	Apr. 58	18.6	June 58	18.6
	100 MW	July 58	18.6	Apr. 59	11.7	July 59	11.7
	200 MW	May 60	6.2	Dec. 60	4.6	Mar. 61	1.8
	400 MW	Mar. 62	−5.0	July 62	−5.0	July 62	−5.0
2	0 MW	Dec. 56	31.3	Apr. 57	27.4	Dec. 57	22.0
	100 MW	Dec. 57	22.0	June 58	18.6	July 58	18.6
	200 MW	Dec. 58	13.9	May 59	11.7	May 60	6.2
	400 MW	Apr. 61	1.5	Nov. 61	0	Mar. 62	−5.0

the next unit should be added to the system for various assumptions, but also the corresponding percentage of reserve available in the system at that time.

The method just presented essentially assumes that there are no errors in the forecasting of customer demands. However, in practice, if no adjustments are made for errors in forecasting, shortages will occur with less frequency (than anticipated above) 50 per cent of the time (since the forecast will be high 50 per cent of the time), and shortages will occur with more frequency 50 per cent of the time (since the forecast will be low 50 per cent of the time). Accordingly, an additional amount of reserve capacity is required to provide a margin of safety against such errors, that is, in order to reduce the percentage of time with which more frequent shortages will occur or, equivalently, in order to increase the percentage of time during which fewer shortages will occur.

Calculations were made, based on a four-year forecast, showing the additional reserve capacity required for various percentage levels. Results are shown in Table 3.

Table 3

ADDITIONAL RESERVES REQUIRED BECAUSE OF
FORECASTING ERRORS

Per Cent of Time Fewer Than Max. Allowable No. of Shortages	Per Cent Additional Reserves Required
60	2.1
70	4.3
75	5.6
80	7.0
85	8.7
90	10.7
95	13.7
97.5	16.3
99	19.4
99.5	21.5

Analyses were also made of the economics associated with various values for:

1. Probability of unit forced outage: 1 and 2 per cent.
2. Maximum allowable risk of shortage for 1 day in 2 years, 1 day in 5 years, and 1 day in 10 years.
3. Additional power available from the interconnection: 0 MW, 100 MW, 200 MW, and 400 MW.
4. Incremental cost of purchasing new 340 MW-generating units as compared with 240-MW generating units: $0 million, $1 million, $2 million, $4 million, and $8 million. (That is, a system which involved the addition of new 340-MW units was compared with one adding 240-MW units for various cost differentials.)

These analyses were based on the method discussed earlier in this paper and yielded the results discussed below.

Effect of a Rigid Preventative Maintenance Program

As mentioned earlier, the company system experienced forced outages only 1 per cent of the time rather than the national average of 2 per cent, because of an excellent preventative maintenance policy. This has resulted in a reduction of forced outages that reduce the capacity requirements, and, hence, result in substantial gross cost savings. These savings must then be compared with the increased cost of maintenance required to obtain the 1 per cent forced outage rate in order to determine whether or not the rigid maintenance program is economically justified. The gross savings due to this more rigid maintenance program is given in Table 4. (The numbers in Table 4 represent the annual savings obtained by comparing the costs for a 1 per cent unit forced outrage rate with those for a 2 per cent unit forced outrage rate.)

Table 4

ADDITIONAL COSTS, 2% OUTAGE RATE vs. 1% OUTAGE RATE

Size of Units Subsequently Added	Maximum Allowable Risk of Shortage								
	1 day/2 yrs			1 day/5 yrs			1 day/10 yrs		
240 MW	1.3*	1.1	0.4	1.8	1.3	0.5	1.9	1.7	1.0
340 MW	1.2	1.0	0.6	2.2	1.7	1.2	2.4	1.9	1.2
	100	200	400	100	200	400	100	200	400
	Additional power available (MW)								

* Figures shown are in millions of dollars per year.

Maximum Allowable Risk of Shortage

In this study, the "cost of shortage" and "maximum allowable risk of shortage" have been used rather interchangeably. Ideally, one would like to be able to determine the costs caused by shortage (including the impact on customer good-will, loss of future sales, etc.) and thereby arrive at a definite answer to the reserve question. However, the costs caused by shortage are not known nor are they easily determined. Hence, the alternate approach of analyzing several maximum allowable risks of shortage was used. Thus, although management is obliged to decide upon a suitable shortage policy, it is nevertheless supplied with a firm quantitative basis for establishing this policy.

Table 5 shows the cost reductions associated with shortage policies of 1 day in 2 years and 1 day in 5 years as compared with a policy of maximum acceptable risk of shortage of 1 day in 10 years.

Table 5

REDUCTION IN COSTS FOR RISK OF SHORTAGE GREATER THAN
1 DAY IN 10 YEARS

Risk of Shortage	Size of New Units	Probability of Forced Outage							
		1%				2%			
1 day/5 yrs	240 MW	1.0*	0.8	0.3	0.2	1.0	0.9	0.7	0.6
	340 MW	1.0	0.9	0.6	0.3	1.0	1.2	0.8	0.3
1 day/2 yrs	240 MW	1.9	1.5	1.0	0.3	2.0	2.0	1.7	0.9
	340 MW	2.4	1.7	1.1	0.4	2.3	3.0	2.0	0.9
		0	100	200	400	0	100	200	400
		Additional power available (MW)							

* Figures shown are in millions of dollars per year.

Additional Power Available from the Interconnection

Throughout this paper it has been apparent that a very important factor is the amount of power available from the interconnection. Thus, in applying Table 1, varying the level of the amount of power available from the interconnection would affect whether or not additional capacity must be added. In addition, as the other tables show, the costs and savings vary quite markedly with the amount of such additional power.

Table 6

EVALUATION OF INTERCONNECTION (BASE 100 MW)

ADDITIONAL POWER AVAILABLE	SIZE OF NEW UNITS	PROBABILITY OF FORCED OUTAGE					
		1%			2%		
0 MW	240 MW	−2.0	−1.9	−1.6	−2.0	−1.9	−2.0
	340 MW	−2.5	−2.4	−1.8	−2.0	−2.2	−2.8
200 MW	240 MW	1.8*	1.3	1.5	2.0	1.9	1.7
	340 MW	2.0	1.7	1.3	2.5	2.2	1.5
400 MW	240 MW	3.8	3.1	2.6	4.7	4.4	3.5
	340 MW	4.2	3.6	2.8	5.5	4.6	3.4
		1 day/ 10 yrs	1 day/ 5 yrs	1 day/ 2 yrs	1 day/ 10 yrs	1 day/ 5 yrs	1 day/ 2 yrs
		Maximum allowable risk of shortage					

* Figures shown are in millions of dollars per year.

Accordingly, analyses were made of the differences in costs associated with power available from the interconnection in amounts of 0 MW, 100 MW, 200 MW, and 400 MW. The amount of 100 MW was used as a base and all costs were compared accordingly. The results are given in Table 6.

As mentioned earlier, a table such as Table 6 thus furnishes management with a sound basis for determining the amount of power for which it should contract from the interconnection.

Determination of Size of New Units to Be Added to the System

A highly essential question which must be answered in planning for the expansion of a utility system is that of determining the most economic size of unit to be added to the system. Two basic plans of expansion were considered: (1) each new unit is of size 240 MW or (2) each new unit is of size 340 MW. Since actual purchase costs were not known and will vary with time, computations were made for various incremental cost levels, thus enabling one to determine those purchase cost levels for which one unit is more economical than the other. These comparisons, using the 240-MW unit as a base, are given in Table 7, and are obtained by taking into account: (1) fixed charges

Table 7

COMPARISON OF 240 MW AND 340 MW UNITS

PROBABILITY OF OUTAGE, %	ADDITIONAL PURCHASE COST OF 340 MW vs. 240 MW	MAXIMUM ACCEPTABLE RISK OF SHORTAGE											
		1 day/10 yrs				1 day/5 yrs				1 day/2 yrs			
1	0	3.7*	7.7	7.6	8.1	3.9	7.8	9.9	9.4	8.8	9.0	5.5	8.3
	1.0	2.3	6.3	6.5	7.3	2.5	6.6	8.9	8.6	7.5	7.8	4.6	7.5
	2.0	0.9	5.0	5.4	6.5	1.1	5.4	7.9	7.8	6.1	6.6	3.6	6.7
	4.0	−1.9	2.4	3.3	4.8	−1.6	2.9	5.9	6.3	3.5	4.2	1.7	5.2
	8.0	−7.1	−2.7	−0.8	1.7	−6.7	−1.7	2.2	3.3	−1.6	−0.2	−1.9	2.3
2	0	2.1	2.2	7.1	6.9	1.3	5.1	7.3	3.0	4.8	11.4	8.4	6.2
	1.0	0.7	0.8	5.8	6.0	−0.1	3.7	6.0	2.2	3.4	10.4	7.3	5.4
	2.0	−0.7	−0.6	4.5	5.0	−1.5	2.4	4.8	1.3	2.0	9.0	6.2	4.6
	4.0	−3.5	−3.4	2.0	3.2	−4.3	−0.3	2.0	−0.4	−0.8	6.4	4.1	2.9
	8.0	−8.8	−8.6	−2.8	−0.4	−9.5	−5.3	−2.2	−3.7	−6.1	1.4	0	−0.2
		0	100	200	400	0	100	200	400	0	100	200	400
		Additional power available (MW)											

* Figures are in millions of dollars for period 1958–1967. The negative values indicate the conditions under which the 240-MW generator is preferable to the 340-MW generator.

on capital equipment, and (2) differential costs in (*a*) coal, (*b*) labor, and (*c*) maintenance.

SUMMARY

This paper, then, presents a method for determining when additional generating capacity should be added to an electric utility system and also for determining the optimum size of units to be added. The conclusions, however, presuppose that management has already made certain decisions:

1. What probability of unit forced outage to use. That is, what should be the preventative maintenance policy?
2. What is the maximum allowable risk of shortage?
3. What amount of power is to be made available through the interconnection?
4. What safety level is deemed essential for protection against forecasting errors?

Once having answered these questions (with the assistance of cost comparisons such as are provided in this paper), one can then readily determine when new units should be added to the system and what the size of these units should be.

REFERENCES

1. "Forced Outage Rate of High Pressure Steam Turbines and Boilers," *Combustion* (October, 1954), pp. 57–61.

2. "An Investigation of the Economic Size of Steam-Electric Generating Units," *Combustion* (February, 1955), pp. 57–64.

3. G. CALABRESE. "Determination of Reserve Capacity by the Probability Method—Effect on Interconnections," *A. I. E. E. Transactions,* Vol. LXIX, Part II (1950), pp. 1018–20.

4. ———, "Determination of Reserve Capacity by the Probability Method," *A. I. E. E. Transactions,* Vol. LXVIII, Part II (1949), pp. 1681–88.

5. WATCHORN. "Elements of System Capacity Requirements," *A. I. E. E. Transactions,* Vol. LXX, Part I (1951), pp. 1163–80.

6. H. T. STRANDRUD. "Determination of Generator Stand-By Reserve," *A. I. E. E. Transactions,* Vol. LXIX, PART II (1950), pp. 179–87.

7. W. J. LYMAN. "Calculating Probability of Generating Capacity Outages," *A. I. E. E. Transactions,* Vol. LXV (1945), pp. 1471–77.

8. H. P. SEELYE. "Outrage Expectancy as a Basis for Generator Reserve," *A. I. E. E. Transactions,* Vol. LXV (1946), pp. 1483–88.

9. E. D. AYRES. *Probability Methods for Generator Capacity Reserves,* Special report to C. E. I., September 24, 1954.

10. G. CALABRESE. *System Generation Reserve Requirements,* prepared monograph submitted to the Subcommittee on the Application of Probability Methods to Power System Problems, July 9, 1953.

CASE 11

Scale of Operations—An Empirical Study[1]

EDWARD H. BOWMAN[2]

Some points of special interest in this paper are:

a) The assumption of circular and uniform sales density territory areas.
b) The small sample size (10).
c) The boundaries of the analysis (e.g., the combination and location of the particular plants not handled).
d) The results of the decision rule at the extremes of the parameter estimates.
e) Management's own decisions and decision process.

This study concerns the optimum size of an ice cream branch plant and territory. The company operated ten plants covering a seven-state area. At the time of the study, management was uncertain as to even the approximate size of an optimum plant. The study revealed that about six larger plants would be a better system. The company now operates six plants and is considering cutting this number still further.

This paper reports one phase of a larger research project that involves the attempted application of several methods of analysis or models to one set of manufacturing problems. The problems are those posed by one company's system of ice cream branch plants.

[1] *Operations Research,* June, 1958. Reprinted by permission. The research in connection with this paper has been partly supported by the Sloan Research Fund of MIT's School of Industrial Management and the U.S. Army Ordnance Corps. Thanks are due several individuals of the cooperating company for their assistance and to Mr. T. A. Mangelsdorf and Mr. A. G. Grasberg, Graduate Assistants of M.I.T. A briefer version of this paper was presented at the Fifth Annual Meeting of the Operations Research Society of America in Philadelphia on May 10, 1957.

[2] Yale University.

THE PROBLEM

At the time of this study the company operated ten ice cream plants over an extended multistate area. The plants were essentially homogeneous and self-sufficient within their areas. The basic question being asked in this study was, *what is the optimum size for this company's ice cream plants?*

The relation between price asked and quantity sold is not part of this study. In addition it was felt that the customers will neither know nor care where their ice cream originates. Therefore, it is assumed for this study that both total sales and product mix were given. An answer to the question of optimum size plants then would also answer the question of an optimum number of plants. The study was not addressed to the proper location of the individual plants in the system.

The answer given to the question raised on the basis of this analysis is that nine out of ten of the plants are too small, most of them about half their optimum size, and that therefore the best number of plants would be five or six. The analysis leading to this conclusion follows.

The basic nature of the method of analysis used here is to attempt to relate quantitatively the variations that do exist in actual costs per gallon between plants to variations in other important factors, some of which may be manipulated by management. If insight into these relations may be gained from present experience, then changes in these other variables may be made by management in order to reduce the cost per gallon.

A MEASURE OF EFFECTIVENESS

With the restriction that total sales and product mix were given, it was determined that the objective was to attempt to minimize the cost per gallon of ice cream. This objective function, cost per gallon, itself, presented two problems, i.e., what was a cost and what was a gallon?

The cost used in this study was essentially a value added type or conversion cost. It included the costs of manufacturing and distribution without the raw-material costs. Actually, each plant was well beyond economies of scale with respect to raw-material procurement as all deliveries of milk and cream—the major components—were by tank car. In addition, the company itself, rather than the individual plants, contracts for these raw materials on a long-term basis. The company's own accounting system was relied upon to determine what costs occurred at the different plants in the given year under study. That is, the company kept books for each plant, including the usual labor accounts

—direct, indirect, supervisory—supplies, local taxes, depreciation, transportation, etc. Obviously, accounting decisions with respect to allocating long-term expenses to a given time period had been made, e.g., the proportion of equipment depreciation to allot to this year. In addition to the accounting costs, opportunity costs for capital invested in plant, equipment, and inventory were also included. In order to do this, the replacement cost of each plant was determined, and this was multiplied by the company's opportunity cost of capital. Had the company not invested capital in a particular plant, the capital could have been used elsewhere in the firm and the value of its use elsewhere denied by this plant must be considered as part of the cost of operating the plant. Though in some cases such "interest" costs might be important, here they were relatively small. That is, the decision sought would not be sensitive to the cost of capital used. As it was the total cost of the plant that was of interest for this analysis, there was no need nor desire to allocate these costs to the various products.

With respect to a measure of gallons, the company had developed for its own purposes a "gallon-equivalent" system. With respect to pint, quart, gallon, and three-gallon packages, the conversion was the obvious one to gallon equivalents. For specialty products, it was necessary to determine the net weight including, for instance, a chocolate coating, and convert this weight into gallon equivalents of ice cream. Though, of course, the unit of measure lacks complete homogeneity, it is unlikely that this could seriously influence the analysis. This is due to the fact that the product mix each plant manufactures was explicitly considered as one of the variables that influence the cost per gallon. That is, allowance was made in the model predicting cost per gallon for the higher labor content in specialty products, e.g., ice cream cups, popsickles, etc.

It is interesting to note at this point that having determined the measure of effectiveness, cost per gallon equivalent, an initial check was made of the variation in this measure between plants. It turned out that the comparison of the highest to the lowest cost plant revealed a difference of more than two to one (as shown in Table 1).

THE MODEL

It was felt that the following variables were the major influences on differences in the cost per gallon between plants:

1. Volume of product manufactured by each plant.
2. Area size of the territory served by each plant.

3. Product mix manufactured at each plant.
4. Labor rates at the particular plant location.

The larger the volume handled by a plant, the lower the cost per unit was expected to be. For virtually any kind of an economic activity, there tend to be certain fixed costs such as, for instance, the plant manager's or night watchman's salary. The larger the number of units to which this cost is assigned or allocated, the lower the cost per unit.

The larger the area of the territory served by a plant, the higher the costs were expected to be. This was due mainly to the fact that the trucks would have to travel farther from the plant out into the territory and back again. As a gross approximation, this travel from the plant corresponds to spokes on a wheel or circle radii. Such a radius varies with the square root of the area, and therefore it was felt that the cost would increase approximately with the square root of the area.

The higher the amount of labor input required for a gallon of a plant's products, the higher costs were expected to be. Specialty items per gallon equivalent require substantially more labor than regular products. All plants do not make the same proportion of each product, i.e., mix of product differs. The company had developed for its own purposes a measure of the relative labor input into each product, and for each plant had computed a weighted average of this measure.

The higher the labor rates in the area, the higher the costs per gallon were expected to be. Actually, most of the cost involved in the conversion process was a labor cost—direct, indirect, and supervisory. Therefore, it was felt that all of the previously mentioned costs would increase somewhat as labor rates increased.

Two other factors were carried beyond the early stages of the analysis but were ultimately not used: (a) The number of retail outlets in a territory was found not to affect the cost per gallon significantly. (b) Technology differences between plants, though certainly of potential importance in some branch plant systems, were judged of no significance between these particular ice cream plants.

The model, as developed, was as follows: [3]

$$C = L \left(a + b/V + c\sqrt{A} + d\,M \right). \tag{1}$$

Here, a, b, c, d are constant parameters; the variables have the following meanings:

---

[3] Though a model like $C = L^{\alpha}\,V^{\beta}\,A^{\gamma}\,M^{\delta}$ might have been employed using a regression on logarithms, it was felt that a direct sum of the cost components would more closely describe the actual circumstances. That is, it would give a better description of the physical and economic behavior, not necessarily a better statistical fit.

C = Cost of manufacturing and distribution per 1,000-gallon equivalents not including raw material costs. This is the total cost for each plant secured from the company's books for the one-year period being used as the empirical base of the study divided by the plant's volume.

L = Labor rates at the plant expressed as the average hourly wage payment.

V = Volume manufactured and distributed by the plant during the year expressed in 1,000-gallon equivalents.

A = Area serviced by the plant expressed in square miles, and determined by placing a grid over the map of each of the territories.

M = Mix of product expressed as a ratio of the average "labor content" of the plant's products to the labor content of the company's least costly product, i.e., the variable allowing for high labor input into some products.

$C, L, V, A,$ and M vary throughout the system of plants with their actual values determined for each of the plants. On the other hand, $a, b, c,$ and d are treated as constant parameters of the system, and their values must be estimated. The same basic model (not including dM) was applied with some success to bulk plants (warehouses) of a major oil company, and to warehouses of another type of food processer.[4]

The underlying rationale of the analysis is that the ten plants examined are a small sample from an infinite number of similar (possible) plants. The analysis infers from this sample that other plants in the same parent population with different configurations of the influencing variables will yield different (and in some cases lower) costs per gallon. Prediction of such costs is sought. The parameters of the system ($a, b, c,$ and d) were estimated by standard least-squares multiple regression.

To summarize the procedures so far:

1. A measure of effectiveness, cost per gallon, was chosen.
2. Ten "observations" were taken with actual cost per gallon as the dependent variable and labor rates, product volume, territory area, and plant product mix for that year as the independent variables. All observations covered a one-year period.
3. A model that related the dependent to the independent variables was constructed from studying the problem (not the data).
4. Using the actual data "observed," the system parameters of the model were estimated by least-squares regression.

TESTING THE MODEL

Several tests of the model were made: (a) the significance of the estimates of the separate parameters was tested, and (b) the model was used to "predict" the costs of the plants to compare against the actual

[4] E. H. Bowman and J. B. Stewart, "A Model for Scale of Operations," *Journal of Marketing*, January, 1956.

costs. This comparison is shown first in Table 1. The *actual cost* is the cost per gallon, *C*, the total cost for each plant for the particular year divided by the volume of that plant that year expressed in 1,000-gallon equivalents. The *predicted cost* was calculated for each plant by inserting that plant's particular values of *L*, *V*, *A*, and *M* (labor rates, volume, area, and product mix) into the model that now has the regression estimates of the system parameters *a*, *b*, *c*, and *d*. The model then "predicts" a cost for the plant. All costs (and only costs) are coded

Table 1

	Predicted Cost	Actual Cost	Ratio, Predicted/Actual
Plant No. 1	98	98	1.00
Plant No. 2	87	87	1.00
Plant No. 3	117	105	1.11
Plant No. 4	82	63	1.30
Plant No. 5	98	134	.73
Plant No. 6	118	118	1.00
Plant No. 7	92	87	1.06
Plant No. 8	109	90	1.21
Plant No. 9	115	141	.82
Plant No. 10	170	167	1.02

on a consistent basis, and may be considered analogous to cents per gallon.

The multiple-correlation coefficient for the comparison shown in Table 1 (with the error approximately normally distributed) is $R = 0.868$, which has a significance greater than 0.005. Adjusted for the relation between the number of unknowns (four) and the small sample size (ten) the adjusted multiple correlation coefficient is $R = 0.80$.[5]

Using the point estimates of the parameters, and the computed estimate of their standard deviations, the significance levels from a one-tail "*t*" test (as economic reasoning ruled out the other tail), with the coefficients equal to zero as the null hypothesis, were as shown in Table 2.

Admittedly, parameter *c* can hardly be called significant at this level. However, if the null hypothesis of $c = 0$ is accepted, then the decision

Table 2

Statistic	t	Significance Level
b	3.459	>0.005
c	0.816	>0.22
d	1.413	>0.10
$R[f(b,c,d)]$	4.276	>0.005

[5] M. Ezekiel, *Methods of Correlation Analysis* (New York: John Wiley & Sons, Inc., 1941).

rule that this analysis is seeking will call for one very large plant to serve the whole territory. In other words, *if* cost per gallon does *not* vary with territory area and it decreased with increasing volume, then the larger the plant the better. This point reappears later. For the moment at least, the analysis will accept all the point estimates (for *a*, *b*, *c*, and *d*).

DECISION RULE

Having determined the model that would in some sense predict the cost per gallon at a plant, given the plant's labor rates, volume, area, and product mix, the next step was to see how the variables in this model could be manipulated to minimize cost per gallon. On the assumption that the model represents the real world, if this minimum could be found in the model, then the branch plant system could be altered according to the model to yield the minimum cost per gallon of ice cream.

The decision rule sought was an expression for the optimum *size* plant. Neither the average labor rate nor the product mix would *necessarily* vary with an alteration by management in the volume of a plant. This is not true of area. With total sales for the company given or fixed, if the volume of a plant is to be increased (for instance), then the area of the territory served by the plant would have to be increased to pick up the additional customers to purchase this volume. It was necessary then to establish this relation between volume of production (and sales) and territory area. This relation was labelled sales density and noted by K, where $K = V/A$. This expression for sales density was in terms of sales volume (1000-gallon equivalents) per square mile, and was treated as a constant *within* each plant's territory.

The substitution, $A = V/K$ can then be made in the model:

$$C = L\left(a + b/V + c\sqrt{A} + dM\right), \qquad (2)$$
$$C = L\left(a + b/V + c\sqrt{V/K} + dM\right); \qquad (3)$$

and the derivative taken with respect to V (the decision variable), and equated to zero to reveal the optimum volume;

$$dC/dV = -Lb/V^2 + \tfrac{1}{2}Lc\,(V/K)^{-1/2} = 0$$
$$V_{opt} = K^{1/3}\,(2b/c)^{2/3}. \qquad (4)$$

The optimum value then is a function of b and c, cost parameters of the system, and K, defined as the sales density of the territory. This is the decision rule that has been sought by the analysis. It is an expression for the "best" size of the company's ice cream plants based on the company's own technology, methods, and costs. The appropriate values of K (the sales density of the particular region), and b and c (the point estimates of the parameter values for the whole system) are inserted into the decision rule, equation (4), in order to determine the optimum volume for each plant. This information is presented in Table 3. The ratio of costs in Table 3 was determined by inserting first the actual volume and then the optimum volume in the cost predicting model, equation (2).

Table 3

	Ratio of Actual Volume to Optimum Volume	Ratio of Predicted Cost at Actual Volume to Predicted Cost at Optimum Volume
Plant No. 1	1.50	1.01
Plant No. 2	0.72	1.02
Plant No. 3	0.60	1.03
Plant No. 4	0.53	1.06
Plant No. 5	0.54	1.05
Plant No. 6	0.54	1.05
Plant No. 7	0.53	1.04
Plant No. 8	0.49	1.05
Plant No. 9	0.38	1.11
Plant No. 10	0.15	1.63

It can be seen from Table 3 that according to this analysis, except for Plant No. 1, all the plants are operating at too small a volume. Half of them are operating at about half their optimum volume, while two are substantially below this figure. Taking total sales as given, then it appears that the company should operate five or six plants rather than ten. As an example, plants 1, 2, 3, 5, 7, and 9, all operating at their calculated *optimum* volumes, together would produce just about the total sales volume of all ten plants at their old volumes; that is, the total sales that are given. An extension of the cost premium paid by the company for operating the smaller plants as suggested by the last column in Table 3 indicates that a total premium of approximately $230,000 per year has been incurred as a result of operating the small plants. That is, the total sales volume could have been supplied by fewer larger plants with this yearly dollar savings.

ADDENDA TO THE DECISION RULE

According to the model, and depending on a territory's sale density, a plant that varies 50 per cent from optimum on the small side incurs a 5 to 8 per cent cost premium while a plant that varies 50 per cent from optimum on the large side incurs only a 1 or 2 per cent cost premium. Therefore, the analysis indicates not only that most plants should be larger, but if an error is to be made, it is better to make it on the large side.

Considering the fact that the parameter values used for b and c are point estimates, and that the estimating procedure presents distributions of these parameters, a case could be made for combining the economic cost functions $(b/V + c\sqrt{V/K})$ with the statistical distributions (of b and c) in order to carry out an explicit minimization of expected value rather than using the point estimates. While this was not done here, the following calculations served somewhat the same purpose.

The decision rule developed by the analysis centers around the ratio b/c, i.e., $V_{Opt} = K^{1/3}(2b/c)^{2/3}$. Both b and c have been estimated by least squares regression. The point can now be made again that the estimate of c had a relatively large standard deviation (significance level >0.22).

A sensitivity check was made on the *limits* of the decision rule. Using the standard deviation estimates developed in the regression computation, one confidence interval of 80 per cent was placed around the point estimate of $b,$ and another around the point estimate of c. As the distributions are assumed symmetrical, b and c would be outside their own limits 10 per cent of the time at either extreme. So far, this analysis reveals that virtually all of the plants are too small; however, if b were enough smaller and c were enough larger this would not be the case.

The value below which b could be expected in 10 per cent of the estimates, and the value above which c could be expected in 10 per cent of the estimates were determined. If independent, this would happen simultaneously in only 1 per cent of the estimates (0.1×0.1). With these new values, the plants that this present analysis reveals are about half their optimum size would be just about their optimum size, e.g., rather than 0.54 to 0.49, the ratio of actual to optimum size would be 1.09 to 0.97. This extreme (on the small side) answer for plant size, however, would be very unlikely. To give some balance to the picture, the large extreme (with $0.1 \times 0.1 = 0.01$ probability) was computed to be an infinite size plant, or to make it more meaningful that the company should make all their ice cream in only one plant. This is similar to accepting the null hypothesis that c (the coefficient of area) is not significant, i.e., cost per gallon does not increase with an area increase.

MANAGEMENT'S DECISION PROCESS

This analysis was carried on with the cooperation of several members of the ice cream company but independent of the decision-making group in the firm. While the optimum size of the company's plants would not be seriously recommended as *precise* answers following this analysis, considering the model explained only about two-thirds (0.8^2) of the cost variance, it was felt that the company's plants were too small, and that a system with fewer and larger plants would be a less costly one. Sometime after this study was completed (and to the best of our knowledge independent of it), the company started to make some changes. *They closed Plants Nos. 10, 4, 6, and 8.* In other words, they arrived at just about the system recommended by this analysis (i.e., size and number of plants, as no attention was given in this analysis as to which plants to close).

A check back with the company (our cooperating individuals) yielded the company's rationale. The management group suspected they had too many plants. Most of the plants had been acquired (with customers) rather than purposefully built. From the company's books and accounting cost models, they estimated, item by item, in the chart of accounts what costs would be saved by closing a particular plant (essentially manufacturing costs), and what costs would be increased at the adjacent plants (essentially manufacturing and transportation costs). According to the *company's* analysis, Plant No. 10 was studied and closed as it had a particularly poor layout. Plant No. 4 was studied and closed as its space was needed for storage for sales purposes. Plant No. 6 was studied and closed because it was built for another purpose originally and also the company desired to increase the operations of Plant No. 5, the adjoining plant. Plant No. 8 was studied and closed because it was becoming one of the most costly plants, as it is in a very difficult and high cost labor market.

It is interesting to note that the company is now considering going still further with their consolidations, possibly even to a three-plant system.

CASE 12

Some Models of Inventory and an Application[1]

ELIEZER NADDOR[2]

Some points of special interest in this paper are:

a) The tabular or numerical approach to solving the problem at the end of the paper.
b) The use of integer weeks for possible cycle lengths.
c) A model was chosen "to facilitate use of computers."
d) The differences between the various decision rules developed.
e) The specific costs needed for shortage or runout for the various models and the application.
f) The meaning of "optimum" casting interval in the application described.

This paper is concerned with two topics: (1) the development of mathematical models for several simple inventory situations, and (2) an industrial application of a mathematical model of inventory. Because T. M. Whitin has described in detail in this journal the present state of research in inventory control,[3] no attempt will be made to provide a review here. This paper is not an attempt to solve the "general inventory problem." On the contrary, the object is to deal with specific situations, and with an illustrative industrial application. The emphasis

---

[1] *Management Science*, July, 1956. Reprinted by permission. The material in this paper has been presented in two parts: at the first national meeting of The Institute of Management Sciences, Pittsburgh, October 21–22, 1954, and at the meeting of the Operations Research Society of America, Washington, November 19–20, 1954.

[2] Case Institute of Technology. Professor Naddor is now at Johns Hopkins University.

[3] T. M. Whitin, "Inventory Control Research," *Management Science*, November 1, 1954.

is on methodology of approach rather than on a general solution.

We shall first deal with four simple inventory situations, and we shall develop suitable models for them. The simplilcity of the situations lies in considering a minimum number of factors and in making certain assumptions regarding these factors. We then describe the application of one of the models to an industrial Operations Research study which involved the developed of decision rules with regard to frequency of building inventories and their sizes.

SOME MODELS OF INVENTORY

The models to be discussed below will be concerned with answering the question: What should be the optimum inventory level at the beginning of a period over which uncertain requirements for inventory will occur? More specifically, the situation to be studied may be described as follows: We are at the beginning of a planning period, say, at

Figure 1

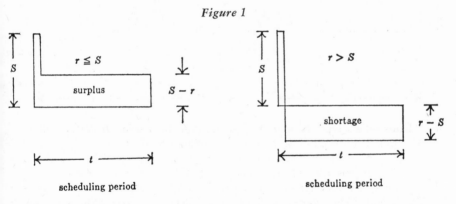

the beginning of a month. At that time we have in stock a certain amount of inventory, and we must make the decision: To what level should we increase the inventory, so that we shall be able to satisfy uncertain requirements during the coming month? The level may be either too high or too low. If it is too high, a surplus in inventory will arise, the costs associated with which are the costs of carrying inventories (cost of money, storage, handling, taxes, obsolescence, paper work, overhead, etc.). If the level is too low, shortages will arise, which are usually more costly than the costs of surpluses (loss of profit, loss of good will or even loss of customers). An optimum inventory level will be such as to minimize the total expected cost associated with surpluses and shortages. Let us now specify what factors will be considered in the models to be developed:

Input—will be denoted by q; depending on the situation, q will represent a quantity to be produced, or purchased; we shall assume that the time required to obtain q is relatively small; so that if the quantity in stock at the beginning of the planning period is s, and q is scheduled, then we shall have $S = s + q$ as the inventory level virtually at the beginning of the period to be studied. We shall assume that input will occur at regular equal intervals—the scheduling periods.

Output—will be denoted by r; r may represent the quantity required, or sold; we shall assume that r is a variable which can be estimated in the form of a probability density distribution function, $f(r)$; two patterns of output will be considered; instantaneous and continuous (see Figure 1 and Figure 2).

Figure 2

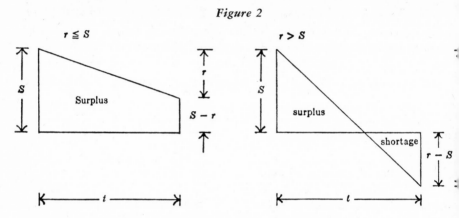

Units—Two types of units will be dealt with: continuous (as in the case of sale of gasoline) or discrete (sale of automobiles).

Costs—It will be assumed that the only relevant costs will be cost of carrying surpluses in inventory and the costs incurred when there are shortages in inventory; c_1 will denote the cost of carrying a surplus of one unit for one interval of time; c_2 will denote the corresponding cost for shortage; we shall assume that for a given situation c_1 and c_2 are constant, i.e., the unit cost does not depend on the total quantity involved nor on the length of time the quantity is carried; $C(S)$ will denote the total expected costs associated with an inventory level of S.

Thus, the models to be considered make the following assumptions:

1. The time required to obtain any input is virtually zero.
2. Decisions regarding input are made at regular equal intervals and only then.
3. Output can be estimated by a density distribution function.
4. Costs of carrying surpluses and shortages in inventory are linear in quantity and in time.

In addition, the following assumptions with regard to pattern of output and units are made for the specific models:

	OUTPUT	
	Instantaneous (Fig. 1)	Continuous (Fig. 2)
Units		
Continuous...........	Model I	Model II
Discrete..............	Model III	Model IV

Model I

Let us assume that the period starts with an inventory level of S. Two situations may arise, depending on the relation of r to S (see Fig. 1). In the case of a surplus the cost will be $c_1(S - r)t$, and in the case of a shortage $c_2(r - S)t$ so that the total expected cost $C(S)$ associated with an inventory level of S will be:

$$C(S) = \int_0^S c_1(S - r)tf(r)\, dr + \int_S^\infty c_2(r - S)tf(r)\, dr \qquad (1)$$

In order to find the optimum S we proceed as follows: From equation (1) by differentiating we have:

$$\begin{aligned}
\frac{dC}{dS} &= c_1 t \int_0^S f(r)\, dr - c_2 t \int_S^\infty f(r)\, dr \\
&= c_1 t F(S) - c_2 t[1 - F(S)] \qquad (2) \\
&= [(c_1 + c_2)F(S) - c_2]t
\end{aligned}$$

Where

$$F(S) = \int_0^S f(r)\, dr$$

$C(S)$ will have a relative extreme (maximum or minimum) at S_0 if

$$\left.\frac{dC}{dS}\right|_{S=S_0} = 0.$$

Therefore, from equation (2), we have as a necessary condition for an extreme value,

$$(c_1 + c_2)F(S_0) - c_2 = 0$$

or

$$F(S_0) = \frac{c_2}{c_1 + c_2} \qquad (3)$$

Since

$$\left.\frac{d^2C}{dS^2}\right|_{S=S_0} = [c_1 f(S_0) + c_2 f(S_0)]t = (c_1 + c_2)f(S_0)t$$

and since c_1 and c_2 are not both zero, and since $f(S) \geqq 0$ then

$$\left.\frac{d^2C}{dS^2}\right|_{=S_0} \geqq 0$$

If the inequality holds, then S_0 gives the minimum. If the equality holds, then $f(S_0) = 0$. But $f(r)$ is a continuous function and $f(r) \geqq 0$. Therefore, if $f(S_0) = 0$, then $f(r)$ has a minimum at S_0, namely zero. It follows that $C(S)$ has a minimum at $S = S_0$. Therefore, $S = S_0$ satisfying $F(S_0) = c_2/(c_1 + c_2)$ gives a minimum of $C(S)$.

Example 1: Suppose the demand density distribution per week has been found to be: $f(r) = .02 - .0002r$ with r varying from 0 to 100. The cost of carrying a surplus of one unit per month is estimated at 1 cent and the corresponding cost of a shortage at 15 cents. The optimum inventory level at the beginning of each week can be found as follows:

$$F(S) = \int_0^S (.02 - .0002r)\, dr = .02S - .0001S^2$$

$$\frac{c_2}{c_1 + c_2} = \frac{\dfrac{15}{4}}{\dfrac{1}{4} + \dfrac{15}{4}} = \frac{15}{16}$$

Hence

$$.02S_0 - .0001S_0^2 = \frac{15}{16}$$

Therefore

$$S_0 = 75 \text{ lbs.}$$

Equation (3) has an interesting interpretation. If we rearrange the terms we can get:

$$\frac{F(S_0)}{1 - F(S_0)} = \frac{c_2}{c_1}$$

Now, the expected frequency of occurrence of surpluses when we start with S is $\int_0^S f(r)\, dr = F(S)$ and the expected frequency of occurrence of shortages is $1 - F(S)$. Equation (3) can therefore be interpreted as follows: To find the inventory level that will minimize the expected costs, choose that level which will give the ratio of expected frequency of surplus to that of shortage to be inversely proportionate to the corresponding costs of surplus and shortage.

Model II

This model is similar to Model I, except that the output r will be assumed to occur continuously during the scheduling period. Here, again two typical situations arise, depending on the relation of r to S (see Fig. 2). When $r \leq S$ the cost will be $c_1(S - r/2)t$ and when $r > S$ the cost will be

$$c_1 \frac{S}{2} \frac{S}{r} t + c_2 \frac{r - S}{2} \frac{r - S}{r} t ,$$

so that the expected total cost associated with an inventory level of S will be:

$$C(S) = \int_0^S c_1 \left(S - \frac{r}{2} \right) tf(r)\, dr + \int_S^\infty c_1 \frac{S^2}{2r} tf(r)\, dr + \int_S^\infty c_2 \frac{(r - S)^2}{2r} tf(r)\, dr \quad (4)$$

In order to find the optimum S in this case, we proceed in a manner similar to that adopted for Model I:

$$\frac{dC}{dS} = c_1 t \int_0^S f(r)\, dr + c_1 t \int_S^\infty \frac{S}{r} f(r) - c_2 t \int_S^\infty \frac{r - S}{r} f(r)\, dr$$

$$= \{c_1 F(S) + c_1 G(S) - c_2[1 - F(S)] + c_2 G(S)\} t$$

$$= \{(c_1 + c_2)[F(S) + G(S)] - c_2\} t = \{(c_1 + c_2)L(S) - c_2\} t$$

Where:

$$L(S) = F(S) + G(S) .$$

$F(S)$ was defined earlier and

$$G(S) = S \int_S^\infty \frac{f(r)}{r}\, dr$$

$C(S)$ will have a relative extreme at S_0 if:

$$\left. \frac{dC}{dS} \right|_{S=S_0} = 0$$

or if:

$$L(S_0) = \frac{c_2}{c_1 + c_2} \quad (5)$$

Now:

$$\frac{d^2C}{dS^2} = (c_1 + c_2)t \int_S^\infty \frac{f(r)}{r}\, dr > 0$$

Hence equation (5) specifies completely the condition for finding the optimum inventory level S_0.

Example 2: There are 1.12 units on hand. The demand density is $f(r) = re^{-r}$. The cost of a shortage is estimated to be 20 times larger than the cost of a surplus. Find the optimum input.

Here: $L(S) = \int_0^S re^{-r}\, dr + S \int_S^\infty e^{-r}\, dr = 1 - e^{-s}$ and $\dfrac{c_2}{c_1 + c_2} = \dfrac{19}{20}$

Using (5) we have:

$$1 - e^{-S_0} = \frac{19}{20}$$

Hence $S_0 = 3.04$ and the optimum input, q, will be: $q = S_0 - s = 3.04 - 1.12 = 1.92$. Equation (5) has a similar interpretation to that of equation (3). For an inventory level of S units we find that the expected frequency of occurrences of surpluses is

$$\int_0^S f(r)\, dr + \int_S^\infty \frac{S}{r} f(r)\, dr = L(S)$$

and the frequency of occurrence of shortages is $1 - L(S)$. If we rewrite equation (5) we get:

$$\frac{L(S_0)}{1 - L(S_0)} = \frac{c_2}{c_1}$$

Equation (5) can therefore be interpreted exactly as equation (3): the inventory level which minimizes expected costs, is that level which gives the ratio of expected frequency of occurrence of surplus to that of frequency of occurrence of shortage to be inversely proportionate to the corresponding costs of surplus and shortage.

Model III

This model is similar to Model I, except that we shall be dealing with discrete units. The expected cost can be developed as in Model I, leading to:

$$C(S) = \sum_0^S c_1 (S - r) t f(r) + \sum_{S+1}^\infty c_2 (r - S) t f(r) \tag{6}$$

To find the optimum inventory level we proceed as follows: We first substitute $(S + 1)$ for S in equation (6), obtaining:

$$C(S + 1) = \left\{ c_1 \sum_{r=0}^{S+1} (S + 1 - r) f(r) + c_2 \sum_{r=S+2}^\infty (r - S - 1) f(r) \right\} t$$

$$= \left\{ c_1 \sum_0^S (S - r) f(r) + c_1 \sum_0^S f(r) \right.$$

$$\left. + c_2 \sum_{S+1}^\infty (r - S) f(r) - c_2 \sum_{S+1}^\infty f(r) \right\} t$$

$$= C(S) + \{ (c_1 + c_2) F(S) - c_2 \} t$$

Where

$$F(S) = \sum_0^S f(r)$$

Similarly,

$$C(S - 1) = C(S) - \{(c_1 + c_2)F(S - 1) - c_2\}t$$

Consider, now, S_0 such that

and

$$\left.\begin{array}{c} (c_1 + c_2)F(S_0) - c_2 \geqq 0 \\[4pt] -(c_1 + c_2)F(S_0 - 1) + c_2 \geqq 0 \end{array}\right\} \qquad (7)$$

For any integer S' larger than S_0 and for any integer S'' smaller than S_0, inequations (7) would hold since $F(S)$ is nondecreasing for increasing S. Hence, if inequations (7) hold, then

$$C(S'') \geqq C(S_0) \text{ for } S'' < S_0 ,$$

and

$$C(S') \geqq C(S_0) \text{ for } S' > S_0 .$$

We have thus found the value of S which minimizes the total expected cost; namely, S_0 satisfying inequalities (7). These inequalities can be re-arranged to give

$$F(S_0 - 1) \leqq \frac{c_2}{c_1 + c_2} \leqq F(S_0) \qquad (8)$$

Example 3[4]*:* There are certain rather expensive items (some costing over $100,000 each) known as "insurance spares" which are generally procured at the time a new class of ships is under construction. These spares are bought even though it is known that it is very unlikely that any of them will ever be needed and that they cannot be used on any ship except of that particular class. They are procured in order to provide insurance against the rather serious loss which would be suffered if one of these spares were not available when needed. Also the initial procurement of these spares is intended to be the only procure-ment during the lifetime of the ships of that class, because it is ex-tremely difficult and costly to procure these spares at a later date.

Suppose, for example, that spares cost $100,000 each and that a loss of $10,000,000 is suffered for each spare that is needed when there is none available in stock. Further suppose that the probabilities that

---

[4] See J. Laderman, S. B. Littauer, and L. Weiss, "The Inventory Problem," *Journal of the American Statistical Association*, Volume XLVIII (December, 1953), pp. 717–32.

spares will be needed as replacements during the lifeterm of the class of ships discussed are:

No. of Spares Required	Probability
1	.0400
2	.0100
3	.0010
4	.0002
5 or more	.0000

How many spare parts should be procured?

This example meets the assumptions of Model III. Here $c_1 = \$100,000$, $c_2 = \$9,900,000$, $F(0) = .9488$, $F(1) = .9888$, $F(2) = .9988$, $F(3) = .9998$, $F(4) = 1.0000$. Since $c_2/(c_1 + c_2) = .9900$ and since $F(1) < .9900 < F(2)$, we conclude by (8) that the optimum number of spare parts to be ordered is $S_0 = 2$.

Model IV

This model is similar to Model II, except that we shall develop the cost equation for discrete units.

By a reasoning similar to that used in the derivation of equation (4) we obtain for the present case:

$$C(S) = \sum_0^S c_1\left(S - \frac{r}{2}\right) tf(r) + \sum_{S+1}^{\infty} c_1 \frac{S^2}{2r} tf(r) + \sum_{S+1}^{\infty} c_2 \frac{(r-S)^2}{2r} tf(r) \qquad (9)$$

We proceed to find S_0: Substituting $(S + 1)$ for S in equation (9) yields

$$C(S + 1) = \left\{ c_1 \sum_0^{S+1}\left(S + 1 - \frac{r}{2}\right)f(r) + c_1 \sum_{S+2}^{\infty} \frac{(S+1)^2}{2r}f(r) \right.$$
$$\left. + c_2 \sum_{S+2}^{\infty} \frac{(r-S-1)^2}{2r}f(r) \right\} t \qquad (10)$$

Now

$$c_1 \sum_0^{S+1}\left(S + 1 - \frac{r}{2}\right)f(r) = c_1 \sum_0^S\left(S + 1 - \frac{r}{2}\right)f(r)$$
$$+ c_1\left(S + 1 - \frac{S+1}{2}\right)f(S + 1)$$
$$= c_1 \sum_0^S\left(S - \frac{r}{2}\right)f(r) + c_1 \sum_0^S f(r)$$
$$+ c_1\left(\frac{S+1}{2}\right)f(S + 1)$$

Similarly

$$c_1 \sum_{S+2}^{\infty} \frac{(S+1)^2}{2r} f(r) = c_1 \sum_{S+1}^{\infty} \frac{S^2}{2r} f(r) + c_1 S \sum_{S+1}^{\infty} \frac{f(r)}{r} + \frac{c_1}{2} \sum_{S+1}^{\infty} \frac{f(r)}{r}$$
$$- c_1 \frac{S+1}{2} f(S+1)$$

and

$$c_2 \sum_{S+2}^{\infty} \frac{(r-S-1)^2}{2r} f(r) = c_2 \sum_{S+1}^{\infty} \frac{(r-S)^2}{2r} f(r) - c_2 \sum_{S+1}^{\infty} f(r)$$
$$+ S c_2 \sum_{S+1}^{\infty} \frac{f(r)}{r} + \frac{1}{2} c_2 \sum_{S+1}^{\infty} \frac{f(r)}{r}.$$

Therefore, from equations (9) and (10), it follows that

$$C(S+1) = C(S) + \left\{ (c_1 + c_2) \left[F(S) + (S + \tfrac{1}{2}) \sum_{S+1}^{\infty} \frac{f(r)}{r} \right] - c_2 \right\} t \quad (11)$$

Next, let

$$L(S) = F(S) + (S + \tfrac{1}{2}) \sum_{S+1}^{\infty} \frac{f(r)}{r}$$

then, from equation (14),

$$C(S+1) = C(S) + \{(c_1 + c_2) L(S) - c_2\} t$$

Similarly, substituting $(S-1)$ for S in equation (12), we obtain:

$$C(S-1) = C(S) - \{(c_1 + c_2) L(S-1) - c_2\} t \quad (13)$$

Now, $L(S)$ is a nondecreasing function of S. This can be proved as follows:

$$L(S+1) = F(S+1) + (S + 1 + \tfrac{1}{2}) \sum_{S+2}^{\infty} \frac{f(r)}{r}$$

$$= F(S) + f(S+1) + (S + \tfrac{1}{2}) \sum_{S+1}^{\infty} \frac{f(r)}{r} - \frac{(S + \tfrac{1}{2})}{(S+1)} f(S+1)$$
$$+ \sum_{S+1}^{\infty} \frac{f(r)}{r} - \frac{f(S+1)}{S+1}$$

$$= L(S) - \frac{1}{2} \frac{f(S+1)}{S+1} + \sum_{S+1}^{\infty} \frac{f(r)}{r}$$

Hence

$$L(S + 1) = L(S) + \sum_{S+2}^{\infty} \frac{f(r)}{r} + \frac{1}{2} \frac{f(S + 1)}{S + 1}$$

But since

$$\sum_{S+2}^{\infty} \frac{f(r)}{r} + \frac{1}{2} \frac{f(S + 1)}{S + 1} \geqq 0$$

then we have

$$L(S + 1) \geqq L(S) .$$

Consider, now, S_0 such that

$$\left.\begin{array}{c} (c_1 + c_2)L(S_0) - c_2 \geqq 0 \\[2mm] -(c_1 + c_2)L(S_0 - 1) + c_2 \geqq 0 \end{array}\right\} \tag{14}$$

and

For any $S' > S_0$ and $S'' < S_0$, inequations (14) and hold since $L(S)$ is non-decreasing. Hence,

$$C(S'') \geqq C(S_0), \qquad S'' < S_0$$

and

$$(S') \geqq C(S_0), \qquad S' > S_0 .$$

Therefore, the value of S which minimizes the total expected cost is that value S_0 which satisfies inequations (14) or, by rearrangement, the inequalities

$$L(S_0 - 1) \leqq \frac{c_2}{c_1 + c_2} \leqq L(S_0) \tag{15}$$

where

$$L(S) = F(S) + (S + \tfrac{1}{2}) \sum_{S+1}^{\infty} \frac{f(r)}{r} .$$

Example 4: The discrete density for sales is given by:

$$f(0) = .1 \quad f(1) = .2 \quad f(2) = .2 \quad f(3) = .3 \quad f(4) = .1 \quad f(5) = .1$$

c_1 is \$1.00. There is currently being maintained an inventory level of 3 units. Assuming that this is an optimum level, what, then, is c_2? We first compute $L(2)$ and $L(3)$. This can be done best as shown in Table 1. From (15) we have:

$$.8625 < \frac{c_2}{1.00 + c_2} < .9575$$

Hence

$$\$6.27 < c_2 < \$22.53 .$$

If 3 is an optimum inventory level, then this implies that the cost of being short one unit lies between \$6.27 and \$22.53, and it is not necessary to estimate c_2 any more accurately in order to show that the current policy is optimum.

Table 1

r,S	$f(r)$	$F(S)$	$\dfrac{f(r)}{r}$	$\displaystyle\sum_{S+1}^{\infty} \dfrac{f(r)}{r}$	$(S+\tfrac{1}{2})\displaystyle\sum_{S+1}^{\infty}\dfrac{f(r)}{r}$	$L(S)$
0	.1	.1000	∞	.4450	.2225	.3225
1	.2	.3000	.2000	.2450	.3675	.6675
2	.2	.5000	.1000	.1450	.3625	.8625
3	.3	.8000	.1000	.0450	.1575	.9575
4	.1	.9000	.0250	.0200	.0900	.9900
5	.1	1.0000	.0200	.0000	.0000	1.0000

AN APPLICATION

We shall now describe an industrial situation which called for the development of a mathematical model of inventory. The Subject Company produces among other things bi-metalic and tri-metalic strip material from which it fabricates finished components. One stage in the production cycle are the casting operations. They consist of casting molten copper-lead alloys on strip steel. In this preliminary series of operations, raw materials are converted into a secondary raw material, from which form fabrication into the finished product takes place. In the past there has been a limited amount of cast material prepared for banking purposes. Management has requested that research be carried out with regard to the casting operations and the banking of cast materials to accomplish the following purposes:

1. To enable the company, through the customer schedulers and allied personnel, to render improved customer service.
2. To increase the effectiveness of the casting lines without increasing the total cost of cast materials.
3. To reduce or eliminate lead time required for the casting operations.

The team composed of company and Case personnel chose the copper alloy on steel casting lines as the first area for research. In the past there was no sure way of determining which materials from these lines and how much of each cast material should be stocked. Hence it often happened that rush orders required material other than that in bank or in greater quantity than the amount available. The amount in the bank was also governed by fear of obsolescence, fear of material deterioration due to atmospheric conditions while material was in storage, and by the desire to keep a minimum of all types of inventories including cast material.

Preliminary study revealed that in order to minimize set-up costs, shop orders requiring the same widths of steel should be cast concurrently. Changes in alloys and/or gauge of steel could then be readily accommodated with no appreciable increase in set-ups. (This procedure was actually being followed to a great degree in the past.) All cast items having the same widths were said to belong to the same family. The following questions thus arose:

1. What is the best casting cycle for each family?
2. Which items within each family should be banked?
3. How should optimum inventory levels for banked items be determined?
4. What would be the expected maximum and average total inventories?
5. What would be the expected costs associated with the maintenance of banks of cast material?

The research has resulted in the development of mathematical and conceptual tools which can be used to answer these questions. Approximate methods have also been developed to obtain quick estimates. These estimates showed that: (a) Although the frequency of casting cycles in practice is within the range of the best frequencies, the amounts banked for stock are not sufficient, (b) that the storage facilities for the increased optimum inventories were available, (c) that the total costs associated with the maintenance of inventories, which included costs of obsolescence and deterioration, were relatively small compared to the advantages to be gained: greater customer satisfaction through reduction of lead time, and smoother internal operations within the company.

Management, therefore, gave its consent to the building up of banks of cast material. This is currently being carried out.

Space allotted to this paper will not allow to include all the models developed in connection with this project. We shall confine our attention to one of the basic models only.

We consider the following: Given a family of n items. The setup cost associated with the family is c_3. For each item i in the family the costs of surplus and shortage of one unit per one interval are c_{1i} and c_{2i} respectively. Also for each item in the family $f_i(r)$ will be the discrete density of requirements over one interval of time. The problem is to find: (a) How often should the family be cast? (b) What is the optimum inventory level for each item in the family?

Let us assume that the family will be cast every t intervals. The inventory situation for each item in the family may be represented by diagrams such as those of Model II, since the casting operation is relatively short, and since the demands for cast material are continuous. From past data it was possible to evaluate the density distribution function $f_i(r/t)$ for each item in the family for various scheduling periods, t. Since, however, $f_i(r/t)$ was expressed for discrete units (this was done to facilitate use of computers) we have to use Model IV for cost equations and optimum level finding. If we use this model we can find for each item and for various scheduling periods t its optimum inventory level, $S_i(t)_0$ [by (15)] and the corresponding expected costs $C(S_i(t)_0)$ (by replacing S with $S_i(t)_0$ in (9)). Thus, if the family is cast every t intervals, the expected cost per interval of time will be:

$$C(t) = \frac{1}{t}\left[\sum_{i}^{n} C(S_i(t)_0) + c_3\right] \qquad (16)$$

To minimize the expected cost, t must be chosen suitably. We shall illustrate the procedure by a relatively simple example:

Example 5: A family consists of 2 items. The costs and densities of requirements with respect to these items are:

	Item 1		Item 2	
c_1 (Cost of surplus per unit per week)....	$2		$5	
c_2 (Cost of shortage per unit per week)..	$130		$60	
Density of requirements per week.......	r	$f_1(r)$	r	$f_2(r)$
	0	.4	0	.2
	1	.3	1	.5
	2	.2	2	.3
	3	.1		

The setup cost for the family is $18. How often should the family be cast, and what are the optimum inventory levels of the two items of the family?

We first assume that the family will be cast every week. Model IV is used to find the optimum inventory level for item 1 and for item 2. A table (Table 2) is prepared as in Example 4. The last 4 columns of the table will be used for computing the expected cost. It can be shown that equation (9) can be rearranged to give:

$$C(S) = \left\{(c_1 + c_2)S\left[F(S) + \frac{H(S)}{2} + \frac{G(S)}{2}\right] - c_1\frac{\bar{r}}{2} - c_2 S\right\}t \qquad (17)$$

Where:

$$F(S) = \sum_0^S f(r); \quad H(S) = \frac{1}{S}\sum_{S+1}^{\infty} rf(r); \quad G(S) = S\sum_{S+1}^{\infty}\frac{f(r)}{r} \text{ and } \bar{r} = \sum_0^{\infty} rf(r)$$

We next compute $c_{2i}/(c_{1i} + c_{2i})$ for the two items:

$$\frac{c_{21}}{c_{11} + c_{21}} = \frac{130}{2 + 130} = .985 \qquad \frac{c_{22}}{c_{12} + c_{22}} = \frac{60}{5 + 60} = .923$$

Hence by (15) $S_1(1)_0 = 3$ and $S_2(1)_0 = 1$ since $L_1(2) < .985 < L_1(3)$ and $L_2(0) < .923 < L_2(1)$.

Using (17) we find that: $C_1(3) = \$5.00$ and $C_2(1) = \$7.13$. These results have the following meaning: If the family will be cast every week, then the optimum inventory levels for items 1 and 2 are 3 and 1 respectively. For such levels the expected costs associated with surpluses and shortages in inventory will be $5.00 and $7.13 respectively. If we now add the setup cost to these costs we shall find by (16)

Table 2

r, S	$f(r)$	$F(S)$	$\dfrac{f(r)}{r}$	$\sum\limits_{S+1}^{\infty} \dfrac{f(r)}{r}$	$\sum\limits_{.S+1}^{\infty} \dfrac{(S+\frac{1}{2})}{r} f(r)$	$L(S)$	$rf(r)$	$\sum\limits_{S+1}^{\infty} rf(r)$	$H(S)$	$G(S)$
					Item 1					
0	.4	.4	∞	.43333	.216665	.616665	0	1.0	∞	0
1	.3	.7	.30000	.13333	.199995	.899995	.3	.7	.700000	.13333
2	.2	.9	.10000	.03333	.083325	.983325	.4	.3	.15000	.06666
3	.1	1.0	.03333	0	0	1.000000	.3	0	0	0
					Item 2					
0	.2	.2	∞	.65000	.325000	.525000	0	1.1	∞	0
1	.5	.7	.50000	.15000	.225000	.925000	.5	.6	.600000	.15000
2	.3	1.0	.15000	0	0	1.000000	.6	0	0	0

the total expected costs per week for the family, if cast every week:
$C(1) = 1/1[5.00 + 7.13 + 18.00] = \$30.13$.

In order to find the total expected costs for the family for a scheduling period of two weeks a similar procedure is adopted. However, the corresponding densities have to be computed first. We readily find, by use of simple probability considerations, the densities for two weeks (this can be done if we assume statistical independence for the two weeks distributions). These densities are used in the preparation of Table 3. The values of $c_{2i}/(c_{1i} + c_{2i})$ are unaltered. Hence, by (15) for the two weeks cycle: $S_1(2)_0 = 4$ and $S_2(2)_0 = 3$ since $L_1(3) < .985 < L_1(4)$ and $L_2(2) < .923 < L_2(3)$. By (17) and the above table we find that: $C_1(4) = \$13.94$ and $C_2(3) = \$20.46$. Hence, by (16), for casting every two weeks, the total expected costs per week for the family will be: $C(2) = \frac{1}{2}[13.94 + 20.46 + 18.00] = \$26.20$. Thus, if the family will be cast every two weeks, then the expected costs per week of holding inventories (surpluses and shortages) and the costs of set ups will be $26.20. The optimum inventory levels, in that case, will be 4 for item 1 and 3 for item 2.

We next investigate the total cost for casting every three weeks. The computations are similar to those given before. The following are the results for $t = 3$ weeks:

$$S_1(3)_0 = 5 \qquad S_2(3)_0 = 4 \qquad C(3) = \$28.18$$

Table 3

r, S	$f(r)$	$F(S)$	$\dfrac{f(r)}{r}$	$\displaystyle\sum_{s+1}^{\infty} \dfrac{f(r)}{r}$	$(S+\tfrac{1}{2})\displaystyle\sum_{s+1}^{\infty}\dfrac{f(r)}{r}$	$L(S)$	$rf(r)$	$\displaystyle\sum_{s+1}^{\infty} rf(r)$	$H(S)$	$G(S)$
				Item 1						
0	.16	.16	∞	.46634	.233170	.393170	0	2.00	∞	0
1	.24	.40	.24000	.22634	.339510	.739510	.24	1.76	1.76000	.22634
2	.25	.65	.12500	.10134	.253350	.903350	.50	1.26	.63000	.20268
3	.20	.85	.06667	.03467	.121345	.971345	.60	.66	.22000	.10401
4	.10	.95	.02500	.00967	.043515	.993515	.40	.26	.06500	.03868
5	.04	.99	.00800	.00167	.009185	.999185	.20	.06	.01200	.00835
6	.01	1.00	.00167	0	0	1.000000	.06	0	0	0
				Item 2						
0	.04	.04	∞	.50750	.253750	.293750	0	2.20	∞	0
1	.20	.24	.20000	.30750	.461250	.701250	.20	2.00	2.00000	.30750
2	.37	.61	.18500	.12250	.306250	.916250	.74	1.26	.63000	.24500
3	.30	.91	.10000	.02250	.078750	.988750	.90	.36	.12000	.06750
4	.09	1.00	.02250	0	0	1.000000	.36	0	0	0

This last result shows that the two weeks gives a relative minimum. It can be shown that the function $C(t)$ of (16) is a convex function; hence, we do not have to find $C(t)$ for other values of t. Our problem has been solved: The family should be cast every 2 weeks; the optimum inventory level for item 1 is 4 and the optimum inventory level for item 2 is 3; the expected weekly costs associated with this policy, covering inventory carrying costs (surplus and shortage) and set up costs, will be $26.20.

This procedure was carried out for 14 families of about 30 items each. All the computation could be performed with relative ease on an IBM 604. The final results stated the frequency of casting for each family, the optimum inventory levels of all cast items, the expected total costs and the expected inventories which will be carried.

CASE 13

Economic Equipment Policies:
An Evaluation[1]

VERNON L. SMITH[2]

Some points of special interest in this paper are:

a) The empirical work at an industry level on obsolescence.

b) The inclusion of a factor in the general equipment replacement model to take account of differences in performance of successive members of the chain of machines, and the rationale and statistical justification for this factor.

c) The leveling off of maintenance expense and the associated rationale.

d) The estimates made of the functions necessary for a solution of the model.

e) The determination made of the sensitivity of firm profits to difference in replacement decisions.

f) The use of equipment theory as a guide in the choice of equipment type.

g) The statement that the "machine" contemplated by the model is really a "capacity unit."

h) Delayed replacement as a cheap source of capital for an expanding firm.

---

[1] *Management Science,* October, 1957. Reprinted by permission.

[2] Purdue University. This research was conducted in the author's capacity as a member of the research staff of the Harvard Economic Research Project and as a part of his doctoral dissertation at Harvard University during the academic year 1954–1955. The author is indebted to Professor W. W. Leontief, Dr. E. B. Gilboy and Dr. Anne P. Carter for many helpful comments. The revision of an earlier form of the present manuscript was supported by the Office of Naval Research under contract with the Management Sciences Research Group of Purdue University directed by Dr. A. Charnes. In many ways the author's greatest debt is to Mr. M. C. Benton, Jr., Vice President and Treasurer of the McLean Trucking Company, for his kind cooperation in supplying much of the information without which this study would hardly have been possible. This debt is acknowledged with pleasure. The author has also had the benefit of many valuable comments by his referee, Mr. Bertram Rifas. The author, of course, takes full responsibility for any errors or weaknesses.

The present paper summarizes the results of a detailed empirical investigation of the theory of economic equipment policy as applied to one important kind of industrial equipment, *viz* line-haul truck-tractor power units. The objective of this research was to ascertain, for a type of equipment which is perhaps best suited to exact replacement analysis, the quantitative importance to the firm of following optimal policies in replacement and in the choice of equipment type. Also it was desired to compare actual with optimal policies in a concrete case.

THEORY

Consider a firm engaged in a process of production requiring units of a particular class of industrial equipment, such as trucks, metal working machines, chemical reactors, pumping equipment, and so forth. Suppose, for the sake of reducing the problem to its most essential elements, that the equipment employed by the firm is all of the same make, model and vintage.

Also, for the present, let the common assumption be entertained, that output and therefore the stock of machines is held constant. An economic replacement policy for the firm is defined as one that optimally spaces the purchases and retirements of the firm's stock of equipment. This is determined by finding that period of equipment service that maximizes the present value of the net earnings profile of the present and all future equipment in the chain of renewals extending as far into the future as the firm's profit horizon. If that horizon is taken to be infinite, then mathematically the problem is to maximize[3] with respect to

$$v = \sum_{k=0}^{\infty} e^{-\rho k L} \left\{ \int_0^L Q(kL, t)e^{-\rho t}\,dt - p + S(L)e^{-\rho L} \right\} \qquad (1.1)$$

L, where v is the present value of the net earnings profile per unit of equipment, ρ is the continuous rate of interest, L is the period of equipment service in, say, years, p is the initial cost per unit of the equipment under consideration, and $S(L)$ is its market resale value after L years of service.

The function $Q(kL,t)$ represents the earnings or quasi-rent of a unit of equipment net only of its operating costs, as a function of its age t and the point in calendar time, kL, when the equipment was purchased

---

[3] This is essentially the expression for present value used by Preinreich, Lutz, Alchian, and others, except that differences in the performance of successive members of the infinite machine chain are taken into account explicitly by inclusion of the discrete variable kL. G. A. D. Preinreich, "The Economic Life of Industrial Equipment," *Econometrica*, Vol. VIII, No. 1 (January, 1940), p. 12. Fredric and Vera Lutz, *The Theory of Investment of the Firm* (Princeton University Press, 1951). Armen A. Alchian, *Economic Replacement Policy*, The RAND Corporation, Santa Monica, California, April 12, 1952.

new. It is technological—or more accurately, structural—change, affecting the performance of successive new models of equipment, that causes equipment earnings to depend upon the calendar time that has elapsed up to the point at which the kth replacement is made.

A graph of $Q(kL,t)$ is shown in Figure 1 for the special case in which Q is *linear* in kL and t, *i.e.*, where

$$Q(kL, t) = A + \alpha kL - \beta t; \quad k = 0, 1, 2, \cdot \qquad (1.2)$$

and the origin is the point in calendar time at which the present equipment was placed in service. The term $A + \alpha kL$ is the obsolescence

Figure 1

GRAPH OF QUASI-RENT PROFILE $Q(kL,t)$

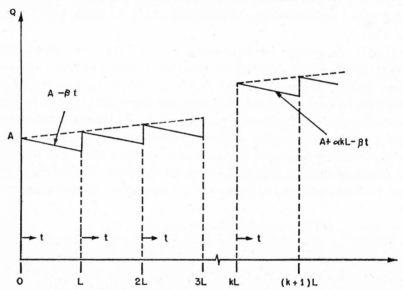

function as measured by the effect of structural change on the initial earnings of the new equipment that becomes available each year. It is assumed that structural change does not alter the (in this case linear) shape of the earnings profile, but increases the *initial* intercept rate of earnings of new equipment at the rate of α dollars/year/year. After an asset has been in service L years it will have accumulated an obsolescence of αL dollars/year relative to the newest model then available.[4]

---

[4] The term $\alpha + \beta$ is what George Terborgh (*Dynamic Equipment Policy* [New York: McGraw-Hill Book Co., Inc., 1949]) calls the inferiority gradient or the total rate at which an existing installation develops inferiority relative to the most recently available model. In the present treatment the inferiority gradient has been divided into an obsolescence component α and a deterioration component β.

If $R(kL,t)$ is the gross revenue rate and $E(kL,t)$ the operating expense rate of the equipment, then the quasi-rent function can be written as

$$Q(kL,\ t) = R(kL,\ t) - E(kL,\ t) \tag{1.3}$$

In general one will expect $R(kL,t)$ to be a nondecreasing function of kL, and a nonincreasing function of t, while $E(kL,t)$ will be a nonincreasing function of kL, and a nondecreasing function of t. As a rule, revenue will be expected to fall and expenses rise with age, while revenue will rise and expenses fall with technological advance.

ESTIMATES OF OBSOLESCENCE

Motor trucking equipment fits, perhaps better than any other kind of equipment, the obsolescence assumptions of the model contained in equation (1.1). The technical changes which have taken place have been neither sporadic nor spectacular but have proceeded at a steady, pedestrian pace from year to year since the initial development of the industry. Therefore, the assumption of continuity in the development of obsolescence does not appear to be in serious violation of the facts. This situation is likely to prevail for those kinds of industrial equipment which employ the internal combustion engine as a prime mover. The internal combustion engine is an excellent example of equipment which has enjoyed almost continuous change with no single technical alteration being of striking importance. This is particularly evident in time series of such engineering variables as compression ratio, thermal efficiency, horsepower per pound of engine weight, and so forth.[5]

Specifically, motor trucks have experienced two broad kinds of technological change which may impinge upon revenue and/or operating cost to an important extent.

One class of technological improvement has involved changes in the design and construction of vehicles so that greater payloads can be carried without violating the maximum over-all legal limits placed upon gross weight, axle load, length, width and height. These changes have taken, among others, the following forms: (1) reduced vehicle tare (unladen) weight, through the use of lighter materials and weight saving designs, which permit larger payloads without increasing gross weight; (2) the use of multiple axle tractor-trailer designs which permit larger gross weights without increasing axle loadings; and (3) design changes which have shortened the tractor and lengthened the

---

[5] See *e.g.* A. F. Denham, *20 Years' Progress in Commercial Motor Vehicles*, Automotive Council for War Production, 1942, chaps. 4–6 *passim*.

trailer units permitting larger payloads without violating state limits on length, width and height.

The impact of these changes on trucking operations is seen quite clearly in the time series of average load for all intercity common carriers of freight. Figure 2 shows how average loads have risen steadily during the period 1943–1952. The empirical equation of this trend is given by the expression:

$$Z = B_Z T + A_Z = 0.09T + 8.25 + 0.09\,(T_0 - 1943) \qquad (2.1)$$

where Z is the average load in tons, and T_0 is the year chosen for the

Figure 2

AVERAGE LOAD TREND; CLASS I INTERCITY COMMON CARRIERS OF GENERAL AND OTHER THAN GENERAL FREIGHT

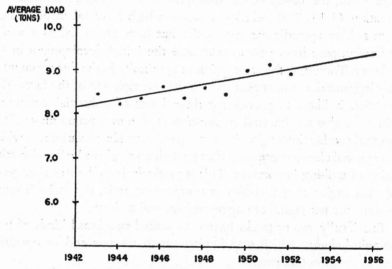

Source: Interstate Commerce Commission, Statistics of Class I Motor Carriers, Bureau of Transport Economics and Statistics, 1943–1952, Washington, D. C.

origin. This equation shows that average load has risen at the rate of about .09 tons or 180 pounds per year.

If it is intended that this trend in average load be used as a basis for developing an economic measure of the obsolescence of intercity motor vehicles, it is important that it be attributable to factors which require individual companies to shift from old to new equipment in order to reap the benefits of a larger average payload. The empirical evidence seems to suggest that this is the case.[6] Since, by and large, vehicle

---

[6] For a much more careful discussion of this point see the author's doctoral dissertation "A Theoretical and Empirical Inquiry into the Economic Replacement of Capital Equipment," Harvard University, 1955.

operating costs tend to vary a great deal more with mileage than with load, the value of the increased ton-mileage made possible by the observed rise in average load will represent, approximately, an average net contribution to the profits of individual firms and, consequently, will serve as a direct measure of what we shall call capacity obsolescence. One qualification to be noted in using the full observed increase in average load as a measure of truck-tractor obsolescence is the fact that some changes, such as the use of lighter materials in semi-trailers, cause an increase in average load independently of the power units. Another possible qualification pertains to the fact that increases in state weight limits may account for at least some of the upward average load trend in Figure 2. However, insofar as the full benefits from increases in state weight limits cannot be enjoyed without the acquisition of larger capacity tractors, this would not be a qualification. All factors considered, it would appear that the observed growth in average load is an upper limit to a measure of the physical capacity obsolescence of truck-tractors.

The gross earnings of the intercity power units operated by a firm which co-operated in the present study is about $0.0183 per ton-mile. Using this figure the capacity obsolescence of a vehicle develops at the rate of (0.0183) (0.09) $m = 0.00165$ m dollars per year, where m is the annual mileage (rate of equipment utilization) of the vehicle in revenue service. For this firm, annual mileage per vehicle, m, averages 105,000 miles per year, and therefore capacity obsolescence grows at the rate of $173 per year. Note that the impact of obsolescence on the firm's equipment is due not only to conditions existing outside the firm but depends directly upon the rate of equipment utilization, m. The rate of obsolescence is much greater for a firm that employs its equipment to the fullest extent than for a firm whose equipment remains idle much of the time.

The other broad class of technological change which must be taken into account is that associated with improvements in internal combustion engine technology. These improvements have tended to reduce fuel requirements for given operating conditions, and to increase engine horsepower. As a result of experimental studies by the National Research Council[7] and the Oregon State Highway Commission[8] of the

---

[7] National Research Council, Highway Research Board, "Time and Gasoline Consumption in Motor Truck Operation," Research Report No. 9-A, Washington, D.C., 1950.

[8] Oregon State Highway Commission, "The Effect of Highway Designs on Vehicle Speed and Fuel Consumption," Highway Department Technical Bulletin No. 5, 1937.

operating performance of motor trucks under commercial conditions, it is possible to make fairly accurate estimates of fuel obsolescence (the effect of reductions in fuel requirements on operating cost), and horsepower obsolescence (the effect of increased horsepower on operating cost).

These studies have established the structural relation shown in (2.2) between fuel consumption, g, in gallons per mile, and gross vehicle weight, W, in pounds:

$$g = aW^b, \qquad a > 0, 0 < b < 1. \qquad (2.2)$$

The parameters a and b depend, for given equipment technology, on the average rate of rise and fall of the highway over which hauls are performed. The rate of rise and fall is measured by the total vertical rise and fall of a highway route in feet divided by the length of the route in hundreds of feet. Since the Oregon study applied to 1935 and 1936 model trucks while the National Research Council study applied to 1948 model trucks, the values of the parameters a and b for the two studies provide a means of comparing the two technologies. Such a comparison shows that for a given W, g has fallen substantially over this 12 year period, but the corresponding rise in W, due to rising average load, wiped out most of this advantage. Consequently, the indicated fuel savings are very small. Furthermore, it is very questionable as to whether the remaining net fuel savings are wholly attributable to engine changes since the fuel itself has improved and thereby raised the performance of both old and new models. For these various reasons fuel obsolescence will, on balance, be considered negligible.

The National Research Council study[9] found the time of travel τ, in minutes per mile of motor trucks to depend upon the gross weight to net horsepower ratio U, in pounds per net horsepower, according to the relation

$$\tau = A_\tau + B_\tau U \qquad A_\tau, B_\tau > 0 \qquad (2.3)$$

where the parameters A_τ and B_τ depend upon the rate of rise and fall. For a rate of rise and fall of 2 feet per hundred feet, (2.3) becomes

$$\tau = 1.0416 + 0.001984\, U \qquad (2.4)$$

It is clear from (2.3) that if the weight to horsepower ratio of motor trucks has tended to fall with model improvements, then this may be an important source of obsolescence. Reductions in time of travel will reduce equipment investment, and speed deliveries—the latter having uncertain, but favorable effects upon revenue.

---

[9] *Op. cit.*

Estimates of the average gross weight to net horsepower ratio for 1940, 1947 and 1953 vehicles are shown in Table 1. These computations show that in spite of the average load trend in Figure 2 the average weight to net horsepower ratio fell from the 1940–1947 war

Table 1

CALCULATION OF AVERAGE WEIGHT TO POWER RATIO FOR 1940, 1947 AND 1953

I	II	III	IV	V
Year	Average Load (Z)*	Average Unladen Weight of Tractor-Trailer Units†	Average Net Maximum Brake Horsepower (P)†	Gross Weight to Net Horsepower Ratio $\dfrac{W}{P} = \dfrac{II + III}{IV}$
1940	13,560	16,580	103.6	291
1947	16,720	20,030	117	314
1953	18,600	18,656	152.1	245

Sources:
* From the graph in Figure 2.
† The unladen weight of power units was computed from specifications published in the *Commercial Car Journal,* April, 1940 and April, 1953. The unladen weight of trailers was computed from samples taken from the ICC Motor Carrier Reports. The author is indebted to the Bureau of Transport Economics and Statistics for access to these records.

period down to 1953.[10] If a linear trend is fitted to these three observations, then U is given by

$$U = A_u - B_u T = 305 - 3.75(T_0 - 1940) - 3.75\ T \qquad (2.5)$$

Hence the weight to power ratio has fallen at the rate of 3.75 pounds per horsepower per year. If it is assumed that savings in travel time are worth $3.00 per hour (or $0.05 per minute), then at a mileage rate of 105,000 miles per year a truck-tractor will develop horsepower obsolescence at the rate of $(0.05)\ (0.001984)\ (3.47)\ (105,000) = \$39$ per year.

ESTIMATES OF OPERATING COST

Turning now to operating costs, let it be borne in mind that, for replacement analysis, only those costs that vary with age (or cumulative mileage) are significant. Costs that are independent of the age and

---

[10] Parenthetically it is of interest to note in Table 1 that unladen tractor-trailer weight appears to have risen from 1940–1947, and then to have declined from 1947–1953. Apart from the usual qualifications relating to sampling error, it is suggested that the following explanation satisfactorily accounts for these changes: During the war years, 1940–1947, when replacement equipment was unavailable, the lighter equipment tended to be discarded relatively early because of the much heavier loads that were permitted to roll during the war emergency. From 1947–1953 the wartime stock of equipment was replaced by lighter units giving rise to a falling average weight trend. The over-all upward trend in unladen weights from 1940–1953 indicates that the use of lighter construction materials has been more than offset by the use of larger engines, larger transmissions, and larger trucks.

mileage of a truck are important in deciding which of several alternative types of vehicle are best, but have no bearing on the computation of the optimal period of service of a given type of vehicle, provided that the vehicle in question is to be replaced by one of similar design. If the current operating equipment is to be replaced by units with a different fixed operating cost performance (i.e. not taken into account by the linear obsolescence function) then these costs are important in computing when it is optimal to change over to the new units.

Motor trucks seem to incur at least two important costs which vary with cumulative mileage, *viz.* fuel expense and maintenance expense. In the empirical analysis to follow the structural dependence of these costs on current and cumulative mileage will be determined, then the utilization function, or the relation of the mileage rate to the period of service, will be studied. The latter will serve as a transformation function for changing structural cost equations into functions depending upon the length of service rather than mileage. This approach has the advantage that it permits us to deduce the consequences of rates of equipment utilization other than those observed for the sample of vehicles to be studied.

The fuel and maintenance cost equations that were obtained are based upon the operation of a sample of 240 1951 model truck-tractors that were purchased new by a for-hire trucking firm, and placed in service in 1951. These units were all of the same make, model, and type (diesel powered), and were used in the same type of service. The sample was chosen so as to hold as constant as possible such extraneous variables as differences in operating conditions and type of service. The sample was considered sufficiently large so that such influences as differences in driver behavior might be expected to be random.

For these units monthly observations on mileage and fuel consumption, and quarterly observations on repair cost were available for a period of service of about three and one-half years from the time the vehicles were first placed in service.

Analysis of these data shows that quarterly repair cost per mile depends upon cumulative mileage as follows:

$$r = \frac{\Delta R}{\Delta M} = a_r(1 - e^{-b_r M}) = 0.026(1 - e^{-1.31 \cdot 10^{-5} M}). \tag{3.1}$$

where r = quarterly repair cost in dollars per mile.
             R = quarterly repair cost in dollars per vehicle.
             M = cumulative mileage per vehicle.

The graph of (3.1) is shown in Figure 3.

It is interesting and enlightening to provide some interpretation of the result contained in Figure 3 which shows that repair cost per mile begins at zero when a vehicle is placed in service and rises at a uniformly declining rate, reaching a horizontal plateau around 300,000 miles. Of course, the nature of this function is going to depend partly on the firm's maintenance policies; it is not a technical relation in the strict sense, as it reflects suboptimal behavior. Assuming, however, that the general characteristics of this function hold for typical truck maintenance policies, what explanation can be advanced for this result?

Reflection will show that a relatively simple stochastic failure model will generate this observed maintenance cost function. When a truck is new, each of its component parts is new, and each of these parts is subject to a probability failure density, with age (mileage) an independent variate. These probability densities will, in general, be different and have different expected values. As a vehicle renders mileage service these parts begin to fail, with the parts of lowest expected life tending to fail first and so forth. Very few parts fail early in service, while more and more fail in later service. Hence, the maintenance cost curve tends to rise. Eventually, however, the past replacement of parts creates a truck with a more even age distribution of component parts, rather than a distribution heavily biased by relatively new parts as is the case in the early periods of service. Once the ages of the many component parts begin to fall into a wider distribution, the failure of individual parts tends to become random with the average maintenance cost rate approaching a constant level.

It is believed that this explanation will describe adequately the behavior of any complex mechanical system composed of a large number of component parts, such as automotive equipment, pumping equipment, various kinds of automatic conveying and mechanical fabricating equipment and so on. Therefore, one might expect the repair cost function of Figure 3 to be typical of many complex mechanical systems.

It is obvious from ordinary experience that a major determinate of current fuel consumption is current miles, but it is not obvious *a priori* that the rate of fuel consumption need rise with cumulative mileage. If, for example, fuel consumption is dependent more on an engine being well "tuned" than on its state of wear, then fuel consumption may not increase with cumulative mileage. Indeed an old engine may present less internal friction than a new one, tending to *reduce* fuel consumption. Of course, it is well known that oil consumption increases with mileage in internal combustion engines because of "blow-by" past the piston rings and it may be that fuel consumption will increase for related reasons.

The facts were easily established from the data. A simple linear

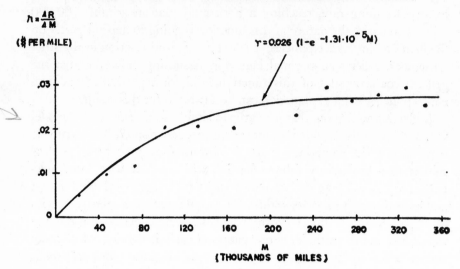

Figure 3

AVERAGE REPAIR COST PER MILE VERSUS CUMULATIVE MILES

regression of cumulative mileage on fuel consumption per mile was computed yielding the relation:

$$f = \frac{\Delta F}{\Delta M} = A_f + B_f M = 0.1786 + 1.7355 \cdot 10^{-8}M \qquad (3.2)$$

where
f = monthly fuel consumption in gallons per mile
F = monthly fuel consumption in gallons per vehicle
M = cumulative mileage per vehicle.

The graph (3.2) is shown in Figure 4.

Also from the data, cumulative mileage is found to be approximately proportional to the period of service, i.e.

$$M = \overline{m}t = 105,000\ t \qquad (3.3)$$

where t = period of service in years. In other words current mileage m in miles per year is

$$m = \frac{\Delta M}{\Delta T} = \overline{m} = 105,000 \qquad (3.4)$$

From (3.3) and (3.4) the repair cost function in (3.1) can be written

$$r_t = \frac{\Delta R}{\Delta t} = rm = a_r(1 - e^{-b_r mt})m = (0.026)(1 - e^{-1.31 \cdot 10^{-5}mt})m \qquad (3\cdot5)$$

and the fuel equation (3.2) can be written

$$f_t = \frac{\Delta F}{\Delta t} = fm = (A_f + B_f mt)m = (0.1786 + 1.7355 \cdot 10^{-8}mt)m \qquad (3.6)$$

Figure 4

AVERAGE FUEL CONSUMPTION VERSUS CUMULATIVE MILES

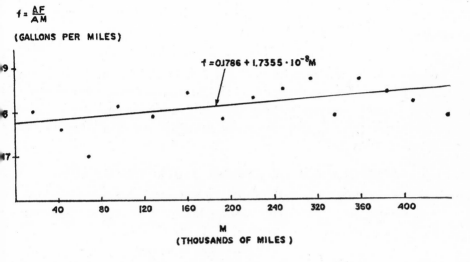

$f = \frac{\Delta F}{\Delta M}$

(GALLONS PER MILES)

$f = 0.1786 + 1.7355 \cdot 10^{-8}M$

M

(THOUSANDS OF MILES)

These transformations convert the technical repair and fuel equations into input flows.

ESTIMATION OF RESALE VALUE FUNCTION

The remaining function for which we require an empirical estimate is the resale value function. A common view that one finds in both the theoretical and the trade literature is that units of industrial equipment, particularly trucks, tend to fall in value during their first year by a constant proportion of their new price, and then to decline in value at a constant percentage rate per year thereafter.[11]

However, data obtained from the Truck Blue Book[12] indicates that resale values decline at a constant linear rate after the first year—at least for the first five or six years. In Figure 5 is shown the course of resale values for the make and model of vehicle for which we have obtained cost data. This model has a list price new of slightly over $8,000 in 1954 and 1955. The same model was produced in each of the years 1950 through 1953. Therefore, it was possible to obtain the resale value of this model over a five year period at 1954 prices. From the figure it is seen that the resale value drops abruptly to $4,400 after one

[11] See Alchian, *op. cit.*, pp. 17–18.

[12] *Blue Book Appraisals and Specifications*, Truck Section, National Used Car Market Report, Inc., Chicago, February 1, 1954.

year, and thereafter declines in value at the average rate of $575 per year.[13]

Expressed as a proportion of the new price, the resale value (salvage) function becomes

$$S = B - \lambda L = (0.615 - 0.0706\ L)p \qquad (4.1)$$

where p is the truck's price new and L is its age in years. The form (4.1) is used because the price p in which we shall be interested is the price actually paid by the firm, not the manufacturer's list price. For example, in the case under study, the firm paid over $1,500 below the usual list price.

COMPUTATION OF OPTIMAL TRUCK SERVICE LIFE

From the above empirical estimates we can now proceed to adapt the replacement model in section 1 for application to motor trucks. Using (2.1) the gross revenue function in (1.3) can be written

$$R(kL,\ t) = p_z Zm = p_z m[B_z T + A_z] = p_z m[B_z kL + A_z] \qquad (5.1)$$

where p_z is revenue per ton-mile. It is seen that revenue does not depend upon service time t, but does depend upon technological changes affecting average load.

The total of those operating expenses which vary significantly with age and/or technological change will be composed of fuel outlays, maintenance expenses, and costs associated with vehicle time of travel. That is, from (2.3), (2.5), (3.5) and (3.6),

$$E(kL,\ t) = p_\tau[A_\tau + B_\tau(A_u - B_u kL)]m + p_f m(A_f + B_f mt) + a_\tau(1 - e^{-brmt})m \qquad (5.2)$$

where p_τ is the cost saving per minute reduction in travel time τ. If we let

$$
\begin{aligned}
A &= p_z A_z m - p_f A_f m - p_\tau(A_\tau + B_\tau A_u)m - a_\tau m \\
\alpha &= p_z B_z m + p_\tau B_\tau B_u m \\
\beta &= p_f B_f m^2 \\
a &= a_\tau m \\
b &= b_\tau m
\end{aligned}
\qquad (5.3)
$$

then from (5.1) and (5.2), we obtain, upon simplification,

$$Q(kL,\ t) = A + k\alpha L - \beta t + ae^{-bt} \qquad (5.4)$$

---

[13] The abrupt initial decline in the market value of any durable good is due to such factors as the nontransferability of manufacturer's guarantees; the greater uncertainty in regard to the reliability of used goods, or even new goods which are not purchased directly from manufacturer's outlets; and the greater purchasing cost of used goods, due to the necessity of more careful inspection and appraisal by the buyer.

Using (5.4) and the resale value function (4.1) the expression (1.1) takes the empirical form

$$v = \sum_{k=0}^{\infty} e^{-pkL} \left\{ \int_0^L (A + k\alpha L - \beta t + ae^{-bt})e^{-\rho t}\,dt \right.$$

$$\left. - p + (B - \gamma L)e^{-\rho L} \right\} \quad (5.5)$$

From the various numerical estimates of the indicated parameters (which are summarized in the appendix) we are now in a position to

Figure 5
DECLINE IN VEHICLE RESALE VALUE WITH AGE

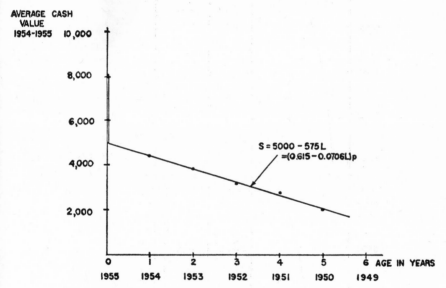

Source: Truck Section, Blue Book Appraisals Specifications, National Used Car Market Report, Inc., Chicago, Illinois, February 1, 1955.

compute the optimal economic life L^0. Since it is the estimate of α, the time rate of obsolescence, that is likely to be most in question, the computations were carried out for two values of α. If the full trend in average load is taken as the measure of truck-tractor obsolescence, then α is about \$200 per year per year. In this case maximizing v gives an optimal service period $L^0 \cong 3.2$ years.

On the other hand assuming $\alpha = 100$ gives $L^0 = 4.2$ years.

In Figure 6 appears the empirical graphs of $\pi = \rho v$ (the constant annual income stream equivalent to v), for $\alpha = 100$ and for $\alpha = 200$.

An optimal service period of 3 to 4 years is about 1 to 2 years shorter than the actual replacement behavior of the firm in question.

But the interesting fact revealed in Figure 6 is the relative insensitivity of optimal profit to replacement errors. As is indicated by the dotted lines on the curve for $\alpha = 200$ replacement anywhere between

Figure 6

VARIATION IN VEHICLE EARNINGS WITH LENGTH OF SERVICE PERIOD

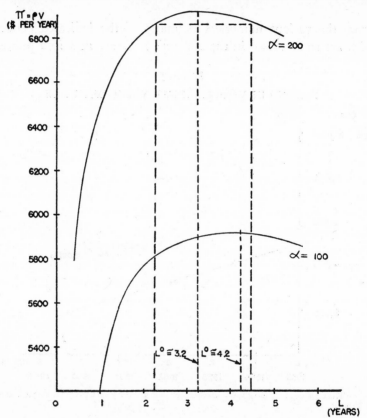

2.2 years and 4.4 years will lead to losses of at most $50 short of the exact optimum. In other words a failure to replace optimally by this margin will not cost more than $50 per year per vehicle. This is a loss of $12,000 per year for all 240 vehicles; but as a proportion of the firm's net annual profits prorated to this portion of its fleet, this represents a profit loss of only 1.86 per cent. This percentage is still smaller for the case $\alpha = 100$. Consequently, a delay in replacement of somewhat more than one year beyond the optimal trade-in point leads to a penalty of less than 2 per cent of profit.

This is a remarkable result especially when one considers that on the average about ⅔ of the total investment of trucking firms is in the form of trucking equipment (i.e. capital goods of intermediate durability requiring regular maintenance). It would seem that this of all industries would find equipment *replacement* policies of considerable importance, yet precision in such policies turns out to be of minor significance. It is not argued that it makes no difference when equipment is replaced. Rather the point is that profits are not sufficiently sensitive to replacement that the firm is likely to miss the optimum by a costly margin, even when using relatively crude techniques of analysis.

As a corollary to these empirical results one important weakness of the classical replacement model is brought into sharp focus. If a delay of a year or two or even longer causes a relatively small decline in profit as computed from the present *pure replacement* model, then to a growing firm requiring an expanding stock of capital, "delayed replacement" may be a cheap source of capital. If the firm can always obtain as much additional capital as is desired at the constant rate ρ, then it will never pay to delay replacement. But if a rate above ρ must be offered to attract additional capital for growth and/or the firm is faced by capital rationing, then replacement according to the above model will be premature. In these circumstances replacement will be "delayed" as long as the consequent reduction in profit on the present capacity is more than offset by the addition to profit resulting from the added capacity. Hence, replacement policy cannot in strict accuracy be divorced from expansion policy, for, unless the capital market is perfect, postponed replacement may be a rational internal source of capital that can be used for expansion.

REPLACEMENT THEORY AND THE ECONOMIC CHOICE OF EQUIPMENT

When we consider the use of equipment theory as a guide to the optimal choice of equipment type, the conclusions may be quite different from those above. It may make a considerable difference to a firm's profit whether, for example under certain operating conditions, diesel equipment is chosen rather than gasoline, or heavy equipment rather than light. For every set of operating conditions, there will be a commercially available type of equipment which is best, and, whether this or some other equipment is chosen, may have a considerable bearing upon net earnings.

To obtain some empirical test of the importance of equipment type it was decided to analyze the diesel versus gasoline issue. Diesel equipment has both advantages and disadvantages relative to gasoline pow-ered equipment. The enormous advantage is, of course, savings in fuel. Diesel fuel consumption is only 60 to 70 per cent of gasoline fuel consumption because of the greater thermal efficiency of diesel units, and in many areas diesel fuel is cheaper than gasoline. However, on the debit side diesel units cost more and are heavier, thereby reducing maximum payloads. The diesel units also present somewhat higher repair bills than do gasoline units used under comparable conditions. It is clear from these observations that the question of diesel versus gaso-line units depends crucially upon those factors which affect fuel con-sumption. If vehicles are employed under conditions which cause fuel expenses to bulk large in total expenses, then diesel units will be superior to gasoline units and *vice versa*. Therefore, one would expect diesel units to be preferable to gasoline units where service demands require heavy loads, high mileages, or where the geographical terrain is mountainous, since any of these conditions will promote high fuel costs.

Estimates were made of the fuel, price and maintenance cost pa-rameters for gasoline units in the same weight class as the above diesel units. Then for both types of equipment maximum profit, $\pi^0 = \pi/L = L^0$ corresponding to an optimal spacing of replacements was determined as a function of current mileage, m. These functions are shown graphically in Figure 7. From the figure it is clear that for mileage rates of less than 40,000 per year, gasoline units yield a higher profit than diesel; while for mileages above 40,000 the reverse is true. These results are fully consistent with the following observed practices: (1) Usually only gasoline units are used in local service where mileages and loads are small, (2) the long-haul heavy-load operations in the Rocky Mountain and Pacific regions are heavily dominated by diesel units, and (3) the short-haul light-load operations in New England are more frequently performed by gasoline units.

The results also show that using the wrong kind of equipment may be quite costly. For the firm used in our case study, with mileages averaging 105,000, the loss from operating 240 gasoline rather than diesel tractors is estimated at $67,100 per year or 10.4 per cent of net earnings. This difference would be even more striking if a heavier class of vehicle were involved or if the terrain were more rugged.

We conclude that equipment theory may be a very useful tool as a guide in the choice of equipment. The savings that can be made are substantial and, furthermore, it may not be obvious which type of equipment is best without moderately sophisticated analysis, particu-larly in cases where the rate of technological change and the relation

Figure 7

MAXIMUM PROFIT VERSUS MILES PER YEAR FOR
DIESEL AND GASOLINE VEHICLES

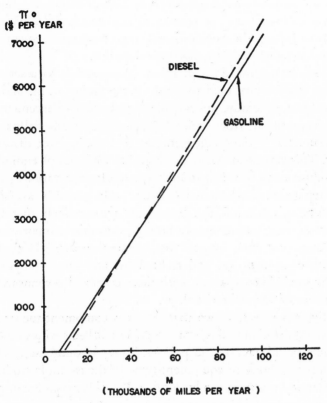

between operating costs and age is different for different types of equipment.

SUMMARY AND COMMENTS

This paper has attempted careful estimates of the obsolescence and deterioration components of truck-tractor revenues and costs on the assumption of continuity in the development of these components. The results, therefore, indicate an approximate general forecast of the optimal economic life of this equipment. The precise timing of replacement is another matter and should take account of details hardly touched upon here. For example, the availability and cost of capital to the company at the time replacement is contemplated could clearly be of dominating importance. Indeed, since replacement delays are not expected to be very costly, it has been concluded that where the firm is faced by capital rationing or a rising supply curve of capital, it will pay to delay replacement during a period of expansion. This, by the way, is consistent with the results obtained from a study by Yance[14] of the investment behavior of railroads wherein it was found that the railroads reduce the retirement rate of boxcars whenever there is a need to expand the stock of boxcars. Normal replacements are thus postponed to facilitate an expansion of the stock.

With these qualifications in mind, it seems fair to assert that the results of this inquiry tend to show that trucking firms, and perhaps business firms generally, are not likely to follow replacement policies that deviate seriously from optimal policies. This is especially true when we measure the deviation in terms of the relative cost of alternative policies. This conclusion need not apply to all types of equipment nor to all industries since it is certainly possible for the various parameters of the replacement problem to assume values which would yield a sensitive profit optimum. But it does not appear likely that such conditions will occur often, simply because the only components of cost and revenue that enter into the replacement decision are those which vary with equipment age and technology, and these components are normally small in comparison with those costs and revenues which are independent of age and technology.

Finally, it has been shown that, whereas equipment theory may not be a business decision tool which can effect marked savings by establishing more rational replacement policies, it may be quite useful as a guide to the optimal choice of equipment type. In the example studied it was found that under certain conditions diesel trucking equipment can effect considerable economies over gasoline equipment.

It has been noted that one of the defects of classical replacement theory is its failure to account explicitly for the interdependence between replacement and expansion policy. The theory contains another defect which is a corollary to this, *viz.* the measurement of the various terms of the present value function (1.1) on a "machine" basis. This practice is no doubt due to the fact that it is the machine unit which is physically replaced. But where obsolescence takes the form of increasing the output capacity of individual machine units this formulation is incorrect, for it allocates the earnings of additions to equipment capacity to that which is only replacement capacity. Hence, in equation (1.1) "machines" ought really to be measured in terms of capacity units and replaced so as to maximize profit or minimize cost per unit of capacity.

---

[14] Joseph Yance, "Investment Behavior in the Railroad Industry" (Ph.D. Thesis, Harvard University, 1955), p. 49 and *passim.*

It is capacity not the stock of machines which must be held constant in replacement analysis.

The revenue component of quasi-rent will then be constant as it should be. The question of changes in revenue should never arise, since if any output dimension is altered when a machine is replaced by a new one, then, by definition, the replacement is not literal. The prudency of the addition or contraction which is thereby made cannot be decided without further information, such as the shape of the demand curve for the machines' output. For optimal *pure* replacement decisions we require knowledge of cost conditions only. An optimal pure replacement policy can be thought of as one which allows the firm to operate along the lowest possible cost-output curve.

APPENDIX

Numerical Value of the Parameters In Equation (5.3) and (5.5)

1. Obsolescence Parameters

A_z = 10.6 tons (1950) B_z = 0.09 tons/years
A_u = 270 pounds/horsepower B_u = 3.75 pounds/horsepower/ year

A = 1.0416 minutes/mile B = 0.001984 minutes/mile/ pound/horsepower

2. Performance and Utilization Parameters

m = 105,000 miles/year A_f = 0.1786 gallons/mile
a_r = 0.026 dollars/year B_f = 1.7355 gallons/mile^2
b_r = 1.31 · 10^{-5}/mile

3. Prices

p = 6556 dollars p_f = 0.20 dollars/gallon
p_r = 0.05 dollars/minute p_s = 0.0183 dollars/ton-mile

4. Parameters of $Q(kL, t)$

A = 5775 dollars/year
β = 36.40 dollars/year^2 $\alpha = \begin{cases} 200 \\ 100 \end{cases}$ dollars/year^2
b = 0.08/year
                                  a = 2730 dollars/year

CASE 14

Manufacturing Progress Functions[1]

WERNER Z. HIRSCH[2]

Some points of special interest in this paper are:

   a. The distinction made between technical knowledge and productive facilities and especially the implication that liberalized tolerances, special tools and holding devices, improvement of layout and work place are changes in technical knowledge, as opposed to productive facilities.
   b. The alternative uses of logarithmic and arithmetic relations because of improved fit.
   c. The assembling progress was not only more rapid than the machining progress but also more consistently so.
   d. When small lots were scheduled, in order to spread the fixed cost of setting up the machines, no less than 20–25 units were machined.
   e. The several uses of the results of the analysis.

Most economic cost studies have been concerned primarily with the relation of cost to rate of output. Short-run costs are usually said to be those associated with variation in the utilization of fixed plant or other facilities, whereas long-run cost encompasses changes in the size and kind of plant. Strictly, then, the distinction is based upon the degree of adaptation of all input factors to rate of output.[3] However, cost may vary because of changes in technical knowledge.[4] Economists have ex-

[1] *Review of Economics and Statistics,* May, 1952. Reprinted by permission.

[2] Washington University. The author would like to express his gratitude to the Bureau of Business and Economic Research of the University of California for financial support of this study.

[3] J. Dean, *Managerial Economics* (New York, 1951), p. 262.

[4] We accept Professor Carlson's distinction between a change in the technical organization of the productive services and a change in the technical knowledge. According to

plicitly excluded all irreversible changes in technology. Most long-run cost theories, for instance, are timeless; one future point in time is selected at which output rate and facilities are permitted to change. That such a cost function, particularly its height, will be affected by improvements in technical knowledge is beyond doubt.

It is convenient to clarify the issue of the different cost functions by referring to production functions, which express the net relation between the input of variable productive factors and output during a given production period, under the assumption of a given plant and technical knowledge. From the production function we can derive a static short-run cost function, which also assumes a given plant and technical knowledge. Long-run cost permits changes in the size and kind of plant, but assumes stability in technical knowledge. Thus, a long-run cost function is related to points on different production functions, each point involving a different plant while using the same technical knowledge. There can be a cost function which permits changes in technical knowledge but not in plant and other facilities. In a sense this is a dynamic cost function. If direct labor is the cost we consider, we shall speak about a (unit) learning or progress function. This expresses the net relation between the amount of direct labor needed to produce one product-unit and the cumulative units produced in a given facility. The progress function thus permits us to estimate the amount of direct labor needed to manufacture the nth unit, from n, the cumulative number of the product-unit. The function is related to a number of points on different production functions involving successive changes in technical knowledge in a given facility.

In this study we will analyze data of a large United States machine builder, who has been one of the largest machine tool[5] manufacturers for about three quarters of a century. Since the end of World War II the company has also manufactured textile and construction machinery. Of its twenty products, seven have been selected for an empirical analysis. They are either new products or new models. Machine 1 is a new

---

Carlson, "A change in the former is a reversible process; a change in the latter is not. When, after a change, a group of productive services revert to their initial combination, the optimal technical organization and the optimal output from the combination will be the same as before the first change took place, provided the technical knowledge is constant. For every service combination there exists one and only one optimal organization and only one maximum output. A change in technical knowledge, on the other hand, implies that the optimal organization and the maximum output from *the same* service combination have changed." See S. Carlson, *A Study on the Pure Theory of Production* (Stockholm, 1939), pp. 15–16.

[5] Machine tools are power-driven machines, not portable by hand, which cut, hammer, or squeeze metal.

semiautomatic machine tool and machines 2–5 are new automatic machine tools which differ greatly in the functions they perform, weight, labor requirement, etc. Machine 6 is a textile machine and machine 7 is a multipurpose construction machine. Production is carried out in one large plant. During the period under consideration, 1946–50, the monthly direct labor force varied from 930 to 3,600 men.

The production process is very complicated, calling for high professional skills. It is divided into machining of parts and their assembly. Each month top management decides on a production schedule which instructs the production manager to have ready for shipment by a given date a given number of machines of each type. Thus, the lot size being determined, the production manager orders certain parts (about 20,000) to be manufactured in the shop, and others (about 10,000) to be purchased from suppliers. After all parts are ready, they are assembled, first into small units and finally into the complete machine. Each machine has a separate assembly floor. As a crew of given size will assemble a particular unit, the assembly process involves fixed proportions between parts and labor. The rate of output is increased primarily by having more crews of given sizes assemble additional units.

In the following pages we will: (1) analyze the labor requirement–production volume relation, (2) discuss the nature of the progress function, (3) present empirically derived progress functions for seven different products, and (4) apply these findings.

LABOR REQUIREMENT–PRODUCTION VOLUME RELATION

The economist's interest in short-run costs is focused on the net effect of the output rate on cost in a given facility, isolating the influence of all other variables. Among the empirical measurements of this relation Professor J. Dean's work indubitably deserves special mention.[6]

However, cost-output analyses of products whose production extends over long periods of time and is in lots of overlapping production periods (e.g., production of ships, aircraft, and complicated machinery) offer additional problems, because it is often not meaningful to talk about a daily or monthly output. If the production period is six months (after a period of gestation) a plant produces 240 units per annum either by starting a lot of 40 units every second month or one of 20 units every month. In the first case, at any one point in time work will be done on three lots of 40 units each, and in the second on six lots of

---

[6] J. Dean, *op. cit.*, pp. 272–90.

20 units each. Thus, the number of different operations as well as their scale varies, while the average monthly or annual production is the same. Frequently, however, successive lots and intervals vary. In the case of some of the machines analyzed lots varied from 18 to 70 units and—if we neglect the strike[7]—lot intervals from 1 to 2 months. Under these circumstances the production in successive time periods is too heterogeneous to permit useful comparisons of annual output rates.

Although there is no stability in terms of annual production, there is stability in terms of lots, which are self-contained units in which machining and assembling take place. The lot size reveals how often each operation congealed in a machine is carried out at one time, making it a good measure of intensity and scale of operation. If lot intervals did not change, lot size would also be a good measure of output rate. With scheduling by and large on a monthly basis, there was much greater stability in lot intervals than lot size. Therefore, lot size was used as a measure of the rate of production.

For the empirical analysis of the direct labor-lot size relation we selected the two products with the largest variation in the size of successive lots, i.e., a textile machine and a semiautomatic machine tool. The analysis extends over the five years 1946–50, during which time practically no changes in management or plant and equipment occurred. While the textile machine analysis encompasses the first 21 lots with about 600 machines, the machine tool analysis covers 27 lots with about 500 machines. The production period varied in length from about seven months in the early lots to five in the later ones. As for all other machines the data were obtained by recording the number of man-hours required for each machining and assembling operation of a product. By adding up the labor input which is congealed in successive machining operations, the machining-hour input of a given part is obtained. A similar method is used with respect to assembling. The total machining-hours are added to the total assembling-hours. They give the total direct labor input of a given product. This information was collected for machines lot by lot.

Statistical Analysis and Findings

Throughout this study the labor requirement data were adjusted by an arbitrary constant to avoid showing the exact cost level. We selected average and not total labor input relations for analysis, because it

---

[7] Toward the end of the period analyzed there was a six months' strike which was won by the management.

provides a more powerful test of curvilinearity.[8] We selected the following general functional relationships (where the functions in one case are on rectangular coordinates and in the other on logarithmic coordinates):

$$x_1 = a_{1.234} + b_{12.34}x_2 + b_{13.24}x_3 + b_{14.23}x_4 \text{ and}$$
$$x_1 = a_{1.23} + b_{12.3}x_2 + b_{13.2}x_3 ;$$

where: a = the intercept on the x_1-axis
b = slope
x_1 = direct labor requirement per machine
x_2 = cumulative lot number
x_3 = lot size
x_4 = average direct labor plant employment.[9]

For the textile machine (machine 6) the calculated equation is:

$$x_1 = 898.87 - 16.25 \ x_2 - 1.49 \ x_3 + .02 \ x_4$$
$$(8.60) \quad (1.96) \quad (.50)$$

where the figures in brackets are t-ratios. Using a .05 level of significance, only the relation between cumulative lot number, i.e., change in technical knowledge, and labor requirement ($b_{12.34}$) was significant during the period analyzed. Both lot size and average (direct labor) factory employment had insignificant effects on labor requirements.[10]

The coefficients of multiple correlation ($\bar{R}_{1.234}$) and multiple determination ($\bar{R}^2_{1.234}$) adjusted for degrees of freedom are .94 and .88 respectively, while the adjusted coefficient of determination ($\bar{r}^2_{12}$) is .87. Thus, on the average, during 1946–50 about 87 per cent of the changes in direct labor requirements were associated with changes in technical knowledge, while changes in lot size and factory employment had no significant effect.

For the machine tool (machine 1) the following functional relation was selected:

$$\bar{x}_1 = a_{1.23} + b_{12.3} \ \bar{x}_2 + b_{13.2} \ x_3,$$

---

[8] If the average function is curvilinear, the total function assumes a very complicated curvilinear relation, possibly around a straight line. Thus there is too great a temptation to fit a linear total function which in turn involves a horizontal average function. Furthermore, a slight curvature in the total function is associated with a substantial curvature in the average function.

[9] We considered the desirability of introducing "length of production period" as a variable to obtain information on labor requirement-rate of output relation. As the length decreases gradually in successive lots from seven to five months, we decided that this change is nothing but a reflection of the learning process, properly reflected already in x_2.

[10] The partial correlation coefficients are:

$$r_{12.34} = .9109$$
$$r_{13.24} = .4494$$
$$r_{14.23} = .1370,$$

with r for $P = .05$ and $n = 16$ being .4683.

where the bars indicate that the data are in a logarithmic form. A logarithmic relation was chosen between x_1 and x_2 in line with the nature of the progress function, as discussed in a later section.[11] Empirical analyses were made for total direct labor, machining, and assembling requirements.

In the case of total direct labor requirement, the values are:

$$\bar{x}_1 = 2.9959 - .3120\,\bar{x}_2 + .000004\,x_3.$$

The corresponding correlation coefficients are:

$$r_{12.3} = .9592$$
$$r_{13.2} = .0011$$
$$\bar{R}_{1.23} = .9570$$
$$\bar{R}^2_{1.23} = .9158.$$

We checked the residuals of x_3 and also calculated logarithmic regressions. The following are the results:

$$\bar{x}_1 = 2.9757 - .3093\,\bar{x}_2 + .0143\,\bar{x}_3$$
$$r_{12.3} = .9568$$
$$r_{13.2} = .1198$$
$$\bar{R}_{1.23} = .9573$$
$$\bar{R}^2_{1.23} = .9165.$$

The logarithmic regressions and the residuals revealed no curvilinear relation.

In spite of these results, we also analyzed the machining and assembling requirement with regard to the effect of lot size. There was still a possibility that they might be related, yet in an offsetting fashion.

For the relation between machining requirement and lot size the following values were obtained:

$$\bar{x}_1 = 2.5516 - .1224\,\bar{x}_2 - .0047\,x_3$$
$$r_{12.3} = .5118$$
$$r_{13.2} = .3853$$
$$\bar{R}_{1.23} = .8156$$
$$\bar{R}^2_{1.23} = .6652.$$

Since a test of the residuals revealed no curvilinearity, we conclude that during 1946–50 there was no significant relation between machining requirement and lot size. A similar statement can be made in regard to the assembling requirement and lot size, where we found that

$$\bar{x}_1 = 2.7989 - .4830\,\bar{x}_2 + .0052\,x_3$$

---

[11] For the textile machine a non-logarithmic relation was selected because of the improved fit.

and

$$r_{12.3} = .9469$$
$$r_{13.2} = .4626$$
$$\bar{R}_{1.23} = .9525$$
$$\bar{R}^2_{1.23} = .9073.$$

Conclusions

The relation between direct labor requirement and lot size in the machining and assembling of a textile machine and a semiautomatic machine tool (both of which had wider lot size variations than any of the other products) appears of little consequence. This phenomenon can be explained, at least partly, by the fact that both machining and assembling involve relatively fixed combinations of labor and equipment. Although in machining the setting-up process is fixed regardless of the number of parts machined at one time, labor savings are very small beyond 25 unit lots. This is illustrated in Chart 1 for one of the machine tools. After a substantial reduction in labor requirement in the case of very small lots, the function, which is a hyperbola, begins to level off around 20–25 unit lots.

NATURE OF THE PROGRESS PROCESS AND FUNCTION

As long as changes in technical knowledge take place there will be a negative labor requirement–cumulative output relation. We can divide the forces underlying the progress function into four groups:

a) Progress of Direct Labor. A worker, whatever his skill, will require more time for doing a job the first time than he will later. It will also be more tiring for him. In the machining of parts a new assignment will require, for instance, more time for blueprint reading and setting-up of the machine. The assembly worker discovers time-saving techniques. His movements become routinized and well adapted to the task.

b) Progress of Management. The managerial learning process results in improvements in production and labor scheduling and in the flow of materials and labor into and within the plant.[12] Furthermore, backward integration to steady and expedite the flow of materials, improvements in the coordination between engineering and manufacturing, and better production control techniques can be instituted.

c) Progress of the Engineering Department. Design engineers like to play safe and make sure that the new design will perform the desired

---

[12] That this is generally recognized is evident from the fact that in establishing time standards many companies, including this machine builder, double the delay allowance and increase the fatigue allowance for new operations.

function. As experience is gained, the more economically minded management calls for liberalized tolerances and redesign of certain parts, all of which will save money without impairing the performance of the machine. Furthermore, the early lots of a new design are manufactured under conditions appropriate for the well-entrenched models, but not necessarily for the new model. Learning leads then to the use and improvement of special tools and holding devices, increasing the number of operations performed by a laborer at a time; improvement in the

Chart 1

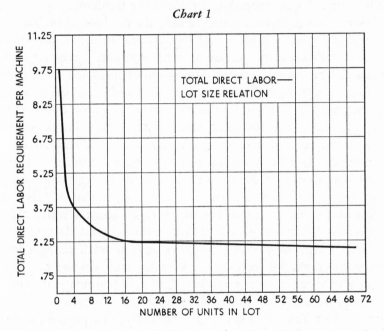

layout of the plant and individual work place; improvement in the routing and handling of material in the plant; and use of improved and better suited materials and equipment.

d) Progress of Material Suppliers. Many outside suppliers experience similar processes, leading to a speedier and more reliable flow of material and equipment, possibly of superior quality.

The learning process of the various groups in a firm is highly interrelated. Direct labor in the course of its work often recognizes improvement possibilities. If this information is passed on to the engineering department, they can jointly implement the improvement. Because of this interdependence, management, engineer, and direct labor must be in close contact through joint meetings, shop visits by engineer and management, and the "suggestion box." A similar effort is needed to benefit from progress outside the firm.

Empirical Progress Functions

By plotting machining, assembling, and total direct labor requirement, respectively, against cumulative output on rectangular coordinates, a substantial curvilinearity is apparent, which all but disappears on logarithmic coordinates. A linear relation on logarithmic coordinates reveals a high correlation with little, if any, curvilinearity in the residuals. Of 19 progress functions fitted, only 5 had a correlation coefficient smaller than .85 (after adjusting for degrees of freedom).

Obviously these measures concern only the mechanical fit. The logical justification of a constant relative decline in labor requirement associated with a relative increase in cumulative output requires further discussion. The period over which progress is measured only extends over five to six years, during which no more than 27 lots, i.e., about 600 machines, were completed. Furthermore, there is reason to expect that the average rate of improvement usually declines with increasing experience, in this case cumulative lot number. Such a relation can be approximated by a hyperbola on rectangular coordinates or a straight line on logarithmic coordinates. If, for instance, the regression or *progress elasticity* coefficient is about −.32, it means that a 1 per cent increase in cumulative output is on the average associated with a .32 per cent decrease in labor requirement. While the progress elasticity, as all elasticity concepts in economics, applies only to small changes in the progress functions, we are usually concerned with a wider range, e.g., doubling of cumulative output. We shall call percentage declines in labor requirement associated with a doubling of cumulative output *progress ratios.* The progress ratio corresponding to a progress elasticity of −.32 is about 20, i.e., by doubling the cumulative output, total direct labor requirement declines by about 20 per cent.[13] While the average percentage decline per lot is 20 from lot 1 to 2, it is only 10 from lot 2 to 4, 5 from lot 4 to 8, 2.5 from lot 8 to 16, 1.25 from lot 16 to 32, .6 from lot 32 to 64, etc. Thus, after 30–40 lots have been completed, further labor savings are very small.

In line with all these considerations, we specified the following functional relationship for the progress function:

$$\bar{x}_1 = a + b\bar{x}_2, \text{ or}$$
$$x_1 = ax_2{}^b,$$

---

[13] $x_1 = ax_2{}^b$. If $b = -.32$, $x_1 = a\, x_2{}^{-.32}$
$$x'_1 = a\,(2x_2)^{-.32}$$
$$\frac{x'_1}{x_1} = 2^{-.32} = .80.$$

where the same notation is used as before, and b is the slope of the curve (between 0 and -1).

Total Direct Labor Progress Function. In Chart 2 we present the total direct labor progress function of a semiautomatic machine tool (machine 1). The adjusted correlation coefficient, $\bar{r}_{12}$, is .96. The data, consisting of 27 lots totaling about 500 machines, cover the period 1946–50. The progress elasticity coefficient is $-.29$ and the corre-

Chart 2

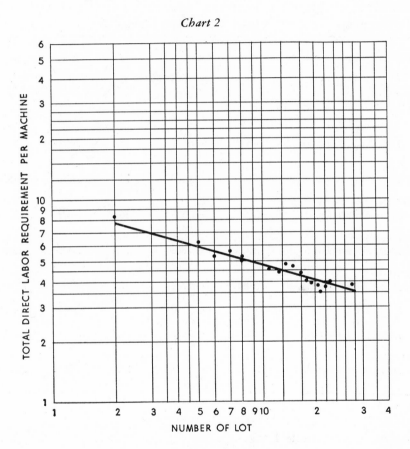

sponding progress ratio 18. Concerning the confidence that can be placed in the results, it is clear that since we are working with time series there is the obvious danger that the data are serially correlated. By using only every second observation, any significant serial correlation that had existed was eliminated without any major effect on the regression coefficient, correlation coefficient, and height. The t-ratio remained sufficiently large. The same is true with regard to other machines (see Tables 1 and 3).

In the absence of serial correlation, the standard error of the regression coefficient gains in importance. As the t-ratio is about 15, we can accept the findings with confidence (see Table 1).

Table 1

ANALYSIS OF TOTAL DIRECT LABOR PROGRESS FUNCTIONS OF SEVEN DIFFERENT MACHINES BUILT BY ONE MANUFACTURER, 1946–50

Machine	a_{12}	b_{12} Progress Elasticity*	Progress Ratio	$\bar{r}_{12}$	$r_{z,\,z-1}$†
Machine 1					
Every observation	3.3251	−.2868 (15.2)	18.1	.9653	.4883
Every 2nd observation	3.3394	−.2917 (14.4)	18.3	.9557	.0849
Machine 2					
Every observation	3.7537	−.2996 (23.4)	18.8	.8900	.6517
Every 2nd observation	3.7498	−.2933 (6.90)	18.4	.9064	.2358
Machine 3					
Every observation	3.7872	−.3370 (8.0)	20.8	.9150	.5182
Machine 4					
Every observation	3.7001	−.2595 (4.2)	16.5	.8373	.1513
Machine 5					
Every observation	3.1989	−.2868 (3.9)	18.1	.8563	.4643
Machine 6					
Every observation	3.5051	−.2774 (7.5)	17.5	.8894	.7599
Every 2nd observation	3.4029	−.2350 (4.8)	15.1	.8684	.2482
Every 3rd observation	3.3872	−.2313 (4.2)	14.8	.8414	.0707
Machine 7					
Every observation	3.1706	−.3233 (5.8)	20.0	.9061	.2782

* Figures in parentheses are t-ratios.
† Coefficient of correlation of lag residuals, where $z = x_1 - x'_1$.

Chart 3 and Table 1 together reveal that the fit is quite good. The adjusted correlation coefficient varies between .84 and .96. Only in the case of machine 6 could the fit be improved by using a straight line functional relation on rectangular coordinates.[14] The difference in fit was not great, i.e., .89 compared to .94.

Major interest rests with the slope of the progress function and in

14 For the functional relation $x_1 = a + b\,x_2$, we found

using every observation:
$x_1 = 897.91 - .7025\,x_2$
$S_{b12} = .0585$
$\bar{r}_{12} = .9385$
$\bar{r}^2_{12} = .8807$
$r_{z,z-1} = .6434$

using every second observation:
$x_1 = 901.5031 - .7158\,x_2$
$S_{b12} = .0260$
$\bar{r}_{12} = .9391$
$\bar{r}^2_{12} = .8820$
$r_{z,z-1} = .0265$

particular with the progress ratio, which varied among the seven machines between 16.5 and 20.8 per cent. The corresponding progress elasticities are −.26 and −.34. The mean progress ratio and elasticity are 18.5 and −.30.

Chart 3

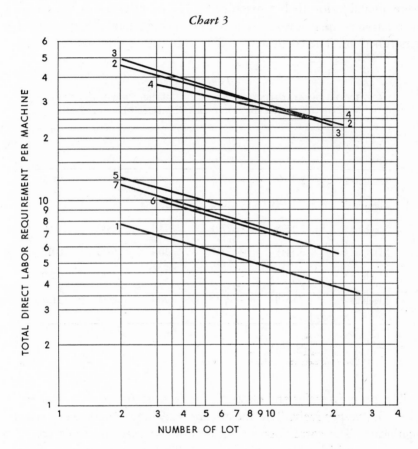

A test of equality of the regression coefficients was made and is summarized in Table 4. We will use a .01 level of significance as the criterion of whether the progress elasticities and ratios of different products could have come from the same universe, i.e., whether we can, with confidence, use these derived means as a basis for prediction. The pooled or mean progress ratio and progress elasticity of all machines are 18.5 and −.30 respectively. They can be used even at a .04 level of significance. This is the more interesting because of the heterogeneous nature of the products, which include machine tools, textile machines, and construction machinery. Similar results were obtained for the automatic machine tools as well as all machine tools (see Table 4).

Concerning the height of the total direct labor progress functions, little regularity prevails. This was to be expected because height depends primarily on the complexity of the product. The same also holds for the height of machining and assembling functions.

Machining Progress Functions. Machining and assembling data were available for all but machine 6. The fit in terms of the adjusted correlation coefficient is not as good as that of the total direct labor progress functions. The coefficients range from .69 to .99 (see Table 2).[15]

Table 2

ANALYSIS OF MACHINING PROGRESS FUNCTIONS OF SEVEN
MACHINES BUILT BY ONE MANUFACTURER, 1946–50

Machine*	a_{12}	b_{12} Progress Elasticity †	Progress Ratio	$\bar{r}_{12}$	$r_{s,\,s-1}$ ‡
Machine 1	2.5607	−.0956 (3.6)	6.4	.6933	.8251
Machine 2	3.4168	−.2036 (18.8)	13.2	.8500	.5636
Machine 3	3.4298	−.2194 (6.7)	14.1	.8812	.4960
Machine 4	3.3445	−.1517 (2.7)	10.4	.6965	.0017
Machine 5	2.9011	−.2088 (15.2)	13.5	.9912	.0000
Machine 7	2.8578	−.3243 (4.7)	20.1	.8668	.1122

* Every observation.
† Figures in parentheses are t-ratios.
‡ Coefficient of correlation at lag residuals, where $z = x_: - x'_1$.

The progress ratios and elasticities vary from 6.4 to 20.1 and −.10 to −.32, respectively. The means are 12.9 and −.20. They are insignificant. The corresponding means for the machine tools are 11.5 and −.18, which also cannot be used. The same is not true for the automatic machine tools with means of 12.7 and −.196, which are significant even at .05 level.

Assembling Progress Functions. The adjusted correlation coefficients vary in magnitude from .59 to .92 (see Table 3). With the small number of observations available for machines 5 and 7, the coefficients are statistically insignificant. The progress ratios range from 19.0 to 28.6 with 24.6 the mean. (The corresponding progress elasticities are −.30 to −.48 with −.41 the mean.) If we could neglect the relatively

---

[15] Progress was slowest in the machining of parts for the semiautomatic machine tool. This may partly be explained by the fact that the parts of this machine were most closely related to the company's previous work.

small correlation coefficients of machines 5 and 7, we could use the mean values. The mean progress ratio and elasticity for the machine tools are 26.3 and —.44. They can be used even at a .05 significance level.

Machining versus Assembling Progress. Chart 6 portrays machining, assembling, and total direct labor progress functions in regard to machine 2. The adjusted coefficients of correlation vary between .85 and .89. The machining progress ratio (and elasticity) is 13.2 (and —.20)

Table 3

ANALYSIS OF ASSEMBLING PROGRESS FUNCTIONS OF SEVEN MACHINES
BUILT BY ONE MANUFACTURER, 1946–50

Machine	a_{12}	b_{12} Progress Elasticity*	Progress Ratio	$\bar{r}_{12}$	$r_{z,\,z-1}$†
Machine 1					
Every observation	3.4412	—.4627	27.5	.9047	.7533
		(8.8)			
Every 2nd observation	3.4618	—.4726	28.0	.9247	.5872
		(8.0)			
Machine 2					
Every observation	3.5009	—.4241	25.5	.8899	.5693
		(22.9)			
Machine 3					
Every observation	3.5543	—.4854	28.6	.9168	.3586
		(7.9)			
Machine 4					
Every observation	3.4669	—.3918	23.7	.8929	.4601
		(5.4)			
Machine 5					
Every observation	2.8941	—.3779	23.2	.6595	.4518
		(2.3)			
Machine 7					
Every observation	2.8622	—.3033	19.0	.5921	.3483
		(2.3)			

* Figures in parentheses are t-ratios.
† Coefficient of correlation of lag residuals, where $z = x_1 - x'_1$.

as compared to an assembling progress ratio (and elasticity) of 25.5 (and —.42). Both are statistically significant (their t-ratio is about 20). Thus the assembling progress is much faster than the machining progress. That this holds with regard to all seven machines can be seen in Chart 7. The average assembling progress ratio (and elasticity) of the machine tools and construction machine is 24.6 (and —.41), compared with 12.9 (and —.20) for the average machining progress ratio (and elasticity). The assembling ratios range from 19 to 28.6 and the machining ratios from 6.4 to 20.1. The assembling progress, therefore, was not only more rapid than the machining progress but also more consistently so.[16]

Conclusions. Having established earlier the relative importance of changes in technical knowledge, we can now point to some regularity in

Chart 4

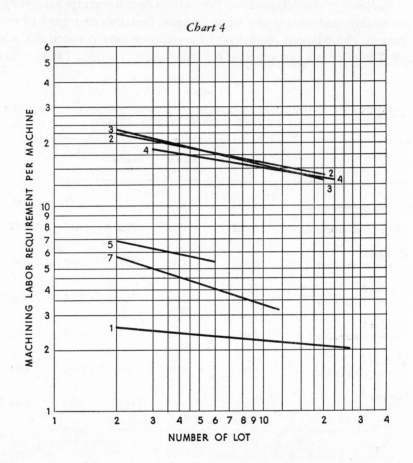

NUMBER OF LOT

these changes. The progress elasticity is constant over a five-year output. On the average, direct labor requirement decreased about 18.5 per cent with each doubling of cumulative output. Most of the progress was in the assembling of parts.

---

[16] This assumes that in the presence of more observations for machines 5 and 7, the assembling elasticity would not have changed much and thus become significant. That machining progress was slower than assembling progress does not reflect on the relative capacity of workers to learn. Instead, it means that there is apparently less place for machining progress in such forms as liberalization of tolerances, minor design improvements, better tools, etc., than there is for assembling progress in such forms as improvements in plant layout, routing of material and managerial coordination, learning by assembling crews, etc.

Chart 5

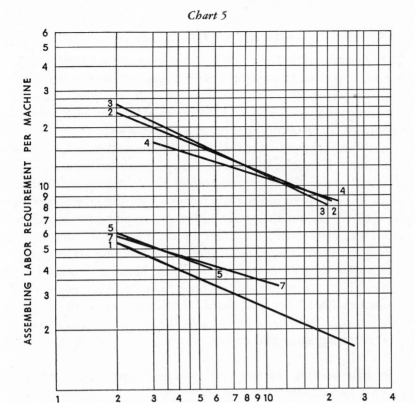

Chart 6

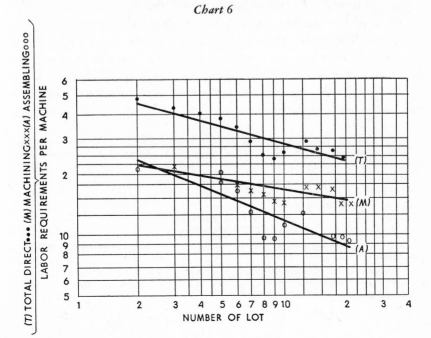

APPLICATION OF FINDINGS

Determination of Lot Size. When demand increases rapidly, as in a rearmament period, management must decide whether increasing lot sizes or producing lots at shorter intervals will prove more desirable. Labor savings may come about by economies of lot scale, effect of size of preceding lot, lot frequency, and passage of time *per se.*

It was shown above that within limits the economies of lot scale are insignificant.[17] Similarly, the size of the preceding lot appears to have little effect on unit labor requirement of the following lot. This was revealed by an analysis of the two machines with the greatest variation in lot size.[18] A six months' strike, although stopping only learning by direct labor, may clarify the effect of the passage of time and lot frequency. As production is most intensive in the later stages, completion lags were used to measure lot intervals. Machine 6 is used as an example.[19] The average monthly decline in labor requirement of the 17 prestrike lots was 1.7 per cent; that of the first poststrike lot 0.6 and of the second 6.5. The later lots fell into the general prestrike pattern. Although management and engineers continued to learn, the average monthly reduction in the first poststrike lot is only about one-third of the prestrike average. In the next lot labor apparently regained its experience and implemented improvements made by management and engineers during the strike, thus increasing productivity substantially. Passage of time *per se,* except for short periods of gestation, can explain but little of the learning process. Instead, lot frequency appears most important. The more often lots are scheduled the more opportunities there are for everybody to recognize, introduce, and test improvements and the fewer opportunities to forget what was learned before.

Therefore, with the present know-how and setup, lots should be relatively small; 20–30 units may be machined and 10–20 assembled at

---

[17] Although lots varied in size from 10 to 70 units, the actual range of the machining of parts was between 20–25 and 70. When small lots were scheduled, in order to spread the fixed cost of setting up the machines, no less than 20–25 units were machined.

[18] The correlation between the reduction in direct labor requirement per machine from lot x to lot $x + 1$ expressed as a percentage of the unit labor requirement in lot x and the size of lot x was found to be:

    1) .3447 for machine 1, and
    2) .0001 for machine 6.

With the number of observations exceeding 15 in both cases, the correlation is statistically insignificant.

[19] The reason for selecting this machine is that lots which were scheduled before the strike were also completed before its beginning; and all post strike lots were not worked on before the strike.

a time.[20] If smaller lots are needed, machining can be done for two or three lots at a time. Large demand increases call not so much for larger lots as for more frequent ones. This conclusion is also consistent with the firm's profit policy.

Chart 7

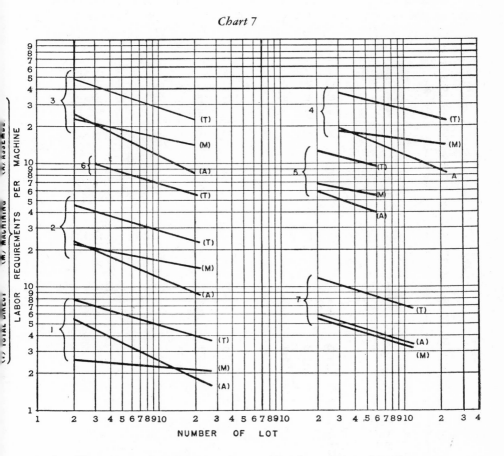

Cost Forecasts. Assuming a given scale of operation, hourly wages for direct and indirect labor, and the amount of indirect labor needed, the total unit cost can be calculated with the help of a progress elasticity estimate. Expected material, overhead, and indirect labor cost, together

---

[20] The importance of this issue may be illustrated by an example. Let us assume that: (1) the progress ratio is 20; (2) in one case, lots of 20 units are scheduled every month, and in the second, lots of 80 every four months; and (3) progress is exclusively associated with the frequency of production. Under these assumptions, in the first case the 640th machine would call for about 33 per cent of the labor that went into the first one; in the second case for about 51 per cent. If the first machine had required 5,000 direct labor hours at $2.00 an hour, which is not uncommon, the first method could save around $1,800 in direct labor cost of the 640th machine. Even if, as indicated before, not all progress is associated with production frequency, the savings still will be substantial.

Table 4

SUMMARY OF TEST OF EQUALITY OF PROGRESS ELASTICITIES AND RATIOS, 1946–50

H_0—Hypothesis Tested	H_1—Alternative Hypothesis $H_1 = H_0$	Fisher's Z Calculated	Degrees of Freedom	Z_{mn} ($\alpha = .05$)	Z_m ($\alpha = .01$)	Action Taken*	Mean Progress Elasticity	Mean Progress Ratio (Per Cent)
1. Total Direct Labor Regression Coefficients are equal for:								
all seven machines	Not all coefficients are equal	.4332	$m = 6,$ $n = 68$	.3900	.5500	Accept H_0 for $\alpha = .04$	−.2958	18.5
all five machine tools	"	.5258	$m = 4,$ $n = 47$	.4700	.6283	Accept H_0 for $\alpha = .038$	−.2939	18.4
all four automatic m-tools	"	.4847	$m = 3,$ $n = 30$	.5362		Accept H_0 for $\alpha = .05$	−.2957	18.5
2. Machining Labor Regression Coefficients are equal for:								
all six machines	"	2.7000	$m = 5,$ $n = 52$	.5900	.5900	Reject H_0	−.2006	12.9
all five machine tools	"	2.0400	$m = 4,$ $n = 47$		.6283	Reject H_0	−.1758	11.5
all four automatic m-tools	"	.4630	$m = 3,$ $n = 30$	.5362		Accept H_0 for $\alpha = .05$	−.1959	12.7
3. Assembling Labor Regression Coefficients are equal for:								
all six machines	"	.5498	$m = 5,$ $n = 52$		.5900	Accept H_0 for $\alpha = .01$	−.4075	24.6
all five machine tools	"	.3253	$m = 4,$ $n = 47$	.4700		Accept H_0 for $\alpha = .05$	−.4387	26.3
all four automatic m-tools	"	.3613	$m = 3,$ $n = 30$	.5362		Accept H_0 for $\alpha = .05$	−.4198	25.3

* If H_0 is rejected it means that the progress elasticity (and ratio) coefficients are statistically unequal; if H_0 is accepted at a given level of significance, it means that the coefficients are equal at that level of significance.

with average hourly wages of direct labor, can be reduced to dollars per direct labor hour. By adjusting the estimate of the progress function by this figure the cumulative total cost function is obtained. Such rough estimates usually suffice to decide whether the design is marketable at a profit. After a few lots have been completed the early estimates can be checked and, if necessary, adjusted. After allowing for changes in plant scale and inaccuracies in the estimate, the product can be priced.[21]

Often in planning new products and in negotiating contracts, management likes to estimate the cumulative labor requirement, wage bill, and total cost of a given production schedule. As we specified the unit progress function to be $x_1 = ax_2{}^b$, the cumulative progress function can be written as the integral of the unit progress function or:

$$X_1 = x_1 \int dx_1 = a \int x_2{}^b \, dx_2 = \frac{a}{b+1} x_2{}^{b+1}$$

where X_1 is the cumulative direct labor requirement. For instance if $a = 6{,}000$ man-hours, $b = -.30$, and $x_2 = 1{,}000$ machines, $X_1 = \dfrac{6{,}000}{.7} (10^3)^{.7} = 1{,}080{,}000$ man-hours.

Similar information can be obtained after some units have already been completed. Let L be the number of machines for which the total labor requirement or cost is to be estimated, K the number of machines already completed, and $x_1 = ax_2{}^b$ the unit progress function with coefficients determined for this type of machine. Then:

$$X_L = \sum_{K}^{K+L} x_1 = \int_{K}^{K+L} x_2{}^b \, dx_2 \, .$$

Thus, for instance, if we use the same values for a and b as before, the second thousand units would require about 675,000 man-hours of direct labor.

Labor Scheduling. Labor requirement forecasts to facilitate hiring and training of workers are of particular importance in the building of machine tools because of the wide demand fluctuations and need for high skills. Let us assume that we expect a direct labor progress ratio of

---

[21] This method was tried with regard to one machine. It was estimated that in the early lots the product would cost more than $15,000 while the possible price could be no more than $8,000. Over a three-year period the product was redesigned. When production started the actual direct labor requirement for machines in the second lot was ascertained, a progress ratio of 18 per cent assumed, and a progress function in terms of total unit cost estimated. On this basis a price below $8,000 was established which—consistent with the firm's pricing policy—would be maintained for many years, except for adjustments for major price level changes.

Chart 8

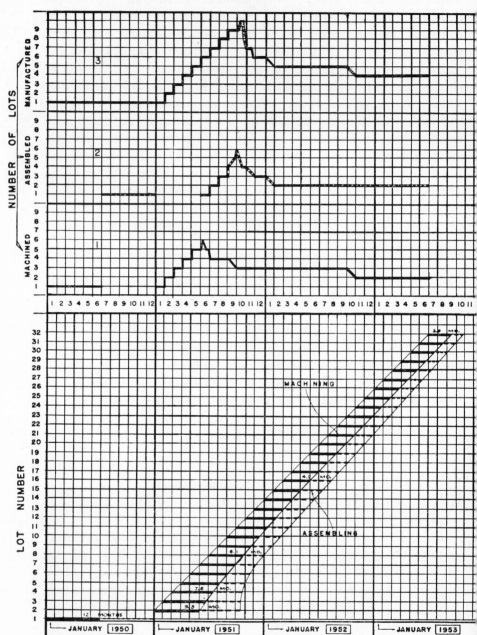

20, a machining progress ratio of 14, and an assembling progress ratio of 26, with the machining and assembling periods initially equal. Also, we may assume that progress finds its expression in a shortening of successive production periods. Thus, for instance, in January 1950 a pilot unit was started and successfully completed one year thereafter. In January 1951, a monthly scheduling of 20 machines was decided upon. Based on the progress ratio we can estimate the length of successive production periods, e.g., the second is 9.5, the fourth 7.6, the eighth 6.1, the sixteenth 4.9, and the thirty-second 3.9 months.

These changes are portrayed in Chart 8, from which we can read off how many lots are worked on in any one month. In order to know the types of labor required, we must break down manufacturing into major operations. We have done this only for machining and assembling (the first represented by full and the second by broken line). In the upper part of the chart the number of lots on which machining, assembling, and thus manufacturing is carried on in successive months is presented. In addition to the qualitative statement, management can make quantitative ones by estimating the labor requirements of separate operations. The same procedure can be used to forecast not only labor requirements, but also, depending on the circumstances, equipment requirements, pace of output, lot intervals, lot sizes, etc.

Conclusion

This study is an attempt to call attention to certain dynamic cost aspects, i.e., irreversible changes in technology. The empirical inquiry into machine building illustrates the relative importance of the effect of changes in technical knowledge and in production volume on the requirement of direct labor. While the first is of paramount importance, the influence of the latter appears insignificant. Although we do not know whether this is an isolated case, we are inclined to expect similar results in other plants producing large and complicated machinery, particularly if the work is organized in lots. In such cases, relatively fixed combinations of labor and equipment are used, while engineer, management, and direct labor have a wide-open field for contributing labor-saving improvements.[22]

The company's progress in machine building, if expressed in internal labor savings, exhibits a remarkable degree of regularity. The progress ratio and elasticity are about constant. Their magnitudes, based on the analysis of seven out of twenty products, appear to be about 18.5 and —.30 respectively. Thus, in 1946–50 doubling cumulative output was on the average associated with a decrease of about 18.5 per cent in direct labor requirement. Of the company's twenty products, the production of eight was initiated during 1946–50. During this period

---

[22] This holds in particular if production is neither carried out by a single man nor by an assembly line technique, but an intermediate degree of labor specialization with operational frequency at its best prevails.

productivity in the manufacture of these eight products increased on the average by about 10–12 per cent per annum, while the annual productivity increase with regard to the twelve "old" machines was about 1½–2 per cent. The average annual productivity increase of the whole plant was about 5–6 per cent.

In an attempt to gain a better understanding of the fields in which progress is made, the machining of parts, as well as their assembly, was analyzed. It was found that the assembling progress was much more rapid and more consistently so than the machining progress.

Empirical estimates of progress functions can be used on a firm as well as national level for numerous purposes. With regard to managerial decisions, applications were presented in three separate fields. First, we discussed the problem of determining lot sizes and frequencies and showed that it would be in the interest of the machine builder to produce in relatively small lots of 20–30 units each. Assembling may be carried out in even smaller lots and then machining of parts would be done for two or three lots at a time. Thus, large demand increases should be translated into more frequent lots and not excessively large ones. The opposite holds if demand falls off. Second, we presented a technique to forecast labor requirement and cost as an aid in determining whether a new design will find a market and, if so, at what price it should be offered. Third, we showed how progress functions can help in scheduling labor, material, and the balanced use of equipment.

Progress function estimates are perhaps of even greater use for national planning in such areas as industry or nationwide forecasts of labor requirements and cost, allocation of labor and materials, and calculation of the magnitude of contracts which will furnish the proper production base by a given date.[23]

---

[23] Because of the present interest in estimating production bases for various products under the rearmament program, we shall indicate how the base and pre-M-Day contracts can be calculated wtih the help of progress functions. The production base is the cumulative output by M-Day. As most plants can absorb direct labor at a more or less given rate, which can be closely estimated from previous experience, we must decide only how many units (A) must be produced in the post-M-Day period. Thus, having a requirement of A units to be produced after M-Day with a fixed input of X_1 direct man-hours, we must solve for x_2

$$X_1 \Sigma x_1 = a \int_{x_2}^{x_2 + A} x_2{}^b \, dx_2,$$

using the same notation as before. The solution to find x_2 takes the form:

$$X_1 = \Sigma x_1 = \frac{a(x_2 + A)^{1+b} - a \, x_2{}^{1+b}}{1 + b}$$

$$\frac{X_1 (1 + b)}{a} = (x_2 + A)^{1+b} - x_2{}^{1+b}$$

It is naturally much too early to generalize about the nature and extent of changes in technical knowledge. Besides the present progress study of machine building there are two other progress studies both of which use World War II data. The progress ratio of the wartime production of airframes in the United States was found to be about 20.[24] For the wartime production of Liberty ships, Victory ships, tankers, and standard cargo vessels, the progress ratio ranged from 16 to 22.[25] The question, thus, arises—and certainly warrants further study—whether in certain United States plants and industries there is perhaps a rather similar pace of progress and, if so, of what magnitude. Although in all three studies the progress ratio was around 18–20 per cent, much further work is needed before generalizations can be attempted.

---

and must be solved by trial and error. By solving for x_2 we know what the cumulative output of the given machine must be by M-Day in order to permit the production of A units of the same item after M-Day. By the same method we can also estimate output by time period after M-Day. See also H. Bergman, "A Mathematical Method of Calculating Labor Requirements and Optimum Production Output," *Econometrica*, Vol. XIX (February, 1951), pp. 49–50.

[24] A. Alchian, "An Airframe Production Function," Project RAND Paper, P-108, 1949, p. 4.

[25] A. D. Searle and C. S. Gody, "Productivity Increases in Selected Wartime Shipbuilding Programs," *Monthly Labor Review*, Vol. LXI, No. 6 (1945), p. 1132.

CASE 15

A Plant-Warehouse System with Variable Lead Times and Variable Re-order Levels[1]

PAUL A. STRASSMANN[2]

Some points of special interest in this paper are:

 a. The method used in selecting the allocation interval.
 b. The cost functions used for inventory and employment change costs.
 c. The use of a delivery standard to "price" back orders.
 d. The separation of back orders into those due to human error and those due to forecast error.
 e. The interaction between quarterly planning activities and weekly planning activities.

INTRODUCTION

An analyst, in approaching the design of an integrated factory warehouse decision system, finds out that existing operations research theory concentrates on the rigorous solution of only limited and selected segments of the complex relationship between production and distribution. The fixed or economic order quantity re-ordering practice most frequently discussed in O/R literature results in an undesirable fluctuation in orders at the plant. If the manufacturer owns both the plants and the warehouses, he must incorporate an order smoothing decision rule into his system which must necessarily modify the size of the economic order quantity.

The fixed re-order point (or trigger point) is likewise an undesirable

---

[1] *Management Technology,* June, 1962. Reprinted by permission.
[2] Manager, Computer Systems, General Foods Corporation.

restriction on the operation of a system attempting to optimize both factory and distribution costs. At the times when the sales rate is below the rate of production a particular re-order point may not be reached at all. Conversely, at times of high sales, the re-order point may be reached repeatedly with the ultimate consequence of lengthening the lead times at the plant.

Whether to design the system on the assumption of fixed or statistically varying lead times is another dilemma. In an integrated system, the imposition of a short fixed lead time on a factory by a warehouse is not realistic because the urgency of supply varies depending on the phase of the sales cycle. Unduly liberal fixed lead times, on the other hand, penalize the system by excessive permanent safety stocks. A statistical model based on sampled actual lead times is also difficult to justify. The shape of a particular lead time distribution function has a causal basis in the inter-relationships between warehouse ordering practices and plant production patterns. Calculating safety stocks on the basis of these lead time distributions, which include transactions having varying degrees of priority, results in heavy inventories.

The question of selecting an optimal production scheduling and inventory descision (or review) period must be also answered. The necessity of examining inventory levels and fixing production schedules varies from time-to-time, from product-to-product and is clearly related to policies adapted with respect to order quantities, re-order points and lead times. A number of secondary relationships affecting the design of the system place important restrictions on the design of an integrated system. These are:

(a) Shipment Consolidation—Regardless of order quantity or re-order point, such things as the product mix, frequency of shipments and predictability of economic shipment quantities may govern the plant to warehouse movements.

(b) Economic Production Lot Size—Superimposed on ordering patterns of individual warehouses are the effects of aggregate order quantities and the cyclical or counter-cyclical peaking of demand for products manufactured on joint facilities.

(c) Organization Limitations—The organizational status of warehouse administration, raw materials procurement, managerial control over cascaded (or subassembly) steps in the process, availability of computer facilities, sales promotional practices, strength of divisional vs. plant production planning staffs are significant limitations which must necessarily dictate the feasible operating features of an integrated system.

This paper describes design features of a decentralized plant-warehouse inventory system operating successfully and providing decision rules for ordering, producing and shipping well over $250,000,000 worth of relatively low cost grocery products from over 10 plants to 16 nationally located distribution centers. The product line consists of over 250 items, most of which are distributed nationally. Individual plants report operationally to different divisions. All warehouses are administered by a single division. Due to the large volume and bulk of products, all warehousing is done as close as possible to the ultimate sales destina-

Exhibit I

SCHEMATIC OUTLINE OF MULTI-DIVISIONAL, MULTI-PLANT AND MULTI-WAREHOUSE DISTRIBUTION SYSTEM

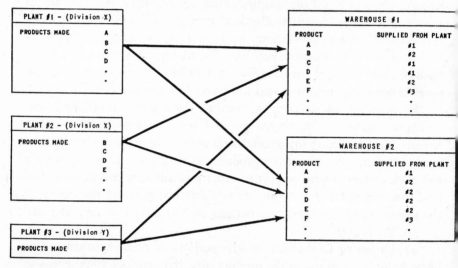

tion, with insignificant amounts held at the factory level. Hence, the problem of inventory management is inseparable from the problem of production and traffic scheduling and any statements about cost savings can be made from the point of view of minimizing warehousing plus transportation plus production plus customer service costs. This requirement is reinforced by placing the total cost responsibility for manufacturing and distribution with the producing divisions. Consequently, the warehouse managers do not make ordering decisions. Exhibit I describes diagrammatically the distribution system.

ALLOCATION OF WAREHOUSES TO PLANT FOR SERVICE

Two principal considerations led to fixing (for a stipulated planning period of one year) the "service responsibility" for supplying a given warehouse with a specific product for items manufactured in a number of plants. If the "service responsibility" was not assigned in advance, each supply decision would have to be made by referring all demands to a centralized scheduling staff. Apart from the costliness of such an arrangement in terms of personnel, communications and "noise" generated, all system transactions would be penalized by 3–4 additional days of lead time. A simple, worksheet simulation identified both the "steady state" effect (on safety stocks) and "dynamic effect" (on response characteristics to instantaneous sales peaks) of the two system design alternatives and substantiated the recommendation to eliminate functions performed by a centralized staff of order dispatchers. Another consideration for fixing the "service responsibility" was the appreciation of the fact that short-term transfers of demands from borderline warehouses back and forth among plants to meet short-term demands actually results in oscillations of aggregate production levels while total long-term demand remains constant. The system now provides for a routine allocation of warehouses to plants using the Ford-Fulkerson method on an IBM 704. The allocation decision is scheduled to be made about four months prior to start of a fiscal year and prior to each plant submitting next year's standard manufacturing costs (the latter being based on the volume of production allocated each plant). The allocation decision is then rechecked about two weeks before the start of the fiscal year using latest standard variable cost data.

Despite the fixed assignment of "service responsibility" the desirable flexibility of centralized order dispatching has been retained by distributing to all plants information concerning weekly stock status, sales and supply urgency for all warehouses storing products for which a plant has production facilities. Using this information, the plant planning manager may, at critical times, request inter-warehouse trans-shipments from a borderline location serviced by another plant. The man hour production equivalents of such transfers are later reconciled among plants themselves. Only rare instances of conflict concerning priority in expediting are referred to the central production planning staff.

SEASONAL PLANNING

Inasmuch as most grocery products exhibit seasonal sales patterns, the decision period for long run smoothing of production levels is one year. Two weeks before the start of each fiscal year, each plant submits a formal inventory and production plan proposal for four fiscal quarters ahead. The annual plan is based on moving average projections of past sales for product groups, by sales districts, as modified by latest marketing and operational plans.

Exhibit II illustrates the basic approach to seasonal employment stabilization. Extreme employment (uniform employment) and inventory (uniform inventory) policies are set forth and their consequences priced out for each plant separately. The least cost inventory and employment policy is then calculated and a feasible annual production plan is set forth meeting a number of additional restrictions such as vacation shut-downs, process limitations, crop and sales season requirements, etc.

Exhibit II

SEASONAL EMPLOYMENT STABILIZATION POLICIES

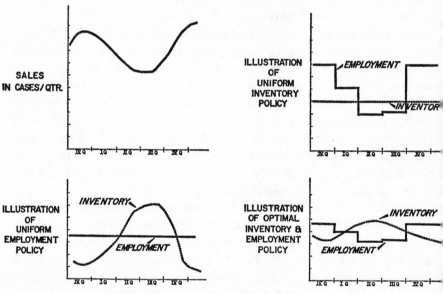

To arrive at a cost of smoothed employment, each plant represents a unique production smoothing problem due to peculiarities of the product mix assigned to it, amplitude and phasing of the aggregate seasonal sales curve, labor contents of its product line as well as distinctly non-continuous increments in the operating scale of various departments. This non-homogeneity immediately ruled out analytic approaches.[2a] Instead, each plant prepares two "Manpower Balances," one for a variable and the other for a uniform employment plant. The "Manpower Balance" concept is outlined in Exhibit III. The uniform employment plan balances manpower from quarter-to-quarter so that plant employment remains constant. The labor man-shifts for each product are

[2a] Such as Holt, Modigliani, Muth and Simon's: *Planning Production, Inventories, and Work Force* (Englewood Cliffs, N.J.: Prentice Hall, Inc., 1960).

Exhibit III

Plant _____ #_

MANPOWER BALANCE   Prepared By   JOHN DOE   Date 4/5/61

'62

Uniform Employment Plan

PRODUCT GROUP or DEPARTMENT	JUNE QUARTER 63 Operating Days					SEPTEMBER QUARTER 48 Operating Days					DECEMBER QUARTER 61 Operating Days					MARCH QUARTER 63 Operating Days				
	MEN	SHIFTS	SCHED.	AVAIL.	DIFF.	MEN	SHIFTS	SCHED.	AVAIL.	DIFF.	MEN	SHIFTS	SCHED.	AVAIL.	DIFF.	MEN	SHIFTS	SCHED.	AVAIL.	DIFF.
Product A Pkg.	4	47	188	252	+64	4	44	176	192	+16	4	50	200	244	+44	4	57	228	252	+24
" B "	4	42	168	0	-168	4	4	16	0	-16	4	11	44	0	-44	4	6	24	0	-24
" C "	2	23	46	63	+17	2	24	48	48	0	2	18	36	61	+25	2	19	38	63	+25
" A,B,C	6	63^1	378	378	0	6	46^2	276	288	+12	6	59^3	354	366	+12	5	63^3	378	378	0
Product D Pkg.	3	30	90	189	+99	3	48	144	144	0	3	61	183	183	0	3	63	189	189	0
" E "	5	58	153	189	+36	5	80	208	144	-64	3	51	153	183	+30	3	63	189	189	0
" (process) D,E	6^4	37	222	378	+156	6^4	48	288	288	0	6^4	54	324	366	+42	6^4	64	384	378	0
a Overtime ft																6	-1	-6		
Product F (6)	8	15	120	0	-120															
Supervision	4·		218			4		179			4		236			4		250		
Service & Handle			84	0	-84			52		+52			109		-109			25		-25
Total Man Shifts			1667		≤ 0			1335		≤ 0			1639		≤ 0			1699		≤ 0
Employment			27					28^5					27					27		
- 8.5 hr. Day																				
- 10.0 hr. Day																				
- 8.0 hr. Day																				
- shift operation																				
- hire 1 girl for special assignment																				
- Controlled by plant																				

converted into anticipated production volumes using standard shift production rates corresponding to the particular shift levels (or machine configuration) chosen and are then compared to corresponding quarterly sales volume projections, as shown in Exhibit IV.

The variable employment "Manpower Balance" shows the extent of fluctuation in plant labor, in terms of men, to meet the aggregate seasonal sales curve. Sub-totals can be used to identify (by department and/or labor skill) manpower fluctuations, the feasibility of scaling up or down production levels and the interchangeability of personnel. Net employment additions or deletions are then multiplied by approved employment fluctuation unit costs reflecting the seniority level of personnel involved, projected duration of the seasonal layoff or other peculiarities of the local labor market (such as availability of a skilled labor pool not desiring year-round employment).

The formulation and approval of a cost scale for employment variation is resolved well in advance of the annual planning process at the management level, the scale being set separately for each plant. In many instances, a feasible variable employment "Manpower Balance" of necessity results in some accumulation of seasonal inventories. The

Exhibit IV

Plant: #1							Sheet ___ of ___
FY: '62			SEASONAL INVENTORY		Prepared By: JOHN DOE		
☒ UNIFORM EMPLOYMENT PLAN			ACCUMULATION SCHEDULE		Approved By:		
☐ VARIABLE EMPLOYMENT PLAN - TRIAL # ___							

Prod-uct		Current Inventory Accumulation MARCH Qtr.	PLANNED DATA				
			JUNE Qtr.	SEPT. Qtr.	DECEMBER Qtr.	MARCH Qtr.	TOTAL
A	Sales Volume		110,000	86,850	100,650	113,550	411,050
	Scheduled Production		94,000	88,000	100,000	114,000	396,000
	Inventory Change		- 16,000	+ 1,150	- 650	+ 450	
	Cum. Inventory Change	+ 16,200	+ 200	+ 1,350	+ 700	+ 1,150	
	Cost of Cum. Inv. Change		$ 12.00	$ 81.00	$ 42.00	$ 69.00	$ 204.00
B	Sales Volume		7,640	9,500	7,000	7,100	31,240
	Scheduled Production		21,000	2,000	5,500	3,000	31,500
	Inventory Change		+ 13,360	- 7,500	- 1,500	- 4,100	
	Cum. Inventory Change	0	+ 13,360	+ 5,860	+ 4,360	+ 260	
	Cost of Cum. Inv. Change		$ 334.00	$ 146.00	$ 109.00	$ 7.00	$ 596.00
C	Sales Volume		9,418	9,768	7,027	7,832	34,235
	Scheduled Production		9,418	9,768	7,027	7,832	34,235
	Inventory Change		0	0	0	0	
	Cum. Inventory Change	0	0	0	0	0	
	Cost of Cum. Inv. Change		0	0	0	0	$ 0
D	Sales Volume		30,189	95,250	91,897	108,881	326,217
	Scheduled Production		52,800	76,800	97,600	100,800	328,000
	Inventory Change		+ 22,611	- 18,450	+ 5,703	- 8,081	
	Cum. Inventory Change	0	+ 22,611	+ 4,161	+ 9,864	+ 1,783	
	Cost of Cum. Inv. Change		$ 1,355	$ 250	$ 592	$ 107	$ 2,304
M	Sales Volume		133,224	161,500	158,124	198,822	651,670
	Scheduled Production		118,400	153,600	163,200	201,600	636,800
	Inventory Change		- 14,824	- 7,900	+ 5,076	+ 2,778	
	Cum. Inventory Change	+ 30,857	+ 16,033	+ 8,133	+ 13,209	+ 15,987	
	Cost of Cum. Inv. Change		$ 1,603	$ 813	$ 1,321	$ 1,599	$ 5,336
	Sales Volume						
	Scheduled Production						
	Inventory Change						
	Cum. Inventory Change						
	Cost of Cum. Inv. Change		PRODUCT	INV. CARRY COST PER QTR.			
	Sales Volume		A	.06 per case			
	Scheduled Production		B	.025 " "			
	Inventory Change		C	- -			
	Cum. Inventory Change		D	.06 " "			
	Cost of Cum. Inv. Change		E	.10 " "			

variable costs of such inventories must then be added to the priced out cost of employment variation. Similarly, fluctuation in production levels in phase with seasonal variation of sales may increase variable production costs by forcing departures from optimal process or machine load configurations. Such costs are additive to the cost of employment variation. The computation of the least cost seasonal employment is performed as follows:

Given: A = Cost of employment fluctuation
a_1 = Minimum feasible cost of seasonal inventories corresponding to A
a_2 = Loss in efficiency due to non-optimal scheduling
B = Cost of inventory accumulation corresponding to level employment
X = Inventory accumulation function with a lower limit of 0 (no employment stabilization inventory accumulation) and an upper limit of 1 (maximum inventory accumulation possible)

We can assume that

$$Y_u = \text{cost of uniform employment} = f(x) = (B - a_1) \cdot x + a_1$$

and that

$$Y_v = \text{cost of variable employment} = f(x) = (A + a_1 + a_2) \cdot (1 - x)^2$$

Inasmuch as the values of A; a_1; a_2 and B cannot be derived analytically, they are established empirically using trial and error techniques partially illustrated in Exhibits III and IV.

The quadratic approximation of the cost of variable employment has been shown to give a reasonably close representation of factory cost relationships. Incremental costs for small changes in output levels are relatively small. As fluctuations in seasonal output levels become larger, the number of people affected as well as their seniority rapidly increases. The non-linearity of the variable employment curve is then due both to cut-backs in indirect labor in addition to variable labor (assumed as linear) as well as due to steeply increasing employment variation unit costs. Seasonal planning costs will be then:

$$TC = Y_u + Y_v = (B - a_1) \cdot x + a_1 + (A + a_1 + a_2)(1 - x)^2$$
$$= Bx - a_1x + a_1 + (A + a_1 + a_2)(1 - 2x + x^2)$$

as shown in Exhibit V.

Exhibit V

SEASONAL PLANNING COST RELATIONSHIPS

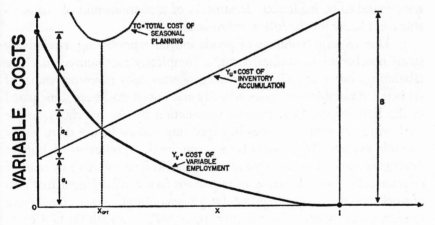

To find minimum seasonal planning costs

$$\frac{d(TC)}{dx} = B - a_1 - 2(A + a_1 + a_2) + 2x(A + a_1 + a_2) = 0$$

then

$$x_{opt} = 1 - \frac{B - a_1}{2(A + a_1 + a_2)}$$

Due to limits on value of $0 \leqq X \leqq 1$ a compromise solution between extreme employment or inventory policies exists only if:

$$B - a_1 < 2(A + a_1 + a_2)$$

This means that if the incremental cost of accumulating seasonal inventories is more than twice the total cost of employment variation, the latter policy should be preferred in all cases.

The allocation of optimum seasonal inventory accumulations to individual products is finally accomplished by re-working the "Manpower Balance" and "Seasonal Inventory Accumulation Schedule" to assure that high labor content products are scheduled preferentially into seasonal inventory surplus, that shelf life and frequent packaging changes do not conflict with the accumulation plan and that economic scheduling of incremental production levels is feasible.

SETTING THE AVAILABILITY STANDARD

Since the size of safety inventories, which are necessary to maintain availability (service) at warehouses are an important factor in short-term production planning, the criteria and techniques for determining their size become a matter of primary concern in the plant-warehouse system design. Standard references on the question of valuation of an out-of-stock occurrence or setting an arbitrary availability percentage were found to be inadequate treatments of a phenomenon of considerable complexity for the following reasons:

1. Due to large volumes of goods moved representing a relatively small number of individual items, a completely mechanized machine tabulating system at each warehouse generates daily inventory status of all items. Availability is reviewed daily and out-of-stocks are anticipated in the light of the local marketing situation by the warehouse order clerk who may initiate a series of expediting actions before there is any tangible evidence of an out-of-stock condition. Application of human intelligence to call for advance action is particularly effective in cases of extreme sales demands and is an important factor in keeping actual out-of-stocks in the range required by an exceedingly keen competitive market. (e.g. substantially better than 99% availability). Consequently, the size of safety inventories is determined to an important extent by "expediting costs" such as:

   a. Inter-warehouse trans-shipments;
   b. Less than carload or less than truckload shipments;
   c. Cost penalties arising from departures from an optimum plant production schedule;
   d. Overtime;
   e. Uneconomic procurement practices for raw and packaging materials.

2. The duration of a particular out-of-stock condition is of great importance. The prevailing practice of assigning a unit cost to an out-of-

stock occurrence has not been found to be satisfactory. The fact that it is virtually impossible to obtain agreement on the cost of a "customer non-service" occurrence testifies clearly that this approach is not meaningful. Distributors of grocery products do not necessarily expect full and continuous service out of a distribution warehouse instantaneously, for all products and at all times. The availability of stocks in the customer's own distribution channels and the relative importance of being fully stocked at the grocery shelf level results in most cases in a penalty to the manufacturer's sales organization only if over a period of time promised delivery deadlines are not met.

3. The relative priority to maintain a fixed availability standard varies from time-to-time and changes depending on product involved, location and condition of sale (such as a "promotion," market test or new product introduction). Furthermore, an out-of-stock occurrence at the warehouse (distribution center) level does not necessarily result in lost sales to ultimate customers inasmuch as a large portion of shipments from a warehouse go to distributors and not to retail stores.

In order to cope with the restrictions discussed above, the following system policies have been adopted:

1. Each product group or location is assigned an agreed upon "delivery standard" in days. If this standard is, for instance, two days, a least cost expediting action must be taken to assure delivery within two days after the out-of-stock is reported. All out-of-stocks are tabulated daily and counted daily until the item becomes available. For instance, 100 items reported as being out-of-stock for three days would be tallied as 300 out-of-stock occurrences.

2. All expediting actions taken within a month are costed out, classified and reported to the central production planning staff.

3. Charts similar to ones used in quality control are maintained to aid in identification of local out-of-control situations and to aid the central staff in evaluation of plant scheduling performance. Consistent above-or-below standard out-of-stock experiences are reviewed to identify their cause and to aid in taking corrective actions.

The information obtained as a result of the above policies is then used to calculate the optimum system factors of safety (K) for each product group and/or warehouse location.[3] Exhibit VI portrays the technique used. The approach differs in many respects from the conventional treatment of the problem. First, the costs of a lost sale or loss of good will are hidden in the expediting costs which are a function of the

---

[3] The factor of safety is used here in the same sense as outlined by R. G. Brown in *Statistical Forecasting for Inventory Control* (New York: McGraw-Hill Book Co., Inc., 1959).

"delivery standard." Although this is not an explicit way of identifying the extent of penalty due to item unavailability, operationally this represents a method which lends itself to clear communication of relative service priorities. Changing an item from two to three day delivery standard can be understood, administered and measured easier than increasing the "service standard," for instance from 99.75 to 99.90%. Secondly, individual expediting occurrences may be measured and analyzed to yield significant information for improving the performance of the system and for taking corrective actions where human error can be easily hidden by phenomena presumed to be "statistical."

Exhibit VI

SERVICE STANDARD DETERMINATION

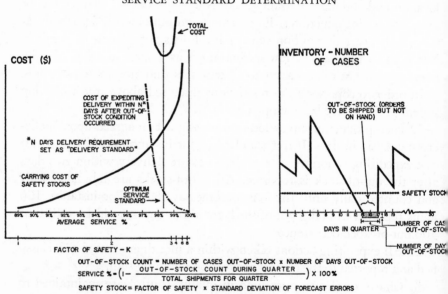

The fundamental premise on which this approach is based is the observed fact that out-of-stocks do not occur only because demand and lead times are statistically variable. Failure to communicate marketing developments, hesitancy on the part of the plant to alter schedules or take corrective action that may adversely affect manufacturing costs, hold-up of raw material supplies by quality control due to poor vendor performance, delays by advertising in releasing approved copy for change of packaging, etc. ultimately account for a large share of "forecasting errors" and "lead time variations" causing out-of-stocks. Unless a mechanism is developed for making the variable system costs causally traceable, the extreme ranges of the statistical distributions of lead time and of error in sales forecast will be incorporated uncritically into various inventory safety levels. The long-term consequence of such an approach will be the embalmment of the status quo into theoretically correctly computed safety parameters. The other important difference in approach to system design is that the optimum availability standard, computed as illustrated in Exhibit VI and defined as

$$\text{Availability } (\%) = \frac{\text{Orders (in units)} - \text{out-of-stock count (cumulative method)}}{\text{Orders (in units)}} \times 100$$

is attributed solely to the statistical distribution of forecast errors. This assumption holds true in a system where lead time is a controllable system element due to the following policies:

1. Weekly, plants receive forecasts of detailed production and shipping requirements, by week, eight weeks ahead.[4] Hence, availability of equipment capacity and transportation means can be planned well in advance and plans reviewed as the day of action approaches.

2. The reliability of the transportation system is known reasonably well and the actual routing of shipments is subject to continuous monitoring.

3. A daily warning signal is generated as a matter of routine and as a by-product of the warehouses' daily perpetual stock record updating. Such a signal is originated if a warehouse reaches an availability point where action can be taken only on an expedited basis. To make sure that a plant knows how to respond to such a "warehouse minimum" message, each plant establishes quarterly warehouse minimum levels at which the warehouse is required to originate a teletype message. As a rule, the warehouse minimum level is higher than that of the warehouse safety stock and is computed using the least re-supply time which may be economical for a particular plant-warehouse configuration.

4. Although the plant's production schedule can be planned ahead reasonably in advance (up to eight weeks) and raw materials availability has been designed to satisfy availability criteria for finished goods, the plant is specifically prohibited from finalizing production schedules until the latest sales and re-supply priority computations arrive at the plant two to three days before the start of the production week.[5]

---

[4] For detail see the "weekly planning" section of this paper.

[5] Design criteria for a factory raw materials inventory policy shall be discussed in a separate paper. There are significant relationships between ratios of finished goods inventories at the distribution warehouse, plant warehouse levels and raw materials inventories at the plant and supplier warehouses. Attempts to minimize inventories at any of these four levels in a plant-warehouse logistic system may seriously penalize the system as a whole.

COST OF CARRYING INVENTORIES

The application of a single percentage figure (usually ranging from 10%–30%) to the value of an inventoried item, as a method of pricing out the cost of carrying inventory per annum, is the most frequently quoted approach currently in use. If there are relatively few items in a product line, the lack of correlation between the size of an item and its value as well as the general bulkiness of grocery products per unit justify a more rigorous treatment of this parameter which affects a large number of system relationships. The cost of carrying inventory is defined as:

(a) Warehousing Cost (warehousing cost per sq. ft. per annum reduced to cost per case per annum). Unless a company already owns substantial amounts of vacant warehousing space, the warehousing cost used in computations should be the marginal cost for additional space at prevailing commercial rates.

(b) Taxes and insurance, per case.

(c) Net variable cost of capital tied up in inventories—For purposes of inventory valuation in a distribution decision system only direct variable costs should be used to measure the amount of funds tied up in inventories. Fixed charges and factory overhead should be subtracted from the cost-of-goods used for valuation for accounting purposes. Similarly, if the manufacturing process involves a conversion from raw materials which are purchased in substantial supply regardless of the short term requirements of the conversion process (such as in the case of purchasing an annual crop or buying a substantial supply of a raw material as protection against a price increase or supply failure) the inclusion of such raw materials in the valuation of inventories is incorrect. The timing of the conversion of raw materials into finished goods (creation of inventories) should not be affected by the fact that the raw material will remain available regardless of actions taken.

Another problem arises when an interest rate must be selected representing the percentage per annum costs of funds employed in inventories. The divisional controllers are confronted with conflicting considerations if inventories represent a large portion of total funds employed. Invariably, they will tend to select the interest rate applicable to the divisional return on investment of funds employed which leads to obviously fallacious inventory decisions.[6] The correct approach is to use a return on investment rate for an investment having a risk comparable

---

[6] See article by John Dearden in the *Harvard Business Review*, May–June, 1961, p. 76.

to creation of inventories. For a staple product, this rate would approach the cost of long-term corporate borrowing. For new products, promotional items, merchandise subject to sudden price decline, obsolescence or spoilage, etc., the investment in inventories should be based on a discounted valuation of probabilities that inventory losses will take place in the future.

QUARTERLY PLANNING

Since fiscal and marketing objectives are re-appraised quarterly, adjustments in the annual plan are easiest to accomplish during the first two weeks of each quarter. At this time over-fulfillment or underfulfillment of last quarter's sales targets has been identified and detailed product promotional activities for the current quarter have been communicated to plants.

At the end of the first two weeks of each quarter, each plant submits for approval to the divisional production planning staff a formal quarterly production and inventory accumulation plan illustrated partially as Exhibits VII and VIII. A minimum cost production and inventory plan is found by pricing out inventory accumulations and comparing this cost with the cost of varying production levels which would eliminate increases in inventories.[7] This is illustrated in Exhibit IX. The quarterly planning process is completed by determining the minimum and maximum levels for inventories to apply during the next planning period, as follows:

(a) Minimum Inventory—This amount is read off the computer run described in the "weekly planning" section of this paper and represents K standard deviations of forecast errors for the lead time of one week. If the review period increases, such as during plant shutdown for vacations, the minimum inventory corresponding to the shutdown period (in weeks) would be used.

(b) Manufacturing Cycle or Shipping Frequency—Upon completion of a production lot, the size of warehouse inventories will be determined either by the frequency of the manufacturing cycle (in week's supply) or by the frequency of economic shipments to the particular warehouse location. For instance, if product Q is manufactured once every three weeks at plant X, but the most economic shipping method (by rail) to warehouse #4 allows scheduling of car-lot deliveries only once every five weeks, the "shipping frequency" shall

---

[7] Due to cycling of a large number of products through identical equipment, the technique outlined in Magee's *Production Scheduling and Inventory Control* (New York: McGraw-Hill Book Co., Inc., 1958), pp. 58, 59, 310–12, was found particularly helpful.

Exhibit VII

PLANNED PRODUCTION REQUIREMENTS

QUARTER: JUNE QTR.   FY 62

PLANT: #1
PREPARED BY: JOHN DOE
APPROVED: _____   PLANT MANAGER
APPROVED: _____   DATE: _____

PRODUCT CODE	PRODUCT DESCRIPTION	LAST QUARTER-END INVENTORIES				NEXT QUARTER-END INVENTORIES								
		(1) WAREHOUSE	(2) TRANSIT	(3) PLANT	(4) = (1)+(2)+(3) TOTAL	(5) WAREHOUSE SAFETY	(6) WHSE. PROTECTION ADJ. WEEKS / QUANTITY	(7) SEASONAL ACCUMULATION	(8) PROJECTED IN-TRANSIT	(9) PROJECTED PLANT	(10) = (5)+(6)+(7)+(8)+(9) PLANNED TOTAL	(11) = (10)-(4) INVENTORY ADJUSTMENT	(12) WAREHOUSE SHIPMENT FORECAST	(13) = (12)+(11) QUARTER PRODUCTION REQUIREMENTS
	Product A	54,326	16,453	3,451	74,230	38,030	— / —	+ 200	16,000	4,000	58,230	−16,000	110,000	94,000
	Product B	5,780	100	70	5,950	5,250	— / —	+13,360	700	—	19,310	+13,360	7,640	21,000
	Product C	0	0	494	494	0	— / —	+ 0	—	494	494	0	9,418	9,418
	Product D	15,347	2,570	178	17,895	13,351	— / —	+22,611	4,000	544	40,506	+22,611	30,189	52,800
	Product E	32,293	18,190	5,006	55,489	20,034	0.4 / 4,598	+16,033	—	—	40,665	−14,824	133,224	118,400

Exhibit VIII

PRODUCTION PLAN

QUARTER: JUNE QTR. FY 62

PLANT: #1
PREPARED BY: JOHN DOE
APPROVED: _____
APPROVED: _____ PLANT MANAGER
DATE _____

PRODUCT CODE	PRODUCTION REQUIREMENTS	Wk 1 MACH SHFTS	Wk 1 PRODUCTION	Wk 2 MACH SHFTS	Wk 2 PRODUCTION	Wk 3 MACH SHFTS	Wk 3 PRODUCTION	Wk 4 MACH SHFTS	Wk 4 PRODUCTION	Wk 5 MACH SHFTS	Wk 5 PRODUCTION	Wk 6 MACH SHFTS	Wk 6 PRODUCTION	Wk 7 MACH SHFTS	Wk 7 PRODUCTION	Wk 8 MACH SHFTS	Wk 8 PRODUCTION	Wk 9 MACH SHFTS	Wk 9 PRODUCTION	Wk 10 MACH SHFTS	Wk 10 PRODUCTION	Wk 11 MACH SHFTS	Wk 11 PRODUCTION	Wk 12 MACH SHFTS	Wk 12 PRODUCTION	Wk 13 MACH SHFTS	Wk 13 PRODUCTION	TOTAL PRODUCTION SCHEDULED	NEXT QTR 1st Wk MACH SHFTS	NEXT QTR 1st Wk PRODUCTION	NEXT QTR 2nd Wk MACH SHFTS	NEXT QTR 2nd Wk PRODUCTION
A	94,000	4	8,000	4	8,000	4	8,000	4	8,000	3	6,000	3	6,000	3	6,000	4	8,000	4	8,000	4	8,000	4	8,000	3	6,000	3	6,000	94,000	5	10,000	5	10,000
B	21,000	4	2,000	4	2,000	4	2,000	0						5	2,500	4	2,000	4	2,000	4	2,000	4	2,000	5	2,500	4	2,000	21,000		0		0
C	9,418 – 80# Bags	2	800	2	800	2	800	0	1		400	2	800	2	800	2	800	2	800	2	800	2	800	2	800	3	1,200	9,600	2	800	2	800
D	52,800	5	8,000	5	8,000	4	6,400	0			0		0	4	6,400	4	6,400	4	6,400	4	6,400	3	4,800		0		0	52,800	5	8,000	5	8,000
E	118,400	5	16,000	5	16,000	4	12,800	0			0		0		0		0	3	9,600	5	16,000	5	16,000	5	16,000	5	16,000	118,400	5	16,000	5	16,000

Exhibit IX

QUARTERLY TRIAL PRODUCTION PLAN COMPUTATION

Plant: **#1**   Prepared by: ___JOHN DOE___   Date: ___4/5/61___

PRODUCT GROUP: ___D___

WEEK NO.	NO. OF SHIFTS	☐ UNIFORM ☒ TRIAL PRODUCTION PLAN (1)	QUARTERLY CYCLE FACTOR (2)	VARIABLE PROD. PLAN (SHIPMENTS) (3)	INVENTORY ACCUMULATION (1) - (3)	TOTAL INVENTORY ACCUMULATION	COST OF TRIAL PROD. PLAN
Carry-Over, Seasonal or Cycle Inventory					0	0	
1	5	8,000	0.8	1,855	+ 6,145	+ 6,145	$ 28
2	5	8,000	0.8	1,855	+ 6,145	+12,290	$ 57
3	4	6,400	1.0	2,320	+ 4,080	+16,370	$ 75
4	0	0	1.0	2,320	- 2,320	+14,050	$ 65
5	0	0	0.7	1,625	- 1,625	+12,425	$ 57
6	0	0	1.0	2,320	- 2,320	+10,105	$ 47
7	4	6,400	1.0	2,320	+ 4,080	+14,185	$ 65
8	4	6,400	1.0	2,320	+ 4,080	+18,265	$ 84
9	4	6,400	1.0	2,320	+ 4,080	+22,345	$ 104
10	4	6,400	1.0	2,320	+ 4,080	+26,425	$ 122
11	3	4,800	1.0	2,320	+ 2,480	+ 28,905	$ 134
12	0	0	1.3	3,019	- 3,019	+ 25,886	$ 120
13	0	0	1.4	3,275	- 3,275	+22,611	$ 104
QTR. TOTAL	33	52,800	13.0	30,189	-	+ 22,611	$1,062
1							
2							

COMMENTS: _____

_____

_____

govern in determination of the maximum inventories at warehouse #4 for a product made at X. Similarly, if shipments are made weekly, the "manufacturing cycle frequency" would govern.

(c) Seasonal and Quarterly Cycle Inventories—Allowances for

these accumulations are made and the value of the maximum inventory level raised accordingly.

(d) Additional Protection—For a number of reasons, such as accumulation for a promotion, anticipation of price changes, equipment modifications, etc., management may wish to raise the allowable maximum inventory levels by providing additional supplies of specific items.

A tabulation of the maximum and minimum factors in terms of weeks' supply is then made which is translated into maximum case limits. At the same time, a computation is made of "warehouse minima" by taking the minimum inventory levels (from the plant's point of view) and increasing them by a time factor representing plant to warehouse lead time on an expedited basis. The "warehouse minima" are inserted into the perpetual inventory records maintained by IBM tabulating equipment at each warehouse and reviewed daily. If the quantity available is less than the "warehouse minimum" this fact is immediately reported by teletype to the plant. It should be noted that

Exhibit X

THE MIN.—MAX. INVENTORY CONTROL CONCEPT

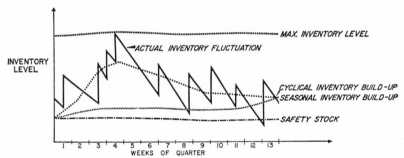

this communication allows for reaction on an expedited basis only and is not used to make the routine replenishment decision. The primary significance of the daily "warehouse minimum" signal on an exception basis is that it allows reduction of safety levels even further than theoretically deemed feasible by a weekly review frequency. The decision rules discussed under the minimum-maximum concept above are summarized in a graphical form as Exhibit X, which indicates how plants are given considerable latitude in optimizing their short-run inventory, production, transportation and customer service costs subject to the following restrictions:

(a) Plants shall always schedule shipments to warehouses so that the actual inventory, projected one review period ahead, shall not fall below in the minimum inventory level.

(b) Plants shall always schedule shipments to warehouses so that the actual inventory shall not exceed the *maximum* inventory level.

The practical consequences of these decision rules is that plants are allowed to re-allocate instantaneously (without divisional action) production capacity and manpower to items experiencing short-term sales increases even if such sales are substantially in excess of budgeted amounts. As a corollary, plants are not allowed to produce in amounts which would result in inventories in excess of the minimum limit if sales slow down even though the planned production levels have been set for the anticipated sales levels. Divisional approval is necessary only if the aggregate effect of short-term sales fluctuations require a modification of the annual plan.

WEEKLY PLANNING

The plant's decision to produce and ship is postponed to the latest time period possible. This rule is theoretically justifiable because both the age of information on which decisions are made, as well as the frequency of decisions, have a significant influence on the aggregate lead time and response characteristics to transient disturbances built into the system. Applying techniques of "industrial dynamics" to the old inventory system (outlined in Exhibit XI), the average lead time of six weeks (with an upper range of 12.3 weeks) was reduced by changing to the information system shown in Exhibit XII. The major differences between the new and the old information loops are:

1. Orders placed for future delivery are "phased out" by date and automatically deducted from available inventories.

2. The four weeks moving average has been replaced by an exponentially weighted moving average forecasting function,[8] which is believed to eliminate the lagging features of the moving average and makes allowance for seasonal and trend components of sales curves.

3. Shortening the review frequency from two weeks to one week.

4. Eliminating the lead time component attributable to the procurement of raw materials establishing a raw materials forecasting system consistent with management of finished goods inventories.

5. Eliminating the warehouse to division reporting lag (see paragraph 2 of the paper).

These measures have reduced the average lead time from six weeks to three weeks. But the most significant element in reducing inventories has been the reduction of the upper range of lead times from twelve

---

[8] See Peter R. Winters, "Forecasting Sales by Exponentially Weighted Moving Averages," *Management Science*, Vol. VI, No. 3.

Exhibit XI

PRODUCTION—INVENTORY MANAGEMENT SYSTEM

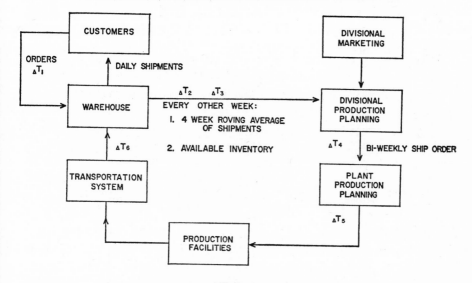

DELAYS IN OLD SYSTEM

DELAY	EXPLANATION	AVERAGE DURATION (Weeks)	RANGE	CUMULATIVE VALUE (Weeks)
ΔT_1	ORDERS PLACED FOR FUTURE DELIVERY	0.6	0.2 – 2.0	0.6
ΔT_2	SENSITIVITY OF 4 WEEKS MOVING AVERAGE	2.0	0 – 4.0	2.6
ΔT_3	REPORTING LAG — WAREHOUSE TO DIVISION	0.5	0.5 – 0.8	3.1
ΔT_4	PRODUCTION SCHEDULING TIME	0.2	0 – 0.5	3.3
ΔT_5	PRODUCTION TIME	1.7	0.2 – 3.0	5.0
ΔT_6	TRANSIT TIME	1.0	0.5 – 2.0	6.0
	TOTAL	6.0	1.4 – 12.3	

weeks to four weeks. Since it is the unpredictability of the range of demand rather than the demand average that determines the size of safety stocks each system element must be carefully analyzed for maximum delays which are generated by it. This experience has demonstrated that the first step in the design of an integrated inventory production scheduling decision making system should be a detailed flow chart of the logic and time elements of the existing system. This is to be followed by evaluation of institutional, communication and data processing limitations which determine the lowest attainable levels of lead time.

The new communication system provides for teletype transmission of information about sales and stocks to a central location where a report illustrated as Exhibit XIII is prepared and mailed (over the weekend) to each plant. The significance of the various elements on the computer run is explained as Exhibit XIV.

Exhibit XII

INVENTORY MANAGEMENT SYSTEM COMMUNICATIONS

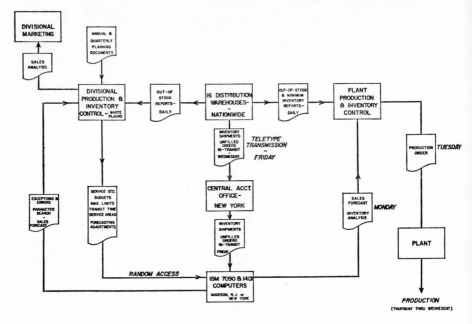

The forecasts shown on the computer output are made cumulatively, one through eight weeks ahead, each week of a 13 week quarter. This means that at the end of the fifth week in a quarter, the first projection of quarter-end sales can be made by adding actual for quarter-to-date plus an eight week sales forecast.

This process is repeated weekly with improved accuracy inasmuch as the quarter-end forecast includes an ever increasing fraction of actual sales, providing thereby significant information for sales analysis purposes. The forecasting equations are based on Winter's paper (*op. cit.*) and are used to compute cumulative forecasts F, at time t for n periods ahead where $1 \leqq n \leqq 8$. Then

$$F_{t,n} = \bar{S}_{t,1} + \bar{S}_{t,2} + \cdots + \bar{S}_{t,n}$$

where $\bar{S}_{t,n}$ is forecast shipments in period $(t + n)$. Similarly, the cumulative actual shipments, A, during these periods are given by

$$A_{t,n} = S_{t,1} + \cdots + S_{t,2}$$

Exhibit XIII

DATE 02/08/1962
PROD. 20337

	1	2	3	4	5	6	7	8	9	10	11	12	13	CUM QTR FORCAST	QTRLY BUDGET
					MAX	INV		UNSHP		TRANS		GP	W/TR NP		
PLT CHICAGO W/H CINCINNATI					K= 2.5	1239.	678.		55		GP 2.2	W/TR 0.7 NP 1.5		
CUM ACT+FORCST	1280.	0.	0.	0.	0.		145.	303.	514.	650.	784.	946.	1206.	1903.	2300.
SAFETY	604.	0.	0.	0.	0.	697.	200.	275.	281.	316.	392.	463.	509.		
PROD. FORECAST	0.	0.	0.	0.	0.	257.	0.	171.	136.	134.	163.	260.	74.		
ORDER REQUIRED	0.	0.	0.	0.	0.	0.	0.	171.	171.	210.	165.	0.	0.		
PLT HOBOKEN W/H CLIFTON					K= 2.5	900.	603.		96		GP 1.8	W/TR 0.1 NP 1.7		
CUM ACT+FORCST	1098.	0.	0.	0.	0.		137.	251.	400.	561.	743.	845.	1016.	1552.	1410.
SAFETY	638.	0.	0.	0.	0.	536.	200.	293.	418.	468.	584.	586.	624.		
PROD. FORECAST	82.	0.	0.	0.	0.	140.	0.	38.	148.	162.	181.	102.	171.		
ORDER REQUIRED	0.	0.	0.	0.	0.	0.	0.	38.	273.	96.	0.	0.	0.		
PLT CHICAGO W/H DETROIT					K= 2.5	1193.	988.		60		GP 3.5	W/TR 0.6 NP 2.9		
CUM ACT+FORCST	1175.	0.	0.	0.	0.		150.	315.	479.	611.	773.	889.	1098.	1774.	1990.
SAFETY	770.	0.	0.	0.	0.	676.	184.	263.	339.	430.	522.	619.	701.		
PROD. FORECAST	0.	0.	0.	0.	0.	214.	0.	0.	113.	162.	115.	210.	76.		
ORDER REQUIRED	0.	0.	0.	0.	0.	0.	0.	0.	113.	242.	0.	0.	0.		
PLT CHICAGO W/H CHICAGO					K= 2.5	2205.	778.		173		GP 1.0	W/TR 0.1 NP 0.9		
CUM ACT+FORCST	2200.	0.	0.	0.	0.		320.	590.	863.	1131.	1370.	1634.	2067.	3313.	4100.
SAFETY	1322.	0.	0.	0.	0.	1246.	308.	491.	645.	788.	961.	1084.	1218.		
PROD. FORECAST	133.	0.	0.	0.	0.	301.	23.	270.	273.	268.	239.	264.	433.		
ORDER REQUIRED	0.	0.	0.	0.	0.	0.	23.	454.	426.	411.	318.	0.	0.		
PLT CHICAGO W/H YOUNGSTOWN					K= 2.5	1850.	1017.		178		GP 2.3	W/TR 0.7 NP 1.6		
CUM ACT+FORCST	1522.	0.	0.	0.	0.		207.	407.	634.	812.	1021.	1203.	1452.	2437.	3340.
SAFETY	1143.	0.	0.	0.	0.	985.	294.	325.	440.	556.	724.	859.	1025.		
PROD. FORECAST	0.	0.	0.	0.	0.	215.	0.	179.	209.	182.	249.	70.			
ORDER REQUIRED	0.	0.	0.	0.	0.	0.	0.	234.	295.	377.	250.	0.	0.		
PLT CHICAGO W/H ATLANTA					K= 2.5	2008.	1553.		51		GP 2.7	W/TR 0.9 NP 1.8		
CUM ACT+FORCST	2485.	0.	0.	0.	0.		354.	640.	971.	1258.	1616.	1886.	2326.	3525.	3570.
SAFETY	1182.	0.	0.	0.	0.	1199.	337.	503.	666.	733.	847.	953.	1078.		
PROD. FORECAST	0.	0.	0.	0.	0.	624.	0.	135.	287.	358.	270.	440.	158.		
ORDER REQUIRED	0.	0.	0.	0.	0.	0.	0.	135.	354.	336.	270.	0.	0.		
CHICAGO	0.	0.	0.	0.	0.	0.	138.	1313.	1901.	2003.	1226.	2542.	193.	0. ORDER SUM	1368. PROD. SUM
	200.						138.	1033.	1402.	1469.	1449.	785.			
HOBOKEN	0.	0.	0.	0.	0.	0.	0.	38.	381.	814.	383.	193.		0. ORDER SUM	356. PROD. SUM
	82.						0.	38.	256.	691.	572.	785.	356.		

The difference between cumulative forecast shipments and cumulative actual shipments is represented by $E_{t,n}$ where

$$E_{t,n} = F_{t,n} - A_{t,n}$$

Since for any value of n we have p different error estimates (where p depends on the number of data in the computer and internal Q_2 over which the forecast has been simulated), the standard deviation for an n period forecast is computed from the root-mean-square of these p estimates as follows:

$$\sigma_n = \sqrt{\frac{(\Sigma E^2)_n}{p}}$$

The program computes σ_n for $n = 1, 2 \cdots 8$ and saves the results for multiplication by the safety factor K which can be chosen individually

Exhibit XIV

EXPLANATION OF COMPUTER OUTPUT

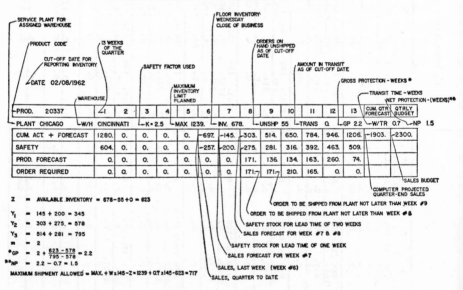

for each product warehouse location. The safety stock in each of the cumulative forecasts is then $X_n = K \cdot \sigma_n$ and the total inventory requirement Y_n is given by

$$Y_n = F_{t,n} + X_n$$

Due to the scarcity of input data in the proper format, the system was started up initially with only 26 sales data intervals (two cycles of 13 weeks each) per time series for each of the 4,000 time series involved.

Although this amount of data is an absolute minimum it represented such a vast improvement over the existing four weeks moving average that the cost of additional input data for the system start-up was not considered practical.

The computer operations are classified according to the "pilot" or "production" mode. During the "pilot" mode initial values of the trend, seasonal factors and smoothed shipments are computed. Then simulation without forecasting takes place over an interval Q_1 to test out the effect of three weighting factors (smoothing constants) on the system. Another simulation, over an interval Q_2 simulates the exponential smoothing equations to arrive at reasonable values of the standard deviation of forecast errors. A further option may be exercised wherein as many as six different values may be supplied for each of the weighting factors to determine one combination which would minimize the standard deviation of forecast errors n periods ahead. Inasmuch as only one forecasting period can be selected for the criterion of optimality, the minimum value of σ_2 has been selected because the production lead time of three weeks (from the date of the data) represents closest the existing planning horizon of the plants. In the "production mode," no simulation takes place and maximum advantage is taken of the exponentially moving average equations to up-date the time series with a minimum of historical data. The economies of exponential smoothing are apparent from the following data:

1. Compute time on IBM 7090: 4.4 minutes per 1,000 time series in "production mode"[9]

2. Input edit time on IBM 1401: 4 minutes per 1,000 time series. The order computation by the computer is based on the concept of "Gross Protection" which is analogous to the widely used concept of "weeks of supply" except that the length of time over which the existing stocks will suffice takes into account both the shape of the short-term sales forecast curve and the forecast requirements for safety stocks. The order computations are based on the following method:

If Z = amount available at the warehouse = inventory plus intransit less unshipped order at time t

W = weeks-in-transit, plant-to-warehouse using most economical means of transportation

R_i = order required (outbound shipment from plant to warehouse) at time $t = i$

m = number of the last forecast in which Z exceeds Y_n

---

[9] The program efficiency is due to work by the Computer Usage Company of New York and their Senior Analyst, J. H. G. Kelly.

GP = Gross Protection (number of weeks' existing supply would last with a confidence implicit in the $K \cdot \sigma_n$ safety stocks

NP = Net Protection (the number of the week in which the first replenishment shipment must leave the plant in order to maintain inventories at the warehouse above safety stocks)

then

$$GP = m + \frac{Z - Y_m}{Y_{m+1} - Y_m}$$

and

$$NP = GP - W$$

The "order" amounts are then determined as follows:

$$R_i = 0 \qquad \text{for } i \leqq m$$

$$R_i = Y_i - Z \qquad \text{for } i = m + 1$$
$$R_i = Y_i - Y_{i-1} \qquad \text{for } i \geqq m + 2$$

The R_i values are shifted on the computer output on the line "Order Required" in accordance with the lowest value of NP to calendarize the outbound shipment into its proper production week. Due to the restriction, however, that inventory shall not exceed a planned maximum (see par. 6), the R_i values are truncated so that

$$\sum R_i \leqq \text{Maximum inventory} - Z + \bar{S}_{t,n} \cdot W$$

The usefulness of the output format is manifold as illustrated by the following cases:

1. The plant totals of R_i values lend themselves to quick determination of order requirements, by item, up to eight weeks ahead. This allows improved short-term manpower scheduling.

2. The NP values act as true "priority indexes" for action. NP's which are negative or less than one are expedited. Code locations having NP's larger than one can be ranked according to priority of shipment, lowest values of NP having the highest urgency. For all practical purposes, items with GP in excess of eight ($GP = OVR$) are disregarded.

3. When sales trail behind production output, the surplus inventories can be distributed with uniform risk by equalizing result NP's up to the allowable maximum inventory level. Conversely, when sales exceed current production levels, the NP index allows uniform spreading of the out-of-stock risks.

4. The plant summary labelled "production forecast" totals are used for raw materials management and procurement. Scheduled production

one, two and three weeks ahead is key punched into cards, converted into ingredients requirements by the materials "explosion" technique, compared against available stocks and safety requirements to yield a phased out raw materials ordering schedule.

5. The increase in safety stocks with lengthened lead times is used in computations to influence diverse system decisions such as:

(a) Optimum economic order quantities using non-linear relationships of inventory costs as a function of batch size.

(b) Optimum length of vacation shut down or equipment change-over.

(c) Production requirements for promotions.

CONCLUDING REMARKS

The system described in this paper has been successfully operational since the Spring of 1961 and is generally known as the COPT system (abbreviation for *Cost Opt*imization). Less than eight months were spent designing and installing the features discussed. The primary reason for the rapid introduction and relatively low development costs can be found in the close cooperation between the production scheduling personnel and the operations research consultant. The inadequacies and contradictory tendencies of the old scheduling system confronted the operating personnel daily. Consequently, they were in a position to set forth the fundamental criteria for measures which should eliminate the identified problems. The major difficulty encountered was in education of personnel on the clerical level who actually make the majority of production scheduling, shipping and inventory decisions. The concept of making decisions which optimize costs of the overall system rather than minimize individually factors such as out-of-stock, inventory investment, warehouse floor space, realization of in-transit privileges, etc., were exceedingly difficult to get across. A partial answer to this was found by writing a detailed procedural manual which outlines in sequential format individual decision-making steps which have to be taken by each individual operating the system.

CASE 16

Consistency and Optimality in Managerial Decision Making[1,2]

E. H. BOWMAN[3]

Some points of special interest in this paper are:

a. The revised form of the rule used for regression in the aggregate scheduling cases.
b. The Management Coefficients Theory "axioms."
c. The implied problems of *using* the theory as a heuristic.
d. The statistical fit and savings of the naïve model for the plant size illustration.

This paper reports some research, ideas, and theory about managerial decision making. The first research projects dealt with are aggregate production and employment scheduling. From this is developed the idea that management's own (past) decisions can be incorporated into a system of improving their present decisions. Decision rules are developed, with the coefficients in the rules derived from management's past decisions (rather than from a cost or value model). Half a dozen test cases are used to illustrate and test these ideas (theory). Some rationale about decision making in organizations and criteria surfaces is supplied to help interpret the major ideas presented.

This paper reports some research in managerial decision making, as well as the ideas and a theory stemming from this research. Presented

[1] *Management Science*, January, 1963. Reprinted by permission.

[2] Draft of a paper given at the Conference on Factory Scheduling at Carnegie Institute's Graduate School of Industrial Administration, May 12, 1961.

[3] Yale University. The research underlying this paper was in part sponsored by the MIT Operations Research Center contract with the Army Office of Ordnance Research (DA-19-020-ORD-2684) and the MIT School of Industrial Management Sloan Research Fund. A number of graduate students have helped with this research, particularly Mr. Howard Kunreuther.

here is a combination of description and prescription. It combines the talents of the manager with those of the analyst in a method and in a theory. The method is pragmatic rather than utopian in that it offers one way of starting with the managers' actual decisions and building on them to reach a better system.

A referee has summarized this paper as follows: "that managerial decisions might be improved more by making them more consistent from one time to another than by approaches purporting to give 'optimal solutions' to explicit cost models . . . especially for problems where intangibles (run-out costs, delay penalties) must otherwise be estimated or assumed." Though this is a normative statement, it is derived from a number of descriptive concepts (about the world in which we live) which may be of equal interest.

The paper is organized essentially in the sequence in which the research was performed and the ideas generated. The problems, research, and decision rules of production scheduling are set forth first. They introduce the cause of this paper. Next, the approach of using management's own past decisions in order to improve present decisions is described. The theory is then set forth in a more general form, after which several additional empirical tests of the theory are described. Finally, the ideas are summarized. Further questions of validity, generality, and operationality must be answered by future research.

PRODUCTION SCHEDULING DECISION RULES

The research which led up to the more basic ideas presented here dealt with the general problem of production and employment scheduling. This work is set forth in some detail in order to convey the spirit of the research.

A very simple decision rule for production scheduling might be:

$$P_t = S_t$$

where P_t represents production scheduled in time period t, and S_t represents sales expected in time period t. In this case production would match all fluctuations up and down in sales, and the rule might not be considered a very good one. An extension might be:

$$P_t = S_t + x(P_{t-1} - S_t)$$

where x is a decision rule coefficient to be specified between zero and one, and P_{t-1} represents production in the previous time period. If $x = 1$, then the sales terms cancel out, and production in this period equals production in the previous time period (i.e., with no fluctuation). A value for x between zero and one will supply a damping mechanism in this case, where production does change but not as quickly as sales.[4]

However, using this rule (where production does not necessarily match sales each period) would cause inventories to fluctuate. In order to offer some control of these inventory levels the rule may be further extended:

$$P_t = S_t + x(P_{t-1} - S_t) + y(I_N - I_{t-1})$$

where y is also a decision rule coefficient to be specified between zero and one, I_N represents a concept of "Normal" inventory (possibly an easier label than optimum inventory), and I_{t-1} represents the amount of inventory at the end of the previous period.

Because it is desirable to take into account the anticipated future sales (in the near term), the rule should be extended further:

$$P_t = \sum_{i=t}^{i=t+n} a_i \hat{S}_i + x(P_{t-1} - S_t) + y(I_N - I_{t-1})$$

$$(a_t > a_{t+1} > a_{t+2} > \cdots a_{t+n})$$

with the a_i's representing weighting coefficients of the sales forecasts, $\hat{S}_i$, for future periods.

While such a decision rule could be further extended and elaborated, this will suffice for our introduction. The production scheduling behavior of a firm following such a rule would be critically influenced by the numbers supplied for the coefficients, $a_t \ldots a_n$, x, y, and I_N (which may be conceived of as a number for the moment). Different sets of numbers in the coefficients would result in different behavior patterns through time. Some patterns would undoubtedly be preferable to others. The challenge, of course, is to determine the preferred set of coefficients. Three methods for making this determination are listed below:

1) Simulation (experimentation)
2) Analysis
3) Management Decisions

Simulation seems to require no justification at present. Many uses are being made today of this activity in universities and in industry,[5] partic-

---

[4] This rule may be converted into the more standard feed-back form:

$$P_t = P_{t-1} + (1 - x)(S_t - P_{t-1}).$$

[5] See for a large example Jay Forrester, *Industrial Dynamics* (Cambridge: MIT Press; and New York: John Wiley & Sons, Inc., 1961).

ularly where the mathematics of a more deductive solution scheme break down. Mathematical analysis may be possible even in problems as complex as this.[6] For industrial problems which are framed in less complex form mathematical analysis is not uncommon. A different source (management decisions) for these decision rule coefficients is developed later in this paper.

THE HMMS DECISION RULES

The production and employment scheduling problem faced by most manufacturing firms, where in each scheduling period both a production quantity and an employment level must be chosen, has been analysed in research work by Holt, Modigliani, Muth, and Simon (HMMS) on a paint company. Working with quadratic cost forms, and a long term scheduling horizon the following production and work force rules were derived:

$$P_t = +.463\ O_t \quad +.993\ W_{t-1} + 153 - .464\ I_{t-1}$$
$$+.234\ O_{t+1}$$
$$+.111\ O_{t+2}$$
$$\vdots \ \ O_{t+11}$$
$$W_t = +.0101\ O_t \quad +.743\ W_{t-1} + 2.09 - .010\ I_{t-1}$$
$$+.0088\ O_{t+1}$$
$$+.0071\ O_{t+2}$$
$$\vdots \ \ O_{t+11}$$

where the subscripts are time period notation, P stands for production, W for workers, O for sales orders, and I for inventory. The analyses leading to these decision rules are quite involved and will not be described here, as it is not essential to the major ideas presented in this paper. They may be found in the literature.[7]

It is important to explain, however, that the rule *and* the coefficients —the numbers .463, .993, 153, −.464,—were derived by mathematical analysis from the cost structure model of this one paint factory studied. Had the company followed these rules, the physical behavior pattern and, therefore, the costs of the behavior would have been different. The HMMS group present the following normalized summary cost data for three cases:

----

[6] See especially Holt, Modigliani, Muth and Simon, *Planning Production, Inventories, and Work Force* (Englewood Cliffs, N.J.: Prentice-Hall, Inc., 1960).

[7] "A Linear Decision Rule for Production and Employment Scheduling," by Holt, Modigliani, and Simon, *Management Science*, October, 1955; and "Derivation of a Linear Decision Rule for Production and Employment," by Holt, Modigliani, and Muth, *Management Science*, January, 1956. Reprinted as Case 6 in this book; also included in *Planning Production, Inventories, and Work Force* by Holt, Modigliani, Muth, and Simon (Englewood Cliffs, N.J.: Prentice-Hall, Inc., 1960).

PAINT COMPANY

	1949–53 (Korean War included)	1952–54
Decision Rule (perfect forecast)..................	100%	
Decision Rule (moving average forecast)...........	110%	100%
Company Performance..........................	139%	108.5%
(cost base about $3,000,000)		

Since the decision rules require estimates of future sales over the next 12 months, both the actual sales (now known and entitled perfect forecast), and a moving average forecast (entitled naive forecast) were used to reconstruct the behavior of the system over the years listed. The total costs (normalized to 100%) for the company's own behavior, and that from the decision rules, is given. It can be seen that the decision rule consistently used would have shown an appreciable cost saving.

OTHER APPLICATIONS

In our research, we applied the HMMS analysis previously cited to the production and employment scheduling problems of an ice cream company,[8] a chocolate company,[9] and a candy company.[10]

The results, in the same form as before, were as follows:

	Ice Cream	Chocolate	Candy
Decision Rule (perfect forecast)....................	100%	100%	100%
Decision Rule (moving average forecast)...........	104.9%	102.0%	103.5%
Company Performance...........................	105.4%	105.3%	111.5%
Approximate Cost Base..........................	$500,000	$150,000	$1,500,000

With less margin of improvement, it appeared that the linear decision rules, derived from the quadratic approximations to the costs structures of each firm might have resulted in the cost savings shown.

BEHAVIOR AND STATISTICAL REGRESSION

The author of the chocolate company thesis was requested to do a statistical least squares regression of the company's actual scheduling

---

[8] "An Application of a Linear Decision Rule for Production and Employment Scheduling" by Rien T. van der Velde, MIT Master's thesis, 1957.

[9] "An Empirical Study of Actual and Optimum Decision Rules for Production and Employment Scheduling," Wallace Crowston, MIT Master's thesis, 1958.

[10] Constructed from "Production and Inventory Control, Analysis of the Decision-Making Process," Clinton M. Jones, MIT Master's thesis, 1958.

behavior against the linear decision rule. He added another variable, sales contracted for the next 6 months, and used a sales level which was derived from exponentially weighted past sales. For the W_t rule he obtained a multiple correlation coefficient of $r = .971$. For the P_t rule he obtained a multiple correlation coefficient of $r = .87$. In other words, the *form* of these rules gave a pretty fair indication of the chocolate company managers' decisions. That is, the managers were sensitive to these same variables in their decision behavior.

We then did a graphical multiple regression for the candy company using these rules (with a single "sales level" figure). Again we obtained a fair correlation with the addition that more inventory was "tolerated" in the busy half of the year.

Next for all four companies—paint, ice cream, chocolate, and candy—we did a statistical least squares regression for the company management scheduling behavior on the "open form" of the decision rules, e.g.,

$$P_t = a + b_1\hat{S}_1 + b_2\hat{S}_2 + b_3\hat{S}_3 + b_4\hat{S}_4 + b_5\hat{S}_5 + b_6W_{t-1} + b_7I_{t-1}$$

These regressions gave us rather poor results. The sales estimates, $\hat{S}$, were highly correlated, and the t tests on the coefficients came out poorly.

With advice concerning regression, "Use all the good restrictions you have—you'll get better estimates," we were able to use the feedback form (modified) of the original decision rules.[11]

The versions of the decision rules developed for regression were:

$$\Delta W_t = b_1[\bar{S}_{2-4} - (\bar{S}/\bar{W})W_{t-1}] + b_2[S_t(\bar{I}/\bar{S}) - I_{t-1}] + a_1$$

$$P_t = b_3W_t + b_4[(\bar{W}/\bar{S})\bar{S}_{2-4} - W_t] + b_5[S_t(\bar{I}/\bar{S}) - I_{t-1}] + a_2$$

where W, P, and I are as given before, S_t represents actual sales in the current period, $\bar{S}_{2-4}$ represents average actual sales in the next three periods, and $\bar{S}$, $\bar{W}$, and $\bar{I}$ represent averages of these variables over the total period of investigation. These rules are a bit simpler though they follow from the feed back rules which Yance proves equivalent to the Carnegie rules. The exact form of the rules is not important for this paper, though the modification using variables which are the normalized differences between variables, e.g., $[S_t(\bar{I}/\bar{S}) - I_{t-1}]$, permitted a more meaningful regression to be made. Using these rules as the form, regressions were done for the four companies to obtain the (estimates

---

[11] The HMMS rules had been factored into feedback form by Joseph V. Yance in his unpublished paper, "Marshallian Elements in the Carnegie Tech Rules."

of) decision rule coefficients from management's actual behavior. These gave significant correlations which permitted the development described next.

COSTING THE REGRESSION RULES

With the feed back production and employment scheduling rules, and with the coefficients developed from management's own scheduling behavior, it was possible to reconstruct (simulate) the companies' scheduling behavior following these rules (with moving average forecast) as was done in the original work. The results are as shown in the table.

	Ice Cream	Chocolate	Candy	Paint
Decision Rule (perfect).....	100%	100%	100%	100%
Decision Rule (move.av.)...	104.9%	102.0%	103.3%	110%
Company Performance......	105.3%	105.3%	111.4%	139.5%
Management Coefficients....	102.3%	100.0%	124.1%[12]	124.7%[13]
Correlation	$W_t, r = .78$	$W_t, r = .57$	$W_t, r = .73$	$W_t, r = .40$
	$P_t, r = .97$	$P_t, r = .93$	$P_t, r = .86$	$P_t, r = .66$

As can be seen from the table, in all cases but the candy company, using the decision rules with the coefficients supplied by regression of management's own behavior, and a rather simple estimating scheme for future sales, the costs would have been less than the company's actual behavior. In the Ice Cream Company and the Chocolate Company, it would have been even cheaper than the decision rule derived from the standard quantitative analysis and the same sales forecasting scheme.

Several points of explanation may help. It is suspected that the somewhat surprising results of better performance with the managers' coefficients than that supplied by the analysis is due to the fact that the *analysis* is optimum only in the sense that the quadratic cost models from which the rules were derived is a perfect fit for these costs. This, of course, is not the case. It is important to keep in mind that *optimization* is always of a (mathematical) model, which hopefully bears some resemblance to important facets of the real world. The graphical multiple regression done earlier on the candy company (the refuting case here) suggests that had the split inventory policy between slack and busy times of the year been permitted in the rule, the then adjusted management coefficients rule would have been better.

---

[12] Using a perfect sales forecast would have reduced this to 112.5%.

[13] This figure must be viewed with some reservation as we were working with the publications and working papers from HMMS, not the data as such. We could not reconstruct some of their costs, and the five years are '50–'54 rather than '49–'53, though both cover the extreme years of the Korean War.

THE MANAGEMENT COEFFICIENTS THEORY

An attempt at something like an axiomatic treatment of these concepts is presented *in order to stimulate more ideas*:

1) Experienced managers are quite aware of and sensitive to the criteria of a system.

2) Experienced managers are aware of the system variables which influence these criteria.

3) Managers, in their present position through a process of natural screening, make decisions, i.e., implicitly operate decision rules, with a sense and intuition which relates the variables to the criteria imperfectly —*but more erratic than biased.*

4) Most cost or criteria surfaces as a function of the decision variables are shallow, dish-shaped at the bottom (top) and even with bias in the manager's behavior, it is the far out (variance) examples of behavior which are really expensive or damaging.

5) If manager's behavior had paralleled the decision rules with their average or mean coefficients, their experience would have been better according to the (their) criteria.

It seems useful to attempt an explanation of why decision rules derived from management's own average behavior might yield better results than the aggregate behavior itself. Man seems to respond to selective cues in his environment—particular things seem to catch his attention at times (the last telephone call), while at other times it is a different set of stimuli. Not only is this selective cueing the case, but a threshold concept seems to apply. He may respond not at all up to some point and then overrespond beyond that. It is this type of behavior which helps explain the variance in the organization's (or its management's) behavior.

Departures of the decision making behavior of management from the preferred results, in this sense then can be divided or factored into two components, one which in the manner of a grand average departing from some preferred figure, we call bias (which causes a relatively small critera loss due to the dish shaped bottom of the criteria surface), and one which representing individual occurrences of experience departing from the grand average, we call variance (which causes larger critera losses due to the individual occurrences up the sides of the criteria dish-shaped surface). It is the latter and more important component which seems to offer the tempting possibility of elimination through the use of decision rules incorporating coefficients derived from management's own recurrent behavior.

What can be done with this management coefficients theory?

1) It may yield fresh insight into a management problem or a decision process—it may lead to further ideas. (This is operational in an academic world.) [14]

  a) Several approaches to the same problem are often of benefit.
  b) Patterns of behavior variance against the decision rule may point to missed elements in the analysis.
  c) It gives us a chance to see (indirectly) the criteria through the manager's eyes (or action).

2) Sampling in the current system may be possible—e.g., with 10,000 items in inventory, maybe the managers will look carefully at 100, and make the necessary decisions for these 100; then these 100 items (along with their relevant variables) may be used in estimating the coefficients in the decision rules for the 10,000–100 items (an inventory test case is given later in the paper).

3) Balance the present system structure—e.g., with many branch plants, it may be possible to arrange a better configuration of plant sizes (a plant size test case is given later in the paper).

4) Let the manager look at the decision rule with his regression coefficients and then decide what his decision will be, e.g., run in parallel with joint feed back between manager and rules. [15]

5) Decouple the manager, but record his decisions. (This is not seriously offered as a suggestion but just to stimulate ideas). The manager has continual access to his changing environment—he makes his decisions—these are filed and this operation (e.g., production and employment scheduling) is determined by the decision rule (not his decision). Then periodically the decision rule is updated from the file of recent decisions. The idea here is to eliminate the effects of the variance in decision behavior, while at the same time permitting the decision rule to reflect the current environment.

6) If the theory can be verified where it is felt that the system

---

[14] Harlow Shapely, the Harvard astronomer, in reviewing *The Universe at Large* by Hermann Bondi, includes "It is not the purpose of any scientific theory," wisely remarks Dr. Bondi, "to be infallible or final or true. Its purpose is to be fertile; to suggest new observations that suggest new ramifications of the subject."

[15] March and Simon, *Organizations* (New York: John Wiley & Sons, Inc., 1958), p. 209, state: ". . . since there is no reason to suppose that *any* technique of decision-making, whether centralized or decentralized, will bring the organization into the neighborhood of a genuine 'optimum', the search for decision mechanisms cannot take criteria of optimization too seriously, but must seek 'workable' techniques for satisficing. The exploration of decision-making techniques along these lines is still in a very undeveloped state . . . A number of decision rules for production control and scheduling decisions in individual firms have been developed—but again with only small forays beyond the familiar terrain of optimization." The new theory departs a bit from this familiar terrain.

criteria can be measured (as in the cases presented in this paper), then some assurance might exist for using it where the criteria can't be measured.[16]

7) Automatic decision making (by computer) to save executive time will require decision rules with coefficients—these may be supplied by regression.

8) At the bounds of analysis, the new theory may help structure the system. Where aggregation is used in the analysis and the question is raised as to what happens when the clerk breaks open the aggregate, rules with regression coefficients can be supplied.

The management coefficients theory is, of course, not without its problems. It may kill the goose that lays the golden eggs. The manager may follow the rule with his past (average) coefficients, and not adjust to new conditions as they take place. March and Simon[17] make the distinction between a) short run adaptation as problem solving (here, using the decision rule as fulcrum), and b) long run adaptation as learning (here, using the manager to modify decision rules). The problem is how to bypass (a) without inhibiting (b).

PLANT SIZE

As an additional check on the theory presented here an analysis described in the *Operations Research* journal[18] was reexamined. The study concerned the question of the optimum size ice cream plant for a particular company operating ten plants over a seven state area. For purposes here, the analysis need not be repeated, but it led up to a decision rule for the optimum volume plant:

$$V_{opt} = (K)^{1/3}(2b/c)^{2/3}$$

where K was the sales density in thousand gallons per square mile (per year), and b and c were particular cost factors relevant to the ice cream production and distribution system. Had the system been restructured

---

[16] Herbert Simon in *The New Science of Management Decision* (New York: Harper & Bros., 1961), makes several statements relevant to this idea. If the new theory offers anything then the first quotation is not necessarily true—p. 17, (talking about operations research) ". . . The model will call for certain parameters of its structure (the system) to be estimated before it can be applied in a particular situation. Hence, it is necessary that there be ways of making actual numerical estimates of these parameters (he is talking about the system not the decision rules derived therefrom) of sufficient accuracy for the practical task at hand."

The second quotation, however, is cited for reinforcement here—p. 18. "For the operations research approach to work, nothing has to be exact—it just has to be close enough to give better results than could be obtained by common sense without the mathematics."

[17] March and Simon, *op. cit.*, p. 170.

[18] E. H. Bowman, "Scale of Operations—An Empirical Study," *Journal of the Operations Research Society of America*, May–June, 1958. Case 11 in this book.

according to the analysis and decision rule, gross cost savings appeared to be available. These along with the results of the new theory are presented in the table.

		Savings
Original	$V_{opt} = (K)^{1/3}(2b/c)^{2/3}$	\$207,000
Regression (first model)	$V = (K)^{1/3} d_1$	\$133,000
Regression (naive model)	$V = a + d_2K$	\$ 20,000

Using the same decision rule form (with $(K)^{1/3}$ as the independent variable and permitting no intercept, $a = O$), the company's actual plant volumes were used to estimate d_1, the decision rule coefficient. Had the plant system then been restructured using their own (behavior) coefficient in the decision rule, the projected gross cost savings would be \$133,000.

For test purposes a naive decision rule, $V = a + d_2K$, was used in the same manner—it included the relevant variable, sales density, but not to the "right" power, as well as permitting an intercept a. Here a and d_2 were estimated from the actual plants, and as can be seen the savings are quite small. In other words, *any old decision rule will not do.* It is certain that the most simple, $V = \bar{V}$, i.e., have all plants the average size, would have been more costly for the firm than the present arrangement.

It is interesting to note that the naive rule actually gave a better fit to the data. While it is the cost savings rather than the good fit which is the choice here, if a collaboration were now in existence between the analyst and the managers, this point would be worthy of discussion and reflection for both parties. That is, the new theory might be a very useful part of a more general analytic procedure, rather than being *directly* prescriptive.

KENNEDY AIRCRAFT SPARES

A further check was made on the new theory using the basic work of a thesis[19] dealing with a spare parts inventory maintained at Kennedy Airport. Waiting line theory had been used for the inventory analysis with an n channel service facility for n pieces of an item. An idle channel corresponded to an item in stock; a busy channel corresponded to an empty space; no queues were allowed.

---

[19] Giyora Doeh, "Overhauled Spares Inventory for Aircraft Components," MIT Master's thesis, 1958.

For the management coefficients theory test, an extremely simple decision rule was developed:[20]

$$\text{Spares} = a + bx$$

$$x = \frac{\text{usage during repair cycle}}{\text{unit price of item}}$$

The thesis studied in some detail ten stock items of widely scattered characteristics. For our purposes, the results are shown below.

	Company Actual	Thesis Analysis	New Theory
Investment	$17,000	$16,000	$16,500
Stock-outs in 6 years	186	69	143

From this small sample, at least, the simple decision ruled with the coefficients (a and b) would have saved half as much investment and one third as many run outs as the analysis. No more detailed analysis was made here.

OTHER APPLICATIONS

In a very detailed study of equipment replacement policies in the trucking industry,[21] a number of conclusions supporting ideas presented here are found. A well accepted model[22] was used with empirical data from industry studies. The following items were determined:

A. Estimates of obsolescence
   a) carrying capacity of trailer
   b) internal combustion engine technology
B. Estimates of operating cost
   a) fuel
   b) maintenance

---

[20] For an incremental approach:
  Δ Cost = Δ Gain
  Unit Cost = (Δ prob)(run out cost)
  Let Δ prob α (1/spares) (usage), with tail of hyperbola a rough approximation to tail of poisson distribution.
  Then, Unit Cost α (usage/spares) (run out cost) and Spares α (usage/unit cost) (run out cost)

[21] Vernon Smith, "Economic Equipment Policies: An Evaluation," *Management Science*, October, 1957.

[22] $V = \displaystyle\sum_{K=0}^{\infty} e^{-pkl} \left\{ \int^{L} Q(KL, t)e^{-pt}\, dt - p + S(L)e^{-pL} \right\}$

The study resulted in very flat curves of total yearly average value as a function of equipment life. Replacement anywhere between 2.2 years and 4.4 years will lead to losses of at most $50 short of "exact" optimum. Smith reports:

"This is a remarkable result especially when one considers that on the average about ⅔ of the total investment of trucking firms is in the form of trucking equipment (i.e., capital goods of intermediate durability requiring regular maintenance). It would seem that this of all industries would find equipment *replacement* policies of considerable importance, yet precision in such policies turns out to be of minor significance. It is not argued that it makes no difference when equipment is replaced. Rather the point is that profits are not sufficiently sensitive to replacement that the firm is likely to miss the optimum by a costly margin even when using relatively crude methods of analysis."

He also states that an optimum service period of 3 to 4 years is about 1 to 2 years shorter than the actual replacement behavior of the firm in question.

He then goes on to explain that delayed replacement in effect is a relatively cheap source of capital for this firm. This is equivalent to saying that the management senses a somewhat different criteria surface than his analysis explicitly considers. Regression of behavior should permit this sensing to be incorporated in the decision rule.

A good deal of interest today seems to exist in heuristics and management problem solving. While these processes may be largely programmatic and qualitative, some coefficients are embedded therein. The question of how far to go down some path or how many of these parts to combine may still require parameters. Where this is so, observation and regression of experienced problem solvers may be helpful.

For a case in point, a thesis student has been working on heuristics for a dispatching rule to be associated with a key process in an aircraft plant. The question involves the order in which waiting parts should proceed through the equipment. He has identified four characteristics (e.g., cost, due date) of the parts which are relevant for this sequencing (dispatching). He needs coefficients to weight these characteristics. Simulation had already occurred to him. He agreed that analysis, at least conceptually, might be possible. The new theory suggests to him that he might obtain from the shop the actual dispatching decisions by the men directly involved on a long list of parts along with their characteristics in order to do a regression for the weighting coefficients.

The management coefficients theory says something about the behavior of managers and their organizations. There seems to be no apparent reason why these ideas should apply to production only and not marketing or industrial organizations only and not governmental, or even microeconomic problems only and not macroeconomic as well. But, perhaps this overstates the case.

SUMMARY

The gist of the management coefficients theory is a relatively simple notion:

a) In their decision making behavior, managers and/or their organizations can be *conceived* of as decision rule coefficient estimators, (not that they explicitly *are* coefficient estimators).

b) It is the variance in the decision making rather than the bias that hurts due to dish-shaped criteria surfaces.

c) A decision rule with mean coefficients estimated from management's behavior should be better than actual performance.

d) It may be better than a rule with coefficients supplied by traditional analysis.

e) Systematic and comparative studies using this idea may lead to further ideas.

APPENDIXES

I. Glossary of Symbols

A	Arrival rate to some servicing facility.
α	Producer's risk or probability of an error of the first kind (rejection of null hypothesis when true).
AOQ	Average outgoing quality.
$AOQL$	Average outgoing quality limit.
AQL	Acceptable quality level.
ASN	Average sample number.
A_2	Control chart factor giving limits on $\bar{x}$ (see Table F in Appendix).
B	In-place value of a piece of equipment.
β	Consumer's risk or probability of an error of the second kind (acceptance of null hypothesis when not true).
b_j	Amount of jth capacity available.
C	Cost.
C_d	Cost of a defect per unit.
C_i	Cost of inspection per unit.
C_m	Machine cost.
C_o	Cost of output.
C_s	Cost of service.
C_1	Cost of an error of the first kind.
C_2	Cost of an error of the second kind.
c	Number of columns in an analysis of variance.
c, c_a	Acceptance number (number of defects which will accept the null hypothesis).
c'	Number of defects in a sample.
D_3	Control chart factor giving lower limit on R (see Table F in the Appendix).
D_4	Control chart factor giving upper limit on R.
d_2	Expected value of relative range (see w).
ΔC	Incremental cost.
ΔG	Incremental gain.
ϵ	Amount of artificial quantity used to fill up a route in order to resolve degeneracy in transportation method of linear programming.
$E(x)$	Expected value of x.
E_t	Annual expense.
$E(t)$	Expenses incurred in operating equipment (rate).
e	$2.71828+ =$ base of natural logs.
F	Variance ratio for Snedecor's test $= \dfrac{s_{x_1}{}^2 \sigma_{x_2}{}^2}{s_{x_2}{}^2 \sigma_{x_1}{}^2}$.

F_i	Fixed cost per sample.
G	Annual change in expenses.
G_i	Number of items to be produced in an inspection interval, i.
g	Number of items per cell in analysis of variance.
h_1, h_2	Zero ordinates in number of defects for sequential sampling.
I	Carrying charges per unit per year in economic lot calculations.
I	Number of items inspected per lot.
i	Interest rate in per cent per year.
k	Standard normal deviate.
k	Servicing constant.
k	Inspection interval.
k_d	Cost of an undetected defect.
k_e	Cost of mistakenly inferring that the process has changed to some state when it has not.
k_i	Cost of inspection per piece.
λ	Lagrange multiplier.
LCL_p	Lower control limit for fraction defective.
LCL_R	Lower control limit for range.
$LCL_{\bar{x}}$	Lower control limit for $\bar{x}$.
$LTFD$	Lot tolerance fraction defective.
$M_{T'}$	Overhaul cost at time T'.
m	Machine running time per time unit.
m	Expected number of defects per unit.
N	Number of inspection intervals per period.
N	Number of units assigned to a service facility.
N, n	Number of items in a sample.
P	"Pay-off" period for an investment.
P_a	Probability of acceptance.
P_{aj}	Probability of acceptance in the jth state.
P_i	Profit per unit of ith product.
P_j	Probability of jth state.
$Pr(x)$	Probability of x.
$P(x)$	Probability of an event up to x (between 0 and x).
$P(X\|\mu)$	Probability of x given μ.
$P_\text{I}\|k$	Probability of inferring the process has changed when it has not given k.
$P_{\text{II}-j}$	Probability of failing to detect a change to jth state given k.
p	Estimate of process average based on a sample.
p_j	Fraction defective in jth state.
$p(x)$	Probability of an event x (between x and $x + dx$).
p_1	Acceptable quality level.
p_2	Lot tolerance fraction defective.
p'	Process average.
$\bar{p}$	Fraction defective of an inspection lot of size n.
π	Stockout cost per unit demanded but not available.
Q	Lot size in economic lot size calculations.
Q_t	Annual earnings.
$Q(t)$	Earnings of an investment (rate).

R	Annual usage of an item.
R	Range of a sample.
R_t	Annual revenue.
$R(t)$	Revenue earned by an investment (rate).
$\bar{R}$	Average range.
r	Coefficient of correlation.
r	Number of rows in an analysis of variance.
r	Reorder point.
r^2	Coefficient of determination.
S	Lot size in sampling inspection.
S	Setup cost in economic lot calculations.
S	Servicing rate in waiting-line theory.
$\hat{S}_i$	Sales forecast for period i.
$S(T)$	Salvage value of an investment at time T.
$S'(T)$	First derivative of $S(T)$ with respect to T.
s	Servicing time per time unit.
s	Slope of reject, accept lines in sequential sampling.
s_c	Estimate of standard deviation of defects-per-unit.
s_p	Estimate of standard deviation of fraction defective.
s_R	Estimate of standard deviation of a population of ranges.
s_x	Estimate of population standard deviation based on a sample.
s_x^2	Estimate of population variance based on a sample.
$s_{\bar{x}}$	Estimate of standard deviation of a population of means.
s_s	Estimate of standard deviation of a population of standard deviations.
σ_c	Standard deviation of defects-per-unit.
σ_p	Standard deviation of fraction defective.
σ_R	Standard deviation of a population of ranges.
σ_s	Standard deviation of a population of standard deviations.
σ_x	Population standard deviation.
$\sigma_{\bar{x}}$	Standard deviation of a population of means.
T	Life of a piece of equipment.
TC	Total cost.
TVC	Total variable cost.
t_{ij}	Time to produce ith product on jth capacity.
U	Usage during lead time.
UCL_p	Upper control limit for fraction defective.
UCL_R	Upper control limit for range.
$UCL_{\bar{x}}$	Upper control limit for $\bar{x}$.
μ	Population mean.
$\mu_{\bar{x}}$	Mean of a population of means.
V	Present worth of return on investment.
V	Variable cost.
v_i	Value of an event if it occurs.
var( )	Variance of variable in parentheses.
W	Annual warehousing cost per unit stored.
w	Waiting time per time unit.
w	Relative range (R/σ_x).
x_i	Amount of ith product.

x_i	Value of a variable.
$\bar{x}$	Mean of a set of values of a variable.
$\bar{\bar{x}}$	Estimate of the mean of a population of means.
Z	Profit.
Z	Difference between two means in standard deviation units.
$\left[\dfrac{a}{b}\right]$	Largest integer value which includes the quotient a/b.

II. Tables

TABLE A

Cumulative Probabilities of the Normal Probability Distribution*
(Areas under the Normal Curve from $-\infty$ to z)

z	.00	.01	.02	.03	.04	.05	.06	.07	.08	.09
.0	.5000	.5040	.5080	.5120	.5160	.5199	.5239	.5279	.5319	.5359
.1	.5398	.5438	.5478	.5517	.5557	.5596	.5636	.5675	.5714	.5753
.2	.5793	.5832	.5871	.5910	.5948	.5987	.6026	.6064	.6103	.6141
.3	.6179	.6217	.6255	.6293	.6331	.6368	.6406	.6443	.6480	.6517
.4	.6554	.6591	.6628	.6664	.6700	.6736	.6772	.6808	.6844	.6879
.5	.6915	.6950	.6985	.7019	.7054	.7088	.7123	.7157	.7190	.7224
.6	.7257	.7291	.7324	.7357	.7389	.7422	.7454	.7486	.7517	.7549
.7	.7580	.7611	.7642	.7673	.7704	.7734	.7764	.7794	.7823	.7852
.8	.7881	.7910	.7939	.7967	.7995	.8023	.8051	.8078	.8106	.8133
.9	.8159	.8186	.8212	.8238	.8264	.8289	.8315	.8340	.8365	.8389
1.0	.8413	.8438	.8461	.8485	.8508	.8531	.8554	.8577	.8599	.8621
1.1	.8643	.8665	.8686	.8708	.8729	.8749	.8770	.8790	.8810	.8830
1.2	.8849	.8869	.8888	.8907	.8925	.8944	.8962	.8980	.8997	.9015
1.3	.9032	.9049	.9066	.9082	.9099	.9115	.9131	.9147	.9162	.9177
1.4	.9192	.9207	.9222	.9236	.9251	.9265	.9279	.9292	.9306	.9319
1.5	.9332	.9345	.9357	.9370	.9382	.9394	.9406	.9418	.9429	.9441
1.6	.9452	.9463	.9474	.9484	.9495	.9505	.9515	.9525	.9535	.9545
1.7	.9554	.9564	.9573	.9582	.9591	.9599	.9608	.9616	.9625	.9633
1.8	.9641	.9649	.9656	.9664	.9671	.9678	.9686	.9693	.9699	.9706
1.9	.9713	.9719	.9726	.9732	.9738	.9744	.9750	.9756	.9761	.9767
2.0	.9772	.9778	.9783	.9788	.9793	.9798	.9803	.9808	.9812	.9817
2.1	.9821	.9826	.9830	.9834	.9838	.9842	.9846	.9850	.9854	.9857
2.2	.9861	.9864	.9868	.9871	.9875	.9878	.9881	.9884	.9887	.9890
2.3	.9893	.9896	.9898	.9901	.9904	.9906	.9909	.9911	.9913	.9916
2.4	.9918	.9920	.9922	.9925	.9927	.9929	.9931	.9932	.9934	.9936
2.5	.9938	.9940	.9941	.9943	.9945	.9946	.9948	.9949	.9951	.9952
2.6	.9953	.9955	.9956	.9957	.9959	.9960	.9961	.9962	.9963	.9964
2.7	.9965	.9966	.9967	.9968	.9969	.9970	.9971	.9972	.9973	.9974
2.8	.9974	.9975	.9976	.9977	.9977	.9978	.9979	.9979	.9980	.9981
2.9	.9981	.9982	.9982	.9983	.9984	.9984	.9985	.9985	.9986	.9986
3.0	.9987	.9987	.9987	.9988	.9988	.9989	.9989	.9989	.9990	.9990
3.1	.9990	.9991	.9991	.9991	.9992	.9992	.9992	.9992	.9993	.9993
3.2	.9993	.9993	.9994	.9994	.9994	.9994	.9994	.9995	.9995	.9995
3.3	.9995	.9995	.9995	.9996	.9996	.9996	.9996	.9996	.9996	.9997
3.4	.9997	.9997	.9997	.9997	.9997	.9997	.9997	.9997	.9997	.9998

z	1.282	1.645	1.960	2.326	2.576	3.090	3.291	3.891	4.417
F (z)	.90	.95	.975	.99	.995	.999	.9995	.99995	.999995
2[1 - F(z)]	.20	.10	.05	.02	.01	.002	.001	.0001	.00001

* Table A is reprinted with permission from A. M. Mood, *Introduction to the Theory of Statistics* (New York: McGraw-Hill Book Co., Inc., 1950), p. 423.

TABLE B

PERCENTAGE POINTS OF THE χ^2 DISTRIBUTION*

EACH entry is a per cent point of χ^2. It is exceeded by the proportion (P) of values of χ^2 listed in the column heading for the number of degrees of freedom (n) given in the stub.

n	$P=.99$	.98	.95	.90	.80	.70	.50	.30	.20	.10	.05	.02	.01
1	.000157	.000628	.00393	.0158	.0642	.148	.455	1.074	1.642	2.706	3.841	5.412	6.635
2	.0201	.0404	.103	.211	.446	.713	1.386	2.408	3.219	4.605	5.991	7.824	9.210
3	.115	.185	.352	.584	1.005	1.424	2.366	3.665	4.642	6.251	7.815	9.837	11.345
4	.297	.429	.711	1.064	1.649	2.195	3.357	4.878	5.989	7.779	9.488	11.668	13.277
5	.554	.752	1.145	1.610	2.343	3.000	4.351	6.064	7.289	9.236	11.070	13.388	15.086
6	.872	1.134	1.635	2.204	3.070	3.828	5.348	7.231	8.558	10.645	12.592	15.033	16.812
7	1.239	1.564	2.167	2.833	3.822	4.671	6.346	8.383	9.803	12.017	14.067	16.622	18.475
8	1.646	2.032	2.733	3.490	4.594	5.527	7.344	9.524	11.030	13.362	15.507	18.168	20.090
9	2.088	2.532	3.325	4.168	5.380	6.393	8.343	10.656	12.242	14.684	16.919	19.679	21.666
10	2.558	3.059	3.940	4.865	6.179	7.267	9.342	11.781	13.442	15.987	18.307	21.161	23.209
11	3.053	3.609	4.575	5.578	6.989	8.148	10.341	12.899	14.631	17.275	19.675	22.618	24.725
12	3.571	4.178	5.226	6.304	7.807	9.034	11.340	14.011	15.812	18.549	21.026	24.054	26.217
13	4.107	4.765	5.892	7.042	8.634	9.926	12.340	15.119	16.985	19.812	22.362	25.472	27.688
14	4.660	5.368	6.571	7.790	9.467	10.821	13.339	16.222	18.151	21.064	23.685	26.873	29.141
15	5.229	5.985	7.261	8.547	10.307	11.721	14.339	17.322	19.311	22.307	24.996	28.259	30.578
16	5.812	6.614	7.962	9.312	11.152	12.624	15.338	18.418	20.465	23.542	26.296	29.633	32.000
17	6.408	7.255	8.672	10.085	12.002	13.531	16.338	19.511	21.615	24.769	27.587	30.995	33.409
18	7.015	7.906	9.390	10.865	12.857	14.440	17.338	20.601	22.760	25.989	28.869	32.346	34.805
19	7.633	8.567	10.117	11.651	13.716	15.352	18.338	21.689	23.900	27.204	30.144	33.687	36.191
20	8.260	9.237	10.851	12.443	14.578	16.266	19.337	22.775	25.038	28.412	31.410	35.020	37.566
21	8.897	9.915	11.591	13.240	15.445	17.182	20.337	23.858	26.171	29.615	32.671	36.343	38.932
22	9.542	10.600	12.338	14.041	16.314	18.101	21.337	24.939	27.301	30.813	33.924	37.659	40.289
23	10.196	11.293	13.091	14.848	17.187	19.021	22.337	26.018	28.429	32.007	35.172	38.968	41.638
24	10.856	11.992	13.848	15.659	18.062	19.943	23.337	27.096	29.553	33.196	36.415	40.270	42.980
25	11.524	12.697	14.611	16.473	18.940	20.867	24.337	28.172	30.675	34.382	37.652	41.566	44.314
26	12.198	13.409	15.379	17.292	19.820	21.792	25.336	29.246	31.795	35.563	38.885	42.856	45.642
27	12.879	14.125	16.151	18.114	20.703	22.719	26.336	30.319	32.912	36.741	40.113	44.140	46.963
28	13.565	14.847	16.928	18.939	21.588	23.647	27.336	31.391	34.027	37.916	41.337	45.419	48.278
29	14.256	15.574	17.708	19.768	22.475	24.577	28.336	32.461	35.139	39.087	42.557	46.693	49.588
30	14.953	16.306	18.493	20.599	23.364	25.508	29.336	33.530	36.250	40.256	43.773	47.962	50.892

For larger values of n, the expression $\sqrt{2\chi^2} - \sqrt{2n-1}$ may be used as a normal deviate with unit variance.

* Reprinted from Table III, pp. 112–13, of R. A. Fisher, *Statistical Methods for Research Workers* (11th ed.), published by Oliver and Boyd, Ltd, Edinburgh, by permission of author and publishers.

TABLE C

PERCENTAGE POINTS OF THE t DISTRIBUTION*

(Probabilities refer to the sum of the two-tail areas. For a single tail divide the probability by 2)

Probability (P).

n	·9	·8	·7	·6	·5	·4	·3	·2	·1	·05	·02	·01	·001
1	·158	·325	·510	·727	1·000	1·376	1·963	3·078	6·314	12·706	31·821	63·657	636·619
2	·142	·289	·445	·617	·816	1·061	1·386	1·886	2·920	4·303	6·965	9·925	31·598
3	·137	·277	·424	·584	·765	·978	1·250	1·638	2·353	3·182	4·541	5·841	12·941
4	·134	·271	·414	·569	·741	·941	1·190	1·533	2·132	2·776	3·747	4·604	8·610
5	·132	·267	·408	·559	·727	·920	1·156	1·476	2·015	2·571	3·365	4·032	6·859
6	·131	·265	·404	·553	·718	·906	1·134	1·440	1·943	2·447	3·143	3·707	5·959
7	·130	·263	·402	·549	·711	·896	1·119	1·415	1·895	2·365	2·998	3·499	5·405
8	·130	·262	·399	·546	·706	·889	1·108	1·397	1·860	2·306	2·896	3·355	5·041
9	·129	·261	·398	·543	·703	·883	1·100	1·383	1·833	2·262	2·821	3·250	4·781
10	·129	·260	·397	·542	·700	·879	1·093	1·372	1·812	2·228	2·764	3·169	4·587
11	·129	·260	·396	·540	·697	·876	1·088	1·363	1·796	2·201	2·718	3·106	4·437
12	·128	·259	·395	·539	·695	·873	1·083	1·356	1·782	2·179	2·681	3·055	4·318
13	·128	·259	·394	·538	·694	·870	1·079	1·350	1·771	2·160	2·650	3·012	4·221
14	·128	·258	·393	·537	·692	·868	1·076	1.345	1·761	2·145	2·624	2·977	4·140
15	·128	·258	·393	·536	·691	·866	1·074	1·341	1·753	2·131	2·602	2·947	4·073
16	·128	·258	·392	·535	·690	·865	1·071	1·337	1·746	2·120	2·583	2·921	4·015
17	·128	·257	·392	·534	·689	·863	1·069	1·333	1·740	2·110	2·567	2·898	3·965
18	·127	·257	·392	·534	·688	·862	1·067	1·330	1·734	2·101	2·552	2·878	3·922
19	·127	·257	·391	·533	·688	·861	1·066	1·328	1·729	2·093	2·539	2·861	3·883
20	·127	·257	·391	·533	·687	·860	1·064	1·325	1·725	2·086	2·528	2·845	3·850
21	·127	·257	·391	·532	·686	·859	1·063	1·323	1·721	2·080	2·518	2·831	3·819
22	·127	·256	·390	·532	·686	·858	1·061	1·321	1·717	2·074	2·508	2·819	3·792
23	·127	·256	·390	·532	·685	·858	1·060	1·319	1·714	2·069	2·500	2·807	3·767
24	·127	·256	·390	·531	·685	·857	1·059	1·318	1·711	2·064	2·492	2·797	3·745
25	·127	·256	·390	·531	·684	·856	1·058	1·316	1·708	2·060	2·485	2·787	3·725
26	·127	·256	·390	·531	·684	·856	1·058	1·315	1·706	2·056	2·479	2·779	3·707
27	·127	·256	·389	·531	·684	·855	1·057	1·314	1·703	2·052	2·473	2·771	3·690
28	·127	·256	·389	·530	·683	·855	1·056	1·313	1·701	2·048	2·467	2·763	3·674
29	·127	·256	·389	·530	·683	·854	1·055	1·311	1·699	2·045	2·462	2·756	3·659
30	·127	·256	·389	·530	·683	·854	1·055	1·310	1·697	2·042	2·457	2·750	3·646
40	·126	·255	·388	·529	·681	·851	1·050	1·303	1·684	2·021	2·423	2·704	3·551
60	·126	·254	·387	·527	·679	·848	1·046	1·296	1·671	2·000	2·390	2·660	3·460
120	·126	·254	·386	·526	·677	·845	1·041	1·289	1·658	1·980	2·358	2·617	3·373
∞	·126	·253	·385	·524	·674	·842	1·036	1·282	1·645	1·960	2·326	2·576	3·291

* Table C is reprinted from Table III of R. A. Fisher and F. Yates, *Statistical Tables for Biological, Agricultural and Medical Research* published by Oliver & Boyd, Ltd., Edinburgh, by permission of the authors and publishers.

TABLE D

PERCENTAGE POINTS OF THE DISTRIBUTION OF THE RELATIVE RANGE $w = R/\sigma'$, NORMAL UNIVERSE*

N	Mean w or d_2	σ_w'	Probability That w Is Less than or Equal to Tabular Entry									
			0.001	0.005	0.010	0.025	0.050	0.950	0.975	0.990	0.995	0.999
2	1.128	0.8525	0.00	0.01	0.02	0.04	0.09	2.77	3.17	3.64	3.97	4.65
3	1.693	0.8884	0.06	0.13	0.19	0.30	0.43	3.31	3.68	4.12	4.42	5.06
4	2.059	0.8798	0.20	0.34	0.43	0.59	0.76	3.63	3.98	4.40	4.69	5.31
5	2.326	0.8641	0.37	0.55	0.66	0.85	1.03	3.86	4.20	4.60	4.89	5.48
6	2.534	0.8480	0.54	0.75	0.87	1.06	1.25	4.03	4.36	4.76	5.03	5.62
7	2.704	0.833	0.69	0.92	1.05	1.25	1.44	4.17	4.49	4.88	5.15	5.73
8	2.847	0.820	0.83	1.08	1.20	1.41	1.60	4.29	4.61	4.99	5.26	5.82
9	2.970	0.808	0.96	1.21	1.34	1.55	1.74	4.39	4.70	5.08	5.34	5.90
10	3.078	0.797	1.08	1.33	1.47	1.67	1.86	4.47	4.79	5.16	5.42	5.97
11	3.173	0.787	1.20	1.45	1.58	1.78	1.97	4.55	4.86	5.23	5.49	6.04
12	3.258	0.778	1.30	1.55	1.68	1.88	2.07	4.62	4.92	5.29	5.54	6.09

* Probabilities reproduced with permission from E. S. Pearson, "The Probability Integral of the Range in Samples of N Observations from a Normal Population," *Biometrika*, Vol. XXXII (1941–42), pp. 301–8. Mean and σ' reproduced with permission from E. S. Pearson, "The Percentage Limits for the Distribution of Range in Samples from a Normal Population," *Biometrika*, Vol. XXIV (1932), pp. 404–17.

847

TABLE E
PERCENTAGE POINTS OF THE F DISTRIBUTION

EACH entry is the per cent point of F which is exceeded by the proportion of values of F listed at the head of its column for degrees of freedom n_1 listed in the major caption and n_2 listed in the stub.

n_2	$n_1 = 1$			$n_1 = 2$			$n_1 = 3$			$n_1 = 4$			$n_1 = 5$		
	.05	.01	.001	.05	.01	.001	.05	.01	.001	.05	.01	.001	.05	.01	.001
1	161.45	4,052.2	405,284	199.50	4,999.5	500,000	215.71	5,403.3	540,379	224.58	5,624.6	562,500	230.16	5,763.7	576,405
2	18.513	98.503	998.5	19.000	99.000	999.0	19.164	99.166	999.2	19.247	99.249	999.2	19.296	99.299	999.3
3	10.128	34.116	167.5	9.552	30.817	148.5	9.277	29.457	141.1	9.117	28.710	137.1	9.014	28.237	134.6
4	7.709	21.198	74.14	6.944	18.000	61.25	6.591	16.694	56.18	6.388	15.977	53.44	6.256	15.522	51.71
5	6.608	16.258	47.04	5.786	13.274	36.61	5.410	12.060	33.20	5.192	11.392	31.09	5.050	10.967	29.75
6	5.987	13.745	35.51	5.143	10.925	27.00	4.757	9.779	23.70	4.534	9.148	21.90	4.387	8.746	20.81
7	5.591	12.246	29.22	4.737	9.547	21.69	4.347	8.451	18.77	4.120	7.847	17.19	3.972	7.460	16.21
8	5.318	11.259	25.42	4.459	8.649	18.49	4.066	7.591	15.83	3.838	7.006	14.39	3.688	6.632	13.49
9	5.117	10.561	22.86	4.256	8.022	16.39	3.863	6.992	13.90	3.633	6.422	12.56	3.482	6.057	11.71
10	4.965	10.044	21.04	4.103	7.559	14.91	3.708	6.552	12.55	3.478	5.994	11.28	3.326	5.636	10.48
11	4.844	9.646	19.69	3.982	7.206	13.81	3.587	6.217	11.56	3.357	5.663	10.35	3.204	5.316	9.58
12	4.747	9.330	18.64	3.885	6.927	12.97	3.490	5.953	10.80	3.259	5.412	9.63	3.106	5.064	8.89
13	4.667	9.074	17.81	3.806	6.701	12.31	3.410	5.739	10.21	3.179	5.205	9.07	3.025	4.862	8.35
14	4.600	8.862	17.14	3.739	6.515	11.78	3.344	5.564	9.73	3.112	5.035	8.62	2.958	4.695	7.92
15	4.543	8.683	16.59	3.682	6.359	11.34	3.287	5.417	9.34	3.056	4.893	8.25	2.901	4.556	7.57
16	4.494	8.531	16.12	3.634	6.226	10.97	3.239	5.292	9.00	3.007	4.773	7.94	2.852	4.437	7.27
17	4.451	8.400	15.72	3.592	6.112	10.66	3.197	5.185	8.73	2.965	4.669	7.68	2.810	4.336	7.02
18	4.414	8.285	15.38	3.555	6.013	10.39	3.160	5.092	8.49	2.928	4.579	7.46	2.773	4.248	6.81
19	4.381	8.185	15.08	3.522	5.926	10.16	3.127	5.010	8.28	2.895	4.500	7.26	2.740	4.171	6.61
20	4.351	8.096	14.82	3.493	5.849	9.95	3.098	4.938	8.10	2.866	4.431	7.10	2.711	4.103	6.46
21	4.325	8.017	14.59	3.467	5.780	9.77	3.072	4.874	7.94	2.840	4.369	6.95	2.685	4.042	6.32
22	4.301	7.945	14.38	3.443	5.719	9.61	3.049	4.817	7.80	2.817	4.313	6.81	2.661	3.988	6.19
23	4.279	7.881	14.19	3.422	5.664	9.47	3.028	4.765	7.67	2.795	4.264	6.69	2.640	3.939	6.08
24	4.260	7.823	14.03	3.403	5.614	9.34	3.009	4.718	7.55	2.776	4.218	6.59	2.621	3.895	5.98
25	4.242	7.770	13.88	3.385	5.568	9.22	2.991	4.676	7.45	2.759	4.177	6.49	2.603	3.855	5.88
26	4.225	7.721	13.74	3.369	5.526	9.12	2.975	4.637	7.36	2.743	4.140	6.41	2.587	3.818	5.80
27	4.210	7.677	13.61	3.354	5.488	9.02	2.960	4.601	7.27	2.728	4.106	6.33	2.572	3.785	5.73
28	4.196	7.636	13.50	3.340	5.453	8.93	2.947	4.568	7.19	2.714	4.074	6.25	2.558	3.754	5.66
29	4.183	7.598	13.39	3.328	5.421	8.85	2.934	4.538	7.12	2.701	4.045	6.19	2.545	3.725	5.59
30	4.171	7.563	13.29	3.316	5.390	8.77	2.922	4.510	7.05	2.690	4.018	6.12	2.534	3.699	5.53
40	4.085	7.314	12.61	3.232	5.178	8.25	2.839	4.313	6.60	2.606	3.828	5.70	2.450	3.514	5.13
60	4.001	7.077	11.97	3.150	4.977	7.76	2.758	4.126	6.17	2.525	3.649	5.31	2.368	3.339	4.76
120	3.920	6.851	11.38	3.072	4.786	7.31	2.680	3.949	5.79	2.447	3.480	4.95	2.290	3.174	4.42
∞	3.841	6.635	10.83	2.996	4.605	6.91	2.605	3.782	5.42	2.372	3.319	4.62	2.214	3.017	4.10

TABLE E—(Continued)

n_2	$n_1 = 6$ .05	$n_1 = 6$ .01	$n_1 = 6$ .001	$n_1 = 8$ .05	$n_1 = 8$ .01	$n_1 = 8$ .001	$n_1 = 12$ .05	$n_1 = 12$ .01	$n_1 = 12$ .001	$n_1 = 24$ .05	$n_1 = 24$ .01	$n_1 = 24$ .001	$n_1 = \infty$ .05	$n_1 = \infty$ .01	$n_1 = \infty$ .001
1	233.99	5,859.0	585,937	238.88	5,981.6	598,144	243.91	6,106.3	610,667	249.05	6,234.6	623,497	254.32	6,366.0	636,619
2	19.330	99.332	999.3	19.371	99.374	999.3	19.413	99.416	999.4	19.454	99.458	999.5	19.496	99.501	999.5
3	8.941	27.911	132.8	8.845	27.489	130.6	8.745	27.052	128.3	8.638	26.598	125.9	8.527	26.125	123.5
4	6.163	15.207	50.53	6.041	14.799	49.00	5.912	14.374	47.41	5.774	13.929	45.77	5.628	13.463	44.05
5	4.950	10.672	28.84	4.818	10.289	27.64	4.678	9.888	26.42	4.527	9.467	25.14	4.365	9.020	23.78
6	4.284	8.466	20.03	4.147	8.102	19.03	4.000	7.718	17.99	3.841	7.313	16.89	3.669	6.880	15.75
7	3.866	7.191	15.52	3.726	6.840	14.63	3.575	6.469	13.71	3.410	6.074	12.73	3.230	5.650	11.69
8	3.581	6.371	12.86	3.438	6.029	12.04	3.284	5.667	11.19	3.115	5.279	10.30	2.928	4.859	9.34
9	3.374	5.802	11.13	3.230	5.467	10.37	3.073	5.111	9.57	2.900	4.729	8.72	2.707	4.311	7.81
10	3.217	5.386	9.92	3.072	5.057	9.20	2.913	4.706	8.45	2.737	4.327	7.64	2.538	3.909	6.76
11	3.095	5.069	9.05	2.948	4.745	8.35	2.788	4.397	7.63	2.609	4.021	6.85	2.405	3.602	6.00
12	2.996	4.821	8.38	2.849	4.499	7.71	2.687	4.155	7.00	2.505	3.780	6.25	2.296	3.361	5.42
13	2.915	4.620	7.86	2.767	4.302	7.21	2.604	3.960	6.52	2.420	3.587	5.78	2.206	3.165	4.97
14	2.848	4.456	7.43	2.699	4.140	6.80	2.534	3.800	6.13	2.349	3.427	5.41	2.131	3.004	4.60
15	2.790	4.318	7.09	2.641	4.004	6.47	2.475	3.666	5.81	2.288	3.294	5.10	2.066	2.868	4.31
16	2.741	4.202	6.81	2.591	3.890	6.19	2.425	3.553	5.55	2.235	3.181	4.85	2.010	2.753	4.06
17	2.699	4.102	6.56	2.548	3.791	5.96	2.381	3.455	5.32	2.190	3.083	4.63	1.960	2.653	3.85
18	2.661	4.015	6.35	2.510	3.705	5.76	2.342	3.371	5.13	2.150	2.999	4.45	1.917	2.566	3.67
19	2.628	3.939	6.18	2.477	3.631	5.59	2.308	3.296	4.97	2.114	2.925	4.29	1.878	2.489	3.52
20	2.599	3.871	6.02	2.447	3.564	5.44	2.278	3.231	4.82	2.083	2.859	4.15	1.843	2.421	3.38
21	2.573	3.812	5.88	2.421	3.506	5.31	2.250	3.173	4.70	2.054	2.801	4.03	1.812	2.360	3.26
22	2.549	3.758	5.76	2.397	3.453	5.19	2.226	3.121	4.58	2.028	2.749	3.92	1.783	2.305	3.15
23	2.528	3.710	5.65	2.375	3.406	5.09	2.204	3.074	4.48	2.005	2.702	3.82	1.757	2.256	3.05
24	2.508	3.667	5.55	2.355	3.363	4.99	2.183	3.032	4.39	1.984	2.659	3.74	1.733	2.211	2.97
25	2.490	3.627	5.46	2.337	3.324	4.91	2.165	2.993	4.31	1.964	2.620	3.66	1.711	2.169	2.89
26	2.474	3.591	5.38	2.321	3.288	4.83	2.148	2.953	4.24	1.946	2.585	3.59	1.691	2.132	2.82
27	2.459	3.558	5.31	2.305	3.256	4.76	2.132	2.926	4.17	1.930	2.552	3.52	1.672	2.096	2.75
28	2.445	3.528	5.24	2.291	3.226	4.69	2.118	2.896	4.11	1.915	2.522	3.46	1.654	2.064	2.70
29	2.432	3.499	5.18	2.278	3.198	4.64	2.104	2.869	4.05	1.901	2.495	3.41	1.638	2.034	2.64
30	2.421	3.474	5.12	2.266	3.173	4.58	2.092	2.843	4.00	1.887	2.469	3.36	1.622	2.006	2.59
40	2.336	3.291	4.73	2.180	2.993	4.21	2.004	2.665	3.64	1.793	2.288	3.01	1.509	1.805	2.23
60	2.254	3.119	4.37	2.097	2.823	3.87	1.917	2.496	3.31	1.700	2.115	2.69	1.389	1.601	1.90
120	2.175	2.956	4.04	2.016	2.663	3.55	1.834	2.336	3.02	1.608	1.950	2.40	1.254	1.380	1.56
∞	2.099	2.802	3.74	1.938	2.511	3.27	1.752	2.185	2.74	1.517	1.791	2.13	1.000	1.000	1.00

SOURCE: Frederick E. Croxton and Dudley J. Cowden, *Practical Business Statistics* (2d ed.; New York: Prentice-Hall, Inc., 1948), pp. 514 and 515. Reprinted by permission of the publisher.

Values of F at the .05 and .01 points were taken, by permission, from Maxine Merrington and Catherine M. Thompson, "New Tables of Statistical Variables," *Biometrika*, Vol. XXXIII, Part 1, pp. 80, 81, 84, and 85. Values of F at the .001 point were taken from Table V of R. A. Fisher and F. Yates, *Statistical Tables for Biological, Agricultural and Medical Research*, Oliver and Boyd Ltd., Edinburgh, 1938, by permission of the author and publishers. The first reference gives F values to five digits at the .50, .25, .10, .05, .025, .01, and .005 points and for values of n_1 in addition to those shown in the above table. The second reference gives F values to three or more digits at the .20, .05, .01, and .001 points.

TABLE F
FACTORS USEFUL IN THE CONSTRUCTION OF CONTROL CHARTS*

Number of Observations in Sample, N	Chart for Averages			Chart for Standard Deviations						Chart for Ranges						
	Factors for Control Limits			Factors for Central Line		Factors for Control Limits				Factors for Central Line		Factors for Control Limits				
	A	A_1	A_2	c_2	$1/c_2$	B_1	B_2	B_3	B_4	d_2	$1/d_2$	d_3	D_1	D_2	D_3	D_4
2	2.121	3.760	1.880	0.5642	1.7725	0	1.843	0	3.267	1.128	0.8865	0.853	0	3.686	0	3.267
3	1.732	2.394	1.023	0.7236	1.3820	0	1.858	0	2.568	1.693	0.5907	0.888	0	4.358	0	2.575
4	1.500	1.880	0.729	0.7979	1.2533	0	1.808	0	2.266	2.059	0.4857	0.880	0	4.698	0	2.282
5	1.342	1.596	0.577	0.8407	1.1894	0	1.756	0	2.089	2.326	0.4299	0.864	0	4.918	0	2.115
6	1.225	1.410	0.483	0.8686	1.1512	0.026	1.711	0.030	1.970	2.534	0.3946	0.848	0	5.078	0	2.004
7	1.134	1.277	0.419	0.8882	1.1259	0.105	1.672	0.118	1.882	2.704	0.3698	0.833	0.205	5.203	0.076	1.924
8	1.061	1.175	0.373	0.9027	1.1078	0.167	1.638	0.185	1.815	2.847	0.3512	0.820	0.387	5.307	0.136	1.864
9	1.000	1.094	0.337	0.9139	1.0942	0.219	1.609	0.239	1.761	2.970	0.3367	0.808	0.546	5.394	0.184	1.816
10	0.949	1.028	0.308	0.9227	1.0837	0.262	1.584	0.284	1.716	3.078	0.3249	0.797	0.687	5.469	0.223	1.777
11	0.905	0.973	0.285	0.9300	1.0753	0.299	1.561	0.321	1.679	3.173	0.3152	0.787	0.812	5.534	0.256	1.744
12	0.866	0.925	0.266	0.9359	1.0684	0.331	1.541	0.354	1.646	3.258	0.3069	0.778	0.924	5.592	0.284	1.716
13	0.832	0.884	0.249	0.9410	1.0627	0.359	1.523	0.382	1.618	3.336	0.2998	0.770	1.026	5.646	0.308	1.692
14	0.802	0.848	0.235	0.9453	1.0579	0.384	1.507	0.406	1.594	3.407	0.2935	0.762	1.121	5.693	0.329	1.671
15	0.775	0.816	0.223	0.9490	1.0537	0.406	1.492	0.428	1.572	3.472	0.2880	0.755	1.207	5.737	0.348	1.652
16	0.750	0.788	0.212	0.9523	1.0501	0.427	1.478	0.448	1.552	3.532	0.2831	0.749	1.285	5.779	0.364	1.636
17	0.728	0.762	0.203	0.9551	1.0470	0.445	1.465	0.466	1.534	3.588	0.2787	0.743	1.359	5.817	0.379	1.621
18	0.707	0.738	0.194	0.9576	1.0442	0.461	1.454	0.482	1.518	3.640	0.2747	0.738	1.426	5.854	0.392	1.608
19	0.688	0.717	0.187	0.9599	1.0418	0.477	1.443	0.497	1.503	3.689	0.2711	0.733	1.490	5.888	0.404	1.596
20	0.671	0.697	0.180	0.9619	1.0396	0.491	1.433	0.510	1.490	3.735	0.2677	0.729	1.548	5.922	0.414	1.586
21	0.655	0.679	0.173	0.9638	1.0376	0.504	1.424	0.523	1.477	3.778	0.2647	0.724	1.606	5.950	0.425	1.575
22	0.640	0.662	0.167	0.9655	1.0358	0.516	1.415	0.534	1.466	3.819	0.2618	0.720	1.659	5.979	0.434	1.566
23	0.626	0.647	0.162	0.9670	1.0342	0.527	1.407	0.545	1.455	3.858	0.2592	0.716	1.710	6.006	0.443	1.557
24	0.612	0.632	0.157	0.9684	1.0327	0.538	1.399	0.555	1.445	3.895	0.2567	0.712	1.759	6.031	0.452	1.548
25	0.600	0.619	0.153	0.9696	1.0313	0.548	1.392	0.565	1.435	3.931	0.2544	0.709	1.804	6.058	0.459	1.541
Over 25	$\dfrac{3}{\sqrt{n}}$	$\dfrac{3}{\sqrt{n}}$				*	**	*	**							

$$*\,1 - \frac{3}{\sqrt{2n}} \qquad\qquad **\,1 + \frac{3}{\sqrt{2n}}$$

Chart	Central Line	3σ Control Limits
$\bar{X}$	$\bar{X}$	$\bar{X} \pm A_1 s_x$ or $\bar{X} \pm A_2 \bar{R}$
	μ_x	$\mu_x \pm A\sigma_x$
R	$\bar{R}$	$D_3\bar{R}$ and $D_4\bar{R}$
	$d_2\sigma_x$	$D_1\sigma_x$ and $D_2\sigma_x$
σ_x	s_x	$B_3 s_x$ and $B_4 s_x$
	σ_x	$B_1\sigma_x$ and $B_2\sigma_x$

Definitions: $A = 3/\sqrt{n}$, $A_1 = \dfrac{3}{c_2\sqrt{n}}$, $A_2 = \dfrac{3}{d_2\sqrt{n}}$, $B_1 = c_2 - K$,

$B_2 = c_2 + K$, $B_3 = 1 - \dfrac{K}{c_2}$, $B_4 = 1 + \dfrac{K}{c_2}$, $D_1 = d_2 - 3d_3$, $D_2 = d_2 + 3d_3$,

$D_3 = 1 - 3\dfrac{d_3}{d_2}$, and $D_4 = 1 + 3\dfrac{d_3}{d_2}$, where $K = 3\sqrt{\dfrac{(n-1)}{n}} - c_2{}^2$.

Note that d_2 and d_3 are the same as mean w and σ_w' appearing in Table D and have the same original source.

Warning: The fourth significant figures for D_1, D_2, D_3, and D_4 are in doubt for N greater than 5.

* Reproduced with permission from Table B2 of the *A.S.T.M. Manual on Quality Control of Materials*, p. 115. The c_2 factor is also given in Table 29 of W. A. Shewhart, *Economic Control of Quality of Manufactured Product* (New York: D. Van Nostrand & Co., 1931), p. 185.

TABLE G

TABLE OF RANDOM NUMBERS*

Line\Col.	(1)	(2)	(3)	(4)	(5)	(6)	(7)	(8)	(9)	(10)	(11)	(12)	(13)	(14)
1	10480	15011	01536	02011	81647	91646	69179	14194	62590	36207	20969	99570	91291	90700
2	22368	46573	25595	85393	30995	89198	27982	53402	93965	34095	52666	19174	39615	99505
3	24130	48360	22527	97265	76393	64809	15179	24830	49340	32081	30680	19655	63348	58629
4	42167	93093	06243	61680	07856	16376	39440	53537	71341	57004	00849	74917	97758	16379
5	37570	39975	81837	16656	06121	91782	60468	81305	49684	60672	14110	06927	01263	54613
6	77921	06907	11008	42751	27756	53498	18602	70659	90655	15053	21916	81825	44394	42880
7	99562	72905	56420	69994	98872	31016	71194	18738	44013	48840	63213	21069	10634	12952
8	96301	91977	05463	07972	18876	20922	94595	56869	69014	60045	18425	84903	42508	32307
9	89579	14342	63661	10281	17453	18103	57740	84378	25331	12566	58678	44947	05585	56941
10	85475	36857	53342	53988	53060	59533	38867	62300	08158	17983	16439	11458	18593	64952
11	28918	69578	88231	33276	70997	79936	56865	05859	90106	31595	01547	85590	91610	78188
12	63553	40961	48235	03427	49626	69445	18663	72695	52180	20847	12234	90511	33703	90322
13	09429	93969	52636	92737	88974	33488	36320	17617	30015	08272	84115	27156	30613	74952
14	10365	61129	87529	85689	48237	52267	67689	93394	01511	26358	85104	20285	29975	89868
15	07119	97336	71048	08178	77233	13916	47564	81056	97735	85977	29372	74461	28551	90707
16	51085	12765	51821	51259	77452	16308	60756	92144	49442	53900	70960	63990	75601	40719
17	02368	21382	52404	60268	89368	19885	55322	44819	01188	65255	64835	44919	05944	55157
18	01011	54092	33362	94904	31273	04146	18594	29852	71585	85030	51132	01915	92747	64951
19	52162	53916	46369	58586	23216	14513	83149	98736	23495	64350	94738	17752	35156	35749
20	07056	97628	33787	09998	42698	06691	76988	13602	51851	46104	88916	19509	25625	58104
21	48663	91245	85828	14346	09172	30168	90229	04734	59193	22178	30421	61666	99904	32812
22	54164	58492	22421	74103	47070	25306	76468	26384	58151	06646	21524	15227	96909	44592
23	32639	32363	05597	24200	13363	38005	94342	28728	35806	06912	17012	64161	18296	22851
24	29334	27001	87637	87308	58731	00256	45834	15398	46557	41135	10367	07684	36188	18510
25	02488	33062	28834	07351	19731	92420	60952	61280	50001	67658	32586	86679	50720	94953
26	81525	72295	04839	96423	24878	82651	66566	14778	76797	14780	13300	87074	79666	95725
27	29676	20591	68086	26432	46901	20849	89768	81536	86645	12659	92259	57102	80428	25280
28	00742	57392	39064	66432	84673	40027	32832	61362	98947	96067	64760	64584	96096	98253
29	05366	04213	25669	26422	44407	44048	37937	63904	45766	66134	75470	66520	34693	90449
30	91921	26418	64117	94305	26766	25940	39972	22209	71500	64568	91402	42416	07844	69618
31	00582	04711	87917	77341	42206	35126	74087	99547	81817	42607	43808	76655	62028	76630
32	00725	69884	62797	56170	86324	88072	76222	36086	84637	93161	76038	65855	77919	88006
33	69011	65795	95876	55293	18988	27354	26575	08625	40801	59920	29841	80150	12777	48501
34	25976	57948	29888	88604	67917	48708	18912	82271	65424	69774	33611	54262	85963	03547
35	09763	83473	73577	12908	30883	18317	28290	35797	05998	41688	34952	37888	38917	88050
36	91567	42595	27958	30134	04024	86385	29880	99730	55536	84855	29080	09250	79656	73211
37	17955	56349	90999	49127	20044	59931	06115	20542	18059	02008	73708	83517	36103	42791
38	46503	18584	18845	49618	02304	51038	20655	58727	28168	15475	56942	53389	20562	87338
39	92157	89634	94824	78171	84610	82834	09922	25417	44137	48413	25555	21246	35509	20468
40	14577	62765	35605	81263	39667	47358	56873	56307	61607	49518	89656	20103	77490	18062
41	98427	07523	33362	64270	01638	92477	66969	98420	04880	45585	46565	04102	46880	45709
42	34914	63976	88720	82765	34476	17032	87589	40836	32427	70002	70663	88863	77775	69348
43	70060	28277	39475	46473	23219	53416	94970	25832	69975	94884	19661	72828	00102	66794
44	53976	54914	06990	67245	68350	82948	11398	42878	80287	88267	47363	46634	06541	97809
45	76072	29515	40980	07391	58745	25774	22987	80059	39911	96189	41151	14222	60697	59583
46	90725	52210	83974	29992	65831	38857	50490	83765	55657	14361	31720	57375	56228	41546
47	64364	67412	33339	31926	14883	24413	59744	92351	97473	89286	35931	04110	23726	51900
48	08962	00358	31662	25388	61642	34072	81249	35648	56891	69352	48373	45578	78547	81788
49	95012	68379	93526	70765	10592	04542	76463	54328	02349	17247	28865	14777	62730	92277
50	15664	10493	20492	38391	91132	21999	59516	81652	27195	48223	46751	22923	32261	85653

* Reproduced from Interstate Commerce Commission, Bureau of Transport Economics and Statistics, *Table of 105,000 Random Decimal Digits*, Statement

TABLE 5—(Continued)

Line\Col.	(1)	(2)	(3)	(4)	(5)	(6)	(7)	(8)	(9)	(10)	(11)	(12)	(13)	(14)
51	18408	81899	04153	53381	79401	21438	83035	92350	36693	31238	59649	91754	72772	02338
52	17611	86845	00470	91962	79012	13092	02638	24823	94730	06691	89528	91286	86105	73000
53	35104	35101	54376	87637	79021	43060	88244	71015	18765	02881	23152	12245	16516	91202
54	57491	16700	23107	59132	15059	33132	82716	71035	99803	74353	06868	30422	16703	91403
56	16631	35006	85909	98275	32030	53790	16815	69298	82732	35467	73117	32523	38480	44437
57	96973	35202	82591	78985	38003	14890	14305	54598	35975	19687	73134	91826	60333	19346
58	31693	64238	14340	82671	31767	44489	64758	75519	16554	31613	18146	08930	85001	98346
59	31162	19477	13633	27889	47914	02584	04750	20061	72152	03139	13486	08930	85001	87820
61	03931	33309	57047	74211	63445	17361	62825	39908	05607	91284	68833	35570	38818	46920
62	07408	33278	42708	10154	89917	15564	39272	38825	73115	86662	89977	74496	51906	99378
63	07094	33060	42077	25354	58911	55454	64535	88815	05005	51117	47589	95574	62565	66092
64	09253	02400	08204	35447	18949	65402	43542	31352	00099	94107	77569	50975	52644	66534
65	16151	18108	08265	14577	81959	46942	17537	53363	00033	57107	77510	06625	28725	34191
66	21457	40742	29820	96788	29400	21840	15035	34537	33310	06116	95240	15995	16578	06004
67	21581	57802	03125	89720	10583	37621	47075	42080	97544	48625	68995	04436	57802	15297
68	55612	37809	84595	57370	10597	48761	07075	60433	64889	94884	58845	45250	03288	93342
69	44657	04909	01827	37089	37374	60563	23970	63543	64089	43785	69113	14226	02559	50502
70	91340	09234	64099	81171	37374	61023	43997	11052	80641	73772	89201	71725	99531	50501
71	91227	21117	36296	24296	84676	55468	35216	14486	17899	68607	41867	14951	91696	85065
72	50001	36243	62825	29052	78131	39148	51519	16685	82790	15033	57148	92820	83737	92294
73	65390	32441	68997	85063	06107	69618	25484	37421	85184	50349	91440	94202	37887	79840
74	27504	76948	36764	35372	89095	64847	86556	49490	39734	95070	94136	95920	43800	24920
75	37169	49134	94911	54167	00819	00648	09654	49490	34761	82601	02853	74300	00275	48280
76	11508	70225	51111	38351	19444	66499	71945	91599	17842	68607	84081	66938	93654	59894
77	37449	30311	06694	19444	10573	15765	11271	54854	84051	71196	16549	40107	33100	52924
78	46515	81295	05944	10323	52141	30130	43990	37866	65134	60790	58345	81075	74818	79864
79	30986	24095	99241	35808	10523	75028	68013	40265	25798	07301	14580	35869	74818	46987
80	63798	64499	90740	35097	11417	78148	08991	42865	92530	08531	03577	18356	81250	54238
81	82486	65046	99254	67632	43218	04734	21366	64816	52003	81125	84704	52689	53875	83556
82	21885	82908	74247	43218	43564	51690	21369	23796	52740	41540	59166	27934	27991	29648
83	60336	32689	92074	60535	63554	40136	54862	29750	85020	15410	11925	54870	14805	29148
84	43937	76465	20103	25251	80110	33960	25742	24400	85248	00024	01544	51035	06995	41585
85	97656	63175	89303	16207	57510	92037	21942	08611	39078	44302	85477	10036	84095	48201
86	03299	01221	05418	30000	57550	92037	79752	86367	21216	98442	03076	56615	91511	75928
87	79626	06486	04754	38017	64045	96973	25058	26014	33478	88844	08544	12178	22178	50548
88	85636	01366	47740	37064	66440	04754	03024	24001	34071	60457	17963	15818	37168	47908
89	18039	14150	07600	30007	66644	41675	07032	24010	86078	06004	21700	58216	33065	57567
91	79556	29068	04142	16203	15387	12856	66227	38358	22478	73377	88732	09444	82558	05250
92	92608	82530	27055	02643	34090	12077	62085	63863	11034	39721	80023	51601	34925	57031
93	23982	25036	27094	35797	42096	01358	19480	63789	11540	97041	37518	61707	35000	85117
94	09915	30300	07694	67294	53835	07144	10084	60383	86654	96548	79102	81817	28111	40123
95	59037	33300	06669	87383	12689	01762	24242	12918	40098	43718	07799	76530	71255	52350
96	42488	78077	69882	61657	34136	79180	97526	43092	40098	73577	80799	76530	71255	64239
97	46773	86735	61657	31204	79666	40829	43092	53000	55430	53216	95787	42557	80672
98	59725	45404	61657	16588	34136	33073	09534	76038	41297	09548	10436	37572	63022
99	48237	01715	52667	65082	31204	43072	89536	90110	86537	62738	19636	51113	02647

TABLE H*

VALUES OF e^{-x}

x	e^{-x} Value	x	e^{-x} Value	x	e^{-x} Value
0.00	1.00000	0.45	.63763	0.90	.40657
0.01	.99005	0.46	.63128	0.91	.40252
0.02	.98020	0.47	.62500	0.92	.39852
0.03	.97045	0.48	.61878	0.93	.39455
0.04	.96079	0.49	.61263	0.94	.39063
0.05	.95123	0.50	.60653	0.95	.38674
0.06	.94176	0.51	.60050	0.96	.38289
0.07	.93239	0.52	.59452	0.97	.37908
0.08	.92312	0.53	.58860	0.98	.37531
0.09	.91393	0.54	.58275	0.99	.37158
0.10	.90484	0.55	.57965	1.00	.36788
0.11	.89583	0.56	.57121	1.01	.36422
0.12	.88692	0.57	.56553	1.02	.36060
0.13	.87809	0.58	.55990	1.03	.35701
0.14	.86936	0.59	.55433	1.04	.35345
0.15	.86071	0.60	.54881	1.05	.34994
0.16	.85214	0.61	.54335	1.06	.34646
0.17	.84366	0.62	.53794	1.07	.34301
0.18	.83527	0.63	.53259	1.08	.33960
0.19	.82696	0.64	.52729	1.09	.33622
0.20	.81873	0.65	.52205	1.10	.33287
0.21	.81058	0.66	.61685	1.11	.32956
0.22	.80252	0.67	.51171	1.12	.32628
0.23	.79453	0.68	.50662	1.13	.32303
0.24	.78663	0.69	.50158	1.14	.31982
0.25	.77880	0.70	.49659	1.15	.31664
0.26	.77105	0.71	.49164	1.16	.31349
0.27	.76338	0.72	.48675	1.17	.31037
0.28	.75578	0.73	.48191	1.18	.30728
0.29	.74826	0.74	.47711	1.19	.30422
0.30	.74082	0.75	.47237	1.20	.30119
0.31	.73345	0.76	.46767	1.21	.28920
0.32	.72615	0.77	.46301	1.22	.29523
0.33	.71892	0.78	.45841	1.23	.29229
0.34	.71177	0.79	.45384	1.24	.28938
0.35	.70469	0.80	.44933	1.25	.28650
0.36	.69768	0.81	.44486	1.26	.28365
0.37	.69073	0.82	.44043	1.27	.28083
0.38	.68386	0.83	.43605	1.28	.27804
0.39	.67706	0.84	.43171	1.29	.27527
0.40	.67032	0.85	.42741	1.30	.27253
0.41	.66365	0.86	.42316	1.31	.26982
0.42	.65705	0.87	.41895	1.32	.26714
0.43	.65051	0.88	.41478	1.33	.26448
0.44	.64404	0.89	.41066	1.34	.26185

TABLE H—(*Continued*)

x	e^{-x} Value	x	e^{-x} Value	x	e^{-x} Value
1.35	.25924	1.80	.16530	2.25	.10540
1.36	.25666	1.81	.16365	2.26	.10435
1.37	.25411	1.82	.16203	2.27	.10331
1.38	.25158	1.83	.16041	2.28	.10228
1.39	.24908	1.84	.15882	2.29	.10127
1.40	.24660	1.85	.15742	2.30	.10026
1.41	.24414	1.86	.15567	2.31	.09926
1.42	.24171	1.87	.15412	2.32	.09827
1.43	.23931	1.88	.15259	2.33	.09730
1.44	.23693	1.89	.15107	2.34	.09633
1.45	.23457	1.90	.14957	2.35	.09537
1.46	.23224	1.91	.14808	2.36	.09442
1.47	.22993	1.92	.14661	2.37	.09348
1.48	.22764	1.93	.14515	2.38	.09255
1.49	.22537	1.94	.14370	2.39	.09163
1.50	.22313	1.95	.14227	2.40	.09072
1.51	.22091	1.96	.14086	2.41	.08982
1.52	.21871	1.97	.13946	2.42	.08892
1.53	.21654	1.98	.13807	2.43	.08804
1.54	.21438	1.99	.13670	2.44	.08716
1.55	.21225	2.00	.13534	2.45	.08629
1.56	.21014	2.01	.13399	2.46	.08543
1.57	.20805	2.02	.13266	2.47	.08458
1.58	.20598	2.03	.13134	2.48	.08374
1.59	.20393	2.04	.13003	2.49	.08291
1.60	.20190	2.05	.12873	2.50	.08208
1.61	.19989	2.06	.12745	2.51	.08127
1.62	.19790	2.07	.12619	2.52	.08046
1.63	.19593	2.08	.12493	2.53	.07966
1.64	.19398	2.09	.12369	2.54	.07887
1.65	.19205	2.10	.12246	2.55	.07808
1.66	.19014	2.11	.12124	2.56	.07730
1.67	.18825	2.12	.12003	2.57	.07654
1.68	.18637	2.13	.11884	2.58	.07577
1.69	.18452	2.14	.11765	2.59	.07502
1.70	.18268	2.15	.11648	2.60	.07427
1.71	.18087	2.16	.11533	2.61	.07353
1.72	.17907	2.17	.11418	2.62	.07280
1.73	.17728	2.18	.11304	2.63	.07208
1.74	.17552	2.19	.11192	2.64	.07136
1.75	.17377	2.20	.11080	2.65	.07065
1.76	.17204	2.21	.10970	2.66	.06995
1.77	.17033	2.22	.10861	2.67	.06925
1.78	.16864	2.23	.10753	2.68	.06856
1.79	.16696	2.24	.10646	2.69	.06788

TABLE H—(*Continued*)

x	e^{-x} Value	x	e^{-x} Value	x	e^{-x} Value
2.70	.06721	2.95	.05234	4.00	.01832
2.71	.06654	2.96	.05182	4.10	.01657
2.72	.06587	2.97	.05130	4.20	.01500
2.73	.06522	2.98	.05079	4.30	.01357
2.74	.06457	2.99	.05029	4.40	.01227
2.75	.06393	3.00	.04979	4.50	.01111
2.76	.06329	3.05	.04736	4.60	.01005
2.77	.06266	3.10	.04505	4.70	.00910
2.78	.06204	3.15	.04285	4.80	.00823
2.79	.06142	3.20	.04076	4.90	.00745
2.80	.06081	3.25	.03877	5.00	.00674
2.81	.06020	3.30	.03688	5.10	.00610
2.82	.05961	3.35	.03508	5.20	.00552
2.83	.05901	3.40	.03337	5.30	.00499
2.84	.05843	3.45	.03175	5.40	.00452
2.85	.05784	3.50	.03020	5.50	.00409
2.86	.05727	3.55	.02872	5.60	.00370
2.87	.05670	3.60	.02732	5.70	.00335
2.88	.05613	3.65	.02599	5.80	.00303
2.89	.05558	3.70	.02472	5.90	.00274
2.90	.05502	3.75	.02352	6.00	.00248
2.91	.05448	3.80	.02237	6.25	.00193
2.92	.05393	3.85	.02128	6.50	.00150
2.93	.05340	3.90	.02024	6.75	.00117
2.94	.05287	3.95	.01925	7.00	.00091
				7.50	.00055
				8.00	.00034
				8.50	.00020
				9.00	.00012
				9.50	.00007
				10.00	.00005

* Table H is taken from Table XV of Burington: *Handbook of Mathematical Tables and Formulas*, 2nd Edition, published by Handbook Publishers, Inc., Sandusky, Ohio, by permission of the author and publishers.

III. Simulation Languages

A simulation model can be executed by hand computation, as illustrated in the previous chapter, but in general poses such formidable computational requirements as to make this approach infeasible, except for the most simple situations. The use of a computer requires that a program be prepared, and, in fact, the model and the program are in most cases not distinguishable one from another. In order to illustrate the use of computers in simulation, several programs will be constructed using various languages in wide use for this purpose. At the same time we must recognize that this treatment is by no means exhaustive with respect to computer languages or simulation techniques.

ALGEBRAIC LANGUAGES

There are a number of algebraic languages available which are more or less well suited to the construction of simulation models. Examples of these are ALGOL, FORTRAN, and MAD. FORTRAN is a widely used language, and we shall use it to model the demand during lead time problems of Chapter 11. A flow chart of the process is shown in Figure A–1, and a program written in FORTRAN to carry out this process is given below.

As can be seen, the logic given for this process earlier is carried out repetitively, and records are kept of the frequency with which various demands occur. The only nonstandard part of the program is the function GRN (for get random number). Everything else is in standard form for a FORTRAN processor (an IBM 1620 was used to execute this program). Given a random number generator, input of the kind shown in Table A–1 would be processed by this program and result in output as shown in Table A–2. The relative frequencies shown are estimates of the probabilities of interest whose goodness is a function of the random number generating process used. Without laboring the point, it is very difficult to obtain a generator which is both fast and unbiased at the level of precision required by the analysis. A great deal of effort has gone into this aspect of simulation, and one is well advised to pay some attention to this aspect of any simulation.

Figure A–1

FLOW CHART OF DEMAND DURING LEAD TIME PROGRAM

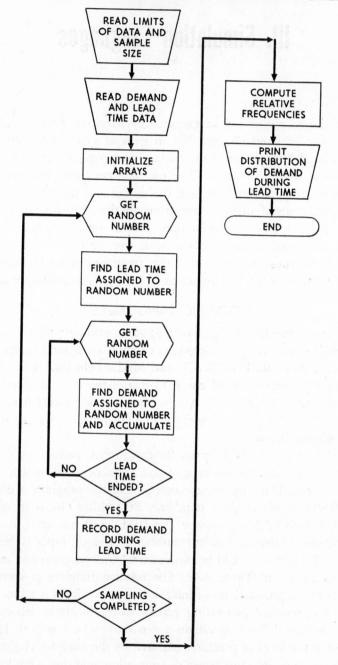

```
C    PROGRAM TO ESTIMATE THE PROBABILITIES OF DEMAND DURING LEAD TIME
     DIMENSION PX(50),PT(20),PU(200),PL(200)
C                                                    READ INPUTS
  21 READ 101,N,MINT,MAXT,MINX,INC,MINXT,MAXXT,NOBS
     READ 102,IEND,RAND
     IF(IEND)99,3,3
   3 NOXS=(N-MINX)/INC+1
     DO 5 I=1,NOXS,3
   5 READ 103,PX(I),PX(I+1),PX(I+2)
     DO 15 I=MINT,MAXT,3
  15 READ 103,PT(I),PT(I+1),PT(I+2)
                                                    INITIALIZE
     DO 7 I=1,200
     PU(I)=0.
   7 PL(I)=0.
C                                                    BEGIN SAMPLING
     DO 74 I=1,NOBS
     ISUMU=0
C                                                    FIND LEAD TIME
     RAND=GRN(RAND)
     DO 47 KK=MINT,MAXT
     IF(RAND-PT(KK))46,46,47
  46 JR=KK
     GO TO 48
  47 CONTINUE
                                                    FIND DEMANDS
  48 DO 58 L=1,JR
     RAND=GRN(RAND)
     DO 57 NN=1,NOXS
     IF(RAND-PX(NN))56,56,57
  56 JL=NN
     GO TO 58
  57 CONTINUE
  58 ISUMU=ISUMU+(JL-1)*INC+MINX
     IU=(ISUMU-MINX)/INC+1
  74 PU(IU)=PU(IU)+1.
C                                  CALCULATE RELATIVE FREQUENCIES
     NPUS=(N*MAXT-MINX)/INC+1
     PNOBS=NOBS
     DO 76 I=1,NPUS
  76 PU(I)=PU(I)/PNOBS
     PL(1)=PU(1)
     DO 82 I=2,NPUS
  82 PL(I)=PL(I-1)+PU(I)
     MINOT=(MINXT-MINX)/INC+1
     MAXOT=(MAXXT-MINX)/INC+1
     DO 88 I=1,NPUS
  88 PU(I)=1.-PL(I)
     DO 94 I=MINOT,MAXOT
     LOB=(I-1)*INC+MINX
C                                                    PRINT OUTPUTS
     IF(SENSE SWITCH 1)201,202
 201 PUNCH 102,LOB,PU(I)
 202 IF(SENSE SWITCH 2)203,94
 203 PRINT 102,LOB,PU(I)
  94 CONTINUE
     GO TO 21
  99 STOP 99
 101 FORMAT(8I5)
 102 FORMAT(I5,F6.4)
 103 FORMAT(3F6.4)
     END
```

Table A–1

INPUT DATA FOR DEMAND DURING LEAD TIME PROGRAM

Demand/Day	Probability	Cumulative Probability	Lead Time in Days	Probability	Cumulative Probability
0	0.10	0.0999	3	0.20	0.1999
1	0.20	0.2999	4	0.45	0.5499
2	0.30	0.5999	5	0.25	0.8999
3	0.20	0.7999	6	0.10	0.9999
4	0.15	0.9499			
5	0.05	0.9999			

N = 5, MINT = 3, MAXT = 6, MINX = 0, INC = 1, MINXT = 0, MAXXT = 30, NOBS = 200.

Table A–2

OUTPUT OF DEMAND DURING LEAD
TIME PROGRAM

Demand during Lead Time	Cumulative Probability
0	1.0000
1	0.9950
2	0.9900
3	0.9850
4	0.9350
5	0.8700
6	0.7900
7	0.6900
8	0.5950
9	0.5150
10	0.4100
11	0.3550
12	0.2450
13	0.2000
14	0.1300
15	0.0900
16	0.5000
17	0.0350
18	0.0300
19	0.0250
20	0.0050

SIMSCRIPT[1]

This language developed expressly for easing the task of constructing system simulation models includes all of the capability of an algebraic language with additional features of interest in simulation.

Any digital simulation consists of a numerical description of the "Status" of the simulated system. This Status is modified at various points in simulated time by occurrences which may be called "Events." SIMSCRIPT provides a standardized definition-form for specifying the Status description. It also automatically provides a main timing routine to keep track of simulated time and the occurrence of Events. An "Event Routine" is then written for each kind of Event, describing how the Status is to change. The SIMSCRIPT source-language is specifically designed to facilitate the formulation and programming of these Event Routines.

In particular, the following operations may each be accomplished by a single source-language statement: the allocation or return of storage space for temporary variables, the filing of items into or out of "Sets," the accumulation of information across simulated time, the summariza-

---

[1] Adapted with permission from H. M. Markowitz, Bernard Hausner, H. W. Karr, *Simscript: A Simulation Programming Language* (New York: Prentice-Hall, Inc., 1963).

tion of information at a point in time, and the finding of minimum or maximum over collections of items meeting specified conditions. Additional features include subscripted subscripts to any level, and a memory-layout philosophy which affords considerable flexibility in making program modifications and which permits both source and object programs to be "dimension-free." A "Report Generator" is also provided which permits the user to specify the form, content, and repetition of printed output on a layout form from which an output routine is generated without further programming.

Although SIMSCRIPT was developed for simulation problems, and the present exposition is presented in terms of simulation problems, SIMSCRIPT is actually a general programming system that is also readily usable for nonsimulation problems.

Status Description

In SIMSCRIPT, the "Status" of the simulated system is defined in terms of what are called *Entities, Attributes* of Entities, and *Sets* of Entities.

Any type of unit to be independently identified in the simulation, such as a truck, a species of animal, a chair, or a bank loan, is called an "Entity."

Each type of Entity is in turn described by enumerating its particular "Attributes." The Attributes of a truck might include its initial cost, its payload, and its operating cost per mile; those of a bank loan might include the amount due, the due date, and the interest rate.

A Status description may comprise any number of different types of Entities; there can also be any number of Entities of a particular type. Entities are considered to be of the same type if their Attribute names are identical; the values of these Attributes may of course be different. Two bank loans, for example, may have different due dates, although both have an Attribute called "due date." Whether or not something is to be considered an Entity or an Attribute of an Entity depends on whether it is to be independently identified in the simulation. Interrelationships among individual Entities may be depicted in the Status description by grouping the Entities into "Sets;" for example: "passengers holding reservations for flight 72," or "requisitions on backorder at depot 3." Entities may be members of Sets and also owners of Sets.

Event Routines and Timing

A separate subprogram must be written for each different kind of Event, describing how it changes the Status. There may be any number of different kinds of Events, and a particular kind of Event may occur repeatedly and at any desired point in simulated time.

Each kind of Event is enumerated in what is called an "Events List." Based on this Events List, SIMSCRIPT automatically generates a main Timing routine which keeps track of simulated time and calls the various Event routines in the proper sequence. In SIMSCRIPT simulation programs, time is advanced by variable-increments rather than being broken into a sequence of fixed increments. Therefore, Events may occur at any desired point in simulated time. When the execution of a particular Event routine is finished, simulated time is immediately advanced to the time of the next most imminent Event, whether it be seconds, hours, or days away, and the appropriate Event Routine is automatically called. The intervening time periods when no Status changes occur are skipped. The SIMSCRIPT Timing routine permits the occurrence of both "Endogenous Events" (those caused by previous Events within the simulation) and "Exogenous Events" (those introduced from outside the simulation by means of an "Exogenous Event Tape").

For purposes of discussion, the various operations performed by Event routines (or by subroutines on which they call) may be grouped under the following headings:

1. Changing the Status of individual Entities
2. Causing or cancelling future Events
3. Executing decision rules
4. Accumulating and analyzing results
5. Printing results

Changing the Status of an Entity

Since Status is defined in terms of Entities, Attributes, and Sets, an Entity can change its Status in only three ways:

1. It can come into or go out of existence (i.e., be created or destroyed)
2. It can change an Attribute value
3. It can change a Set membership

SIMSCRIPT provides a number of commands especially adapted to making these changes.

Creating or Destroying an Entity

To create a record in memory for a new Entity that is just coming into existence (for example, a new bank loan) it is necessary merely to write a single statement, such as "CREATE LOAN." This record will be in whatever configuration was specified on the Definition Form. If the bank loan is going out of existence, the statement "DESTROY

LOAN" will zero out the record of its Attributes and make the storage space available to subsequent "CREATE" statements. Entities that may be created and destroyed are either "Temporary Entities" or "Event Notices."

Changing an Attribute Value

SIMSCRIPT uses a "LET" statement to change an Attribute value arithmetically. For example, a statement like the following could set the current stock of an item equal to the previous stock plus receipts:

LET STOCK(ITEM) = STOCK(ITEM) + RCPTS(ITEM)

If this computation were to be done for each item on a list, the statement could read:

LET STOCK(ITEM) = STOCK(ITEM) + RCPTS(ITEM), FOR EACH ITEM OF LIST

In these examples, "STOCK" and "RCPTS" are Attributes of "ITEM," and "LIST" is a Set of ITEMS.

Changing a Set Membership

SIMSCRIPT provides special statements such as "FILE ITEM IN LIST" or "REMOVE FIRST ITEM FROM LIST" for transferring Entities into and out of Sets.

While the preceding examples are not exhaustive, they demonstrate that in changing the Status of an Entity, a single SIMSCRIPT statement is sufficient to create or destroy it, change an Attribute value, or change a Set membership.

Causing and Canceling Events

To help keep track of Events, SIMSCRIPT provides a special kind of Temporary Entity called an "Event Notice." Event Notices have the same properties as Temporary Entities: they may be created and destroyed, have Attributes, and be members and owners of Sets. The programming steps for causing a future Event are:

1. Creating an "Event Notice" for the particular Event
2. Posting the values of its Attributes, as required
3. Scheduling its occurence

For example, if an order is shipped to a base, its arrival following a transit-time delay might be caused by the following statements:

```
CREATE ARRVL
STORE ORDER IN ITEM(ARRVL)
STORE BASE IN DESTN(ARRVL)
CAUSE ARRVL AT TIME + TRANT
```

Prior to its occurrence, this Event could be cancelled by the statement "CANCEL ARRVL."

Executing Decision Rules

In Event routines, it is usually necessary to perform tests or computations in order to decide how Status should change and what future Events should be caused or cancelled. For making simple decisions, an assortment of "IF" and "GO TO" statements are provided. In addition, SIMSCRIPT provides "FIND MAX," "FIND MIN," and "FIND FIRST" statements. For example,

FIND LEVEL = MIN OF STOCK(ITEM, BASE), FOR ITEM = (1)(N), FOR EACH BASE OF ZI, WITH (PRICE(ITEM))GR(CAT(2))

In cases where more complex decision rules are desired, the source language provides a full complement of arithmetic and control-statements so that any desired algorithm may be programmed.

Accumulating and Analyzing Results

Data describing simulation results may be accumulated, and analyzed, by progressively changing the values of certain Attributes through standard arithmetic and control operations. However, some accumulation and analysis operations are required so often that special commands are provided.

The integral of an Attribute value may be accumulated over time by an ACCUMULATE statement, such as:

ACCUMULATE STOCK(ITEM) INTO CURSK(ITEM) SINCE LAST(ITEM)

Certain frequently desired statistical quantities may be computed by a COMPUTE statement, such as:

COMPUTE M, S, V = MEAN, STD-DEV, VARIANCE OF PRICE(ITEM), FOR EVERY ITEM OF JOB

Printed Output

Printed output in SIMSCRIPT programs normally comes from the "SIMSCRIPT Report Generator," which generates output routines based on the contents of the "Report Generator Layout Form" in Figure A–2. The form and content of the printed output are specified on the Layout Form by what are called "Form Lines" and Content Lines." Any desired text may be specified in a Form Line by writing the characters into the print positions where it is desired to have them appear. Numerical fields for printing the values of Attributes are specified by inserting asterisks in the desired print positions. Any Form Line containing one or more numerical fields must be followed by a Content Line which lists the names of the Attributes whose values are to be printed in the numerical fields. A variety of other control features are also provided in the SIMSCRIPT Report Generator.

Example of the Use of SIMSCRIPT

The maintenance problem of Chapter 11 provides us with a vehicle for using this language. The following is a list of the program and Figures A–3 and A–4 are the definition form and report generating program respectively.

```
        SIMULATION
        EVENTS
            3 EXOGENOUS
                    BEGIN(1)
                    FINIS(2)
                    FINAL(3)
            1 ENDOGENOUS
                    ARRVL
        END



        EXOG EVENT BEGIN
        SAVE EVENT CARD
        DO TO 10, FOR I=(1)(NV)
        CREATE ARRVL
        LET NOV(ARRVL)=I
        LET TME(ARRVL)=TIME
        CAUSE ARRVL AT TIME + TVFA
        FILE ARRVL IN LIST
     10 LOOP
        READ MPLCY,NR,AVL
        FORMAT (2I5,M4.2)
        LET TOTIM=0.
        LET RTIME=0.
        LET GAVRT=0.
        LET AVRT=0.
        LET STIME=TIME
        LET PTIME = TIME
        LET NT = 0
        CALL SPACE
        RETURN
        END



        ENDOG EVENT ARRVL
        LET N=NOV(ARRVL)
        REMOVE ARRVL FROM LIST
        IF(MPLCY)EQ(4),GO TO 4
        LET RTIME = RTIME + RT(MPLCY)
        LET TME(ARRVL) = TIME+RT(MPLCY)
        CAUSE ARRVL AT TME(ARRVL) +TVFA
        FILE ARRVL IN LIST
        GO TO (1,2,3),MPLCY
      1 RETURN
      2 IF(N)LE(NIV),GO TO 20
     11 DO TO 10, FOR EACH ARRVL OF LIST, WITH(NOV(ARRVL))GR(NIV), AND
        X(NOV(ARRVL))NE(N)
        CANCEL ARRVL
        LET TME(ARRVL)=TIME + RT(2)
        CAUSE ARRVL AT TME(ARRVL) + TVFA
     10 REPEAT 11
        RETURN
     20 DO TO 40, FOR EACH ARRVL OF LIST, WITH(NOV(ARRVL))LE(NIV), AND
        X(NOV(ARRVL))NE(N)
        CANCEL ARRVL
        LET TME(ARRVL)=TIME + RT(2)
        CAUSE ARRVL AT TME(ARRVL) + TVFA
     40 REPEAT 20
        RETURN
```

```
3 DO TO 50,FOR EACH ARRVL OF LIST, WITH(NOV(ARRVL))NE(N)
  CANCEL ARRVL
  LET TME(ARRVL)=TIME+RT(3)
  CAUSE ARRVL AT TME(ARRVL) + TVFA
50 REPEAT 3
   RETURN
 4 LET RTI = RT(1)
   STORE ARRVL IN FAIL
   LET NRA = 0
61 DO TO 60,FOR EACH ARRVL OF LIST,WITH(NOV(ARRVL))LE(NIV), AND(TIME-
   X TME(ARRVL))GE(AVC)
   LET NRA = NRA + 1
60 REPEAT 61
   IF(NRA) EQ(0),GO TO 71
   IF(N) GR(NIV),LET RTI=RTI+RT(4)
   LET RTI = RTI + FLOATF(NRA)*RT(5)
   LET NRA = 0
71 DO TO 70,FOR EACH ARRVL OF LIST,WITH(NOV(ARRVL))GR(NIV), AND
   X(TIME-TME(ARRVL))GE(AVL)
   LET NRA = NRA + 1
70 REPEAT 71
   IF(NRA) EQ(0), GO TO 90
   IF(N)LE(NIV),LET RTI=RTI+RT(4)
   LET RTI = RTI + FLOATF(NRA)*RT(5)
90 LET RTIME=RTIME+RTI
81 DO TO 80,FOR EACH ARRVL OF LIST,WITH(TIME-TME(ARRVL))GE(AVL)
   CANCEL ARRVL
   LET TME(ARRVL) = TIME + RTI
   CAUSE ARRVL AT TIME+RTI+TVFA
80 REPEAT 81
   STORE FAIL IN ARRVL
   LET TME(ARRVL)=TIME+RTI
   CAUSE ARRVL AT TME(ARRVL)+TVFA
   FILE ARRVL IN LIST
   RETURN
   END


   EXOG EVENT FINIS
   LET TOTIM= OTIM+RTIME
   LET AVRT = 1. - (RTIME/(TIME - PTIME))
   LET GAVRT = 1. -(TOTIM/(TIME - STIME))
   LET NT=NT+1
   CALL INREP
   LET RTIME=0.
   LET PTIME = TIME
   IF(NT)LS(NR), GO TO 20
II DO TO IO,FOR EACH ARRVL OF LIST
   REMOVE ARRVL FROM LIST
   CANCEL ARRVL
   DESTROY ARRVL
IO REPEAT II
20 RETURN
   END


   EXOG EVENT FINAL
   CALL EXITM
   RETURN
   END
```

The events list is self-explanatory with event BEGIN used to start a simulation for a given policy. The first failure on each valve is defined as a temporary entity ARRVL which occurs at a time selected at random from an input distribution labeled TVFA. The failures are filed in a ranked set based on time of failure and the policy to be followed is read from the event card. After initializing some variables and setting up the printer for reports, control is returned to the main timing routine.

Event ARRVL processes failures according to one of the four defined policies. For example, policy 1 requires the valve that has failed to be repaired and this is recorded by adding to repair time (RTIME) the time required for a single valve repair job, setting up the time at which this valve will fail again, and returning control to the main timing routine. Policy 2 cancels failures which are now slated to occur later on the bank of valves being repaired, records repair times for all of these valves, and sets up the next failure event for each.

Event FINIS computes cumulative repair time, average utilization during the reporting period just past, cumulative utilization, and reports the results to date. If a run is finished, the list of failures is cleared, otherwise control returns to the timing routine for continuation of this run. In order for a different policy to be evaluated, an event card for event BEGIN must be processed specifying the new policy. Event FINAL merely stops all processing.

In Figure A–4 (p. 848) is shown an example of the reports generated by the program. One measure of effectiveness is shown in Figure A–5 (p. 849), the utilization of the equipment in which this is defined as operating time as a proportion of total time. Here it can be seen that policy 3 is decidedly inferior while policies 1 and 4 are virtually indistinguishable in terms of this measure. Of course, other measures could be devised and would be easy to evaluate given this program.

General Purpose Systems Simulator[2]

The program to be described here is called the General Purpose Systems Simulator, or GPSS, and it has been written for operation on the IBM 704, 709 and 7090/94. The program allows the user to study the logical structure of a system, to follow the flow of traffic through the system, and to measure the effects of blocking caused by the need to time-share parts of the system or caused by limiting the capacity of parts of the system. Outputs of the program give information on:

1. The amount of traffic that flows through the complete system or through part of the system.
2. The average time and the distribution of time for traffic to pass through the complete system or between selected points of the system.
3. The extent to which elements of the system are loaded, together with the distribution of the occupancy of storage elements in the system.
4. The maximum and the average queue lengths occurring at various parts of the system, together with the distribution of the occupancies of the queues.

---

[2] Adapted with permission from G. Gordon, "A General Purpose Systems Simulator," *IBM Systems Journal,* Vol. I (September, 1962).

Figure A-2

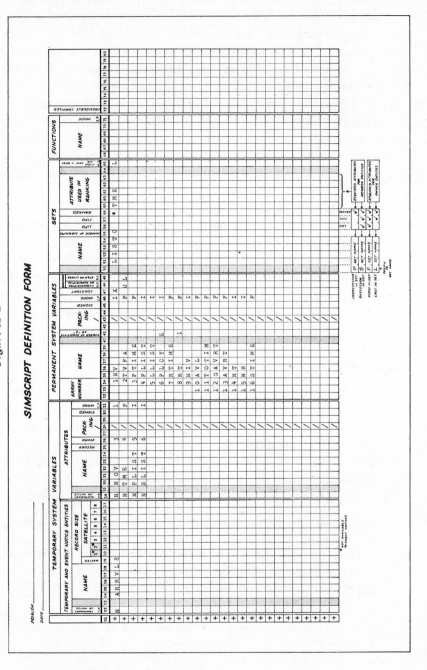

SIMSCRIPT DEFINITION FORM

Figure A-3

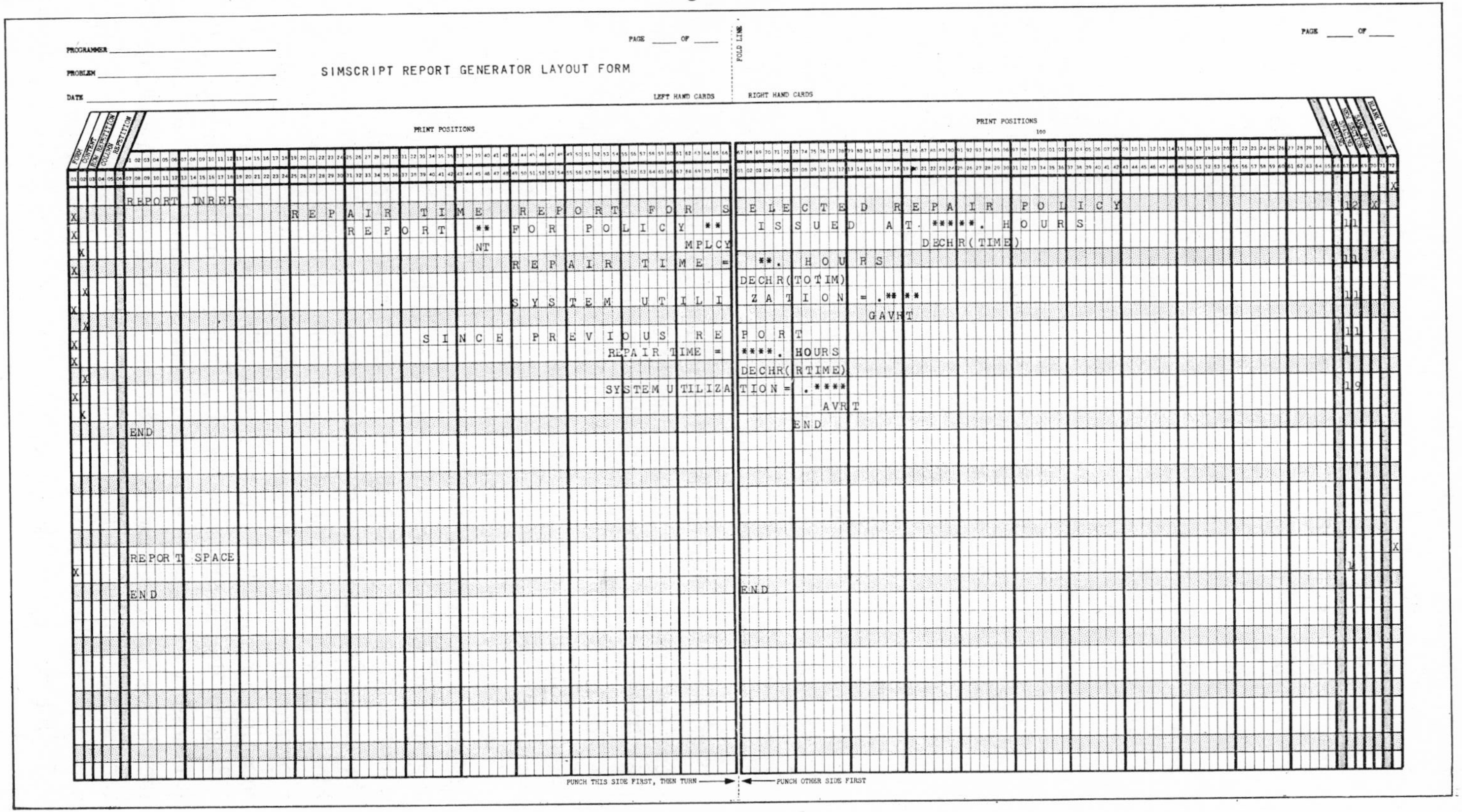

SIMSCRIPT REPORT GENERATOR LAYOUT FORM

PROGRAMMER _____ PAGE ____ OF ____

PROBLEM _____

DATE _____

PAGE ____ OF ____

PRINT POSITIONS

REPORT INREP

REPORT TIME = ** REPORT FOR POLICY **
FOR POLICY = MPLCY
REPAIR TIME = TIME
SYSTEM UTILLI
SINCE PREVIOUS RE
REPAIR TIME =
SYSTEM UTILIZZA

REPORT SPACE
END
END

SELECTED REPAIR POLICY
AT. *****. HOURS
ISSUED DECHR(TIME)
**. HOURS
DECHR(TOTIM)
ZATION = .**
PORT ***** GAVHT
HOURS
DECHR(RTIME)
TION = .***** AVRT
END
END

PRINT POSITIONS 100

PAGE ____ OF ____

Figure A–4

REPORTS GENERATED BY MAINTENANCE POLICY PROGRAM

```
REPAIR   TIME   REPORT   FOR   SELECTED   REPAIR   POLICY

     REPORT   3  FOR   POLICY   1   ISSUED   AT   7200.  HOURS
            REPAIR   TIME  = 277.  HOURS
           SYSTEM   UTILI ZATION = .9615
      SINCE   PREVIOUS   REPORT
                   REPAIR TIME =    90. HOURS
                   SYSTEM UTILIZATION = .9625




REPAIR   TIME   REPORT   FOR   SELECTED   REPAIR   POLICY

     REPORT   4  FOR   POLICY   1   ISSUED   AT   9600.  HOURS
            REPAIR   TIME  = 375.  HOURS
           SYSTEM   UTILI ZATION = .9609
      SINCE   PREVIOUS   REPORT
                   REPAIR TIME =    97. HOURS
                   SYSTEM UTILIZATION = .9594
```

Statistical variations can be introduced in the simulation and arrangements are made to sample the state of the system at various points of time. The effect of assigning levels of priority to units of traffic can be studied. It is also possible to simulate the effects of peak loads by varying the load on the system with time or by varying speeds of operation with load.

The program is based on the use of block diagrams as a means of describing the structure and action of a system. The method of describing systems with a block diagram is well known. Each block of the diagram represents a step in the action of the system and lines joining the blocks indicate the sequence of events that can occur. To make a block diagram description of a system serve as the input to a simulation program, however, a number of conditions must be met. First, the meaning of the blocks used in the diagram cannot be left to the individual user but must be clearly defined to the program. Secondly, it is necessary to associate with each block a number, that will be called the block time, to represent the execution time of the action the block is simulating. Thirdly, conventions need to be established to control the way in which the selection of the succession of blocks is made.

Each block type is distinguished by a name which is descriptive of its

Figure A–5

UTILIZATION AS A FUNCTION OF OPERATING HOURS FOR VARIOUS
REPAIR POLICIES

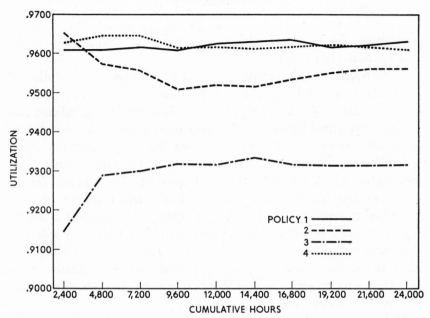

action and it is also given a characteristic symbol to be used when drawing block diagrams. When the block diagram is complete, each individual block is also given an identification number called the block number.

The block time is an integer giving the number of time units required for the action represented by the block. The magnitude of the time unit is determined by the program user. The unit is not specifically entered in the program but is implied by entering all times throughout the block diagram in terms of this same basic time unit.

The time required for the action being represented by a block is not always well defined. It may be an ill-defined quantity or it may vary over a range of values, often in a random manner. A simple rectangular distribution of time can be introduced at any block by specifying two numbers, the *mean* and the *spread* for the block. Whenever the program refers to the block, it will choose at random a block time between the values of mean minus spread and mean plus spread, with equal probability being given to each integer in this range. If the block time does not vary, the spread is set to zero to make the block time a constant value equal to the mean. If desired, the mean may also be set to zero to represent actions that take no time or take a negligible amount of time compared with the basic time unit. If a more precise random distribution is known or the variation of block times is not random but depends upon some factor associated with the system, use can be made of tables of numbers referred to as *functions* to introduce a more accurate representation of the block time.

To represent the alternative courses of action that may be followed by the system, more than one line may leave a block. Correspondingly, one block may be entered by way of more than one line to indicate that the step represented by that block occurs in more than one sequence of events. The convention is made that, with the exception of one block type called the BRANCH block, not more than two lines may lead from a given block. On the other hand, no restriction is placed on the number of lines leading into a given block. If a larger number of paths is required to represent the results of a particular decision, it is always possible to use a network of blocks with zero block time, that will lead to the required number of alternative paths. The BRANCH block type that was just mentioned is a block that allows many alternative paths and can be used to avoid such networks when the choice between paths follows some simple rules.

All block types other than those that represent terminal points of the system, can have two exits. The exits are distinguished by referring to them as exits 1 and 2 and they are defined by giving the number of the block to which the exit leads. If there are two possible exits from a block, a number called the *selection factor,* S, must be given at that block to determine the choice between the exits. The selection factor can be used to make two types of decisions in determining the exit to be followed from a block. If the selection factor is set between 0 and 1 then a random choice will be made on every occasion an exit is made. The probability of choosing exit 1 will be $1 - S$, and the probability of choosing exit 2 will be S.

The other method of deciding between exits is to choose exit 1 if next block 1 is available at the time of the decision and take exit 2 if exit 1 is not available. If neither exit is available then the first exit to become available is selected. This mode of operation is indicated by setting S equal to 1. It is an important mode of operation that can be used to simulate alternative lines of action in the system when some component of the system is found to be busy.

The system represented by the block diagram is operating upon certain basic units that move through the system. The nature of these units depend upon the system. For example: in a communication system the units might be messages; in a traffic study they might be people or vehicles; in a data processing system they might be records and so on. For convenience, the unit is referred to in the simulation as a *transaction*. The simulation proceeds by creating transactions to represent these units and moving the transactions through the block diagram in the same manner as the units would progress through the system represented by the block diagram.

The system being studied will also involve certain physical components which operate upon the transactions individually or in groups as they proceed through the system. To simulate the effects of these components, the simulation includes elements referred to as *items of equipment*. Certain of the block types are concerned with the interaction between transactions and items of equipment.

The principal property of an item of equipment that is of interest in a simulation study is the limit of its capacity to handle transactions simultaneously. The existence of such limits can cause congestion and a significant part of any system simulation is concerned with measuring the effects that these limits have on the overall performance of a system.

A distinction is made between two types of equipment according to whether the capacity for handling transactions is limited to one transaction or more than one transaction. An item of equipment that can handle only one transaction at a time is called a *facility*. An item of equipment that can handle many transactions simultaneously, up to a specified limit, is called a *storage*. They are identified by number and the block types that are concerned with equipment refer to the number of the particular item of equipment they employ. Because of the capacity limits set by equipment, blocks that employ equipment can cause congestion when the equipment is fully engaged by transactions. These blocks will then be unavailable to a transaction attempting to enter. In these circumstances, the transaction can be made to wait until room is made available, or it can be diverted to some other course of action by use of the selection factor described before.

Items of equipment that do not correspond to a system component are sometimes introduced into a simulation to effect control over the flow of transactions. If, for example, there are two or more parts of a system such that only one part can be in use at a time, entrance to any one part can be made contingent upon seizing a facility that will then block off the other parts. Similarly, taking up capacity in a storage can be made to limit the number of transactions allowed in any one part of a system. Some of the basic block types will now be described, and an example using these blocks will then be given to illustrate the method of using the program. A more complete description of the program can be found in reference [2]

Figure A–6 illustrates four block types concerned with creating, destroying and moving transactions without involving equipment. The block type called ORIGINATE creates transactions and enters them into the simulation. The block time of this type represents the interval of time between successive creations. Creation of transactions continues even if the transactions are unable to leave the ORIGINATE block when the exit blocks are unavailable. For this reason, the mean at an ORIGINATE block may not be set at zero since this would represent an infinite rate of generation. A TERMINATE block removes transactions from the system the instant they enter the TERMINATE block. This block therefore has no block time nor does it have any exits.

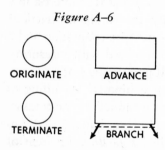

Figure A–6

ORIGINATE   ADVANCE

TERMINATE   BRANCH

An ADVANCE block is used to represent any action requiring time but not involving equipment. Since it does not involve equipment it cannot cause congestion; it is often used, therefore, with a zero block time as a buffer at the exit of a block using equipment to ensure that the equipment is released. It may also be used with zero time and a selection factor of 1 to precede a block using equipment in order to divert transactions when the equipment is busy.

The BRANCH block is similar to an ADVANCE but it allows many exits from the block. The selection of the exit follows special rules, however, in that the selection factor must be either 0 or 1. In the former case, a random selection from all possible exits is made with equal probability being given to each. With $S = 1$, an attempt is made to leave by the lowest numbered exit; if this is unavailable, the next highest is tried and so on. If all exits are busy, the transaction waits for the first exit to become available.

Figure A–6 shows a group of three blocks concerned with the use of facilities. In each case the flag on the side of the block symbol is used to carry the number of the facility associated with the block.

The HOLD block allows a transaction that enters the block to engage the facility for as long as the transaction remains in the block. The SEIZE block allows a transaction to engage the facility upon entering the block. The transaction, however, keeps control of the facility when it leaves the SEIZE block and remains in control until it enters a RELEASE block associated with the same facility. Between the points at which the transaction seizes the facility and releases the facility any number of blocks may be inserted to represent the actions followed by the transaction while it has control of the facility. The same facility may be mentioned at many different points of the block diagram indicating the different places in the system requiring its use.

In Figure A–7 there are three blocks associated with storages, the associated storage being numbered in the flag attached to the symbol. The actions of these blocks are analogous to the three facility type blocks of Figure A–8. The STORE block allows a transaction to occupy space in the storage associated with the block for as long as the transaction is in the block. The ENTER block allows a transaction to take up

Figure A–7   *Figure A–8*

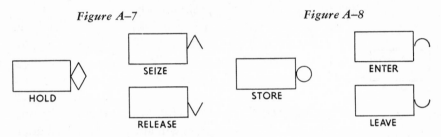

space in the storage but the space is not given back until a transaction enters a LEAVE block.

Three modes of operation are allowed for each of these blocks, differing in the amount of space that is controlled by the transaction. In a *normal* mode, only one unit of space is involved. In a *parameter* mode, the amount of space depends upon a number called a parameter that is associated with the transaction. The generation and use of parameters will be described later. In the third mode, called the *total* mode, the entire storage is filled or emptied as the transaction takes up or gives back space.

The same storage may be referred to by several blocks each employing any of the modes. A common count is maintained of the total space occupied by all such blocks. Any time there is insufficient space available for a transaction it will be refused entrance to a STORE or ENTER block but other transactions requiring less space may still be able to advance. An important distinction exists between the way the program treats transactions engaging facilities and entering storage. The transaction that engages a facility at a SEIZE block is the only transaction that may release the facility. In the case of a storage, however, one transaction can take up the space at an ENTER block while a different transaction can give back the space at a LEAVE block.

One of the main objects of using a simulation program is to gather statistics about the estimated performance of the system being simulated. Some of the blocks are concerned with gathering statistics rather than representing system actions. These are illustrated in Figure A–9. As has been pointed out, blocks involving equipment can cause congestion if the equipment involved is busy. As a result blocks that do not use equipment, such as the ADVANCE, may contain any number of transactions waiting for equipment to become available. The program will maintain such transactions in a queue which is served on a first-come first-served basis. The program will not, however, maintain any statistics about these queues unless they occur in a QUEUE block. These blocks, therefore, are placed in positions where congestion is anticipated, such as immediately in front of a HOLD block. The program will measure the average queue size and the maximum queue size occurring in each QUEUE block. If desired, the program will also give the distribution of the queue length sampled at uniform intervals of time. The number of the queue is indicated in the flag attached to the QUEUE block symbol.

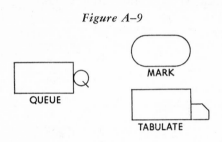

Figure A–9

QUEUE

MARK

TABULATE

Another important set of statistics that are frequently wanted are the transit times of transactions in getting from one point of the system to another. These statistics can be gathered by using MARK and TABULATE blocks. The program makes a note of the current clock time on each transaction that enters a MARK block. Later, when the transaction arrives at a TABULATE block, the program notes the clock time upon arrival, subtracts the MARK time placed on the transaction by the MARK block and enters the difference in a table. The table associated with a TABULATE block is numbered in the flag attached to the block symbol. Each table maintains frequency counts of the number of entries falling in each tabulation interval. The tabulation intervals are set by the program user at the beginning of the simulation run.

A Sample Program

As an example of how the program is used, consider the problem of measuring the flow of traffic through a supermarket. Shoppers enter a supermarket, but before shopping they must each get a basket. The number of baskets is limited to 150 and if none is available the shopper leaves the supermarket without shopping. Having obtained a basket, the shopper spends some time shopping, checks out at a counter and then leaves, returning the basket on the way out. Two types of shopper will be assumed, express shoppers, and nonexpress, or normal shoppers. Separate check-out facilities are available for the two types of shopper. For the express shopper there is only one counter but for the normal shopper there are 7 counters.

Figure A–10 illustrates the section of the block diagram concerned with the actions of getting a basket. An ORIGINATE block creates transactions, each representing one shopper. The convention adopted in drawing the blocks is that the block number is placed at the top center of the block and the mean and spread, if any, are placed at the center, separated by a colon. The mean is at the left end and the spread on the right. The ORIGINATE block, for example, is block number 1 and has a mean of 36 units and a spread of 18. The unit of time chosen in this example is 1 second so that the average time between arrivals is 36 seconds, but the time may vary from 18 to 54 seconds.

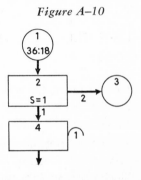

Figure A–10

To represent the baskets, a storage, number 1, is defined with a capacity of 150, equal to the number of baskets. To get a basket, the transaction representing the shopper must move into an ENTER block, number 4, associated with storage number 1. The attempt to enter is made through an ADVANCE block, number 2, with zero block time and S = 1. The ENTER block is at exit 1 of this ADVANCE block so the transaction will move into the ENTER block if there is space available in storage 1, that is, if there is a basket available. If this is not so, the transaction moves to a TERMINATE block, number 3, indicating that the shopper leaves because no basket is available.

Having got a basket the shopper moves into the supermarket and shops. This part of the simulation is illustrated in Figure A–11. One factor to be measured in this simulation will be the time shoppers spend in the supermarket. The transactions are therefore sent to a MARK block to note on each transaction the time at which shopping begins. The MARK block is also used to divide the flow of transactions into two streams representing the express and normal shoppers. It will be assumed that 25 per cent of the shoppers are express so a selection factor of 0.25 is set in the MARK block. Shopping will be represented by simple ADVANCE blocks, one for each type of shopper. The average shopping time is set to be 44 minutes for the normal and 7 minutes 20 seconds for the express shoppers. When the transaction leaves these ADVANCE blocks, shopping is complete and the shoppers move to the check-out counters.

The check-out section of the block diagram is represented in Figure A–12. It is to be expected that there will be congestion at the counters and the program will be arranged to measure the queues. The transactions therefore go to one of two QUEUE blocks immediately preceding the blocks representing the check-out equipment. Since there is only one check-out counter for express shoppers, this counter will be represented by a facility number 1 and a HOLD block is used to represent the action of occupying the check-out counter. Each transaction representing an express shopper moves, in turn, into the

Figure A–11

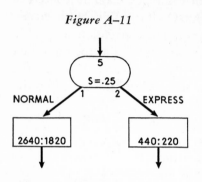

HOLD block for service and occupies the counter for a time ranging from ½ to 1½ minutes. It then moves on making room for the next shopper in the queue.

For the normal shoppers, there are seven check-out counters and these are represented by a storage, number 2, of capacity 7. The STORE block operates in a normal mode so that up to seven transactions at a time can be in the STORE block. Each stays for a time varying between 3 and 9 minutes and then moves on.

Having left the check-out counter, the customers prepare to leave the supermarket. Both streams are brought together at this point, and move to the section illustrated in Figure A–13.

Each transaction was marked at the time of beginning to shop. Since they are now about to leave the supermarket, the transactions are sent to a TABULATE block to enter into Table 1 a measure of the total time

Figure A–12   *Figure A–13*

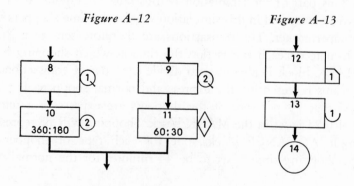

the shopper spent in the supermarket. The basket is then returned by entering a LEAVE block that returns the space taken up at the ENTER block. Finally, the transactions are removed at a TERMINATE block.

The complete diagram appears as shown in Figure A–14. Each block is numbered and the exits for each block are identified. One card is punched for each block. The cards have a simple fixed field format. Figure A–15 illustrates the completed coding form from which the cards for this problem are punched.

Included in the coding form are certain control cards required to describe the simulation run. A JOB card identifies the beginning of the problem deck and a START card defines the end of the problem deck. REMARKS cards allow comments to be printed in the output listing. The START card in this case indicates that the run begins at zero time with an initially empty condition and that the simulation is to run until 1200 shoppers have passed through the supermarket. For each storage used in the simulation a CAPACITY card defines the capacity of each storage. For each table associated with a TABULATE block a TABLE card defines the tabulation intervals. In this case Table 1 has intervals of 500 units beginning at 500 as lower unit.

One output that can be obtained from the program is a count of the number of times a block is entered.

Figure A–14

If this information is required for a block, a 1 is entered in column 65 of the BLOCK card. The 3 entered for the TERMINATE block indicates that not only is a block count to be gathered but, in addition, the entries to this block count toward the end of the simulation.

When the simulation is completed, a series of outputs are printed and these are illustrated in Figure A–16. The first output, not shown in

Figure A–15

IBM

GENERAL PURPOSE SYSTEM SIMULATOR
(BLOCK CARDS)

PROBLEM	ELEMENTARY SUPERMARKET MODEL			PAGE 1 OF 1
CODER	NEWMAN			DATE JULY 2, 1962

FIELD NO.	1	2	3	4	5	6	7	8	9	10	11	12	13	14	15	16
	BLOCK TYPE	BLOCK NUMBER	MEAN	SPREAD	PRIORITY	FUNT. NO.	SELECT FACTOR	TAG OR MODE	NEXT BLOCK 1	NEXT BLOCK 2	TABLE NO. OF ASSIGN FUNT.	FACILITY NO.	STORE NO.	QUEUE NO.	BLOCK COUNT	REMARKS
	2	11	15	21	27	31	33	37	41	45	49	53	57	61	65	66
JOB	SUPERMARKET, ELEMENTARY MODEL															
REMARKS	ILLUSTRATES BASIC MODEL BUILDING AND SYSTEMS STUDY METHODS.															
REMARKS	BASIC TIME UNIT IS 1, SECOND															
REMARKS																
ORIGINATE	1	36	18					2						1	
ADVANCE	2					1		4	3					1	
TERMINATE	3													1	
ENTER	4							5							
CAPACITY	1	150										1			
MARK	5					.25		6	7					1	
ADVANCE	6	2640	1320					8						1	
ADVANCE	7	440	220					9						1	
QUEUE	8							10					1	1	
QUEUE	9							11					2	1	
STORE	10	360	180					12				2		1	
CAPACITY	2	7													
HOLD	11	60	30					12			1			1	
TABULATE	12							13		1				1	
TABLE	1	500	500												
LEAVE	13							14				1		1	
TERMINATE	14														
START	0	1200												3	
END															

Figure A–16, is a listing of the input cards defining the problem. The time at which the simulation ended is shown, followed by the block counts that have been mentioned. Information is then given about each facility, storage and queue in the simulation. For the facilities, the program gives the fraction of total time for which the facility was engaged.

Figure A–16

OUTPUT OF SUPERMARKET SIMULATION

NO TIMES BLOCKS ENT				TIME END SIM 47640	
BLOCK	COUNT	BLOCK	COUNT	BLOCK	COUNT
1	1313	2	1312	3	
4	1312	5	1312	6	965
7	347	8	910	9	345
10	862	11	345	12	1200
13	1200	14	1200		

FACILITY NR 1   FRACTION OF TIME IN USE 0.4278

STORE NR	STORAGE CAPACITY	AVERAGE UTILIZATION
1	150	0.5962
2	7	0.9367

QUEUE NR	MAX QUEUE LGTH	AV QUEUE LGTH
1	50	27.1471
2	4	0.1360

TABLE NUMBER 1 MODE 0   TOTAL NUMBER IN TABLE 1200
TOTAL TIME IN TABLE 3971800   MEAN OF TABLE 3309.833
VARIANCE OF TABLE 3789437.0938

LIMIT	NO	PER CENT	CUM	MULT OF MEAN
500	148	12.33	12.33	0.1511
1000	196	16.33	28.67	0.3021
1500		0.00	28.67	0.4532
2000	4	0.33	29.00	0.6043
2500	9	0.75	29.75	0.7553
3000	55	4.58	34.33	0.9064
3500	91	7.58	41.92	1.0575
4000	127	10.58	52.50	1.2085
4500	161	13.42	65.92	1.3596
5000	148	12.33	78.25	1.5107
5500	135	11.25	89.50	1.6617
6000	91	7.58	97.08	1.8128
6500	31	2.58	99.67	1.9638
7000	4	0.33	100.00	2.1149
7500		0.00	100.00	2.2660
		0.00	100.00	2.4170

For the storages, the average occupancy is given and for the queues, the average and maximum queue lengths are shown. Finally, the tables of statistics that were requested are printed.

The block times that are not zero or constant in this example have all been represented by means and spreads giving random selections from simple rectangular distributions. One important respect in which the problem can be elaborated is to use functions and parameters to introduce more realism in these block times and the complete system includes this capability.

The description given here is of course not complete and the interested reader is referred to the GPSS III manual listed in the References below which represents a later version of the program than the one described in this chapter. It is hoped that the nature of this language, and some insight into its capability, has been obtained.

REFERENCES

1. "General Purpose Systems Simulator III: Introduction," IBM *Application Program.* 1965.

2. MARKOWITZ, H. M.; BERNARD HAUSNER; KARR, H. W. *Simscript: A Simulation Programming Language.* Englewood Cliffs, N.J.: Prentice-Hall, Inc., 1963.

3. ORGANICK, E. I. *A FORTRAN Primer.* Reading, Mass.: Addison-Wesley Press, 1963.

INDEX

Index

This book has been set on the Linotype in 12 and 10 point Garamond No. 3, leaded 1 point. Chapter numbers are in 18 point, and chapter titles in 24 point, Alternate Gothic. Case numbers and titles are in 18 point Alternate Gothic. The size of the type page is 27 by 46½ picas.